EARTH SCIENCE

Edward J. Tarbuck
Frederick K. Lutgens

Both Illinois Central College, Emeritus

Illustrated by
Dennis Tasa

The Earth Science
program has been developed to meet
teachers' goals and help every student
achieve success. Print and digital
program components help students
connect science to the world around them
and master the state assessment.

Sandstone formation in the Paria
Canyon-Vermillion Cliffs
Wilderness, Arizona

SAVVAS
LEARNING COMPANY

EARTH SCIENCE

Print Components

Student Edition
Teacher's Edition
Progress Monitoring Assessments,
   Teacher's Edition)
Test Prep Workbook
Lesson Plans
Laboratory Manual
Laboratory Manual, Teacher's Edition
Guided Reading and Study Workbook, Level A
Guided Reading and Study Workbook, Level A, Teacher's Edition
Guided Reading and Study Workbook, Level B
Guided Reading and Study Workbook, Level B, Teacher's Edition
Chapter Tests and Answer Key

Technology Components

Student Edition eText
Teacher's Edition eText
ExamView® CD-ROM
GEODe CD-ROM
Virtual Earth Science Lab CD with Lab Manual

Cover Sandstone formations in the Paria Canyon—Vermillion Cliffs Wilderness, Arizona.

Photographs Photo locators denoted as follows: Top (T), Center (C), Bottom (B), Left (L), Right (R), Background (Bkgd)

Front Cover Jim Lopes/Shutterstock; **Back Cover** (Bkgrd) Jim Lopes/Shutterstock, (L) Joseph C. Justice Jr./iStockphoto, (CL) S. Solum/Photolink/Getty Images, (CR) Mary Terriberry/Shutterstock, (R) amygdala_imagery/iStockphoto.

Front Matter T1, Jim Lopes/Shutterstock; T2 ©Stone Nature Photography/Alamy Images; T3 (TL) E. J. Tarbuck; T4 (TL) Michael Wysession, (Bkgrd) Art Wolfe, Inc; T5 Fred Ward/Blackstar; T6 Michael Medford/Getty Images; T8 Gary Yeowell/ Getty Images; T15 Diane N. Ennis/Shutterstock. Additional credits appear on pages 806 and 807, which constitute an extension of this copyright page.

Student Edition ISBN-13: 978-1-32320587-7
Teacher's Edition ISBN-13: 978-1-32320588-4

Student Edition ISBN-10: 1-32-320587-X
Teacher's Edition ISBN-10: 1-32-320588-8

11 22

SAVVAS
LEARNING COMPANY

About the Authors

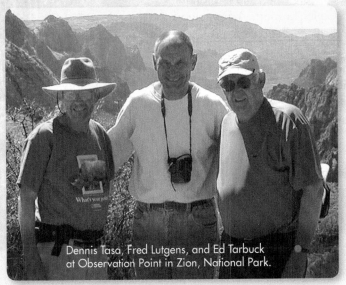

Dennis Tasa, Fred Lutgens, and Ed Tarbuck at Observation Point in Zion, National Park.

Edward J. Tarbuck served twenty-nine years as Professor of geosciences at Illinois Central College. During twenty of those years, he was also Chair of the Math, Science and Engineering Department. He now holds a place as Professor Emeritus at Illinois Central College.

Frederick K. Lutgens For thirty years, Frederick K. Lutgens served as Professor of geosciences at Illinois Central College. During his career, he was awarded "The Faculty Who Make a Difference" honor in recognition of his outstanding academic performance and dedication to students. He is also Professor Emeritus at Illinois Central College.

Tarbuck and Lutgens The term *synergistic* applies to the combined efforts of Tarbuck and Lutgens, two names widely recognized and respected in the field of geosciences. Early in their careers, they shared frustrations with the limited availability of textbooks designed for non-majors. Out of their dilemma sprang a series of textbooks that are used nation-wide and have been published in English, Spanish, Italian, and Korean. They have co-authored close to sixty editions of college textbooks including *Earth Science*, now in its 13th edition, *Earth: Introduction to Physical Geology*, and *The Atmosphere*. Tarbuck and Lutgens have received several publishing honors including the *Texty Award* for *Earth* and the *McGuffey Award* for *Earth Science*, both from the Text and Academic Authors Association.

Illustrations by Dennis Tasa Dennis Tasa has been illustrating college textbooks since 1978, specializing in the area of geology and geography. In 1993, he expanded his illustration work to develop and produce Earth Science educational CD-ROMs. Dennis has won numerous awards for his illustration and software products including EDDIE Awards by ComputEd Education Software Review for both Middle School and High School Science; Silver Awards; Summit Creative Awards; and the Children's Software and New Media Review School All Star Award.

It is with great pride that Savvas brings the talents of this superb author team to the high school class-room.

Salt marsh in Chincoteague National Wildlife Refuge, Virginia

Consultants/Reviewers

High School Earth Science Consultant, Writer, and Reviewer

Michael Wysession received his Ph.D. in geophysics from Northwestern University in 1991. He is an Associate Professor in Earth and Planetary Sciences at Washington University in St. Louis, Missouri. He is an author on more than fifty scientific publications. For his research, he was awarded a Packard Foundation Fellowship, and in 1996 was awarded a Presidential Faculty Fellowship at the White House.

In addition to teaching, writing, and research, Dr. Wysession is internationally known for his work in geoscience education and outreach. He was the Earth and Space Science Design Team Leader for the National Research Council report, *A Framework for K–12 Science Education.* Professor Wysession was also on the organizing committee for the writing of the Next Generation Science Standards, based upon the NRC's *A Framework for K–12 Science Education.*

Content Reviewers

Glen C. Kroeger, Ph.D.
Associate Professor and Chair
Geosciences Department
Trinity University
San Antonio, Texas

George S. Mumford, Ph.D.
Professor of Astronomy, Emeritus
Tufts University
Medford, Massachusetts

Scott M. Rochette, Ph.D.
Department of the Earth Sciences
State University of New York
Brockport, New York

Ronald Sass, Ph.D.
Professor of Ecology and
Evolutionary Biology, Emeritus
Rice University
Houston, Texas

Paul R. Stoddard, Ph.D.
Department of Geology and
Environmental Geosciences
Northern Illinois University
DeKalb, Illinois

Teacher Reviewers

Helen A. Bastin
Bloomington High School North
Bloomington, Indiana

David R. Blakely
Arlington High School
Arlington, Massachusetts

Joseph M. Bosco, Jr.
New Britain High School
New Britain, Connecticut

Jeffrey C. Callister
Earth Science Teacher (ret.)
Newburgh Free Academy
Newburgh, New York

Jo A. Combs
Broward County Schools
Ft. Lauderdale, Florida

Scott Cordell
Earth Science Teacher
Armarillo, Texas

Elizabeth Elixman Campbell
Warren Central High School
Indianapolis, Indiana

Glen Dolphin
Union-Endicott High School
Endicott, New York

Richard P. Filson
Edison High School
Stockton, California

Greg J. Geisen
New Albany High School
New Albany, Indiana

Amy Hall
Vista del Lago High School
Moreno Valley, California

Georgina Koch Hidalgo
Miami-Dade County Public Schools
Miami, Florida

Kristine J. Kelley
Wilkes Central High School
Wilkesboro, North Carolina

Kevin Leineweber
Tippecanoe School Corporation
Lafayette, Indiana

Marian J. Marley
Wilkes Central High School
Wilkesboro, North Carolina

Bruce A. Mellin
Brooks School
North Andover, Massachusetts

Michael Passow
White Plains Middle School
White Plains, New York

Jean Pennycook
Fresno Unified School District
Fresno, California

Gregory S. Small
William Henry Harrison High School
Evansville, Indiana

Thomas J. Vaughn
Arlington High School
Arlington, Massachusetts

Donald G. Wafer
Muncie Central High School
Muncie, Indiana

Jeffrey A. Williams
New Albany High School
New Albany, Indiana

Bryce Canyon National Park, Utah

Contents

Three sapphires

Death Valley, California

A rainbow displaying the colors of visible light

Labs and Activities

Try It!

Quick Lab

Exploration Lab

Features

Earth & Space

Earth & Its Resources

Earth & Its Systems

Earth & History

How Earth Works

Map It

EARTH SCIENCE

Focus and Engage

At the beginning of each chapter, the Big Idea focuses on a major theme of Earth Science. Launch each chapter with an engaging visual and an inquiry activity to build excitement and a deeper understanding of the theme.

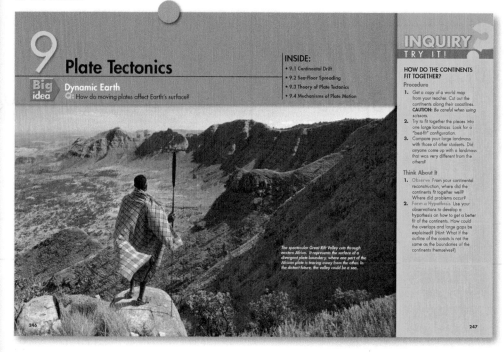

- Student Edition
- Teacher's Edition
- Progress Monitoring Assessments, Teacher's Edition
- Standardized Test Prep Workbook
- ExamView® CD-ROM
- Student Edition eText
- Teacher's Edition eText

---

9 Plate Tectonics

Big idea
Dynamic Earth
Q: How do moving plates affect Earth's surface?

INSIDE:
- 9.1 Continental Drift
- 9.2 Sea-Floor Spreading
- 9.3 Theory of Plate Tectonics
- 9.4 Mechanisms of Plate Motion

INQUIRY
TRY IT!

HOW DO THE CONTINENTS FIT TOGETHER?
Procedure
1. Get a copy of a world map from your teacher. Cut out the continents along their coastlines. **CAUTION:** Be careful when using scissors.
2. Try to fit together the pieces into one large landmass. Look for a "best-fit" configuration.
3. Compare your large landmass with those of other students. Did anyone come up with a landmass that was very different from the others?

Think About It
1. Observe From your continental reconstruction, where did the continents fit together well? Where did problems occur?
2. Form a Hypothesis Use your observations to develop a hypothesis on how to get a better fit of the continents. How could the overlaps and large gaps be explained? [Hint: What if the outline of the coasts is not the same as the boundaries of the continents themselves?]

The spectacular Great Rift Valley cuts through eastern Africa. It represents the surface of a divergent plate boundary, where one part of the African plate is tearing away from the other. In the distant future, the valley could be a sea.

246 | 247

9.1 Continental Drift

At the beginning of each lesson, **Key Questions** and **Reading Strategies** help you unlock the lesson content.

Key Questions

🔑 What is the hypothesis of continental drift?

🔑 What evidence supported continental drift?

🔑 Why was Wegener's hypothesis rejected?

Vocabulary
- continental drift
- Pangaea

Reading Strategy
Summarize Copy the table. Fill it in as you read to summarize the evidence of continental drift.

MORE THAN 300 years that accurately showed the maps, people noticed that of a jigsaw puzzle. Few pe until the early twentieth c at the fit of the continents

The Continent

A German scientist, Alfre between the coastlines on Ocean. As you can see in and Africa are an approxi Wegener proposed his rad
🔑 **According to Wege continents had once been** He called this supercontin
Wegener also hypothes

Key Questions

🔑 **What is the hypothesis of continental drift?**

🔑 **What evidence supported continental drift?**

🔑 **Why was Wegener's hypothesis rejected?**

Vocabulary
- continental drift
- Pangaea

Reading Strategy
Summarize Copy the table. Fill it in as you read to summarize the evidence of continental drift.

Explore Through Inquiry

Explore the Big Ideas through Inquiry with the hands-on **Try It!** activities at the beginning of each chapter. **Quick Labs** and full-length chapter **Exploration Labs** help you explore Earth Science in depth.

Use Visuals to Explore

Use the **Map It** feature to build your map and visual learning skills while deepening your understanding of the science content.

MAP IT!
ACTIVITY

In **Figure 4**, note the volcanoes encircling the Pacific basin, known as the "Ring of Fire."
Infer How are the volcanoes in the middle of the Atlantic Ocean related to a plate boundary?

FIGURE 4 Major Volcanoes

Assess Your Understanding

Review content and apply concepts with the lesson and chapter assessments. Then use the Standardized Test Prep pages to prepare for standardized tests.

Standards at a Glance

The Next Generation Science Standards identify the key scientific ideas and practices that all students should learn by the time they graduate from high school. Each standard is written as a performance expectation that integrates three dimensions: science and engineering practices (SEP), disciplinary core ideas (DCI), and crosscutting concepts (CCC). This blending of practices for doing science, content for *knowing* science, and themes for *connecting* science is what makes the Next Generation Science Standards a unique shift in science education.

This table provides a curriculum alignment for *Savvas Earth Science* to the Next Generation Science Standards for high school Earth sciences plus relevant Engineering standards. Use this table to help you in your transition to the new standards.

NGSS Performance Expectations	
HS-ESS1 Earth's Place in the Universe	**Where You Will Find It**
HS-ESS1-1. Develop a model based on evidence to illustrate the life span of the sun and the role of nuclear fusion in the sun's core to release energy that eventually reaches Earth in the form of radiation.	Lessons 24.3, 25.2
HS-ESS1-2. Construct an explanation of the Big Bang theory based on astronomical evidence of light spectra, motion of distant galaxies, and composition of matter in the universe.	Lessons 24.1, 24.3, 25.1–25.3 Chapter 1 Earth & Space
HS-ESS1-3. Communicate scientific ideas about the way stars, over their life cycle, produce elements.	Lessons 24.3, 25.1, 25.2
HS-ESS1-4. Use mathematical or computational representations to predict the motion of orbiting objects in the solar system.	Lesson 22.1
HS-ESS1-5. Evaluate evidence of the past and current movements of continental and oceanic crust and the theory of plate tectonics to explain the ages of crustal rocks.	Lessons 9.1–9.3, 10.1, 11.3 Chapters 9, 10 Try It
HS-ESS1-6. Apply scientific reasoning and evidence from ancient Earth materials, meteorites, and other planetary surfaces to construct an account of Earth's formation and early history.	Lessons 12.1–12.3, 22.3, 23.1
HS-ESS2 Earth's Systems	**Where You Will Find It**
HS-ESS2-1. Develop a model to illustrate how Earth's internal and surface processes operate at different spatial and temporal scales to form continental and ocean-floor features.	Lessons 9.3–9.4, 11.2–11.3 Chapters 9, 11 Quick Lab Chapters 9, 14 Exploration Lab Chapters 9, 11 Earth & Its Systems Chapter 10 How Earth Works Chapter 10 Map It
HS-ESS2-2. Analyze geoscience data to make the claim that one change to Earth's surface can create feedbacks that cause changes to other Earth systems.	Lessons 1.4, 13.1, 21.3 Chapter 9 Earth & Its Systems Chapter 9 Map It
HS-ESS2-3. Develop a model based on evidence of Earth's interior to describe the cycling of matter by thermal convection.	Lessons 8.4, 9.2–9.4 Chapter 9 Map It

NGSS Performance Expectations

HS-ESS2 Earth's Systems	Where You Will Find It
HS-ESS2-4. Use a model to describe how variations in the flow of energy into and out of Earth's systems result in changes in climate.	Lessons 15.2–15.3, 17.1–17.2, 21.1, 21.3 Chapters 17, 21 Try It Chapter 21 Quick Lab Chapter 17 Exploration Lab Chapter 19 Earth & Its Systems Chapter 12 Earth & History
HS-ESS2-5. Plan and conduct an investigation of the properties of water and its effects on Earth materials and surface processes.	Lessons 5.1, 6.1–6.3, 7.2, 10.1, 17.3, 18.1, 21.3 Chapters 5, 6, 18 Try It Chapter 7, 15 Exploration Lab Chapter 7 How Earth Works
HS-ESS2-6. Develop a quantitative model to describe the cycling of carbon among the hydrosphere, atmosphere, geosphere, and biosphere.	Lesson 13.1, 21.3 Chapter 3 Earth & Its Systems
HS-ESS2-7. Construct an argument based on evidence about the simultaneous coevolution of Earth's systems and life on Earth.	Lessons 13.1–13.2

NGSS Performance Expectations

HS-ESS3 Earth and Human Activity	Where You Will Find It
HS-ESS3-1. Construct an explanation based on evidence for how the availability of natural resources, occurrence of natural hazards, and changes in climate have influenced human activity.	Lessons 4.1–4.4, 6.2, 8.3, 20.3, 21.3 Chapter 8 Try It Chapter 21 Exploration Lab Chapters 8, 20 How Earth Works
HS-ESS3-2. Evaluate competing design solutions for developing, managing, and utilizing energy and mineral resources based on cost-benefit ratios.*	Lessons 4.1–4.2, 4.4 Chapter 4 Try It Chapter 4 Exploration Lab Chapter 4 Earth & Its Resources Chapter 4 Map It
HS-ESS3-3. Create a computational simulation to illustrate the relationships among management of natural resources, the sustainability of human populations, and biodiversity.	Lessons 4.1–4.4 Chapter 4 Map It
HS-ESS3-4. Evaluate or refine a technological solution that reduces impacts of human activities on natural systems.*	Lesson 4.4, 21.3 Chapter 4 Exploration Lab Chapter 6 Earth & Its Resources
HS-ESS3-5. Analyze geoscience data and the results from global climate models to make an evidence-based forecast of the current rate of global or regional climate change and associated future impacts to Earth systems.	Lesson 21.3 Chapter 21 Try It Chapter 21 Exploration Lab
HS-ESS3-6. Use a computational representation to illustrate the relationships among Earth systems and how those relationships are being modified due to human activity.	Lesson 21.3 Chapter 21 Exploration Lab Chapter 17 How Earth Works

NGSS Performance Expectations

HS-ETS1 Engineering Design	Where You Will Find It
HS-ETS1-1. Analyze a major global challenge to specify qualitative and quantitative criteria and constraints for solutions that account for societal needs and wants.	Lesson 21.3 Chapter 21 Exploration Lab
HS-ETS1-2. Design a solution to a complex real-world problem by breaking it down into smaller, more manageable problems that can be solved through engineering.	Lesson 4.2, 21.3 Chapter 21 Exploration Lab
HS-ETS1-3. Evaluate a solution to a complex real-world problem based on prioritized criteria and trade-offs that account for a range of constraints, including cost, safety, reliability, and aesthetics, as well as possible social, cultural, and environmental impacts.	Lessons 4.1–4.2
HS-ETS1-4. Use a computer simulation to model the impact of proposed solutions to a complex real-world problem with numerous criteria and constraints on interactions within and between systems relevant to the problem.	Lesson 21.3 Chapter 21 Exploration Lab

Materials List

Savvas Earth Science has a wide range of activities. Some use materials that are listed in the tables below. You can use the tables to help you plan your activities and order supplies. Visit Savvas.com for information on how to order materials. Materials in the tables with an ◆ are school supplied.

Consumable

Item	*Quantity	Chapter
Aluminum foil	1 sheet	14 Lab
◆ Apple	1	12.1 TI
Antacid tablet	5	5 Lab
◆ Carton, juice		
1.89-L	1	4 Lab
946-mL	1	4 Lab
240-mL	1	4 Lab
Clay, modeling	1 piece	3.4 QL, 14 Lab
◆ Club soda	2 bottles	10.1 QL
Cotton ball	3	6 Lab
Food coloring	1	15 Lab
Glitter	1/4 tsp	20.1 TI
Hydrochloric acid solution	4 mL	3 Lab
Hydrochloric acid solution, dilute	5 mL	2 Lab
◆ Ice crystals	250 mL	7.1 TI
◆ Ice cube	12	5 Lab, 15 Lab, 18.1 TI
Knife, plastic	1	3.4 QL
Leaf sample	1	12.1 TI
Marker, permanent	1	10.1 TI
Markers, felt-tip (water-based ink)	1 set	3 Lab, 21.1 TI
Masking tape	4 strips	21.1 QL
Notebook	1	25 Lab
◆ Orange seed	1	12.1 TI
Paper, 5-m adding machine tape	1	13 Lab
Paper, 6-m adding machine tape	1	23 Lab
Paper, black construction	1 sheet	17.1 TI

Item	*Quantity	Chapter
Paper, graph	1 sheet	5 Lab, 12 Lab, 14 Lab, 15 Lab, 16 Lab, 17 Lab
Paper, tracing	1 sheet	11 Lab, 20 Lab
◆ Paper, white	1 sheet	4.1 TI, 19 Lab, 22 Lab, 24.1 TI
	2 sheets	14.1 TI
◆ Paper, white unlined	1 sheet	9.1 TI, 23.1 TI, 24 Lab
Paper towels	1 roll	2 Lab, 10.1 QL, 20.1 TI, 21.1 QL
Pen	1	21.1 TI
Pencil	1	4.1 TI, 8 Lab, 9 Lab, 11 Lab, 13 Lab, 14 Lab, 16 Lab, 17.1 TI, 19 Lab, 20 Lab, 21 Lab, 22 Lab, 23.1 TI, 24.1 TI, 24 Lab
Pencils, colored	1 set	10 Lab, 15 Lab, 17 Lab, 23 Lab
Plastic putty	1 chunk	11.1 TI
◆ Raisin	1	12.1 TI
Rubber band, large, thick	1	11.1 TI
Salt, non-iodized	4–5 tbsp	14.4 QL
Sand sample	1	6 Lab, 14.1 TI, 17 Lab, 21.1 QL, 22.1 TI
Sand, coarse	1	6 Lab
Soap, liquid 30-mL	1	20.1 TI
Stick, flat wooden	2	17 Lab
Stick, thin, wooden 25-cm	1	11.1 TI
String	20–35 cm	23.1 TI
Tape, duct	10-cm strip	20.1 TI
Tape, removable	4 strips	20 Lab
Tape, transparent	4 strips	23.1 TI, 24 Lab
Thread, thin	2 cm	2 Lab
◆ Water, distilled	3 mL	3 Lab

Key: TI = Try It   QL = Quick Lab   Lab = End-of-Chapter Lab   ◆ = School Supplied   * = Quantities per group

Materials List (continued)

Consumable

Item	*Quantity	Chapter
◆ Water, hot	200 mL	5 Lab
◆ Water, noncarbonated	2 bottles	10.1 QL

Item	*Quantity	Chapter
◆ Water, room temperature		18 Lab
Wax paper, 20-cm square	2	3.4 QL

Nonconsumable

Item	*Quantity	Chapter
Air Movement in Pressure Cells	1 copy	19 Lab
Anthracite sample	1	3 Lab
Augite sample	1	2 Lab
Balance	1	2 Lab, 14.4 QL
Ball, different-sized	3	22.1 TI
Ball, small rubber	1	15.1 TI
Basalt sample	1	3.1 TI, 3 Lab
◆ Basketball	1	22 Lab
Beaker, 100-mL	1	6 Lab, 15 Lab
Beaker, 250-mL	2	5 Lab, 7.1 TI, 17 Lab, 18.1 TI
Beaker, 400-mL	1	14.4 QL
Bituminous coal	1	3 Lab
Board, short	2	19.1 TI
Bone, small	1	12.1 TI
◆ Book, large	1 2	8.1 TI 19.1 TI
Bottle, 1-L plastic	2	20.1 TI
Calcite sample	1	2.1 TI, 2 Lab
Calculator	1	9.1 QL, 9 Lab, 18 Lab, 23 Lab
Cardboard box, large	1	24 Lab
Cardboard box, small	1	24 Lab
Cardboard sheet, (20 cm × 20 cm)	1	23.1 TI
Clay sample	1	14.1 TI
Common Minerals, pp. 54–55	1 copy	2 Lab
Compass, drawing	1	1 Lab, 8 Lab

Item	*Quantity	Chapter
Conglomerate sample	1	3 Lab
Container, clear plastic	1	14.1 TI, 22.1 TI
Container, clear plastic, rectangular	1	16.1 TI
Container, identical	2	21.1 QL
Container, with lid 1-L	1	5.1 TI
Fan, Table Top, 3-speed	1	16.1 TI
Feldspar sample	1	2 Lab
Fluorite sample	1	2 Lab
Fossil sample (or replica)	variety	13.1 TI
Funnel, small	1	6 Lab
Geologic Time Scale, p. 357	1 copy	12 Lab
Glass jar, clear	1	5.1 TI
Globe	1	1 Lab
Gneiss sample	1	3.1 TI, 3 Lab
Goggles, safety	1	2.1 TI
Graduated cylinder, 100-mL	2	6 Lab, 15 Lab
Graduated cylinder, 500-mL	2	15.1 TI
Graduated cylinder, 50-mL	1	2 Lab
Granite sample	1	3.1 TI, 3 Lab
Gypsum sample	1	2 Lab
Hair sample	1	12.1 TI
Halite sample	1	2.1 TI, 2 Lab
Hammer	1	2.1 TI, 2 Lab
Hand lens	1	2.1 TI, 2 Lab, 3.1 TI, 5.1 TI, 14.1 TI

Nonconsumable

Item	*Quantity	Chapter
Hornblende sample	1	2 Lab
Insect wing - Sphynx Moth	1	12.1 TI
Knife, steel blade	1	2 Lab
Knife, table	1	7.1 TI
Lamp	1	22 Lab
Light source	1	17 Lab
Limestone sample	1	3.1 TI, 3 Lab
Magnetite sample	1	2 Lab
Magnifying glass	1	7.1 TI, 12.1 TI
Map, p. 241	1 copy	8 Lab
Map, world	1	1 Lab, 8 Lab, 9.1 TI, 10.1 TI
Marble sample	1	3.1 TI, 3 Lab
Meter stick	1	13 Lab, 22.1 TI, 23 Lab
Mica sample	1	2 Lab
Microscope	1	12.1 TI
Northern Hemisphere, p. 550	1 copy	19 Lab
Obsidian sample	1	3 Lab
Olivine sample	1	2 Lab
Penlight	1	25 Lab
◆ Penny	1	2 Lab
Plastic bead, small, round	20–30	3.4 QL
Plate, glass	1	2 Lab
Protractor	1	1 Lab, 11 Lab
Psychrometer	1	18 Lab
Pushpin	2	23.1 TI
Pyrite sample	1	2 Lab
◆ Resource object	5–10	4.1 TI
Ring stand	1	17 Lab
Rock, small	5–10	5.1 TI
Ruler, metric (30-cm)	1	1 Lab, 4 Lab, 9 Lab, 16.1 TI, 20 Lab, 22.1 TI, 23.1 TI, 24 Lab
Sandstone sample	1	3.1 TI, 3 Lab

Item	*Quantity	Chapter
Scalpel	1	14 Lab
Scissors	1	2 Lab, 4 Lab, 9.1 TI, 20.1 TI
Seashell	1	12.1 TI
Seismogram, p. 223	1 copy	8.2 QL
Shale sample	1	3 Lab
Shoe box	1	14 Lab
Slate sample	1	3 Lab
◆ Softball	1	22 Lab
Soil sample, potting	1	6 Lab
Southern Hemisphere, p. 551	1 copy	19 Lab
Spoon, table	1	14.4 QL
Spring scale	1	2 Lab
Star Charts (Appendix)	1 copy	25 Lab
◆ Stick, small	1	12.1 TI
Stirring rod	1	14.4 QL, 15 Lab
Strainer	1	5.1 TI
Streak plate	1	2 Lab
Talc sample	1	2 Lab
Telescope	1	24 Lab
Temperature Curves Graph p. 301	1 copy	10 Lab
Tennis ball	1	19.1 TI
Test tube	2	15 Lab
Thermometer	2	5 Lab, 17 Lab, 18.1 TI
Thermometer, laboratory	2	21.1 QL
Tooth, small	1	12.1 TI
Topographic Map, p. 211	1	7 Lab
Travel-time Graph, p. 225	1 copy	8.2 QL
Washer, flat rubber 3/8" hole	1	20.1 TI
Watch or clock with a second hand	1	5 Lab, 6 Lab, 14.1 TI, 19.1 TI, 21.1 QL
Wood block	2	19.1 TI

1 Introduction to Earth Science Planning Guide

BIGIDEA: EARTH'S MATERIALS AND SYSTEMS

Lesson Objectives		Activities
1.1 What Is Earth Science? pp. 2–5 1.1 **Define** Earth science. 1.2 **Describe** the formation of Earth and the solar system.		TE Teacher Demo: Separation and Density, p. 4 L2 LM Laboratory Skills Checkup 1, 2, 3, 4 L1
1.2 A View of Earth, pp. 7–10 1.3 **Describe** Earth's four major spheres. 1.4 **Differentiate** among the three parts of the geosphere. 1.5 **Explain** the theory of plate tectonics and its value to Earth science.		TE Teacher Demo: Earth's Layers, p. 8 L2 TE Teacher Demo: Convection and Plates, p. 10 L2 LM Evaluating Precision L1 LM The International System of Units (SI) L1
1.3 Representing Earth's Surface, pp. 11–17 1.6 **Locate** points on Earth's surface by their latitude and longitude. 1.7 **Describe** the advantages and disadvantages of different types of maps. 1.8 **Explain** what makes topographic maps different from other maps.		TE Teacher Demo: Conic and Gnomonic Projections, p. 13 L2 LM Using a Topographic Map to Create a Landform L2
1.4 Earth System Science, pp. 18–22 1.9 **Describe** the primary goal of Earth system science and **define** the term *system*. 1.10 **Describe** Earth's two major sources of energy. 1.11 **Explain** how humans affect Earth's systems. 1.12 **Distinguish** between renewable and nonrenewable resources.		TE Build Science Skills, p. 22 L2
1.5 What Is Scientific Inquiry? pp. 23–24 1.13 **Define** the terms *hypothesis* and *theory*.		LM Measuring Volume and Temperature L1

Chapter Features and Labs

Try It Developing Your Observation Skills, p. 1		
Earth & Space Earth's Place in the Universe, p. 6		
Earth & Space Studying Earth from Space, p. 25		
Exploration Lab Determining Latitude and Longitude, pp. 26–27		

Ability Levels

L1 For students who need additional help
L2 For all students
L3 For students who need to be challenged

Components

SE	Student Edition	LP	Lesson Plans
TE	Teacher's Edition	AA	Active Art
LM	Laboratory Manual	PD	Planet Diary
CT	Chapter Tests	GEODe	Geode CD-ROM
GRSW	Guided Reading & Study Workbook	eText	
CTB	Computer Test Bank		

Resources	Lesson Assessment
GRSW Lesson 1.1 LP Lesson Planning 1.1	SE Lesson 1.1 Assessment, p. 5 eText Lesson 1.1
GRSW Lesson 1.2 LP Lesson Planning 1.2	SE Lesson 1.2 Assessment, p. 10 eText Lesson 1.2
GRSW Lesson 1.3 LP Lesson Planning 1.3 AA Topographic Map PD GPS	SE Lesson 1.3 Assessment, p. 17 eText Lesson 1.3
GRSW Lesson 1.4 LP Lesson Planning 1.4	SE Lesson 1.4 Assessment, p. 22 eText Lesson 1.4
GRSW Lesson 1.5 LP Lesson Planning 1.5	SE Lesson 1.5 Assessment, p. 24 eText Lesson 1.5

Materials for Activities and Labs

Quantities for each group

STUDENT EDITION

Exploration Lab, pp. 26–27
globe, protractor, ruler, compass or round object for tracing, pencil, world map

TEACHER'S EDITION

Teacher Demo, p. 4
2 large glass jars with lids, 100 mL sand, 100 mL rock salt, 100 mL sugar, 100 mL water, 100 mL vegetable oil, 100 mL corn syrup

Teacher Demo, p. 8
hard-boiled egg, knife

Teacher Demo, p. 10
hot plate; deep, wide glass container such as a lasagna pan; diluted tomato soup; large, thin sponges; scissors; tongs

Teacher Demo, p. 13
small globe, blank transparency sheet

Build Science Skills, p. 22
pictures of houses underwater due to a flood (natural or human-made), pictures of buildings damaged by an earthquake, pictures of a coastal home being swept out to sea due to beach erosion

Assessment

CHAPTER ASSESSMENT
SE Assessment, pp. 29–30
CT Chapter 1 Test
CTB Chapter 1
eText Chapter 1

21st Century Learning

Creativity and Intellectual Curiosity: What Science Subject Interests You?, TE p. 28

Common Themes

Michael Wysession
Washington University

Earth science involves the study of Earth and its neighbors in the solar system. Earth science is very interdisciplinary, involving aspects of geology, chemistry, physics, and biology.

Space and Time Earth is located in the outer part of the Milky Way galaxy. Earth and the rest of the solar system formed about 4.56 billion years ago and are about one-third the age of the universe. Gravity caused Earth to form layers based upon density. Going from the center out, Earth consists of a metal core, rocky mantle and crust, liquid ocean, and a gaseous atmosphere. The biosphere, which is an important geological agent, is found in the geosphere, hydrosphere, and atmosphere. Earth's surface is best represented on a globe, though maps are more convenient. There are many different ways of projecting the globe onto a two-dimensional map, and many different kinds of maps such as topographic and geologic maps.

Forces and Motion Plate tectonics, involving the lateral motions of pieces of Earth's surface, is ultimately responsible for the formation and structure of the continents, and provides the framework for understanding modern Earth science.

Earth as a System Earth System Science is an approach to viewing Earth as the result of many different interconnected systems. Environmental science is an aspect of Earth science that is concerned with issues related to the human impact on our planet such as the use of natural resources and the alteration of Earth's surface.

EARTH SCIENCE REFRESHER

Uniformitarianism vs. Catastrophism

In the 18th and 19th centuries, many debates in geology focused on how Earth formed. Scientists often took one of two polarized views. Catastrophists, often with a theological interest, envisioned a world that formed rapidly in a series of "catastrophic" events. Uniformitarians, with a more naturalist view, thought the Earth formed over an unimaginably long period of time from the slow, continual geologic processes seen today. It turned out that both were right to some degree: Earth formed relatively rapidly in a catastrophic manner 4.56 billion years ago, but has cooled slowly and relatively continuously since then.

Most processes in Earth science occur over a spectrum of scales that can be seen as catastrophic at one end and continual at the other. There are thousands of earthquakes that occur every day, part of a continual cracking and bending of the plates, but it is the rare catastrophic ones that release the most energy and account for most of the plate motion. Small volcanic eruptions occur continuously, but it is the occasional enormous eruption that adds so much gas and dust into the atmosphere that global climates are changed. It is estimated that about three tons of cometary and meteoroid debris enters Earth's atmosphere each day, mostly in the form of

> **Address Misconceptions**
>
> *Students may think that Earth and the Milky Way are at the center of the universe. They may have inferred this from learning that almost all galaxies are moving away from the Milky Way in all directions.* For a strategy that helps to overcome this misconception, see **Address Misconceptions** on **TE p. 6.**

Students may think that only human actions can seriously affect the environment. Use the example of the eruption of Mount St. Helens to emphasize that natural events can have widespread and negative effects on the environment. For a strategy that helps to overcome this misconception, see **Address Misconceptions** on TE p. 20.

tiny grains. However, separated by tens or hundreds of millions of years, impacts from large asteroids have likely caused mass extinctions and indelibly altered the course of life through their chance collisions. And, of course, in each of these examples, there is a full spectrum of activity covering all the intermediate levels as well. So be aware, when teaching all aspects of Earth Science, from streams and floods to folding and faulting, that the same process occurs at many scales, and can be seen from both a Uniformitarian and a Catastrophist point of view.

Biogeosciences

One of the most exciting new areas of research and discovery in the Earth sciences concerns the incorporation of biology. It turns out that a huge number of geochemical processes that once were thought to occur inorganically are now known to be caused by or catalyzed by bacteria and other single-celled organisms. Bacteria have been found everywhere there is water, including within the tiny pore spaces between mineral grains of rocks deep beneath Earth's surface! Many minerals are made by biological processes, and it is now realized that Earth's geology would be very different if it were not for the presence of life. As a result, there are a rapidly growing number of biologists now working in university geology departments, and the areas of biogeology and biogeochemistry are where some of the most exciting new research is being done.

BUILD READING LITERACY
Anticipation Guide
Stimulating Interest in a Topic

Strategy Engage students actively with a selection by activating prior knowledge, arousing interest, and helping establish purposes for reading. Generate a series of statements related to the topic of a passage for students to respond to and discuss before reading. Choose a passage from this chapter, such as Section 1.4, pp. 18–22, and prepare a set of statements ahead of time.

Example

1. Prior to class, read through the passage and identify major concepts and details.

2. Construct an anticipation guide as follows:

• Write 5–10 short, but thought-provoking, declarative statements about the most important concepts featured in the section.

• If students are likely to have misconceptions about the topic, be sure to include statements that address those misconceptions.

• The statements could be in either a true-false or an agree-disagree format.

• To the left of each statement, put a blank for student responses.

3. Before assigning the section to read, either display the guide on the board or on an overhead, or distribute individual worksheets. Students can respond to the statements individually or as a group.

4. Discuss students' responses, asking students to support their answers using examples from past experience or prior reading.

5. Then, have students read the section, evaluating the statements from the anticipation guide as they read.

6. After reading, revisit the guide, encouraging students to compare and contrast their current ones. Have students quote information from the passage to support their decisions.

See TE p. 8 for a script on how to use the anticipation guide strategy with students. For additional Build Reading Literacy strategies, see TE pp. 2, 3, 8, 9, 12, 19, and 23.

ASSESS PRIOR KNOWLEDGE

Use the Chapter Pretest below to assess students' prior knowledge. As needed, review these concepts.

Review Science Concepts

Lesson 1.1 Review the parts of the solar system, and the concept that the solar system is just one part of the Milky Way galaxy, which is just one part of the universe. Review with students that denser objects sink while less dense objects float. This will help students understand how Earth's layers formed.

Lesson 1.2 Remind students that Earth's liquid water and atmosphere make it unique among the planets.

Lesson 1.3 Have students recall the locations of North America, the equator, the prime meridian, and the International Date Line on a world map. Review the compass rose (N-S-E-W).

Lesson 1.4 Review the concept of a system. Discuss living and nonliving (biotic and abiotic) factors in the environment.

Lesson 1.5 Encourage students to recall the idea that an observation is something you notice with your senses.

Review Math Skills

Ratio Students will need to understand ratios and how ratios can be written (as a fraction or with a colon). Direct students to the Math Skills in the Skills Handbook at the end of the student text.

1 Introduction to Earth Science

Big idea **Earth's Materials and Systems**
Q: What is the basic structure of Earth?

Chapter Pretest

1. True or False: Our solar system consists only of Earth and the sun. *(False)*

2. Object A is denser than water. If object A is dropped into a cup of water, what will happen to the object? *(c)*
  a. Object A will float on top of the water.
  b. Object A will float in the middle of the water.
  c. Object A will sink to the bottom of the cup.

3. What is Earth known to have that other planets in our solar system are not known to have? *(c)*
  a. an atmosphere   **b.** volcanoes
  c. liquid water   **d.** rings

4. What is the name of the imaginary horizontal line that goes around Earth's middle? *(a)*
  a. equator   **b.** prime meridian
  c. international date line

5. Which of these imaginary lines crosses through Greenwich, England? *(b)*
  a. equator   **b.** prime meridian
  c. international date line

6. Fill in the locations for west, east, and south on the compass rose to the right.

$$W \underset{S}{\overset{N}{+}} E$$

7. What is a storm that brings strong winds, heavy rains, and coastal flooding? *(b)*
  a. tornado   **b.** hurricane
  c. tsunami

INSIDE:

Systems of air, rock, water—and life—are all connected in this magnificent landscape at Moraine Lake, Banff National Park in the Canadian Rockies.

INQUIRY
TRY IT!

DEVELOPING YOUR OBSERVATION SKILLS

Procedure

Study the photograph on this page. Note the nonliving and living features that make up the landscape.

Think About It

1. **Observe** What features can you identify in the photograph?
2. **Infer** How do you think this lake was formed?
3. **Design an Experiment** If you were an Earth scientist, how could you use this photograph in your work?

1

ENGAGE/EXPLORE

INQUIRY
TRY IT!

DEVELOPING YOUR OBSERVATION SKILLS   L2

Purpose This eye-catching photo should intrigue your students.

Skills Observe, Infer

Prep Time 5 minutes

Materials textbook

Class Time 10 minutes

Teaching Tip Some students may have difficulty identifying the water line that separates the land and sky from their reflection in the water. Once this line is indicated to students, they should be able to see that much of the bottom half of the image is a reflection.

Expected Outcome Students will observe mountains, water, clouds, and a glacier (snow and ice). Students are also likely to observe the living things in the photograph, including the trees and the hiker.

Think About It

1. Features include mountains, water, clouds, ice, snow, and a glacier.
2. Students may note the glaciers and infer that the lake resulted from the melting of glacial ice.
3. This photograph could be used to observe cloud types and predict the weather. This photograph could be used to study the shape and structure of the mountains to determine their geologic history. An Earth scientist can infer from this picture that past glaciation has shaped the mountains, and uplifting caused by tectonic plate movements built these mountains.

LESSON 1.1

1 FOCUS

Lesson Objectives
1.1 **Define** Earth science.
1.2 **Describe** the formation of Earth and the solar system.

Build Vocabulary `L2`
Word Parts Ask students to use a dictionary to determine the meanings of the following word parts:
geo- (Earth);   *astro-* (outer space); *-ology* (study of); *-ography* (study of); *-onomy* (study of)
Based on this discussion and their prior knowledge, have students predict the meaning of this lesson's vocabulary words. Then, have students look up the words in the Glossary to check their predictions and make any necessary corrections. *Meteorology* will likely present a problem, with most students predicting that it is the study of meteors, rather than the study of the atmosphere.

Reading Strategy `L2`
a. Earth, earthquakes, mountains, volcanoes, Earth's history
b. oceanography
c. composition and movements of seawater, coastal processes, seafloor topography, marine life
d. meteorology
e. atmosphere, weather, climate
f. astronomy
g. universe, solar system

2 INSTRUCT

Build Reading Literacy `L1`
Refer to **p. 216D** in **Chapter 8,** which provides guidelines for comparing and contrasting.

Compare and Contrast Have students create a table to compare and contrast physical geology and historical geology. They should fill in their table as they read the first part of this lesson. Areas to consider include the focus of each area and examples of what is studied.
Visual

Key Questions

 What is the study of Earth science?

 How did Earth and the solar system form?

Vocabulary
- Earth science • geology
- oceanography
- meteorology • astronomy

Reading Strategy
Categorize As you read about the different branches of Earth science, fill in the column with the name of each branch and list some of the things that are studied in the other column.

geology	a. ____?____	
b. ____?____	c. ____?____	
d. ____?____	e. ____?____	
f. ____?____	g. ____?____	

FIGURE 1 Studying Earth's Past
Paleontologists study fossils— remains of life from the distant past—to learn how life forms have changed through time.
Pose Questions *What questions do you have about this fossil?*

THE SPECTACULAR ERUPTION of a volcano, the dramatic scenery of a rocky coast, and the destructive power of a hurricane are all subjects for Earth science. The study of Earth science deals with many fascinating and practical questions about our environment. What forces shape the features of our landscape, from the tallest of mountains to the deepest of valleys? What causes ocean tides? Why does our daily weather change? Is our climate changing? How old is Earth? What is an ice age like? Will there be another?

Understanding Earth is not an easy task because our planet is continually changing. Earth is a dynamic planet with a long and complex history.

Overview of Earth Science
Earth science is the name for the group of sciences that studies Earth and its neighbors in space. The field of Earth science includes many subdivisions, including geology, oceanography, meteorology, and astronomy.

Geology Units 1 through 4 of this textbook focus on the science of **geology,** a word that means "study of Earth." Geochemistry, geophysics, geobiology, and paleontology are all areas of study within geology.

Geology is divided into two broad areas—historical geology and physical geology. The aim of historical geology is to understand Earth's long history. Historical geology tries to establish a timeline of the vast number of physical and biological changes that have occurred in the past.

Physical geology includes the examination of the materials that make up Earth and the possible explanations for the many processes that shape our planet. Processes below the surface create earthquakes, build mountains, and produce volcanoes. Processes at the surface break rock apart and create diverse landforms. Erosion by water, wind, and ice results in different landscapes. You will learn how rocks and minerals form due to Earth's internal and external processes. Understanding the origin of rocks and minerals is an important part of understanding Earth.

FIGURE 2 Studying the Oceans
Oceanographers study all aspects of the ocean—the chemistry of its waters, the geology of its seafloor, the physics of its interactions with the atmosphere, and the biology of its organisms.

☑ **Reading Checkpoint** *What are the two main areas of geology?*

Oceanography Unit 5 is devoted to **oceanography,** the scientific study of the oceans. Oceanography integrates the sciences of chemistry, physics, geology, and biology in understanding oceanic phenomena. Oceanographers study the composition and movements of seawater, as well as coastal processes, seafloor topography, and marine life.

Meteorology Unit 6 examines the composition of Earth's atmosphere. The combined effects of Earth's motions and energy from the sun cause the atmosphere to produce different weather conditions. This, in turn, creates the basic pattern of global climates. **Meteorology** is the study of the atmosphere and the processes that produce weather and climate. Like oceanography, meteorology also involves other branches of science.

Astronomy Unit 7 focuses on **astronomy,** the study of the universe. All objects in space, including Earth, are subject to the same physical laws. Learning about the other members of our solar system and the universe beyond helps us, therefore, to better understand Earth. Astronomy is useful in probing the origins of our own environment.

Throughout its long existence, Earth has been changing. In fact, it is changing as you read this page and will continue to do so. Sometimes the changes are rapid and violent, such as when tornadoes, landslides, or volcanic eruptions occur. Many changes, however, take place so gradually that they may go unnoticed during a lifetime.

Introduction to Earth Science **3**

Use Community Resources L2

The USGS (United States Geological Survey) has a network of regional offices where geologists study geological phenomena at local, regional, and global levels. Their activities include monitoring earthquake activity, mapping subsurface rock formations, and providing the public with information about geologic events such as floods and landslides. Ask a USGS geologist from a local office to talk to the class about what geologists do at their jobs. Ask students to prepare questions in advance. **Interpersonal**

Build Reading Literacy L1

Refer to **p. 186D** in **Chapter 7,** which provides guidelines for relating text and visuals.

Relate Text and Visuals Have students turn to Figure 3 on the next page for a visual representation of the nebular hypothesis. Have them read the figure caption, then use the figure to describe the major steps in the nebular hypothesis. *(Solar system begins as cloud of dust and gases. Cloud starts to rotate and collapse. Heated center forms the sun. Cooling creates solid particles. Collisions create asteroid-sized bodies. Asteroids form the inner planets. Lighter materials and gases form the outer planets.)* **Visual**

Answers

Figure 1 *Sample answers: How old is it? Where was it found?*

☑ **Reading Checkpoint** *The two main areas of geology are physical geology and historical geology.*

Differentiated Instruction

ENGLISH LANGUAGE LEARNERS Students should use the words and word parts they just learned, along with their prior knowledge, to define the following words: *oceanographer, meteorologist, geologist, geological,* *astronaut, astronomer.* Students should then use a dictionary to check their definitions. Review the correct meanings of these words with students when they are finished.

LESSON 1.1

Use Visuals

Figure 3 Have students study the diagram illustrating the nebular theory. **Ask:** What do all stages of this theory have in common? *(In all stages, the system is spinning.)* What was the first stage in the development of our solar system? *(Our solar system began as an enormous cloud of gas and dust.)* Challenge students to make a timeline or flowchart of the key events in the formation of our solar system. *(Students should make a timeline or flowchart based on steps A through E given in the figure caption.)*
Visual, Logical

(Teacher **Demo**)

SEPARATION AND DENSITY

Purpose Students see how substances separate based on density.

Materials 2 large glass jars with lids, 100 mL sand, 100 mL rock salt, 100 mL sugar, 100 mL water, 100 mL vegetable oil, 100 mL corn syrup

Procedure At the start of the class, place all of the solids in one jar and all the liquids in another jar. Put the lids on both jars and shake them carefully. Let the jars settle during the class. Then, have the students look at them. **Ask:** Why did the liquids separate? *(Differences in density made the liquids rise or fall and separate.)* Why didn't the solids separate? *(The solid particles were unable to move past each other.)* What state was Earth most likely in when it separated into layers? *(The materials that made up Earth must have been molten or nearly molten.)*

Expected Outcome The liquids will separate into different layers. The solids will remain mixed.
Visual, Logical

Formation of Earth

Earth is one of several planets that revolve around the sun in our solar system. Scientists understand that Earth and the other planets formed during the same time span and from the same material as the sun.

The Nebular Theory The nebular theory is the most widely accepted model for explaining the formation of the solar system. ▭ The nebular theory suggests that the bodies of our solar system evolved from an enormous rotating cloud called the solar nebula. It was made up mostly of hydrogen and helium, with a small percentage of heavier elements. Some key points of the nebular theory are summarized in **Figure 3**.

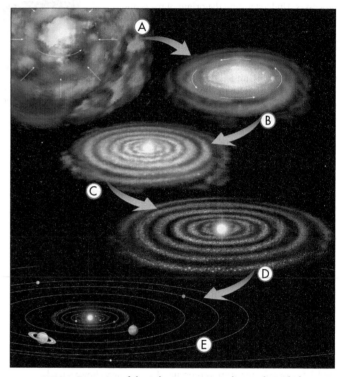

FIGURE 3 Formation of the Solar System According to the Nebular Theory A Our solar system began as an enormous cloud of dust and gases made up mostly of hydrogen and helium with a small percentage of heavier elements. **B** This cloud, called a *nebula*, started to rotate and collapse toward the center of the cloud. Heat was generated at the center, which eventually formed the sun. **C** Cooling of the nebula caused rocky and metallic materials to form tiny solid particles. **D** Repeated collisions of these particles resulted in the formation of asteroid-sized bodies. **E** These asteroids eventually combined to form the four inner planets—Mercury, Venus, Earth, and Mars. The lighter materials and gases combined farther away from the center to form the four outer planets—Jupiter, Saturn, Uranus, and Neptune.

Facts and Figures

As Earth was forming, density differences caused denser materials to sink to Earth's core, while less dense materials escaped to the atmosphere. Density differences continue to shape Earth today. Today's volcanic eruptions are generally caused by less dense magma and gases rising up through the mantle until they penetrate the crust, resulting in a volcanic eruption. This is an example of the principle of uniformitarianism, which is essential to the study of geology. This principle states that the processes that exist on Earth today are identical to the processes that existed on Earth in the distant past. This principle allows geologists to make useful inferences based on contemporary observations.

During the formation of the solar system, the inner planets were characterized by high temperatures and weak fields of gravity. As a result, the inner planets were not able to hold onto the lighter gases of the nebular cloud. The lightest gases, hydrogen and helium, were whisked away toward the heavier planets by the solar wind. Earth, Mars, and Venus were able to retain some heavier gases including water vapor and carbon dioxide. The materials that formed the outer planets contained mostly hydrogen and helium, but also high percentages of water, carbon dioxide, ammonia, and methane, in addition to rock and metal cores. Because of their large size, the outer planets' gravity was strong enough to hold all of these gases.

Layers Form on Earth Shortly after Earth formed, the decay of radioactive elements, combined with heat released by colliding particles, produced some melting of its interior. This allowed the denser elements, mostly iron and nickel, to sink to Earth's center because of gravity. The less dense, rocky components floated outward, toward the surface. This sinking and floating is believed to still be occurring, but on a much smaller scale. As a result of this process, Earth's solid interior is not made of uniform materials; it consists of distinct layers with different properties.

An important result of the layering process is that gaseous materials were allowed to escape from Earth's interior, just as gases escape today during volcanic eruptions. In this way, an atmosphere consisting mainly of the released gases gradually formed along with the ocean.

☑ **Reading Checkpoint** *Why does Earth have layers?*

Build Science Skills `L2`

Infer Based on the information in this lesson, ask students to infer which of Earth's layers is the densest. Have students turn ahead in the text to Figure 6 on p. 8 to see a diagram of Earth's layers.
Logical

3 ASSESS

Evaluate Understanding `L2`

To assess students' knowledge of lesson content, ask them to answer the Key Questions at the beginning of this lesson.

Reteach `L1`

Have students use Figure 3 to explain in their own words the formation of our solar system.

1.1 Assessment

Review Key Concepts

1. What are the sciences that are included in Earth science?

2. What topics are included in the study of physical geology?

3. Explain how physical geology differs from historical geology.

4. Describe the nebular theory.

Think Critically

5. **Infer** Would meteorology be a useful science to apply to the study of Mercury, the innermost and smallest planet? Explain.

6. **Relate Cause and Effect** Where did gases in Earth's atmosphere come from?

7. **Form a Hypothesis** Suppose that as Earth formed, all lighter elements were released to surrounding space. How might this affect the structure of Earth today?

CONNECTING CONCEPTS

8. **Summarize** Earth science includes many different areas of study. Why is it important to include all of these areas in the study of Earth and the solar system?

Introduction to Earth Science **5**

Answers

☑ **Reading Checkpoint** *Earth has layers because denser elements sank to Earth's center and less dense elements floated to the surface.*

Assessment Answers

1. geology, oceanography, meteorology, and astronomy
2. Sample answers: volcanoes, mountain building, erosion, and earthquakes.
3. Historical geology's aim is to understand Earth's history. Physical geology's aim is to understand the processes that shape Earth.
4. The solar system evolved from the solar nebula. As the cloud began to rotate, it collapsed toward the center, where the sun

formed. Cooling of the cloud caused rocky and metallic materials to form the inner planets. The outer planets formed from lighter materials and gases.
5. No, because Mercury has no atmosphere. Planets with no atmospheres would have no meteorological processes occurring on them. Therefore, meteorology would not be very useful in studying this planet.

6. Earth's atmosphere consists of gases that were released from within the planet.
7. Earth probably would not have layers defined by their density.
8. All of the spheres on Earth interact. To understand Earth's existence and history, it is important to study all aspects of Earth together.

Earth's Place in the Universe L2

Background

The Milky Way is a collection of several hundred billion stars, the oldest of which is about 10 billion years. It is one of a cluster of approximately 28 galaxies, called the *Local Group,* that exists in our region of the universe. Initially, the oldest stars in the Milky Way formed from nearly pure hydrogen. Later, succeeding generations of younger stars, including our sun, would have heavier, more complex atoms available for their formation.

Teaching Tips

- As students read the feature and look at Figure 4, have them make a timeline of the events shown from the Big Bang to the present.
- While reading the feature, have students create a flowchart showing the chain of events starting with the Big Bang and ending with the formation of our sun and the planets of our solar system. *(Big Bang → Protons and neutrons appear → Hydrogen and helium form → Hydrogen and helium condense into clouds → Galaxies and galaxy clusters form and start spreading apart → Clouds of gas and dust collapse, forming stars → Stars become supernovas → Nebula, enriched from supernovas, contracts, rotates, and flattens → Planets and our sun form)*

Address **Misconceptions** L2

Students may think that the Milky Way is at the center of the universe. They may have inferred this from learning that almost all galaxies are moving away from the Milky Way in all directions. To dispel this misconception, have students mark with a black marker a number of dots on a partially inflated balloon. Blow up the balloon and observe what happens to the dots. They all move away from each other, as do almost all galaxies. All points in the universe can be thought of as being the center of the universe, as everything else is moving away from everything else.
Visual

Earth's Place in the Universe

For centuries, people who have gazed at the night sky have wondered about the nature of the universe, Earth's place within it, and whether or not we are alone.

Today, continuous discoveries in astronomy contribute to our knowledge about the origin of the universe, the formation and evolution of stars, and how Earth came into existence.

The realization that the universe is immense and orderly began in the early 1900s. Edwin Hubble and other scientists demonstrated that the Milky Way galaxy is one of hundreds of billions of galaxies, each of which contains billions of stars. Evidence indicates that Earth, its materials, and all living things are the result of the "Big Bang". The Big Bang theory is illustrated in **Figure 4.**

According to the theory, the universe began between 13 and 14 billion years ago as a dense, hot, massive amount of material exploded with violent force. Within about one second, the temperature of the expanding universe cooled to approximately 10 billion degrees. Basic atomic particles called protons and neutrons began to appear. After a few minutes, atoms of the simplest elements—hydrogen and helium—had formed. The initial conversion of energy to matter in the young universe was completed.

During the first billion years or so, matter (essentially hydrogen and helium) in the expanding universe clumped together to form enormous clouds that eventually collapsed to become galaxies and clusters of galaxies. Inside these collapsing clouds, smaller concentrations of matter formed into stars. One of the billions of galaxies to form was the Milky Way. The Milky Way galaxy is where our solar system—our sun, Earth, and neighboring planets—resides.

During the life of most stars, energy is produced as hydrogen nuclei fuse together to form helium. During this process, called nuclear fusion, matter is converted to energy. Stars begin to die when their nuclear fuel is used up. Massive stars often have explosive deaths. During these events, called supernovas, nuclear fusion produces atoms such as oxygen, carbon, and iron. These atoms may become the materials that make up future generations of stars. From the debris scattered during the death of a preexisting star, our sun, and the solar system formed.

Our star, the sun, is at the very least a second-generation star. Along with the planets in our solar system, the sun began forming nearly 5 billion years ago from a large interstellar cloud called a nebula. This nebula consisted of dust particles and gases enriched in heavy elements from a supernova explosion. Gravitational energy caused the nebula to contract, rotate, and flatten. Inside, smaller concentrations of matter began condensing to form the planets. At the center of the nebula there was sufficient pressure and heat to initiate hydrogen nuclear fusion, and our sun was born.

It has been said that all life on Earth is related to the stars. This is true because the atoms in our bodies, and everything else on Earth, owe their origin to a supernova event that occurred billions of years ago, trillions of kilometers away.

FIGURE 4 Big Bang Theory Between 13 and 14 billion years ago, a huge explosion sent all of the universe's matter flying outward at great speed. After a few billion years, the material cooled and condensed into the first stars and galaxies. About 5 billion years ago, our solar system began forming in a galaxy that is now called the Milky Way galaxy.

1.2 A View of Earth

A VIEW SUCH as the one in **Figure 5A** provided the *Apollo 8* astronauts with a unique view of our home. Seen from space, Earth is breathtaking in its beauty. Such an image reminds us that our home is, after all, a planet—small, self-contained, and in some ways even fragile.

If you look closely at Earth from space, you may see that it is much more than rock and soil. As shown in **Figure 5B**, the swirling clouds and the vast global ocean emphasize the importance of water on our planet.

Earth's Major Spheres

Earth's physical environment is traditionally divided into three major spheres—spheres of air, rock, and water. However, our environment is characterized by the continuous interactions of air and rock, rock and water, and water and air. A fourth sphere, consisting of all living things, interacts with all three of the physical spheres. **Earth can be thought of as having four major spheres: the atmosphere, hydrosphere, geosphere, and biosphere.**

FIGURE 5 A View of Our Planet A This view, named *Earthrise*, greeted the *Apollo 8* astronauts as their spacecraft emerged from behind the moon. **B** Africa and Arabia are prominent in this image of Earth taken from *Apollo 17*. The tan areas are desert regions. The bands of clouds over central Africa are associated with rainforests. Antarctica, which is covered by glacial ice, is visible at the south pole. The dark blue oceans and white swirling clouds remind us of the importance of oceans and the atmosphere.

Key Questions

What are the four major spheres into which Earth is divided?

What defines the three main parts of the solid Earth?

What theory explains the position of continents and the occurrence of volcanoes and earthquakes?

Vocabulary

- atmosphere • hydrosphere
- geosphere • core
- mantle • crust • biosphere

Reading Strategy

Predict Before you read, predict the meaning of the vocabulary words. After you read, revise your definition if your prediction was incorrect.

Vocabulary Term	Before You Read	After You Read
atmosphere	a. ?	b. ?
hydrosphere	c. ?	d. ?
geosphere	e. ?	f. ?
core	g. ?	h. ?
mantle	i. ?	j. ?
crust	k. ?	l. ?
biosphere	m. ?	n. ?

1 FOCUS

Lesson Objectives
1.3 **Describe** Earth's four major spheres.
1.4 **Differentiate** among the three parts of the geosphere.
1.5 **Explain** the theory of plate tectonics and its value to Earth science.

Build Vocabulary
Word Parts Explain to students that *hydro-* relates to water and *atmos-* relates to air. Have them use this information, along with prior knowledge, to predict the meaning of the vocabulary words for this lesson.

Reading Strategy
Sample answers:
a. ball of water
b. all water on Earth
c. ball of air
d. gaseous envelope surrounding Earth
e. ball of rock
f. solid part of Earth below the atmosphere and oceans
g. ball of living things
h. all life on Earth
i. center of Earth
j. dense inner sphere
k. ledge
l. less dense middle layer
m. outer envelope
n. light, thin outer layer

2 INSTRUCT

Use Visuals L1
Figure 5 This image of Earth was taken by astronauts in space. **Ask:** Which of Earth's features are visible from space? *(oceans, continents, clouds)* What does the color of the land that is visible tell you about the climate in those regions? *(Brown indicates a desert climate. Green indicates a wet climate.)* What other Earth features do you think would be visible from space? *(smoke from forest fires and city lights at night)* Who might find images from space useful? *(meteorologists, geologists, oceanographers)*
Visual, Verbal

LESSON 1.2

Build Reading Literacy **L1**

Refer to **p. 1D,** which provides guidelines for guided anticipation.

Anticipation Guide Ask students to respond to the following questions in writing before they read this lesson. Have students check their answers and make changes as needed after they finish reading the lesson. Students should answer True or False to the following series of statements:

- The atmosphere contains all of the water on Earth. *(F)*
- Groundwater is part of Earth's hydrosphere. *(T)*
- Earth's atmosphere does nothing to protect us from the sun's radiation. *(F)*
- There is no crust under Earth's oceans. *(F)*
- Earth's crust is the same thickness under land as under water. *(F)*
- The only layer of Earth that is solid is the crust. *(F)*
- The biosphere affects all other spheres of Earth. *(T)*

Verbal

Teacher **Demo**

EARTH'S LAYERS **L2**

Purpose Provide students with a three-dimensional model of Earth's layered structure.

Materials hard-boiled egg, knife

Procedure Show students a hard-boiled egg. Crack the shell in several places so pieces of shell can slide a bit over the white of the egg. Tell students the shell of the egg represents Earth's crust, which is a thin layer, cracked and broken into plates that can move. Cut the egg in half. Show students that the white of the egg represents Earth's mantle, and the yolk of the egg represents Earth's core.

Expected Outcome Students will be able to relate the structure of the egg to the structure of Earth and can use this representation to make a mental model of what Earth's layers look like.

Visual, Logical

Atmosphere A life-sustaining, thin, gaseous envelope called the **atmosphere** surrounds Earth. It reaches more than 100 kilometers above Earth, yet 90 percent is found within just 16 kilometers of Earth's surface. This thin blanket of air is an important part of Earth. It provides the air that we breathe. It protects us from the sun's intense heat and dangerous radiation. The energy exchanges between space, the atmosphere, and Earth's surface produce weather and climate.

Hydrosphere Water is what makes Earth unique. All of the water on Earth makes up the **hydrosphere.** The portion of the hydrosphere that controls frozen water is often referred to as the *cryosphere.* Continually on the move, water evaporates from the oceans to the atmosphere, falls back to Earth as rain, and runs back to the ocean. The oceans account for approximately 97 percent of the water on Earth. The remaining 3 percent is fresh water and is present in groundwater, streams, lakes, and glaciers. These freshwater sources are responsible for sustaining life and creating many of Earth's varied landforms.

The properties of water and its distribution are major factors that affect life on Earth. Living things require liquid water. Fortunately, much of Earth has temperatures at which water remains in the liquid state. The availability of water also helps to determine where many organisms, including humans, can live. For example, fewer people live in desert areas than in areas where water is abundant.

Geosphere Lying beneath both the atmosphere and the ocean is the **geosphere,** which is mostly solid. 🔊 **Because the geosphere is not uniform, it is divided into three main parts based on differences in composition—the core, the mantle, and the crust.** In **Figure 6,** you can see the inner sphere that is the **core,** rich in iron and nickel; the **mantle** of high-density rock; and the thin **crust** of low-density rock.

FIGURE 6 Earth's Interior Earth's crust, mantle, and core are divided into different layers based on physical properties and chemical composition.

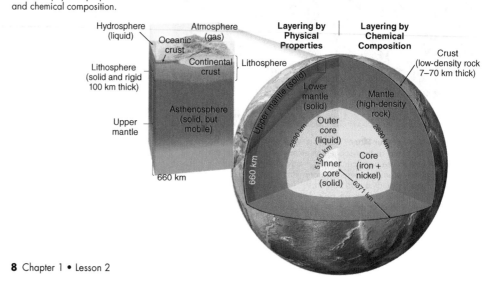

Differentiated Instruction

SPECIAL NEEDS Have students with special needs draw labeled pictures illustrating each of Earth's four major spheres: hydrosphere, atmosphere, geosphere, and biosphere. Be sure they include Earth's layers in their sketch of the geosphere. They can use Figure 6 as a guide.

The crust is not uniform in thickness. It is thinnest beneath the oceans and thickest beneath the continents. The crust and uppermost mantle make up a rigid outer layer called the *lithosphere*. Below the lithosphere are additional layers. The physical properties of these layers vary due to the effects of high temperatures and pressures deep within Earth. Beneath the lithosphere, the rocks, though solid, are able to slowly flow. This region is called the *asthenosphere*. Beneath the asthenosphere, the rock becomes more dense. This region of Earth is the lower mantle. Below the mantle, the outer core is liquid, while the inner core is solid.

Biosphere The **biosphere** includes all life on Earth. It is concentrated in a zone that extends from the ocean floor upward for several kilometers into the atmosphere. Plants and animals depend on the physical environment for life. However, organisms do more than just respond to their physical environment. Through countless interactions, organisms help maintain and alter their physical environment. Without life, the makeup and nature of the solid Earth, hydrosphere, and atmosphere would be very different.

☑ **Reading Checkpoint** What are Earth's four major spheres?

FIGURE 7 Interacting Spheres
Elements of the atmosphere, hydrosphere, geosphere, and biosphere are visible in this mountain scene. Infer *What organisms might be part of the biosphere in the environment shown in this photo?*

Earth's Changing Surface

Earth is a dynamic planet, which means that it is always changing. If we could go back in time a billion years or more, we would find a planet with a dramatically different surface from what we see today. Such prominent features as the Grand Canyon, the Rocky Mountains, and the Appalachian Mountains did not exist. We would find that the continents had different shapes and were located in different positions than those of today. Within the last several decades, scientists have learned a great deal about the inner workings of our planet. Their work has contributed to an understanding of how Earth's surface changes.

Destructive and Constructive Forces Two types of forces shape Earth's surface. *Destructive forces* such as weathering and erosion work to wear away high points and flatten out the surface. *Constructive forces* such as mountain building and volcanism build up the surface by raising the land and depositing new material in the form of lava. These constructive forces depend on Earth's internal heat for their source of energy.

Introduction to Earth Science **9**

LESSON 1.2

CONVECTION AND PLATES `L2`

Purpose Students observe how heat from within Earth can move plates.

Materials hot plate; deep, wide glass container such as a lasagna pan; diluted tomato soup; large, thin sponges, cut into rough plate shapes; scissors; tongs

Procedure Fill the container about halfway with tomato soup, and put it on the hot plate. Slowly heat it until convection cells form (soup rising in the center and falling at the edges). Use the tongs to place the sponges on the surface of the soup. Have students observe what happens to the sponges. (If necessary, review the concept of convection.)
Ask: Why is the soup moving? *(Heat from below produces convection cells.)* Why do the "plates" move? *(The moving soup carried the plates along with it.)* How is the actual movement of Earth's plates different from this demonstration? *(Because the molten rock in the mantle is solid, it is slower-moving than the soup.)*

Safety Caution students not to touch the hot container or soup.

Expected Outcome The heat will produce convection cells that move the sponges around.
Visual, Logical

3 ASSESS

Evaluate Understanding `L2`

Have students make posters showing Earth's layers and spheres. Students should label their drawings with the terms crust, mantle, core, hydrosphere, biosphere, and atmosphere.

Reteach `L1`

Use Figure 8 to review Earth's plates and the concept of plate tectonics.

Assessment Answers

1. lake: hydrosphere, meadow: geosphere, canyon: geosphere, clouds: atmosphere
2. core, mantle, and crust
3. The geosphere is layered because it consists of different materials with varying properties.
4. the model of plate tectonics
5. Earth's plates drift slowly and continuously upon the asthenosphere.

Theory of Plate Tectonics In the early twentieth century, a revolutionary idea was proposed that the continents had moved about on Earth's surface. This idea contradicted the accepted view that the continents and ocean basins are stationary features on the planet. More than 50 years passed before enough data were collected to support and transform this hypothesis to the widely accepted theory of plate tectonics. **The theory of plate tectonics provided geologists with a model to explain how continents move and earthquakes and volcanic eruptions occur.**

FIGURE 8 Earth's Plates
Earth's lithosphere is broken up in to numerous plates. Note that some of the plates encompass an entire continent and a large part of the seafloor.

According to the theory of plate tectonics, Earth's lithosphere is broken into several individual sections called *plates*, as shown in **Figure 8.** These plates, which lie upon the asthenosphere, drift slowly and continuously across Earth's surface. Their motion is a result of the unequal distribution of heat deep within Earth. As you will later learn, the movement of Earth's plates ultimately generates earthquakes, volcanic activity, and the deformation of large masses of rock into mountains.

1.2 Assessment

Review Key Concepts

1. Which of Earth's spheres do each of these features belong to: lake, meadow, canyon, clouds?

2. What are the three main parts of the geosphere?

3. Why is the geosphere layered?

4. What model helps scientists explain earthquakes and volcanic eruptions?

5. Describe the motion of Earth's lithospheric plates.

6. Describe an example of how water moves through the hydrosphere.

Think Critically

7. **Review** Describe the layer upon which Earth's lithospheric plates float.

8. **Apply Concepts** Describe a situation in which two or more of Earth's spheres are interacting.

9. **Classify** Choose a branch of Earth science. List how some of its studies relate to Earth's different spheres.

BIGIDEA
EARTH'S MATERIALS AND SYSTEMS

10. **Explain** You have learned that Earth is a dynamic planet. Explain how features in each of Earth's interacting spheres are changing over time.

6. Sample answer: Water in a lake evaporates into the atmosphere. The water vapor condenses and falls from the clouds into the lake as rain and the cycle begins again.
7. The asthenosphere is solid but able to flow slowly.
8. Sample answers: waves (hydrosphere) crashing onto the shore (geosphere); birds (biosphere) flying in the sky (atmosphere)
9. Sample answer: meteorology: cloud cover—atmosphere; rain storms—hydrosphere and atmosphere

10. Students' answers could include discussions of the hydrosphere (sea level changes), atmosphere (weather and climate changes), geosphere (erosion of topsoil, earthquake occurrence), and biosphere (evolution of living things).

1.3 Representing Earth's Surface

LONG AGO, people had to rely on maps made by travelers and explorers. During the twentieth century, photographs of the land surface taken from airplanes became important tools in map-making. Later, satellite images provided even more accurate data about Earth's surface.

Determining Location

In addition to accurate data, mapmakers need a way of precisely describing the location of features on Earth's surface. Mapmakers use a global grid to help determine location.

Latitude and Longitude Scientists use two special Earth measurements to describe location. The distance around Earth is measured in degrees. **Latitude is the distance north or south of the equator, measured in degrees. Longitude is the distance east or west of the prime meridian, measured in degrees.** Lines of latitude and longitude form a global grid, as shown in **Figure 9.**

Lines of latitude are east-west circles around the globe. All points on the circle have the same latitude. One degree of latitude is equal to about 111 km on Earth's surface. The line of latitude around the middle of the globe, at 0°, is the *equator*. The equator divides Earth in two. Each half is called a *hemisphere*. The equator divides Earth into the northern and southern hemispheres.

Key Questions

🔑 **What lines on a globe are used to indicate location?**

🔑 **What problems do mapmakers face when making maps?**

🔑 **How do topographic maps differ from other maps?**

Vocabulary

- latitude • longitude
- topographic map
- contour line
- contour interval

Reading Strategy

Monitor Your Understanding Preview the Key Concepts, topic headings, vocabulary, and figures in this lesson. List two things you expect to learn. After reading, state what you learned about each item you listed.

What I Expect to Learn	What I Learned
a. ___?___	b. ___?___
c. ___?___	d. ___?___

FIGURE 9 Global Grid Lines of latitude and longitude form a global grid.

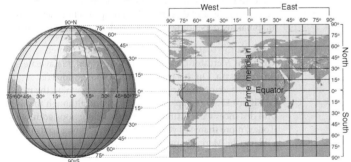

Introduction to Earth Science **11**

1 FOCUS

Lesson Objectives

1.6 **Locate** points on Earth's surface by their latitude and longitude.

1.7 **Describe** the advantages and disadvantages of different types of maps.

1.8 **Explain** what makes topographic maps different from other maps.

Build Vocabulary [L2]

Paraphrase Have students look up the vocabulary words for this lesson in the Glossary and then rewrite the definitions in their own words. Help students remember that latitude lines run horizontally across Earth with the mnemonic "L̲a̲t̲ lies f̲l̲a̲t̲." Similarly, help them see that l̲o̲n̲g̲itude lines run the "l̲o̲n̲g̲ way" over Earth.

Reading Strategy [L2]

Sample answers:

a. I expect to learn about latitude and longitude.

b. Latitude lines measure degrees north and south of the equator; longitude lines measure degrees east and west of the prime meridian.

c. I expect to learn about different types of maps.

d. There are many different types of maps. Maps are hard to make accurately. Different map types have different advantages and disadvantages.

2 INSTRUCT

Use Visuals [L1]

Figure 9 Help students find the point that is at 45°N, 75°W. **Ask:** What major city is near this point? *(Montreal, Canada)* If an earthquake occurred near this point, are people at 30°N, 60°E likely to feel it? Why or why not? *(No, 30°N, 60°E is in the Western Hemisphere and Montreal is in the Eastern Hemisphere.)*
Visual, Logical

Use Visuals L1

Figure 10 Use this diagram to explain the concepts of latitude and longitude and how they are measured. Emphasize that although latitude and longitude are usually shown on Earth's surface, they are actually measured inside Earth. **Ask:** From which point is latitude measured? *(the equator)* From which point is longitude measured? *(the prime meridian)*
Visual, Logical

Build Reading Literacy L1

Refer to **p. 124D** in **Chapter 5,** which provides guidelines for summarizing.

Summarize Have students write a summary of this lesson that includes each map type and its advantages and disadvantages. This can be done as a table. Here is an example:

Map Type	Advantages	Disadvantages
Mercator projection	Rectangular; longitude lines are parallel; directions shown accurately	Sizes and distances distorted
Robinson projection	Most distances, sizes, and shapes are accurate	Distortions around the map edges
Conic projection	Great accuracy over small areas; good for road and weather maps	Lots of distortion on most of the map
Gnomonic projection	Reliably shows the shortest distance between two points	Exact distances and directions are distorted

Visual, Verbal

FIGURE 10 Prime Meridian
The prime meridian (0° longitude) passes through Greenwich, England.

Lines of longitude run north and south. The prime meridian marks 0° of longitude, as shown in **Figure 10.** Earth is 360° in circumference. The prime meridian and the 180° meridian divide Earth into eastern and western hemispheres. A degree of longitude varies in size; it is about 111 km near the equator and decreases to zero as the meridians meet at the poles.

Degrees of latitude and longitude are further divided into smaller units called minutes (') and seconds ("). There are 60 minutes per degree and 60 seconds per minute. One minute of latitude is equivalent to about 1.85 km. One minute of longitude is also about 1.85 km at the equator, but decreases towards the poles. The global grid allows you to state the absolute location of any place on Earth. For example, the Greenwich Royal Observatory in Greenwich, England, is located at 0° 0' 0" longitude and 51° 28' 38" north latitude.

☑ **Reading Checkpoint** *What is the prime meridian?*

Globes As people explored Earth, they collected information about the shapes and sizes of islands, continents, and bodies of water. Mapmakers wanted to present this information accurately. The best way was to put the information on a model, or globe, with the same round shape as Earth itself. By using an accurate shape for Earth, mapmakers could show the continents and oceans of Earth much as they really are. The only difference would be the scale, or relative size. However, there is a problem with globes. A globe can't be detailed enough to be useful for finding directions and at the same time small enough to be convenient for everyday use.

Representing the Globe

A map is a flat representation of Earth's surface. But Earth is spherical. Can all of Earth's features be accurately represented on a flat surface without distorting them? No. **No matter what kind of map is made, some portion of the surface will always be too small, too big, or out of place. Mapmakers have, however, found ways to limit the distortion of shape, size, distance, and direction.** Various projections are used in mapmaking depending on the intended purpose of the map.

FIGURE 11 Mercator Projection
To make a Mercator projection map, mapmakers have to carve an image of Earth's surface into slices and then stretch the slices into rectangles. Stretching the slices enlarges parts of the map. The enlargement becomes greater toward the north and south poles. **Observe** *What areas on the map appear larger than they should?*

Mercator Projection In 1569, a mapmaker named Gerardus Mercator created a map to help sailors navigate around Earth. On this map, the lines of longitude are parallel, making this grid rectangular, as shown on the map in **Figure 11.** The map was useful because, although the sizes and distances were distorted, it showed directions accurately. Today, more than 400 years later, many seagoing navigators still use the Mercator projection map to guide them.

12 Chapter 1 • Lesson 3

Differentiated Instruction

SPECIAL NEEDS Students can more easily locate positions on a map using latitude and longitude coordinates by using the following procedure. First, help students orient themselves to the map by locating the equator and the prime meridian. Have students go over those two key points using a highlighter and extend the lines out to the edge of the paper. Next, have students write *N* in the left and right margins above the equator, and *S* in the left and right margins below the equator. Students should write *W* in the margins above and below the map west of the prime meridian, and write *E* in the margins above and below the map east of the prime meridian.

Robinson Projection In an attempt to minimize overall distortion while showing the entire world at once, the geographer Arthur H. Robinson developed a map based on tables of coordinates. Robinson projection maps show most distances, sizes, and shapes accurately. However, a Robinson projection does have its distortions, especially in areas around the edges of the map. You can see a Robinson projection map in **Figure 12.**

FIGURE 12 Robinson Projection A rounded Robinson projection map is useful for seeing the entire world all at once.

Conic Projection Conic projection maps are made by wrapping a cone of paper around a globe at a particular line of latitude, as shown in **Figure 13.** Various points and lines are then projected onto the paper. There is almost no distortion along the line of latitude that's in contact with the cone, but there can be much distortion in areas away from this latitude. Because accuracy is great over a small area, conic projections are commonly used to make road and weather maps.

FIGURE 13 Conic Projection Conic projections are useful for making road maps and weather maps because there is little distortion over small areas.

Gnomonic Projection As shown in **Figure 14,** gnomonic projections are made by placing a piece of paper on a globe so that it touches a single point on the globe's surface. Various points and lines are then projected onto the paper. Although distances and directions are distorted on these maps, they are useful to sailors and navigators because they show with great accuracy the shortest distance between two points.

☑ **Reading Checkpoint** *What major problem must mapmakers overcome?*

FIGURE 14 Gnomonic Projection Gnomonic projections allow sailors to accurately determine distance and direction across the oceans. *Interpret Maps What region on this map has the least distortion?*

Introduction to Earth Science **13**

LESSON 1.3

Topographic Maps

Sometimes, it is useful to know a region's *topography,* or surface features. A **topographic map** represents Earth's three-dimensional surface in two dimensions. ◖▭ **Topographic maps differ from other maps in that they show elevation using contour lines.** Most also show the presence of bodies of water, roads, place names, government and public buildings, and political boundaries. These maps are important for geologists, hikers, campers, and anyone else interested in the three-dimensional lay of the land.

Contour Lines A **contour line** is used to indicate the elevation of the land. Elevation refers to the height above sea level. **Figure 15** illustrates how contour lines are determined. Every position along a single contour line is the same elevation. Adjacent contour lines represent a change in elevation. The **contour interval** tells you the difference in elevation between adjacent lines.

In a topographic map, such as the one in **Figure 16,** every fifth line is bold and labeled with the elevation. This bolded line is called an *index contour.* The steepness of an area can be determined by examining a map. Lines that are closer together indicate a steeper slope, while lines farther apart indicate a gentler slope. Contour lines never touch or intersect, except where there is a vertical cliff.

A series of contour lines that form roughly concentric circle represent a hill. Hachure marks, or "tick marks", on contour lines are a series of short strokes that point towards lower elevation. Roughly concentric contours with hachure marks indicate a depression, which is a landform sunken below the surrounding area. Note several depressions in the map in Figure 16.

☑ **Reading Checkpoint** *How do topographic maps indicate changes in elevation?*

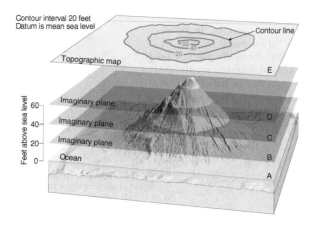

FIGURE 15 Determining Contour Lines Every point on the same plane has the same elevation. A contour line connects points of similar elevation along the surface feature. The contour interval here is 20 feet.

14 Chapter 1 • Lesson 3

Facts and Figures

Topographic maps contain a great deal of information. Each map has a legend that gives information about the map and the symbols used on it. The legend lists the title of the map (usually a major feature), the dates the map was produced and revised, and the latitude and longitude. There is a small diagram showing the map's location in the state and the names of adjacent maps. A small box contains the contour interval and the scale as a ratio and as scale bars in miles, feet, and kilometers/meters. A magnetic declination diagram shows the differences in degrees among true north, grid north, and magnetic north. A long list explains the symbols shown on the map, which can include contour lines, depressions, ocean depth lines, boundaries, survey markers, forests, fields, built-up areas, buildings, roads, and railways.

SCALE 1:24 000

KILOMETERS

METERS

MILES

FEET

CONTOUR INTERVAL 10 FEET

Scale

Scale In using a map, it is necessary to be able to determine distances on the map and then translate them to the real world. Therefore, to be useful, a map must be drawn to scale. A map's *scale* represents the relationship between distance on the map and actual distance on Earth's surface. Look at the scale on the map in Figure 16. The ratio reads 1 : 24,000. This means that 1 unit on the map is equal to 24,000 units on the ground. The unit may stand for anything. For example, we usually use inches or centimeters for our units. One centimeter on the map represents 24,000 centimeters on the ground; 1 inch on the map equals 24,000 inches on the ground.

A 1 : 24,000 scale map is also known as a 7.5-minute quadrangle, one of the most widely used maps produced by the United States Geological Survey (USGS). The USGS is a federal scientific agency that researches the landscape of the United States and produces maps of the country at various scales.

In addition to a ratio scale, another type of scale provided on a map is a bar scale, also shown in Figure 16. This allows you to use a ruler to measure the distance on the map and then line the ruler up to the bar to quickly determine the actual distance represented.

FIGURE 16 Topographic Map
This is a very small portion of the Dundee, Wisconson, 7.5-minute quadrangle produced by the USGS, showing the Kettle Moraine region. Contour lines are shown in brown. Interpret Maps *What is the contour interval on this map?*

Integrate Math

Work With Ratios Working with a map key to determine actual distances often requires the use of ratios, a topic taught in math class. Explain the following process to your students. If a map legend has 1:24,000, this suggests that 1 unit (centimeters or inches) on the map is equal to 24,000 units (centimeters or inches) on Earth. To determine how many kilometers 1 cm on the map would equal, set up a ratio (using the conversion factor 1 km = 100,000 cm), as follows:

$$\frac{1\ km}{100,000\ cm} = \frac{x\ km}{24,000\ cm}$$

then solve the ratio by cross-multiplication. The result will be that 1 cm on the map represents 0.24 km on Earth. Because 1:24,000 represents a ratio, it does not matter what unit is used as long as the map's unit matches the unit on Earth. This ratio would allow students to determine how many inches on Earth corresponded to inches on the map.
Logical

Direct students to the **Math Skills** in the **Skills and Reference Handbook** at the end of the student text for additional help.

Use Community Resources

Geologic maps are used by research scientists, government agencies, and mining companies. Ask a geologist from a local college, university, mining company, or government agency to talk to the class about how geologic maps are made, what information they show, and how they are used. Ask students to prepare questions in advance.
Interpersonal

Answers

Figure 16 *10 feet*

☑ **Reading Checkpoint** *Topographic maps indicate changes in elevation with contour lines. Lines closer together indicate a steeper slope.*

LESSON 1.3

Use Visuals L1

Figure 17 Tell students that the different colors and textures in the map represent different rock types and formations.
Ask: What rocks are represented with light purple in the map? *(Rocks from the Hermit Formation)* What color is given to rocks from the Holocene and Pleistocene epochs? *(yellow)*
Visual, Logical

Integrate Social Studies L2

Space Age The successful launch of *Sputnik* by the Soviet Union was a significant event in the Cold War era. It marked the beginning of the Space Age and was the first victory in the space race between the United States and the Soviet Union. In response, the United States accelerated its efforts to launch its own satellite.

FIGURE 17 Geologic Map
This map shows a small segment of the Grand Canyon in Arizona. Each color and pattern represents a different type of rock. Only a partial key is shown here.

Geologic Maps In addition to topography, it is often desirable to know the type and age of the rocks that are exposed, or crop out, at the surface. **A map that shows the type and age of exposed rocks is called a geologic map.** An example of a geologic map is shown in **Figure 17.** Once individual rock formations are identified and mapped, each rock formation is assigned a color and sometimes a pattern. A key provides the information needed to learn what formations are present on the map. A geologic map is often overlayed on top of a topographic map.

Facts and Figures

The first satellite to orbit Earth was called *Sputnik.* The Soviet Union launched it on October 4, 1957. It was a 23-inch, 184-pound metal ball containing a thermometer, a battery, and a radio transmitter. On its exterior, four whip antennas transmitted short-wave frequencies between 20 and 40 MHz, common frequencies intended to make *Sputnik's* presence obvious to the world, and particularly to the United States. *Sputnik* orbited Earth for 92 days before burning up in Earth's atmosphere.

Satellites and Information Technology

🔑 **Today's technology provides us with the ability to more precisely analyze Earth's physical properties.** Scientists now use satellites and computers to send and receive data. These data are converted into usable forms such as images and accurate maps.

The process of collecting data about Earth from a distance, such as from satellites orbiting in space, is called *remote sensing.* Satellites use remote sensing to produce views of Earth that scientists use to study rivers, oceans, fires, pollution, natural resources, and many other topics. How might a scientist use the image in **Figure 18?**

We can use satellite technology in our daily lives, too. For example, Global Positioning Systems (GPS) can provide maps in our cars and mobile phones to help us reach our destinations. GPS consists of an instrument that receives signals from satellites to compute the user's latitude and longitude as well as speed, direction, and elevation. GPS is an important tool for navigation by ships and airplanes. Scientists use GPS to track wildlife, to study earthquakes, to measure erosion, and for many other purposes. Remote sensing, GPS, and other information technologies are valuable tools for Earth scientists. Some people, however, worry that these technologies can also have negative effects, such as loss of privacy.

FIGURE 18 Wildfires from Space Satellite images like this one helped firefighters and officials manage the 2011 wildfire in Apache National Forest—the largest wildfire in Arizona history. This colorized image shows the vegetation (green), burn scar (dark red), ongoing fires (bright red), and smoke (blue).

PLANET DIARY

For links about **GPS,**
go to PlanetDiary.com/HSES.

1.3 Assessment

Review Key Concepts 🔑

1. Describe the two sets of lines that are used on globes and some maps.

2. What happens to the images on the globe when they are transferred to a flat surface?

3. What is the purpose of contour lines on topographic maps?

4. What two lines mark zero degrees on the globe? In which directions do these lines run?

5. Why is the Mercator projection map still in use today?

6. What types of advanced technology are used in mapmaking today?

Think Critically

7. **Apply Concepts** Why are there so many different types of maps?

8. **Interpret Maps** An area on a topographic map has the following contour line configuration: First, the lines are fairly widely spaced. Then they are closely spaced. Finally, they form concentric circles. Describe the topography represented by these lines.

MATH PRACTICE

9. **Measure** Use the bar scale on Figure 16 to determine the approximate distance between the center of Spruce Lake and the center of Cedar Lake. Record your answer in feet, miles, and kilometers.

Introduction to Earth Science **17**

3 ASSESS

Evaluate Understanding ⬛L2

Give students a topographic map that includes latitude and longitude. Have them locate specific features on the map, such as hills and depressions, based on the shapes of the contour lines. Have students determine the latitude and longitude of these features. Give students the latitude and longitude of a few sites of interest on the map and have them tell you what they find at each of those locations.

Reteach ⬛L1

Have students answer the Assessment questions in small groups. Assign the lower ability students to answer the Review Key Concepts questions and the higher ability students to answer the Think Critically questions. Have partners then share and discuss their answers. Once all groups are finished, have students report their answers to the class. Clarify concepts as needed.

Assessment Answers

1. Lines of latitude are east-west circles around the globe. Lines of longitude run north and south.
2. They become distorted.
3. Contour lines indicate elevation.
4. The lines are the equator, which runs east and west, and the prime meridian, which runs north and south.

5. It is useful to sailors because although size and shape are distorted, it shows directions accurately.
6. Sample answer: satellites, computers, high-powered telescopes, sonar, GPS, VLBI
7. Each type of map is particularly useful in some capacity. Conic projections are good for small-scale maps such as road maps. Topographic maps help geologists and hikers. Mercator projections help sailors to navigate.

8. The land starts out relatively flat and rises steeply to the top of a hill.
9. About 4000 feet, 0.75 miles, 1.2 kilometers

1 FOCUS

Lesson Objectives

1.9 **Describe** the primary goal of Earth system science and **define** the term *system.*

1.10 **Describe** Earth's two major sources of energy.

1.11 **Explain** how humans affect Earth's systems.

1.12 **Distinguish** between renewable and nonrenewable resources.

Build Vocabulary L2

Word Forms Have students predict the meanings of *open system* and *closed system* based on their prior knowledge of the words *open, closed,* and *system.* Have students verify their predictions by reading the lesson.

Reading Strategy L2

Earth System Science

A. What is a System?

1. System—any size group of interacting parts forming a whole
2. Types of Systems—closed and open

B. Earth as a System

1. Earth has two energy sources—the sun and Earth's interior.
2. The parts of the Earth system are linked so a change in one part can cause changes in all the other parts.

2 INSTRUCT

Build Science Skills L2

Use Analogies The text gives an analogy of a car's cooling system to a natural system. Challenge students to think of other analogies between human-made and natural systems. They should write a description of the analogy they choose, including diagrams if appropriate. The descriptions should explain how the analogies are similar to the actual process and different from it.

Verbal, Logical

1.4 Earth System Science

Key Questions

 How is Earth a system?

How is Earth a system?

What is a system?

Where does the energy come from that powers Earth's systems?

How do humans affect Earth's systems?

What makes a resource renewable or nonrenewable?

Vocabulary

• system

Reading Strategy

Outline As you read, make an outline of the most important ideas in this lesson. Begin with the section title, then list the orange headings as the next step of the outline. Expand your outline as needed.

I. Earth System Science

    A. What is a System?
        1. _____?_____
        2. _____?_____
    B. _____?_____

AS WE STUDY EARTH, we see that it is a dynamic planet with many separate but interactive parts or spheres. Earth scientists are studying how these spheres are interconnected. This way of looking at Earth is called Earth system science. **The aim of Earth system science is to understand Earth as a system made up of numerous interacting parts, or subsystems.** Instead of studying only one branch of science, such as geology, chemistry, biology, or physics, Earth system science tries to put together what we know from our study of all of these fields of science. Using this type of approach, we hope to understand and solve many of our global environmental problems.

What Is a System?

Most of us hear and use the term *system* frequently. You might use your city's transportation system to get to school. A news report might inform us of an approaching weather system. We know that Earth is just a small part of the much larger solar system.

Interacting Parts **A system can be any size group of interacting parts that form a complex whole.** Most natural systems are driven by sources of energy that move matter and/or energy from one place to another. A simple analogy is a car's cooling system. It contains a liquid (usually water and antifreeze) that is driven from the engine to the radiator and back again. The role of the cooling system is to transfer the heat generated by combustion in the engine to the radiator, where moving air removes the heat from the system.

Open and Closed Systems The car's cooling system is an example of a *closed system.* Here energy moves freely in and out of the system, but no matter enters or leaves the system. In the case of the car's cooling system, the matter is the liquid. By contrast, most natural systems are *open systems.* Here both energy and matter flow into and out of the system. In a river system, for example, the amount of water flowing in the channel can vary a great deal. At one time or place, the river may be fuller than it is at another time or place.

☑ **Reading Checkpoint** *What is Earth system science?*

Earth as a System

The Earth system is characterized by processes that occur over distances that range in size from millimeters to thousands of kilometers. Likewise, time scales for Earth's processes range from milliseconds to billions of years. For example, a torrential downpour over a region may last just a few minutes, while a mountain range is built up over millions of years. Despite this great range in distance and time, many processes are connected. A change in one component can influence the entire system.

Energy Sources The Earth system is powered by energy from two sources. **One source is the sun, which drives external processes that occur in the atmosphere, hydrosphere, and at Earth's surface.** Weather and climate, ocean circulation, and erosion are driven by energy from the sun. **Earth's interior is the second source of energy.** Intense heat remains in Earth's interior from when the planet formed. Heat is also generated continuously by the decay of radioactive elements. These sources power the internal processes that produce volcanoes, earthquakes, and mountains.

Linked Effects Because the parts of the Earth system are linked, a change in one part can produce changes in any or all of the other parts. For example, when a volcano erupts, it affects many aspects of the atmosphere, geosphere, hydrosphere, and biosphere.

During a volcanic eruption, ash and gases might be blown high into the atmosphere and influence the amount of solar energy that can reach Earth's surface. The result could be a drop in air temperatures over the entire hemisphere. Lava flow from the volcano may block a nearby valley, influencing the region's drainage system by creating a lake or causing streams to change course.

Over time, soil will develop on the lava or ash-covered surface and, as shown in **Figure 19**, plants and animals will populate the area again. This new soil will reflect the interactions among many parts of the Earth system—the original volcanic material, the type and rate of weathering, and the impact of biological activity. Of course, there would also be significant changes in the biosphere. Some organisms and their habitats would be eliminated by the lava and ash, while new settings for life, such as the lake, would be created. The potential climate change could also have an effect on some life-forms.

☑ **Reading Checkpoint** *How do we know that Earth's systems are connected?*

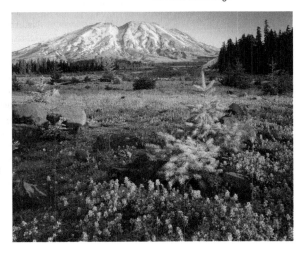

FIGURE 19 Biosphere Changes When Mount St. Helens erupted in 1980, the area shown here was buried by a volcanic mudflow. Now, plants are reestablished and new soil is forming.

LESSON 1.4

Address **Misconceptions**   L2

Students may think that only human actions can seriously affect the environment. Use the example of the eruption of Mount St. Helens to emphasize that natural events can have widespread and negative effects on the environment. The 1980 eruptions spread ash over much of eastern Washington. About 500 square kilometers of forest were destroyed or damaged. Most large animals in the area were killed by the blast, but some small animals survived. More than 20 years later, the area is still fairly barren. It may take at least 200 years for the forest to be restored to its previous state. Large mammals such as elk have already repopulated the area, along with birds, insects, and small mammals. To reinforce this idea, ask interested students to research the environmental impact of more recent events, such as the 2010 earthquakes in Haiti and Chile, the 2011 earthquake in Japan, or the 2011 tornado in Joplin, Missouri.

Use Visuals   L1

Figure 20 This flood was caused by the action of humans. **Ask:** What was the actual cause of this flood? *(building the Aswan Dam)* What are some ways humans can cause floods or make them worse? *(by clearing forests, building cities, and constructing dams)*
Visual, Logical

FIGURE 20 Environmental Impacts The Aswan Dam in Egypt was built to provide water for generating electricity and for irrigating crops. But the dam also flooded historic sites and prevented the annual floods that helped keep soils in the Nile River Valley fertile.

Role of Humans Humans play an important role in the Earth system. **Our actions produce changes in all of the other parts of the Earth system.** When we burn gasoline and coal, build breakwaters along a shoreline, dispose of our wastes, and clear the land, we cause other parts of the Earth system to respond, often in unforeseen ways. Throughout this book, you will learn about many of Earth's subsystems, such as the hydrologic (water) system, the tectonic (mountain-building) system, and the climate system. Remember that these components and we humans are all part of the complex interacting whole we call the Earth system.

People and the Environment

Environment refers to everything that surrounds and influences an organism. Some aspects of the environment are biological and social. Others are nonliving such as water, air, soil, and rock, as well as conditions such as temperature, humidity, and sunlight. These nonliving factors make up our physical environment. Because studying the Earth sciences leads to an understanding of the physical environment, most of Earth science can be characterized as environmental science.

Environmental Science *Environmental science* is the study of how the natural world works, how people affect the environment, and how the environment affects people. A key focus of environmental science is the relationship between people and the natural environment. For example, we can dramatically influence natural processes. A river flooding is natural, but the size and frequency of flooding can be changed by human activities such as clearing forests, building cities, and constructing dams. Unfortunately, natural systems do not always adjust to artificial changes in ways we can anticipate. An alteration to the environment that was intended to benefit society may also have some negative effects, as shown in **Figure 20.**

Earth's Resources Natural resources are an important part of the Earth system. A *natural resource* is any material obtained from Earth. Earth's resources include water and soil, metallic and nonmetallic minerals, and energy. Together they form the foundation of modern civilization. The Earth sciences consider not only the formation and occurrence of these vital resources but also how to maintain supplies and the environmental impact of their mining and use.

Resources are commonly divided into two broad categories—renewable resources and nonrenewable resources. **Renewable resources can be replenished over relatively short time spans.** Common examples are plants and animals for food, natural fibers for clothing, and forest products for lumber and paper. Energy from flowing water, wind, and the sun is also considered a renewable resource.

Facts and Figures

One of the reasons it is often difficult to predict how natural systems will respond to unexpected changes is the prevalence of positive and negative feedback mechanisms. Processes that feed into changes, making them more severe, are considered positive feedback. As humans put more carbon dioxide into the air, Earth may hold more of the sun's heat and begin to warm. This warming may cause snow and ice near the poles to melt. This melting may make Earth absorb more of the sun's rays, thus increasing Earth's temperature further. This is an example of positive feedback. Negative feedback mechanisms work to return the system to the way it was before the change. For example, an increase in Earth's temperature may result in an increase in evaporation, and then an increase in clouds. Clouds cause Earth to reflect more of the sun's rays back into space, cooling Earth back down.

Metals such as iron, aluminum, and copper plus our most important fuels—oil, natural gas, and coal—are classified as nonrenewable resources. **Although nonrenewable resources continue to form, the processes that create them are so slow that it takes millions of years for significant deposits to accumulate.** Earth contains limited quantities of these materials. Although some nonrenewable resources, such as aluminum, can be used over and over again, others, such as oil, cannot. When the present supplies are exhausted, there will be no more.

☑ **Reading Checkpoint** *How do renewable and nonrenewable resources differ?*

Population Effects on Resources The graph in **Figure 21** shows that Earth's human population is growing exponentially. Although it took until the beginning of the nineteenth century for the population to reach 1 billion, just 130 years were needed for the population to double to 2 billion. Between 1930 and 1975, the figure doubled again to 4 billion. Another 2 billion people were added to the population over the next 25 years. By 2010, nearly 7 billion people inhabited Earth. Clearly, as population grows, so does the demand for resources. However, the rate of mineral and energy resource usage has increased more rapidly than the overall growth of the population.

How long will the remaining supplies of basic resources last? How long can we sustain the rising standard of living in today's industrialized countries and still provide for the growing needs of developing regions? How much environmental deterioration are we willing to accept to obtain basic resources? Can alternatives be found? If we are to cope with the increasing demand on resources and a growing world population, it is important that we have some understanding of our present and potential resources.

Environmental Problems

In addition to the search for mineral and energy resources, the Earth sciences must also examine environmental problems. Some of these problems are local, some are regional, and still others are global. Humans are a major cause of environmental problems, such as the one shown in **Figure 22. Significant threats to the environment include air pollution, acid rain, ozone depletion, and global climate change.** The loss of fertile soils to erosion, the disposal of toxic wastes, and the contamination and depletion of water resources are also of considerable concern. The list of environmental problems continues to grow.

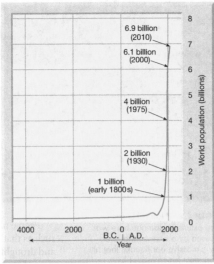

FIGURE 21 Growth of World Population The world population grew from 1 billion to nearly 7 billion in only about 200 years.

FIGURE 22 Air Pollution The air quality in many cities is affected by pollution. This photo shows the haze over Guangzhou, China. **Infer** *What may have contributed to this air pollution problem?*

Introduction to Earth Science **21**

Build Science Skills
L2

Solve Problems Explain that when supplies of a nonrenewable resource start running low, it is often possible to substitute some other resource. Have students work in small groups to brainstorm and research alternatives to oil that can be used when all of our oil supplies have been exhausted. If students are having trouble getting started, suggest that they focus on transportation and power generation. Areas students can investigate include natural gas, coal, biodiesel, nuclear power, wind power, and solar power. Have each group present their results to the class.
Interpersonal, Logical

Address **Misconceptions**   L2

Students may think that the world population is expected to continue to increase indefinitely. Tell students that many demographers (scientists who study changes in human populations) expect population growth to slow down over the next 100 years. In fact, some predict that the total population may even decrease. The reason for this is that in many developed countries, people are not having enough children to replace themselves. Most current population growth is occurring in developing countries. However, as those countries develop, their birth rates are also expected to fall.

Answers

☑ **Reading Checkpoint** *Renewable resources can be replenished over a relatively short time span. Nonrenewable resources take millions of years to accumulate.*

Figure 22 *Sample answer: home heating, motor vehicles, industry, power plants*

LESSON 1.4

Build Science Skills `L2`

Student Activity: Infer Discuss with students that events such as earthquakes, landslides, floods, hurricanes, beach erosion from coastal storms, and drought are natural processes. Help students understand that these natural processes become hazards only when people try to live where these processes occur. Provide small groups of students with one or more pictures of damage from natural disasters. Some examples to use would be flooded homes, a coastal home about to be carried out to sea, buildings damaged by an earthquake, or urban flooding due to too much paved land. **Ask:** What happened here? How could this disaster have been prevented? *(Sample answer: This home is being carried out to sea because it was built too close to the ocean. These homes were flooded because they were built on a flood plain. This building was destroyed because it was built too close to a fault line.)* Have students infer the answers to these two questions, and then share their ideas with the class. Use this as an opportunity to introduce students to various Earth events and processes that will be studied later in the year.
Visual

3 ASSESS

Evaluate Understanding `L2`

Ask students to write a five-question quiz on this lesson along with an answer key. Then have students ask one another the questions.

Reteach `L1`

Use the outlines students created for this chapter's reading strategy to review the main ideas from this lesson.

FIGURE 23 Natural Disaster
The extensive damage here was caused by a tsunami triggered by a massive earthquake that hit northeast Japan in 2011.

People must also cope with natural hazards and their effects, such as that shown in **Figure 23**. Earthquakes, floods, hurricanes, and drought are some of the many environmental risks. Of course, natural hazards are simply natural processes. They become hazards only when people try to live where these processes occur.

It is clear that as world population continues to grow, pressures on the environment will increase as well. Therefore, an understanding of Earth is essential for the management and use of basic resources. It is also essential for dealing with the human impact on the environment and minimizing the effects of natural hazards. Knowledge about Earth and how it works is necessary to our survival and well being. Earth is the only suitable habitat we have, and its resources are limited.

1.4 Assessment

Review Key Concepts 🔑

1. Why do scientists study Earth as a system?

2. If a system is a collection of interacting parts, what happens when one of the parts is changed?

3. What are the two sources of energy that power Earth's systems?

4. List three ways that humans affect Earth's systems.

5. Large numbers of tiny ocean organisms die every day, fall to the ocean floor, are buried, and will be converted to oil and natural gas. Why are these two fuels considered nonrenewable?

Think Critically

6. Use Analogies Describe the parts of a tree that comprise the tree as a system.

7. Evaluate Is it possible for humans to avoid having an effect on Earth's systems? Explain.

8. Apply Concepts How can scientists help to prevent a natural process from becoming an environmental hazard?

CONNECTING CONCEPTS

9. Communicate In Lesson 1.3, you learned about geologic maps. How might data from geologic maps help land use planners in determining where to build communities?

Assessment Answers

1. Because Earth has many separate parts, but these parts are interconnected
2. Other parts may also change.
3. The sources are the sun and reactions in Earth's interior.
4. Sample answer: contaminating water, polluting air, disposing of toxic waste
5. It takes too long (millions of years) for the organisms to be converted into fuel.

6. Roots transport food and water up through the trunk, which holds the tree upright. The trunk transports food and serves as support for branches and leaves. Leaves help keep the tree moist and shaded and release excess water through pores.
7. Sample answer: No, simply breathing changes the atmosphere around you or stepping on the grass may affect the biosphere beneath your foot.

8. Sample answer: They can analyze an area to see if it is safe to live there. If the land is unstable or subject to flooding, they may make recommendations that people not choose to live there.
9. Sample answers: Geologic maps can help land use planners analyze the rock structure and landforms in the area to see if it is safe to live there; the possibility of earthquakes; the availability of mineral resources

1.5 What Is Scientific Inquiry?

EARTH SCIENTISTS, like all scientists, are guided by the basic assumption that through careful, systematic study, events in the natural world can be understood and explained. The knowledge gathered can be used to make useful predictions. For example, by understanding weather patterns, meteorologists can predict the path of a hurricane.

The Process of Science

Scientific inquiry refers to the diverse ways in which scientists study the natural world and propose explanations based on the evidence they gather. The dynamic process of science involves observing, asking questions, developing hypotheses, making and testing predictions, and analyzing and interpreting results. Scientists take various paths using these scientific methods, depending on the questions they are investigating and the resources available to them.

Developing Hypotheses Scientific inquiry often begins as scientists pose questions and collect data through observation and measurement. ▭ **Scientists try to explain how or why things happen in the manner observed by stating a hypothesis. A hypothesis is a scientific explanation for a set of observations that can be tested in ways that support or reject it.** Scientists often explore more than one hypothesis at the same time. A hypothesis must be rigorously tested and analyzed before it can be accepted by the scientific community.

Testing Hypotheses Testing a hypothesis often involves designing an experiment that keeps track of various factors that can change, called *variables*. Examples of variables include temperature, amount of sunlight, and time. In a *controlled experiment*, only one variable is changed while all other variables are kept unchanged, or controlled. When experimental data does not fit with a hypothesis, the hypothesis may be modified or discarded altogether. An example of a discarded hypothesis is the Earth-centered model of the universe.

Experiments are just one way that scientists test their hypotheses. Observational studies provide another key source of data. In an observational study, scientists look for evidence in the natural world that would help confirm or contradict the predictions generated by their hypotheses. You can learn more about scientific skills and methods, including science safety procedures, in the Skills Handbook in the Appendix.

Key Questions

▭ **What is a hypothesis?**

▭ **What is a theory?**

Vocabulary
• hypothesis • theory

Reading Strategy

Compare and Contrast Complete the Venn diagram by listing the ways hypothesis and theory are alike and how they differ.

hypothesis   theory

▌1▐ FOCUS

Lesson Objectives
1.13 **Define** the terms *hypothesis* and *theory*.

Build Vocabulary   L2
Word Meanings Before they read the lesson, have students write down definitions for *hypothesis* and *theory*. As they read the lesson, have them note the scientific definitions of these terms and compare them to their definitions.

Reading Strategy   L2
Hypothesis: an idea someone wants to test; Theory: an explanation that is supported by evidence and widely accepted; Similarities: could be proven wrong, can be tested

▌2▐ INSTRUCT

Build Reading Literacy   L1
Refer to **p. 446D** in **Chapter 16,** which provides guidelines for sequencing.

Sequence Tell students to make a flowchart showing the steps involved in developing and testing hypotheses. *(Sample response: Pose questions and collect data → Develop a hypothesis → Test hypothesis (experiment, observational study) → Accept, modify, or reject hypothesis)* Have students check their flowchart against the sequence of steps provided in the Process of Science section of the text. **Visual, Verbal**

LESSON 1.5

(Address **Misconceptions**)   L2

Students often think that a scientific theory is an ultimate truth, and therefore can never be changed. This is not true. A theory is only accepted if a multitude of tests support the theory. However, if even one scientist finds a situation where the theory fails, that theory is again called into question and must be revised or replaced. For this reason, science is constantly changing.
Verbal

Integrate Language Arts   L2

Represent Definitions There are many definitions for the word *model*. Have students use a dictionary to write down as many definitions of the word as possible. Then have them draw or cut out pictures representing these definitions. Help students determine which definition is most appropriate in this lesson.
Visual, Verbal

3 ASSESS

Evaluate Understanding   L2

Give students several examples of theories and laws in science. Discuss the examples and have students come up with their own definitions of *scientific theory* and *scientific law*.

Reteach   L1

Have students illustrate each step of the scientific method on the flowchart they made earlier. Help students understand that scientists do not always perform these steps in the same sequence. Often, the process of science loops back on itself. There is no one set way to "do" science.
Visual

Scientific Knowlege

An important aspect of scientific inquiry is the sharing of ideas and communication of results to the scientific community. The scientific community, through critical review and replication of data, helps to verify the accuracy of results and contributes to the establishment of scientific theories.

Scientific Theories In science, a **theory** is a well-established, highly reliable explanation of a natural or physical phenomenon. 🔑 **A scientific theory unifies a broad range of observations and hypotheses and enables scientists to make accurate predictions about new situations.** Tested by multiple independent researchers, a theory is well supported by evidence and widely accepted by the scientific community. For example, the theory of plate tectonics provides the framework for understanding the origin of continents and ocean basins, plus the occurrence of mountains, earthquakes, and volcanoes.

Scientific Laws Laws differ from theories. A scientific law is a concise, specific statement that summarizes a pattern found in nature. Laws describe how some aspect of the world is expected to behave in a certain situation. For example, the laws of planetary motion describe the way planets move around the sun. In general, laws describe relationships but do not attempt to explain why the relationships exist. Similar to theories, laws are based on repeatable observations and are widely accepted by the scientific community.

1.5 Assessment

Review Key Concepts 🔑

1. Why is science considered to be a dynamic process?

2. What is a controlled experiment?

3. How are observational studies useful in scientific investigations?

4. What is the difference between a scientific theory and a hypothesis?

Think Critically

5. Apply Concepts What happens if more than one hypothesis is put forward to explain the same observations?

6. Apply Concepts Why is it necessary to use careful and systematic methods when carrying out scientific investigations?

7. Design an Experiment While carrying out an investigation, a scientist observes some unexpected results. What are the scientist's next steps?

WRITING IN SCIENCE

8. Communicate It may take a long time for the scientific community to accept a theory, such as the theory of plate tectonics. Write a paragraph suggesting how the use of proper scientific methods helps a scientific explanation gain acceptance as a theory.

Assessment Answers

1. Sample answer: Scientists take various paths in their quest to learn more about the world; experiments are repeated; hypotheses are tested and retested
2. An experiment where only one variable is changed while all other variables are kept unchanged
3. They provide data that help confirm or contradict hypotheses

4. A theory may encompass many hypotheses.
5. They are all tested and analyzed.
6. To be accepted by the scientific community, data must be able to be replicated and results verified for accuracy. By using systematic methods, this can be done.
7. Sample answer: The scientist should record his/her observations and any data that can be recorded. The scientist should continue carrying out the experiment, reanalyze the hypothesis, retest the hypothesis, or modify it if necessary.

8. Sample answer: Many scientists around the world repeat the same observations, experiments, and record similar results. The theory is consistently supported time and time again. Advise students that they can find out more about the theory of plate tectonics in Chapter 9.

Studying Earth From Space

Scientific data are gathered in many ways, such as laboratory studies, field observations, and field measurements. Satellite images like the one in **Figure 24** are another useful source of data. Such images provide perspectives that are difficult to get from more traditional sources. The high-tech instruments aboard many satellites enable scientists to gather information from remote regions where data are otherwise scarce. The image in Figure 24 makes use of ASTER technology.

ASTER stands for Advanced Spaceborne Thermal Emission and Reflection Radiometer. Because different materials reflect and give off energy in different ways, ASTER can provide detailed information about the composition of Earth's surface. Figure 24 is a three-dimensional view looking north over Death Valley, California. The data have been computer enhanced to exaggerate the color variations that indicate differences in types of surface materials.

FIGURE 24 This satellite image shows detailed information about the composition of surface materials in Death Valley, California. It was produced by superimposing nighttime thermal infrared data, acquired on April 7, 2000, over topographic data from the U.S. Geological Survey. (Image courtesy of NASA)

Salt deposits on the floor of Death Valley appear in different shades of colors. These colors indicate the presence of sulfate, carbonate, and chloride minerals. The Panamint Mountains lie to the west and the Black Mountains lie to the east.

Both mountain ranges are made up of sedimentary limestones, sandstones, shales, and metamorphic rocks. The bright red areas are dominated by the mineral quartz, found in sandstone; the green areas are limestone.

Studying Earth From Space L2

Background ASTER is an imaging instrument that obtains detailed maps of land surface temperature. It flies on a satellite called Terra, which was launched in 1999. ASTER is part of NASA's Earth Observing System (EOS), which is a series of satellites, a science component, and a data system. EOS will help scientists develop a deeper understanding of Earth as an integrated system—the interactions among the biosphere, hydrosphere, lithosphere, and atmosphere.

Teaching Tips

- As students read the feature and look at Figure 24, have them identify on the image the various regions described in the text.
- Explain to students that this image does not show the true colors of Death Valley as seen from space. Instead, the colors were inserted by scientists to indicate differences in surface composition.
  Ask: What do you think this image would look like in true color? *(Because Death Valley is a desert, it would be mostly tan in color.)* Based on the information given on what the colors indicate, what is the composition of the most distant mountains in the image? *(mostly limestone, with some sandstone and a little bit of salt)*
- Have students research ASTER and EOS on NASA's web site and prepare a report to the class.

Visual, Logical

DETERMINING LATITUDE AND LONGITUDE L2

Objective
In this activity, students will:
- measure angles with a protractor in order to draw and label latitude and longitude lines accurately.
- locate points on Earth's surface using their latitude and longitude.

Skills Interpret, Measure, Infer

Prep Time 15 minutes

Class Time 30 minutes

Teaching Tip Some students will not remember how to use a protractor. Provide small-group instruction for these students before starting the lab.

Expected Outcome Students will understand how the measurements for latitude and longitude lines were made by early mapmakers and will create a diagram that looks like the following:

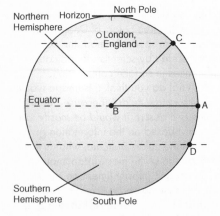

Answers to Procedure Questions
1–4 See sketch above.
3. The latitude is 45°N.
4. 25°S
5. Answers will vary depending on the globe used.
6. A: 30°N latitude, B: 5°S latitude, C: 55°N latitude, D: 35°S latitude, E: 0° latitude, F: 20°N latitude
7. A: 56°N 37°E, B: 29°S 31°E, C: Answers will vary depending on where students live.
8. Answers will vary depending on where students live.
9. See sketch above.

Determining Latitude and Longitude

Problem How are latitude and longitude calculated, and how do they indicate a particular location's position on the globe?

Materials globe, protractor, ruler, compass or round object for tracing, pencil, world map

Skills Interpret Visuals, Measure, Infer

Connect to the Big idea Using maps and globes to find places and features on Earth's surface is an essential skill required of all Earth scientists. The grid that is formed by lines of latitude and longitude form the basis for locating points on Earth. Latitude lines indicate north-south distance, and longitude lines indicate east-west distance. Degrees are used to mark latitude and longitude distances on Earth's surface. Degrees can be divided into 60 equal parts called minutes ('), and a minute of angle can be divided into 60 parts called seconds ("). Thus, 31°10'20" means 31 degrees, 10 minutes, and 20 seconds. This exercise will introduce you to the systems used for determining location on Earth.

Procedure
Part A: Determining Latitude

1. **Figure A** represents Earth, with point B its center. Draw this figure on a separate piece of paper. Locate the equator on a globe. Sketch and label the equator on your diagram. Label the Northern Hemisphere and Southern Hemisphere on your diagram.

2. On your diagram, make an angle by drawing a line from point A on the equator to point B (the center of Earth). Then extend the line from point B to point C in the Northern Hemisphere. The angle you have drawn (∠ABC) is 45°. By definition of latitude, point C is located at 45° N latitude.

3. Draw a line on your figure through point C that is also parallel to the equator. What is the latitude at all points on this line? Record this number on the line.

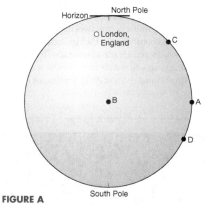

FIGURE A

4. Using a protractor, measure ∠ABD on your paper. Then draw a line parallel to the equator that also goes through point D. Label the line with its proper latitude.

5. How many degrees of latitude separate the latitude lines (or parallels) on the globe that you are using? Record this on your paper.

6. Refer to **Figure B**. Determine the latitude for each point A–F. Be sure to indicate whether it is north or south of the equator and include the word "latitude." Record these numbers on your paper.

7. Use a globe or map to locate the cities listed below. On your paper, record their latitude to the nearest degree.
   A. Moscow, Russia
   B. Durban, South Africa
   C. Your home city

8. Use the globe or map to give the name of a city or feature that is equally as far south of the equator as your home city is north.

Part B: Determining Longitude

9. Locate the prime meridian on **Figure C.** Sketch and label it on your diagram. Label the Eastern and Western Hemispheres.

10. How many degrees of longitude separate each meridian on your globe? Record this on your paper.

11. Refer to Figure C. Determine the longitude for each point A–F. Be sure to indicate whether it is east or west of the Prime Meridian. Record these numbers on your paper.

12. Use the globe or map to give the name of a city or feature that is equally as far east of the prime meridian as your home city is west.

Analyze and Conclude

1. **Apply Concepts** What is the maximum number of 1 degree longitude or latitude lines that can be drawn on a globe?

2. **Compare and Contrast** How are longitude and latitude lines the same and how are they different?

3. **Relate Cause and Effect** The aviation pioneer Amelia Earhart, her flight engineer, and her plane are believed to have been lost somewhere over the Pacific Ocean. It is now thought that the coordinates that she was given for her fuel stop at Howley Island in the Pacific Ocean were wrong. Knowing what you do about how latitude and longitude coordinates are written, why would a wrong number have been so catastrophic for her?

GO FURTHER Use reference books or the Internet to research the number of time zones on Earth. Find out how many there are and draw their boundaries on the figure you created for this lab. What time zone do you live in? What time zone is the location that you chose in question 12? What is the time difference between these two locations?

FIGURE B

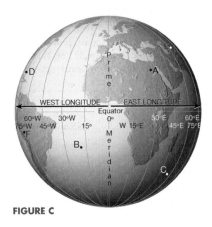

FIGURE C

---

10. Answers will vary depending on the globe used.

11. A: 30°E, B: 20°W, C: 45°E, D: 75°W, E: 65°E, F: 68°W

12. Answers will vary depending on where students live.

Analyze and Conclude

1. 360 longitude lines and 180 latitude lines

2. Both latitude and longitude are measured in degrees. Latitudes are N/S measurements, longitudes are E/W measurements. Lines of latitude all run parallel to each other. Because lines of longitude run north and south, they follow the curvature of Earth and meet at the poles.

3. Earth is very large. Even a mistake of a minute or seconds of a degree may have set her in the wrong direction, unable to spot a small island in the ocean.

GO FURTHER

Answers to the questions depend on where students live.
Visual, Logical

Study Tip

Study Daily

Encourage students to study their notes for a few minutes each day. Advise them to read their notes over, make sure they are complete, add color to sketches, highlight important facts, make flashcards for new vocabulary and concepts, and keep a list of questions related to things they don't understand. This will help your students to follow along in class more easily and do better on exams.

21st Century Learning

Creativity and Intellectual Curiosity

What Science Subject Interests You?
Earth science includes many different topics, such as rocks, water, weather, Earth's movements, and the solar system. Scientists, including earth scientists, study what they are most interested in. Encourage students to discuss what topics interest them most. **Ask:** What topic of Earth science most interests you? What questions would you like answered? Why are you interested in this particular topic? Encourage student to write notes or a blog post about their interests.

Homework Guide

Lesson	Questions
1	1, 11
2	2, 3, 7, 9, 12, 13, 24, 25
3	4–6, 10, 14–16, 27–33, 35
4	17–21, 26, 34, 37
5	8, 22, 23, 36

1 Study Guide

Big idea ▶ Earth's Materials and Systems

1.1 What Is Earth Science?

🔑 Earth science is the name for the group of sciences that studies Earth and its neighbors in space.

🔑 The nebular theory suggests that the bodies of our solar system evolved from an enormous rotating cloud called the solar nebula. It was made up mostly of hydrogen and helium, with a small percentage of heavier elements.

Earth science (2) meteorology (3)
geology (2) astronomy (3)
oceanography (3)

1.2 A View of Earth

🔑 Earth can be thought of as having four major spheres: the atmosphere, hydrosphere, geosphere, and biosphere.

🔑 Because the geosphere is not uniform, it is divided into three main parts based on differences in composition—the core, the mantle, and the crust.

🔑 The theory of plate tectonics provided geologists with a model to explain how continents move and earthquakes and volcanic eruptions occur.

atmosphere (8) mantle (8)
hydrosphere (8) crust (8)
geosphere (8) biosphere (9)
core (8)

1.3 Representing Earth's Surface

🔑 Latitude is the distance north or south of the equator, measured in degrees. Longitude is the distance east or west of the prime meridian, measured in degrees.

🔑 No matter what kind of map is made, some portion of the surface will always be too small, too big, or out of place. Mapmakers have, however, found ways to limit the distortion of shape, size, distance, and direction.

🔑 Topographic maps differ from other maps because topographic maps show elevation.

🔑 A map that shows the type and age of exposed rock is called a geologic map.

🔑 Today's technology provides us with the ability to more precisely analyze Earth's physical properties.

latitude (11) contour line (14)
longitude (11) contour interval (14)
topographic map (14)

1.4 Earth System Science

🔑 The aim of Earth system science is to understand Earth as a system made up of numerous interacting parts, or subsystems.

🔑 A system can be any size group of interacting parts that form a complex whole.

🔑 The sun drives external processes that occur in the atmosphere, hydrosphere, and at Earth's surface. Earth's interior is also a source of energy.

🔑 Human actions produce changes in all other parts of the Earth system.

🔑 Renewable resources can be replenished over relatively short time spans. Nonrenewable resources form over such a long period of time that it takes millions of years for significant deposits to accumulate.

🔑 Significant threats to the environment include air pollution, acid rain, ozone depletion, and global climate change.

system (18)

1.5 What Is Scientific Inquiry?

🔑 A hypothesis is a scientific explanation for a set of observations that can be tested in ways that support or reject it.

🔑 A scientific theory unifies a broad range of observations and hypotheses and enables scientists to make accurate predictions about new situations.

hypothesis (23) theory (24)

Assessment Answers

Review Content

1. b	**2.** a	**3.** c
4. a	**5.** b	**6.** b
7. a	**8.** b	**9.** d
10. b		

Understand Concepts

11. A large cloud of dust and gas formed, then began to rotate and collapse. Heat increased toward the center, forming the sun. As cooling progressed, the cloud condensed into rocky and metallic materials that eventually became the inner planets. The outer planets formed mainly from gases.

12. mountains—geosphere; lakes—hydrosphere; trees—biosphere; clouds—atmosphere; ice—hydrosphere; snow—hydrosphere

1 Assessment

Review Content

Choose the letter that best answers the question or completes the statement.

1. The science that deals with the study of the atmosphere is
   a. oceanography.   c. geology.
   b. meteorology.   d. astronomy.

2. What caused Earth to develop layers as it cooled?
   a. differences in density
   b. the magnetic field
   c. the speed of rotation
   d. escaping gases

3. What drives the process of plate tectonics, the currently accepted explanation for the movement of drifting continents?
   a. gravity
   b. ocean currents
   c. unequal heat distribution
   d. earthquakes

4. Lines of latitude describe position
   a. north or south of the equator.
   b. east or west of the equator.
   c. north or south of the prime meridian.
   d. east or west of the prime meridian.

5. The Robinson map projection is considered very useful because
   a. all of the continents are the same size.
   b. most distances, sizes, and shapes are accurate.
   c. it shows landmasses in three dimensions.
   d. features along latitude lines are accurate.

6. Which of the following types of map would best show the three dimensions of Earth's surface?
   a. road map   c. weather map
   b. topographic map   d. tectonic map

7. Which of the following is the outermost of Earth's major spheres?
   a. atmosphere   c. hydrosphere
   b. biosphere   d. geosphere

8. What makes a hypothesis scientifically useful?
   a. Many people think it is a good idea.
   b. It can be tested.
   c. It contains numerical data.
   d. It applies directly to Earth science.

9. The theory that Earth's lithosphere is broken into large sections that move is called
   a. biosphere.   c. nebular.
   b. global positioning.   d. plate tectonics.

10. On a topographic map, contour lines that are closer together indicate
    a. forest.   c. a mountain top.
    b. a steeper slope.   d. roads.

Understand Concepts

11. Briefly list the events that led to the formation of the solar system.

12. Which of Earth's spheres do mountains, lakes, trees, clouds, ice, and snow represent?

13. List the four parts of the geosphere indicated at the letters in the figure below.

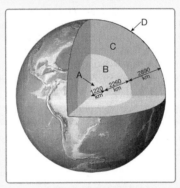

14. The Mercator projection map shows Earth's features on a grid. Why is this map useful to sailors?

15. Why is the contour interval included on a topographic map?

16. How is remote sensing useful to Earth scientists?

13. A—inner core; B—outer core; C—mantle; D—crust
14. It shows directions accurately.
15. It tells you the change in elevation from line to line.
16. Sample answer: Remote sensing enables scientists to study Earth's features and processes from a distance.

ASSESSMENT

17. Matter does not enter or leave a closed system, but energy moves freely in and out.
18. soil, air, water, rocks
19. The sources are the sun and Earth's interior.
20. It must be replenished over a relatively short period of time.
21. Sample answers: earthquakes, floods, landslides, hurricanes, drought
22. data collection, development of hypotheses, observation and experimentation to test hypotheses, acceptance, modification, or rejection of hypotheses

Think Critically

23. A hypothesis is a possible explanation for how or why an observed phenomena happens. A scientific theory is formed after a hypothesis has been well tested and accepted by the scientific community as the best explanation for certain observable facts.
24. Humans can't drink ocean water. Because only 3 percent of Earth's water is fresh water, we only have a small amount of water available to us.
25. Most of Earth's life forms need oxygen to live. Our atmosphere contains oxygen. If Earth had no atmosphere, there would be no oxygen, and most organisms would not be able to survive.
26. Sample answers: atmosphere—less oxygen released into the air, less carbon dioxide absorbed, less water vapor present; biosphere—fewer trees in the area, loss of habitat for tree-dwelling organisms; geosphere—increased erosion from absence of tree roots, less physical weathering from tree roots in the area; hydrosphere—less water vapor released into the air, which results in less water returning to the ground in the form of precipitation
27. Great Plains—the contour interval would be small because the elevation changes slowly over larger distances; Colorado—the contour interval would be high because the elevation changes greatly over a short distance. If the contour interval was small, the map would have to be very large in order to correctly show the changes in elevation and the topography of the area.

Math Skills

28. 1 km 5 approximately 0.6 mile
29. 7.5 km
30. one fourth around the globe; one third around the globe

30 Chapter 1

---

17. What happens to matter and energy in a closed system?
18. What types of factors make up our nonliving environment?
19. What are the two sources of energy for the Earth system?
20. What requirement must be satisfied in order for a resource to be considered renewable?
21. List at least four natural environmental hazards that people must cope with.
22. Briefly describe the steps that most scientific investigations involve.

Critical Thinking

23. Compare and Contrast How is a scientific hypothesis different from a scientific theory?
24. Apply Concepts If oceans cover nearly 71 percent of Earth's surface, why is it important to conserve water?
25. Infer Explain the following statement: If Earth had no atmosphere, our planet would be lifeless.
26. Form a Hypothesis Predict what the effect might be on some of Earth's systems if a forest is cut down for lumber.
27. Compare and Contrast As part of the Great Plains of the United States, the state of Kansas has relatively flat topography. On the other hand, portions of the state of Colorado are mountainous. Describe how the contour interval and the contour lines might vary on topographic maps of these two states.

Math Skills

Use the map scale to answer Questions 28 and 29.

28. Interpret Visuals Approximately how many miles is 1 kilometer equal to?
29. Calculate If 1 kilometer is equal to 1 centimeter on the map, what is the distance in km between two cities that are 7.5 cm apart?

30 Chapter 1 • Assessment

---

30. Calculate Recall that Earth is divided into 360 degrees. If you travel to a location that is 90 degrees east from the prime meridian, how far around the globe have you gone? What about a location that is 120 degrees east from the prime meridian?

Map Skills

Use the topographic map in Figure 16 on page 15 to answer Questions 31–33.

31. Interpret Maps Compare and contrast the topography of Spruce Lake Bog National Landmark and Dundee Mountain. What do the contour lines indicate?
32. Interpret Maps About how wide is Spruce Lake at its widest point from east to west?
33. Interpret Maps What can you infer about Camp Vista?

Concepts in Action

34. Apply Concepts List at least three examples of how you influence one or more of Earth's major spheres in your daily life.
35. Apply Concepts A local company wants to open a new quarry for extracting limestone, a rock useful in construction. Explain what type of map they should use to determine if limestone is present in your area.
36. Form an Opinion A friend's scientific experiment yielded results that do not support her hypothesis. She thinks that the investigation has failed. Do you agree? What advice regarding the scientific process might you give your friend?
37. Writing in Science You are given the opportunity to address the city council about the proposed construction of a factory by the river in your community. Prepare a list of questions about the project that you would like to ask the city council and the building engineers before deciding whether or not you would support the project.

Map Skills

31. With few contour lines, the area near Spruce Lake Bog National Landmark is relatively flat. The closely spaced contours indicate that Dundee Mountain is steep.
32. about a quarter mile across
33. It is located in an area of lower elevation.

Concepts in Action

34. Sample answers: hydrosphere—You use water everyday for bathing, washing clothes, and cooking; atmosphere—driving to school

burns gasoline, which emits pollutants into the air; using a clothes dryer releases hot air.
35. The company should use a geologic map. This map will give them information on the local rock types, whether limestone is present, and the extent of the rock formations.
36. Sample answer: The experiment should be repeated and the hypothesis modified, if necessary, based on data collected.
37. Students should include a discussion on the impact on Earth's spheres and the interaction among the spheres and the factory.

Standardized Test Prep

Standardized Test Prep

1 D
2 G
3 B
4 H
5 D

Choose the letter that *best* answers the question or completes the statement.

1 The "sphere" that strongly influences the other three "spheres," because without life their makeup and nature would be much different, is the—
  A atmosphere
  B hydrosphere
  C geosphere
  D biosphere

2 The science that includes the study of the composition and movements of water, as well as coastal processes, the seafloor, and marine life is—
  F geology
  G oceanography
  H meteorology
  J astronomy

3 Which of these situations is(are) an example of an open system?
I. a car's cooling system
II. a boiling teakettle
III. a loaf of bread in a sealed plastic bag
IV. a river flowing through a canyon
  A I only
  B II & IV
  C I & III
  D I, II, III & IV

Use the figure below to answer Question 4.

4 The latitude and longitude for point A on the map are—
  F 60°N latitude, 30°E longitude
  G 60°E latitude, 30°N longitude
  H 30°N latitude, 60°E longitude
  J 30°S latitude, 60°W longitude

5 In order for a hypothesis to become accepted by the scientific community—
  A the hypothesis must first become a scientific law
  B evidence for the hypothesis must be published in the newspaper
  C the hypothesis must be rejected and then modified
  D the hypothesis must be rigorously tested and supported by evidence

If You Have Trouble With . . .

Question	1	2	3	4	5
See Lesson	1.2	1.1	1.4	1.3	1.5

2 Minerals Planning Guide

Lesson Objectives		Activities
2.1 Matter, pp. 34–43 2.1 **Explain** how elements are related to minerals. 2.2 **Identify** the kinds of particles that make up atoms. 2.3 **Explain** the differences between ions and isotopes. 2.4 **Explain** what compounds are and **describe** why they form. 2.5 **Compare and contrast** the three major types of chemical bonds.		**TE** Teacher Demo: Isotopes and Numbers, p. 38 〔L2〕 **TE** Teacher Demo: Comparing Bonds, p. 42 〔L2〕
2.2 Minerals, pp. 44–49 2.6 **List** five characteristics of minerals. 2.7 **Describe** the processes that result in mineral formation. 2.8 **Explain** how minerals can be classified. 2.9 **List** some of the major groups of minerals.		**TE** Teacher Demo: Crytallization of Sulfur, p. 45 〔L2〕 **TE** Teacher Demo: Precipitation of a Mineral, p. 46 〔L2〕 **TE** Build Science Skills, p. 48 〔L2〕
2.3 Properties of Minerals, pp. 50–55 2.10 **Explain** why color is often not a useful property in identifying minerals. 2.11 **Define** the terms *luster, crystal form, streak,* and *Mohs scale.* 2.12 **Distinguish** between cleavage and fracture. 2.13 **Explain** density and how it can be used to identify substances. 2.14 **Describe** some other properties that can be used to identify minerals.		**TE** Build Science Skills, p. 54 〔L2〕 **TE** Evaluate Understanding, p. 55 〔L2〕
Chapter Features and Labs		
Try It How Are a Group of Minerals Alike and Different?, p. 33		**LM** Crystal Systems 〔L3〕
Earth & Its Resources Gemstones, pp. 56–57		
Exploration Lab Mineral Identification, pp. 58–59		

Ability Levels

L1	For students who need additional help
L2	For all students
L3	For students who need to be challenged

Components

SE	Student Edition	LP	Lesson Plans
TE	Teacher's Edition	AA	Active Art
LM	Laboratory Manual	PD	Planet Diary
CT	Chapter Tests	GEODe	Geode CD-ROM
GRSW	Guided Reading & Study Workbook	eText	
CTB	Computer Test Bank		

Resources	Lesson Assessment
GRSW Lesson 2.1 **LP** Lesson Planning 2.1	**SE** Lesson 2.1 Assessment, p. 43 **eText** Lesson 2.1
GRSW Lesson 2.2 **LP** Lesson Planning 2.2 **PD** Minerals **GEODe** Earth Materials: Rock Cycle	**SE** Lesson 2.2 Assessment, p. 49 **eText** Lesson 2.2
GRSW Lesson 2.2 **LP** Lesson Planning 2.2 **AA** Crystal System	**SE** Lesson 2.3 Assessment, p. 55 **eText** Lesson 2.3

Materials for Activities and Labs

Quantities for each group

STUDENT EDITION

Try It, p. 33
hand lenses, small hammers, safety goggles, samples of the colorless varieties of fluorite, quartz, halite, and calcite

Exploration Lab, p. 58
mineral samples, hand lens, streak plate, copper penny, steel knife blade, glass plate, piece of quartz, dilute hydrochloric acid, magnet, hammer, 50-mL graduated cylinder, tap water, balance, thin thread, scissors, paper or cloth towels, Table 2 on pp. 54–55

TEACHER'S EDITION

Teacher Demo, p. 38
overhead projector, red and green gummy candies

Teacher Demo, p. 42
rock salt, chalk, copper wire, hammer, goggles

Teacher Demo, p. 45
two crucibles, 50-mL beaker, water, teaspoon, sulfur powder, tongs, Bunsen burner, magnifying glass

Teacher Demo, p. 46
rock salt, spoon warm water, 400-mL beaker, shallow pan or tray

Build Science Skills, p. 48
modeling clay or gumdrops, toothpicks

Build Science Skills, p. 54
small samples of calcite and dolomite, goggles, gloves, dropper bottles of dilute HCl

Evaluate Understanding, p. 55
4 or 5 mineral samples of varying hardness (unidentified)

Assessment

CHAPTER ASSESSMENT
SE Assessment, pp. 61–62
CT Chapter 2 Test
CTB Chapter 2
eText Chapter 2

21st Century Learning

Global Awareness and Economic Literacy:
How are minerals used?, TE p. 60

Common Themes

Michael Wysession
Washington University

Earth is mostly made of rock (2/3 by weight, 5/6 by volume). These rocks are made of minerals. There are more than 3800 different named minerals, though most rocks are made of only a small number of these.

Matter and Energy Atoms combine naturally to form minerals. Atoms consist of a nucleus, containing protons and neutrons, surrounded by clouds of electrons. Atoms have different properties when they occur as different isotopes (varying numbers of neutrons) and ions (varying numbers of electrons).

Forces and Motion Atoms bond in several different ways, including covalent, ionic, and metallic bonding. The electrical charge of ions and their sizes determine which atoms can combine in a stable manner to form minerals. Mineral grains or crystals are the accumulation of enormous numbers of atoms or ions bonding with a particular repeating structure. The manner in which the three-dimensional crystal lattice of atoms is constructed determines the mineral's characteristics, such as crystal form, luster, color, streak, hardness, fracture, cleavage, and density.

Earth as a System Most minerals form from the crystallization of magma, which is molten rock. Minerals can also form through precipitation, or by the alteration of existing minerals through changes in temperature and pressure. Because of the high abundance of the elements oxygen and silicon, most rocks are silicates, which usually involve combinations of silicon-oxygen tetrahedra with other elements.

EARTH SCIENCE REFRESHER

Why Are Particular Minerals Abundant?

1. Stellar Nucleosynthesis. The products of a pre-solar nebula depend upon the reactants available. While most hydrogen and helium (and a small amount of lithium) formed during the Big Bang, Earth's other elements formed much later. The oxygen, carbon, and other atoms larger than helium form within stars, and are ejected into space during a star's supernova phase. When our solar system formed, the planets were made from the remains of stars that were "dead" — had finished their fusion stages. The stellar production of these larger elements, called nucleosynthesis, does not make equal amounts of all elements. In terms of mass, Earth's principal elements are iron (35 percent), oxygen (30 percent), silicon (15 percent), magnesium (13 percent), nickel (2.4 percent), sulfur (1.9 percent), calcium (1.1 percent), and aluminum (1.1 percent). These elements are made more abundantly within stars than other elements. Most of the iron, nickel, and sulfur sank to form Earth's core. The rest are the primary elements available for minerals and rocks.

2. Earth's location in the solar system. As you will see in Chapter 23, different planets have different compositions.

> **Address Misconceptions**
>
> *Many students think that atoms become positively charged as a result of gaining protons.* However, electrons are the only subatomic particles that can be removed from or added to an atom during a chemical reaction. For a strategy that helps to overcome this misconception, see **Address Misconceptions** on TE p. 40.

Students may think that the minerals discussed in this chapter are the same as the minerals found in vitamin pills. They are related but not the same. In earth science, a mineral is a naturally occurring inorganic crystalline solid. In contrast, minerals found in vitamin pills are inorganic compounds made in the laboratory that contain elements needed by the body. For a strategy that helps to overcome this misconception, see **Address Misconceptions** on **TE p. 44.**

Planets close to the sun are metal-rich. Planets a bit farther out, such as Earth, are rock-rich. Planets farther from the sun are gas-rich and ice-rich. This is a result of the temperatures in the solar system when the planets were forming. Had Earth been closer or farther from the sun, the abundances of elements available to make minerals and rocks would have been different.

3. Electrical charge and ion size compatibility. Chapter 2 describes how the electrical charges of compounds must add to zero for the compound to be stable. In addition, compounds that have ion sizes that fit together well tend to be more stable, and so these are the minerals that we tend to find in nature. One way to think of this is that, because atoms are always oscillating, if the ions don't fit together well, their vibrations create an unstable compound structure. Stable minerals have atoms that fit together well. When minerals are pushed to greater depths, their ions get reduced in size. Negative ions, which are usually larger, are compressed more easily than positive ions. This compression can change the relative sizes of the ions, and minerals that were stable at the surface may now become unstable. When this happens, mineral structures will fall apart and rearrange into the more compatible structures of new minerals.

BUILD READING LITERACY
Preview

Skim Ahead to Understand Text Organization

Strategy Get an advance idea of how the text is organized and activate prior knowledge. This prereading strategy involves skimming the titles, headings, visuals, and boldfaced text. Like checking a roadmap before beginning a trip, previewing helps the reader to recall familiar material and to prepare to learn new material. Before students begin to read, select a portion of Chapter 2 for them to preview, such as pp. 34–35.

Example

1. Ask students to look at the chapter title, section titles, and heads. Tell them to notice whether the terms and concepts mentioned are familiar or unfamiliar.

2. Have students look at the Reading Focus for the specific section to be previewed.

3. Ask students to compare the key concepts and the boldfaced statements in the section.

4. Have students look at the visuals in the section and (where possible) relate each to a specific heading.

5. You may wish to have students prepare a study guide using the headings, key concept questions, and vocabulary as categories in a chart showing the section organization. Have students read the selected pages in depth, filling in the chart with details as they read.

See TE p. 50 for a script on how to use this strategy with students. For additional strategies, see TE pp. 34, 42, and 45.

CHAPTER 2

ASSESS PRIOR KNOWLEDGE

Use the Chapter Pretest below to assess students' prior knowledge. As needed, review these concepts.

Review Science Concepts

Lesson 2.1 Review the information about elements that can be derived from the periodic table. Review the basic structure of atoms.

Lesson 2.2 Review the naming of simple chemical compounds. Recall what a precipitate is.

Lesson 2.3 Review SI measurement units and density.

Review Math Skills

Line Graphs Review with students what a line graph shows and how the axes should be labeled.

Direct students to the **Math Skills** in the **Skills Handbook** at the end of the student text.

2 Minerals

Big idea Earth's Materials and Systems

Q: What are minerals and why are they important?

32

Chapter Pretest

1. What are the three particles that make up atoms? *(b)*
  a. protons, isotopes, and electrons
  b. protons, neutrons, and electrons
  c. protons, isotopes, and neutrons
  d. neutrons, isotopes, and electrons

2. What are the main types of chemical bonds? *(ionic bonds, covalent bonds, metallic bonds)*

3. What elements make up NaCl? *(c)*
  a. sodium and carbon
  b. sodium and calcium
  c. sodium and chlorine
  d. nitrogen and chlorine

4. True or False: A precipitate forms from dissolved substances *(True)*

5. A 1-cubic-centimeter sample of a mineral has a mass of 2 grams. What is the density of the mineral? *(c)*
  a. 1   **b.** 1 g/cm^3
  c. 2 g/cm^3 **d.** 2

6. How is data shown on a line graph? *(a series of points joined by a line)*

The structures in this cave are giant natural crystals of the mineral gypsum. They formed about 300 meters below the desert in northern Mexico. The geologist is wearing a suit that protects against the high temperature (50°C) of the cave.

INQUIRY
TRY IT!

HOW ARE A GROUP OF MINERALS ALIKE AND DIFFERENT?

Procedure

1. Obtain several mineral samples from your teacher. Examine them closely.
2. Design a data table in which you can record your observations.
3. Record at least three ways that the samples are alike. Also record three ways that the samples are different.
4. Classify the minerals into two groups based on your observations. Give reasons for your classification scheme.
5. Put on safety goggles. Gently strike each sample with a hammer and observe the pieces of each sample. If necessary, use these results to reclassify the minerals into two groups.

Think About It

1. **Observe** What kinds of characteristics did you observe in all of the samples?
2. **Compare and Contrast** How did the samples differ?
3. **Classify** Each of the minerals you just observed belongs to a different group. Design a scheme for how these minerals might be classified into four different groups.

33

ENGAGE/EXPLORE

HOW ARE A GROUP OF MINERALS ALIKE AND DIFFERENT?   L2

Purpose In this activity, students will classify several mineral samples by observing similarities and differences among the samples.

Skills Observe, Compare and Contrast, Classify

Prep Time 10–15 minutes

Materials hand lenses, small hammers, safety goggles, samples of the colorless varieties of fluorite, quartz, halite, and calcite

Class Time 20–25 minutes

Safety Students need to wear safety goggles during this activity. Remind students to handle the hammers carefully and not to taste any of the minerals.

Teaching Tips
- Label the samples with permanent markers or numbered pieces of masking tape before distributing them to students.
- The breakage surfaces will vary among the minerals. Halite and calcite should break to produce three planar surfaces; fluorite will produce four. Quartz will break to form uneven surfaces that resemble broken glass.

Expected Outcome Students shouldn't have problems noting similarities and differences among the substances. Students should be able to describe at least one unique characteristic of each mineral.

Think About It
1. Similarities might include size and/or shape and possibly heft (the estimated weight of a mineral when held in the hand). Other similarities include color, transparency, and the fact that each mineral is a solid.
2. Depending on the samples used, the minerals may vary in size and shape. The way in which each mineral breaks is also unique. If students did the test for solubility, the dissolving of the halite is another difference.
3. Accept all reasonable responses. The most likely schemes will be by size, shape, color, luster, and shattering ability.

2.1 Matter

Lesson Objectives

2.1 **Explain** how elements are related to minerals.

2.2 **Identify** the kinds of particles that make up atoms.

2.3 **Explain** the differences between ions and isotopes.

2.4 **Explain** what compounds are and **describe** why they form.

2.5 **Compare and contrast** the three major types of chemical bonds.

Build Vocabulary L2

Concept Map Have students construct a concept map using the terms *chemical bond, ionic bond, covalent bond,* and *metallic bond.* The main concept *(chemical bond)* should be at the top. Tell students to place the terms in ovals and list the characteristics of each type of bond underneath the oval. For each type of bond, students should include some examples and their properties.

Reading Strategy L2

Differences Electron is much less massive than proton and neutron; electron is negatively charged, proton is positively charged, neutron is not charged.
Similarities All are subatomic particles.

2 INSTRUCT

Build Reading Literacy L1

Refer to **p. 392D** in **Chapter 14,** which provides guidelines for this strategy.

Preview Have students preview the lesson (pp. 34–43), focusing their attention on headings, visuals, and boldfaced material.
Ask: Based on your preview, which figure in the lesson do you think contains the most information? *(Figure 2 on pp. 36–37)* Based on your preview, name three classes of elements. *(metals, nonmetals, and metalloids)*
Visual, Verbal

Key Questions

⬡ **What is an element?**

⬡ **What particles make up atoms?**

⬡ **What are isotopes?**

⬡ **What are compounds and why do they form?**

⬡ **How do chemical bonds differ?**

Vocabulary

- element • atomic number
- energy level • isotope
- mass number • compound
- chemical bond • ion
- ionic bond • covalent bond
- metallic bond

Reading Strategy

Compare and Contrast
Copy the graphic organizer. As you read, complete the organizer to compare and contrast protons, neutrons, and electrons.

Protons	Electrons	Neutrons
Differences		
Similarities		

YOU AND EVERYTHING else in the universe are made of matter. *Matter* is anything that has volume and mass. On Earth, matter usually exists in one of three states—solid, liquid, or gas. A solid is a type of matter that has a definite shape and a definite volume. Rocks are examples of solids. A liquid is matter that has a definite volume, but not a definite shape. Earth's oceans, rivers, and lakes are liquids. A gas is matter that has neither a definite shape nor a definite volume. Earth's atmosphere contains gases.

Elements and the Periodic Table

You may already know the names of several elements. For example, carbon, oxygen, and gold. ⬡ **An element is a substance that cannot be broken down into simpler substances by chemical or physical means.** There are more than 100 known elements, and new elements continue to be discovered. Of these, about 90 occur naturally; the others are produced in laboratories.

The elements have been organized by their properties in a table called the periodic table, which is shown in **Figure 2** later in this lesson. You see from the table that the name of each element is represented by a symbol consisting of one, two, or three letters. Symbols provide a shorthand way of representing an element. Each element is also known by a number called its atomic number, which is shown above each symbol on the table. For example, the atomic number of carbon is 6, oxygen is 8, and gold is 79. You will learn more about atomic number on the next page.

The rows in the periodic table are called periods. The number of elements in a period varies. Period 1, for example, contains only two elements. These elements are hydrogen (H) and helium (He). Period 2 contains the elements lithium (Li) through neon (Ne). Periods 4 and 5 each contain 18 elements while Period 6 includes 32 elements.

The columns in the periodic table are called groups. Note that there are 18 groups. All the elements within a group have similar physical and chemical properties.

The most common elements found on Earth's surface are listed in **Table 1.** Six of these eight elements are classified as metals. Metals have specific properties such as the ability to be shaped and drawn into wire. Metals are also good conductors of heat and electricity. These common elements in Table 1 combine in thousands of ways with other elements to form all the materials found on Earth.

Atoms

All elements are made of atoms. ▭ **An *atom* is the smallest particle of an element that retains the characteristics of that element.** An atom is so small it can only be viewed using highly specialized instruments.

Atoms consist of smaller particles called subatomic particles. The major subatomic particles are protons, neutrons, and electrons. The central core of an atom is called the *nucleus*. *Protons* are subatomic particles with a positive charge that are found in the nucleus. *Neutrons* are subatomic particles with no charge that are also found in the nucleus. *Electrons*, which are subatomic particles with negative electrical charges, surround the nucleus of an atom.

Subatomic particles are not unique to any specific element. For example, a proton found in a hydrogen atom is essentially the same as a proton found in an atom of any other element.

Protons and Neutrons A proton has about the same mass as a neutron. Hydrogen atoms have only a single proton in their nuclei. Some types of atoms contain more than 100 protons. The number of protons in the nucleus of an atom is called the **atomic number.** All atoms with six protons, for example, are carbon atoms. Likewise, every atom with eight protons is an oxygen atom.

The number of neutrons in the nucleus can vary. For example, all atoms of carbon have six protons. However, some carbon atoms have six neutrons, other carbon atoms have seven neutrons, and still others have eight or more neutrons.

Atoms have the same number of protons and electrons. Carbon atoms have six protons and therefore six electrons. Oxygen atoms have eight protons, with eight electrons surrounding the nucleus.

Electrons An electron is the smallest of the three subatomic particles in an atom. Each electron has a mass of about 1/1840 the mass of a proton or a neutron. Electrons rapidly move about the nucleus in a sphere-shaped negative zone. You can picture moving electrons by imagining a cloud of negative charges surrounding the nucleus, as shown in **Figure 1.** At any one moment in time the electrons will be located somewhere within that cloud.

Electrons occupy regions called **energy levels.** Each energy level contains a certain number of electrons. Interactions among electrons in the highest energy levels explains how atoms chemically combine with other atoms.

☑ **Reading Checkpoint** *How are electrons, protons, and neutrons alike and how are they different?*

Table 1 Most Common Elements on Earth's Surface	
Element	**Approximate Percentage by Weight**
Oxygen (O)	46.6
Silicon (Si)	27.7
Aluminum (Al)	8.1
Iron (Fe)	5.0
Calcium (Ca)	3.6
Sodium (Na)	2.8
Potassium (K)	2.6
Magnesium (Mg)	2.1
All others	1.7

Source: Data from Brian Mason.

FIGURE 1 Electron Cloud Model of an Atom Electrons can be located anywhere within a cloud-like sphere surrounding the nucleus. Notice that the cloud is denser near the nucleus.

Draw Conclusions *What do you think this means about the chance of finding electrons near the nucleus compared with the outer edges of the sphere?*

- Protons (charge +1)
- Neutrons (charge 0)
- Electrons (charge –1)

Electron cloud →

Nucleus —

Minerals **35**

Build Math Skills ▣ L2

Use Tables and Graphs Have students convert Table 1 into a circle graph. **Ask:** Why would a circle graph be a good alternative way to show the information in Table 1? *(A circle graph shows the parts that make up a whole, just as the elements listed in the table make up a whole—100 percent of the elements in the continental crust.)* Suggest that students first estimate the size of each wedge of the circle graph and draw the graph accordingly. Then have them precisely draw the graph by first multiplying each percent by 360° to find the central angle of each wedge. They can then use a protractor to draw each central angle on a circle. Students can compare their estimates with their precise graphs. Some students may wish to use software to make their graphs. **Ask:** What advantage does a circle graph have over a table of percentages? *(The sizes of the wedges of the graph often make it easier to compare different quantities.)* **Visual, Logical**

Integrate Biology ▣ L2

Cell Nucleus Students may know that most cells in living organisms also have a structure called a nucleus. Inform students that the cell's nucleus contains the cell's genetic, or hereditary, material. **Ask:** How are an atom's nucleus and a cell's nucleus similar? *(They are both central structures of a basic unit.)* How are the two nuclei different? *(The cell nucleus controls the activities of the cell. The atomic nucleus does not have a similar function.)* **Logical**

Differentiated Instruction

ENGLISH LANGUAGE LEARNERS
To help students understand the idea of energy levels, have them work in pairs to think of everyday situations that involve different levels. Examples might include dresser drawers, shelves in a bookshelf, and bleachers in a gym. Ask students how these analogies are different from energy levels in atoms. *(Energy levels are not physical objects and are not evenly spaced.)* If you have a bookshelf in the class, have students place marbles on different levels to represent electrons.

Answers

Figure 1 *Electrons occupy the energy levels near the nucleus first and are therefore more likely to be found nearer to the nucleus.*

☑ **Reading Checkpoint** *They all are subatomic particles that make up atoms. Protons have positive electrical charges, neutrons have no charge, and electrons have negative charges. Protons and neutrons are found in an atom's nucleus. Electrons move about the nucleus.*

LESSON 2.1

Use Visuals L1

Figure 2 Use this figure to discuss how information is shown on a periodic table. **Ask:** What are the boldfaced single or double letters, such as *H* and *Li*? *(symbols for each element)* What is the number above each symbol? *(the element's atomic number)* What is the number below each symbol? *(the element's atomic mass)* What do the colors of the boxes indicate? *(They show whether an element is a metal, transition metal, nonmetal, noble gas, lanthanide, or actinide.)*
Visual, Logical

Build Science Skills L2

Use Tables and Graphs Use the data in Figure 2 to show the advantage of arranging elements by atomic number instead of atomic mass. Make a large graph with atomic number on the horizontal axis and atomic mass on the vertical axis for elements 1 through 20. Draw straight lines between the points. **Ask:** What does the graph show about the general relationship between atomic number and atomic mass? *(As the atomic number increases, so does the atomic mass.)* Are there any points on the graph that do not follow the pattern? *(Yes, the atomic mass of element 18, argon, is greater than the atomic mass of element 19, potassium.)* Point out that arranging the elements strictly by increasing atomic mass would result in some elements with unlike properties being grouped together.
Visual, Logical

Integrate Chemistry L2

There is a fourth state of matter called the plasma state. In the plasma state, matter consists of ions and free electrons. The plasma state exists only at high temperatures. The glowing gas in a fluorescent lamp, the sun, and other stars are in the plasma state.
Logical

PERIODIC TABLE OF THE ELEMENTS

FIGURE 2 Categories of Elements
Metals—elements that are good conductors of heat and electric current

Nonmetals—elements that are poor conductors of heat and electric current

Metalloids—elements with properties that are somewhat similar to metals and nonmetals

—Atomic number
—Electrons in each energy level
—Element symbol
—Element name
—Atomic mass†

†The atomic masses in parentheses are the mass numbers of the longest-lived isotope of elements for which a standard atomic mass cannot be defined.

Elements 104–118 are the transactinide elements.

Lanthanide Series

Actinide Series

Facts and Figures

Although plutonium is classified as a synthetic element, traces of plutonium isotopes Pu-238 and Pu-239 appear at low concentrations (about one part per 1011) in pitchblende, a uranium ore. In 1971, Darlene Hoffman, a scientist at Los Alamos National Laboratory, discovered traces of Pu-244 in Precambrian rocks. Because this isotope has a half-life of about 82 million years, it probably existed when Earth formed.

Representative Elements
- Alkali Metals
- Alkaline Earth Metals
- Other Metals
- Metalloids
- Nonmetals
- Noble Gases

Transition Elements
- Transition metals
- Inner transition metals

C	Solid
Br	Liquid
He	Gas
Tc	Not found in nature

13 3A	14 4A	15 5A	16 6A	17 7A	18 8A
					2 **He** Helium 4.0026
5 **B** Boron 10.81	6 **C** Carbon 12.011	7 **N** Nitrogen 14.007	8 **O** Oxygen 15.999	9 **F** Fluorine 18.998	10 **Ne** Neon 20.179
13 **Al** Aluminum 26.982	14 **Si** Silicon 28.086	15 **P** Phosphorus 30.974	16 **S** Sulfur 32.06	17 **Cl** Chlorine 35.453	18 **Ar** Argon 39.948

10	11 1B	12 2B						
28 **Ni** Nickel 58.71	29 **Cu** Copper 63.546	30 **Zn** Zinc 65.38	31 **Ga** Gallium 69.72	32 **Ge** Germanium 72.59	33 **As** Arsenic 74.922	34 **Se** Selenium 78.96	35 **Br** Bromine 79.904	36 **Kr** Krypton 83.80
46 **Pd** Palladium 106.4	47 **Ag** Silver 107.87	48 **Cd** Cadmium 112.41	49 **In** Indium 114.82	50 **Sn** Tin 118.69	51 **Sb** Antimony 121.75	52 **Te** Tellurium 127.60	53 **I** Iodine 126.90	54 **Xe** Xenon 131.30
78 **Pt** Platinum 195.09	79 **Au** Gold 196.97	80 **Hg** Mercury 200.59	81 **Tl** Thallium 204.37	82 **Pb** Lead 207.2	83 **Bi** Bismuth 208.98	84 **Po** Polonium (209)	85 **At** Astatine (210)	86 **Rn** Radon (222)
110 **Ds** Darmstadtium (269)	111 **Rg** Roentgenium (272)	112 **Cn** Copernicium (277)	*113 **Uut** Ununtrium (284)	*114 **Uuq** Ununquadium (289)	*115 **Uup** Ununpentium (288)	116 **Uuh** Ununhexium (293)	*117 **Uus** Ununseptium Classification pending	*118 **Uuo** Ununoctium (299)

*Discovery reported but not verified

63 **Eu** Europium 151.96	64 **Gd** Gadolinium 157.25	65 **Tb** Terbium 158.93	66 **Dy** Dysprosium 162.50	67 **Ho** Holmium 164.93	68 **Er** Erbium 167.26	69 **Tm** Thulium 168.93	70 **Yb** Ytterbium 173.04
95 **Am** Americium (243)	96 **Cm** Curium (247)	97 **Bk** Berkelium (247)	98 **Cf** Californium (251)	99 **Es** Einsteinium (252)	100 **Fm** Fermium (257)	101 **Md** Mendelevium (258)	102 **No** Nobelium (259)

Integrate Language Arts [L2]

Elements 113, 114, 115, 116, 117, and 118 have not been named yet. Scientists can propose names for new elements, but the International Union of Pure and Applied Chemistry has final approval. Until new elements receive official names, chemists refer to them by their Latin-based atomic numbers. For example, element 114 is called ununquadium, Latin for one-one-four. Increase students' familiarity with the periodic table by discussing some of the strategies used to name elements (scientists, geographic locations, mythological characters).
Verbal, Portfolio

Build Science Skills [L2]

Compare and Contrast For this activity, display or distribute a periodic table that is several years old. You might use one from an older textbook. To illustrate the dynamic nature of science, have students compare Figure 2 to the older periodic table. **Ask:** What differences do you notice between the two periodic tables? (Depending on when the older table was printed, the number of elements may vary and some elements in Period 7 may not have assigned names. Some values for atomic mass are likely to vary.) Make a list of responses on the board. Then **ask:** How will the periodic table change in the future? (Unnamed elements will be assigned official names and more elements may be discovered.)
Visual, Verbal

Calculate An electron has a mass of 9.11×10^{-28} g. Have students calculate a more exact ratio between the mass of a proton and the mass of an electron. If necessary, review *ratio*: a dimensionless number used to compare two values. *(The mass of a proton is 1.674×10^{-24} g. 1.674×10^{-24} g/9.11×10^{-28} g = 1838)* The ratio is actually 1836:1. The error is due to rounding.
Logical

Build Science Skills L2

Calculate Oxygen-18 has a mass number of 18 and 10 neutrons in its nucleus. Oxygen-17 has a mass number of 17 and 9 neutrons. **Ask:** What is the atomic number of oxygen? *(8)*
Logical

(Teacher **Demo**)

ISOTOPES AND NUMBERS L2

Purpose Students will observe the relationships among number of protons, number of neutrons, atomic number, and mass number for different isotopes.

Materials overhead projector, red and green gummy candies

Procedure Explain that the green candies represent neutrons and the red candies represent protons. Model a carbon-12 nucleus by placing a group of 6 red candies and 6 green candies on the overhead. Ask students to count the number of candies (particles) to determine the mass number of the carbon atom *(12)*. Then ask students what the atomic number is for carbon *(6)*. Then remove a red candy (proton) and ask if the atom is still carbon *(no)*. Replace the red candy and add a green candy (neutron). Ask students if the atom is still carbon *(yes)*. Then **ask:** How is this atom different from the original one? *(The atom is a different isotope, carbon-13.)* Show students the appropriate notation for representing isotopes: element name with mass number or element symbol with mass number and atomic number.

carbon-13 or $^{13}_{6}\text{C}$

Expected Outcomes Students should gain a familiarity with mass numbers, atomic numbers, and isotopes.
Visual

Isotopes

Atoms of the same element always have the same number of protons. For example, every carbon atom has 6 protons. Carbon is element number 6 on the periodic table. But the number of neutrons for atoms of the same element can vary. **Atoms with the same number of protons but different numbers of neutrons are isotopes of an element.** Isotopes of the same element are labeled using a convention called the mass number and with the element's name or symbol. The **mass number** of an atom is the total mass of the atom expressed in atomic mass units (amu). A proton and a neutron each have a mass of one amu. Recall that the mass of an electron is so small that the number of electrons has no effect on the mass number of an atom. Therefore, an atom's mass number is the sum of the masses of the protons and neutrons in its nucleus.

Carbon has 15 different isotopes. Models for three of these are shown in **Figure 3.** Carbon-12 makes up almost 99 percent of all carbon on Earth. Carbon-12 has 6 protons and 6 neutrons. Carbon-13 makes up much of the remaining naturally occurring carbon atoms on Earth. Carbon-13 has 6 protons and 7 neutrons. Carbon-14, with 6 protons and 8 neutrons, is relatively rare.

The nuclei of most atoms are stable. However, many elements have atoms whose nuclei are unstable. Such atoms disintegrate through a process called *radioactive decay*. During radioactive decay, unstable atoms give off energy and particles. Carbon-14 is an example of a radioactive isotope.

In nature, radioactive decay occurs at a constant rate. For example, it takes 5730 years for one half of any size sample of carbon-14 to decay. Since the rate of decay is measurable, radioactive atoms can be used to determine the ages of fossils, rocks, and minerals. Since the element carbon is found in living things, carbon-14 is used to determine the age of many fossils.

☑ **Reading Checkpoint** *What are isotopes?*

FIGURE 3 Nuclei of Isotopes of Carbon These three isotopes of carbon occur naturally. The remaining dozen isotopes of carbon are manufactured in laboratories.
Compare and Contrast *How are the nuclei of these isotopes the same, and how do they differ?*

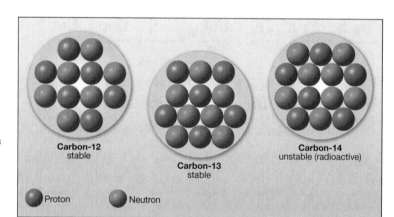

Facts and Figures

Carbon-14 can be used to find the ages of some objects. Carbon-14 is formed continuously by natural processes in the atmosphere. Carbon in the atmosphere reacts with oxygen to form carbon dioxide. Plants take in carbon dioxide during photosynthesis, the process by which they use energy in sunlight to make food. Initially, the ratio of carbon-14 to carbon-12 is the same in plants as it is in the atmosphere. The same is true for an animal that eats a plant. After a plant or animal dies, though, it no longer takes in carbon. The carbon-14 gradually undergoes radioactive decay to form nitrogen-14 with a half-life of 5730 years. The age of an object containing plant or animal material can be determined by comparing the ratio of carbon-14 to carbon-12 in the object to the ratio of these isotopes in the atmosphere. If the ratio of carbon-14 to carbon-12 in the object is one-quarter the ratio of carbon-14 to carbon-12 in the atmosphere, for example, then two half-lives, or 11,460 years, have passed since the plant or animal was alive.

Why Atoms Bond

Most matter exists in nature as a chemical combination of two or more elements. Chemical combinations of elements are called compounds. **A compound is a substance that consists of two or more elements that are chemically combined in specific proportions.** For example, the elements sodium and chlorine combine to form a compound called sodium chloride.

The elements in a compound are held together by forces called **chemical bonds.** Chemical bonds involve the interaction between negative electrons and positive nuclei. When two or more elements combine to form compounds, the atoms of the elements gain, lose, or share electrons.

Some elements are more reactive than others. The most reactive elements are found in Groups 1 and 17. The more reactive an element is, the more likely it will combine with another element and form a compound.

The most stable (least reactive) elements are found in Group 18. These elements are stable largely because their highest energy levels contain the maximum number of electrons. Reactive elements form compounds in order to make their electron structures more like the elements in Group 18. **When an atom's highest energy level does not contain the maximum number of electrons, the atom is likely to form a chemical bond with one or more other atoms.**

Look at **Figure 4.** It shows the shorthand way of representing the number of electrons in the highest energy level. Electrons in the highest energy level are sometimes called *valence electrons.* For example, neon has eight valence electrons, which is the maximum number of electrons in the highest energy level. So neon, argon, and krypton are stable elements. Most of the other elements in the table have incomplete highest energy levels. This means these elements are reactive and would be most likely to form chemical bonds. The principal types of chemical bonds are ionic bonds, covalent bonds, and metallic bonds.

FIGURE 4 Electron Dot Diagrams In an electron dot diagram, each dot represents an electron in the atom's highest energy level. These electrons are sometimes called valence electrons. **Observe** *How many valence electrons do sodium (Na) and chlorine (Cl) have?*

Electron Dot Diagrams for Some Representative Elements

Group							
1	2	13	14	15	16	17	18
H·							He:
Li·	·Be·	·B·	·C·	·N·	:O·	:F·	:Ne:
Na·	·Mg·	·Al·	·Si·	·P·	:S·	:Cl·	:Ar:
K·	·Ca·	·Ga·	·Ge·	·As·	:Se·	:Br·	:Kr:

Minerals **39**

Predict Emphasize that, except for hydrogen and helium, the dots in an electron dot diagram do not represent all of the electrons in an atom, just the valence electrons.

Have students look at Figure 4. Ask them to predict the electron dot diagrams for rubidium, strontium, indium, tin, antimony, tellurium, iodine, and xenon. *(These elements—Rb, Sr, In, Sn, Sb, Te, I, and Xe—have the same valence electron configurations as the elements directly above them in the periodic table.)* **Logical, Visual**

Answers

Figure 3 *The nuclei of the carbon isotopes all have the same number of protons, and thus, the same atomic number, but each has a different number of neutrons.*

Figure 4 *Sodium has one electron in its outer energy level (valence electron) and chlorine has seven.*

☑ **Reading Checkpoint** *Isotopes are atoms of the same element with the same number of protons but different numbers of neutrons.*

LESSON 2.1

Many students think that atoms become positively charged as a result of gaining protons. Challenge this misconception by explaining that electrons are the only subatomic particles that can be removed from or added to an atom during a chemical reaction. Remind students that protons are bound into the nuclei of atoms and cannot be removed or added during chemical reactions.
Logical

Integrate Chemistry · L2

Ionic Compounds and Conduction
Tell students that solid ionic compounds are poor conductors of electricity whereas melted ionic compounds are good conductors. Tell them that for an electric current to flow through a substance, charged particles must be able to move from one place to another. In a solid ionic crystal, the ions are fixed in a lattice. **Ask:** Why can't ionic solids conduct electricity? *(Because the ions are in fixed positions, they cannot conduct current.)* What happens if the solid is melted? *(The ions are freed from the lattice.)* Why is the melted solid a good conductor of electricity? *(The ions can move around and conduct a current.)*
Logical

Use Visuals · L1

Figure 5 Use this diagram to explain how an ionic compound forms. **Ask:** What happens to the sodium atom when it loses an electron? *(It becomes a positive ion.)* What happens to a chlorine atom when it gains an electron? *(It becomes a negative ion.)* What happens to the two ions? *(They are attracted to each other and form a compound.)*
Visual, Logical

Types of Chemical Bonds

Ionic Bonds If an atom loses an electron, it has more protons than electrons. This results in a positive charge. An atom that gains one or more electrons has more electrons than protons. This results in a negative charge. An atom that possesses an electric charge is called an **ion**. Opposite charges attract. So, ions with positive charges are attracted to ions with negative charges. **Ionic bonds form between positive and negative ions.**

Compounds that contain ionic bonds are called *ionic compounds.* Sodium chloride, or table salt, is an example of an ionic compound. Salt forms when sodium (Na) reacts with chlorine (Cl) as shown in **Figure 5.** Sodium is very unstable and reactive. Sodium atoms lose one electron and become positive ions. Chlorine atoms gain one electron and become negative ions. These oppositely charged ions are attracted to each other and form the compound sodium chloride.

The properties of a compound are different from the properties of the elements in the compound. Sodium is a soft, silvery metal that reacts vigorously with water. If you held it in your hand, sodium could burn your skin. Chlorine is a green poisonous gas. When chemically combined, these atoms produce table salt, the familiar crystalline solid that is used to flavor food.

☑ **Reading Checkpoint** *What happens when two or more atoms form an ionic bond?*

VISUAL SUMMARY

FORMATION OF SODIUM CHLORIDE

FIGURE 5 A Sodium atoms transfer one electron each to the highest energy levels of chlorine atoms. Both ions now have filled highest energy levels. **B** The positive and negative ions attract each other and form a crystalline solid with a rigid structure.

$$Ca \overset{\textstyle\frown}{\underset{\textstyle\smile}{}} + \begin{array}{c} F \\ F \end{array} \longrightarrow Ca^{2+} \quad \begin{array}{c} F^- \\ F^- \end{array}$$

FIGURE 6 Ionic Compound
A Calcium flouride is an ionic compound that forms when calcium reacts with fluorine.

B The dots shown with the element's symbol represent the electrons in the highest energy levels of the ions.

Explain *What happens to the electrons in calcium atoms and fluorine atoms when calcium flouride forms?*

Figure 6 shows calcium fluoride, another common ionic compound. Our model for ionic bonding suggests that one calcium atom transfers two electrons from its highest energy level to two atoms of fluorine. This transfer gives all atoms the right numbers of electrons in their highest energy levels.

Ionic compounds are rigid solids with high melting and boiling points. These compounds are poor conductors of electricity in their solid states. When melted, however, many ionic compounds are good conductors of electricity. Most ionic compounds consist of elements from Groups 1 and 2 on the periodic table reacting with elements from Groups 16 and 17.

☑ **Reading Checkpoint** *What are some properties of ionic compounds?*

Covalent Bonds ⬤ **Covalent bonds form when atoms share electrons.** Compounds with covalent bonds are called *covalent compounds.* **Figure 7A** on the next page shows silicon dioxide (quartz), one of the most common covalent compounds on Earth. Silicon dioxide forms when one silicon atom and two oxygen atoms share electrons in their highest energy levels.

Covalent compounds generally have different properties than ionic compounds. For example, while ionic compounds have high melting and boiling points, many covalent compounds have low melting and boiling points. Sodium chloride, an ionic compound, boils at 1413°C. Water, a covalent compound, boils at 100°C. Covalent compounds also are poor conductors of electricity, even when melted.

The smallest particle of a covalent compound that shows the properties of that compound is a molecule. A *molecule* is a neutral group of atoms joined by one or more covalent bonds. Water, for example, consists of molecules. These molecules are made of two hydrogen atoms covalently bonded to one oxygen atom. The many gases that make up Earth's atmosphere, including hydrogen, oxygen, nitrogen, and carbon dioxide, also consist of molecules.

Minerals **41**

Build Reading Literacy **L1**

Refer to **p. 502D** in **Chapter 18,** which provides guidelines for this strategy.

Visualize Tell students that forming a mental image of concepts they are learning helps them remember new concepts. After students have read about ionic, covalent, and metallic bonds, have them visualize models for each type of bond. Then encourage students to draw diagrams that demonstrate the differences among these three types of bonds.

Visual

(Teacher **Demo**)

COMPARING BONDS **L2**

Purpose Students observe differences in the properties of substances with different bonds.

Materials rock salt, chalk, copper wire, hammer, goggles

Procedure Take students outside to an open area. Allow them to examine the samples of rock salt, chalk, and copper wire. Have students stand back a safe distance. Put on goggles, then place each sample on a hard surface and hit it with a hammer. Invite students to observe how each sample looks after being pounded with the hammer.

Expected Outcomes The rock salt and chalk shatter because they are ionic and covalent substances, respectively. The copper wire changes shape instead of shattering because metals are malleable.
Visual

In a molecule, each atom exerts a pulling force on the electrons that are being shared. When the atoms in a molecule pull equally on the shared electrons, the electrons are shared equally. Molecules of hydrogen (H_2), oxygen (O_2), and chlorine (Cl_2) are examples of covalent bonds with equally shared electrons.

However, in some covalent bonds the electrons are not shared equally. **Figure 7B** shows a model of a molecule of water—one example of covalent bonds with unequal electron sharing. In a water molecule, an oxygen and two hydrogen atoms are pulling on the shared electrons. But the pulling force of oxygen is greater than the pulling force of hydrogen. As a result, the shared electrons are being pulled away from the hydrogen atoms toward the oxygen atom. The hydrogen atoms gain a slight positive charge. And the oxygen atom gains a slight negative charge. The unequal sharing of electrons results in a weak positive side and a weak negative side of the molecule.

Look again at the model of the water molecule below. Notice that the two hydrogen atoms are located on one side of the oxygen atom. So the water molecule can be said to have a hydrogen side and an oxygen side. Since the oxygen atom has a slight negative charge, the oxygen side of the water molecule has a weak negative pole. Conversely, the hydrogen atoms have a slight positive charge so the hydrogen side of the water molecule has a weak positive pole. A covalent bond that produces a molecule with negative and positive poles is called a *polar bond*.

Polar bonds give molecules unique properties. For example, many different kinds of compounds dissolve in water. Water's ability to dissolve compounds is related to the polar bonds in water molecules. Other examples of molecules with polar bonds are hydrogen chloride (HCl) and ammonia (NH_3).

H_2O

FIGURE 7 Examples of Covalent Bonds—
A Quartz is a covalent compound that forms when oxygen and silicon atoms bond.

B Water forms when hydrogen and oxygen share electrons.

Facts and Figures

Unlike ionic and covalent compounds, metals are malleable and ductile. Metal ions are held together in a "sea of electrons" referred to as the metallic bond. When a piece of metal is deformed, the ions move to new positions. The piece of metal does not break because the ions are still attracted to the electrons.

FIGURE 8 Metallic Bonds
A Metals form bonds when metallic atoms share electrons.

B Metallic bonds give metals, such as copper, their characteristic properties. Metals can be easily shaped and pulled into wire.

Metallic Bonds **Metallic bonds form when electrons are shared by metal ions.** A model for this kind of bond is shown in **Figure 8A**. Sharing a pool of electrons gives metals their characteristic properties. Using the model you can see how an electrical current is easily carried through the pool of electrons. If electrons were added to one end of a metal, other electrons leave the opposite end.

Metals are malleable, which means that they can be easily shaped. You've observed this property when you wrapped aluminum foil around food or crushed an aluminum can. Metals are also ductile, meaning that they can be drawn into thin wires without breaking. The wiring in your school or home is probably made of the metal copper. Metals are excellent conductors of electricity.

 Assessment

Review Key Concepts

1. What is an element?

2. What kinds of particles make up atoms?

3. What are isotopes?

4. What are compounds and how do they form?

5. Contrast ionic, covalent, and metallic bonds.

Think Critically

6. **Compare and Contrast** Compare and contrast solids, liquids, and gases.

7. **Apply Concepts** Which elements in Table 1 are metals?

8. **Apply Concepts** A magnesium atom has two valence electrons. A chlorine atom needs one electron to fill its highest energy level. If magnesium reacts with chlorine, which type of bond will most likely form? Explain.

9. **Apply Concepts** Which elements in the periodic table might combine with oxygen to form compounds similar to magnesium oxide (MgO)?

MATH PRACTICE

10. **Interpret Data** The isotopes of carbon have 2 to 16 neutrons. Use this information to make a table that shows the 15 isotopes of carbon and the atomic number and mass number of each.

Minerals **43**

Minerals **43**

1 FOCUS

Lesson Objectives

2.6 **List** five characteristics of minerals.

2.7 **Describe** the processes that result in mineral formation.

2.8 **Explain** how minerals can be classified.

2.9 **List** some of the major groups of minerals.

Build Vocabulary   L2

Word Parts Help students understand the meaning of the word *tetrahedron* by breaking the word down into parts. The part *tetra* comes from the Greek word for "four." The part *hedron* comes from the Greek word for "face." So a tetrahedron is a shape that has four faces.

Reading Strategy   L2

Silicates: made of tetrahedra; quartz; feldspar

Carbonates: contain carbon, oxygen, and one or more other metallic elements; calcite; dolomite

Oxides: contain oxygen, and one or more other elements; rutile; corundum

Sulfate and sulfides: contain sulfur; gypsum; galena

Halides: contain a halogen ion plus one or more other elements; halite; fluorite

Native elements: substances that exist as free elements; gold; silver

2 INSTRUCT

(Address **Misconceptions**)   L2

Students may think that the minerals discussed in this chapter are the same as the minerals found in vitamin pills. They are related, but not the same. In earth science, a mineral is a naturally occurring inorganic crystalline solid. In contrast, minerals found in vitamin pills are inorganic compounds made in the laboratory that contain elements needed by the body. Many elements needed by the body are metals such as calcium, potassium, phosphorus, magnesium, and iron.

Logical

2.2 Minerals

Key Questions

What are five characteristics of a mineral?

What processes result in the formation of minerals?

How can minerals be classified?

What are some of the major groups of minerals?

Vocabulary

• mineral • silicate
• silicon-oxygen tetrahedron

Reading Strategy

Preview Copy the organizer below. Skim the material on mineral groups on pages 47 to 49. Place each group name into one of the ovals in the organizer. As you read this section, complete the organizer with characteristics and examples of each major mineral group.

LOOK AT THE SALT shaker in **Figure 9B.** Did you know that each part of the salt shaker, including the salt, is made of elements or compounds that either are minerals or that are obtained from minerals? In fact, practically every manufactured product that you might use in a typical day contains materials obtained from minerals. What minerals do you probably use regularly? The "lead" in your pencils is actually a soft black mineral called graphite. Most body powders and many kinds of make-up contain finely ground bits of the mineral talc. Your dentist's drill bits contain tiny pieces of the mineral diamond. It is hard enough to drill through your tooth enamel. The mineral quartz is the main ingredient in the windows in your school and the drinking glasses in your family's kitchen. What do all of these minerals have in common? How do they differ?

FIGURE 9 Many Objects Are Made From Minerals A Table salt is the mineral halite. **B** Glass is made from the mineral quartz. The aluminum top comes from bauxite.

Minerals

A dictionary provides several definitions for "mineral." In Earth science, the term has a specific meaning. **A mineral is a naturally occurring, inorganic solid with an orderly crystalline structure and a definite chemical composition.** All minerals share the following characteristics:

1. **Naturally occurring** A mineral forms by natural geologic processes. Therefore, synthetic gems (made by people), such as synthetic diamonds and rubies, are not considered minerals.

2. **Solid substance** Minerals are solids within the temperature ranges that are normal for Earth's surface.

3. **Orderly crystalline structure** The atoms of minerals are arranged in an orderly and repetitive manner and form crystals. Halite and opal contain the same elements. Halite is a mineral because it has a definite crystal structure. Opal does not have an orderly internal structure, so opal is not a mineral.

4. **Definite chemical composition** Most minerals are chemical compounds made of two or more elements. For example, halite is a compound containing one sodium atom and one chlorine atom (NaCl). A few minerals, such as gold and silver, consist of a single element (native form).

5. **Generally considered inorganic** Most minerals are inorganic crystalline solids found in nature. Halite (table salt) is an example. However, sugar, another crystalline solid, is not a mineral because it is an organic compound. Sugar comes from sugar beets or sugar cane. Many marine animals secrete inorganic compounds, such as calcium carbonate (calcite). The shell of a clam is an example. Calcite is considered a mineral, even though it comes from an animal.

How Minerals Form

Minerals form under a wide variety of conditions. For example, minerals called silicates often form deep under Earth's surface where temperatures and pressures are very high. Most of the minerals known as carbonates form in warm, shallow ocean waters. Most clay minerals form at or near Earth's surface when existing minerals are exposed to weathering. Still other minerals form when rocks are subjected to changes in pressure or temperature. **There are four major processes by which minerals form: crystallization from magma, precipitation, changes in pressure and temperature, and formation from hydrothermal solutions.**

Crystallization From Magma Magma is molten rock that forms deep within Earth. As magma cools, elements combine to form minerals such as those shown in **Figure 10** on the next page. The first minerals to crystallize from magma are usually those rich in iron, calcium, and magnesium. As minerals continue to form, the composition of the magma changes. Minerals rich in sodium, potassium, and aluminum then form.

Build Reading Literacy

Refer to **p. 334D** in **Chapter 12,** which provides guidelines for this strategy.

Outline Have students read the text on pp. 45–49 about how minerals form and mineral groups. Encourage students to use the headings as major divisions in an outline. Have students refer to their outlines when answering the questions in the Lesson 2.2 Assessment.
Verbal, Logical

(Teacher **Demo**)

CRYSTALLIZATION OF SULFUR

Purpose Students observe how the rate of cooling of a mineral affects crystal size.

Materials two crucibles, 50-mL beaker, water, teaspoon, sulfur powder, tongs, Bunsen burner, magnifying glass

Procedure Put a teaspoon of powdered sulfur into one of the crucibles. Using tongs, hold the crucible near the burner flame until the sulfur melts. Set the crucible aside to cool. Put a teaspoon of powdered sulfur into the second crucible. Put about 200 mL of water in the beaker. Melt the sulfur in the second crucible and carefully pour the molten sulfur into the beaker. Pour off the water. When the first crucible has cooled, allow students to look at the crystals using the magnifying glass.

Safety Wear goggles, apron, and heat-resistant mitts while melting the sulfur. Make sure students are at a safe distance from the crucible and flame and that the room is well ventilated.

Expected Outcome The sulfur in the first crucible, which cooled slowly, will have bigger crystals than the sulfur that cooled quickly.
Visual, Logical

LESSON 2.2

PRECIPITATION OF A MINERAL L2

Purpose Students observe how a mineral can form by precipitation.

Materials rock salt, spoon warm water, 400-mL beaker, shallow pan or tray

Procedure Out of view of students, add rock salt spoon by spoon to a beaker of warm water, stirring as you go. Stop when no more salt will dissolve. Show the beaker to students and ask them if there is a mineral in it. Most will say no. Then pour the liquid into the pan and leave it in a warm and/or sunny spot. (If you don't have a suitable warm and/or sunny spot or want to save time, pour some of the solution into an evaporation dish and heat it on a hot plate.) When the water has evaporated, show the pan to students and ask them to identify the substance in it *(halite crystals).*

Expected Outcome As the water evaporates, the salt will precipitate out of the solution and form crystals.
Visual, Logical

Build Science Skills L2

Infer Sometimes rocks are buried deep under Earth's surface. When they reach the surface again they are often changed into a different type of rock. Ask students why this happens. *(The rocks are subjected to great heat and pressure deep below Earth's surface. The heat and pressure cause reactions that change the minerals and thus produce new types of rocks.)*
Logical

FIGURE 10 Minerals From Magma These minerals can form from crystallization of magma.

Feldspar

Quartz

Muscovite

Hornblende

Precipitation The water in Earth's lakes, rivers, ponds, oceans, and beneath its surface contains many dissolved substances. When this water evaporates, some of the dissolved substances can react to form minerals. Changes in water temperature may also cause dissolved material to precipitate out of a body of water. Generally, as water temperature increases, the amount of dissolved material in the water can increase. But when water temperature decreases, the maximum amount of dissolved material in water decreases. As the water cools, the minerals are left behind, or *precipitated,* out of the water. Two common minerals that form in this way are shown in **Figure 11.**

Pressure and Temperature Some minerals, including talc and muscovite, form when existing minerals are subjected to changes in pressure and temperature. An increase in pressure can cause a mineral to recrystallize while still solid. The atoms are simply rearranged to form more compact minerals. Changes in temperature can also cause certain minerals to become unstable. Under these conditions, new minerals form, which are stable at the new temperature. Before a method for manufacturing sheet glass was invented, sheets of muscovite were mined and used in buildings as window panes. Today, muscovite has many uses, including as windows in wood stoves.

Hydrothermal Solutions A hydrothermal solution is a very hot mixture of water and dissolved substances. Hydrothermal solutions have temperatures between about 100°C and 300°C. When these solutions come into contact with existing minerals, chemical reactions take place that form new minerals. Also, when such solutions cool, some of the elements in them combine to form minerals such as quartz and pyrite. The sulfur minerals in the sample shown in **Figure 12** formed from thermal solutions.

☑ **Reading Checkpoint** *Describe what happens when a mineral is subjected to changes in pressure or temperature.*

FIGURE 11 Minerals From Precipitation
A This limestone cave formation is an obvious example of precipitation.

B Halite and calcite are also formed by precipitation.

Facts and Figures

Judging from the enormous number of known minerals, one might think that a large number of elements are needed to make them. Surprisingly, the bulk of these minerals are made up of only eight elements. These elements, in order of abundance, are oxygen (O), silicon (Si), aluminum (Al), iron (Fe), calcium (Ca), sodium (Na), potassium (K), and magnesium (Mg). These eight elements represent over 98 percent by weight of the continental crust. The two most abundant elements, oxygen and silicon, comprise nearly three-fourths of Earth's continental crust. These elements are the main building blocks of silicates. The most common group of silicates, the feldspars, compose over 50 percent of Earth's crust. Quartz is the second most abundant mineral in the continental crust. It is a silicate made mostly of oxygen and silicon.

Mineral Groups

Over 4000 minerals have been named, and several new ones are identified each year. Only a few dozen, however, are known as common minerals. 🔑 **Common minerals, together with the thousands of others that form on Earth, can be classified into groups based on their composition.** Some of the more common mineral groups include silicates, carbonates, oxides, sulfates and sulfides, halides, and native elements.

Silicates Silicon and oxygen are the most abundant elements on Earth's surface. 🔑 **Silicon and oxygen combine to form a structure called the silicon-oxygen tetrahedron.** The **silicon-oxygen tetrahedron** is a structure composed of four oxygen atoms surrounding a central silicon atom. The structure is shown in **Figure 13A**. **Silicates** are minerals that have the silicon-oxygen tetrahedron as their basic structure. Silicates are the most abundant groups of minerals on Earth. The tetrahedron provides the framework of every silicate mineral. Except for a few silicate minerals, such as pure quartz, most silicates also contain one or more other elements.

Silicon-oxygen tetrahedra can join in a variety of ways, as you can see in **Figure 14** on the next page. Silicon-oxygen bonds are very strong. Some minerals, such as olivine, are made of millions of single tetrahedra. In minerals such as augite, the tetrahedra join to form single chains. Double chains are formed in minerals such as hornblende. Micas are silicates in which the tetrahedra join to form sheets. Three-dimensional structures are found in silicates such as quartz and feldspar. As you will see, the internal structure of a mineral affects its properties.

☑ **Reading Checkpoint** *What is the silicon-oxygen tetrahedron, and in how many ways can it combine?*

FIGURE 12 Minerals From Hydrothermal Solutions Bornite (blue and purple) and chalcopyrite (gold) are sulfur minerals that form from hydrothermal solutions.

PLANET DIARY

For links to learn more about **Minerals,** visit PlanetDiary.com/HSES.

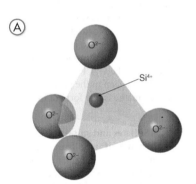

FIGURE 13 The Silicon-Oxygen Tetrahedron
A A tetrahedron is a shape with four triangular faces. The silicon-oxygen tetrahedron has one silicon atom in the middle and an oxygen atom at each of the four corners.

B Quartz is the most common silicate mineral. A typical piece of quartz like this contains millions of silicon-oxygen tetrahedra.

Minerals **47**

Address **Misconceptions** [L2]

Students may think that the silicates described in this lesson are the same materials as those in silicon computer chips or silicone sealant. They are different materials, although all three contain silicon. Silicon chips are made from pure silicon, which does not contain the oxygen found in silicates. Silicone is an artificially-made silicon-oxygen polymer gel that feels rubbery and is water repellent, chemically inert, and stable at extreme temperatures.
Verbal

Use Visuals [L1]

Figure 13 Use this diagram to explain the basic structure of silicates. **Ask:** What is the atom at the center of the tetrahedron? *(a silicon atom)* What are the four atoms at the corners of the tetrahedron? *(oxygen atoms)* Why is this structure called a tetrahedron? *(it has four sides, or faces)*
Visual

Answers

☑ **Reading Checkpoint** *The mineral often becomes unstable, and its atoms react to form a new mineral.*

☑ **Reading Checkpoint** *The silicon-oxygen tetrahedron consists of one silicon atom and four oxygen atoms and provides the framework of every silicate mineral. These tetrahedra can join to form single chains, double chains, sheets, and three-dimensional networks. In these arrangements the corner oxygen atoms are shared between silicon atoms so the ratio is not necessarily 1 to 4.*

Differentiated Instruction

ENGLISH LANGUAGE LEARNERS To help students learn and understand the names of the different mineral groups, have them focus on the roots of the names and ignore the endings. The beginning of *silicates,* for example, is *silic-*. This is similar to *silicon* and indicates that silicates contain silicon.

Have students go though all the other names, isolate the beginnings of the names, and figure out what the name indicates about what elements the minerals contain *(carbonates: carbon-, carbon; oxides: ox-, oxygen; sulfates and sulfides: sulf-, sulfur; halides: hal-, halogens).*

LESSON 2.2

Build Science Skills

Student Activity: Use Models Have students use Figures 13 and 14 to build models of the various silicate structures. They can use plastic foam balls, modeling clay, or gumdrops to represent silicon and oxygen atoms and toothpicks to represent chemical bonds. First have each student build several silicon-oxygen tetrahedra as shown in Figure 13. Then have students work in groups to combine their tetrahedra into chains and other structures as shown in Figure 14.
Kinesthetic, Visual, Logical

Use Visuals

Figure 14 Use this diagram to explain the different structures that silicate tetrahedra can form. **Ask:** How does a single chain form? *(A series of tetrahedra are joined together end-to-end.)* How are double chains formed? *(Two single chains are joined together side-by-side.)* How are sheets formed? *(Many single chains are joined together side-by-side.)*
Visual

FIGURE 14 Silicate Structures
Silicate structures are chains, sheets, and three-dimensional networks.
Form a Hypothesis *What type of chemical bond is formed by silicon atoms in an SiO₄ tetrahedron?*

Silicate Structures

Single tetrahedrons

Single chains

Double chains

Sheets

Three-dimensional networks

Recall that most silicate minerals crystallize from magma as it cools. This cooling can occur at or near Earth's surface, where temperatures and pressures are relatively low. The formation of silicates can also occur at great depths, where temperatures and pressures are high. The place of formation and the chemical composition of the magma determine which silicate minerals will form. For example, the silicate olivine crystallizes at temperatures of about 1200°C. Quartz crystallizes at about 700°C.

Some silicate minerals form at Earth's surface when existing minerals are exposed to weathering. Clay minerals, which are silicates, form this way. Other silicate minerals form under the extreme pressures that occur with mountain building. Therefore, silicate minerals can often provide scientists with clues about the conditions in which the minerals formed.

To date, more than 800 silicate minerals have been identified and they make up more than 90 percent of Earth's surface. All the remaining minerals are sometimes grouped together and classified as nonsilicates. The nonsilicates include carbonates, oxides, sulfates and sulfides, halides, and the native elements.

Carbonates Carbonates are the second most common mineral group. **Carbonates are minerals that contain the elements carbon, oxygen, and one or more other metallic elements.** Calcite ($CaCO_3$), which contains the metal calcium, is the most common carbonate mineral. Many marine animals secrete the mineral calcite. Dolomite is another carbonate mineral that contains magnesium and calcium. Both limestone and marble are rocks composed of carbonate minerals. Both types of rock are used in building and construction.

Oxides **Oxides are minerals that contain oxygen and one or more other elements, which are usually metals.** Some oxides, including the mineral called rutile (TiO_2), form as magma cools deep beneath Earth's surface. Rutile is titanium oxide. Other oxides, such as corundum (Al_2O_3), form when existing minerals are subjected to changes in temperature and pressure. Corundum is aluminum oxide. Still other oxides, such as hematite (Fe_2O_3), form when existing minerals are exposed to oxygen in the presence of water or moisture in the air. Hematite is one form of iron oxide.

Sulfates and Sulfides **Sulfates and sulfides are minerals that contain the element sulfur.** Sulfates, including anhydrite ($CaSO_4$) and gypsum ($CaSO_4 \cdot 2H_2O$), form when mineral-rich waters evaporate. Sulfides, which include the minerals galena (PbS), sphalerite (ZnS), and pyrite (FeS_2), often form from thermal, or hot-water, solutions. **Figure 15** shows two of these sulfides.

Halides **Halides are minerals that contain a halogen ion plus one or more other elements.** Halogens are elements from Group 17 of the periodic table. This group includes the elements fluorine (F) and chlorine (Cl). The mineral halite (NaCl), table salt, is a common halide. Fluorite (CaF_2) is also a common halide and is used in making steel. It forms when salt water evaporates.

Native Elements **Native elements are minerals that only contain one element or type of atom.** You are probably familiar with some native elements, such as gold (Au), silver (Ag), copper (Cu), sulfur (S), and carbon (C). The reason that native metals are so rare is that most metal atoms readily combine with the abundant element oxygen and form oxides.

FIGURE 15 Sulfides
A Galena is a sulfide mineral that can be mined for its lead.

B Pyrite, another sulfide, is often called fool's gold.

Use Community Resources L2

Invite a geologist from a local college or company to visit the classroom and discuss different groups of minerals with students. Ask the geologist to bring in samples from each group of minerals to show to students. **Visual, Interpersonal**

3 ASSESS

Evaluate Understanding L2

Have students describe the four major processes by which minerals can form.

Reteach L1

Review the five characteristics that a material must have to be considered a mineral. Have students list and define all of the science terms used in the description of the five characteristics. Then review each of the five points again to be sure students understand them.

2.2 Assessment

Review Key Concepts

1. What are five characteristics of a mineral?

2. Describe four processes that result in the formation of minerals.

3. How can minerals be classified?

4. Name the major groups of minerals, and give at least two examples of minerals in each group.

Think Critically

5. **Compare and Contrast** Compare and contrast sulfates and sulfides.

6. **Draw Conclusions** When hit with a hammer, quartz shows an uneven breakage pattern. Using Figure 14, what can you suggest about its structure?

7. **Apply Concepts** To which mineral group does each of the following minerals belong: bornite (Cu_5FeS_4), cuprite (Cu_2O), magnesite ($MgCO_3$), and barite ($BaSO_4$)?

BIGIDEA EARTH'S MATERIALS AND SYSTEMS

8. **Explain** Write a paragraph that describes what minerals are. Be sure to include the five characteristics that all minerals share.

Minerals **49**

Answers

Figure 14 *covalent*

Assessment Answers

1. A mineral is a natural, inorganic solid with an orderly internal structure and a definite chemical composition.
2. Crystallization occurs when minerals form as magma cools. Minerals form through precipitation as waters rich in dissolved substances evaporate. Changes in pressure and temperature can cause the atoms in a mineral to change places to form a new mineral. Precipitation from hydrothermal solutions is another way in which minerals form.

3. according to their compositions
4. silicates (quartz, feldspars, augite, olivine, and micas); carbonates (calcite, dolomite); oxides (rutile, corundum, hematite); sulfates (anhydrite, gypsum); sulfides (galena, pyrite, sphalerite); halides (fluorite, halite); native elements (gold, silver, copper, sulfur, diamond)
5. Both contain sulfur. Sulfates also contain oxygen and a metallic element. Sulfides contain only sulfur and one or more other metallic elements.

6. The tetrahedra that combine to form quartz share very strong bonds, resulting in an uneven breakage.
7. Bornite is a sulfide mineral, cuprite is an oxide, magnesite is a carbonate mineral, and barite is a sulfate.
8. Students should explain the five characteristics listed in Answer 1.

2.3 Properties of Minerals

❶ FOCUS

Lesson Objectives
2.10 **Explain** why color is often not a useful property in identifying minerals.

2.11 **Define** the terms *luster, crystal form, streak,* and Mohs scale.

2.12 **Distinguish** between cleavage and fracture.

2.13 **Explain** density and how it can be used to identify substances.

2.14 **Describe** some other properties that can be used to identify minerals.

Build Vocabulary [L2]
Paraphrase As students read the lesson, have them look for the vocabulary terms that describe properties of minerals. For each term, have students write a definition in their own words. If students are having trouble, use mineral samples to demonstrate each of the properties.

Reading Strategy [L2]
A.1 Often not used to identify minerals
A.2 Small amounts of different elements can give the same mineral different colors.
B.1 The color of a mineral in its powdered form
B.2 Doesn't usually vary from sample to sample

❷ INSTRUCT

Build Reading Literacy [L1]
Refer to **p. 32D** in this chapter, which provides guidelines for this strategy.

Preview Before they read the lesson, have students skim the headings, visuals, and boldfaced sentences and terms to preview how the text is organized. Have students note any unfamiliar terms and concepts and make notes about these as they read the lesson.
Verbal

2.3 Properties of Minerals

Key Questions

🔑 *What properties can be used to identify minerals?*

🔑 *What is the Mohs scale?*

🔑 *What are some distinctive properties of minerals?*

Vocabulary
- streak • luster
- crystal form • hardness
- Mohs scale • cleavage
- fracture • density

Reading Strategy
Outline Before you read, make an outline of this section, following the format below. Use the orange headings as the main topics. As you read, add supporting details.

I. Properties of Minerals
A. Color
1. _____
2. _____
B. Streak
1. _____
2. _____

AS YOU CAN SEE from the photographs in this chapter, minerals occur in different colors and shapes. Minerals also vary in the way they reflect light and in the way in which they break. Some minerals are harder than others and some minerals smell like rotten eggs. Still other minerals attract objects containing iron. All of these characteristics, or properties, of minerals can be used to identify them.

Color
One of the first things you might notice about a mineral is its color. While color is unique to some minerals, this property is often not useful in identifying many minerals. 🔑 **Small amounts of different elements can give the same mineral different colors.** You can see examples of this in **Figure 16**.

FIGURE 16 Color Small amounts of different elements give these sapphires their distinct colors.
Observe *Why is color often not a useful property in mineral identification?*

Streak
🔑 **Streak is the color of a mineral in its powdered form.** Streak is obtained by rubbing a mineral across a streak plate, a piece of unglazed (rough) porcelain. While the color of a mineral may vary from sample to sample, the streak usually doesn't. Therefore, streak can be a good indicator.

Luster

🔑 **Luster is used to describe how light is reflected from the surface of a mineral.** Minerals that have the appearance of metals, regardless of their color, are said to have a metallic luster. The piece of copper shown in **Figure 17A** has a metallic luster. Minerals with a nonmetallic luster are described by many adjectives. These include vitreous or glassy, like the quartz crystals in Figure 13B. Other types of mineral luster include pearly, silky, and earthy. Diamond, shown in **Figure 17B,** has an adamantine, or brilliant, luster. Some minerals appear somewhat metallic and are said to have a sub-metallic luster. Streak can also show the difference between minerals with metallic lusters and minerals with nonmetallic lusters. Metallic minerals generally have a dense, dark streak. Minerals with nonmetallic lusters do not have such streaks.

FIGURE 17 Luster
A The mineral copper has a metallic luster.

B The brilliant luster of diamond is also known as an adamantine luster.

Crystal Form

A *crystal* is a three-dimensional, orderly arrangement of atoms. This arrangement gives minerals their shape. 🔑 **Crystal form is the visible expression of a mineral's internal arrangement of atoms.** Every mineral has a crystal form based on one of six distinct crystal systems. All the minerals that belong to a given crystal system have crystals of the same shape. For example, fluorite in **Figure 18** belongs to the cubic crystal system. Quartz has hexagonal (six-sided) crystals and belongs to the hexagonal crystal system.

Usually, when a mineral forms slowly and without space restrictions, it will develop into a crystal with well-formed faces—sides, top, and bottom. Most of the time, however, minerals compete for space. This crowding results in an intergrown mass of small crystals. When this happens, the crystal form is not as noticeable.

☑ **Reading Checkpoint** *What two conditions produce crystals with well-defined faces?*

FIGURE 18 Crystal Form Fluorite often forms cubic crystals.

Minerals **51**

Integrate Chemistry L2

Streak Color There are several reasons a mineral's streak color may differ from the color of the mineral itself. Some translucent minerals are colored by trace impurities of other elements. These colors are visible in a large sample because light passes through the impurities before reaching the eye. A streak will often not show this coloring effect and will appear white instead. Also, the structure and surface coatings of a sample may affect its color. Again, the streak will not show these effects and will instead show the true color of the mineral. Have students research how streak can be used to distinguish gold from iron pyrite. *(Samples of both have a gold color. Gold has a golden streak but iron pyrite has a greenish-black streak.)*
Logical

Integrate Physics L2

Causes of Luster The type of luster a mineral displays depends on how light interacts with the surface of the sample. If most of the light is reflected or absorbed, the mineral will have a metallic luster. A few minerals allow a small amount of light to penetrate, and have submetallic luster. Nonmetallic luster occurs when light can pass through the sample. If the mineral has a high index of refraction (the amount that light bends when it is passing through the mineral), such as diamond, the luster is described as adamantine. Minerals with lower indices of refraction have glassy or vitreous luster.
Logical, Visual

Use Visuals L1

Figure 18 Show students a sample of rock salt. Have students compare these crystals with the fluorite crystals in Figure 18. **Ask:** How are the crystals similar? How are they different? *(Similar: both cubic; Different: colors)*
Visual

Differentiated Instruction

BEHAVIORALLY DISORDERED For students who have difficulty concentrating on reading or class lectures, have them explore mineral samples on their own to learn about the properties of minerals. Students can work on their own or in small groups to explore three to five minerals. Encourage students to take notes about each mineral's color, luster, crystal form, streak, hardness, cleavage, fracture, and density.

Answers

Figure 16 *The same mineral can be different colors.*

☑ **Reading Checkpoint** *unrestricted space and a slow rate of formation*

LESSON 2.3

Use Visuals `L1`

Figure 19 Have students use the Mohs scale of hardness to give the hardness ranges for the following descriptions: a mineral that can be scratched by your fingernail *(less than 2.5)*, a mineral that cannot be scratched by your fingernail and cannot scratch glass *(2.5 to 5.5)*, a mineral that scratches glass *(greater than 5.5)*.
Visual

Build Science Skills `L1`

Infer Ask: What does the use of a pencil tell you about the hardness of graphite? *(Graphite, or pencil "lead," is a very soft mineral because it leaves a mark, or streak, when rubbed against paper or most surfaces.)* What can you say about the hardness of chalk versus the hardness of a chalkboard? *(Chalk is softer than the board.)* What kind of minerals could you not test for streak when using a streak plate? *(Minerals that are harder than the streak plate will not leave a streak; instead they will scratch the plate.)*
Logical

Integrate Language Arts `L2`

Origin of the Names Mica and Muscovite Tell students that the name "mica" probably came from the Latin word *micare,* which means "to shine" and refers to mica's appearance. Muscovite, a common type of mica, was named after the old Russian state of Muscovy. In the 1300s, it was common in Muscovy to use mica as a substitute for glass, so it was called muscovy glass. Biotite is another common type of mica. Have students research the origin of that name. *(It was named for J. B. Biot, a French physicist.)*
Verbal

Hardness

When you think of minerals, you probably imagine substances that are fairly hard. But, did you know that you can scratch some minerals with your fingernail? The scratch test is one method used to identify minerals. **Hardness** is a measure of the resistance of a mineral to being scratched. You can identify the hardness of a mineral by rubbing it against another object of known hardness. One object will scratch the other, unless both objects have the same hardness.

Geologists use a standard hardness scale called the Mohs scale. The Mohs scale consists of 10 index minerals arranged from 10 (hardest) to 1 (softest). The Mohs scale of hardness is illustrated in **Figure 19.** Notice that some of the index minerals are talc, calcite, and quartz. Any mineral of unknown hardness can be rubbed against these index minerals to determine its hardness. Other objects can also be used to determine hardness. Your fingernail, for example, has a hardness of 2.5. A copper penny has a hardness of 3.5. A piece of glass has a hardness of about 5.5. Look again at Figure 19. The mineral gypsum, which has a Mohs hardness of 2, can be easily scratched by your fingernail. The mineral calcite, which resembles gypsum, has a hardness of 3. Calcite cannot be scratched by your fingernail. Calcite, which can resemble the mineral quartz, cannot scratch glass, because its hardness is less than 5.5. Quartz, the hardest of the common minerals with a Mohs hardness of 7, will scratch a glass plate. Diamond, the hardest mineral on Earth, can scratch any other mineral.

☑ **Reading Checkpoint** *Describe three or four of the most useful properties for identifying unknown minerals.*

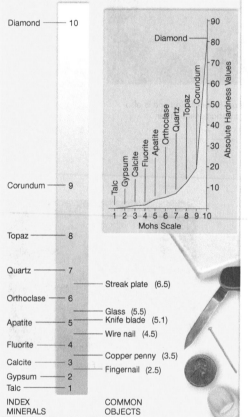

FIGURE 19
Mohs Scale of Hardness
Common objects can be used with the Mohs scale to determine mineral hardness.
Interpret Graphs *A mineral has a hardness of 4.2. Which common items on the chart will that mineral scratch?*

Cleavage

In the atomic structure of a mineral, some bonds are weaker than others. These weak bonds are places where a mineral will break when it is stressed. **Cleavage is the tendency of a mineral to cleave, or break, along flat, even surfaces.**

Minerals called micas show the simplest type of cleavage. Because the micas have weak bonds in one direction, they cleave to form thin, flat sheets, as shown in **Figure 20A.** Look again at Figure 14. Can you see the relationship between mica's internal structure and the cleavage it shows? Mica, and all other silicates, tend to cleave between the silicon-oxygen structures rather than across them. This is because the silicon-oxygen bonds are strong. The sheet structure of mica causes the mineral to cleave into flat plates.

Some minerals have cleavage in more than one direction. Look back at Figure 11. Halite has three directions of cleavage. The cleavage planes of halite meet at 90-degree angles. Calcite also has three directions of cleavage. The cleavage planes of calcite, however, meet at 75-degree angles.

Fracture

Minerals that do not show cleavage when broken are said to fracture. Fracture is the uneven breakage of a mineral. Both mica and quartz contain silicon-oxygen bonds. However, quartz has equally strong silicon-oxygen bonds in all directions. Therefore, quartz fractures instead of cleaving like the micas. Like cleavage, there are different kinds of fracture. Minerals that break into smooth, curved surfaces like the quartz in **Figure 20B** have a curved, glassy (conchoidal) fracture. Other minerals, such as asbestos, break into splinters or fibers. Many minerals have an irregular fracture.

☑ **Reading Checkpoint** *How are cleavage and fracture different?*

Density

Density is a property of all matter and is the ratio of an object's mass to its volume. Density is a ratio and can be expressed using the following equation.

$$\frac{mass\ (m)}{Volume\ (V)} = Density\ (D)$$

Suppose a sample of lead, for example, has a mass of 113 grams and a volume of 10 cubic centimeters. You can calculate the density of lead by dividing its mass by its volume—113 grams divided by 10 cubic centimeters equals 11.3 grams per cubic centimeter. Several different samples of the same pure mineral will have the same density. So, density can be used to help identify minerals. For example, suppose you had an unknown sample and you determined its density was 7.5 g/cm³. You could use the chart on the next page to determine which mineral this sample might be.

FIGURE 20 Cleavage and Fracture A Mica has cleavage in one direction and therefore cleaves into thin sheets. **B** The bonds in quartz are very strong in all directions, causing quartz to display conchoidal fracture.

Use Visuals L1

Figure 20 Use these photographs to explain fracture and cleavage. **Ask:** What is cleavage? *(the tendency of a mineral to break along flat, even surfaces)* Which mineral shows cleavage? *(mica)* What is fracture? *(the uneven breakage of a mineral)* Which mineral shows fracture? *(quartz)* **Visual**

Integrate Chemistry L2

Density and Atomic Mass Specific gravity was once used to distinguish minerals. The specific gravity of a mineral is the ratio of the mineral's density to the density of a reference substance. However, today geologists use density. Density depends mainly on the chemical composition of a mineral. Minerals made of elements with high atomic masses generally have higher densities than minerals made of atoms with low atomic masses. Tell students that the mineral galena contains large amounts of lead, which has a high atomic mass. **Ask:** Would you expect the density of galena to be relatively low or high? *(high)* Tell students that the mineral quartz is made up of silicon and oxygen, which have low atomic masses. Would you expect the density of quartz to be relatively low or high? *(low)* **Logical**

Answers

Figure 19 *copper penny and fingernail*

☑ **Reading Checkpoint** *Hardness, streak, luster, and density are the most definitive properties that can be used to identify minerals.*

☑ **Reading Checkpoint** *Cleavage is the tendency for a mineral to break along flat, even surfaces. Fracture is the uneven breakage of a mineral.*

Facts and Figures

Like mica, asbestos is a sheet-forming mineral. However, unlike flat sheets of mica, sheets of asbestos roll up in a tight needle-like formation. These needles can cause serious damage to lungs if inhaled. Before people realized that asbestos caused a health risk, it was a popular insulation material. Now, many older buildings must undergo expensive asbestos removal in order to be safe.

Use Community Resources L2

As noted on p. 49, invite a geologist from a local college or company to visit the classroom and discuss properties of minerals with students. Ask the geologist to bring in samples of unusual minerals and demonstrate their properties to students.
Visual, Interpersonal

Build Science Skills L2

Student Activity: Design Experiments Give each student or group of students two mineral samples. Tell them only that one is calcite and the other is dolomite. Have students design an activity they could do without any additional materials or equipment to determine the identities of the two samples. *(Try to scratch the samples with each other. The one that is scratched is softer and is calcite.)* Then ask students how they might identify the samples using additional materials. *(Place dilute hydrochloric acid on each sample to see if it fizzes.)* Have them carry out their experiment. Be sure students wear safety goggles and gloves when using the hydrochloric acid. Dispense the acid in small dropper bottles and be sure it is diluted.
Logical

Table 2 Some Common Minerals and Their Properties					
Name	Chemical Formula and Mineral Group	Common Color(s)	Density (g/cm³)	Hardness	Comments
Quartz	SiO_2 silicates	colorless, milky white, pink, brown	2.65	7	glassy luster; conchoidal fractures
Orthoclase feldspar	$KAlSi_3O_8$ silicates	white to pink	2.57	6	cleaves in two directions at 90°
Plagioclase feldspar	$(Na,Ca)AlSi_3O_8$ silicates	white to gray	2.69*	6	cleaves in two directions at 90°; striations common
Galena	PbS sulfides	metallic silver	7.5*	2.5	cleaves in three directions at 90°; lead gray streak
Pyrite	FeS_2 sulfides	brassy yellow	5.02	6–6.5	fractures; forms cubic crystals; greenish-black streak
Sulfur	S native elements	yellow	2.07*	1.5–2.5	fractures; yellow streak smells like rotten eggs
Fluorite	CaF_2 halides	colorless, purple	3.18	4	perfect cleavage in three directions; glassy luster
Olivine	$(Mg,Fe)_2SiO_4$ silicates	green, yellowish-green	3.82*	6.5–7	fractures; glassy luster; often has granular texture
Calcite	$CaCO_3$ carbonates	colorless, gray	2.71	3	bubbles with HCl; cleaves in three directions
Talc	$Mg_3Si_4O_{10}(OH)_2$ silicates	pale green, gray, white	2.75*	1	pearly luster; feels greasy; cleaves in one direction
Gypsum	$CaSO_4 \cdot 2H_2O$ sulfates	colorless, white, gray	2.32	2	glassy or pearly luster; cleaves in three directions
Muscovite mica	$KAl_3Si_3O_{10}(OH)_2$ silicates	colorless in thin sheets to brown	2.82*	2–2.5	silky to pearly luster; cleaves in one direction to form flexible sheets

* Average density of the mineral

FIGURE 21 An Example of Distinctive Properties Calcite shows the property of double refraction.

Distinctive Properties of Minerals

Some minerals can be recognized by other distinctive properties. Talc and graphite, for example, both have distinctive feels. Talc feels soapy. Graphite feels greasy. Metallic minerals, such as gold, silver, and copper, are easily shaped. Some minerals, such as magnetite and hematite, are magnetic. Magnetite will attract paper clips and small nails. When a piece of transparent calcite is placed over printed material, the lines appear doubled, as **Figure 21** shows. This property is called double refraction. Streaks of a few minerals that contain sulfur smell like rotten eggs. A droplet of hydrochloric acid will cause carbonate minerals, such as calcite, to fizz.

A mineral's properties depend on the elements that make up the mineral (its composition) and how the atoms are arranged (its structure). **Table 2** lists some of the more common minerals and their properties.

Table 2 Some Common Minerals and Their Properties, continued

Name	Chemical Formula and Mineral Group	Common Color(s)	Density (g/cm³)	Hardness	Comments
Biotite mica	K(Mg,Fe)$_3$(AlSi$_3$O$_{10}$) (OH)$_2$ silicates	dark green to brown to black	3.0*	2.5–3	perfect cleavage in one direction to form flexible sheets
Halite	NaCl halides	colorless, white	2.16	2.5	has a salty taste; dissolves in water; cleaves in three directions
Augite	(Ca, Na)(Mg, Fe, Al) (Si, Al)$_2$O$_6$ silicates	dark green to black	3.3*	5–6	glassy luster; cleaves in two directions; crystals have 8-sided cross section
Hornblende	(Ca, Na)$_{2-3}$(Mg, Fe, Al)$_5$ Si$_6$(Si, Al)$_2$O$_{22}$(OH)$_2$ silicates	dark green to black	3.2*	5–6	glassy luster; cleaves in two directions; crystals have 6-sided cross section
Hematite	Fe$_2$O$_3$ oxides	reddish brown to black	5.26	5.5–6.5	metallic luster in crystals; dull luster in earthy variety; dark red streak; weakly magnetic
Dolomite	CaMg(CO$_3$)$_2$ carbonates	pink, colorless, white, gray	2.85	3.5–4	does not react to HCl as quickly as calcite; cleaves in three directions
Magnetite	Fe$_3$O$_4$ oxides	black	5.18	6	metallic luster; black streak; strongly magnetic
Copper	Cu native elements	copper-red on fresh surface	8.9	2.5–3	metallic luster; fractures; can be easily shaped
Graphite	C native elements	black to gray	2.3	1–2	black to gray streak; marks paper; feels slippery

2.3 Assessment

Review Key Concepts 🔑

1. Describe five common properties of minerals that can be used to identify them.

2. How is the Mohs scale used?

3. What are some unique properties that can be used to identify minerals?

Think Critically

4. **Apply Concepts** What kind of luster do the minerals shown in Figure 15 have? Explain your choice.

5. **Apply Concepts** Hornblende is a double-chain silicate. How many planes of cleavage do you think hornblende has when it breaks? Explain your answer.

6. **Apply Concepts** A mineral scratches a piece of fluorite but cannot be scratched by a piece of glass. What is this mineral's hardness?

CONNECTING CONCEPTS

7. **Classify** Choose one of the minerals pictured in this chapter. Find out to which mineral system it belongs as well as its luster, streak, hardness, density, and whether it cleaves or fractures. Also note any unique properties of the mineral.

Minerals **55**

Integrate Social Studies L2

Mining Economics Mineral resources are Earth's storehouse of minerals that can be recovered for use. The term *ore* refers to useful metallic minerals that can be mined at a profit. For pure elements, the element must be concentrated well above the level of its average crustal abundance to be worth mining. Copper must be present at about 100 times its average concentration, whereas for aluminum the ratio is only 4. Have students research the history of the copper mine at Bingham Canyon, Utah. (*It is one of the largest open-pit mines on Earth. Mining was halted in 1985 because it was uneconomic but later restarted with new equipment that made it profitable.*)
Verbal, Logical

❸ ASSESS

Evaluate Understanding L2

Provide students with 4 or 5 unidentified minerals. Challenge students to place the minerals in order of hardness from softest to hardest. They should rub any two of the minerals together and repeat this process until they can determine the order of hardness. Remind students that a harder mineral will scratch a softer mineral and a softer mineral may leave a streak on a harder mineral. After rubbing two minerals together, students may need to rub the mark with their finger to tell if it is a scratch or a streak.

Reteach L2

Begin an outline of the lesson based on the Reading Strategy presented on p. 50. List only the lesson's headings and do not add supporting details. Complete the outline as a class, adding definitions of difficult terms as well as other supporting details.

Gemstones L2

Background

- How can diamond and graphite be made of the same material (carbon) but form such different minerals? You could make a diamond out of your pencil if you could squeeze it hard enough. The pressure would compress the carbon atoms of the graphite together until they eventually formed the strong covalent bonds of diamond. In fact, this is roughly how synthetic diamonds are made: by squeezing carbon very tightly. Natural diamonds are thought to form more than 150 km beneath Earth's surface, where the pressures are very high. The diamonds that we find at the surface have been brought up from deep within Earth by geologic processes.

- Pure quartz, containing only SiO_2, is clear and colorless. However, natural quartz comes in many color varieties that form when different elements are contained in the crystal structure. If small amounts of titanium and iron are included, the result is rose quartz. The inclusion of manganese produces purple amethyst. The inclusion of aluminum produces smoky quartz.

- A precious gemstone that has gained in popularity in recent years is tanzanite. Mined only in the east-African country of Tanzania, tanzanite was discovered in 1967. Its color ranges from a light purplish blue to the more prized deep blues. The most prized stones are deep blue rimmed in a purplish hue. This hydrated calcium aluminum silicate is actually the blue variety of the gemstone called zoisite. But the jeweler Louis Comfort Tiffany, who popularized the gem after its discovery, thought that the correct name of *blue zoisite* was too reminiscent of the word *suicide*. So he suggested *tanzanite* instead.

Precious stones have been prized by people since ancient times. Unfortunately, much misinformation exists about the nature of gems and the minerals of which they are composed. Part of the misinformation stems from the ancient practice of grouping precious stones by color rather than mineral makeup. For example, the more common red spinels were often passed off to royalty as rubies, which are more valuable gems. Even today, when modern techniques of mineral identification are commonplace, yellow quartz is frequently sold as topaz.

What's In a Name?

Compounding the confusion is the fact that many gems have names that are different from their mineral names. For example, diamond is composed of the mineral of the same name, whereas sapphire is a form of corundum, an aluminum oxide-rich mineral. Although pure aluminum oxide is colorless, a tiny amount of a foreign element can produce a vividly colored gemstone. Therefore, depending on the impurity, sapphires of nearly every color exist. Pure aluminum oxide with trace amounts of titanium and iron produce the most prized blue sapphires. If the mineral corundum contains enough chromium, it exhibits a brilliant red color, and the gem is called ruby. Large gem-quality rubies are much rarer than diamonds and thus command a very high price.

If the specimen is not suitable as a gem, it simply goes by the mineral name corundum. Although common corundum is not a gemstone, it does have value as an abrasive material. Whereas two gems—rubies and sapphires—are composed of the mineral corundum, quartz is the parent mineral of more than a dozen gems. **Table 3** lists some well-known gemstones and their mineral names.

Precious or Semiprecious?

What makes a gem a gem instead of just another mineral? Basically, certain mineral specimens, when cut and polished, possess beauty of such quality that they can command a price that makes the process of producing the gem profitable. Gemstones can be divided into two categories: precious and semiprecious. A *precious* gem has beauty, durability, size, and rarity, whereas a *semiprecious* gem usually has only one or two of these qualities. The gems that have traditionally enjoyed the highest esteem are diamonds, rubies, sapphires, emeralds, and some varieties of opal. All other gemstones are classified as semiprecious. It should be noted, however, that large, high-quality specimens of semiprecious stones can often command a very high price.

FIGURE 22 Two Forms of the Mineral Beryl Emerald is the dark green variety of the mineral beryl. More common blue-green beryl is aquamarine.

FIGURE 23 Two Examples of Diamond A diamond in the rough looks very different from the brilliant, multi-faceted gem it can become.

Obviously, beauty is the most valuable quality that a gem can possess. Today we prefer translucent stones with evenly tinted colors. The most favored hues appear to be red, blue, green, purple, rose, and yellow. The most prized stones are deep red rubies, blue sapphires, grass-green emeralds, and canary-yellow diamonds. Colorless gems are generally less than desirable except in the case of diamonds that display "flashes of color" known as brilliance.

Notice in **Figure 23** that gemstones in the "rough" are dull and would be passed over by most people as "just another mineral." Gemstones must be cut and polished by experienced artisans before their true beauty can be displayed.

The durability of a gem depends on its hardness—that is, its resistance to abrasion by objects normally encountered in everyday living. For good durability, gems should be as hard or harder than quartz, as defined by the Mohs scale of hardness. One notable exception is opal, which is comparatively soft (hardness 5 to 6.5) and brittle. Opal's esteem comes from its fire, which is a display of a variety of brilliant colors including greens, blues, and reds.

It seems to be human nature to treasure that which is rare. In the case of gemstones, large, high-quality specimens are much rarer than smaller stones. Thus, large rubies, diamonds, and emeralds, which are rare in addition to being beautiful and durable, command the very highest prices.

Table 3 Some Important Gemstones		
Gem	**Mineral Name**	**Prized Hues**
Precious		
Diamond	Diamond	Colorless, yellows
Emerald	Beryl	Greens
Opal	Nonmineral	Brilliant hues
Ruby	Corundum	Reds
Sapphire	Corundum	Blues
Semiprecious		
Alexandrite	Chrysoberyl	Variable
Amethyst	Quartz	Purples
Aquamarine	Beryl	Blue-greens
Cat's-eye	Chrysoberyl	Yellows
Chalcedony	Quartz (agate)	Banded
Citrine	Quartz	Yellows
Garnet	Garnet	Reds, greens
Jade	Jadeite or nephrite	Greens
Moonstone	Feldspar	Transparent blues
Peridot	Olivine	Olive greens
Smoky quartz	Quartz	Browns
Spinel	Spinel	Reds
Topaz	Topaz	Purples, reds
Tourmaline	Tourmaline	Reds, blue-greens
Turquoise	Turquoise	Blues
Zircon	Zircon	Reds

MINERAL IDENTIFICATION L2

Objectives
After completing this activity, students will be able to
- explain some of the simple tests that can be used to identify minerals.
- differentiate among some of the common rock-forming minerals.

Skills Observe, Compare and Contrast, Measure

Prep Time 20 minutes

Advance Prep Order the minerals from a scientific supply house at least one month before you plan to do this activity. Minerals should include several different varieties of quartz, calcite, magnetite, gypsum, talc, feldspars, olivine, fluorite, augite, hornblende, pyrite, halite, and micas. Make sure the mineral samples will fit into the graduated cylinders you plan to use.
- Label the samples with numbers, using a permanent marker so that you can check students' results.
- You may want to assemble mineral testing kits for students to use. These can be easily made by placing one of each testing item—acid bottle, knife, piece of quartz, magnet, streak plate, glass plate, penny, and hand lens—into small, study cardboard boxes. Students can share the minerals to be observed.
- If students do the Go Further exercise, you will need some small hand samples of the following rocks: sandstone, granite, limestone, marble, and schist.

Class Time 45 minutes

Safety Have students wear their safety goggles and aprons during the entire activity. Remind them to take care when breaking the minerals and that only a gentle blow is needed to break most of the samples they will be examining. Also remind students not to taste any of the minerals or the acid.

Teaching Tips
- If you don't want the samples destroyed, have students omit Part C. Alternatively, you can break a set of samples and have them on display for students to observe.
- Stress to students to use only a drop or two of acid to test each of the minerals and to thoroughly wash the samples after testing them with the HCl.

Mineral Identification

Problem How can you use simple tests and tools to identify common minerals?

Materials mineral samples, hand lens, streak plate, copper penny, steel knife blade, glass plate, piece of quartz, dilute hydrochloric acid, magnet, hammer, 50 mL graduated cylinder, tap water, balance, thin thread, scissors, paper or cloth towels, Table 2 in the chapter.

Skills Observing, Comparing and Contrasting, Measuring

Connect to the Big idea Most minerals can be identified by using the properties discussed in this chapter. In this lab, you will use what you have learned about mineral properties and the information in Table 2 (pages 54 and 55) to identify some common rock-forming minerals. In the next chapter, you will learn about rocks, which are mixtures of one or more minerals. Being able to identify minerals will enable you to understand more about the processes that form and change the rocks at and beneath Earth's surface.

Procedure

Part A: Color and Luster

1. Examine each mineral sample with and without the hand lens. Examine both the central part of each mineral as well as the edges of the samples.

2. Record the color and luster of each sample in a data table like the one shown on the next page.

Part B: Streak and Hardness

3. To determine the streak of a mineral, gently drag it across the streak plate and observe the color of the powdered mineral. If a mineral is harder than the streak plate (H = 7), it will not produce a streak.

4. Record the streak color for each mineral in your data table.

5. Use your fingernail, the penny, the glass plate, the knife blade, and the piece of quartz to test the hardness of each mineral. Remember that if a mineral scratches an object, the mineral is harder than the object. If an object scratches a mineral, the mineral is softer than the object.

6. Record the hardness values for each sample in your data table.

Part C: Cleavage and Fracture

7. Cover one of the mineral samples with two layers of paper towel. With your goggles on and everyone out of your way, gently strike the sample with a hammer.

8. Observe the broken mineral pieces. Does the mineral cleave or fracture? *Cleavage* is even surfaces and *fracture* is uneven breakage. Record your observations in your data table.

9. Repeat Steps 7 and 8 for the other minerals.

Part D: Density

10. Using a balance, determine the mass of your mineral sample. Record the mass in the first column under Density.

11. Cut a piece of thread about 20 cm long. Tie a small piece of your mineral sample to one end of the thread.

12. Securely tie the other end of the thread to a pencil or pen.

13. Fill the graduated cylinder about half full with water. Record the volume of the water in the second column under Density.

Data Table

Mineral Number	Color	Luster	Streak	Relative Hardness	Cleavage/ Fracture	Density				Other Properties
						m	V₁	V₂	d	
1										
2										
3										
4										
5										
6										
7										
8										

14. Lower the mineral into the graduated cylinder. Read the volume of the water now. Record the volume in the third column under Density.

15. Calculate the density of the mineral using the following equation:

$$\frac{mass_1}{volume_2 - volume_1}$$

Record this value in the fourth column.

Part E: Other Properties

16. Use the magnet to determine if any of the minerals are magnetic. Record your observations in the data table.

17. Place the transparent minerals over a word on this page to see if any have the property of double refraction. If a mineral has this property, you will see two sets of the word. Record your observations.

18. Compare the feel of the minerals. In the data table, note any differences.

19. Carefully place one or two drops of dilute hydrochloric acid on each mineral. Record your observations. When you are finished with this test, wash the minerals well with tap water to rinse away the acid.

Analyze and Conclude

1. **Identify** Use your data and Table 2 to identify each of the minerals tested.

2. **Evaluate** Which of the properties did you find most useful? Least useful? Give reasons for your answers.

3. **Compare and Contrast** In general, how did the minerals with metallic luster differ from those with non-metallic luster?

4. **Classify** Classify your minerals into at least three groups based on your observations. How does your classification scheme differ from those of at least two other students?

GO FURTHER Obtain some rock samples from your teacher or collect some of your own. Use the hand lens to try to identify the minerals in each rock. Make a table in which to record your observations. Compare your table to the information presented in the Rocks chapter.

Expected Outcome Students should be able to identify at least one-half to three-fourths of the samples accurately by using what they know about mineral properties and the information in Table 2 on pages 54 and 55.

Sample Data
Compare students' data and observations with the information provided in Table 2.

Analyze and Conclude
1. Most students should be able to correctly identify at least half of the minerals provided.
2. Answers will vary, but might include color and luster as the two least useful properties; and density, streak, hardness, and breakage as the most useful.
3. Minerals with metallic luster tend to have higher densities than minerals with non-metallic luster.
4. Students' classification schemes will probably differ, but might be based on similarities and differences in relative hardness, density, luster, type of breakage, or color.

GO FURTHER

Most students will probably be able to identify some of the larger minerals in the rocks. Quartz, feldspar, and hornblende are found in many granites. Quartz is also a major component of many sandstones. Limestone and marble are often mostly calcite.
Visual, Logical

Minerals **59**

Study Tip

Plan Ahead

Tell students to examine their schedules at least a week before the test. They should figure out how much time they will have available to study. Then students should divide up that time and plan when they are going to study each topic covered on the test. Encourage students to review the most important topics first. That way, students can cut the time allotted for reviewing less important topics if they have less time for studying than they expected.

Thinking Visually

The mineral is green, has a glassy luster, and does not appear to have cleavage. The sample also has striations, is transparent or translucent, and illustrates a portion of a distinctive crystal form.

21st Century Learning

Global Awareness and Economic Literacy

How are minerals used?

Minerals mined from Earth have many different uses. Tell students to research to find data, including chemical composition and physical properties, about each of three minerals. Ask students to identify some of the products that are made from each mineral and to list some countries where each mineral is mined. Finally, ask them to produce a single-page information sheet or Web page to present each mineral. Presentations should include tables and images to present the information in a clear and attractive way.

Homework Guide

Lesson	Questions
1	1–3, 10, 11, 17–24
2	4, 5, 12–14, 25–31
3	6–9, 15, 16, 32–34

2 Study Guide

Big idea Earth's Materials and Systems

2.1 Matter

🔑 An element contains only one type of atom. Therefore, an element cannot be broken down, chemically or physically, into a simpler substance.

🔑 An atom is the smallest particle of an element that retains the characteristics of that element.

🔑 Atoms with the same number of protons but different numbers of neutrons are isotopes of an element.

🔑 A compound is a substance that consists of two or more elements that are chemically combined in specific proportions.

🔑 When an atom's highest energy level does not contain the maximum number of electrons, the atom is likely to form a chemical bond with one or more other atoms.

🔑 Ionic bonds form between positive and negative ions. Covalent bonds form when atoms share electrons. Metallic bonds form when electrons are shared by metal ions.

element (34)	chemical bond (39)
atomic number (35)	ion (40)
energy level (35)	ionic bond (40)
isotope (38)	covalent bond (41)
mass number (38)	metallic bond (43)
compound (39)	

2.2 Minerals

🔑 A mineral is a naturally occurring, inorganic solid with an orderly crystalline structure and a definite chemical composition.

🔑 There are four major processes by which minerals form: crystallization from magma, precipitation, changes in pressure and temperature, and formation from hydrothermal solutions.

🔑 Common minerals, together with the thousands of others that form on Earth, can be classified into groups based on their composition.

🔑 Silicates are the most common minerals on Earth and are made of millions of silicon-oxygen

60 Chapter 2 • Study Guide

tetrahedra. Carbonates contain carbon, oxygen, and one or more other elements. Oxides contain oxygen and one or more other elements, usually metals. Sulfates and sulfides are minerals that contain sulfur. Halides contain a halogen ion plus one or more other elements. Native elements are minerals that only contain one element or type of atom.

mineral (45)
silicon-oxygen tetrahedron (47)
silicate (47)

2.3 Properties of Minerals

🔑 Small amounts of different elements can give the same mineral many different colors.

🔑 Streak is the color of a mineral in its powdered form.

🔑 Luster describes how light is reflected from the surface of a mineral.

🔑 Crystal form is the visual expression of a mineral's internal arrangement of atoms.

🔑 The Mohs scale consists of 10 index minerals arranged from 10 (hardest) to 1 (softest).

🔑 Cleavage is the tendency of a mineral to cleave, or break along flat, even surfaces; fracture is uneven breakage.

🔑 Density is a property of all matter and is the ratio of an object's mass to its volume.

🔑 Some minerals can be recognized by other distinctive properties, such as feel and magnetism.

streak (50)	Mohs scale (52)
luster (51)	cleavage (53)
crystal form (51)	fracture (53)
hardness (52)	density (53)

Think Visually

Observe Use what you have learned about minerals and Table 2 to list as many properties as possible of the mineral below.

Assessment Answers

Review Content

1. b	**2.** b	**3.** c
4. a	**5.** d	**6.** b
7. b	**8.** d	**9.** a

Understand Concepts

10. Protons, neutrons, and electrons make up all atoms. Protons are positive particles found in the nucleus of an atom. Neutrons are neutral particles in the nucleus. Electrons are negative particles that orbit an atom's nucleus.

11. Ionic and covalent bonds are forces that hold atoms together in compounds. Ionic bonds form between ions of opposite charge. Covalent bonds form when electrons are shared.

2 Assessment

Review Content

Choose the letter that best answers the question or completes the statement.

1. Which of the following is neutrally charged?
   a. an ion
   b. a compound
   c. an electron
   d. a proton

2. Atoms combine when
   a. their highest electron levels are filled.
   b. their electrons are shared or transferred.
   c. the number of protons and neutrons is the same.
   d. the number of electrons and protons is the same.

3. Compounds with low boiling points have
   a. metallic bonds.
   b. ionic bonds.
   c. covalent bonds.
   d. no chemical bonds.

4. Minerals that form from magma form as the result of
   a. crystallization.
   b. evaporation.
   c. precipitation.
   d. condensation.

5. The mineral barite ($BaSO_4$) is a(n)
   a. oxide.
   b. silicate.
   c. carbonate.
   d. sulfate.

6. Color is often not a useful identification property because
   a. some minerals are colorless.
   b. the same mineral can be different colors.
   c. different minerals can be different colors.
   d. some minerals are single elements.

7. What is a mineral's streak?
   a. the resistance to being scratched
   b. the color of the mineral in powder form
   c. the way in which the mineral reflects light
   d. the way the mineral reacts to hydrochloric acid

8. A particular mineral breaks like a piece of glass does. Which of these describes the breakage?
   a. cleavage
   b. hardness
   c. metallic luster
   d. fracture

9. Mineral properties depend on composition and
   a. structure.
   b. luster.
   c. cleavage.
   d. streak.

Understand Concepts

10. Name the three types of particles found in an atom and explain how they differ.

11. Compare and contrast ionic and covalent bonds.

12. What are five characteristics of a mineral?

13. Explain three ways in which new minerals can form from existing minerals.

14. Contrast the composition of minerals in each of the mineral groups discussed in the chapter.

15. How is cleavage related to a mineral's atomic structure?

16. Give examples of four minerals that can be identified by unique properties. Describe each property.

Use this diagram to answer Questions 17–21.

17. Briefly describe the kind of bond that is formed when two atoms shown in **A** bond.

18. Describe the kind of bond that forms when the atoms shown in **B** bond.

19. Is the atom on the left in **A** an ion? Explain your answer.

20. Use the periodic table to determine the atomic number of the atom on the left side of **A**. What group is this element in?

21. The atoms in **B** contain 17 protons. Are these atoms ions when they bond with each other? Can these atoms form ions when they react with other elements? Explain your answers.

15. Some bonds in minerals are weaker than others. When a mineral is stressed, these bonds break to form flat, even surfaces.

16. Graphite feels greasy; talc feel soapy. Magnetite is attracted to objects containing iron. Calcite has double refraction. Sulfur minerals have unique odors. Some carbonates such as calcite will fizz when exposed to HCl.

17. Because an electron is being transferred from the magnesium to the oxygen, an ionic bond is formed.

18. Because the chlorine atoms share electrons, a covalent bond is formed.

19. Yes, because it contains a different number of electrons than protons.

20. The atomic number is 12. The group is 2 or 2A.

21. No, the model shows them to be covalently bonded forming a molecule. Yes, chlorine atoms form ions when reacting with metals in Groups 1 and 2.

12. The five characteristics of a mineral are that it is naturally occurring, inorganic, solid, has definite internal structure, and has definite chemical composition.

13. New minerals can form from existing minerals when they are subjected to changes in temperature or changes in pressure and when the existing minerals are exposed to water at or near Earth's surface or to hydrothermal solutions.

14. Silicates contain silicon, oxygen, and often one or more other elements. Carbonates are made of carbon, oxygen, and one or more other elements. Oxides contain oxygen and one or more other elements, usually metals. Sulfates contain sulfur, oxygen, and one or more other elements. Sulfides also contain sulfur and one or more metallic elements. Halides are compounds that contain a halogen and one or more other elements. Native elements are minerals that exist as single elements.

ASSESSMENT

Think Critically

22. The atoms are isotopes.

23. KCl; potassium chloride

24. Metals form metallic bonds with one another by sharing a pool of electrons. When a metal is pounded into a sheet or drawn into a wire, the electrons and the metallic ions merely shift their positions.

25. Most silicates crystallize from magma as it cools. Silicates can also form as the result of changes in temperatures and pressures. Some silicate minerals form at Earth's surface when existing minerals are exposed to water. Other silicates form under the extreme pressures associated with mountain building.

26. The mineral might form another mineral as the result of exposure to air and water, or it might react as the result of being subjected to lower pressures and temperatures at Earth's surface.

27. a. carbonate
b. sulfide
c. oxide
d. halide

28. The unit is the silicon-oxygen tetrahedron.

29. They are single chains and double chains.

30. Minerals with these structures will break along planes of weakness, that is, between the oxygen bonds, to form flat, even surfaces.

31. The double chain structure is more complex because more tetrahedra combine to form two chains, rather than one.

Concepts in Action

32. The mineral could be tested for hardness using either another diamond or a piece of corundum. If the mineral is a diamond, it will scratch the corundum and be as hard as the other diamond.

33. Quartz and corundum are often used as abrasives because of their hardness. Graphite is a common lubricant because of its greasiness and softness. Mica is a common ingredient in many kinds of make-up.

34. The volume of the brick is 30 cm × 8 cm × 4 cm = 960 cm³ The mass would equal 960 cm³ × 19.3 g/cm³ 5 18,528 g or 18.5 kg (rounded)

22. Compare and Contrast Three atoms have the same atomic number but different mass numbers. What can you say about the atoms?

23. Predict Potassium metal in Group 1 of the periodic table is very reactive. When placed in chlorine gas, potassium reacts to form a halide compound. Using Figure 4 and the periodic table propose the formula and name for the compound.

24. Form a Hypothesis Why do you think metals can easily be rolled into thin sheets and drawn into wires? (*Hint:* Think about the arrangement of electrons in metals.)

25. Explain Explain the processes that result in the formation of silicate minerals.

26. Form a Hypothesis A mineral forms deep beneath the surface. It reaches Earth's surface during mountain building. Describe two things that might happen to this mineral at the surface.

27. Apply Concepts Classify the following minerals based on their chemical formulas.
a. $NaCO_3$ c. $FeCr_2O_4$
b. PbS d. CaF_2

Use the diagrams to answer Questions 28–31.

28. Identify What is the basic structural unit in these two diagrams?

29. Classify What are the names given to these two silicate structures?

30. Apply Concepts How do these two structures affect mineral breakage?

31. Form a Hypothesis Which of the two structures is more complex? Explain your choice.

32. Apply Concepts Your friend shows you a crystal that he thinks is a diamond. Without asking an expert, how could you tell if the crystal is really a diamond?

33. Apply Concepts Which two minerals discussed in this chapter would be useful as abrasives? Which could be used as a lubricant? Which might be used in sparkly eye shadows?

34. Calculate Gold has a density of 19.3 g/cm³. What would be the mass of a gold brick that is 30 cm long, 8 cm wide, and 4 cm tall?

Performance-Based Assessment

Apply Concepts Go on a scavenger hunt around your school or home to find at least 20 items that are minerals, that contain minerals, or that were obtained from minerals. Make a poster that shows what you found and display it for the class.

Performance-Based Assessment

Students should be able to identify most items that are made of metals and glass. Other items that are minerals or obtained from minerals include table salt, pencil "lead," and gemstones in jewelry. Plastics would not be considered in this scavenger hunt because they are made from petroleum, which is an organic substance.

Standardized Test Prep

Choose the letter that *best* answers the question or completes the statement.

1 Which of the following pairs of minerals and a common usage of the mineral is *not* correct?
A graphite - pencil lead
B diamond - dentist drill bit
C quartz - drinking glasses
D talc - windows

Use the table below to answer Question 2.

Electron Dot Diagrams for Some Representative Elements

2 How many electrons are in the outer energy level of oxygen?
F 5   H 7
G 6   J 8

If You Have Trouble With . . .

Question	1	2	3	4	5
See Lesson	2.2	2.1	2.2	2.3	2.3

3 Which of the following *best* describes a mineral?
A a naturally occurring, inorganic solid, with an orderly crystalline structure
B a naturally occurring, organic solid with an orderly crystalline structure
C the smallest fundamental particle in nature
D the smallest particle of matter that contains the characteristic of an element

Use the graph to answer Question 4.

4 How does talc's hardness on the Mohs scale compare with its absolute hardness?
F Talc's hardness value on the Mohs scale is less than the absolute hardness value.
G Talc's hardness value on the Mohs scale is about the same as the absolute hardness value.
H Talc's hardness value on the Mohs scale is greater than the absolute hardness value.
J Talc's hardness value on the Mohs scale cannot be compared to the absolute hardness value.

5 Which of the following *best* describes the cleavage of a mineral?
A the uneven breakage of a mineral
B a measure of the resistance of a mineral to being scratched
C the reflection of light from the surface of a mineral
D the tendency of a mineral to break along flat, even surfaces

3 Rocks Planning Guide

Lesson Objectives		Activities
3.1 The Rock Cycle, pp. 66–69 3.1 **Define** the term *rock*. 3.2 **Identify** the three major types of rocks and **explain** how they differ. 3.3 **Describe** the rock cycle. 3.4 **List** the processes that transform rock from one type to another.		TE Teacher Demo: Weathering, p. 68 L2 TE Build Science Skills, p. 68 L2
3.2 Igneous Rocks, pp. 70–74 3.5 **Compare and contrast** intrusive and extrusive igneous rocks. 3.6 **Explain** how the rate of cooling affects an igneous rock's texture. 3.7 **Classify** igneous rocks according to texture and composition.		TE Build Science Skills, p. 70 L2 TE Teacher Demo: Crystal Formation, p. 72 L2
3.3 Sedimentary Rocks, pp. 75–79 3.8 **Describe** the major processes involved in the formation of sedimentary rocks. 3.9 **Distinguish** between clastic, chemical, and biochemical sedimentary rocks. 3.10 **Identify** the features that are unique to some sedimentary rocks.		TE Address Misconceptions, p. 76 L2 TE Build Science Skills, p. 76 L2 TE Teacher Demo: Chemical Weathering, p. 77 L2 TE Build Science Skills, p. 78 L2
3.4 Metamorphic Rocks, pp. 80–84 3.11 **Predict** where most metamorphism takes place. 3.12 **Distinguish** contact metamorphism from regional metamorphism. 3.13 **Identify** the three agents of metamorphism and **explain** what changes they cause. 3.14 **Recognize** foliated metamorphic rocks and **describe** how they form. 3.15 **Classify** metamorphic rocks.		TE Build Science Skills, p. 81 L2 SE Quick Lab: Observing Some of the Effects of Pressure on Mineral Grains, p. 83 L2
Chapter Features and Labs		
Try It What Are Some Similarities and Differences Among Rocks? p. 65		LM Classifying Rocks Using a Key L1
Earth & Its Systems The Carbon Cycle, p. 85		
Exploration Lab Rock Identification, pp. 86–87		

Ability Levels	Components		
L1 For students who need additional help	SE Student Edition	LP Lesson Plans	
L2 For all students	TE Teacher's Edition	AA Active Art	
L3 For students who need to be challenged	LM Laboratory Manual	PD Planet Diary	
	CT Chapter Tests	GEODe Geode CD-ROM	
	GRSW Guided Reading & Study Workbook	eText	
	CTB Computer Test Bank		

Resources	Lesson Assessment
GRSW Lesson 3.1 LP Lesson Planning 3.1 AA Rock Cycle GEODe Earth Materials: Rock Cycle	SE Lesson 3.1 Assessment, p. 69 eText Lesson 3.1
GRSW Lesson 3.2 LP Lesson Planning 3.2 PD Igneous Rock GEODe Earth Materials: Igneous Rocks	SE Lesson 3.2 Assessment, p. 74 eText Lesson 3.2
GRSW Lesson 3.3 LP Lesson Planning 3.3 GEODe Earth Materials: Sedimentary Rocks	SE Lesson 3.3 Assessment, p. 79 eText Lesson 3.3
GRSW Lesson 3.4 LP Lesson Planning 3.4 GEODe Earth Materials: Metamorphic Rocks	SE Lesson 3.4 Assessment, p. 84 eText Lesson 3.4

Materials for Activities and Labs

Quantities for each group

STUDENT EDITION

Try It, p. 65
hand lenses; samples of coarse-grained sandstone, limestone, basalt, granite, gneiss, marble

Quick Lab, p. 83
soft modeling clay; 2 pieces of waxed paper (each 20 cm × 20 cm); 20 to 30 small, round, elongated plastic beads; small plastic knife

Exploration Lab, pp. 86–87
rock samples, hand lens, pocket knife, dilute hydrochloric acid, colored pencils

TEACHER'S EDITION

Teacher Demo, p. 68
2-L plastic bottle with cap, water

Build Science Skills, p. 68
simple materials for model-building

Teacher Demo, p. 72
2 shallow pans, 250-mL beaker, water, teaspoon, sulfur powder, thermal mitt, hot plate, magnifying glass

Address Misconceptions, p. 76
vinegar, sample of limestone

Build Science Skills, p. 76
250-mL beaker, stirrers, sand, water, gravel, soil

Teacher Demo, p. 77
calcium carbonate antacid tablet, 250-mL beaker, vinegar

Assessment

CHAPTER ASSESSMENT
SE Assessment, pp. 89–90
CT Chapter 3 Test
CTB Chapter 3
eText Chapter 3

21st Century Learning

Interpersonal and Collaborative Skills: How Can You Play the Rock Cycle? TE p. 88

Common Themes

Rocks are solid mixtures of one or more minerals, organic remains, or glassy material. The study of igneous, sedimentary, and metamorphic rocks is the foundation of geology.

Space and Time Rocks occupy 5/6 of the volume of the geosphere and account for 2/3 of its mass (the rest consists of metal alloys in the core). The oldest rocks are meteorites, more than 4.5 billion years old, which formed at the same time as Earth.

Forces and Motion Igneous, sedimentary, and metamorphic rocks are interconnected by a set of processes called the rock cycle. A common path through the rock cycle is for igneous rock to be weathered, transported, and deposited to eventually become sedimentary rock. Then this sedimentary rock is subjected to high temperatures and pressures that turn it into metamorphic rock. Eventually the metamorphic rock melts to become new igneous rock. However, different geological histories result in different paths through the rock cycle.

Matter and Energy There are many factors that affect the appearance of a rock. For igneous rocks, these factors include the composition and the rate of cooling. For sedimentary rocks, these include the types of sediment compacted (clastic, chemical, biological). For metamorphic rocks, these include the amounts of heat, pressure, and hot fluids the rocks are exposed to.

Earth as a System Rocks are scientifically important because their characteristics provide clues about their formation. This provides geologists with a kind of time machine that lets them learn about conditions long ago.

Michael Wysession
Washington University

EARTH SCIENCE REFRESHER

Different Igneous Rocks

In addition to there being many different kinds of minerals, there are many different kinds of rocks. While this might seem reasonable for sedimentary and metamorphic rocks (after all, if you start with different kinds of sediments or bedrock, you will end up with different sedimentary or metamorphic rocks), why should this be the case for igneous rocks? The reason is that minerals crystallize and melt at different temperatures. This simple fact has given rise to a wide diversity of igneous rock types. Shortly after it formed, the initially molten Earth began to cool and crystallize into a range of igneous rocks.

Bowen's Reaction Series

The process of igneous rock formation is called Bowen's reaction series. As magma rises toward Earth's surface, minerals crystallize out of solution in a particular order. In general, the minerals that crystallize at high temperatures, generally deep beneath Earth's surface, are those associated with mafic and intermediate rocks. Minerals that crystallize at low temperatures, generally closer to the surface, are those associated with felsic rocks. In part, the series is explained by the effect temperature has on the ability of SiO_2 to form complex structures. The lower the temperature, the more complex the structure can be.

Address **Misconceptions**

Students may mistakenly believe that rocks are stronger than the forces of nature. The agents of mechanical and chemical weathering can break down rocks over time. For a strategy that helps to overcome this misconception, see **Address Misconceptions** on **TE p. 76.**

At high temperatures, there are two branches to the reaction series. In one branch, called the discontinuous branch, olivine crystallizes first, then pyroxene, amphibole, and then biotite. In the other branch, called the continuous branch, calcium-rich plagioclase feldspar crystallizes first, gradually changing to sodium-rich at lower temperatures. At lower temperatures, the branches merge and the last minerals to crystallize are potassium feldspar, muscovite, and quartz.

Example of Crystallization: The Palisades Cliffs

There are many examples of the crystallization process, such as the Palisades Cliffs of New Jersey, across the Hudson River from Manhattan. The Palisades formed as an igneous sill, up to 600 m thick, about 200 million years ago when Africa and North America rifted apart. The bottom third of the cliffs are rich in olivine, which crystallized first and settled out to the bottom of the sill. The middle third of the sill is largely made of pyroxene, which crystallized after the olivine. During these processes, the feldspar composition changed from being calcium-rich to sodium-rich, so that sodium-rich feldspar dominates the top third of the cliffs.

Example of Melting: Granite Batholiths

Did you ever wonder why the cores of many mountain ranges, such as the Appalachians or the Sierra-Nevadas, are made of granite? The reason is Bowen's reaction series in reverse. When continents collide, rock gets thrust up (to form mountains) and also down. The rock that is pushed down becomes hotter with depth, and eventually begins to melt. The first minerals to melt are the ones at the bottom of the reaction series: quartz, muscovite, and potassium feldspar, which are the main ingredients of granite. This melt is more buoyant than the surrounding rock, so it rises up into the heart of the mountain range. Here, temperatures are cooler, so the magma crystallizes to form granite. If the plate collision occurs for a long time, a lot of granite can be generated. When erosion removes the mountain tops, the granite batholiths are exposed.

BUILD READING LITERACY
Directed Reading/Thinking Activity (DRTA)

Predict, Read, Confirm, Revise Predictions

Strategy Help students develop their own reading and thinking processes by setting their own purposes for reading. Select a section of Chapter 3 for students to read, such as Lesson 3.1, pp. 66–69. Before modeling the strategy with students, divide the targeted section into approximately four equal portions. Present the steps in the example below.

Example

1. Preview Tell students to survey the section by analyzing the titles, headings, visual elements, and boldfaced type. Have students also read the introductory and concluding paragraphs.

2. Predict/Generate Questions Ask students to hypothesize and predict what they will learn, and to formulate their own "teacher-type" questions to be answered; that is, of the type that a teacher might ask. List students' responses on the board.

3. Read/Evaluate and Refine Predictions Have students read a portion of the section. Pause afterward for students to evaluate their predictions. Discuss any answers they learned to their questions, and any prior misconceptions that were clarified. Ask students to formulate refined predictions and questions based on the new information.

4. Repeat the process for the remaining text portions.

See TE p. 76 for a script on how to use this strategy with students. For additional strategies, see TE pp. 67, 72, and 82.

CHAPTER 3

ASSESS PRIOR KNOWLEDGE

Use the Chapter Pretest below to assess students' prior knowledge. As needed, review these concepts.

Review Science Concepts

Lesson 3.1 Encourage students to recall what they know about different states of matter. Review the structure of an atom.

Lesson 3.2 Review the definition of a mineral. Have students compare and contrast different types of classification systems. Also, discuss the composition of Earth's crust.

Lesson 3.3 and **Lesson 3.4** Have students explain how minerals form. Ask them to describe some tests they could perform to identify minerals.

3 Rocks

Big idea **Earth's Materials and Systems**

Q: What are the different types of rock and how do they form?

Chapter Pretest

1. Describe the strength of bonds between atoms in a solid. *(Atoms in a solid are tightly bound together.)*

2. What is a mineral? *(A mineral is a naturally occurring, inorganic solid with an orderly crystalline structure and a definite chemical composition.)*

3. True or False: Only eight elements make up the bulk of the minerals found in Earth's crust. *(True)*

4. What is the most common mineral group? *(b)*
 a. carbonates **b.** silicates
 c. oxides **d.** halides

5. What are some common properties of minerals? *(crystal form, luster, color, streak, hardness, cleavage, fracture, and specific gravity)*

A climber scales a formation of sedimentary rock in the Dolomite Alps, Italy

INQUIRY
TRY IT!

WHAT ARE SOME SIMILARITIES AND DIFFERENCES AMONG ROCKS?

Procedure

1. Your teacher will provide you with six rock samples. Examine them closely.
2. Record at least three ways in which the rocks are alike.
3. Now determine and record at least three ways in which the rocks differ.
4. Classify the rock samples into three groups based on your observations. Give reasons for your groupings.

Think About It

1. **Compare and Contrast** How are the rock samples similar? How do they differ?
2. **Compare and Contrast** How does your classification scheme compare with the classification schemes of at least two other students? How do they differ?
3. **Form a Hypothesis** Each of the rocks used in this activity belongs to one of the three major groups of rocks. Hypothesize what makes one group of rocks different from the others.

65

ENGAGE/EXPLORE

INQUIRY
TRY IT!

WHAT ARE SOME SIMILARITIES AND DIFFERENCES AMONG ROCKS?   L2

Purpose Students will classify six rocks into three groups using similarities and differences among the rocks.

Skills Observe, Compare and Contrast, Classify

Prep Time 10–15 minutes

Materials hand lenses, samples of coarse-grained sandstone, limestone, basalt, granite, gneiss, and marble

Class Time 20–25 minutes

Teaching Tip Have students note differences and similarities in the way each sample feels when rubbed with the fingers (smooth or rough), the texture of each sample (the size, shape, and arrangement of the minerals in the rock), and the overall color of the rocks (light-colored or dark-colored).

Expected Outcome Students will find that size, texture, color, shape, and composition account for most differences and similarities among the rocks.

Think About It

1. Similarities might include the color, shape, size, texture, or composition of the rocks. Some students might also state that all rocks are solids or that all rocks appear to be mixtures. Differences among the samples include size, shape, composition, color, and texture.

2. Most students will probably attempt to classify the rocks based on color or texture. For example, students might group limestone and marble based on similarities in color and texture. They might use color and mineral composition to place granite and gneiss in the same group. Students might put sandstone and basalt into a group based on their unique textures. Accept any reasonable classification schemes.

3. Accept any reasonable response—color, texture, or composition. Some students might be able to infer that rocks can be classified according to the way they were formed.

1 FOCUS

Lesson Objectives

3.1 **Define** the term *rock*.
3.2 **Identify** the three major types of rocks and **explain** how they differ.
3.3 **Describe** the rock cycle.
3.4 **List** the processes that transform rock from one type to another.

Build Vocabulary [L2]

Cycle Diagram Have students construct a cycle diagram of the rock cycle. Students should use the terms *igneous rock, sedimentary rock, metamorphic rock, sediment, magma,* and *lava* to indicate the materials involved in the rock cycle. The processes of the rock cycle are shown in Figure 3 on p. 68. Tell students to place the terms in ovals and use labeled arrows to indicate how one process leads to another.

Reading Strategy [L2]

a. a solid mixture of one or more minerals
b. rock that forms when magma or lava cools and hardens
c. rock that forms when sediment is lithified
d. loose bits of weathered rock

Confirm that students' tables list the definitions for each of the vocabulary terms from this lesson.

2 INSTRUCT

Use Visuals [L2]

Figure 1 **Ask:** How do the rocks seen in Figure 1 compare? *(Rock A looks dark, smooth, and shiny. Rock B looks light, rough, and dull.)*
Visual

3.1 The Rock Cycle

Key Questions

- What is a rock?
- What are the three major types of rock?
- What is the rock cycle?
- How do igneous, sedimentary, and metamorphic rocks differ?
- What processes transform rocks from one type to another?

Vocabulary

- rock • rock cycle
- magma • lava
- igneous rock
- weathering • sediment
- sedimentary rock
- metamorphic rock

Reading Strategy

Build Vocabulary Copy and expand the table to include each vocabulary term. As you read, write down the definition for each term.

Term	Definition
rock	a. ___?___
igneous rock	b. ___?___
sedimentary rock	c. ___?___
sediments	d. ___?___

FIGURE 1 **Nonmineral Rocks** **A** Obsidian and **B** pumice are two examples of rocks that are not composed of minerals.

MANY OF the most dramatic Earth processes—from volcanic eruptions, to mountain building, to earthquakes—involve rocks. Rocks give us clues about the environment in which they formed. If a rock contains fragments of seashells, for example, you can infer that the rock formed in the ocean. By understanding how rocks form, you can look at a rock and infer whether it formed at Earth's surface or deep below it, at high temperatures or low, and even whether its pieces were transported by water, wind, or ice.

Rocks

What is a rock? **A rock is a solid mass of minerals or mineral-like materials.** As you have learned, a mineral is a naturally occurring, inorganic solid with a crystalline structure. Most rocks are a mix, or aggregate, of many minerals. However, there are a few rocks, such as limestone, that are composed of just one mineral. Then there are rocks that are not made up of minerals at all. For example, obsidian and pumice, shown in **Figure 1,** are made of natural glass. Glass does not have a crystalline structure, so it is not considered a mineral. Coal, which is made of organic material, is another example of a nonmineral rock.

Rocks vary widely in appearance, texture, and composition. They are classified into one of three categories based on how they form. **The three major types of rock are igneous, sedimentary, and metamorphic.** The **rock cycle** summarizes how each of these rock types form and also describes how they can be transformed from one type to another.

☑ **Reading Checkpoint** *What are the three types of rocks?*

The Rock Cycle

The phrase "like a rock" is used to describe something as unchanging. But rocks are in fact always changing as they interact with Earth systems. **The rock cycle is a model that describes the ways in which rocks transform from one type to another.** The processes involved in the rock cycle do not follow a particular order. The following describes just one possible path through the cycle.

We will begin our discussion of the rock cycle deep underground with melted rock called **magma.** You are likely more familiar with **lava,** which is magma that reaches Earth's surface. When magma or lava cools, it crystallizes and forms igneous rock. **Igneous rocks form from cooled magma or lava.**

When exposed at Earth's surface, rocks such as the igneous rock shown in **Figure 2** undergo a process called weathering. **Weathering** is the breakdown of rock. Weathering can be caused by physical or chemical processes. Loose bits of weathered rock are called **sediment.** Sediment is often picked up and moved, or eroded, and then dropped, or deposited, in a new location by water, wind, glaciers, or gravity. Once deposited, pressure exerted over time on the sediments may turn them into sedimentary rock through a process known as *lithification.* **Sedimentary rocks form from layers of weathered, eroded, and deposited sediment.**

Heat, pressure, and fluids can act to change a rock's structure and composition. This process, called *metamorphism,* is usually associated with mountain building. **Metamorphic rocks form when preexisting rocks are altered by pressure, heat, and/or fluids.** If exposed to extreme enough pressure and temperature, rocks may melt to form magma, and the cycle begins again. The rock cycle is summarized in **Figure 3** on the next page.

FIGURE 2 Exposed *El Capitan* is a huge piece of granite in Yosemite National Park that was once buried deep beneath Earth's surface. Now that it is exposed, it weathers and forms sediments.

Rocks **67**

Build Reading Literacy · L1

Refer to **p. 186D** in **Chapter 7,** which provides the guidelines for relating text and visuals.

Relate Text and Visuals Have students read the text on p. 67 and then look at the rock cycle in Figure 3 on p. 68. Have them list parts of the rock cycle that are difficult to understand. Write a few of these concepts on the board. Then have students carefully study Figure 3. Using the list on the board, have volunteers explain how the visual helped them understand the rock cycle. **Verbal, Visual**

Answers

☑ **Reading Checkpoint** *Igneous rocks, sedimentary rocks, and metamorphic rocks are the three major types of rocks.*

Differentiated Instruction

ENGLISH LANGUAGE LEARNERS Encourage students to compile vocabulary terms into a science glossary. Have students consult dictionaries to obtain the pronunciation and definition of each term and then write these items in their glossaries. Model how to use the dictionary to determine the proper pronunciation of difficult words, such as *igneous* or *metamorphic.* Students may also want to draw simple diagrams next to the terms to further help them to remember each word's meaning. To reinforce language skills, have students arrange the terms in alphabetical order.

LESSON 3.1

WEATHERING   **L2**

Purpose Students will observe how ice can be an agent of weathering.

Materials 2-L plastic bottle with cap, water

Procedure Fill the plastic bottle nearly full with water and put on the cap. Have students note the level of the water. Place the bottle in the freezer for several hours, then have students observe the frozen water.

Expected Outcomes Students will observe how the ice expanded and distorted the bottle. Tell them that in a similar way, water can seep through cracks and pores in rocks, then freeze and expand to break apart the rocks.
Visual

Use Visuals   **L1**

Figure 3 Point out that the arrows represent the processes that link each group to the others. **Ask:** What processes form sedimentary rocks? *(weathering, erosion, deposition, and lithification)* What possible changes might a sedimentary rock undergo? *(A sedimentary rock might be broken back down into sediment. Heat and pressure could change it into a metamorphic rock.)* What type of rock is formed by cooling magma or lava? *(igneous rock)* What happens to igneous rock that is weathered? *(It is broken down into sediment.)*
Visual

Build Science Skills   **L2**

Student Activity: Use Models Have students work with a partner to design simple models that show how pressure affects rocks. For example, students can place a heavy textbook on a sandwich or squeeze a piece of modeling clay between their hands.
Kinesthetic, Interpersonal

Alternate Paths

So far, we have described just one path through the rock cycle, as shown with the purple arrows below: Ⓐ Magma or lava cools to form igneous rock. Ⓑ Igneous rock is weathered, eroded, and deposited as sediment. Ⓒ Sediment is lithified forming layers of sedimentary rock. Ⓓ Sedimentary rock is metamorphosed, forming metamorphic rock, such as the slate in **Figure 4.** Ⓔ Metamorphic rock melts, resulting in magma and lava.

VISUAL SUMMARY

ROCK CYCLE

FIGURE 3 Rocks are constantly changing from one form to another through the processes of the rock cycle, shown as lettered arrows in the figure.
*Infer **Why do most sedimentary rocks form near or in water?***

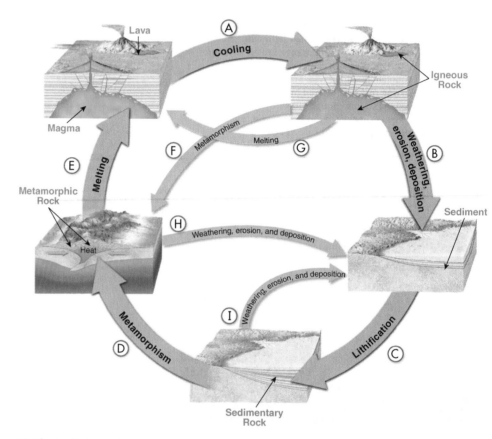

Facts and Figures

Some of the most important accumulations of metals, such as gold, silver, copper, mercury, lead, native platinum, and nickel, are produced by igneous and metamorphic processes. For example, as a large magma body cools, the heavy minerals that crystallize early tend to settle to the lower portion of the magma chamber. This type of process is particularly active in large basaltic magmas where chromite, magnetite, and platinum are occasionally generated. Layers of chromite, an ore of chromium, are mined from such deposits in the Bushveld Complex in South Africa, which contains more than 70 percent of the world's known platinum reserves.

There is not just one path through the cycle, however. The green arrows in Figure 3 show some alternative paths between rock types that are just as likely to occur: Ⓕ Igneous rock is buried and metamorphosed, forming metamorphic rock. Ⓖ Given high enough pressures and temperatures, igneous rock can even melt to form magma and lava. Ⓗ Metamorphic and Ⓘ sedimentary rock are weathered and eroded when exposed at the surface. The deposited sediments can then form sedimentary rock. ⌖ **The processes of melting, cooling, weathering, erosion, deposition, and lithification can transform any type of rock into another.**

These processes are unending. Today, for example, magma under the island of Hawaii is cooling to form igneous rock. As plates collide on the western coast of South America, intense heat and pressure are transforming areas of continental crust to metamorphic rock. In the American west, sediments that were once part of the Rocky Mountains are settling in the Gulf of Mexico and may one day form new layers of sedimentary rock.

FIGURE 4 Slate The roof on this house is made of slate. Slate is a metamorphic rock that forms from the sedimentary rock shale.
Interpret Diagrams *What process turns shale to slate?*

3.1 Assessment

Review Key Concepts ⌖

1. What is a rock?

2. What are the three major types of rocks?

3. How do igneous, sedimentary, and metamorphic rocks differ?

4. What is the rock cycle?

5. What processes are involved in the rock cycle?

Think Critically

6. Compare and Contrast Compare and contrast igneous and metamorphic rocks.

7. Apply Concepts How might a sedimentary rock become an igneous rock?

8. Apply Concepts List in order the processes that could change one sedimentary rock into another sedimentary rock.

BIGIDEA EARTH'S MATERIALS AND SYSTEMS

9. Explain Use your understanding of the rock cycle to explain this statement: *One rock is the raw material for another rock.*

Rocks **69**

Use Community Resources L2

Invite a construction contractor to discuss with the class how various rocks are used as building materials. Ask the contractor to bring in sample supplies for students to examine. Have students prepare by brainstorming questions to ask the contractor about the different qualities of rocks, such as durability and strength.
Verbal

❸ ASSESS

Evaluate Understanding L2

Have students draw sketches illustrating the source of the energy that drives the rock cycle. For example, to represent the interior processes that form igneous rocks, a sketch might show molten material deep inside Earth.

Reteach L2

Use Figure 3 to draw a diagram of the rock cycle that does not include arrows. Make copies of the diagram and distribute it to students. Have students add arrows showing the relationships among the processes of the rock cycle.

Answers

Figure 3 *Because running water carries sediment.*

Figure 4 *metamorphism*

Assessment Answers

1. A solid mass of minerals or mineral-like materials

2. igneous rocks, sedimentary rocks, and metamorphic rocks

3. Rocks differ in the way they form. Igneous rocks form when magma or lava cools and solidifies. Sedimentary rocks form when sediment is compacted and cemented. Metamorphic rocks form when existing rocks are changed by heat, pressure, or solutions.

4. A model that summarizes how each type of rock forms and how they can be transformed from one type to another

5. weathering, erosion, deposition, lithification, metamorphism, melting, and cooling

6. Both form as the result of increases in pressure or temperature. Igneous rock formation involves melting, while the formation of metamorphic rocks does not.

7. The sedimentary rock could become buried at depths where temperatures and pressures were great enough to cause melting. When the melted material (magma) cooled and hardened, an igneous rock would form.

8. weathering, erosion, deposition, and lithification

9. Igneous rocks form from magma, which can be produced when any type of rock melts. Sedimentary rocks form as the result of changes in igneous, sedimentary, or metamorphic rocks. Likewise, metamorphic rocks form when any type of rock is changed by heat, pressure, and/or fluids.

Rocks **69**

❶ FOCUS

Lesson Objectives
3.5 **Compare and contrast** intrusive and extrusive igneous rocks.
3.6 **Explain** how the rate of cooling affects an igneous rock's texture.
3.7 **Classify** igneous rocks according to texture and composition.

Build Vocabulary   L2
Word Parts To help students distinguish between intrusive and extrusive rocks, have them look up the meanings of the prefixes *in-* and *ex-*. Students will find that both prefixes stem from Latin terms. *In-* means "within or into"; *ex-* means "out of" or "outside." Point out that by knowing the meaning of these prefixes, students can better remember which igneous rocks form "within" Earth and which form "outside," or on, Earth's surface.

Reading Strategy   L2
A.1. rock that forms when magma hardens beneath Earth's surface
A.2. Common example of igneous intrusive rock is granite.
B.1. rock that forms when lava hardens
B.2. Common example of igneous extrusive rock is rhyolite.

❷ INSTRUCT

Build Science Skills   L2

Infer Reiterate that magma, which occurs beneath Earth's surface, often cools more slowly than lava, which occurs at Earth's surface. Then have students examine Figure 5. Ask them to use the photograph to infer why lava often cools more quickly than magma. *(Lava is exposed to air and water, which speeds up its cooling rate.)*
Logical

Key Questions

🔑 **How are intrusive and extrusive igneous rocks alike and different?**

🔑 **How does the rate of cooling affect an igneous rock's texture?**

🔑 **How are igneous rocks classified according to composition?**

Vocabulary

- intrusive igneous rock
- extrusive igneous rock
- texture
- granitic composition
- basaltic composition
- andesitic composition

Reading Strategy

Outline Copy the outline and complete it as you read. Include points about how each of these rocks form, some of the characteristics of each rock type, and some examples of each.

```
I. Igneous Rocks
   A. Intrusive Rocks
      1. ____?____
      2. ____?____
   B. Extrusive Rocks
      1. ____?____
      2. ____?____
```

IGNEOUS ROCKS are sometimes called *volcanic rocks*. Recall from the discussion of the rock cycle that igneous rocks form when magma or lava cools and hardens. When the red hot lava shown in **Figure 5** cools, a dark-colored igneous rock called basalt will form. When magma instead cools deep beneath Earth's surface, a very different kind of igneous rock forms. Why?

Formation of Igneous Rocks

The word *igneous* comes from the Latin word *ignis*, which means "fire." While some igneous rock does form at the surface after fiery volcanic eruptions, most forms from magma deep beneath the surface. Geologists describe igneous rocks as either intrusive or extrusive based on where they form.

FIGURE 5 Basaltic Lava Lava from this Hawaiian volcano flows easily over Earth's surface. When the lava cools and hardens, the igneous rock called basalt will form.

FIGURE 6 Igneous Rocks There are two basic ways igneous rocks form.

A Granite, an intrusive igneous rock, forms when magma cools beneath Earth's surface.

B Rhyolite is an extrusive igneous rock that forms when lava cools at Earth's surface.

Intrusive Igneous Rocks Magma is mostly made of oxygen and silicon, with lesser amounts of elements such as aluminum, iron, calcium, sodium, potassium, and magnesium. Magma also contains gases, such as water vapor, that contribute to its relatively low density. Because magma is less dense than the surrounding rock, it slowly works its way to the surface. Most of the time, magma cools and crystallizes before reaching the surface. **Igneous rocks formed from magma beneath Earth's surface are known as intrusive igneous rocks.** Occasionally, intrusive igneous rocks are exposed when overlying rocks are stripped away by weathering and erosion. Mount Rushmore in South Dakota is carved out of exposed granite, an intrusive igneous rock. A sample of granite is shown in **Figure 6A.**

Extrusive Igneous Rocks When magma manages to reach Earth's surface, most of the gases it contains escape. The substance is now called lava. **Igneous rocks formed from lava at Earth's surface are called extrusive igneous rocks.** Extrusive igneous rocks, such as rhyolite, shown in **Figure 6B,** are common in places such as Iceland, which has many active volcanoes.

Classification of Igneous Rocks

Igneous rocks are classified based on more than just where they formed. **Texture and composition together are used to classify igneous rocks.**

Texture A rock's **texture** describes the size, shape, and arrangement of its component parts. The rate of cooling strongly affects an igneous rock's texture. **Slow cooling causes large crystals to form, while rapid cooling results in small crystals.** Why does the rate of cooling affect texture? If molten material cools very slowly, as it tends to do deep beneath Earth's surface, its ions can move over large distances without combining. This results in only a few centers of crystal growth. As they cool, each crystal can grow quite large. When molten material cools quickly, as it tends to do at Earth's surface, its ions quickly lose their motion and combine. This results in a large number of tiny crystals that all compete for space.

PLANET DIARY

For an activity about **Igneous Rocks** visit PlanetDiary.com/HSES

INQUIRY
APPLY IT!

Q: How are magma and lava the same, and how are they different?

A: Both magma and lava are melted rock and their mineral composition may be identical. However, magma is melted material beneath Earth's surface. Lava is melted material at Earth's surface from which most gases have escaped.

LESSON 3.2

Teacher **Demo**

CRYSTAL FORMATION **L2**

Purpose Students will observe how the rate of cooling affects crystal size.

Caution This demonstration should be done in a fume hood or area with very good ventilation. Sulfur fumes can adversely affect students with respiratory problems.

Materials 2 shallow pans, 250-mL beaker, water, teaspoon, sulfur powder, thermal mitt, hot plate, magnifying glass

Procedure Put a teaspoon of sulfur powder into a shallow pan. Heat the pan until the sulfur melts, then place it aside to cool slowly. Heat another teaspoon of sulfur powder in a second shallow pan. Pour the melted sulfur into a beaker half-filled with water so that the sulfur cools quickly. Allow students to view the resulting crystals from both trials with a magnifying glass.

Expected Outcome Students will observe that cooling rates affect the size of crystals— the sulfur that cooled slowly formed larger crystals than the sulfur that cooled quickly.
Visual

Build Reading Literacy **L1**

Refer to **p. 362D** in **Chapter 13,** which provides the guidelines for using prior knowledge.

Use Prior Knowledge Ask students what they think of when they hear the word *texture*. Students will likely say that texture refers to the way an object feels to the touch. Ask them to describe some textures they have felt. *(Sample answers: rough, smooth, sticky, powdery)* Explain that the geologic meaning of *texture* in this lesson refers to the overall appearance of a rock based on the size, shape, and arrangement of its component parts.
Intrapersonal, Verbal

FIGURE 7 Porphyritic Texture
This sample of andesite has a porphyritic texture. Note the large, light-colored crystals surrounded by darker, smaller ones. Describe *How did this rock form?*

▶ *Coarse-Grained and Fine-Grained Texture* Look back at the igneous rocks in Figure 6. The granite, which formed deep underground, has large mineral grains. The rhyolite, which formed at the surface, has grains so small you cannot see them without a magnifying lens. Igneous rocks with large crystals, such as granite, are said to have *coarse-grained texture*. Igneous rocks with small grains, such as rhyolite, are said to have *fine-grained texture*.

▶ *Glassy Texture* Sometimes, lava cools so rapidly at Earth's surface that there is not enough time for the ions to combine and arrange themselves into a network of crystals. Instead, the hardened rock has a random, non-crystalline arrangement of atoms. Igneous rocks formed in this way are said to have a *glassy texture*. Look back at Figure 1. Obsidian is a common, glassy igneous rock that looks like manufactured, dark-colored glass. Pumice, another common, glassy igneous rock, has a very nonglassy appearance due to the presence of escaping gases at the time of formation.

▶ *Porphyritic Texture* Not all minerals crystallize at the same rate. During the slow cooling process beneath the surface of Earth, it is possible for some minerals to form large crystals before other minerals even begin the crystallization process. But what would happen if this mixture of magma and crystals suddenly erupted to the surface? The remaining molten material would cool rapidly around the larger crystals. The resulting rock would have some very large crystals, called *phenocrysts,* surrounded by more fine-grained minerals. Rocks formed by slow and then rapid cooling, such as the andesite in **Figure 7,** are said to have *porphyritic texture*.

☑ **Reading Checkpoint** *How does the rate of cooling of magma or lava affect the texture of igneous rocks?*

Composition Recall that magma contains silicon, oxygen, and smaller amounts of many other elements. As magma and lava cool, their minerals combine to form silicate minerals. Magma and lava that are rich in potassium, sodium, and calcium form light silicates such as quartz, muscovite mica, and feldspars. Magma and lava rich in iron and/or magnesium form dark silicates such as olivine, pyroxenes (such as augite), amphiboles (such as hornblende), and biotite mica. **The relative amounts of light and dark silicates within an igneous rock define its composition.**

▶ *Granitic Composition* Igneous rocks with **granitic composition** are generally light-colored, containing just about 10 to 25 percent dark silicate minerals. Granitic rocks are primarily composed of quartz and feldspars. Granitic rocks are named for granite, a common, coarse-grained granitic rock. Much of the continental crust is made of granite. Rhyolite is an example of a fine-grained granitic rock. Granitic rocks are sometime described as *felsic,* a combination of the words *fel*dspar and *si*lica.

▶ **Basaltic Composition** Igneous rocks with **basaltic composition** contain at least 45 percent magnesium and iron-rich dark silicates, making them generally dark-colored and dense. Basalt, which has a fine-grained texture, is the most common basaltic rock. Most of the ocean floor is made of basalt. Gabbro is a coarse-grained basaltic rock. Basaltic rocks are sometimes described as *mafic*, a term derived from the minerals *m*agnesium and *f*errum, the Latin name for iron.

▶ **Andesitic Composition** Igneous rocks with an intermediate composition between granitic and basaltic are said to have an **andesitic composition**. Andesitic rocks contain 25 to 45 percent dark silicate minerals. Andesitic composition is named for the common, fine-grained volcanic rock andesite. Diorite is a coarse-grained andesitic rock.

To summarize, igneous rocks form when magma or lava cools and hardens. Intrusive igneous rocks form when magma cools and hardens deep within Earth. These rocks tend to have a coarse-grained texture. Extrusive igneous rocks form when lava cools and hardens on Earth's surface. These rocks tend to have a fine-grained texture. The balance of elements present in the magma or lava upon cooling determines an igneous rock's mineral composition. Together, texture and composition are used to classify igneous rocks. A general classification scheme is shown in **Table 1** on the next page.

FIGURE 8 Basaltic Composition Basalt is an igneous rock made mostly of dark-colored silicate minerals. **Infer** *Basalt has a fine-grained texture. What can you infer about the rate of cooling at its formation?*

Integrate Chemistry L2

In the early twentieth century, N. L. Bowen, a geologist, discovered that as magma cools, certain minerals crystallize first at very high temperatures. At successively lower temperatures, other minerals form. Bowen also demonstrated that if a mineral remains in the molten solution after crystallization, it will react with the remaining liquid to produce the next mineral, in a sequence known as Bowen's reaction series. Have students research Bowen's reaction series and compare it with Table 1 on p. 74. **Ask:** What do you notice about the minerals that make up the rocks? *(Each rock group consists of minerals that crystallize in the same temperature range.)* **Logical, Visual**

Answers

Figure 7 *The rock experienced at least two episodes of cooling. Slow cooling resulted in the larger mineral grains. Rapid cooling produced the fine-grained minerals.*

Figure 8 *It cooled quickly.*

☑ **Reading Checkpoint** *A slowly cooling magma or lava will produce rocks in which the mineral grains are relatively large. Quickly cooling molten material will result in rocks with small mineral grains. Lava that cools extremely rapidly will produce a glassy rock. Rocks that form as the result of different cooling rates will have both large and small mineral grains.*

Facts and Figures

Magma is basically a very hot, thick liquid, but it also contains solids and gases. The solids are mineral crystals. The liquid portion of the magma body is composed of ions that move about freely. However, as magma cools, the random movements of the ions slow, and the ions begin to arrange themselves into orderly patterns. This process is called crystallization. Usually not all of the molten material solidifies at the same time. Rather, as it cools, numerous small crystals develop. In a systematic fashion, ions are added to these centers of crystal growth. When the crystals grow large enough for their edges to meet, their growth ceases for lack of space, and crystallization continues elsewhere. Eventually, all of the liquid is transformed into a solid mass of interlocking crystals.

LESSON 3.2

Use Visuals

Table 1 Make sure all students can clearly read the table. If necessary, make enlarged copies of the table for students. **Ask:** Which rocks have the highest percentage of dark minerals? *(basaltic rocks)* Identify a coarse-grained basaltic rock. *(gabbro)* Approximately what percent of an andesitic rock is made of dark minerals? *(25% to 45%)*
Visual

3 ASSESS

Evaluate Understanding   L2

Using Table 1 as a guide, have each student make two tables. One table should show the different textures of igneous rocks. The second table should show the composition of igneous rocks.

Reteach   L1

Use a simple graphic to help summarize the relationship between cooling rate and crystal size in igneous rocks. For example, draw an arrow pointing upward on the board. Label the arrow "Cooling rate." **Ask:** As the rate of cooling increases, what happens to crystal size? *(It decreases.)* To illustrate the answer, draw a downward-pointing arrow next to the first arrow. Label this second arrow "Crystal size."

Table 1 Classification of Major Igneous Rocks

Composition		Granitic	Andesitic	Basaltic
Dominant Minerals		Light silicates	Light and dark silicates	Dark silicates
T E X T U R E Coarse-grained (intrusive)		Granite	Diorite	Gabbro
Fine-grained (extrusive)		Rhyolite	Andesite	Basalt
Porphyritic		"Porphyritic" precedes any of the above names whenever there are appreciable phenocrysts.		
Glassy		Obsidian (compact glass) Pumice (frothy glass)		
Rock Color (based on % of dark minerals)		0% to 25%	25% to 45%	45% to 85%

3.2 Assessment

Review Key Concepts

1. Compare and contrast the formation of intrusive and extrusive igneous rocks.

2. How do coarse-grained igneous rocks form?

3. How are igneous rocks classified according to composition?

4. How do fine-grained igneous rocks form?

5. How do igneous rocks with porphyritic textures form?

Think Critically

6. **Contrast** Contrast basalt and granite in terms of how each forms, the texture of each rock, the color of each rock, and each rock's composition.

7. **Form a Hypothesis** The extrusive igneous rock pumice contains many small holes. Hypothesize how these holes might form.

WRITING IN SCIENCE

8. **Explain** Write a paragraph to explain how one of the igneous rocks pictured in this chapter may have formed.

Assessment Answers

1. Both types of rocks form when molten material cools and solidifies. Intrusive igneous rocks form when magma cools and solidifies deep beneath Earth's surface. Extrusive igneous rocks form when lava cools and hardens at or near Earth's surface.

2. Coarse-grained igneous rocks form when magma or lava cools slowly.

3. Igneous rocks are classified by the relative amounts of light and dark silicate minerals they contain.

4. Fine-grained igneous rocks form when lava or magma cools quickly.

5. Igneous rocks with porphyritic texture form when slowly-cooling magma is exposed to new conditions where it finishes cooling much more rapidly.

6. Granite forms as magma slowly cools below the surface. This slow rate of cooling produces large mineral grains. Most of these minerals are quartz and feldspar, thus granite is light-colored, with a granitic composition. Basalt forms when lava or magma cools quickly. This quick cooling rate results in very small mineral grains. The major minerals in

basalt are dark-colored silicates that give basalt its dark color. A basalt has a basaltic composition.

7. Lava is magma that reaches the surface. As it rises, reduced pressure on the magma causes some of its gases to come out of solution. These gases form bubbles or holes as the molten material cools.

8. Sample answer: Obsidian likely formed when lava reached Earth's surface and cooled very rapidly. Refer to the text and Table 1 to evaluate students' answers.

3.3 Sedimentary Rocks

GEOLOGISTS ESTIMATE that 90 to 95 percent of the outer 16 kilometers (10 miles) of Earth's crust is either igneous or metamorphic rock. However, most of Earth's solid surface, including nearly the entire ocean floor, is covered in sediment or sedimentary rock. Because of their position at or near Earth's surface, sediments and sedimentary rock contain evidence of past conditions and events. As we will see, this group of rocks provides geologists with much of the basic information they need to reconstruct details of Earth's history.

FIGURE 9 Rocks That Tell Tales Geologists can infer a lot about past environmental conditions from these sedimentary rocks in Canyonlands National Park, Utah.

Key Questions

🔑 *What are the major processes involved in the formation of sedimentary rocks?*

🔑 *What are the three types of sedimentary rocks?*

🔑 *What features are unique to some sedimentary rocks?*

Vocabulary

- erosion • deposition
- compaction • cementation
- clastic sedimentary rock
- chemical sedimentary rock
- biochemical sedimentary rock

Reading Strategy

Outline Copy this outline beneath the outline you made for Lesson 2. Complete this outline as you read. Include points about how each of these rocks form, some of the characteristics of each rock type, and some examples of each.

II. Sedimentary Rocks
  A. Clastic Rocks
    1. ____?____
    2. ____?____
  B. Chemical Rocks
    1. ____?____
    2. ____?____
  C. Biochemical Rocks
    1. ____?____
    2. ____?____

1 FOCUS

Lesson Objectives
3.8 **Describe** the major processes involved in the formation of sedimentary rocks.
3.9 **Distinguish** between clastic, chemical, and biochemical sedimentary rocks.
3.10 **Identify** the features that are unique to some sedimentary rocks.

Build Vocabulary L2
LINCS Have students **L**ist the parts of the vocabulary words that they know. For example, *cement* is part of *cementation*. Next, they should **I**magine a mental picture of the term's meaning and describe the image in their own words. Sediments held together by cement might be an image for cementation. Students should then make a **N**ote of a familiar "sound-alike" word. They can **C**onnect the terms by making up a short story about the meaning of the term that incorporates the sound-alike word. Lastly, students should conduct a **S**elf-test by quizzing themselves on the vocabulary terms.

Reading Strategy L2
A.1. rock made up of weathered bits of rocks and minerals
A.2. Common example of clastic sedimentary rock is shale.
B.1. rock that forms when dissolved minerals precipitate from water
B.2. Common example of chemical sedimentary rock is halite.
C.1. Rock that forms from sediments that result from biological processes.
C.2. Common example of biochemical sedimentary rock is limestone.

LESSON 3.3

🟦 INSTRUCT

Build Reading Literacy　🟦L1

Refer to **p. 64D** in **Chapter 3,** which provides the guidelines for directed reading/thinking activity (DRTA).

DRTA Before students read this lesson, have them preview the key concepts, vocabulary terms, and headings. **Ask:** What do you think you will learn in this lesson? *(Sample answer: about the different kinds of sedimentary rocks, how they form, and what they look like)* What type of questions might a teacher ask about this topic? *(Sample answer: How do sedimentary rocks form? How are sedimentary rocks classified?)* List these questions on the board. As students read the lesson, pause to discuss the answers to the questions.
Verbal

⬭ Address **Misconceptions**　🟦L2

Some students may think that rocks are stronger than the agents of mechanical and chemical weathering. To help dispel this misconception, place a few drops of vinegar on a sample of limestone. Have students observe the resulting chemical reaction. **Ask:** What do you think would happen if the acid continued to drip on the rock over a long period? *(The rock would eventually break down or be chemically weathered.)*
Visual, Logical

Build Science Skills　🟦L2

Student Activity: Observe Provide small groups of students with 250-mL beakers, stirrers, sand, water, gravel, and soil. Tell students to half-fill the beakers with water. They should then pour about a handful of each material into the water. Have them stir the mixture, then observe what happens to the materials. **Ask:** Which materials settled on the bottom? Which settled on the top? *(The heavier materials settled on the bottom; the smaller, lighter materials settled on the top.)* What does this activity model? *(the settling out of sediments from a fluid, such as water or air)*
Kinesthetic, Visual

FIGURE 10 Different, Yet the Same Although these two rocks appear quite different, both **A** conglomerate and **B** sandstone are formed by the same processes of weathering, erosion, deposition, compaction, and cementation.

Formation of Sedimentary Rocks

Look at the rocks shown in **Figure 10.** Without doing any research, how would you say they formed? The rock in Figure 10A looks like a bunch of pebbles dropped into a pile of wet sand that then hardened, doesn't it? The rock in 10B just looks like sand that hardened into rock. As it turns out, that is pretty much exactly what happened.

Weathering, Erosion, and Deposition Recall that weathering is any process that breaks down rock. Chemical weathering occurs when the minerals in rocks change into new substances. For example, when oxygen combines with iron, it forms a crumbly layer of iron oxide, or rust, on a rock's surface. Physical weathering is sometimes called mechanical weathering because it occurs when rocks are broken down mechanically. For example, when a tree root forces its way into bedrock, it pushes pieces of rock apart. This type of weathering does not involve a change in a rock's composition.

Weathered sediments do not usually remain in one place for long. 🔑 **Erosion is the picking up and carrying away of sediments.** Usually, sediments are broken down further during this transport phase. When an agent of erosion, such as water, wind, ice, or gravity, loses energy, it drops off its sediment load. This process is called **deposition.** The word *sedimentary* is derived from the Latin word *sedimentum*, meaning "settling." As an agent of erosion slows down, sediments are deposited according to size, with larger sediments settling out before smaller ones.

Compaction and Cementation From studying the rock cycle, we know that deposited sediments can be lithified, or turned into rock. There are two processes involved in lithification: compaction and cementation. 🔑 **Compaction is a process that squeezes, or compacts, sediments.** Compaction is caused by the weight of sediments as they pile on top of each other in layers. The deeper those sediments are buried, the more they are compacted and the firmer they become. During compaction, most of the water between sediment particles is driven out. However, the water leaves behind the minerals it contained. These minerals essentially glue the sediments together. 🔑 **Cementation takes place when dissolved minerals are deposited in the tiny spaces among sediments, binding them together into a solid mass.**

☑ **Reading Checkpoint** *Briefly describe the five major processes involved in the formation of sedimentary rocks.*

Differentiated Instruction

ENGLISH LANGUAGE LEARNERS Compile a classroom library using up-to-date magazines and newspaper articles. Select reading materials that correspond to chapter content. For example, try to find articles that discuss different types of rocks. Avoid academic journals and reference materials with high reading levels. Provide opportunities for ELL students to read the articles in class. This will give them a broader context in which to place this chapter's vocabulary terms and key concepts.

Classification of Sedimentary Rocks

Sandstone, halite (rock salt), and coal are all sedimentary rocks in that they are made of accumulated sediments. However, they each belong to a separate sedimentary rock category because the origin of their sediments differs. ⊂⊃ **Sedimentary rocks are classified into three groups—clastic, chemical, and biochemical.**

Clastic Sedimentary Rocks You are likely most familiar with **clastic sedimentary rocks,** rocks made of sediments that come from preexisting rocks. Many different kinds of minerals are found in clastic sedimentary rocks. The most common are clay minerals and quartz. Clastic sedimentary rocks are further classified according to the size of their sediments. If a rock has sediments that are pebble-sized (2 mm or larger), it is either a conglomerate or a breccia. Conglomerates, such as the one in Figure 10A, have large, rounded sediments. Breccias, such as the one in **Figure 11A,** have large, angular sediments. Angular sediments indicate that the particles have not traveled far enough away from their source to have their corners and rough edges smoothed during transport. Rocks with primarily sand-sized sediments (1/16–2 mm) are called sandstone, and rocks with primarily silt-sized sediments (1/256–1/16 mm) are called siltstones. Shales, such as the one in **Figure 11B,** are made up of very fine, clay-sized (< 1/256 mm) sediments.

Particle size provides useful information about the environment in which the sediment was deposited. The larger the particle size, the more energy required to carry it. Pebbles, for example, are moved by swiftly flowing rivers, rockslides, and glaciers. Less energy is required to move sand and silt. Moreover, recall that sediments settle according to size. If an agent of erosion, such as a river, is carrying sediments of various sizes, the smallest sediments will settle last. So, when a river meets the ocean and begins to deposit its load, the smallest sediments will be deposited the farthest offshore.

Chemical Sedimentary Rocks Rocks made of dissolved sediments that precipitate, or separate, directly from water are called **chemical sedimentary rocks.** Precipitation usually occurs when water evaporates, leaving once-dissolved solids behind. Rock salt is a chemical rock that forms when the mineral halite precipitates from sea water. You can model halite formation by leaving a container of salt water outside in the sun. Over time, the water will evaporate, leaving the salt behind. When dissolved calcite precipitates directly from water, it forms chemical limestones.

☑ **Reading Checkpoint** *Describe the major types of clastic sedimentary rocks.*

FIGURE 11 Clastic Sedimentary Rocks A Breccia and **B** shale are common clastic sedimentary rocks. Infer *Did the shale seen here most likely form in a terrestrial (land) environment or an aquatic environment? Explain.*

LESSON 3.3

Build Science Skills L2

Student Activity: **Experiments**
Have students work in small groups to design an experiment to show how sedimentary rocks form when dissolved minerals precipitate from water. Students should develop a hypothesis and procedure, listing controls, safety measures, and materials to be used. A sample experiment might involve placing table salt in water, then heating the water until it evaporates. If time permits, allow students to carry out their experiments.
Logical, Interpersonal

Use Visuals L1

Figure 13 Ask: Based on its appearance, what can you infer about the rock labeled A? *(It may have formed along a beach or stream bed.)* What can you infer about the rock labeled B? *(It may have formed when wet mud or clay dried and shrank.)*
Visual

FIGURE 12 Biochemical Sedimentary Rock You can see shell fragments that make up this piece of coarse limestone, called coquina.

Biochemical Sedimentary Rocks Rocks made of sediments derived from biological processes are called *organic rocks,* or **biochemical sedimentary rocks.** Living organisms take up dissolved minerals and use them to form their hard and soft tissues. When the organisms die, their bodies are broken down and turned to sediments that can turn to rock. Examples of biochemical rocks include limestone, which is formed primarily from the shells of marine organisms, and coal, which is made up of the remains of swamp plants. Coquina, a type of limestone, is shown in **Figure 12.**

Sedimentary Rock Features

Because sedimentary rocks form at Earth's surface, they often contain clues about past environmental conditions. **Unique features of sedimentary rocks include strata, fossils, ripple marks, and mud cracks. These features indicate how, when, and where the rocks formed.** Sedimentary rock forms in layers called *strata.* Each layer records a period of deposition. Thus, unless disturbed, sedimentary rocks closer to the surface are younger than those that are buried deeper.

Knowing the relative age of sedimentary rock layers can be particularly helpful when the rocks contain fossils. A *fossil* is the remains or trace of ancient life. Only sedimentary rocks contain fossils. In general, a fossil forms when an organism is quickly buried by sediment and then preserved in some way as the sediment is turned to rock. Fossils play a key role in matching up rocks of similar age that are found in different places. You will learn more about this in a later chapter.

Sediments may also preserve information about the environment in which they formed. Ripple marks, like those in **Figure 13A,** indicate that the rock formed in the presence of moving water. Mud cracks, like those in **Figure 13B,** indicate that the rock formed as sediments were drying.

FIGURE 13 Water or No Water? A Ripple marks and **B** mud cracks are features of sedimentary rocks that can be used to learn about the environments in which the rocks formed.

Facts and Figures

When coal is viewed under a magnifying glass, chemically altered leaves, bark, and wood are visible. The materials provide evidence that coal is the end product of the burial of large amounts of plant materials over long periods of time. The initial stage of coal formation is the accumulation of large quantities of plant remains in a swampy environment. Coal then undergoes successive stages of formation. With each stage, higher temperatures and pressures drive off impurities and volatiles, leaving more solid carbon behind.

To summarize, sedimentary rocks form through the processes of erosion, weathering, deposition, compaction, and cementation. Based on the origin of their sediments, there are three basic types: clastic, chemical, and biochemical. Their unique features such as strata, fossils, ripple marks, and mud cracks give clues to when, how, and where they formed.

Table 2 Classification of Major Sedimentary Rocks

Clastic Sedimentary Rocks				Chemical Sedimentary Rocks	
Sediment Type	Sediment size		Rock Name	Composition	Rock Name
Pebble (rounded)	>2 mm		Conglomerate	Calcite (CaCO₃)	Chemical limestone
Pebble (angular)			Breccia	Halite (NaCl)	Rock salt
Sand	1/16 to 2 mm		Sandstone	**Biochemical Sedimentary Rocks**	
Silt	1/16 to 1/256 mm		Siltstone	Composition	Rock Name
Clay	<1/256 mm		Shale	Calcite (CaCO₃)	Biochemical limestone
				Plant remains	Coal

3.3 Assessment

Review Key Concepts 🔑

1. Contrast weathering, erosion, and deposition.

2. Name four clastic sedimentary rocks and explain how these rocks form.

3. What is the difference between a clastic sedimentary rock and a chemical sedimentary rock?

4. Explain how three different features of sedimentary rocks can be used to determine how, where, or when the rocks formed.

5. What is compaction?

6. Where do the cements that hold sediments together come from?

Think Critically

7. Apply Concepts Briefly describe how the rock shown in Figure 12 may have formed.

8. Predict Which type of sediments do you think would undergo more compaction—grains of sand or grains of clay? Explain your choice.

9. Draw Conclusions Suppose you found a sedimentary rock with ripple marks. What could you conclude about the rock?

CONNECTING CONCEPTS

10. Research Choose one of the sedimentary rocks pictured in this section. Find out how the rock is useful to people.

Rocks **79**

Rocks **79**

LESSON 3.4

1 FOCUS

Lesson Objectives
3.11 **Predict** where most metamorphism takes place.
3.12 **Distinguish** contact metamorphism from regional metamorphism.
3.13 **Identify** the three agents of metamorphism and **explain** what changes they cause.
3.14 **Recognize** foliated metamorphic rocks and **describe** how they form.
3.15 **Classify** metamorphic rocks.

Build Vocabulary　L2
Paraphrase Explain vocabulary terms using words students know. For example, *contact metamorphism* occurs when two rocks come into contact with one another. *Regional metamorphism* takes place over a large region. *Foliated metamorphic rocks* have distinct layers. *Nonfoliated metamorphic rocks* do not. Once students are able to distinguish among the vocabulary terms, focus on the processes that cause the different types of metamorphism and the different types of metamorphic rock.

Reading Strategy　L2
A.1. rock that forms when minerals recrystallize at right angles to the direction of pressure
A.2. Common example of foliated metamorphic rock is slate.
B.1. rock that lacks a layered or banded appearance
B.2. Common example of nonfoliated metamorphic rock is marble.

2 INSTRUCT

Use Visuals　L2
Figure 14 Ask students to describe the rocks. *(Sample answer: The rocks are folded and multicolored.)* What force could cause the rocks to fold? *(intense pressure)*
Visual

3.4 Metamorphic Rocks

Key Questions

🔑 *Where does most metamorphism take place?*

🔑 *How is contact metamorphism different from regional metamorphism?*

🔑 *What are three agents of metamorphism, and what kinds of changes does each cause?*

🔑 *What are foliated metamorphic rocks, and how do they form?*

🔑 *How are metamorphic rocks classified?*

Vocabulary
- metamorphism
- contact metamorphism
- regional metamorphism
- hydrothermal solution
- foliated metamorphic rock
- nonfoliated metamorphic rock

Reading Strategy
Outline Copy this outline beneath the outline you made for Lesson 3. Complete it as you read. Include points about how each of these rocks form, some of the characteristics of each rock type, and some examples of each.

> III. Metamorphic Rocks
>   A. Foliated Rocks
>   1. ___?___
>   2. ___?___
>   B. Nonfoliated Rocks
>   1. ___?___
>   2. ___?___

RECALL THAT metamorphic rocks form when existing rocks undergo **metamorphism,** transformation of preexisting rock. A rock that has undergone metamorphism is said to have been metamorphosed. These rocks, such as the one shown in **Figure 14,** tend to be very different from their *parent rocks*—the rocks from which they formed.

Types of Metamorphism
Metamorphism most often occurs in rocks that are buried deeply beneath Earth's crust. Here, they are exposed to an environment that is very different from the one in which they originally formed. 🔑 **Most metamorphic changes occur in the region between the upper mantle and a few kilometers below Earth's surface.** There are two general types of metamorphism: contact metamorphism and regional metamorphism.

FIGURE 14 Deformed Rock Intense pressure not only caused these rocks to fold, but also changed the mineral composition of the parent rock.

Contact Metamorphism When magma forces its way into rock, contact metamorphism may occur. ▭▭ **During contact metamorphism, intruding magma causes localized areas of elevated temperature that alter rock.** Contact metamorphism usually results in minor changes to the parent rock. Marble, shown in **Figure 15,** is sometimes formed from limestone in this way.

Regional Metamorphism When tectonic plates collide and form mountains, large areas of rock are exposed to very high temperatures and pressures. ▭▭ **Regional metamorphism occurs over large areas of Earth's crust, usually during mountain building, and is associated with very high temperatures and pressures.** Regional metamorphism can result in major changes caused by the extreme temperatures and pressures of the upper mantle and lower crust.

FIGURE 15 **Marble** Marble is a common metamorphic rock that can form as the result of contact metamorphism of limestone.

Agents of Metamorphism

We have said repeatedly that metamorphism occurs when rocks are subjected to intense heat and pressure. Heat and pressure, as well as fluids, are called *agents of metamorphism.* ▭▭ **The agents of metamorphism are heat, pressure, and fluids.** Usually, a rock undergoing metamorphosis is exposed to all three of these agents. However, the effect of each agent varies greatly.

Heat The most important agent of metamorphism is heat. Heat provides the energy needed to drive chemical reactions. Some of these reactions cause existing minerals to recrystallize and form larger crystals. Other reactions cause new minerals to form. The heat for metamorphism comes mainly from two sources—magma and the change in temperature with depth. Magma essentially "bakes" any rocks that are in contact with it. Heat also comes from the gradual increase in temperature with depth. In the upper crust, this increase averages between 20°C and 30°C per kilometer.

The temperature needed to change a rock depends on its composition. Minerals become unstable at temperatures higher than those at which they formed. When this happens, they will transform into other minerals that are stable at the new, higher temperature. Thus, rocks composed of minerals that formed deep within Earth's crust will require higher temperatures to metamorphose than those that formed closer to the surface.

☑ **Reading Checkpoint** *Compare and contrast contact and regional metamorphism.*

Rocks **81**

Build Reading Literacy **L1**

Refer to **p.124D** in **Chapter 5,** which provides the guidelines for summarizing.

Summarize Have students read the text under the heading Classification of Metamorphic Rocks. In their own words, have them summarize how metamorphic rocks are classified. *(Sample answer: Metamorphic rocks are classified by texture. There are two kinds of textures—foliated and nonfoliated. Foliated metamorphic rocks have a layered look; nonfoliated metamorphic rocks do not have a layered appearance.)*

Verbal

FIGURE 16 Pressure As a Metamorphic Agent
A Confining pressure is applied in all directions when rocks are buried.

B During mountain building, rocks are subjected to directed pressure, pressure that is greater in one direction than in others.

FIGURE 17 The Effects of Pressure Imagine the tremendous amounts of pressure that caused these rocks to fold.

Pressure There are two types of pressure, as shown in **Figure 16.** *Confining pressure* is pressure associated with burial. Confining pressure occurs equally in all directions and, like temperature, increases with depth. The primary effect of confining pressure is to make rocks more compact and dense. Unlike confining pressure, *directed pressure* is greater in one direction than others. This type of pressure is associated with mountain building and can cause dramatic folds such as those shown **Figure 17.**

Fluids Solutions that surround mineral grains aid in recrystallization by making it easier for dissolved minerals to move. When solutions increase in temperature, reactions among substances can occur at a faster rate. Many of these solutions are associated with magma and are called **hydrothermal solutions.** Hydrothermal solutions promote recrystallization by dissolving original minerals and then depositing new ones. A change in a rock's overall mineral composition is often the result.

Classification of Metamorphic Rocks

Metamorphic rocks are classified into groups based on their texture. **Metamorphic rocks are classified as having either a foliated or nonfoliated texture.**

Foliated Metamorphic Rocks Metamorphic rocks that are formed under high temperatures and elevated, directed pressure may become foliated. **Foliated metamorphic rock** contains minerals that are oriented perpendicular to the direction of greatest pressure. This reorientation of minerals gives foliated metamorphic rocks a layered appearance. When the minerals separate into distinct layers, the rocks appear banded, such as the gneiss shown in **Figure 18A.** Slate, phyllite, schist, and gneiss make up a series of foliated metamorphic rocks that form at increasing temperatures and pressures.

82 Chapter 3 • Lesson 4

Nonfoliated Metamorphic Rocks Metamorphic rocks that are formed under high temperatures and even, confining pressure are not foliated. **Nonfoliated metamorphic rock** lacks a layered or banded appearance. Most nonfoliated metamorphic rocks contain only one mineral and form by contact metamorphism. For example, limestone, the parent rock of marble (**Figure 18B**), is composed entirely of the mineral calcite. When exposed to intruding magma, the calcite crystals recrystallize forming larger, randomly oriented crystals. Quartzite and anthracite are two other common, nonfoliated metamorphic rocks.

☑ **Reading Checkpoint** *Contrast foliated and nonfoliated metamorphic rocks.*

FIGURE 18 Foliated and Nonfoliated Metamorphic rocks have two general textures. **A** Gneiss has a foliated texture. **B** Marble has a nonfoliated texture.
Infer In which direction was pressure exerted on the gneiss?

INQUIRY
QUICK LAB

OBSERVING SOME OF THE EFFECTS OF PRESSURE ON MINERAL GRAINS

Materials
- soft modeling clay • 2 pieces of waxed paper (each 20 cm × 20 cm) • 20–30 small, round, elongated plastic beads • small plastic knife

Procedure
1. Use the clay to form a ball about the size of a golf ball. Randomly place all of the beads into this model rock.
2. Make a sketch of the rock. Label the sketch *Before.*
3. Sandwich the model rock between the two pieces of waxed paper. Use your weight to apply pressure to the model rock.
4. Remove the waxed paper and observe your "metamorphosed" rock.
5. Draw a top view of your rock and label it *After*. Include arrows to show the directions from which you applied pressure.
6. Make a cut through your model rock. Sketch this view of the rock.

Analyze and Conclude
1. **Compare and Contrast** How did the *Before* sketch of your model rock compare with the *After* sketch?
2. **Draw Conclusions** How does pressure affect the mineral grains in a rock?
3. **Infer** Was pressure the only agent of change that affected your rock? Explain.

Rocks **83**

INQUIRY
QUICK LAB

Observing Some of the Effects of Pressure on Mineral Grains L2

Objective
After completing this activity, students will be able to observe the effect of pressure on the rearrangement of mineral grains in a model rock.

Skills Model, Observe, Infer

Prep Time 10 minutes to organize materials

Class Time 15 minutes

Expected Outcome Students will observe that the pressure from opposite directions—from above (their pushing down on the "rock") and below (the table's pushing up on the "rock")—will cause "minerals" to align at right angles to the direction of stress.

Analyze and Conclude
1. The model minerals were randomly distributed throughout the rock before pressure was applied. The minerals aligned themselves at right angles to the direction of stress.
2. Pressure causes the minerals to reorient themselves in the rock.
3. No, heat from the hand and contact with the table also affected the model rock.

Kinesthetic, Visual

Answers

Figure 18 *Pressure was exerted from the sides.*

☑ **Reading Checkpoint** *Foliated metamorphic rocks have a layered or banded appearance. Nonfoliated metamorphic rocks do not have a layered or banded appearance.*

Facts and Figures

Slate is a very fine-grained foliated rock composed of minute mica flakes. The most noteworthy characteristic of slate is its excellent rock cleavage, meaning that it splits easily into flat slabs. This property has made slate a most useful rock for roof and floor tiles, chalkboards, and billiard tables. Slate is most often generated by the low-grade metamorphism of shale, though less frequently it forms from the metamorphism of volcanic ash. Slate can be almost any color, depending on its mineral constituents. Black slate contains organic material; red slate gets it color from iron oxide; and green slate is usually composed of chlorite, a mica-like mineral.

LESSON 3.4

Use Visuals **L1**

Table 3 Ask: What is the parent rock of schist? *(phyllite)* Which has undergone more intense metamorphism, slate or gneiss? Explain your answer. *(Gneiss has undergone more intense metamorphism, as indicated by the arrow in the table.)* Which nonfoliated rock has the finest grains? *(anthracite)*

Visual

3 ASSESS

Evaluate Understanding **L2**

Have students examine Table 3. **Ask:** Generally, what can you say about the relationship between texture and increasing metamorphism that results in foliated rocks? *(The more intense the metamorphism, the courser the texture, or larger the grain size.)*

Reteach **L2**

Have students make tables that compare and contrast contact metamorphism and regional metamorphism.

To summarize, metamorphic rocks form when existing rocks are changed by heat, pressure, and/or fluids. There are two types of metamorphism. Contact metamorphism is often caused when hot magma intrudes into a body of rock. Regional metamorphism is associated with mountain building. The intensity of metamorphism can vary greatly from one environment to another. Samples of shale and its parent rock slate, for example, are often very hard to tell apart. This illustrates that the transition between one rock type to another can be gradual and the changes can be subtle. On the other hand, in more extreme environments, metamorphism can be so complete that the identity of a metamorphic rock's parent rock can not be determined. Metamorphic rocks can be classified by texture as foliated or nonfoliated, as shown in **Table 3.**

Table 3 Classification of Major Metamorphic Rocks

Foliated Metamorphic Rocks			Nonfoliated Metamorphic Rocks		
Parent Rock	Texture	Rock Name	Parent Rock	Texture	Rock Name
Siltstone or Shale		Slate	Limestone		Marble
Slate		Phyllite	Sandstone		Quartzite
Phyllite		Schist	Coal		Anthracite
Schist or Granite		Gneiss			

Increasing metamorphism

3.4 Assessment

Review Key Concepts 🔑

1. Where does most metamorphism take place?

2. Compare and contrast contact metamorphism and regional metamorphism.

3. Name the agents of metamorphism and explain how each changes a rock.

4. What are foliated rocks? How do they form?

5. How are metamorphic rocks classified?

Think Critically

6. **Apply Concepts** What is the major difference between igneous and metamorphic rocks?

7. **Predict** What type of metamorphism, contact or regional, would result in a schist? Explain your choice.

8. **Draw Conclusions** Why can the composition of gneiss vary but overall texture cannot?

WRITING IN SCIENCE

9. **Compare and Contrast** Write a paragraph explaining the major differences and similarities among the three rock groups.

Assessment Answers

1. Most metamorphism takes place in a zone that begins several kilometers below the surface and extends into the upper mantle.

2. Contact metamorphism is caused by locally increased temperatures that occur when magma forces its way into rock. Regional metamorphism occurs over large areas and involves intense heat and directed pressure, usually associated with mountain-building.

3. Heat can cause existing minerals to recrystallize, forming larger mineral crystals, or it can cause new minerals to form. Pressure produces a more compact rock with a greater density. Pressure also can cause folding and minerals to recrystallize. Fluids aid in recrystallization by making it easier for ions to move and by dissolving original minerals and depositing new ones.

4. Foliated rocks have a layered or banded appearance that occurs when minerals realign as the result of directed pressure.

5. Metamorphic rocks can be classified according to their foliated or nonfoliated texture.
6. While both types of rocks form as the result of changes in temperature and pressure, metamorphism does not involve melting.
7. Regional metamorphism; Table 3 indicates that schists result from very intense metamorphism that is generally associated with mountain-building.
8. Gneiss is a foliated rock that forms as the result of directed pressure. However, because the parent rocks of gneisses can vary, so can the compositions of these metamorphic rocks.

9. Sample answer: All are solids that form and change because of Earth processes. All can be classified according to texture and/or composition. The major difference among the three rock types is that each forms in a different way: Igneous rocks form from the cooling of magma or lava; metamorphic rocks form from metamorphism driven by heat, pressure, and/or fluids; and sedimentary rocks form when sediments are turned to rock by compaction and cementation.

The Carbon Cycle

Carbon moves among Earth's major spheres by way of the carbon cycle. The carbon cycle is one of Earth's biogeochemical cycles. A biogeochemical cycle is a cycle in which matter and energy move through the Earth system in a series of steps. These steps in the carbon cycle have different flow characteristics: Some steps involve chemical changes, as when wood is burned, releasing carbon dioxide gas (CO_2). Other steps involve the movement of materials containing carbon. For example, during a volcanic eruption, carbon dioxide gas is released into the atmosphere. Some steps involve the life processes of living things.

At each step in the cycle, carbon is stored for varying lengths of time in different reservoirs, or parts of the Earth system. These reservoirs include the atmosphere, oceans, biomass, fossil fuels, and carbonate rocks. For example, carbon may be part of an organism's biomass for the short span of the organism's lifetime. But the carbon that makes up coal may remain in Earth for millions of years.

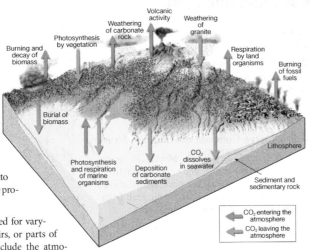

FIGURE 19 The Carbon Cycle

Carbon Dioxide on the Move

In the atmosphere, carbon is found mainly as carbon dioxide. The source of most CO_2 in the atmosphere is thought to be from volcanic activity early in Earth's history. Carbon dioxide moves into and out of the atmosphere by way of photosynthesis, respiration, organic decay, and combustion of organic material.

In photosynthesis, carbon dioxide gas is taken up by plants. Carbon thus becomes part of the compounds, called hydrocarbons, that make up living things. As a result, the biomass of all living organisms on Earth forms a major reservoir of carbon. Respiration, organic decay, and combustion release carbon from this reservoir back into the atmosphere as carbon dioxide.

Carbon and Fossil Fuels

The remains of once living things form another major reservoir of carbon. Some carbon from decayed organic matter

is deposited as sediment. Over long periods of time, this carbon becomes buried. Under the right conditions, some of these carbon-rich deposits are changed to fossil fuels, such as coal. When fossil fuels are burned, carbon dioxide is released.

The Role of Marine Animals

Chemical weathering of certain rocks produces bicarbonate ions that dissolve in water. Rivers and streams carry these ions to the ocean. Here, some organisms extract this substance to produce shells and skeletons made of calcite ($CaCO_3$). When the organisms die, these hard parts settle to the ocean floor and become a sedimentary rock called limestone. If this rock is then exposed at the surface and subjected to chemical weathering, CO_2 is also produced. Use **Figure 19** to follow the carbon cycle.

THE CARBON CYCLE   L2

Background

- During photosynthesis, plants absorb carbon dioxide from the atmosphere and use it to produce the essential organic compounds—complex sugars—that they need for growth. When animals consume plants or other animals that eat plants, the animals use these organic compounds as a source of energy. Then, through the process of respiration, the animals return carbon dioxide to the atmosphere. Plants also return some carbon dioxide to the atmosphere by way of respiration.

- When plants die and decay or are burned, this biomass is oxidized and carbon dioxide is returned to the atmosphere.

- The lithosphere is by far Earth's largest depository of carbon. A variety of rocks contain carbon. The most abundant is limestone. When limestone undergoes chemical weathering, the stored carbon is released into the atmosphere.

Teaching Tips

- Have students contrast different solids that contain carbon, such as coal, diamond, graphite, calcite, and limestone. Have students explain how the carbon is released from each of these components of the lithosphere into Earth's other spheres.

- Write the chemical equations for photosynthesis and respiration below at left on the board or on an overhead transparency to reinforce the fact that the products of one reaction are the reactants of the other reaction.

- Use a clean, empty 2-L bottle, plants, soil, and a thermometer to make a mini-greenhouse to demonstrate how gases in the air, including carbon dioxide, can absorb solar energy.

Photosynthesis

$$\text{energy} + 6CO_2 + 6H_2O \longrightarrow C_6H_{12}O_6 + 6O_2$$

Cellular Respiration

$$6O_2 + C_6H_{12}O_6 \longrightarrow 6CO_2 + 6H_2O + \text{energy}$$

ROCK IDENTIFICATION L2

Objective
After completing this activity, students will be able to differentiate among some of the common rocks.

Skills Observe, Compare and Contrast, Apply Concepts

Prep Time 20 minutes

Advance Prep Order the rock specimens from a scientific supply house at least one month before conducting this activity. Rocks should include anthracite, bituminous coal, granite, gneiss, marble, limestone, basalt, obsidian, shale, slate, a coarse-grained sandstone, quartzite, and conglomerate.

Label the samples with numbers, using a permanent marker so that you can check students' results.

Diluted hydrochloric acid can be prepared using 3.65 mL of concentrated hydrochloric acid diluted to 1 L with distilled water.

Class Time 45 minutes

Safety Students should wear safety goggles, aprons, and gloves. Remind students to take care when testing the rocks for calcite and to thoroughly rinse the samples with fresh tap water to remove the acid.

Teaching Tips
- Students can work in pairs or small groups to complete this investigation.
- Keys or guides to rock identification may be useful for some students.
- Remind students to use only a drop or two of acid to test the rocks for calcite and to thoroughly wash the samples after testing them with the acid.
- Review, if necessary, the properties of some of the more common minerals that students will observe in the rocks, including quartz, calcite, micas, and feldspars.

Rock Identification

Problem How can you use composition and texture to identify common rocks?

Materials rock samples; hand lens; pocket knife; dilute hydrochloric acid; colored pencils; Chapter 2, Table 2; Chapter 3, Tables 1, 2, and 3

Skills Observe, Compare and Contrast, Measure

Connect to the Big idea Most rocks can be easily identified by texture and composition. In this lab, you will use what you have learned about rocks as well as the information on minerals from Chapter 2 to identify some common rocks.

Procedure

1. On a separate sheet of paper, make a copy of the data table shown below. Add any other columns that you think might be useful.

2. Examine each rock specimen with and without the hand lens. Determine and record the overall color of each rock.

3. Try to identify all of the minerals in each rock, using the information in Chapter 2 Table 2. Record your observations.

4. Determine and record the presence of any organic matter in any of the samples.

5. Observe the relationships among the minerals in each rock to determine texture. Refer to Chapter 3 Tables 1, 2, and 3 if necessary. Record your observations.

6. Note and record any other unique observations of the samples.

7. In your data table, make and color a detailed sketch of each sample.

8. Identify each sample as being an igneous rock, a sedimentary rock, or a metamorphic rock.

9. Name each sample. Use the photographs in this chapter and Tables 1, 2, and 3 if necessary.

Data Table						
Rock	Overall Color	Composition	Texture	Sketch	Rock Type	Rock Name
1.						
2.						
3.						
4.						
5.						

86 Chapter 3

Analyze and Conclude

1. **Evaluate** Which of the rock identification characteristics did you find most useful? Which of the characteristics did you find least useful? Give reasons for your answers.

2. **Compare and Contrast** How did identifying rocks compare with the mineral identification lab you did in Chapter 2? How is identifying rocks different from identifying the minerals that compose the rocks?

3. **Apply Concepts** Match the metamorphic rocks with their probable parent rocks.

4. **Apply Concepts** Choose two pairs of rocks used in this investigation. Write a brief description for each pair that explains how one rock can be changed into the other. Refer to a diagram of the rock cycle to help you.

GO FURTHER Obtain permission to collect some local rock samples from a park or nearby road. Use what you have learned about rocks and minerals to identify the rocks. Then write a brief history of each sample to explain how it formed and how it has changed since being formed.

Study Tip

Study With a Partner

Suggest that students pair up as study partners, and spend at least one afternoon a week working together. Students can quiz each other on key concepts, compare notes, and discuss discrepancies.

Interpersonal and Collaborative Skills

How can you play the rock cycle?

Knowledge of the rock cycle is essential to understanding Earth processes. Ask students to work in small groups to develop a board game about the rock cycle. The game should test the players' knowledge of the types of rocks in the cycle as well as some of the key events in the rock cycle. After groups have completed the game, encourage them to exchange games with another group. Then, groups should play and provide feedback about the other group's game. Encourage each group to use the feedback to improve their game.

Homework Guide

Lesson	Questions
1	1–4, 11, 19–22, 36
2	5, 12–14, 23
3	6–8, 10, 15, 16, 24, 25, 29–33, 35
4	9, 17, 18, 26–28, 34, 37

3 Study Guide

Big idea ▶ Earth's Materials and Systems

3.1 The Rock Cycle

🔑 A rock is a solid mass of minerals or mineral-like materials.

🔑 The three major types of rock are igneous, sedimentary, and metamorphic.

🔑 The rock cycle is a model that describes the ways in which rocks transform from one type to another.

🔑 Igneous rocks form from cooled magma or lava.

🔑 Sedimentary rocks form from layers of weathered, eroded, and deposited sediment.

🔑 Metamorphic rocks form when preexisting rocks are altered by pressure, heat, and/or fluids.

🔑 Earth's internal heat and the processes of weathering, erosion, deposition, and lithification can transform any type of rock into another.

rock (66) weathering (67)
rock cycle (66) sediment (67)
magma (67) sedimentary rock (67)
lava (67) metamorphic rock (67)
igneous rock (67)

3.2 Igneous Rocks

🔑 Igneous rocks formed from magma beneath Earth's surface are known as intrusive igneous rocks.

🔑 Igneous rocks formed from lava at Earth's surface are called extrusive igneous rocks.

🔑 Slow cooling of magma or lava causes large crystals to form, while rapid cooling results in small crystals.

🔑 The relative amounts of light and dark silicates within an igneous rock define its composition.

intrusive igneous rock (71)
extrusive igneous rock (71)
texture (71)
granitic composition (72)
basaltic composition (73)
andesitic composition (73)

3.3 Sedimentary Rocks

🔑 Erosion is the picking up and carrying away of sediments.

🔑 Compaction is a process that squeezes, or compacts, sediments.

🔑 Cementation takes place when dissolved minerals are deposited in the tiny spaces among sediments, binding them together into a solid mass.

🔑 Sedimentary rocks are classified into three groups—clastic, chemical, and biochemical.

🔑 Unique features of sedimentary rocks include strata, fossils, ripple marks, and mud cracks. These features indicate how, when, and where the rocks formed.

erosion (76)
deposition (76)
compaction (76)
cementation (76)
clastic sedimentary rock (77)
chemical sedimentary rock (77)
biochemical sedimentary rock (78)

3.4 Metamorphic Rocks

🔑 Most metamorphic changes occur in the region between the upper mantle and a few kilometers below Earth's surface.

🔑 During contact metamorphism, intruding magma causes localized areas of elevated temperature that alter rock.

🔑 Regional metamorphism occurs over large areas of Earth's crust, usually during mountain building, and is associated with very high temperatures and pressures.

🔑 The agents of metamorphism are heat, pressure, and fluids.

🔑 Metamorphic rocks are classified as having either a foliated or nonfoliated texture.

metamorphism (80)
contact metamorphism (81)
regional metamorphism (81)
hydrothermal solution (82)
foliated metamorphic rock (82)
nonfoliated metamorphic rock (83)

Assessment Answers

Review Content

1. a	**2.** b	**3.** b
4. d	**5.** d	**6.** d
7. c	**8.** b	**9.** a
10. a		

Understand Concepts

11. A rock is a solid that is made of minerals or mineral-like materials.

12. Basalt forms when basaltic lava hardens; gabbro, the coarse-grained (intrusive) equivalent of basalt, forms when basaltic magma hardens.

3 Assessment

Review Content

Choose the letter that best answers the question or completes the statement.

1. Which of the following is NOT one of the three major types of rocks?
   a. anthracite
   b. igneous
   c. metamorphic
   d. sedimentary

2. Which of the following is the primary process by which a sedimentary rock transforms into an igneous rock?
   a. metamorphism
   b. melting
   c. erosion
   d. deposition

3. Which of the following would NOT be a major process in the formation of sedimentary rocks?
   a. erosion
   b. melting
   c. deposition
   d. compaction

4. The formation of igneous rocks is powered by
   a. the sun.
   b. compaction.
   c. erosion.
   d. Earth's internal heat.

5. A fine-grained igneous rock forms
   a. deep within Earth.
   b. from magma.
   c. as the result of slow cooling.
   d. as the result of quick cooling.

6. Cementation is one of the final processes involved in the formation of which type of rock?
   a. contact metamorphic
   b. intrusive igneous
   c. extrusive igneous
   d. clastic sedimentary

7. Ripple marks likely indicate that the rock formed
   a. underground.
   b. under a glacier.
   c. in water.
   d. from magma.

8. A major process in the formation of clastic sedimentary rocks is
   a. contact with magma.
   b. cementation.
   c. hardening.
   d. foliation.

9. Metamorphic rocks that have a banded appearance due to the alignment of minerals are called
   a. foliated.
   b. nonfoliated.
   c. clastic.
   d. glassy.

10. Which rock is made of the smallest sediments?
    a. shale
    b. conglomerate
    c. breccia
    d. sandstone

Understand Concepts

11. What is a rock?

12. Which igneous rock forms when basaltic lava hardens? When basaltic magma hardens?

13. A rock has a porphyritic texture. What can you conclude about the rock?

14. How are granite and rhyolite the same, and how do they differ?

15. Explain the two main types of weathering.

16. Why is most of Earth's solid surface composed of sediments or sedimentary rocks?

17. Distinguish between regional and contact metamorphism.

18. What is the difference between shale and slate?

Use the following diagram to answer Questions 19–22.

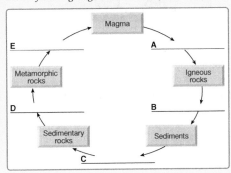

19. What process occurs at point A?

20. What three processes can occur at point B?

21. Name two processes that occur at point C.

22. What two processes occur at points D and E?

17. Regional metamorphism subjects rocks to extreme changes in temperatures and pressures. As a result, the rock undergoes structural and compositional changes. During contact metamorphism, intruding magma causes a rise in temperature of the parent rock. Changes are often slight.

18. Slate is shale that has been metamorphosed.

19. Magma or lava cools and solidifies.

20. weathering, erosion, deposition

21. compaction and cementation

22. metamorphism (D) and melting (E)

13. A porphyritic texture indicates that the rock underwent at least two different episodes of cooling.

14. Both are igneous rocks that have the same basic composition of mostly light silicates. Granite forms slowly, generally deep beneath the surface and therefore is coarse-grained. Rhyolite forms quicker, generally near the surface, and thus is fine-grained.

15. Chemical weathering changes the composition of a rock. Physical weathering breaks the rock into smaller pieces.

16. because erosion occurs at the surface, constantly providing raw sediment that can become sedimentary rock when buried

ASSESSMENT

Think Critically

23. No, if two rocks have the same composition, then they are the intrusive and extrusive equivalents of one another. Thus, they cannot have the same textures.

24. All sedimentary rocks form at or near Earth's surface as a result of weathering, erosion, deposition, compaction, and/ or cementation. Clastic sedimentary rocks, such as sandstone, form from pieces of pre-existing rocks. Chemical sedimentary rocks, such as rock salt, form from sediments that precipitate out of solution. Biochemical sedimentary rocks, such as coal, form from sediments that result from biological processes.

25. The length of time that the sediments that compose the rocks are eroded causes the sediments in a conglomerate to become rounded.

26. Both change rocks. Heat provides the energy needed to drive chemical reactions. Some of these reactions cause existing minerals to recrystallize. Other reactions cause new minerals to form. Pressure can cause changes in composition and texture.

27. heat, pressure, and fluids

28. The metamorphic rocks often have a different composition; they can be foliated, unlike the parent rocks; the minerals might be larger than in the parent rocks; and the metamorphic rocks are often more dense than the rocks from which they formed.

29. coarse-grained

30. sedimentary

31. The rock is a conglomerate: a coarse-grained clastic sedimentary rock.

32. Rocks were weathered to form sediments. The sediments were eroded, deposited, compacted, and cemented to form the rock.

33. This rock could become an igneous rock if it were subjected to increases in temperatures and pressures high enough to cause melting.

Concepts in Action

34. A metamorphic rock will be denser and more compact than its sedimentary parent rock. It will also have a different composition. The layers in a sedimentary rock indicate different periods of deposition whereas the layers in a metamorphic rock are compositional layers.

35. Sedimentary rocks are laid down in layers. If undisturbed, a rock layer is older than layers above it and younger than layers below it.

Think Critically

23. Explain Is it possible for two different types of igneous rocks to have the same composition and the same texture? Explain.

24. Compare and Contrast Compare and contrast the three types of sedimentary rocks and give an example of each type.

25. Form a Hypothesis Think about the sediments that comprise both conglomerate and breccia. What one sedimentary process makes these two rocks different? Explain.

26. Compare and Contrast Compare and contrast the effects of heat and pressure in the formation of metamorphic rocks.

27. Review What are the three agents of metamorphism?

28. Contrast In what ways do metamorphic rocks differ from the sedimentary and igneous rocks from which they form?

Use the photograph to answer Questions 29–33.

29. Observe Describe the texture of the rock.

30. Identify To which of the three major groups of rocks does the rock belong?

31. Classify Classify the rock as specifically as possible.

32. Form a Hypothesis Briefly describe how this rock formed.

33. Apply Concepts Explain how this rock might become an igneous rock.

Concepts in Action

34. Apply Concepts Your friend shows you a rock with distinct layers. How can you and your friend determine if the rock is a sedimentary rock or a metamorphic rock?

35. Apply Concepts Explain how the position of a sedimentary rock layer can provide clues as to its age compared to layers above and below it.

36. Calculate Each year, roughly 9100 kilograms of rock, sand, and gravel are mined for each person in the United States. Calculate how many kilograms of rock, sand, and gravel have been mined for you thus far in your life. Then calculate how much will have been mined when you are 75 years old.

37. Writing in Science Suppose you're a writer for the school newspaper. You have been asked to do a story on one of the rocks described in this chapter. Pick a rock and write a short, newspaper-type story. Include facts about the rock—its texture, mineral composition, and how it formed. Also describe how the rock might change into a rock in each of the other two categories of rocks. Be creative, but scientifically accurate.

Performance-Based Assessment

Apply Concepts Go on a field trip around your house, neighborhood, and community to find at least ten items that are made from rocks or show ways in which rocks are used. Make a poster that shows what you found and display it for the class.

---

36. Sample answer: 9,100 kg/year $\times$ 14 years = 127,400 kg; 9,100 kg/year $\times$ 75 years = 682,500 kg

37. Use the information on the rock cycle and Tables 1, 2, and 3 to evaluate students' newspaper stories' features. Allow time for a few volunteers to read their stories to the class.

Performance-Based Assessment

Provide students with some local references, brochures, or tour guides to get them started, if necessary. As an alternative, plan a class field trip to see the ways in which rocks are an integral part of your community.

Standardized Test Prep

Use the photographs below to answer Questions 1–4. Choose the letter that best answers the question or completes the statement.

1 Which of the rocks has a fine-grained texture?
- A A
- B B
- C C
- D D

2 Which photo shows an igneous rock that formed from rapidly cooling lava?
- F A
- G B
- H C
- J D

3 Which of the rocks formed completely deep beneath the surface?
- A only A
- B only B
- C only D
- D both A and B

4 Which of the following best describes the texture of the rock labeled D?
- F porphyritic
- G glassy
- H fine-grained
- J coarse-grained

Use the photograph below to answer Question 5.

5 What type of rock is shown in the photograph?
- A lava
- B igneous
- C sedimentary
- D metamorphic

6 Which of the following processes involves pressure that causes sediments to combine and form rock?
- F cementation
- G compaction
- H deposition
- J erosion

Tips for Success

Use Visuals Sometimes an answer to a test question requires that you interpret a drawing, a table, or a photograph. When this occurs, carefully study the visual before you read the questions pertaining to it. Refer to the visual again as you read each of the questions to which it pertains.

If You Have Trouble With . . .

Question	1	2	3	4	5	6
See Lesson	3.2	3.2	3.2	3.2	3.2	3.3

Rocks **91**

4 Earth's Resources Planning Guide

BIGIDEA: EARTH'S MATERIALS AND SYSTEMS

Lesson Objectives		Activities	
4.1 Energy and Mineral Resources, pp. 94–101		TE Teacher Demo: Observing Coal, p. 95	L2
4.1 **Distinguish** between renewable and non-renewable resources.		SE Map It: U.S. Coal Fields, p. 95	L2
4.2 **Identity** which energy resources are fossil fuels.		TE Build Science Skills, p. 96	L2
4.3 **Predict** which energy resources might replace dwindling petroleum supplies in the future.		TE Teacher Demo: Recognizing Ore Minerals, p. 99	L2
4.4 **Describe** the processes that concentrate minerals into large deposits as they form.		TE Build Science Skills, p. 100	L2
4.5 **Recognize** how nonmetallic mineral resources are used.			
4.2 Alternative Energy Sources, pp. 102–107		TE Build Science Skills, p. 103	L1
4.6 **Evaluate** the advantages of solar energy.		TE Teacher Demo: Modeling Hydroelectric Power, p. 105	L2
4.7 **Explain** how nuclear power plants use nuclear fission to produce energy.		TE Teacher Demo: Making a Geyser, p. 106	L2
4.8 **Evaluate** wind power's potential for providing energy in the future.			
4.9 **Relate** how hydroelectric power, geothermal nergy, and tidal power contribute to our energy resources.			
4.3 Water, Air, and Land Resources, pp. 108–112		TE Teacher Demo: Motion Accelerates Erosion, p. 111	L2
4.10 **Explain** why fresh water is a vital resource.		TE Map It: Virgin Forests 1620–1992, p. 112	
4.11 **Recognize** why the chemical composition of the atmosphere is important.			
4.12 **Identify** Earth's important land resources.			
4.4 Protecting Resources, pp. 113–116		TE Teacher Demo: Making an Oil Slick, p. 114	L1
4.13 **Identify** the first laws passed to deal with water pollution.			
4.14 **Name** the most important law passed to deal with air pollution.			
4.15 **Explain** what is involved in protecting land resources.			

Chapter Features and Labs

Try It How Can You Determine the Resources You Use?, p. 93		LM Recovering Oil	L2
Earth & Its Resources Bingham Canyon, Utah: The Largest Open-Pit Mine, p. 117		LM Desalinization by Distillation	L3
Exploration Lab Finding the Product that Best Conserves Resources, p. 181			

Ability Levels	Components	
L1 For students who need additional help **L2** For all students **L3** For students who need to be challenged	**SE** Student Edition **TE** Teacher's Edition **LM** Laboratory Manual **CT** Chapter Tests **GRSW** Guided Reading & Study Workbook **CTB** Computer Test Bank	**LP** Lesson Plans **AA** Active Art **PD** Planet Diary **GEODe** Geode CD-ROM **eText**

Resources	Lesson Assessment
GRSW Lesson 4.1 **LP** Lesson Planning 4.1	**SE** Lesson 4.1 Assessment, p. 101 **eText** Lesson 4.1
GRSW Lesson 4.2 **LP** Lesson Planning 4.2	**SE** Lesson 4.2 Assessment, p. 107 **eText** Lesson 4.2
GRSW Lesson 4.3 **LP** Lesson Planning 4.3	**SE** Lesson 4.3 Assessment, p. 112 **eText** Lesson 4.3
GRSW Lesson 4.4 **LP** Lesson Planning 4.4 **PD** Oil Spills	**SE** Lesson 4.4 Assessment, p. 116 **eText** Lesson 4.4

Materials for Activities and Labs

Quantities for each group

STUDENT EDITION

Try It, p. 93
objects that contain resources

Exploration Lab, pp. 118–119
juice cartons (1.89-L, 946-mL, and 240-mL volumes, scissors, metric ruler

TEACHER'S EDITION

Teacher Demo, p. 95
samples of lignite, bituminous, and anthracite

Build Science Skills, p. 96
graduated cylinder or tall jar, vegetable oil, water, gravel, antacid tablet (optional)

Teacher Demo, p. 99
samples of common ore minerals such as pyrite, magnetite, hematite, galena, or graphite

Build Science Skills, p. 100
samples of limestone, cement, and concrete; dilute hyrochloric acid; dropper

Build Science Skills, p. 103
long, narrow potato chip can; scissors; long wooden skewer; tape; 20- × 30-cm piece of transparency film; hot dog

Teacher Demo, p. 105
piece of plastic or transparency film, scissors, plastic straw, straight pin, jar, water, metric ruler

Teacher Demo, p. 106
water; 250- or 500-mL Pyrex flask with tight-fitting, one-hole rubber stopper; glass tube 33–45 cm long; hot plate or Bunsen burner; ring stand; strong, small plastic bowl or container; ice pick or drill; plumber's putty

Teacher Demo, p. 111
2 identical clean 1-L jars with lids, marking pen, water, 2 identical pieces of hard candy, measuring cup

Teacher Demo, p. 114
large, clear, glass bowl; vegetable oil; water; cocoa powder

Assessment

CHAPTER ASSESSMENT
SE Assessment, pp. 121–122
CT Chapter 4 Test
CTB Chapter 4
eText Chapter 4

21st Century Learning

Problem Identification, Formulation, and Solution: Which Energy Source Is Best?, TE p. 120

Before You Teach
Earth's Resources

Michael Wysession
Washington University

Common Themes

Humans are dependent upon Earth for many different resources for survival. Earth science includes the discovery, extraction, and use of these resources.

Space and Time Resources can be roughly divided into renewable and nonrenewable categories. Renewable resources, such as water, food, and solar energy, are replenished over short time scales. Nonrenewable resources, such as coal, oil, and metals, have limited supplies that cannot be replenished.

Forces and Motion Mineral and metal resources become concentrated through a variety of geological processes that include igneous activity, precipitation from hydrothermal solutions, and erosionally-formed placer deposits.

Matter and Energy Humans are dependent upon clean water and air, and therefore the hydrologic cycle and atmospheric processes are vitally important. Human pollution can easily reduce these resources. Humans also rely upon and need to carefully manage land resources such as topsoil and trees. Our society relies heavily upon nonrenewable fossil fuels such as coal, petroleum, natural gas, and uranium (for nuclear power), and is beginning to use tar sands and oil shale. However, there is an increasing trend toward using renewable energy sources such as solar (both active and passive), wind, hydroelectric, geothermal, and tidal power.

Earth as a System Earth's resources will last longer if they are carefully managed, a process called conservation. There is a growing awareness of the need for conservation, including efforts to reduce consumption and to reuse and recycle resources where possible.

EARTH SCIENCE REFRESHER

End of the Cenozoic Era?

Humans have become the most powerful geologic agent of change on Earth's surface. In this context, it is impossible to investigate Earth science from a removed, objective point of view. The study of Earth science must also be a study of humans and human activity because of its remarkable effect on the atmosphere, hydrosphere, geosphere, and even biosphere.

Nowhere else is this as dramatically seen as in the reduction of the number of species of life on Earth. It is hard to quantify the number of species that are currently going extinct. However, because of factors like the deforestation of rain forests and the introduction of foreign species into new environments, it has been estimated that up to 10 percent of the world's species are going extinct every 25 years. Because geologists use periods of mass extinction to define geological time periods, in a very short amount of time we may already have brought about an end to the Cenozoic Era, which has encompassed the past 65 million years.

The morality of the human behaviors that have led to mass extinctions is a topic of debate. In arguing that extinctions may not

> Address **Misconceptions**
>
> *Students may have many misconceptions about nuclear energy. They may think that electricity might be radioactive. And some think that these plants produce power through nuclear explosions.* Nuclear power plants are not that different from coal-burning plants. The heat needed to boil water into steam is produced by burning fossil fuels in a coal-burning power plant. For a strategy that helps to overcome this misconception, see **Address Misconceptions** on TE p. 104.

be wholly bad, some people point out that the asteroid impact that killed off the dinosaurs opened niches for other animals. However, with power should come responsibility, and humans need to be aware of the geological power that they now wield.

Environmental Implications of Resource Use

Humans are by no means the first life-forms to have shaped Earth's surface, nor have they yet had the most impact. Photosynthesizing bacteria created the oxygen in Earth's atmosphere that later allowed for the development of life on the surface of continents. Worms burrowing in ocean sediments have kept carbon dioxide from being locked away, and so have helped keep the climate stable over the past half-billion years. Land plants have covered vast portions of the continents, greatly altering the means and rates of erosion. The remains of ocean life have created the vast layers of the rock limestone. Human activity still pales in comparison.

However, materials that have entered the air as the result of human activities have already significantly affected global warming and the ozone layer in the atmosphere. Water pumping has depleted much of the existing groundwater resources in many areas. The roads and parking lots of urbanized areas have not only reduced groundwater recharge, but greatly increased runoff into streams, worsening the effects of floods. At the same time, many river dams have prevented the occurrence of river flooding and therefore increased the buildup of sediment within the rivers. The human need for energy and mineral resources is resulting in an increasing amount of Earth's surface being stripped away to find these resources. Most significantly, with rising populations and global industrialization, all of these trends will continue to increase, so humans may yet attain the distinction of having altered Earth more than any other species.

CHAPTER 4

ASSESS PRIOR KNOWLEDGE

Use the Chapter Pretest below to assess students' prior knowledge. As needed, review these concepts.

Review Science Concepts

Lesson 4.1 Reviewing rock types and the concept of density ensures that students will understand the structure of oil traps. A review of minerals will enhance understanding of the formation of mineral deposits.

Lesson 4.2 A short discussion of the structure of an atom will enhance students' understanding of nuclear energy.

Lesson 4.3 Reviewing the composition of Earth's atmosphere will give students a baseline for understanding air pollution and the presence of undesirable chemicals in the atmosphere.

Lesson 4.4 A review of minerals and their limited availability will lead students to realize the importance of conservation practices.

Earth's Resources

Big idea — Earth's Materials and Systems
Q: How do people use resources from Earth?

92

Chapter Pretest

1. True or False: The electrons of an atom take part in radioactive decay. *(False)*

2. Which of the following is not a physical property of a mineral? *(c)*
  a. hardness
  b. luster
  c. reactivity

3. Describe briefly the two sources of material that make up sedimentary rocks.

(Sediments that make up sedimentary rocks may originate as solid particles from weathered rocks or as soluble material produced by chemical weathering.)

4. Which gas is present in the greatest concentration in Earth's atmosphere? *(b)*
  a. carbon dioxide
  b. nitrogen
  c. oxygen
  d. ozone

5. What is the difference between a mineral and a rock? *(Minerals have an orderly internal structure and a definite chemical composition. Rocks are usually aggregates of several minerals and thus have a varied chemical composition and no orderly internal structure.)*

6. When might a mineral deposit not be considered an ore? *(when the mineral has no economic value)*

A strip mine in eastern Kentucky

INQUIRY
TRY IT!

HOW CAN YOU DETERMINE THE RESOURCES YOU USE?

Procedure

1. List three objects that you are using now or objects that are around you.
2. Observe the objects. Try to determine which resources they might contain. List possible resources for each object.
3. Your teacher will list several objects chosen by students on the board, along with the resources students believe they contain. Use these lists to answer the following questions.

Think About It

1. **Observe and Analyze** How did you determine the resources that might be in each object?
2. **Design Experiments** How could you actually test each object to determine what resources it contains?

93

ENGAGE/EXPLORE

INQUIRY
TRY IT!

HOW CAN YOU DETERMINE THE RESOURCES YOU USE?   L2

(Address **Misconceptions**)

Students may think that fossil fuels are Earth's only natural resources. Explain that air, water, living things, energy sources, rocks, and minerals all are resources.

Purpose In this activity, students begin to recognize the resources found in everyday objects.

Skills Observe, Design Experiments, Analyze, Evaluate

Prep Time 5 minutes

Materials objects that contain resources

Advance Prep 10 minutes to set out objects

Class Time 10 minutes

Teaching Tip When you gather objects for students to examine, be sure to include some plastic items. This will lead to a discussion of petroleum as a source of plastics and other polymers.

Expected Outcome Students should realize that resources are found in almost all everyday objects.

Think About It

1. Answers will vary. Students will most likely use the physical characteristics of the objects to try to identify the resources.
2. Answers will vary. Students may propose burning the object, physically separating its components, or testing the object with acid or other substances.

LESSON 4.1

1 FOCUS

Lesson Objectives

4.1 **Distinguish** between renewable and nonrenewable resources.

4.2 **Identify** which energy resources are fossil fuels.

4.3 **Predict** which energy resources might replace dwindling petroleum supplies in the future.

4.4 **Describe** the processes that concentrate minerals into large deposits as they form.

4.5 **Recognize** how nonmetallic mineral resources are used.

Build Vocabulary L2

Word Forms Ask students to write a short paragraph explaining how a renewable library book is similar to a renewable resource. After students read the lesson, ask them if their paragraphs must be changed. If so, what changes would they make?

Reading Strategy L2

Answers will vary depending on students' prior knowledge and what they learn from the lesson.

2 INSTRUCT

Integrate Economics L2

Resource Dependence Tell students that modern industries require many different mineral resources. Although some countries have substantial mineral deposits, no nation is self-sufficient. Because deposits are limited in number and location, all countries use trade to fulfill some of their needs. Students can research which countries are major suppliers of various resources and color a world map to show these sources of resources such as aluminum, iron, gold, and copper.

Visual, Kinesthetic

4.1 Energy and Mineral Resources

Key Questions

 What is the difference between renewable and nonrenewable resources?

 Which energy resources are fossil fuels?

 Which energy resources might replace dwindling petroleum supplies in the future?

 What processes concentrate minerals into deposits sufficiently large enough to mine?

 How are nonmetallic mineral resources used?

Vocabulary

• renewable resource
• nonrenewable resource
• fossil fuel • ore

Reading Strategy

Monitor Your Understanding
Copy this table onto a separate piece of paper before you read this section. List what you know about energy and mineral resources in the first column and what you'd like to know in the second column. After you read, list what you have learned in the last column.

Energy and Mineral Resources		
What I Know	What I Would Like to Know	What I Learned
a. ?	c. ?	e. ?
b. ?	d. ?	f. ?

MINERAL AND ENERGY resources are the raw materials for most of the things we use. Mineral resources are used to produce everything from cars to computers to basketballs. Energy resources warm your home, fuel the family car, and light the skyline.

Renewable and Nonrenewable Resources

There are two categories of resources—renewable resources and nonrenewable resources. **A renewable resource can be replenished over fairly short time spans such as months, years, or decades.** Examples are plants and animals for food, natural fibers for clothing, and trees for lumber and paper. Flowing water, wind, and the sun are also renewable resources that supply energy.

 By contrast, a nonrenewable resource takes millions of years to form and accumulate. When the present supply of nonrenewable resources runs out, there won't be any more. Fuels such as coal, oil, and natural gas are nonrenewable. So are important metals such as iron, copper, uranium, and gold.

FIGURE 1 Mineral Resources Miners at work in a gold mine. Gold is a nonrenewable resource.

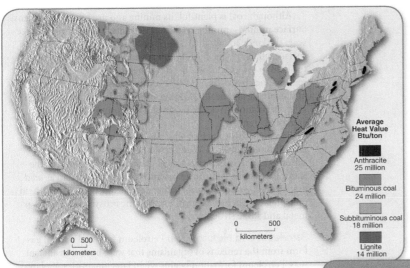

FIGURE 2 U.S. Coal Fields As the map shows, there are coal deposits in many parts of the country.

Earth's population is growing fast, which increases the demand for resources. Because of a rising standard of living, the rate of mineral and energy resource use has climbed faster than population growth. For example, fewer than 6 percent of the world's people live in the United States, but the United States uses more than 20 percent of the world's energy.

Fossil Fuels

More than 85 percent of the electricity used in the United States comes from fossil fuels. A **fossil fuel** is a carbon-containing fuel that formed over millions of years from the remains of living things. **Fossil fuels include coal, petroleum (oil), and natural gas.** Fossil fuels are nonrenewable resources.

Coal Coal forms when heat and pressure transform plant material over millions of years. Coal passes through four stages of development. The first stage, peat, is partially decayed plant material that sometimes looks like soil. Peat may become lignite, which is a sedimentary rock that is often called brown coal. Continued heat and pressure transform lignite into bituminous coal, or soft coal. Bituminous coal is another sedimentary rock. Coal's last stage of development is a metamorphic rock called anthracite or hard coal. As coal develops from peat to anthracite, it becomes harder and releases more heat when burned.

Power plants in the United States primarily use coal to generate electricity. The world has enormous coal reserves. **Figure 2** shows coal fields in the United States.

Earth's Resources **95**

MAP IT!
ACTIVITY

The map in **Figure 2** shows the location of major coal deposits in the United States.
Identify Which type of coal is most plentiful? **Locate** Where are the anthracite deposits in the U.S. located?

Build Reading Literacy **L1**

Refer to **p. 92D,** which provides the guidelines for using context clues.

Use Context Clues Have students explain the meaning of the term *fossil fuels.* The text discussion on how fossil fuels were formed should allow students to infer the meaning of the term. *(Coal, oil, and natural gas are fuels that formed from the remains, or fossils, of once-living organisms.)*
Verbal, Logical

(Teacher **Demo**)

OBSERVING COAL **L2**

Purpose Students compare various stages of coal.

Materials samples of lignite, bituminous, peat, and anthracite (Coal samples are often available from fuel companies, which can be found by entering *fuel companies* and the name of your town or city into an online search engine. Alternatively, you may be able to get coal samples from science supply companies.)

Procedure Obtain samples of various coals. Pass samples around so students can compare them.

Expected Outcomes Anthracite will likely be a shiny dark grey or black. Lignite will not be shiny and will likely be more brown than the other samples. Bituminous coal may have both shiny black and dull grey layers. Students should be able to observe plant fragments within peat samples. Students will be able to break off pieces of lignite and possibly bituminous, but anthracite is too hard to break easily.
Visual

Answers

MAP IT! Bituminous coal is the most plentiful type of coal in the U.S. Anthracite deposits are found in Pennsylvania, Virginia, Rhode Island, and Massachusetts.

Differentiated Instruction

GIFTED Have students research the hydrocarbons that are found in petroleum. They might enjoy drawing structures or making models (using model-building kits or gumdrops and toothpicks) of straight-chain hydrocarbons and some of the simpler ring hydrocarbons. Students can also investigate the process of fractional distillation, in which crude petroleum is separated into different components or fractions according to their boiling points. The various fractions produced range from gasoline to thick asphalts and lubricating grease.

Use Visuals L1

Figure 3 Have students examine the diagram of an oil trap. **Ask:** What prevents the gas and oil from rising to the surface and evaporating? *(a cap rock)* Why does the natural gas collect above the petroleum? *(The gas is less dense than the oil.)* What might happen if tremendous pressure builds up in the oil trap? *(The pressure might force the petroleum up to the surface and cause a "gusher" or oil fountain.)*
Visual, Logical

Build Science Skills L2

Student Activity: Use Models Have students make a model of an oil trap and observe the difference in densities of rock, oil, and water. In a graduated cylinder or tall jar, have students mix equal quantities of vegetable oil, gravel, and water. Tell them to let the mixture stand for 10 minutes and to observe the layers that form. Students will find that the gravel sinks to the bottom of the container and the oil floats on top of the water layer. **Ask:** What would happen if an antacid tablet were dropped into the graduated cylinder? *(Bubbles of carbon dioxide would be produced. The bubbles would rise to the top and dissipate into the air.)* What do the bubbles of carbon dioxide represent? *(natural gas deposits)*
Kinesthetic, Visual

Although coal is plentiful, its mining and use present problems. Surface mining—mining coal from deposits at or near the surface—scars the land. Today, all U.S. surface mines must restore the land surface when mining ends, but the restoration can never return the land to the exact state that it was before mining. Underground mining doesn't scar as much. However, it has been costly in terms of human life and health. Mining is safer today because of federal safety regulations. Yet, the hazards of collapsing roofs and gas explosions remain.

Burning coal—much of which is high in sulfur—also creates air pollution problems. When coal burns, the sulfur becomes sulfur oxides in the air. A series of chemical reactions turns the sulfur oxides into sulfuric acid, which falls to the ground as *acid precipitation*—rain or snow that is more acidic than normal. Acid precipitation can harm forests and aquatic ecosystems, as well as metal and stone structures.

Petroleum and Natural Gas Petroleum (oil) and natural gas form from the remains of organisms that were buried in ancient seas. Petroleum formation begins when large quantities of plant and animal remains become buried in ocean-floor sediments. The sediment protects these remains from oxidation and decay. If sediments continue to build up, over millions of years chemical reactions slowly transform some of the remains into the liquid and gaseous fuels we call petroleum and natural gas.

These materials are gradually squeezed from the sediment layers. The oil and gas then move into nearby rock beds such as sandstone that are *permeable*, meaning that they have spaces through which liquids or gases can pass. The oil and gas are squeezed out of the sedimentary rock layers along with water. Because oil and natural gas are less dense than water, they migrate upward through the water-filled spaces of the enclosing rocks. If nothing stops this upward movement, the fluids will eventually reach the surface.

Sometimes an oil trap—a geologic structure that allows large amounts of fluids to accumulate—stops upward movement of oil and gas. Several geologic structures may act as oil traps, but all have two things in common. First, an oil trap has a permeable reservoir rock that allows oil and gas to collect in large quantities. Second, an oil trap has a cap rock that is nearly impenetrable and so keeps the oil and gas from escaping to the surface. One structure that acts as an oil trap is an anticline. An anticline is an arched series of sedimentary rock layers, as shown in **Figure 3.**

When a drill punctures the cap rock, pressure is released, and the oil and gas move upward toward the drill hole. Then a pump may be needed to lift the oil out. Unrefined oil obtained from the ground is called *crude oil.*

FIGURE 3 Oil Trap Anticlines are common oil traps. The reservoir rock contains water, oil, and natural gas. The fluids collect at the top of the arch with less dense oil and gas on top.
Interpret Diagrams *Why is the water located beneath the oil and gas?*

☑ **Reading Checkpoint** *What two features must an oil trap have?*

Facts and Figures

Different stages of coal have different moisture and heat contents. In general, the lower the moisture content of a coal, the higher the heat content will be. Lignite has a high inherent moisture content, sometimes as high as 45 percent. The heat content of lignite ranges from 9 to 17 million Btu per ton. Bituminous coal has a moisture content that is usually less then 20 percent. The heat content of bituminous coal ranges from 21 to 30 million Btu per ton. Anthracite coal has the lowest moisture content, generally less than 15 percent. The heat content of anthracite ranges from 22 to 28 million Btu per ton.

Tar Sands and Oil Shale

In the years to come, world petroleum supplies will dwindle. 🗝 **Some energy experts believe that fuels derived from tar sands and oil shales could become good substitutes for dwindling petroleum supplies.**

Tar Sands Tar sands, also known as oil sands, are usually mixtures of clay and sand combined with water and varying amounts of a black, thick tar called *bitumen*. Deposits occur in sands and sandstones, as the name suggests, but also in shales and limestones. The oil in these deposits is similar to heavy crude oils pumped from wells. The oil in tar sands, however, is much more resistant to flow and cannot be pumped out easily. The Canadian province of Alberta (**Figure 4**) has one of the largest tar sand deposits.

Some tar sands are mined at the surface, much like the surface mining of coal. The excavated material is then heated with pressurized steam until the bitumen softens and rises. The material is processed to form a substance similar to crude oil. However, extracting and refining tar sands requires a lot of energy—nearly half as much as the end product yields.

Obtaining oil from tar sands has significant environmental drawbacks. Mining tar sands causes substantial land disturbance. Processing also requires large amounts of water. When processing is completed, contaminated water and sediment accumulate in toxic disposal ponds.

Only a small percentage of Alberta's tar sands can be economically recovered by surface mining. Other methods are used to recover deep deposits such as steam injection. The steam heats and softens the bitumen so that it can be pumped to the surface.

☑ **Reading Checkpoint** *What are some environmental drawbacks to mining tar sands?*

Oil Shale Oil shale is a rock that contains a waxy mixture of carbon-containing compounds called *kerogen*. Oil shale can be mined and heated to vaporize the kerogen. The kerogen vapor is processed to remove impurities, and then refined to form a substance similar to crude oil.

Some people see oil shale as a partial solution to dwindling fuel supplies. However, the heat energy in oil shale is only about one-eighth that in crude oil because oil shale contains large amounts of minerals. This mineral material adds costs to the mining, processing, and waste disposal of oil shale.

FIGURE 4 Tar Sand Deposits
In North America, the largest tar sand deposits occur in the Canadian province of Alberta. They contain an estimated reserve of 35 billion barrels of oil.

Earth's Resources **97**

Build Reading Literacy L1

Refer to **p. 124D** in **Chapter 5,** which provides the guidelines for summarizing.

Summarize Have students summarize the process by which tar sands are extracted from their deposits by making a flow diagram. Diagrams should have the various steps of the process labeled. **Ask:** Why are tar sands so much more difficult to extract than petroleum? *(Tar sands are so thick that they do not flow. Thus, they cannot be pumped out of the ground the way crude oil can. Hot fluids are injected into the tar sands to reduce the material's resistance to flow. The material can then be pumped out.)*
Logical

Answers

Figure 3 *The density of water is greater than the densities of oil and gas, so water is located beneath oil and gas.*

☑ **Reading Checkpoint** *permeable reservoir rock to allow oil and gas to collect and a cap rock that keeps oil and gas from escaping*

☑ **Reading Checkpoint** *Processing requires a lot of energy and water and causes the accumulation of contaminated water and sediment in toxic disposal ponds. Mining causes substantial land disturbance.*

Facts and Figures

Oil shales contain an enormous amount of oil. Worldwide, the U.S. Geological Survey estimates that there are more than 3000 billion barrels of oil in shales that could yield more than 38 liters of oil per ton of shale. However, present technology is able to recover less than 200 billion barrels. Still, estimated U.S. resources are about 14 times greater than those of conventionally recoverable oil.

Use Visuals L1

Figure 5 Have students examine the map. **Ask:** Where is the Green River Formation located? *(Northern Colorado, Wyoming, and Utah)* Does this area have abundant water supplies? *(No, the area is semi-arid.)* **Visual, Logical**

Build Science Skills L2

Use Tables and Graphs Have students choose three ores and make a table listing the metal present in each, where in the United States each is mined, and how each is used. Students can list other information about the chosen ores as well. **Intrapersonal, Verbal**

Integrate Chemistry L2

Crystal Size Remind students that the crystal size of minerals that form from magma is determined by how quickly the magma cools. If the rate of cooling is slow, the atoms of the mineral have time to arrange themselves into a large crystal lattice. If cooling is rapid, the atoms have time to arrange themselves only into small crystals. **Visual, Kinesthetic**

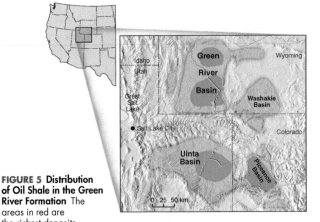

FIGURE 5 Distribution of Oil Shale in the Green River Formation The areas in red are the richest deposits. *Predict Under what circumstances might the mining and processing of oil shale become more economically attractive?*

Roughly half of the world's oil shale supply is in the Green River Formation of Colorado, Utah, and Wyoming, as shown in **Figure 5.** The oil shales are part of sedimentary layers that accumulated at the bottom of two extremely large, shallow lakes 57 to 36 million years ago. The processing of oil shale requires large amounts of water, which is scarce in the semi-arid region where the shales are found. Current technology makes mining oil shale an unprofitable solution.

Formation of Mineral Deposits

Most manufactured products contain substances that come from minerals. Mineral resources are deposits of useful minerals that can be extracted, or removed from the ground. Mineral deposits that are not yet economically or technologically recoverable are also considered mineral resources.

Mineral reserves are deposits from which minerals can be extracted profitably. **Ore** is a useful metallic mineral that can be mined at a profit. Common ore minerals include pyrite, magnetite, hematite, galena, graphite, and sulfur.

The concentration of many minerals in Earth's crust is rather small. A deposit containing a valuable mineral is worthless if the cost of extracting it exceeds the value of the material that is recovered. For example, copper makes up about 0.0135 percent of Earth's crust. However, for a material to be considered a copper ore, it must contain a concentration of about 50 times this amount.

The occurrences of valuable mineral resources are closely related to Earth's rock cycle. The rock cycle includes the formation of igneous, sedimentary, and metamorphic rock as well as the processes of weathering and erosion. **Some of the most important mineral deposits form through igneous processes and from hydrothermal solutions.**

Mineral Resources and Igneous Processes Igneous processes produce important deposits of metallic minerals, such as gold, silver, copper, mercury, lead, platinum, and nickel. For example, as a large body of magma cools, heavy minerals crystallize and settle to the bottom of the magma chamber. Chromite (chromium ore), magnetite (iron ore), and platinum sometimes form this way. Such deposits produced layers of chromite at Montana's Stillwater Complex and the platinum deposit in the Bushveld Complex in South Africa. This deposit contains over 70 percent of the world's known platinum reserves.

98 Chapter 4 • Lesson 1

Hydrothermal Solutions *Hydrothermal (hot-water) solutions* generate some of the best-known and most important ore deposits. Examples of hydrothermal deposits include the gold deposits of the Homestake Mine in South Dakota; the lead, zinc, and silver ores near Coeur D'Alene, Idaho; the silver deposits of the Comstock Lode in Nevada; and the copper ores of Michigan's Keweenaw Peninsula.

Most hydrothermal deposits form from hot, metal-rich fluids that are left over during the late stages of the movement and cooling of magma. **Figure 6** shows how these deposits form. As the magma cools and becomes solid, liquids and various metal ions collect near the top of the magma chamber. These ion-rich solutions can move great distances through the surrounding rock. Some of this fluid moves through fractures in rock or between rock layers. The fluid cools in these openings and the metallic ions separate out of the solution to produce vein deposits, like those shown in **Figure 7**. Many of the most productive gold, silver, and mercury deposits occur as hydrothermal vein deposits.

Placer Deposits *Placer deposits* are formed when eroded high-density minerals settle quickly from moving water while less dense particles remain suspended and continue to move. This settling is a means of sorting in which like-size grains are deposited together due to the density of the particles. Placer deposits usually involve minerals that are not only high in density but are also durable and resistant to chemical change. Common sites of accumulation include sediment deposits on the inside of bends in streams, as well as cracks, depressions, and other streambed irregularities.

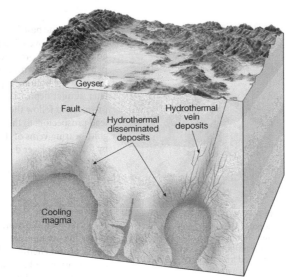

FIGURE 6 Ore From Hydrothermal Solution Mineral-rich hot water seeps into rock fractures, cools, and leaves behind vein deposits.

FIGURE 7 A Vein Deposit Light veins of quartz lace a body of darker gneiss in Washington's North Cascades National Park.

Earth's Resources **99**

Facts and Figures

The term *placer* is probably of Spanish derivation and was used by the early Spanish miners in both North and South America as a name for gold deposits found in the sands and gravels of streams. Originally, the term seems to have meant "sand bank" or "a place in a stream where gold was deposited."

LESSON 4.1

Use Visuals L1

Figure 8 Have students think about prospecting for gold. **Ask:** Why does the gold dust settle to the bottom of the pan? *(The gold dust is denser than the other material suspended in the water.)* Why doesn't the gold dissolve in water? *(Gold is not soluble in water.)*
Visual, Logical

Build Science Skills L2

Student Activity: Design Experiments
When a drop of dilute hydrochloric acid is placed on limestone, it effervesces—bubbles of carbon dioxide are produced. Have students make a hypothesis about whether cement, concrete, and garden lime will effervesce when dilute hydrochloric acid is applied. Encourage students to design an experiment to test their hypothesis. **CAUTION:** Have students submit detailed written descriptions of their planned procedures, and check their plans before allowing them to perform their experiments. Procedures should include safety precautions, including wearing safety goggles and aprons.
Intrapersonal, Logical

FIGURE 8 Panning for Gold Placer deposits led to the California gold rush. Here, a prospector in 1850 swirls his gold pan, separating sand and mud from flecks of gold.

INQUIRY APPLY IT!

Q: *How big was the largest gold nugget ever discovered?*

A: The largest gold nugget ever discovered was the Welcome Stranger Nugget found in 1869 as a placer deposit in the gold-mining region of Victoria, Australia. It weighed a massive 2520 troy ounces (210 pounds, or 95 kilograms). The largest gold nugget known to remain in existence today is the Hand of Faith Nugget, which was found in 1975 near Wedderburn, Victoria, Australia. It was found with a metal detector and weighs 875 troy ounces (73 pounds, or 33 kilograms).

Gold is the best-known placer deposit. In 1848, placer deposits of gold were discovered in California, sparking the famous California gold rush. Early prospectors searched rivers by using a flat-bottomed pan to wash away the sand and gravel and concentrate the gold "dust" at the bottom. **Figure 8** shows this common method. Years later, similar deposits created a gold rush to Alaska. Sometimes prospectors follow the placer deposits upstream. This method may lead prospectors to the original mineral deposit. Miners found the gold-bearing veins of the Mother Lode in California's Sierra Nevadas by following placer deposits.

☑ **Reading Checkpoint** *What are mineral resources?*

Nonmetallic Mineral Resources

🔑 **Nonmetallic mineral resources are extracted and processed either for the nonmetallic elements they contain or for their physical and chemical properties.** People often do not realize the importance of nonmetallic minerals because they see only the products that resulted from their use and not the minerals used to make the products.

Examples of nonmetallic minerals include the fluorite and limestone that are part of the steelmaking process. In addition, minerals such as sylvite are important in the fertilizers needed to grow food. **Table 1** shows how some minerals are used and where they are found.

Nonmetallic mineral resources are divided into two broad groups—building materials and industrial minerals. For example, natural aggregate (crushed stone, sand, and gravel), is an important material used in nearly all building construction.

Some substances, however, have many uses in both construction and industry. Limestone is a good example. As a building material, it is used as crushed rock and building stone. It is also an ingredient in cement. As an industrial mineral, limestone is an ingredient in the manufacture of steel. Farmers also use it to neutralize acidic soils.

Many nonmetallic resources are used for their specific chemical elements or compounds. These resources are important in the manufacture of chemicals and fertilizers. In other cases, their importance is related to their physical properties. Examples include abrasive minerals such as corundum and garnet.

Although industrial minerals are useful, they have drawbacks. Most industrial minerals are not nearly as abundant as minerals used as building materials. Also, manufacturers often must transport nonmetallic minerals long distances, adding to their cost. Unlike most building materials, which need a minimum of processing before use, many industrial minerals require considerable processing to extract the desired substance at the proper degree of purity.

100 Chapter 4 • Lesson 1

Facts and Figures

Our society uses enormous quantities of nonmetallic minerals each year. The per-person consumption of non-fuel resources in the United States totals more than 11 metric tons. About 94 percent of these resources are nonmetallics.

Table 1 Uses and Occurrences of Nonmetallic Minerals

Mineral	Uses	Geological Occurrences
Apatite	Phosphorus fertilizers; detergents	Sedimentary deposits
Asbestos (chrysotile)	Incombustible fibers	Metamorphic alteration
Calcite (limestone)	Aggregate; steelmaking; soil conditioning; chemicals; cement; building stone	Sedimentary deposits
Clay minerals (kaolinite)	Ceramics; china; bricks	Residual product of weathering
Corundum	Gemstones; abrasives	Metamorphic deposits
Diamond	Gemstones; abrasives	Igneous intrusions; placers
Fluorite	Steelmaking; aluminum refining; glass; chemicals	Hydrothermal deposits
Garnet	Abrasives; gemstones	Metamorphic deposits
Graphite	Pencil lead; lubricant; refractories	Metamorphic deposits
Gypsum	Plaster of Paris; wallboard	Evaporite deposits
Halite	Table salt; chemicals; ice control	Evaporite deposits, salt domes
Muscovite	Insulator in electrical applications	Granitic rocks
Quartz	Primary ingredient in glass	Igneous intrusions, sedimentary deposits
Sulfur	Chemicals; sulfuric acid	Natural gas and oil deposits
Sylvite	Potassium fertilizers	Evaporite deposits
Talc	Powder used in paints, cosmetics, etc.	Metamorphic deposits

Use Visuals L1

Table 1 Have students study the table. **Ask:** What is halite, and what are its uses? *(Halite is table salt. In addition to seasoning food, it is used in chemical processes and to melt ice.)* Which mineral listed occurs in igneous intrusions and placers? *(diamond)* Which mineral listed occurs as hydrothermal deposits? *(fluorite)*
Visual, Logical

3 ASSESS

Evaluate Understanding L2

To assess students' knowledge of lesson content, have them list two renewable resources and two nonrenewable resources. Students should explain why each resource listed is renewable or nonrenewable.

Reteach L1

Have students make a poster diagramming the process by which coal is formed. The type of vegetation depicted should be appropriate for the time. *(Large tree ferns and other swamp vegetation were predominant in coal swamps during the Pennsylvanian and Permian periods.)*

4.1 Assessment

Review Key Concepts

1. What is the difference between a renewable and a nonrenewable resource?

2. What are the three major fossil fuels?

3. What are tar sands and oil shale?

4. How do hydrothermal deposits form?

5. What are the two broad categories of nonmetallic mineral resources?

6. Compare and contrast the formation of coal with that of petroleum and natural gas.

Think Critically

7. **Draw Conclusions** Why isn't the use of tar sands more widespread in the United States?

8. **Infer** Explain how following placer deposits upstream would help prospectors find the original deposit.

WRITING IN SCIENCE

9. **Compare and Contrast** Write a paragraph describing the difference in the use of nonmetallic building minerals and nonmetallic industrial minerals.

Earth's Resources **101**

Answers

☑ **Reading Checkpoint** *Mineral resources are Earth materials that are extracted and processed for either the metals or the elements they contain.*

Assessment Answers

1. Renewable resources have unlimited supplies and can be replaced; nonrenewable resources have limited supplies and cannot be replaced.

2. coal, petroleum, natural gas

3. geologic structures that contain low grade hydrocarbons mixed with clay, sand, or shale

4. Hydrothermal deposits form from hot, metal-rich fluids that are left when magma cools. The metal ions collect as mineral deposits in small openings such as rock fractures.

5. building materials and industrial minerals

6. Coal was formed from plant material that collected in swamps. Petroleum and natural gas were formed from plant and animal material that collected and were buried in ancient seas.

7. Most of the world's tar-sand deposits are in Canada. The few deposits in the United States are in California. In addition, mining tar sands has serious environmental drawbacks and is expensive.

8. Placer deposits are minerals that are carried by moving water from a source upstream. By following the deposits upstream, it is possible to find the original deposit.

9. Building materials are abundant, need little processing, need not be pure, and are usually found close to where they are used. Industrial minerals are used for their chemical or physical properties, are relatively scarce, must be extracted and purified, and must be transported.

Earth's Resources **101**

1 FOCUS

Lesson Objectives

4.6 **Evaluate** the advantages of solar energy.

4.7 **Explain** how nuclear power plants use nuclear fission to produce energy.

4.8 **Evaluate** wind power's potential for providing energy in the future.

4.9 **Relate** how hydroelectric power, geothermal energy, and tidal power contribute to our energy resources.

Build Vocabulary **L2**

Word Parts Have students break the word *geothermal* into its parts. They should use a dictionary to find the meaning and derivation of each part. (*Geo-* or *ge-* is a Greek combination form meaning "earth" or "ground." Thermal comes from the Greek word therme meaning "coming from heat." Geothermal energy is heat that comes from within Earth.)

Reading Strategy **L2**

a. solar energy
b. nuclear energy
c. wind energy
d. hydroelectric power
e. geothermal energy
f. tidal power

2 INSTRUCT

Use Visuals **L2**

Figure 9 Have students examine the photo. Tell them that the structures on the ground are tracking mirrors that reflect the solar energy onto a receiver mounted on the tower. **Ask:** What do you think happens to the solar energy once it enters the receiver? *(The solar energy is absorbed by a fluid, typically molten salt or air, and is used to generate steam to power a conventional turbine.)* Can Solar One be used to generate electricity at night? *(No; energy can be stored at night, but not generated at night.)*
Visual, Logical

Key Questions

 What are the advantages of using solar energy?

 How do nuclear power plants use nuclear fission to produce energy?

 What is wind power's potential for providing energy in the future?

 How do hydroelectric power, geothermal energy, and tidal power contribute to our energy resources?

Vocabulary

- hydroelectric power
- geothermal energy

Reading Strategy

Preview Skim the section and start a concept map for the various alternative energy resources.

Alternative Energy Resources
a. ? | b. ? | c. ? | d. ? | e. ? | f. ?

THERE'S NO DOUBT that we live in the age of fossil fuels. These nonrenewable resources supply most of the world's energy, but that can't last forever. As the world population soars, the rate of consumption will climb. This increase in consumption will leave fossil fuel reserves in even shorter supply. One estimate indicates that the supply of recoverable oil may last only another 40 years. In the meantime, the burning of huge quantities of fossil fuels will continue to damage the environment. Our growing demand for energy along with our need for a healthy environment will likely lead to a greater reliance on alternative energy sources.

Solar Energy

Solar energy is by far Earth's most abundant energy resource. Every day, the energy that Earth receives from the sun would power worldwide energy needs for about 25 years. Solar energy far exceeds the amount of Earth's internal energy, or geothermal energy, that is available at or near the surface. Solar energy technologies use the sun's rays to supply heat or electricity. **Solar energy has two advantages: the "fuel" is free, and it is nonpolluting.** The simplest and perhaps most widely used solar energy systems are passive solar collectors such as south-facing windows. As sunlight passes through the glass, objects in the room absorb the sunlight's energy and radiate heat, which warms the air.

FIGURE 9 A Solar Facility Solar One generates electricity in the Mojave Desert near Barstow, California.

More elaborate systems for home heating use an active solar collector. These roof-mounted devices are usually large, blackened boxes covered with glass or plastic. The heat they collect can be transferred by circulating air or liquids through piping. In addition to heating buildings, solar collectors are also used to heat water for domestic and commercial needs.

There are a few drawbacks to solar energy. While the energy collected is free, the necessary equipment and installation are not. A supplemental heating unit is also needed on cloudy days, in the winter, or at night when solar energy is unavailable. However, solar energy is economical in many parts of the United States. Solar power will become even more cost-effective as the prices of fossil fuels increase.

Research is currently underway to improve the technologies for collecting sunlight. Scientists are examining a way to use mirrors to track the sun and keep its rays focused on a receiving tower. **Figure 9** shows a solar collection facility with 2000 mirrors. This facility heats water in pressurized panels to over 500°C by focusing solar energy on a central tower. The superheated water is then transferred to turbines, which are devices that turn electrical generators. Another type of collector, shown in **Figure 10,** uses photovoltaic (solar) cells. They convert the sun's energy directly into electricity.

☑ **Reading Checkpoint** *What are the two main advantages of using solar energy?*

FIGURE 10 Photovoltaic Cells
Solar cells convert sunlight directly into electricity. This array of solar panels is near Sacramento, California.
Apply Concepts *What characteristics would you look for if you were searching for a location for a new solar plant?*

Nuclear Energy

Nuclear power meets about 20 percent of the energy demand of the United States. The fuel for nuclear plants, like the one in **Figure 11,** comes from radioactive materials that release energy through nuclear fission. ☞ **In nuclear fission, the nuclei of heavy atoms such as uranium-235 are bombarded with neutrons. The uranium nuclei then split into smaller nuclei and emit neutrons and heat energy.** The neutrons that are emitted then bombard the nuclei of adjacent uranium atoms, producing a chain reaction. If there is enough fissionable material and if the reaction continues in an uncontrolled manner, fission releases an enormous amount of energy as an atomic explosion.

In a nuclear power plant, however, the fission reaction is controlled by moving neutron-absorbing rods into or out of the nuclear reactor. The result is a controlled nuclear chain reaction that releases great amounts of heat. The heat produces steam that drives turbines. The turbines turn electrical generators, as in most conventional power plants.

FIGURE 11 Diablo Canyon Nuclear Plant Near San Luis Obispo, California Reactors are in the dome-shaped buildings.
Analyze *The location of this plant is controversial because it is close to faults, which are breaks in Earth's crust along which movement can occur. Why would that be a cause for concern?*

Earth's Resources **103**

Students may have many misconceptions about nuclear energy. They may think that the electricity might be radioactive or that nuclear power plants produce power through nuclear explosions. Explain to students that nothing is exploded or burned. Nuclear power plants are not that different from coal-burning plants. The heat needed to boil water into steam is produced by burning fossil fuels in a coal-burning power plant. **Ask:** Where does the heat needed to produce steam come from in a nuclear power plant? *(from splitting certain atoms of uranium)* Once the steam is produced, it turns the blades of a turbine, which causes a generator to produce electricity. **Ask:** Is the process of producing electricity from steam in a nuclear plant the same or different from the process in a coal-burning plant? *(the same; only the method of producing steam is different.)*
Logical

Build Science Skills L2

Apply Concepts Ask: Why are mountain passes good locations for wind farms? *(Most mountain passes have strong, steady winds that sweep through the area.)* What other locations would make good locations for wind farms? *(along a seacoast)*
Intrapersonal, Logical

At one time, energy experts thought nuclear power would be the cheap, clean energy source that would replace fossil fuels. But several obstacles have slowed its development. First, the cost of building safe nuclear facilities has increased. Second, there are hazards associated with the disposal of nuclear wastes. Third, there is concern over the possibility of a serious accident that could allow radioactive materials to escape.

The 1979 accident at Three Mile Island in Pennsylvania made this concern a reality. Some equipment did not function properly, leading to substantial damage to the reactor. Unfortunately, the 1986 accident at Chernobyl in Ukraine was far more serious. Explosions and a fire caused the release of large amounts of radioactive material. Eighteen people died within six weeks of the accident. Thousands more faced an increased risk of death from cancers associated with the fallout. In 2011, an earthquake hit Japan, and a huge wave of water flooded coastal areas. These events caused extensive damage to the reactors at the Fukushima Daiichi nuclear power station north of Tokyo. As with Chernobyl, explosions and fires resulted in the release of radioactive gases. Thousands of people, concerned for their safety, left the area around the power plant in the days following the accident.

☑ **Reading Checkpoint** *What is nuclear fission?*

Wind Energy

According to one estimate, if just the winds of North and South Dakota could be harnessed, they would provide 80 percent of the electrical energy used in the United States. Wind is not a new energy source. People have used it for centuries to power sailing ships and windmills for grinding grains.

In 1980, the federal government started a program to develop wind-power systems, such as the one shown in **Figure 12.** The U.S. Department of Energy set up experimental wind farms in mountain passes with strong, steady winds. One of these facilities, at Altamont Pass near San Francisco, now operates more than 7000 wind turbines. In the year 2004, wind energy supplied about 1.5 percent of California's total electricity—enough to light a large city such as San Francisco.

🔑 **Some experts estimate that in the next 50 to 60 years, wind power could meet between 5 to 10 percent of the country's demand for electricity.** Islands and other isolated regions that must import fuel for generating power are major candidates for wind energy expansion.

The future for wind power looks promising, but there are difficulties. The need for technical advances and the cost of large tracts of land in populated areas are obstacles to development. In addition, windmills are noisy, and the tall towers and rotating blades can harm birds.

FIGURE 12 Capturing Wind Energy These wind turbines are operating near Palm Springs, California.

Facts and Figures

Although many people think wind power is a new development, the use of multiple wind turbines to perform a task is nothing new. Dutch engineers used multiple windmills to drain water from their countryside. The Dutch called these early wind farms *gangs* of windmills, and a group can still be seen southeast of Rotterdam at Kinderdijk. Windmills may also have been the driving force of the industrial revolution in the Netherlands during the eighteenth century. Dutch millers constructed an amazing assembly of more than 700 industrial windmills in a region northwest of Amsterdam. These windmills powered Dutch industry before the use of coal became widespread in the rest of Europe.

FIGURE 13 Glen Canyon Dam and Lake Powell on the Colorado River As dam operators release water in the reservoir, it passes through machinery that drives turbines and produces electricity.

Hydroelectric Power

Like wind, moving water has been an energy source for centuries. The energy that water wheels produce has powered mills and other machinery. Today, the power that falling water generates, known as **hydroelectric power,** drives turbines that produce electricity. In the United States, hydroelectric power plants produce about 5 percent of the country's electricity. Large dams, such as the one in **Figure 13,** are responsible for most of it. The dams allow for a controlled flow of water. ⚙ **The water in a reservoir behind a dam has stored energy that can be released through the dam to produce electricity.**

Hydroelectric power has limitations. For example, although water power is a renewable resource, hydroelectric dams have limited lifetimes. Rivers deposit sediment behind the dam. Eventually, the sediment fills the reservoir. When this happens, the dam can no longer produce power. An example is Egypt's Aswan High Dam on the Nile River, which was completed in the 1960s. It is estimated that half the reservoir will be filled with sediment by 2025. In addition, dams damage the environment by interrupting water flow. Reservoirs behind dams often cover land that was once used for other purposes, such as farming.

The availability of suitable sites is an important limiting factor in the development of hydroelectric power plants. A good site must provide a significant height for the water to fall. It also must have a high rate of flow. Most of the best U.S. sites have already been developed. This limits future expansion of hydroelectric power.

Geothermal Energy

Geothermal energy is harnessed by tapping natural underground reservoirs of steam and hot water. ⚙ **Hot water is used directly for heating, and steam is used to turn turbines to generate electric power.** The reservoirs of steam and hot water occur where subsurface temperatures are high due to relatively recent volcanic activity.

Earth's Resources **105**

Teacher Demo

MODELING HYDROELECTRIC POWER

Purpose Students determine how the amount of energy from falling water increases with increasing height.

Materials piece of plastic or transparency film, scissors, plastic straw, straight pin, jar, water, metric ruler

Procedure Make a pinwheel by cutting a square piece of plastic or transparency film. Attach the pinwheel to a plastic straw by placing a straight pin through the center of the pinwheel and through the straw. Hold the pinwheel over a sink while a student pours a full jar of water on the pinwheel from a measured height. Have students count the number of turns the pinwheel makes. Repeat the procedure several times using the same amount of water and the same rate of flow. Vary only the height of the water jar above the pinwheel.

Expected Outcome The pinwheel should turn faster and make more turns as the water is poured from increasing height.
Visual, Kinesthetic

Integrate Geography

Iceland Inform students that geothermal energy is one of Iceland's greatest natural resources. The capital of Iceland has enjoyed this valuable source of power for more than 60 years. Geothermal heat is used mostly to heat fresh water, which is utilized directly for central heating. Over 89 percent of all the houses in Iceland are heated this way. Geothermal water is also used in swimming pools, for melting snow, farm fishing, drying timber and wool, and heating greenhouses. **Ask:** What can you tell about volcanic activity in Iceland? *(Iceland is volcanically active.)* Do you think Iceland's energy source will last forever? *(Geothermal energy sources can be used up. Eventually, a geothermal field will be depleted.)*
Intrapersonal, Logical

Answers

☑ **Reading Checkpoint** *Nuclear fission is the splitting of an unstable nucleus of an atom into smaller parts, releasing large amounts of energy.*

Earth's Resources **105**

FIGURE 14 Geothermal Energy
The Geysers is the world's largest electricity-generating geothermal facility. Most of the steam wells are about 3,000 meters deep.

Teacher Demo

MAKING A GEYSER L2

Purpose Students model a geyser and observe how it works.

Materials safety goggles; water; 250- or 500-mL Pyrex flask with tight-fitting, one-hole rubber stopper; glass tube 33–45 cm long; hot plate; ring stand; strong, small plastic bowl or container; ice pick or drill; plumber's putty

Safety Use caution when inserting the glass tube into the stopper. Perform this demo behind a safety shield. Have everyone in the room wear goggles.

Procedure Fill the flask with water about 3/4 full. Carefully insert the glass tube in the rubber stopper. Place the stopper in the flask and adjust the tube so that it goes down into the flask about 3/4 of the way to the bottom. Place the flask on the hot plate or on a ring stand just above a Bunsen burner. Drill a hole in a strong, small plastic bowl or container. Work the top of the glass tube into the hole in the bowl and position the bowl on a ring stand above the flask. Plumber's putty can be applied to the bottom of the bowl around the glass tube to keep the bottom of the bowl from leaking. The glass tube should extend up an inch or so into the bowl. The bowl will catch the water from an eruption and also allow the water to flow back into the model. Fill the bowl until water runs down the tube into the flask. Keep adding water until the flask and tube are full. Do not fill the bowl above the top of the glass tube. Turn the hot plate on and allow the water to heat up. Observe how long it takes for an eruption to occur.

Expected Outcomes As the water in the flask turns to steam, pressure builds up inside the flask. Water erupts into the air inside the bowl. After the eruption, water from the bowl should run back down the tube into the flask.
Visual, Kinesthetic

INQUIRY
APPLY IT!

Q: *Is power from ocean waves a practical alternative energy source?*

A: It's being seriously explored now. In November 2000, the world's first commercial wave power station opened on the Scottish island of Islay. It provides power for the United Kingdom. The 500-kilowatt power station uses an oscillating water column, in which incoming waves push air up and down inside a concrete tube that is partly under the ocean's surface. Air rushing in and out of the top of the tube drives a turbine to produce electricity. If the facility succeeds, it could open the door for wave power to become a significant contributor of renewable energy in some coastal areas.

In the United States, areas in several western states use hot water from geothermal sources for heat. The first commercial geothermal power plant in the United States was built in 1960 at The Geysers, shown in **Figure 14**. The Geysers is an important source of electrical power for nearby San Francisco and Oakland. Although production in the plant has declined, it remains the world's premier geothermal field. It continues to provide electrical power with little environmental impact. Geothermal development is now also occurring in Nevada, Utah, and the Imperial Valley of California.

A source of geothermal power may be used up. When hot fluids are pumped from volcanically heated reservoirs, the reservoir often cannot be recharged. The steam and hot water from individual wells usually lasts no more than 10 to 15 years. Engineers must drill more wells to maintain power production. Eventually, the field is depleted.

As with other alternative methods of power production, geothermal sources are not expected to provide a high percentage of the world's growing energy needs. Nevertheless, in regions where people can develop its potential, its use will no doubt grow.

☑ **Reading Checkpoint** *In what two ways is geothermal energy used?*

Tidal Power

Several methods of generating electrical energy from the oceans have been proposed, yet the ocean's energy potential still remains largely untapped. The development of tidal power is one example of energy production from the ocean.

Tides have been a power source for hundreds of years. Beginning in the twelfth century, tides drove water wheels that powered sawmills and mills for grinding grain. During the seventeenth and eighteenth centuries, a tidal mill produced much of Boston's flour. But today's energy demands require more sophisticated ways of using the force created by the continual rise and fall of the ocean.

Facts and Figures

There are 600 to 700 geysers in the world today. Between 400 and 500 of these are found in Yellowstone National Park. Geysers form in areas where groundwater can circulate several thousand feet deep in Earth's crust and be heated by a volcanic heat source. Geysers exist only when certain conditions are present: a volcanic heat source, molten rock (magma) near the surface, water that can circulate near the heat source and become superheated, a "plumbing" system, and silica-rich rocks that can sustain the force that is needed for an eruption.

All over the world, the tides rise and fall each day. **Tidal power can be harnessed by constructing a dam across the mouth of a bay or a tidal river in coastal areas with a large difference between the water levels at high and low tide. The strong in-and-out flow of water that results drives turbines and electric generators.**

An example of this type of dam is shown in **Figure 15.** As you look at the three parts of the illustration, follow the path of the water. Notice that electricity is generated as the water flows out of the dam during low tide. Some tidal-energy facilities also generate electricity during high tide. Some facilities use a generator only and function without a dam.

The largest tidal power plant ever constructed is at the mouth of France's Rance River. Other tidal-energy facilities have been built near Murmansk in Russia, near Taliang in China, and on an arm of the Bay of Fundy in Canada. San Francisco and New York City are both exploring the possibility of harnessing tidal energy.

Tidal power development isn't economical if the difference between the height of high and low tide is small, or if a narrow, enclosed bay isn't available. In addition, tidal stations can harm the environment. However, tidal energy creates little or no pollution. Although the tides will never provide a high portion of the world's ever-increasing energy needs, they are an important source at certain sites.

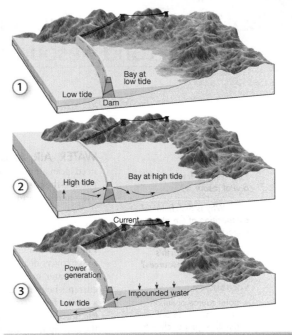

VISUAL SUMMARY

TIDAL DAM

FIGURE 15 1. At low tide, water is at its lowest level on either side of the dam. **2.** At high tide, water flows through a high tunnel. **3.** At low tide, water drives turbines as it flows back to sea through a low tunnel.
Infer *Why is a large tidal range (difference in water level between high and low tide) needed to produce power?*

Use Visuals   L1

Figure 15 Have students study the diagram. **Ask:** What might be a biological disadvantage of a tidal dam? *(The dam probably disrupts marine or coastal ecosystems.)* Which way does water flow through the dam at high tide? *(toward land)* Which way does water flow through the dam at low tide? *(toward the sea)*
Visual, Logical

3 ASSESS

Evaluate Understanding   L2

To assess students' knowledge of lesson content, have each student write three review questions. Invite students to read their review questions to the class. Have the class answer the questions. Continue until everyone has had a turn to read their questions or until unique questions have all been answered.

Reteach   L1

Have students make a table of alternate energy sources, the advantages and disadvantages of each, and whether each source is renewable or nonrenewable.

Answers

Figure 15 *The greater the tidal range, the more potential energy the water will have. This energy is converted to mechanical energy when the turbine's blades turn, then to electrical energy by the generator.*

☑ **Reading Checkpoint** *directly for heating and to turn turbines to generate electricity*

4.2 Assessment

Review Key Concepts

1. What are the advantages and drawbacks of using solar energy?

2. What Earth materials do nuclear power plants use to produce energy?

3. What percentage of our energy might be met by wind power over the next 60 years?

4. What are the advantages and drawbacks of hydroelectric, geothermal, and tidal power?

Think Critically

5. Predict Why will the interest in alternate energy sources probably grow in the future?

6. Classify Identify solar, nuclear, and wind power as renewable or nonrenewable energy sources. Explain your answers.

WRITING IN SCIENCE

7. Explain Write a letter to a family member explaining how tidal power works.

Earth's Resources **107**

Assessment Answers

1. advantages: free and unlimited supply of energy; drawbacks: expensive equipment, supplemental heating unit needed when solar energy is not available
2. Heat produced by the nuclear fission of uranium atoms is used to heat water. The steam drives a turbine that turns an electrical generator, producing electric power.
3. between 5 and 10 percent

4. Hydroelectric—advantages: renewable; drawbacks: dams have finite lifetimes, high water levels needed. Geothermal—advantages: clean; drawbacks: nonrenewable, suitable sites are rare. Tidal—advantages: renewable; drawbacks: limited sites available with enclosed bays and large tidal range
5. Fossil fuel reserves will be in very short supply due to growing demand for energy and for a healthy environment.

6. Solar and wind power are renewable energy sources because the supplies of sunlight and wind are unlimited. Nuclear energy is nonrenewable because the supply of uranium is limited.
7. Students' letters will vary but they should mention that both a large tidal range and a narrow, enclosed bay are requirements for harnessing tidal energy. Letters should also describe how a tidal dam operates and the direction of water flow at high and low tides.

① FOCUS

Lesson Objectives

4.10 **Explain** why fresh water is a vital resource.

4.11 **Recognize** why the chemical composition of the atmosphere is important.

4.12 **Identify** Earth's important land resources.

Build Vocabulary   L2

Paraphrase Before students read the lesson, have them explain what they think *point source* and *nonpoint source* mean. After they have read the lesson, ask students to explain the meanings of the terms in their own words, noting how their definitions have changed, if at all.

Reading Strategy   L2

a. pollution that does not have a specific point of origin

b. runoff, water filtering through piles of waste rock

c. water that flows over the land rather than seeping into the ground

d. waste oil from streets, pesticides off farm fields

e. gases that help maintain a warm temperature near Earth's surface

f. carbon dioxide, methane, water vapor

② INSTRUCT

Use Community Resources   L2

Have students research the water supply in their community. They should find out where their water comes from and how it is treated to make it safe for human use. Additionally, students should research the amount of water that is consumed from each source and how long the current supply is likely to meet your community's needs. The Department of Public Works or the water department will have this information. Students may be able to tour the municipal water treatment plant.

Verbal, Interpersonal

4.3 Water, Air, and Land Resources

Key Questions

🔑 Why is fresh water a vital resource?

🔑 Why is the chemical composition of the atmosphere important?

🔑 What are Earth's important land resources?

Vocabulary

• point source pollution
• nonpoint source pollution
• runoff • global climate change

Reading Strategy

Build Vocabulary Copy the table below. As you read, add definitions and examples to complete the table.

Definitions	Examples
point source pollution: Pollution that can be traced to a location	factory pipes, sewer pipes
nonpoint source pollution: a. ___?___	b. ___?___
runoff: c. ___?___	d. ___?___
greenhouse gas: e. ___?___	f. ___?___

WATER, AIR, AND LAND resources are essential for life. You need clean air and water every day. Soil provides nutrients that allow plants—the basis of our own food supply—to grow. How do people use—and sometimes misuse—these vital resources?

The Water Planet

Figure 16 shows Earth's most prominent feature—water. Liquid water covers nearly 71 percent of Earth's surface. Most of this water is salt water, not fresh water. Oceans have important functions. Their currents help regulate and moderate Earth's climate. They are also a habitat for marine organisms and a vital part of the *water cycle*, the process in which water constantly moves between the oceans, the atmosphere, and the biosphere. Fresh water, however, is what people need in order to live. 🔑 **Each day, people use fresh water in many ways, such as drinking, cooking, bathing, and growing food.** Fresh water—water with little salt dissolved in it—is extremely important. However, Earth's reserves are relatively small—less than one percent of the water on the planet is usable fresh water.

Freshwater Pollution Pollution has contaminated many freshwater supplies. In general, there are two types of water pollution sources—point sources and nonpoint sources. **Point source pollution** is pollution that comes from a known and specific location, such as the factory pipes in **Figure 17**. Other examples include a leaking landfill or storage tank.

FIGURE 16 Water on Earth Oceans cover almost three fourths of Earth's surface.

Nonpoint source pollution is pollution that does not have a specific point of origin. **Runoff,** the water that flows over the land rather than seeping into the ground, often carries nonpoint source pollution. Runoff can carry waste oil from streets. It can wash sediment from construction sites or pesticides off farm fields and lawns. Water filtering through piles of waste rock from coal mines can carry sulfuric acid into rivers or lakes. This contaminated water can kill fish and other aquatic life.

As you can see in **Table 2,** water pollution has adverse health effects. Pollutants can damage the body's major organs and systems, cause birth defects, lead to infectious diseases, and cause certain types of cancers. Contaminated fresh water can sicken or kill aquatic organisms and disrupt ecosystems. In addition, fish and other aquatic life that live in contaminated waters often have concentrated poisons in their flesh. As a result, it is dangerous to eat fish taken from some polluted waters.

☑ **Reading Checkpoint** *What is the difference between a point and a nonpoint water pollution source?*

FIGURE 17 Point Source of Pollution Pollution from point sources, such as these factory pipes, is easy to locate and control.

Table 2 Major Types of Water Pollution			
Type	**Examples**	**Sources**	**Effects**
Disease organisms	Bacteria, viruses	Wastes from people and animals	Typhoid, cholera, dysentery, infectious hepatitis
Wastes that remove oxygen from water	Animal manure and plant debris that bacteria decompose	Sewage, animal feedlots	Great amounts of bacteria can remove oxygen from water, killing fish
Inorganic chemicals	Acids, toxic metals	Industrial effluent, urban runoff, household cleaners	Poisons fresh water and can sicken those who drink it
Organic chemicals	Oil, gasoline, plastic, pesticides, detergent	Farm and yard runoff, industrial waste, household cleaners	Some cancers, disorders of nervous and reproductive systems
Plant fertilizer	Water soluble compounds with nitrate, phosphorus ions	Sewage, manure, farm and garden runoff	Spurs rapid growth of algae that decay and deplete water's oxygen; fish die
Sediment	Soil	Erosion	Disrupts aquatic food webs, clogs lakes and reservoirs, reduces photosynthesis of aquatic plants
Radioactive substances	Radon, uranium, radioactive iodine	Nuclear power plants, uranium ore mining and processing	Some cancers, birth defects, genetic mutations

LESSON 4.3

Use Visuals L1

Figure 19 Have students examine the graphs. **Ask:** What makes up almost half of all air pollution? *(carbon monoxide)* What fraction of pollution sources are industrial processes? *(about 15 percent)* What do you think is the source of most carbon monoxide pollution? *(vehicle exhaust and fuel combustion)*
Visual, Logical

Address **Misconceptions** L2

Students may hold the misconception that there is an actual hole in the sky that lets UV radiation through. Show students NASA satellite photos of ozone distribution so they can read the ozone concentration in the "hole." Explain that ozone is being depleted around the globe but is particularly severe in certain areas, notably above Antarctica. This depletion is actually a temporary depletion of ozone in September and October of each year. In December and January, the "hole" is repaired. The reason for concern is the fact that each year, more ozone is being depleted and less is being repaired. **Ask:** What happens during periods of ozone depletion? *(More UV radiation reaches Earth's surface.)* Why are scientists concerned if the "hole" is repaired each year? *(The hole is not completely repaired, and increasing amounts of ozone are being destroyed.)*
Logical

FIGURE 18 Sources of Air Pollution Cars, trucks, and buses are the biggest sources of air pollution. Laws that control motor vehicle emissions have helped make the air cleaner in many areas.

Primary Pollutants

Volatile Organics 13.6%
Sulfur Oxides 16.4%
Particulates 6.0%
Nitrogen Oxides 14.8%
Carbon Monoxide 49.1%

What They Are

Solid Waste Disposal 2.5%
Industrial Processes 15.0%
Miscellaneous 9.0%
Stationary Source Fuel Combustion 27.3%
Transportation 46.2%

Where They Come From

FIGURE 19 Major Primary Pollutants and Their Sources Percentages are calculated on the basis of weight.
Interpret Graphs *What is the major primary pollutant? What is the major source of air pollution?*

110 Chapter 4 • Lesson 3

Earth's Blanket of Air

Earth's atmosphere is a blanket of nitrogen, oxygen, water vapor, and other gases. **The chemical composition of the atmosphere helps maintain life on Earth.** First and foremost, people and other animals could not live without the oxygen in Earth's atmosphere. But the atmosphere is also part of several cycles, such as the carbon cycle, that make nutrients available to living things.

The atmosphere also makes life on land possible by shielding Earth from harmful solar radiation. There is a layer of protective ozone high in the atmosphere. Ozone is a three-atom form of oxygen that prevents 95 percent of the sun's harmful ultraviolet (UV) radiation from reaching Earth's surface.

Certain gases called *greenhouse gases*—such as carbon dioxide, methane, and water vapor—help maintain a warm temperature near Earth's surface. When solar energy hits Earth, the Earth gives off some of this energy as heat. The gases absorb some heat that Earth radiates, keeping the atmosphere warm enough for living things.

☑ **Reading Checkpoint** *What is the role of ozone in the atmosphere?*

Pollution in the Air Pollution can change the chemical composition of the atmosphere and disrupt its natural processes. Fossil-fuel combustion is the major source of air pollution. Most air pollution comes from motor vehicles and power plants that burn coal or oil. Motor vehicles release carbon monoxide and other pollutants. Some of the pollutants react to form *smog*, a mixture of air pollutants that can form over cities. Power plants release sulfur dioxide and nitrogen oxides. These pollutants combine with water vapor in the air to create acid precipitation. **Figure 19** shows the primary air pollutants and their sources.

The burning of fossil fuels also produces carbon dioxide, a greenhouse gas. The amount of carbon dioxide in the atmosphere has increased since industrialization began in the nineteenth century. This increase has contributed to **global climate change**, which is the unnatural warming of the lower atmosphere and the changes associated with this warming. The warming of the lower atmosphere is also known as *global warming*. Global climate change could lead to enormous changes in Earth's environment. For example, glaciers might melt, and this could contribute to a rise in sea level and coastal flooding.

Chlorofluorocarbons (CFCs), chemicals once used in air conditioners and plastic foam production, destroy ozone in the upper atmosphere. A significant loss of ozone could result in an increased incidence of health problems such as cataracts and skin cancers, because more of the sun's UV radiation would reach Earth's surface. In 1987, an international agreement called for the reduction in the manufacture of CFCs, and today the concentration of ozone in the stratosphere seems to be stabilizing.

Air pollution is a major public health problem. It can cause coughing, wheezing, and headaches, as well as lung, eye, and throat irritation. Long-term health effects include asthma, bronchitis, emphysema, and lung cancer.

Facts and Figures

Primary pollutants are those emitted directly into the troposphere. They pollute the air immediately when they are emitted. Primary pollutants are also dangerous because they may form secondary pollutants when chemical reactions take place among the primary pollutants. The mixture of gases and particles that make up urban smog is a good example of a secondary pollutant. Smog forms when unstable organic compounds and nitrogen oxides from vehicle exhaust react in the presence of sunlight.

Land Resources

Earth's land provides soil and forests, as well as mineral and energy resources. How do land resources impact your daily life? Soil is needed to grow the food you eat. Forests provide lumber for your home, wood for furniture, and pulp for paper. Petroleum provides energy and is in the plastic of your computer and television. Elements such as zinc, copper, and nickel make up the coins in your pocket. Removing and using resources from Earth's crust can take a heavy environmental toll.

Damage to Land Resources There are an estimated 500,000 mines in the United States. Mines are essential because they are the source of many of the mineral resources we need. But mining tears up Earth's surface and destroys vegetation, as you can see in **Figure 20.** It can also cause soil erosion and create pollution that contaminates surrounding soil and water and destroys ecosystems.

Agriculture has many impacts on the land as well. Today, farmers can produce more food per hectare from their land. Extensive irrigation also has allowed many dry areas to be farmed for the first time. But heavy pumping for irrigation of dry areas is depleting the groundwater. And over time, irrigation causes *salinization,* or the build-up of salts in soil. When irrigation water on the soil evaporates, it leaves behind a salty crust. Eventually, the soil becomes useless for plant growth.

Trees must be cut to supply our need for paper and lumber. But the removal of forests, especially through clear-cutting, can damage land. Clear-cutting is the removal of all trees in an area of forest.

FIGURE 20 Effects of Surface Mining Surface mining destroys vegetation, soil, and the contours of Earth's surface. Laws now require mine owners to restore the surface after mining operations cease, but the land cannot be restored to the exact way it was before the mining.

Earth's Resources **111**

Teacher Demo

MOTION ACCELERATES EROSION L2

Purpose Students demonstrate how the motion of water increases the long-term effects of erosion.

Materials 2 identical clean 1-L jars with lids, marking pen, water, 2 identical pieces of hard candy, measuring cup

Procedure Label the jars A and B. Place a piece of candy in each jar. Pour 500 mL of water into each jar. Cover both jars. Place them in a location where both can be seen. Shake jar A once or twice a day. Do not disturb jar B.

Expected Outcome After only 2 days, students should be able to see that the disturbed candy has dissolved much more than the undisturbed candy.
Kinesthetic, Visual

Build Reading Literacy L1

Refer to **p. 246D** in **Chapter 9,** which provides the guidelines for relating cause and effect.

Relate Cause and Effect Have students think about the build-up of salts in soil. **Ask:** Why can salts build up in soil used for intensive farming? *(In order to grow large amounts of crops in an arid area, farmers add heavy applications of fertilizers to support the additional plants. Salts from the fertilizer eventually build up in the soil.)*
Logical

Answers

Figure 19 *The major primary pollutant is carbon monoxide. The major source of air pollution is transportation.*

☑ **Reading Checkpoint** *Ozone absorbs harmful ultraviolet radiation from the sun, thus protecting life.*

LESSON 4.3

Evaluate Understanding [L2]

To assess students' knowledge of lesson content, have them write a short paragraph explaining how ozone can be essential to life when it is in the upper stratosphere, yet a serious pollutant when it is closer to Earth's surface.

Reteach [L1]

Have students summarize their knowledge of water, land, and air resources by making an outline of the lesson. They can use the heads as a guide and add information under each head.

Answers

MAP IT! The amount of virgin forest was much greater in 1620. The eastern half of the United States has lost almost all of its virgin forest. There are now more virgin forests in the western half of the country than in the eastern half.

Assessment Answers

1. People need fresh water for drinking, cooking, bathing, and growing food.
2. The chemical composition of Earth's atmosphere helps to maintain life on Earth.
3. Point source pollution has a known and specific location. Nonpoint source pollution does not have a specific point of origin.

Cleared areas are susceptible to soil erosion. Forest removal also destroys ecosystems and wildlife habitat. The United States actually has more hectares of forest today than it did a century ago. That's because much of the virgin forest (forest that had never been cut down) that was cut long ago has regrown as second-growth forest. This forest is not as diverse as virgin forest—it does not contain as much variety of plant species. Some forestland has also become tree plantations, with even fewer species. As you see in **Figure 21,** the United States has lost most of its virgin forest during the last few centuries.

Finally, land serves as a disposal site. You may have seen landfills and other waste facilities. When disposal is done correctly, there is minimal impact on land. But many old landfills leak harmful wastes that get into soil and underground water. The same is true of buried drums of chemicals, which were often disposed of illegally. Waste is inevitable. But there is a need for ways to reduce it and make the disposal safer.

MAP IT!
ACTIVITY

These maps in **Figure 21** compare the location of virgin forests in the contiguous 48 states of the United States in 1620 and in 1992.

Interpret Maps How has the amount of virgin forest changed? How has the location of virgin forest changed?

Virgin forest, 1620

Remaining areas of virgin forest, 1992

FIGURE 21 Virgin Forests 1620–1992 There is little virgin forest left in the United States today.

4.3 Assessment

Review Key Concepts

1. Why is fresh water a vital resource?
2. Why is the chemical composition of Earth's atmosphere important?
3. What is the difference between point source pollution and nonpoint source pollution?

Think Critically

4. **Relate Cause and Effect** How would the removal of sulfur from coal affect the type of air pollution in a local area? Explain your answer.
5. **Apply Concepts** How would Earth be different if there were no greenhouse gases?

BIGIDEA EARTH'S MATERIALS AND SYSTEMS

6. **Apply Concepts** Write a brief paragraph that connects the following: waste of paper, loss of species diversity of forests, and the increase in second-growth forest area.

4. Removing sulfur from coal would decrease the amount of sulfur oxides in the air. Sulfur oxides combine with water vapor to form acid precipitation, so the acidity of the precipitation both locally and in more distant areas would decrease.
5. Earth would be too cold to sustain life.

6. Student paragraphs should suggest that wasting paper causes more trees to be cut down, resulting in a loss of species due to elimination of their habitat. When trees are clear-cut, the forest eventually will be replaced by a second-growth forest that has greater area but less diversity than the original forest.

4.4 Protecting Resources

EACH YEAR, the paper and wood products that the average American uses are roughly equivalent to a tree that is 30 meters tall. Meanwhile, the population of the United States grows by about 3 million people every year.

As the population grows, people use more and more resources, many of which are nonrenewable. The manufacture and disposal of these products uses enormous amounts of energy and creates pollution, as shown in **Figure 22.** Is there a way to have the products and services we want and still protect resources and create less pollution? Many people think conservation and pollution prevention are the answer. **Conservation** is the careful use of resources. Pollution prevention means stopping pollution from entering the environment.

Between the late 1940s and 1970, a number of serious pollution problems got the public's attention. Severe air pollution events killed hundreds and sickened thousands in the United States and elsewhere. In the late 1960s, many beaches closed due to pollution. An oil spill off the California coast killed wildlife. Then in 1969, Americans watched news reports of Ohio's polluted Cuyahoga River catching fire and burning for days. Incidents such as these made the public and government increasingly concerned about pollution.

FIGURE 22 Polluted Air Strict laws have helped curb air pollution, though it remains a problem.

Key Questions

🔑 **When were the first laws passed to deal with water pollution?**

🔑 **What was the most important law passed to deal with air pollution?**

🔑 **What is involved in protecting land resources?**

Vocabulary

• conservation • compost
• recycling

Reading Strategy

Summarize After reading this section, complete the concept map below to organize what you know about the major laws that help keep water, air, and land resources clean.

1 FOCUS

Lesson Objectives

4.13 **Identify** the first laws passed to deal with water pollution.

4.14 **Name** the most important law passed to deal with air pollution.

4.15 **Explain** what is involved in protecting land resources.

Build Vocabulary L2

Word Forms Have students use a dictionary to find words that are related to the vocabulary term *conservation.* Each word should be used in a sentence. Knowing the meaning of words such as *conservative* and *conserve* will help students understand the concept of conservation.

Reading Strategy L2

a. Clean Water Act
b. Clean Air Act
c. Resource Conservation and Recovery Act
d. Safe Drinking Water Act
e. Comprehensive Environmental Response, Compensation, and Liability Act

2 INSTRUCT

Integrate Biology L2

Oil Spills and Marine Life Ask students if they know why oil spills are dangerous to wildlife. Tell them that oil destroys the insulating ability of fur-bearing mammals, such as sea otters, and the water-repelling abilities of a bird's feathers, thus exposing these animals to cold water and air temperatures. Many marine birds and animals also swallow oil when they try to clean themselves, which can poison them. **Ask:** What is the function of bird feathers? *(They keep the bird warm and waterproofed, and help the bird fly.)* What happens to feathers when they get oiled? *(They become heavy, matted, and soggy.)* **Verbal, Logical**

Use Visuals L1

Table 3 Have students read the information in the table. **Ask:** How should you dispose of old batteries? *(Use a hazardous waste site or collection to dispose of them.)* What happens to household chemicals when they are dumped down a drain? *(They move through sewers into rivers, lakes, or streams.)*
Visual, Logical

(Teacher **Demo**)

MAKING AN OIL SLICK L2

Purpose Students examine the way oil reacts when it mixes with water.

Materials large, clear, glass bowl; vegetable oil; water; cocoa powder

Procedure Mix a little cocoa powder with the oil so it will resemble crude oil. This mixture will make it easier for students to observe the oil. Fill the bowl with water to about 5 cm from the top. Pour some of the oil–cocoa mixture onto the water.

Expected Outcomes Oil and water do not mix, but form two separate layers. The oil, even a little drop, will quickly spread out over the water surface and break up into many little blobs. When oil is spilled onto the ocean, it can be pushed and transported by the wind, currents, and tides because it stays on the top of the water.
Kinesthetic, Visual

Use Visuals L1

Table 4 Have students read the information in the table. **Ask:** How can you use solar energy in your home? *(Allow sunshine in through the windows.)* Name one way you can use your own physical energy instead of fossil fuel energy. *(I can walk or ride a bike instead of using a car.)*

Table 3 How You Can Prevent Water Pollution
• Never pour household chemicals (paints, thinners, cleaners, pesticides, waste oil) down the drain or into the toilet.
• Never dump toxic chemicals in the gutter or onto the ground.
• Don't put items that contain hazardous substances, such as batteries or old computer monitors, into the trash.
• Find out about hazardous waste collection sites and times from your local sanitation or public works department.
• Avoid using hazardous substances in the first place.

PLANET DIARY

For links on effects of **Oil Spills** visit PlanetDiary.com/HSES.

FIGURE 23 Air Sampler Devices such as this monitor air pollutants.

Keeping Water Clean and Safe

Both the public and government officials pressed for action on pollution. **Starting in the 1970s, the federal government passed several laws to prevent or decrease pollution and protect resources.**

America's polluted rivers and lakes got early attention. In 1972, the U.S. Congress passed the Clean Water Act (CWA). Among other provisions, the law requires industries to reduce or eliminate point source pollution of water above ground. The number of sewage treatment plants increased, which eliminated the discharge of raw sewage into many lakes, rivers, and bays. Today, there are still water pollution problems. But because of the CWA, the number of U.S. lakes and streams safe for fishing and swimming has doubled, and the discharge of pollutants by industries has decreased by billions of kilograms a year.

The Safe Drinking Water Act, passed in 1974, helped protect drinking resources. It set maximum contaminant levels for a number of pollutants that could harm the health of people. Public water resources are cleaner today because of this law. See **Table 3** for ways that individuals can help prevent water pollution.

☑ **Reading Checkpoint** *What did the Clean Water Act do?*

Protecting the Air

As lawmakers were tackling water pollution in the 1970s, air pollution was also on the agenda. **In 1970, Congress passed the Clean Air Act, the nation's most important air pollution law.** It established National Ambient Air Quality Standards (NAAQS) for six pollutants known to cause health problems—carbon monoxide, ozone, lead, sulfur dioxide, nitrogen oxides, and particulates (fine particles). Air monitors, such as the one in **Figure 23**, sample the air. If the maximum permissible level of pollutants in the air is exceeded, local authorities must come up with plans to bring these levels down. Since 1970, the total emissions of the six pollutants regulated under the Clean Air Act has decreased 60 percent. This happened despite the fact that over the same time span, energy consumption increased 42 percent and the U.S. population grew by 39 percent.

Today, power plants and motor vehicles use pollution control devices to reduce or eliminate certain pollutants released during fossil fuel combustion. In motor vehicles, devices called catalytic converters change harmful emissions to substances that are less harmful. For example, a catalytic converter changes carbon monoxide into carbon dioxide and water. Power plants are now more likely to use low-sulfur coal. These controls cut down on emissions of sulfur and nitrogen oxides that often produce acid precipitation.

Differentiated Instruction

SPECIAL NEEDS Have students cut out photos from magazines and newspapers that show water usage and conservation. Students can make a poster with these photos, writing a description next to each photo. If enough photos are collected, two posters can be made, one for water usage and the other for conservation methods. Posters can be hung in a school hallway during Conservation Awareness Week or as part of a conservation program.

Increased use of renewable energy sources, such as solar, wind, and hydroelectric power, can also help clear the air. These energy sources cause less air and water pollution than do fossil fuels.

Cars with electric and hybrid (combination of electric and either natural gas, gasoline, or diesel) motors produce fewer or no tailpipe emissions. Several of these lower-emissions vehicles are now available. Some of the hybrid models are also very efficient and get high gas mileage. When a car can go farther on a tank of gas, it uses less fuel and creates less pollution than do cars with low gas mileage.

Energy conservation is an important air pollution control strategy. Fossil-fuel combustion produces most of the electricity in the United States. If we can use less electricity we would have to burn less fossil fuel. Less fossil-fuel combustion means less air pollution. You can see several energy conservation tips in **Table 4.**

☑ **Reading Checkpoint** *What did the Clean Air Act do?*

Caring for Land Resources

🔑 **Protecting land resources involves preventing pollution and managing land resources wisely.** Farmers, loggers, manufacturers, and individuals can all take steps to care for land resources.

Farming Farmers now use many soil conservation practices to prevent the loss of soil and preserve soil fertility. In contour plowing, farmers plow across a hillside rather than up and down the hill. This method of farming decreases water runoff that washes away soil. Another conservation method is strip cropping, in which crops with different nutrient requirements are planted in alternating strips. Strip cropping helps preserve the fertility of soil.

To reduce the chemicals added to soil and crops, some farmers and gardeners now use smaller amounts of pesticides and chemical fertilizers. Natural fertilizers such as compost or animal manure have replaced commercial chemical fertilizers on some fields. **Compost** is partly decomposed organic material that is used as fertilizer. Integrated Pest Management (IPM) uses natural predators or mechanical processes (such as vacuuming pests off leaves) to decrease the number of harmful insects and other organisms.

Forests Selective cutting conserves forest resources. In this method of logging, some trees in an area of a forest are cut, while other trees remain. This practice preserves topsoil as well as the forest habitat. Clear-cutting, on the other hand, removes whole areas of forest and destroys habitats and contributes to the erosion of topsoil.

Table 4 How You Can Save Energy
• Recycle when possible.
• Let the sun in on bright winter days using solar energy to warm rooms.
• Use energy-saving fluorescent bulbs instead of incandescent bulbs where you can.
• Turn off lights when you leave a room. Turn off the radio, TV, or computer when you're not using them.
• Walk or ride a bike when you can.
• When buying electric products, look for the Energy Star sticker which denotes energy-saving products.

Build Reading Literacy L1

Refer to **p. 216D** in **Chapter 8,** which provides the guidelines for comparing and contrasting.

Compare and Contrast Tell students that there are two major methods of forestry. Clear-cutting involves the complete removal of all the trees in an area. In selective logging, only certain trees are removed. Trees left standing form a buffer zone.
Ask: Compare the amount of erosion that would take place with both kinds of forestry practices. *(Clear-cutting exposes bare soil, which is subject to erosion. Selective logging creates buffer zones of trees that slow runoff and prevent any eroded soil from being washed away.)* Do you think forests are a renewable resource? *(Answers will vary. The trees will grow back as a second-growth forest, but it will be less diverse than the virgin forest.)*
Logical

Answers

☑ **Reading Checkpoint** *The Clean Water Act led to an increase in sewage treatment plants; it requires industries to reduce or eliminate point source pollution into surface waters.*

☑ **Reading Checkpoint** *The Clean Air Act established six criteria pollutants and required communities not to exceed certain levels of pollution for these pollutants.*

Facts and Figures

Integrated Pest Management (IPM) practices began in the 1920s. Progress was slow, however, due to the abundance of inexpensive and effective synthetic pesticides and limited knowledge of their long-term effects on organisms and the environment. Rachel Carson's book, *Silent Spring,* brought the effects of chemical pesticides to the public eye in 1962, and IPM practices became more popular. There are several lines of IPM: chemical controls (the use of pheromones to attract and capture pests), cultural controls (crop rotations, sanitation, and pruning), biological controls (introducing predators, parasites, or pest disease organisms), and genetic controls (breeding pest-resistant crops and tolerant plant varieties).

LESSON 4.4

Use Community Resources ⬛L2

Have students investigate recycling programs in their community. If none are available, students may be interested in starting a limited one. If a program exists, students may want to volunteer in some way. Alternatively, students may be interested in participating in a community-wide composting project.
Kinesthetic, Intrapersonal

3 ASSESS

Evaluate Understanding ⬛L2

To assess students' knowledge of lesson content, have them explain the difference between conservation and pollution prevention. (*Conservation is the careful use of resources. Pollution prevention involves ways to prevent pollution from occurring or stopping pollution from entering the environment.*)

Reteach ⬛L1

Have students make a table listing the laws discussed in this lesson. For each law, students should write what it does and what it accomplished.

Answers

☑ **Reading Checkpoint** *The Resource Conservation and Recovery Act requires companies to store, transport, and dispose of hazardous waste according to strict guidelines.*

FIGURE 24 A Recycling Facility Recycling saves resources, reduces energy consumption, and prevents pollution.

Disposal of Waste Some laws reduce the possibility of toxic substances getting into the soil. Sanitary landfills have largely replaced open dumps and old-style landfills. Sanitary landfills have plastic or clay liners that prevent wastes from leaking into the surrounding soil or groundwater. The Resource Conservation and Recovery Act (RCRA) passed in 1976 has decreased the illegal and unsafe dumping of hazardous waste. The law requires companies to store, transport, and dispose of hazardous waste according to strict guidelines. The Comprehensive Environmental Response, Compensation, and Liability Act of 1980 established the Superfund to clean up abandoned hazardous waste sites that are a danger to the public or the environment.

☑ **Reading Checkpoint** *What is the RCRA and what does it do?*

Recycling Creating less waste by using fewer products and recycling products also helps preserve land resources. **Recycling** is the collecting and processing of used items so that they can be made into new products. Many communities now have recycling centers to help with this task. Items that can be recycled include newspapers and magazines, other kinds of paper, plastics, glass bottles, and aluminium containers. By conserving resources and producing less waste, everyone can contribute to a cleaner, healthier future.

4.4 Assessment

Review Key Concepts 🔑

1. When were the first laws passed to deal with water pollution?

2. Identify the most important air pollution control law.

3. What are National Ambient Air Quality Standards?

4. How does selective cutting of forests conserve topsoil?

5. How can gardeners care for land resources?

Think Critically

6. Apply Concepts How can turning off lights when you're not using them help decrease air pollution?

7. Relate Cause and Effect Explain how the Superfund law helps remove sources of underground water pollution.

WRITING IN SCIENCE

8. Explain Write a paragraph explaining how recycling your aluminum soda cans helps conserve resources and energy.

Assessment Answers

1. The first laws were passed in the 1970s. The Clean Water Act was passed in 1972.
2. The Clean Air Act, the most important air pollution law, was passed in 1970.
3. NAAQS are maximum permissible levels of six pollutants known to cause health problems.

4. The trees that are left standing keep topsoil from eroding and washing away.
5. by using less pesticides and inorganic fertilizers; by using compost and Integrated Pest Management
6. When you turn off lights, you use less electricity. Since the fuels that produce electricity cause air pollution, less electricity needed means less fuel used and less pollution produced.

7. The Superfund law mandates the cleaning up of dangerous abandoned hazardous waste sites. This prevents the toxic wastes from leaching out of the site and entering underground water sources.
8. Student paragraphs should include the ideas that the recycling of aluminum soda cans conserves aluminum and produces less waste.

Bingham Canyon, Utah: The Largest Open-Pit Mine

The huge pit shown in **Figure 25** is where a mountain once stood. It's Bingham Canyon copper mine, the largest open-pit mine in the world. The mine, southwest of Salt Lake City, Utah, is 4 kilometers across and covers almost 8 square kilometers.

The mine is so deep—900 meters—that if a steel tower were built at the bottom, it would have to be three times taller than France's Eiffel Tower to reach the pit's rim.

FIGURE 25 An Open-Pit Mine Aerial view of Utah's Bingham Canyon copper mine, the largest open-pit copper mine on Earth

The pit began in the late 1800s as an underground silver and lead mine. Miners later discovered copper. There are similar deposits at several sites in the American Southwest and in a belt from southern Alaska to northern Chile.

The ore at Bingham Canyon formed after magma was intruded to shallow depths. After this, shattering created extensive fractures in the rock. Hydrothermal solutions penetrated these cracks, and ore minerals formed from the hydrothermal solutions.

Although the percentage of copper in the rock is small, the total volume of copper is huge. Ever since open-pit operations started in 1906, some 5 billion tons of material have been removed, yielding more than 1.2 million tons of copper. Miners have also recovered significant amounts of gold, silver, and molybdenum.

The ore body is far from exhausted. The mine's owners plan to remove and process an additional 3 billion tons of material. This mining operation has generated most of Utah's mineral production for more than 80 years. People have called it the "richest hole on Earth."

Like many older mines, the Bingham pit was unregulated during most of its history. Development occurred before today's awareness of the environmental impacts of mining and prior to effective environmental laws. Today, problems of groundwater and surface water contamination, air pollution, and land reclamation are receiving long overdue attention at Bingham Canyon.

Earth's Resources **117**

Bingham Canyon, Utah: The Largest Open-Pit Mine · L2

Background For much of its hundred-year history, Bingham Canyon was owned by Kennecott Copper Corp. However, during the post-1973 oil crisis shake-out, the company was acquired by British Petroleum. It was then sold to Rio Tinto, which operates Bingham Canyon through its subsidiary, Kennecott Utah Copper Corp. The mine employs about 1,400 people and produces about 15 percent of the nation's copper.

Teaching Tips
- Have students research chalcopyrite, the major ore at Bingham Canyon. The formula for chalcopyrite is $CuFeS_2$. The ore is 0.56 percent copper. Chalcopyrite has a metallic luster and a brassy-gold color somewhat less yellow than pyrite.
- Have students make posters showing the processing of copper from mining to grinding and flotation to roasting and smelting to purification by electrolysis.
- Have students make lists of some of the many uses of copper.
- Discuss the importance of copper throughout history, especially in the Bronze Age (bronze is an alloy of tin and copper). Mention the use of copper in brass (an alloy of copper and zinc).
- Tell students that the mine's open pit is one of only a few human-made objects that can be seen from space.
- Have students examine a penny. The composition of the penny has changed several times through the years. Pennies minted in 1943 looked silvery because they were made of zinc-coated steel, due to a shortage of copper. Later, the composition went back to the traditional copper until 1982. After 1982, the composition was changed again, using cheaper zinc for the core and coating the outside with the traditional copper.

Logical

FINDING THE PRODUCT THAT BEST CONSERVES RESOURCES L2

Objectives
In this activity, students will
- measure the dimensions of three different-sized juice cartons.
- calculate the surface area of the three cartons.
- compare the amount of cardboard in the three cartons.
- evaluate the packaging as to which conserves resources the best.

Visual, Logical

Skills Observe, Measure, Calculate, Compare and Contrast, Relate Cause and Effect, Draw Conclusions

Prep Time 10 minutes

Advance Prep Begin to gather juice cartons well in advance of doing this lab.

Class Time 30 minutes

Safety Be careful when using scissors.

Teaching Tip
- Have students bring juice cartons from home. You may be able to get used 240-mL cartons at a day care or preschool facility.
- To save class time, have students cut out and measure the cartons in class and do the calculations at home.
- Have students make three copies of the diagram and write the dimensions directly on the copies. This will ensure that they do not forget to include the bottom of the carton in their calculations.

INQUIRY
EXPLORATION LAB

Finding the Product that Best Conserves Resources

Problem Which packaging conserves resources the best?

Materials 1 1.89-L (64 fl. oz) cardboard juice carton, 1 946-mL (32 fl. oz) cardboard juice carton, 1 240-mL (8 fl. oz) cardboard juice carton, scissors, metric ruler

Caution *Be careful when using scissors.*

Skills Observe, Measure, Calculate, Compare and Contrast, Relate Cause and Effect, Draw Conclusions

Connect to the Big idea When you buy a product, you usually consider factors such as price, brand name, quality, and how much is in the package. But do you consider the amount of resources the package uses? Many products come in packages of different types and materials. You might buy a larger pack if you use a lot, or a small pack if you like the convenience of individual servings. But how much cardboard, plastic, or glass are you using—or wasting—depending on your choice? How about the trees, petroleum, and other resources needed to make those packages? In this lab, you will compare three sets of packages that hold the same amount of juice to determine how your decisions about packaging affect the use of resources.

Procedure

Part A: Determine the Amount of Material in Each Package

1. Work in groups of three or four. Use scissors to cut apart the three cartons your teacher gives your group. Then spread each one out as you see here.

2. Measure the dimensions of the cartons with the ruler.

3. Calculate the area of each carton on a separate sheet of paper. Use these equations:
   - Area of a rectangle:
     $A = l \times w$
     (l = length; w = width)
   - Area of a square:
     $A = s^2$
     (s = length of a side of the square)

Data Table			
	Area of Cardboard in One Carton	Number of Cartons Needed to Hold 1.89 L	Area of Cardboard to Hold 1.89 L
1.89 L		1	
946 mL		2	
240 mL		8	

4. Copy the data table above on a separate sheet of paper. Then record the data you calculated.

Part B: Compare the Amount of Material in the Packages

5. On a separate sheet of paper, calculate how much more cardboard is used when you buy 1.89 L of juice in the two 946-mL cartons instead of one 1.89-L carton.

Use this procedure:

a. Subtract the area of material in the 1.89-L carton from the area of material in the two 946-mL cartons.

b. Divide the answer you get in part a by the area of material in the 1.89-L carton.

c. Multiply the answer you get in Part b by 100. This is how much more material is in the two containers, expressed as a percentage.

6. Repeat this procedure for the material in eight small containers.

Analyze and Conclude

1. **Compare and Contrast** Based on your data, does buying the juice in one large carton or in an 8-pack of small individual cartons use more cardboard? How does buying the juice in two medium-size cartons compare?

2. **Relate Cause and Effect** How does buying the juice in several cartons instead of one large carton impact the use of resources?

3. **Draw Conclusions** Suppose you have determined which set of cardboard cartons uses the least resources. Then you find out that the same size carton of juice comes in plastic and glass as well as cardboard. How would you decide which of these containers would be the best choice, in terms of saving resources?

GO FURTHER Design packaging for an everyday product. The packaging must conserve materials and be recyclable. Write a paragraph that describes your packaging design and explains why you think it is the best solution within the given constraints.

Questioning Strategies

If you want to take 240 mL of juice in your lunch, what can you do that would conserve resources? *(The desired amount of juice can be poured from a large carton into a thermos bottle or plastic container at home.)*

Expected Outcome Students will find that as the size of the carton decreases, the percentage of cardboard to volume increases.

Analyze and Conclude

1. Buying an 8-pack of small cartons uses more cardboard. Buying two medium-size cartons uses more cardboard than one large-size carton but less than an 8-pack.

2. More trees will have to be cut down to supply the materials that make up the additional amount of cardboard.

3. Making plastic uses petroleum, a nonrenewable resource, but the plastic container may be made of recycled plastic. Likewise, a glass container may be made of recycled glass. Without knowing the source of the container material, it would be difficult to reach an informed decision. The container that can be recycled would be the best choice because recycling decreases the use of resources.

GO FURTHER

Have students visit a local supermarket or look around their kitchens and find examples of excessive packaging. They will most likely find individual packets of food in boxes, which may be wrapped. For example, teabags are often individually wrapped and placed in a cardboard box, which is wrapped in cellophane.

Logical, Kinesthetic

Occasionally, Study With a Friend
Divide the class into small groups, and ask each group to make a list of questions that would cover all the Key Concepts in the chapter. Then, have groups exchange lists and answer the questions they receive from another group.

21st Century Learning

Problem Identification, Formulation, and Solution

Which energy source is best?
Energy resources warm homes, fuel cars, and run computers. Ask students to identify the different sources of energy used in the United States and to find out the percentage of total energy used by each source. Encourage them to determine why some sources are used more than others and whether this could cause an energy shortage in the future. Finally, students should propose some possible solutions to this problem and develop a class presentation summarizing their findings.

Homework Guide

Lesson	Questions
1	1–3, 11, 13, 22, 25, 30
2	4, 5, 14, 15, 24, 26, 31
3	6, 7, 12, 16, 27–29, 32
4	8–10, 17, 18, 23, 33

4 Study Guide

Big idea Earth's Materials and Systems

4.1 Energy and Mineral Resources

🔑 A renewable resource can be replenished over fairly short time spans, whereas a nonrenewable resource takes millions of years to form and accumulate.

🔑 Fossil fuels include coal, oil, and natural gas.

🔑 Some energy experts believe that fuels derived from tar sands and oil shales could become good substitutes for dwindling petroleum supplies.

🔑 Some of the most important mineral deposits form through igneous processes and from hydrothermal solutions.

🔑 Nonmetallic mineral resources are extracted and processed either for the nonmetallic elements they contain or for their physical and chemical properties.

renewable resources (94)
nonrenewable resource (94)
fossil fuel (95)
ore (98)

4.2 Alternative Energy Sources

🔑 Solar energy has two advantages: the "fuel" is free, and it's nonpolluting.

🔑 In nuclear fission, the nuclei of heavy atoms such as uranium-235 are bombarded with neutrons. The uranium nuclei then split into smaller nuclei and emit neutrons and heat energy.

🔑 Some experts estimate that in the next 50 to 60 years, wind power could provide between 5 to 10 percent of the country's demand for electricity.

🔑 The water held in a reservoir behind a dam has stored energy that can be released through the dam to produce electric power.

🔑 Hot water is used directly for heating, and steam is used to turn turbines to generate electric power.

🔑 Tidal power is harnessed by constructing a dam across the mouth of a bay or a tidal river in coastal areas with a large difference between the water levels at high and low tide. The strong in-and-out flow that results drives turbines and electric generators.

hydroelectric power (105)
geothermal energy (105)

4.3 Water, Air, and Land Resources

🔑 Each day, people use fresh water in many ways, such as drinking, cooking, bathing, and growing food.

🔑 The chemical composition of the atmosphere helps maintain life on Earth.

🔑 Earth's land provides soil and forests, as well as mineral and energy resources.

point source pollution (108)
nonpoint source pollution (109)
runoff (109)
global warming (110)

4.4 Protecting Resources

🔑 Starting in the 1970s, the federal government passed several laws to prevent or decrease pollution and protect resources.

🔑 In 1970, Congress passed the Clean Air Act, the nation's most important air pollution law.

🔑 Protecting land resources involves preventing pollution and managing land resources wisely.

conservation (113)
compost (115)
recycling (116)

Assessment Answers

Review Content

1. c	**2.** b	**3.** a
4. c	**5.** b	**6.** b
7. d	**8.** a	**9.** d
10. b		

Understand Concepts

11. petroleum, natural gas, coal
12. Burning fossil fuels is a major source of air pollution.
13. A mineral resource is a deposit of useful minerals that can be extracted; an ore is a useful metallic mineral that can be mined at a profit.
14. A collector is a blackened, glass-covered box mounted on a roof. The sun's rays shine on the box and heat the air inside it. The heat warms air or water in pipes that pass through

4 Assessment

Review Content

Choose the letter that best answers the question or completes the statement.

1. Nonrenewable resources are those that
   a. will never run out.
   b. take one or two decades to replace.
   c. have limited supplies.
   d. are contaminated by pollution.

2. Which of the following is a fossil fuel?
   a. uranium   **c.** wood
   b. coal   **d.** ozone

3. Petroleum and natural gas form from
   a. the remains of living things buried in seas long ago.
   b. the decay of radioactive sediments underground.
   c. plant material that collected millions of years ago in swamps.
   d. heating and cooling of magma in underground chambers.

4. Hydroelectric power produces electricity using
   a. the sun's rays.   **c.** moving water.
   b. wind.   **d.** storms.

5. Which of the following substances is a fuel used in nuclear power plants?
   a. sulfur dioxide   **c.** petroleum
   b. uranium   **d.** carbon dioxide

6. Point source pollution comes from sources that are
   a. basically unknown.
   b. directly identifiable.
   c. very small.
   d. dumped illegally.

7. An unnatural warming of the atmosphere near Earth's surface is called
   a. solar wind.
   b. ozone accumulation.
   c. acid precipitation.
   d. global warming.

8. The careful use of resources is
   a. conservation.   **c.** composting.
   b. recycling.   **d.** deposition.

9. The Clean Air Act
   a. makes all air pollution illegal.
   b. limits greenhouse gases in outdoor air.
   c. limits nonpoint source pollution.
   d. set limits on certain pollutants in outdoor air.

10. What type of pollution did the Clean Water Act succeed in limiting?
   a. carbon dioxide
   b. sewage
   c. solid waste
   d. acid precipitation

Understand Concepts

11. What are three major types of fossil fuels?

12. What is a major negative impact of the use of fossil fuels?

13. What is the difference between a mineral resource and an ore?

14. Briefly explain how active solar collectors work.

15. Why do hydroelectric dams have limited lifetimes?

16. Explain why fresh water is a vital resource.

17. How can farmers help protect land resources?

18. When were some of the earliest laws passed to deal with water pollution? Why were they passed at that time?

19. Explain why an anticline might be a good place to search for the earth materials petroleum and natural gas.

20. What are three things that you can do to prevent water pollution?

21. What are three things that you can do to save energy?

20. Answers may include: Never pour household chemicals down the drain, never dump toxic chemicals onto the ground, do not put hazardous materials into the trash.
21. Answers may include: Recycle when possible, turn off lights when you leave a room, walk or ride a bike when you can instead of using a car.

Think Critically

22. Tar sands and oil shale are not a good long-term energy solution because they are nonrenewable, so they can be depleted just as the fossil fuels we use today are being depleted. Extracting and processing these resources also disturbs the land, produces harmful wastes, and requires enormous amounts of energy (tar sands) or water (oil shale).

the box. The pipes bring the heated air or water to areas of the building where they are needed.
15. Sediment builds up behind the dams, which eventually makes them unusable for producing electric power.
16. People need fresh water for drinking, cooking, growing food, and bathing.
17. Farmers can use methods such as contour plowing and strip cropping to reduce soil erosion and nutrient loss. They can also cut down on chemical contamination of soil by using natural fertilizers such as manure and compost, and by using pest-control methods that rely on fewer pesticides, such as Integrated Pest Management.
18. Some of the earliest laws were passed in the 1970s, as the result of a number of serious pollution incidents that got the attention of the public and government officials.
19. Some anticlines act as oil traps that contain petroleum and natural gas. Anticlines keep the petroleum and gas from escaping to the surface.

ASSESSMENT

23. Recycling paper results in decreased need for making new paper. This means preserving forest resources by cutting down fewer trees and using less energy resources to run mills where paper is made. Manufacturing less paper also means that paper mills would produce less pollution.

24. Increased use of alternate energy sources could result in decreased use of fossil fuels, which would make the known resources last longer. Their use also could reduce pollution.

25. A vein deposit of ore can form when hot, metal-rich fluids that form in magma chambers move into fractures in adjacent rock. As the fluids cool, metal separates out of the solution to form metal deposits as veins in the rock.

26. In both cases, the power source turns a turbine, which turns a generator that produces electricity. In a tidal plant, the movement of the tides drives the turbine. In a nuclear plant, the heat created by fission creates steam that drives the turbine.

Analyze Data

27. The graph shows the average surface temperature of the atmosphere between 1860 and 2000.

28. The average temperature has generally been trending upward; the average temperature in 2000 was about 14.4°C.

29. The graph would probably show a lower average surface temperature. The large-scale burning of fossil fuels that began with industrialization gradually raised the amount of the greenhouse gas carbon dioxide in the air, which likely accounts for part of the global temperature rise after that time.

Concepts in Action

30. Limestone can be classified as an industrial mineral and a building material. As a stone used for structures, limestone is a building material. As a soil neutralizer and an ingredient in steel, limestone is an industrial mineral.

31. Possible answer: Facilities take up a lot of space; solar power can't produce power at night or in cloudy weather. Accept any other reasonable answers.

32. Ozone shields Earth from most of the sun's harmful ultraviolet radiation. The loss of ozone means more UV reaches Earth's surface, resulting in a higher incidence of certain health problems such as cataracts and skin cancers.

Think Critically

22. Apply Concepts Some people predict that tar sands and oil shale will one day supply much of our energy needs. Are tar sands and oil shale a good long-term energy solution? Explain.

23. Relate Cause and Effect What effect can recycling paper have on the use of resources and the creation of pollution?

24. Infer How might an increased use of alternative energy sources such as wind and solar radiation affect the lifetime of fossil fuel resources?

25. Summarize Describe how a hydrothermal solution can produce a vein deposit of ore.

26. Compare and Contrast What is the difference between how electricity is produced with tides and how it is produced in a nuclear power plant?

Analyze Data

Use the diagram below to answer Questions 27–29.

27. Use Graphs What does this graph show?

28. Interpret Graphs What is the general temperature trend during the time period shown on the graph? What was the average temperature in 2000?

29. Draw Conclusions How would you expect the graph to be different between 1700 and 1800, before the start of widespread industrialization? Explain.

Concepts in Action

30. Classify Limestone is a nonmetallic mineral that has several uses: as a stone used for structures; as a substance used to neutralize acidic soils; as an ingredient in the manufacture of steel. Should limestone be classified as an industrial mineral or a building mineral? Explain.

31. Analyze Concepts The factors in favor of the use of solar power include the fact that the fuel it uses is free, it's renewable, and it doesn't create pollution. Identify drawbacks of the use of solar power.

32. Summarize What is the effect of the destruction of ozone on human life?

33. Connect Concepts What is the relationship between petroleum production, the increased use of hybrid cars, and the level of air pollutants regulated by the Clean Air Act that are in the air?

Performance-Based Assessment

Draw Conclusions Locate an electric power plant that is in or close to your community. Find out which method it uses to produce electricity. Take into consideration the way the plant produces power, its location, the pollution it produces, and the number of people it serves. Write a short essay on the plant's impact on the environment and on your community in general.

---

33. The increased use of hybrid cars would probably result in less use of fuels such as gasoline, which is made from petroleum. Lower petroleum production would probably be possible. Less burning of fuels such as gasoline would mean less production of gases in auto exhaust that are regulated by the Clean Air Act, such as carbon monoxide, nitrogen oxides, and particulates.

Performance-Based Assessment

Student answers will vary based on the power plants in or near your community. Answers should show students' understanding of the characteristics and impacts of the process used to produce electricity at the plant, and the plant's impact on the environment.

Standardized Test Prep

Standardized Test Prep

1 B
2 G
3 C
4 G
5 D

Tips for Success

Make Logical Connections A cause-and-effect statement may seem to be true when it is actually false. The statement may seem true because the stated cause and effect are both accurate. However, there may be no logical connection between the cause and the effect. In the question below, the opening phrase contains an accurate statement about fossil fuels. But only one answer provides a logical effect of the statement in the opening phrase.

Because fossil fuels are nonrenewable resources,—

  A solar energy is renewable
  B petroleum and natural gas often form together
  C supplies of coal, oil, and natural gas are finite
  D most power plants in the United States use fossil fuels to produce electricity

(Answer: C)

Choose the letter that *best* answers the question or completes the statement.

1 Which one of the substances listed below is a fossil fuel?
  A uranium
  B petroleum
  C carbon dioxide
  D granite

2 Recycling is an important way to reduce resource consumption because—
  F reducing waste is better than recycling it
  G it decreases the use of new resources to make products
  H recycling is not a new way to save resources
  J curbside pick-up makes recycling more convenient in many communities

The line graph below shows U.S. energy consumption between 1970 and 2000, and projected consumption between 2000 and 2020. Use the graph to answer Questions 3 and 4.

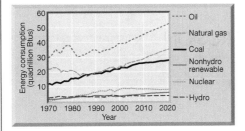

3 Which fuel source had the highest rate of consumption during this period?
  A coal
  B nuclear
  C oil
  D hydroelectric

4 Which renewable energy source is most widely used?
  F coal
  G hydroelectric
  H natural gas
  J nuclear

5 Which of the following is an example of a nonpoint source of pollution of freshwater resources?
  A leaking septic tank
  B outflow pipe from a chemical plant
  C leak from an underground gasoline storage tank
  D oil and salt from highways and roads

If You Have Trouble With . . .

Question	1	2	3	4	5
See Lesson	4.1	4.4	4.1	4.2	4.3

5 Weathering, Soil, and Mass Movements Planning Guide

BIGIDEA: WEATHERING AND EROSION

Lesson Objectives		Activities
5.1 Weathering, pp. 126–132 5.1 **Define** mechanical weathering. 5.2 **Explain** chemical weathering. 5.3 **Identify** the factors that affect the rate of weathering.		TE Build Science Skills, p. 127 L2 TE Teacher Demo: Modeling Exfoliation, p. 128 L2 TE Build Science Skills, p. 129 L2
5.2 Soil, pp. 133–142 5.4 **Recognize** the major components of soil and **list** the most important factors in soil formation. 5.5 **Explain** how soil varies with depth. 5.6 **Compare and contrast** the three common types of soil. 5.7 **Demonstrate** how human activities affect the rate of soil erosion.		TE Teacher Demo: Water Absorption in Different Soils, p. 134 L2 TE Build Science Skills, p. 136 L2 TE Build Science Skills, p. 137 L2 TE Build Science Skills, p. 140 L2
5.3 Mass Movements, pp. 143–147 5.8 **Define** mass movement. 5.9 **Identify** the factors that trigger mass movements. 5.10 **Classify** mass movements.		TE Teacher Demo: Oversteepened Slopes, p. 144 L2
Chapter Features and Labs		
Try It What Causes Weathering? p. 125		LM Some Factors That Affect Soil Erosion L2
How Earth Works pp. 148–149		
Exploration Lab Effect of Temperature on Chemical Weathering, pp. 150–151		

Ability Levels

L1	For students who need additional help
L2	For all students
L3	For students who need to be challenged

Components

SE	Student Edition	LP	Lesson Plans
TE	Teacher's Edition	AA	Active Art
LM	Laboratory Manual	PD	Planet Diary
CT	Chapter Tests	GEODe	Geode CD-ROM
GRSW	Guided Reading & Study Workbook	eText	
CTB	Computer Test Bank		

Resources	Lesson Assessment
GRSW Lesson 5.1 **LP** Lesson Planning 5.1 **GEODe** Sculpturing Earth's Surface: External vs Internal Process	**SE** Lesson 5.1 Assessment, p. 132 **eText** Lesson 5.1
GRSW Lesson 5.2 **LP** Lesson Planning 5.2 **AA** Soil Layers **GEODe** Earth's Materials: Sedimentary Rocks	**SE** Lesson 5.2 Assessment, p. 142 **eText** Lesson 5.2
GRSW Lesson 5.3 **LP** Lesson Planning 5.3 **PD** Mass Movements	**SE** Lesson 5.3 Assessment, p. 142 **eText** Lesson 5.3

Materials for Activities and Labs

Quantities for each group

STUDENT EDITION

Try It, p. 125
1-L plastic container with lid, rocks, water, strainer, clear glass jar, hand lens

Exploration Lab, pp. 150–151
250-mL beaker, thermometer, hot water (40–50°C), ice, 5 antacid tablets, stopwatch, graph paper

TEACHER'S EDITION

Build Science Skills, p. 127
water, container, other materials of students' choice

Teacher Demo, p. 128
large onion, small kitchen knife

Build Science Skills, p. 129
new nail, rusted nail

Teacher Demo, p. 134
sand, silt, clay, water, three plastic cups, nail, 250-mL beaker, paper towel

Build Science Skills, p. 136
hand lens, soil sample

Build Science Skills, p. 137
thermometer, lamp, soil samples

Build Science Skills, p. 140
soil, plastic container, spray bottle with adjustable tip, water

Teacher Demo, p. 144
bag of potting soil, water, cardboard box, plastic knife

Assessment

CHAPTER ASSESSMENT
SE Assessment, pp. 153–154
CT Chapter 5 Test
CTB Chapter 5
eText Chapter 5

21st Century Learning

Self-Direction: How is your town weathering? TE p. 152

Before You Teach
Weathering, Soil, and Mass Movements

Michael Wysession
Washington University

Common Themes

As fast as plate tectonics creates land, weathering destroys it. The ultimate energy source of weathering is the sun, and its major agents are water and gravity. It could be said that the first law of geology is that rocks fall downhill. This occurs as mass movements, which are driven by Earth's gravitational attraction.

Space and Time The entire surface of continents is slowly being destroyed through a combination of mechanical and chemical weathering. Mechanical weathering primarily occurs by frost wedging, unloading (pressure release), and the activities of plants and animals. Chemical weathering occurs through reactions involving water and materials dissolved within it. The rates of weathering are highly variable, and depend upon regional rock types and climate.

Forces and Motion Mass movements involve portions of the ground moving downhill together. They take many different forms, including rockfalls, slides, slumps, flows, and creep. Mass movements can be triggered by too much or too little water, over-steepened slopes, or the occurrence of earthquakes.

Matter and Energy Weathering of rock results in the production of soil, which is vital for most organisms on Earth because it supports plant life. Soil contains a mixture of mineral matter (in differing amounts of sand, silt, and clay), organic matter, water, and air. Soil develops from the top down, and varies greatly depending upon the type of parent rock and regional climate.

Earth as a System Chemical weathering occurs more rapidly when rainwater is acidic, so the formation of acid rain through human industrial activities has greatly increased weathering in some parts of the world.

EARTH SCIENCE REFRESHER

Causes of Chemical Weathering

Chemical weathering is the result of the remarkable properties of water. Because of the polar nature of the water molecule (partial positive charge on hydrogen atoms off to one side of the molecule, the partial negative charge on the oxygen atom off to the other side), all minerals can be disassembled into their ion and atom "building blocks" to some degree by water. This process, called dissolution, is very important in the weathering of minerals like calcite, and therefore for the formation of caves in rocks like limestone, especially if the water is acidic.

When water reacts with carbon dioxide, it creates carbonic acid. This chemical not only enhances dissolution, but performs weathering in another way. When carbonic acid and water react with minerals like feldspar, some of the feldspar's ions are removed, and new minerals are formed. This process, called hydrolysis, is responsible for the weathering of feldspars into clay minerals.

Water chemically reacts with minerals that contain metals like iron in a different manner. In a process called oxidation, water and oxygen react with metal-rich minerals to form new minerals. This process is often called rusting, and the new minerals are the rust.

It is important to establish the difference between the process that occurs when a substance dissolves in water, and the process that occurs when substances react in a water solution. When describing chemical weathering in the chapter, we note that water reacts with gases in the air to form acids or causes oxidation. Water also provides the medium in which soluble ions react.

Chemical Weathering and Climate Change

In addition to being responsible for shaping the surface of the continents, weathering also plays an important role in controlling climate. This is because of carbon dioxide.

Carbon dioxide, which is important in weathering as carbonic acid, is also important in controlling climate because it absorbs radiation emitted by Earth's surface, in the process called the *greenhouse effect.* If a lot of the carbon and oxygen that could form carbon dioxide join to yield carbonic acid instead, Earth's atmosphere contains less carbon dioxide, and global cooling can occur. Interestingly, these two factors—weathering and the greenhouse effect—work counter to each other, and help to stabilize Earth's climate. Carbon dioxide is constantly entering the atmosphere from volcanic eruptions and from the ocean. Higher levels of carbon dioxide in the atmosphere probably lead to a warmer climate, which in turn accelerates weathering. However, this weathering removes carbon dioxide from the atmosphere in the form of carbonic acid, thereby lowering global temperatures again.

An interesting result of the connection between weathering and the greenhouse effect is that plate tectonics can alter global climate. During times of active continental collisions, many new mountains are created. This causes accelerated weathering rates, and therefore increases the removal of carbon dioxide from the atmosphere. The result is that periods of global cooling are associated with periods of mountain building. The overall global cooling trend that has occurred over the past 40 million years has been attributed to the collision of India with Asia and the formation of the Himalayan Mountains.

BUILD READING LITERACY
Summarize
Briefly Restating the Main Ideas

Strategy Help students understand a topic by summarizing part of the chapter. Students read a section of the text and then identify main ideas and supporting details. They summarize what they have read by briefly restating the main concepts in a few sentences. Summarizing can be employed to review brief subsections as well as entire sections and chapters. Have students read the beginning of Lesson 5.1, pp. 126–128.

Example

1. Ask students to carefully read the selected passage. Then, have them review the passage and identify the main ideas. Demonstrate this process by using the bold headings, boldface sentences, and vocabulary as aids in determining what the passage is mostly about. List the main ideas on the board.

2. Direct students to write brief summaries of the passage by restating each of the main ideas in their own words. Remind students to focus on the most important concepts, omitting details and examples. Students should check to be sure that their summaries cover the terms mentioned in the bold headings.

3. Assign the next passage for students to read and summarize. You may want to have students work in small groups to compare their summaries.

4. Have students read and summarize the rest of Lesson 5.1.

See TE p. 139 for a script on how to use this strategy with students. For additional strategies, see TE pp. 127 and 145.

ASSESS PRIOR KNOWLEDGE

Use the Chapter Pretest below to assess students' prior knowledge. As needed, review these concepts.

Review Science Concepts

Lesson 5.1 Review the processes of the rock cycle. In particular, focus on how weathering breaks down rocks.

Lesson 5.2 Reemphasize that the Earth system is made up of numerous interacting subsystems. Discuss how the biosphere interacts with the solid Earth.

Lesson 5.3 Review the definition of *gravity*. Make sure students understand that gravity is a universal force between all objects. Remind students that certain human activities can negatively impact the environment.

5 Weathering, Soil, and Mass Movements

Big idea | **Weathering and Erosion**
Q: What processes break down Earth's surface?

Weathering caused these rocks to fall onto this road in the hills of Bolivia.

124

Chapter Pretest

1. What process breaks down rock into smaller pieces? *(c)*
  a. cementation   **b.** compaction
  c. weathering   **d.** deposition

2. Is weathering classified as an internal or external process? Explain your answer. *(Weathering is an external process. It acts on rocks at or near Earth's surface.)*

3. True or False: The biosphere includes Earth's core, the less dense mantle, and the crust. *(False)*

4. Give one example of how living things interact with their physical environment. *(Sample answer: A beaver may build a dam across a stream and create a large aquatic environment.)*

5. Which statement best describes the force of gravity? *(d)*
  a. Earth's gravity pulls objects toward the center of the planet.

  b. Objects do not have to be in contact with one another to experience the force of gravity.

  c. Gravity is the force that acts between any two objects.

  d. All of the above

6. Describe one positive effect and one negative effect of human activities on the environment. *(Sample answer: A positive effect is creating a wildlife refuge. A negative effect is cutting down a forest.)*

INQUIRY
TRY IT!

WHAT CAUSES WEATHERING?

Procedure

1. Fill a 1-L plastic container about half full of rocks. Add enough water to barely cover the rocks.
2. Place a tight-fitting lid on the container and shake the container vigorously 100 times.
3. Hold a strainer over a clear glass jar. Pour the water and rocks into the strainer.
4. Use a hand lens to observe the bottom and sides of the empty container. Then use the hand lens to observe the water in the glass jar.

Think About It

1. **Observe** What did you see on the bottom or sides of the empty container during Step 4? How did shaking the rock-and-water mixture change the appearance of the water?
2. **Predict** How do you think your observations would change if you put the rocks and water back in the container and repeated Steps 2 through 4 several more times?
3. **Predict** Suppose you found a stream where water ran over a rock ledge into a pool. What would you expect to find at the bottom of the pool?

125

ENGAGE/EXPLORE

INQUIRY
TRY IT!

WHAT CAUSES WEATHERING? L2

Purpose Students will observe how weathering breaks down rocks.

Skills Observe, Predict

Prep Time 10 minutes

Materials 1-L plastic container with lid, rocks, water, strainer, clear glass jar, hand lens

Class Time 15 minutes

Teaching Tips Have students work in pairs to complete the activity. One student can shake the container while the other counts the number of shakes.

If available, you can consider using marble chips in lieu of rocks.

Expected Outcome Shaking the container simulates weathering. Students will observe small rock fragments and other sediments in the bottom of the container and in the water.

Think About It

1. There should be small rock fragments on the bottom or sides of the empty container. The water in the jar may be slightly cloudy, and there may be grit on the bottom of the jar.
2. Sample answer: There would be more rock fragments in the empty container and more grit in the jar, and the water in the jar would become cloudier.
3. rock fragments or other sediment

LESSON 5.1

1 FOCUS

Lesson Objectives
5.1 **Define** mechanical weathering.
5.2 **Explain** chemical weathering.
5.3 **Identify** the factors that affect the rate of weathering.

Build Vocabulary [L2]
Vocabulary Rating Chart Have each student construct a chart with four columns labeled Term, Can Define or Use It, Heard or Seen It, and Don't Know. Students should then write the vocabulary terms *mechanical weathering, frost wedging, talus, exfoliation, and chemical weathering* in column 1 and rate their knowledge of each term by putting a check in one of the other columns. Before reading the text, ask questions that help students anticipate the meaning of the terms based on prior knowledge. For example, **Ask:** What is a wedge used for? *(to force objects apart)* After students have read the lesson, have them revise their charts.

Reading Strategy [L2]
a. process in which physical forces break rock into pieces without changing the rock's mineral composition
b. process in which water enters cracks in a rock, enlarges the cracks by freezing and expanding, and breaks the rock
c. large piles of rock fragments that usually form at the base of cliffs
d. process in which slabs of outer rock separate and break loose
e. the transformation of rock into one or more new compounds

5.1 Weathering

Key Questions
 What is mechanical weathering?

 What is chemical weathering?

 What factors affect the rate of weathering?

Vocabulary
- mechanical weathering
- frost wedging • talus
- exfoliation
- chemical weathering

Reading Strategy
Build Vocabulary Copy the table. As you read the section, define each vocabulary term.

Vocabulary Term	Definition
Mechanical weathering	a. _____ ? _____
Frost wedging	b. _____ ? _____
Talus	c. _____ ? _____
Exfoliation	d. _____ ? _____
Chemical weathering	e. _____ ? _____

EARTH'S SURFACE is constantly changing. Internal forces gradually raise some parts of the surface through mountain building and volcanic activity. At the same time, external processes continually break rock apart and move the debris to lower elevations, as shown in **Figure 1.** The breaking down of rock at or near Earth's surface is called weathering. Weathering is a basic part of the rock cycle and a key process in the Earth system. There are two types of weathering—mechanical and chemical. Though these processes are different, they are at work at the same time.

Mechanical Weathering
If you have walked on gravel you have participated in mechanical weathering. **Mechanical weathering occurs when physical forces break rock into smaller pieces without changing the rock's mineral composition.** Each piece has the same characteristics as the original rock. Breaking a rock into smaller pieces increases the total surface area of the rock. Look at **Figure 2.** When rock is broken apart, more surface area is exposed to chemical weathering.

FIGURE 1
Weathering Ice, rain, and wind are slowly breaking down the rock in this mountain. The rock fragments accumulate in sloped deposits at the base of the mountain.

16 square units ×
6 sides ×
1 cube =
_____
96 square units

4 square units ×
6 sides ×
8 cubes =
_____
192 square units

1 square unit ×
6 sides ×
64 cubes =
_____
384 square units

VISUAL SUMMARY

MECHANICAL WEATHERING AND SURFACE AREA

FIGURE 2 By breaking a rock into smaller pieces, mechanical weathering increases the surface area that can be exposed to chemical weathering. **Calculate** *What would be the total surface area if each of the 64 cubes shown in the right diagram were broken into 8 equal-sized cubes?*

Various events and forces can cause mechanical weathering. 🔑 **In nature, three physical processes are especially important causes of mechanical weathering: frost wedging, unloading, and biological activity.**

Frost Wedging When liquid water freezes, it expands by about 9 percent, exerting a tremendous outward force. This force is great enough to burst water pipes during the winter. In nature, water works its way into every crack in rock. When water freezes and expands, it enlarges the cracks. After many freeze-thaw cycles, the rock breaks into pieces. This process, which is shown in **Figure 3**, is called **frost wedging.** Frost wedging is most common in mountainous regions in the middle latitudes, where daily freezing and thawing often occur. Sections of rock that are wedged loose may tumble into piles called **talus,** which typically form at the base of steep, rocky slopes. Large deposits of talus are visible at the base of the mountains shown in Figure 1.

☑ **Reading Checkpoint** *Explain how water can cause mechanical weathering.*

FIGURE 3 Frost Wedging
Rainwater entered cracks in this boulder. Each time the water froze, it expanded. Eventually, the boulder split.

Weathering, Soil, and Mass Movements **127**

Weathering, Soil, and Mass Movements **127**

LESSON 5.1

FIGURE 4 Unloading and Exfoliation A Uplift and erosion expose a buried mass of igneous rock. Reduced pressure on the rock, called unloading, causes the outer rock layers to expand. They separate from the rest of the rock mass. This process is called exfoliation. **B** The granite layers of Half Dome in Yosemite National Park, California, are undergoing exfoliation.

FIGURE 5 Biological Activity The roots of this tree are causing mechanical weathering by widening the cracks in the rock.

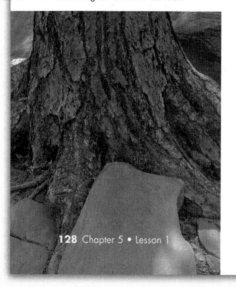

Unloading Large masses of igneous rock may be exposed through uplift and erosion of overlying rocks. When that happens, the pressure exerted on the igneous rock is reduced. This is known as unloading. As illustrated in **Figure 4A,** unloading causes the outer layers of the rock to expand more than the rock below. Slabs of outer rock separate like the layers of an onion and break loose in a process called **exfoliation.** Exfoliation is especially common in rock masses made of granite. It often produces dome-shaped rock formations called exfoliation domes, as shown in **Figure 4B.** Well-known exfoliation domes are Stone Mountain, Georgia, and Liberty Cap, which, like Half Dome, is in Yosemite National Park.

A striking example of the weathering effects of unloading is shown in deep underground mining. Newly cut mine tunnels suddenly reduce the pressure on the surrounding rock. As a result, large rock slabs sometimes explode off the tunnel walls.

Biological Activity The activities of organisms, including plants, burrowing animals, and humans, can also cause mechanical weathering. As **Figure 5** shows, plant roots grow into cracks in rock, wedging the rock apart as they grow. Burrowing animals move rocks to the surface, where weathering is more rapid. Decaying organisms produce compounds called acids that cause chemical weathering. Humans accelerate mechanical weathering through deforestation and blasting in search of minerals or in the creation of new roads.

Chemical Weathering

💬 **Chemical weathering is the transformation of rock into one or more new compounds.** The new compounds remain mostly unchanged as long as the environment in which they formed does not change. You can contrast chemical weathering and mechanical weathering with a sheet of paper. Tearing the paper into small pieces is like mechanical weathering of rock. Burning the paper, which changes it into carbon dioxide and water, is like chemical weathering.

Water Water is the most important agent of chemical weathering. Water promotes chemical weathering by absorbing gases from the atmosphere and the ground. These dissolved substances then chemically react with various minerals. Oxygen dissolved in water reacts easily with certain minerals, forming oxides. For example, iron-rich minerals get a yellow to reddish-brown coating of iron oxide when they react with oxygen. Iron oxide is the rust that forms when iron-containing objects are exposed to water, as shown in **Figure 6.**

Water absorbs carbon dioxide when rain falls through the atmosphere. Water that seeps through the ground also picks up carbon dioxide from decaying organic matter. The carbon dioxide dissolved in water forms carbonic acid. This is the weak acid in carbonated soft drinks. Carbonic acid reacts with many common minerals.

Water in the atmosphere also absorbs sulfur oxides and nitrogen oxides. These oxides are produced by the burning of coal and petroleum. Through a series of chemical reactions, these pollutants are converted into acids that are the major cause of acid precipitation. Acid precipitation accelerates the chemical weathering of stone monuments and structures.

☑ **Reading Checkpoint** *How are water, oxygen, and carbon dioxide involved in chemical weathering?*

Chemical Weathering of Granite To illustrate how chemical weathering can change the properties of rock, let's consider granite. Recall that granite consists mainly of the minerals feldspar and quartz. When granite is exposed to water containing carbonic acid, the feldspar is converted mostly to clay minerals. Quartz, in contrast, is much more resistant to carbonic acid and remains unchanged. As the feldspar slowly changes to clay, the quartz grains are released from the granite. Rivers transport some of this weathered debris to the sea. The tiny clay particles may be carried far from shore. The quartz grains are deposited near the shore where they become the main component of beaches.

FIGURE 6 Rust Oxygen reacted with the iron in these barrels, forming iron oxide, or rust.

Facts and Figures

Weathering creates many important mineral deposits by concentrating minor amounts of metals that are scattered throughout unweathered rock into economically valuable concentrations. Such a transformation can take place in two ways. In one situation, chemical weathering coupled with downward-infiltrating water removes undesired materials from decomposing rock, leaving the desired elements enriched in the upper zones of the soil. The second way is basically the reverse of the first. The desirable elements that are found in low concentrations near the surface are removed and carried to lower zones, where they are redeposited and become more concentrated.

LESSON 5.1

During a student's education, a good deal of emphasis is placed on the scientific method and proper investigation techniques. For this reason, many students mistakenly think that scientific knowledge advances mainly through experimentation. In fact, in several fields, including geology, observation is the key to understanding natural processes. This section offers an excellent opportunity to point out the role of observation in science. Challenge students to brainstorm other fields where observation is crucial to understanding natural processes. *(astronomy, biology, ecology)*
Verbal

Integrate Chemistry

Weathering of Granite The weathering of the potassium feldspar component of granite takes place as follows:

$2KAlSi_3O_8 + 2(H^+ + HCO_3^-) + H_2O \longrightarrow Al_2Si_2O_5(OH)_4 + 2K^+ + 2HCO_3^- + 4SiO_2$.

In this reaction, the hydrogen ions (H^+) attack and replace potassium ions (K^+) in the feldspar structure, thereby disrupting the crystalline network. Once removed, the potassium is available as a nutrient for plants or becomes the soluble salt potassium bicarbonate ($KHCO_3$), which may be incorporated into other minerals or carried to the ocean in dissolved form by streams. Have students summarize the chemical reaction in their own words. *(Potassium feldspar reacts with carbonic acid and water to produce mainly clay minerals and dissolved minerals.)*
Logical

Table 1 Products of Chemical Weathering		
Mineral	**Residual Products**	**Materials in Solution**
Quartz	Quartz grains	Silica
Feldspars	Clay minerals	Silica K^+, Na^+, Ca^{2+}
Amphibole (hornblende)	Clay minerals Limonite Hematite	Silica Ca^{2+}, Mg^{2+}
Olivine	Limonite Hematite	Silica Mg^{2+}

Chemical Weathering of Silicate Minerals Recall that silicate minerals make up most of Earth's crust and are composed largely of just eight elements. When silicate minerals undergo chemical weathering, the sodium, calcium, potassium, and magnesium they contain dissolve and are carried away by groundwater. Iron reacts with oxygen, producing iron oxide. The three remaining elements are aluminum, silicon, and oxygen. These elements usually combine with water and produce clay minerals. **Table 1** lists products of chemical weathering.

Spheroidal Weathering Chemical weathering can change the physical shape of rock as well as its chemical composition. For example, when water enters along the joints in a rock, it weathers the corners and edges most rapidly. These parts of the rock have a greater surface area than the faces have. As a result, the corners and edges become more rounded. The rock takes on a spherical shape, as shown in **Figure 7A**. This process is called spheroidal weathering.

As **Figure 7B** shows, spheroidal weathering sometimes causes the outer layers of a rock to separate from the rock's main body. This can happen when the minerals in the rock turn to clay, which swells by absorbing water. The swelling causes the layers to break loose and fall off. This allows chemical weathering to penetrate deeper into the boulder. Although the effects of this type of spheroidal weathering resemble exfoliation, the two processes are different. Spheroidal weathering is a form of chemical weathering. Exfoliation is caused by unloading. The layers that separate from the rock during exfoliation are not chemically changed.

FIGURE 7 Spheroidal Weathering
A The edges of these granite rocks in California's Joshua Tree National Monument were rounded through spheroidal weathering.

B Spheroidal weathering has caused the outer layers of this rock to loosen and separate.

FIGURE 8 Chemical Weathering of Different Rocks

A This granite gravestone, placed in 1868, shows little evidence of chemical weathering.

B The inscription date (1872) on this marble gravestone is nearly illegible due to chemical weathering.

Apply Concepts In what type of climate would you expect to find gravestones with significant amounts of chemical weathering? In what type of climate would you expect to find gravestones less affected by chemical weathering?

Rate of Weathering

Mechanical weathering affects the rate of chemical weathering. By breaking rock into smaller pieces, mechanical weathering accelerates chemical weathering by increasing the surface area of exposed rock. **Two other factors that affect the rate of weathering are rock characteristics and climate.**

Rock Characteristics Physical characteristics of rock, such as cracks, are important in weathering because they influence the ability of water to penetrate rock. However, a rock's mineral composition also dramatically affects its rate of weathering. You can see this by visiting a cemetery and comparing old gravestones made from different rock types. Gravestones made of granite, like the one in **Figure 8A,** are relatively resistant to chemical weathering. You can easily read the inscriptions on a granite gravestone that is over 100 years old. In contrast, marble gravestones undergo much more rapid chemical weathering, as shown in **Figure 8B.** Marble is composed of calcite (calcium carbonate), which easily dissolves even in weak acids.

Silicates are the most abundant mineral group. Silicates weather in the same sequence as their order of crystallization. Olivine crystallizes first and weathers most rapidly. Quartz, which crystallizes last, is the most resistant to weathering.

Weathering, Soil, and Mass Movements **131**

LESSON 5.1

Build Science Skills L2

Communicate Results Show students a copy or transparency of Bowen's reaction series. Have them note the order of crystallization of minerals. Students can then use the series to sequence the resistance of silicates to weathering, starting with the least resistant mineral. *(olivine, pyroxene, amphibole, biotite mica, potassium feldspar, muscovite mica, and quartz)*
Verbal

3 ASSESS

Evaluate Understanding L2

Have students describe the relationship between burning coal and chemical weathering. *(Oxides produced by burning coal react with water in the atmosphere to create acid precipitation. Acid precipitation, in turn, accelerates rates of chemical weathering.)*

Reteach L1

Show students photographs of several examples of different types of weathering, such as unloading and spheroidal weathering, and have them classify the examples as mechanical or chemical.

Answers

Figure 9 *Weathering is happening most rapidly at the tops of the pinnacles.*

Assessment Answers

1. It does not change.
2. Unloading is the reduction in pressure that happens when a mass of rock is exposed to Earth's surface. It causes the outer layers of the rock to expand, which makes slabs of outer rock separate and break loose.
3. It transforms them into one or more new compounds.

FIGURE 9 Pinnacles These boldly sculpted pinnacles in Utah's Bryce Canyon National Park show differential weathering.
Draw Conclusions *In which parts of these formations is weathering happening most rapidly?*

Climate Climatic factors, especially temperature and moisture, have a strong effect on the rate of weathering. For example, these factors control the frequency of freeze-thaw cycles, which affect the amount of frost wedging. Temperature and moisture also affect the rate of chemical weathering. They influence the kind of vegetation and how much is present. Regions with lush vegetation generally have a thick layer of soil rich in decaying organic matter that releases acids into the water.

The climate most favorable for chemical weathering has high temperatures and abundant moisture. So, chemical weathering is very slow in arid regions. It is also slow in polar regions because the low temperatures there keep moisture locked up as ice.

Differential Weathering Different parts of a rock mass often weather at different rates. This process, called differential weathering, has several causes. Differences in mineral composition are one cause. More resistant rock protrudes as pinnacles, or high peaks, such as those shown in **Figure 9**. Another cause is the variation in the number and spacing of cracks in different parts of a rock mass.

5.1 Assessment

Review Key Concepts

1. What happens to a rock's mineral composition during mechanical weathering?

2. What is unloading? How does it contribute to weathering?

3. How does chemical weathering affect the compounds in rock?

4. Name two rock characteristics and two climatic factors that affect the rate of weathering.

Think Critically

5. Use Analogies Think about the following processes: dissolving a piece of rock salt in a pan of water and grinding a peach pit in a garbage disposal. Which process is more like mechanical weathering, and which is more like chemical weathering?

6. Apply Concepts The level of carbon dioxide in the atmosphere is increasing. How might this affect the rate of chemical weathering of Earth's surface rocks? Explain your reasoning.

MATH PRACTICE

7. Calculate Suppose frost wedging splits a spherical rock 2 m in diameter into two equal-sized hemispheres. Calculate the total surface area of the original rock and of the two hemispheres. (The area of a circle = πr^2, and the surface area of a sphere = $4\pi r^2$, where r is the radius. Use 3.14 as the value of π.)

4. Rock characteristics include cracks and mineral composition; climatic factors include temperature and moisture.
5. mechanical weathering—grinding a peach pit in a garbage disposal; chemical weathering—dissolving a piece of rock salt in water
6. An increased level of carbon dioxide should result in higher levels of carbonic acid, which reacts with many common minerals.

Therefore, the rate of chemical weathering should increase.
7. diameter = 2 m; radius = 1 m; area of sphere = $4\pi(1 \text{ m})^2 = 4\pi \text{ m}^2 = 12.56 \text{ m}^2$; area of two hemispheres = area of sphere + (2 × area of circle) = $4\pi \text{ m}^2 + [2 \times \pi(1 \text{ m})^2] = 4\pi \text{ m}^2 + 2\pi \text{ m}^2 = 6\pi \text{ m}^2 = 18.84 \text{ m}^2$

5.2 Soil

SOIL, an important product of weathering, covers most land surfaces. Along with air and water, it is one of our most important resources. All life depends on a dozen or so elements that come from Earth's crust. Once weathering and other processes create soil, plants absorb the elements as dissolved minerals and make them available to animals, including humans.

Characteristics of Soil

Weathering produces a layer of rock and mineral fragments called **regolith,** which covers nearly all of Earth's land surface. **Soil is the part of the regolith that supports the growth of plants.** Three important characteristics of soil are its composition, texture, and structure.

Soil Composition
Soil has four major components: mineral matter, or broken-down rock; organic matter, or humus, which is the decayed remains of organisms; water; and air. The proportions of these components vary in different soils. **Figure 10** shows that in a good-quality surface soil, mineral matter and organic matter make up half the total volume. The other half consists of pore spaces where air and water circulate. If soil is deprived of water or air, its composition changes and its quality is greatly reduced.

FIGURE 10 Composition by Volume of Good-Quality Soil
Use Graphs *What percentage of this soil consists of water and mineral matter?*

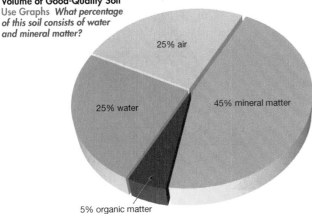

- 25% air
- 45% mineral matter
- 25% water
- 5% organic matter

Key Questions

- What are the major components of soil?

- What are the most important factors in soil formation?

- How does soil vary with depth?

- What are three common types of soil?

- How do human activities affect the rate of soil erosion?

Vocabulary
- regolith • soil
- soil horizon • soil profile
- pedalfer • pedocal
- laterite

Reading Strategy

Compare and Contrast
Copy the table. After you read, compare the three types of soils by completing the table.

Soil Type	Where It's Found
Pedalfer	a. ___?___
Pedocal	b. ___?___
Laterite	c. ___?___

LESSON 5.2

2 INSTRUCT

Use Visuals L1

Figure 11 Give students several sample soil textures, and have them use the diagram to identify the corresponding soil type. For example, **Ask:** What type of soil consists of 60 percent clay, 20 percent sand, and 20 percent silt? *(clay)*
Verbal

Teacher **Demo**

WATER ABSORPTION IN DIFFERENT SOILS L2

Purpose Students will observe the ability of different soils to absorb water.

Materials sand, silt, clay, water, 3 plastic cups, nail, 250-mL beaker, paper towel

Procedure Use the nail to puncture a small hole in the bottom of each cup. Fill one cup halfway with sand. Fill another cup with silt and a third cup with clay. Place the cups on a paper towel. Ask students to predict which soil sample will absorb the most water. Then pour about 50 mL of water into each cup.

Expected Outcomes Students will correctly predict that the silt absorbs the most water. Water rapidly drains out of the sand and does not easily penetrate the clay.
Visual

INQUIRY APPLY IT!

Q: *I've seen photos of footprints left on the lunar surface by astronauts. Does this mean the moon has soil?*

A: Not exactly. The moon has no atmosphere, water, or biological activity. So, the weathering processes that occur on Earth don't take place on the moon. However, the lunar surface is covered by a layer of gray debris called lunar regolith, which was ejected by meteorite impacts over a few billion years. Changes occur so slowly on the lunar surface that the footprints left by the *Apollo* astronauts will probably look fresh for millions of years.

The percentage of organic matter in soil varies greatly. Certain bog soils are composed almost entirely of organic matter. Desert soils may contain only a tiny amount. In soils, organic matter or humus is an essential source of plant nutrients and increases the soil's ability to retain water. Poor soils can be enriched with the addition of humus.

The water and air components of soil are also vital for plant growth. Soil water provides the moisture needed for chemical reactions that sustain life. Soil water holds and carries nutrients in a form that plants can use. Air in the soil, especially oxygen, helps plant roots take in nutrients.

Soil Texture Most soils contain particles of different sizes. Soil texture refers to the proportions of different particle sizes. To classify soil texture, the U.S. Department of Agriculture has established categories based on the percentages of clay, silt, and sand in soil. The diagram in **Figure 11** shows how the percentages differ for each category. For example, point A, near the left-center part of the diagram, represents a soil composed of 40 percent clay, 10 percent silt, and 50 percent sand. Such a soil is called a sandy clay. In soils called loam, which occupy the central part of the diagram, neither clay, silt, nor sand is dominant.

Texture strongly influences a soil's ability to support plant life. Sandy soils may drain and dry out too quickly, while clay-rich soils drain very slowly. Plant roots often have difficulty penetrating soils that contain a high percentage of clay and silt. Loam soils are usually best for plant growth. They retain water better and store more nutrients than do soils composed mainly of clay or sand.

FIGURE 11 Soil-Texture Diagram
The texture of any soil can be represented by a point on this diagram.
Interpret Diagrams *What type of soil consists of 10 percent clay, 60 percent silt, and 30 percent sand?*

Differentiated Instruction

SPECIAL NEEDS Visuals often simplify and clarify key concepts. Take a few moments to ensure that all students correctly interpret photographs, tables, graphs, and diagrams. For example, you can have students plot the data in Figure 10 on p. 133 in a bar graph to assess their understanding of soil composition. You can make copies of Figure 11 on p. 134 and encourage students to draw intersecting lines on the soil-texture diagram, to identify soil type. If students still have difficulty interpreting Figure 11, work through the process together. Pick a point on the diagram to represent a soil sample, then trace a path along the relevant lines to help students identify the percentages of clay, silt, and sand in the sample.

Soil Structure Soil particles usually form clumps that give soils a particular structure. Soil structure determines how easily a soil can be cultivated and how susceptible it is to erosion. Soil structure also affects the ease with which water can penetrate the soil. This, in turn, influences the movement of nutrients to plant roots.

Soil Formation

Soil forms through the complex interaction of several factors. 🗝 **The most important factors in soil formation are parent material, time, climate, organisms, and slope.** Although these factors all interact, we'll examine them separately.

FIGURE 12 Parent Materials and Soils

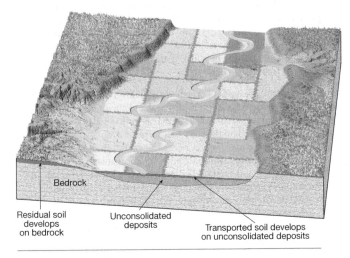

Residual soil develops on bedrock

Bedrock

Unconsolidated deposits

Transported soil develops on unconsolidated deposits

Parent Material The source of the mineral matter in soil is known as the parent material. Notice in **Figure 12** that parent material may be either bedrock or unconsolidated deposits, such as those in a river valley. The soil that forms on bedrock is called residual soil. The soil that forms on unconsolidated deposits is called transported soil. Its parent material was moved from another location by gravity, water, wind, or ice.

☑ **Reading Checkpoint** *What is the difference between residual soil and transported soil?*

Address Misconceptions L2

Show students a sample of soil. Ask them if they think the soil has always existed …in its present form. If they answer yes, students may have misconceptions about the formation of soil. Have them read the key concept sentence on p. 135. Point out that soil evolves over time. In addition, a mature soil may change in response to changes in climate, vegetation, and other factors.
Verbal

Answers

Figure 11 *silty loam*

☑ **Reading Checkpoint** *Residual soil forms on bedrock. Transported soil forms on unconsolidated deposits.*

LESSON 5.2

Integrate Biology   L2

Organic Matter Certain bog soils are composed entirely of organic matter, while desert soils may contain only a tiny percentage of organic matter. Although the quality of organic matter varies substantially among soils, it is the rare soil that completely lacks it. After students have read the text on p. 136, ask them to explain why the interactions between organisms and soil can be thought of as a continuous cycle. *(Organisms die and decay, contributing to soil fertility. Fertile soils nourish organisms, which eventually die and decay, continuing the cycle.)*
Logical

Build Science Skills   L2

Student Activity: Observe Give small groups of students a hand lens and a different soil sample taken from your area. Try to obtain the samples from widely divergent areas, such as a garden, playground, and stream bank. Have students examine the samples and write reports describing the soils. Students should mention soil color, soil texture, and other distinguishing characteristics, such as particle size and the presence of organic matter.
Kinesthetic, Visual

The nature of the parent material influences soils in two ways. First, it affects the rate of weathering and the rate of soil formation. Because unconsolidated deposits are already partly weathered, they provide more surface area for chemical weathering. Therefore, transported soil usually develops more rapidly than residual soil develops. Second, the chemical makeup of the parent material affects the soil's fertility. Fertility influences the types of plants the soil can support.

Time The longer a soil has been forming, the thicker it may become. The parent material largely determines the characteristics of young soils. But as weathering continues, the influence of the parent material can be surpassed by the other factors, especially climate.

Climate Climate has the greatest effect on soil formation. Variations in temperature and precipitation influence the rate, depth, and type of weathering. For example, a hot, wet climate may produce a thick layer of chemically weathered soil. In the same amount of time, a cold, dry climate might produce only a thin layer of mechanically weathered debris. The amount of precipitation also influences soil fertility by affecting the rate at which nutrients are removed from the soil.

Organisms The types of organisms and how many there are in a soil have a major impact on its physical and chemical properties. In fact, scientists name some soils—such as prairie soil, forest soil, and tundra soil—based on the soils' natural vegetation.

Plants are the main source of organic matter in soil. Animals and microorganisms also contribute. Microorganisms, including fungi, bacteria, and single-celled protozoans, play an active role in decomposing organisms. Because organic matter releases nutrients when it decomposes, it contributes to soil fertility.

FIGURE 13 Beneficial Burrowers Earthworms enrich the soil in which they burrow and feed.

Burrowing animals mix the mineral and organic matter in soil. Earthworms, for example, as shown in **Figure 13,** mix soil as they burrow and feed on the organic matter it contains. Holes made by burrowing animals also help water and air to penetrate into soil.

Some bacteria also aid soil fertility. Organisms require nitrogen in order to make amino acids, the building blocks of proteins. Nitrogen is very abundant in the atmosphere, but most organisms cannot absorb it as a gas. As shown in **Figure 14,** certain types of bacteria can take up nitrogen gas. They then produce ammonia, a form of nitrogen that plants can absorb. These nitrogen-fixing bacteria are common on the roots of legumes—plants such as peanuts, beans, and clover.

Much of the ammonia is actually consumed by other bacteria, called nitrifying bacteria. Nitrifying bacteria produce compounds called nitrites and nitrates, which are compounds of nitrogen and oxygen. Nitrate is the most common source of nitrogen for plants. A third type of soil bacteria, called denitrifying bacteria, break down nitrates and release nitrogen gas into the atmosphere, allowing the cycle to continue. Humans are also participants in the cycle.

136 Chapter 5 • Lesson 2

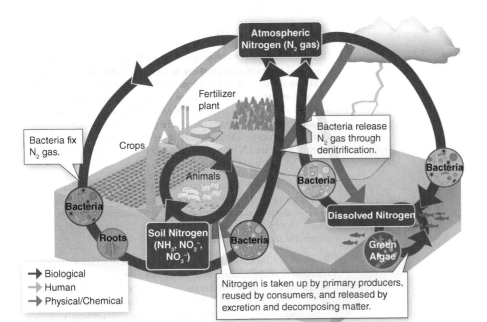

Fertilizer plant

Crops

Bacteria fix N₂ gas.

Atmospheric Nitrogen (N₂ gas)

Bacteria release N₂ gas through denitrification.

Animals

Bacteria

Bacteria

Bacteria

Dissolved Nitrogen

Roots

Soil Nitrogen (NH₃, NO₂⁻, NO₃⁻)

Bacteria

Green Algae

→ Biological
→ Human
→ Physical/Chemical

Nitrogen is taken up by primary producers, reused by consumers, and released by excretion and decomposing matter.

FIGURE 14 The Nitrogen Cycle As part of the nitrogen cycle, certain bacteria absorb nitrogen gas and produce compounds containing nitrogen that plants and algae can use. Human activities now have a considerable effect on the cycle. Large quantities of nitrate fertilizers are applied to soil. Runoff from these fertilized soils, along with sewage, can introduce excess nitrogen to bodies of water, triggering "blooms" of algae that can have negative impacts on ecosystems. **Predict** *How would planting legumes in a field affect the soil's fertility?*

Slope The slope of the land can vary greatly over short distances. Such variations can result in very different soil types. Many of the differences are related to the amount of erosion and the water content of the soil.

On steep slopes, erosion is accelerated. Little water can soak in, so the soil generally holds too little moisture for vigorous plant growth. As a result, soils are usually thin or nonexistent on steep slopes. In contrast, flat areas have little erosion and poor drainage. The waterlogged soils that form in flat areas are typically thick and dark. The dark color results from large amounts of organic matter, or humus, present in such soils.

The direction a slope faces also affects soil formation. In the temperate zone of the Northern Hemisphere, south-facing slopes receive much more sunlight than do north-facing slopes. Consequently, soils on south-facing slopes are usually warmer and drier. In the temperate zone of the Southern Hemisphere, the opposite is true. North-facing slopes receive more sunlight, and their soils tend to be warmer and drier.

☑ **Reading Checkpoint** *Explain how the slope of the land affects soil thickness.*

Build Science Skills

L2

Student Activity: Measure On a sunny day, take students outside and have them measure the temperatures of soils in south-facing slopes and north-facing slopes. If necessary, take along a small spade to loosen the soils. You may wish to insert a thermometer into the soils yourself to avoid breakage accidents. Have students record the temperatures. Students should find that soils in south-facing slopes are warmer than soils in north-facing slopes. If it is not feasible to conduct this activity outside, have students measure the temperatures of two piles of soils. One pile should be placed under a lamp to represent a south-facing slope. The other pile should be placed in the shade to represent a north-facing slope. **Kinesthetic, Visual**

Answers

Figure 14 *Planting legumes would make the soil more fertile by providing nutrients for nitrogen-fixing bacteria.*

☑ **Reading Checkpoint** *Steep slopes have more erosion, so their soil is usually thin or nonexistent. Flat areas have little erosion, so their soils are typically thick.*

Facts and Figures

When Earth is viewed as a system, soil is referred to as an interface, or common boundary where different parts of a system interact. This is an appropriate designation because soil forms where the solid Earth, the atmosphere, the hydrosphere, and the biosphere meet. Soil is a material that develops in response to complex environmental interactions among different parts of the Earth system. Over time, soil gradually evolves to a state of equilibrium or balance with the environment. Soil is dynamic and sensitive to almost every aspect of its environment. When environmental changes occur, such as climate, vegetative cover, or animal activity, the soil responds. Any such change produces a gradual alteration of soil characteristics until a new balance is reached.

Figure 15 This diagram divides a soil profile into three general horizons. Tell students that soil scientists often use a more in-depth approach—they may divide a soil profile into five or more horizons. For example, a typical O horizon is made up of fresh and decomposing organic matter. The E horizon is the zone of leaching, where inorganic soil components are dissolved and carried into lower zones. Based on Figure 15 and the related text on p. 138, have students infer the location of the O horizon and the E horizon. *(The O horizon is the uppermost layer of soil. The E horizon is located between the A horizon and the B horizon.)*
Visual

The Soil Profile

The processes that form soil operate from the surface downward. 🔑 **Soil varies in composition, texture, structure, and color at different depths.** These variations divide the soil into zones known as **soil horizons.** A vertical section through all of the soil horizons is called a **soil profile.** In some soil profiles, the soil horizons blend gradually from one to another. In others, the soil horizons are quite distinct. Mature soils usually have three distinct soil horizons, as shown in **Figure 15.** From the surface downward, these horizons are called the A, B, and C horizons.

A Horizon The A horizon is commonly known as topsoil. Its upper part consists mostly of organic matter, including loose leaves and partly decomposed plant structures. It is teeming with insects, fungi, and microorganisms. The lower part of the A horizon is a mixture of mineral matter and organic matter.

B Horizon The B horizon, or subsoil, contains fine clay particles washed out of the A horizon by water that filters through pore spaces. In some soils, the clay that accumulates in the B horizon forms a compact, impenetrable layer called hardpan. The B horizon is the lower limit of most plant roots and burrowing animals.

C Horizon Located between the B horizon and the unweathered parent material is the C horizon, which contains partially weathered parent material. While the A and B horizons barely resemble the parent material, the C horizon does.

FIGURE 15 Soil Profiles A The A, B, and C horizons have different characteristics. **B** Three soil horizons are visible in this soil profile.
Interpret Photographs *Using the diagram in A as a guide, identify the soil horizons in B.*

Ⓐ
Loose and partly decayed organic matter
A horizon (Topsoil)
Mineral matter mixed with some organic matter
B horizon (Subsoil)
Clay transported from above
C horizon Partially weathered parent material
Unweathered parent material

Ⓑ

Facts and Figures

In a detailed soil profile, the O horizon consists largely of organic material. Its upper portion is primarily plant litter and other recognizable organic debris. Its lower portion is made of humus. Organisms are plentiful in this horizon. The A horizon also is a zone of high biological activity and high levels of humus—up to 30 percent in some instances.

Below the A horizon is the E horizon, a light-colored layer that contains little organic material. As water percolates downward through this zone, finer particles are carried away in a process known as eluviation. The moving water also dissolves soluble inorganic soil components and carries them to lower zones, a process known as leaching. Much

of the material removed by eluviation is deposited in the B horizon, which is also known as the zone of accumulation. In contrast to the C horizon, which is made up of partially altered parent rock, the O, A, E, and B horizons together constitute solum, or true soil.

Soil Types

Recall that climate is the most important factor in soil formation. Climate also has a major effect on the type of soil that forms.

🔑 **Three common types of soil are pedalfer, pedocal, and laterite.**

Pedalfer **Pedalfers** usually form in temperate areas that receive more than 63 cm of precipitation each year. This soil type is present in much of the forested area of the eastern half of the United States. The B horizon in pedalfers contains large amounts of iron oxide and aluminum-rich clays, giving these soils a brown to red-brown color.

Pedocal **Pedocals** are found in the drier western United States in areas that have grasses and brush vegetation. Because chemical weathering is slower in dry climates, pedocals generally contain less clay than pedalfers. Pedocals contain abundant calcite, or calcium carbonate, and are typically a light gray-brown.

FIGURE 16 The Temple at Angkor Wat, Cambodia This temple was constructed of laterite bricks between the years 1113 and 1150.

Laterite **Laterites** form in hot, wet tropical areas. Chemical weathering is intense under such conditions. So laterites are usually deeper than soils that develop over a similar period in temperate areas. The large quantity of water that filters through these soils removes most of the calcite and silica. Iron oxide and aluminum oxide are left behind. The iron oxide gives laterite a distinctive orange or red color.

When dried, laterite becomes very hard and practically waterproof. For centuries, people in portions of South and Southeast Asia have made bricks by digging up laterite, shaping it, and allowing it to harden in the sun. Ancient structures built of laterite bricks, such as the one shown in **Figure 16**, are well preserved even today.

Build Reading Literacy L1

Refer to **p. 124D,** which provides the guidelines for summarizing.

Summarize Ask students to read Soil Types on pp. 139–140. Tell them to carefully review the passage and identify main ideas. Clues to main ideas include headings, key concept statements, and vocabulary terms. List the main ideas on the board. Using the list as a guide, have students write brief summaries of the passage. Encourage students to repeat the procedure for the remainder of the lesson. **Verbal**

Use Community Resources L2

Contact a representative of your county extension agency or the local branch of the state soil conservation district. Ask the representative to discuss your area's soil types with students. He or she can bring in soil-testing kits and discuss ways to reduce soil erosion. **Verbal**

Answers

Figure 15 *The dark horizon at the top is the A horizon. The lighter horizon below it is the B horizon. The horizon below that is the C horizon.*

Erosion and Plant Roots The clearing of a rain forest not only removes the supply of plant nutrients from laterite soils, it also leads to accelerated erosion. When vegetation is present, its roots anchor the soil while its leaves and branches provide a canopy that protects the ground from the full force of frequent heavy rains. Removal of the vegetation also exposes the ground to strong direct sunlight. When baked by the sun, laterites can harden and become nearly impenetrable to water and crop roots. Ask students to summarize how the clearing of a rain forest affects laterite soils. *(The clearing of a rain forest removes the supply of nutrients from the soil, accelerates soil erosion, and exposes laterites to strong direct sunlight.)*
Verbal

Build Science Skills   L2

Student Activity: Observe Take students outside for the following activity. Place a large pile of soil in a plastic container. Obtain a spray bottle with an adjustable tip. Allow students to take turns using the bottle to observe how water erodes soil. Encourage students to experiment with different spray settings to simulate different types of rainfall. A fine mist, for example, would represent a light rain and cause little erosion. A full spray would represent a heavy rainfall and cause heavy erosion.
Visual, Kinesthetic

FIGURE 17 Clearing a Tropical Rain Forest in Borneo The laterite soil cannot support agriculture for more than a few years.

FIGURE 18 Soil Erosion by Raindrops A raindrop can splash soil particles more than a meter away from where it strikes the soil.

Plants that die in a tropical rain forest decompose rapidly because bacterial activity is high in hot and wet climates. As a result, laterite contains almost no organic matter. The roots of living rain forest plants quickly absorb the nutrients released during decomposition. So, even though the vegetation may be dense, the soil itself contains few available nutrients. Most of the nutrients in a tropical rain forest are contained within the plants themselves.

Today, large areas of tropical rain forest are being cleared for timber and to provide land for agriculture, as shown in **Figure 17.** However, laterite is one of the poorest soils for agriculture. Because laterite contains little organic matter and few nutrients, it cannot nourish crops for very long. The nutrients it does have are soon washed out by the plentiful rainwater that filters through the soil. After a few years, the soil in a freshly cleared area may be completely useless for growing crops. Without trees or crop plants to anchor the soil and shield the ground from the full force of heavy rains, the soil erodes quickly. Farmers then abandon the poor, eroded soil and move on to a new patch of forest, which is cut down or burned to produce yet another short-lived farm.

☑ **Reading Checkpoint** *Why is the soil in a tropical rain forest poorly suited for agriculture?*

Soil Erosion

Soils account for just a tiny fraction of all Earth materials, yet they are a vital resource. Because soils are necessary for the growth of rooted plants, they are the foundation of the human life-support system. However, soils are among our most abused resources. The loss of fertile topsoil is a growing problem as human activities disturb more of Earth's surface.

How Water Erodes Soil Soil erosion is a natural part of the constant recycling of Earth materials known as the rock cycle. Water, wind, and other agents move soil from one place to another. Every time it rains, raindrops strike the soil surface with surprising force. As **Figure 18** shows, each drop acts like a tiny bomb, blasting soil particles off the surface. Water flowing across the surface then carries away the dislodged particles. Because thin sheets of water move the soil particles, this process is called sheet erosion.

After flowing as a thin sheet for a short distance, the water forms tiny streams called rills. As more water enters the rills, they erode the soil further, creating trenches known as gullies, like those shown in **Figure 19.** Although most dislodged soil particles do not move far during each rainfall, large quantities eventually make their way downslope to a stream. The stream transports these sediments and eventually deposits them.

Rates of Erosion In the past, soil eroded more slowly than it does today because more land was covered by trees, grasses, and other plants. **Human activities that remove natural vegetation, such as farming, logging, and construction, have greatly accelerated erosion.** Without plants, soil is more easily carried away by wind and water.

Scientists can estimate the rate of erosion due to water by measuring the amount of sediment in rivers. These estimates indicate that before humans appeared, rivers carried approximately 9 trillion kg of sediment to the oceans each year. In contrast, the amount of sediment currently transported to the sea by rivers is approximately 24 trillion kg per year.

Wind generally erodes soil much more slowly than water does. During a prolonged drought, however, strong winds can remove large quantities of soil from unprotected fields. That's exactly what happened during the 1930s in the part of the Great Plains that came to be known as the Dust Bowl. Similar conditions affected the Great Plains in the spring and summer of 2011.

The rate of soil erosion depends on soil characteristics and on factors such as climate, slope, and type and amount of vegetation. In many regions, including about one-third of the world's croplands, soil is eroding faster than it forms. This results in lower productivity, poorer crop quality, and a threatened food supply.

☑ **Reading Checkpoint** *How do human activities affect rates of erosion?*

Integrate Social Studies   L2

The Dust Bowl In the 1930s, the Great Plains experienced a prolonged drought which, combined with the agricultural practices of that era, led to widespread soil erosion. Numerous families were displaced from their farms and emigrated west. Have students research and report on one aspect of the Dust Bowl. For example, they might discuss how much soil was lost or how farmers responded to the crisis by implementing new agricultural techniques. **Verbal**

3 ASSESS

Evaluate Understanding   L2

Have students sketch and label a soil profile showing A, B, and C horizons, along with parent rock.

Reteach   L1

Have students make tables summarizing the three soil types discussed in this lesson. Tables should include characteristics of each soil type and the climate in which it is found.

Assessment Answers

1. mineral matter; organic matter, or humus; water; air

2. Climate influences the rate, depth, and type of weathering, the rate at which nutrients are removed from the soil, and the types of organisms that live on and in the soil.

3. The A horizon, or topsoil, contains a mixture of mineral matter and organic matter, as well as many insects, fungi, and microorganisms. The B horizon, or subsoil, contains fine clay particles washed out of the A horizon. The C horizon contains partially weathered parent material.

Sediment Deposition Another problem caused by excessive soil erosion is the deposition of sediment. Rivers that accumulate sediment must be dredged to remain open for shipping. As sediment settles in reservoirs, they become less useful for storing water, controlling floods, and generating electricity.

Some sediments are contaminated with agricultural pesticides. When these chemicals enter a river or lake, they endanger organisms that live in or use the water, including humans. Sediments also contain soil nutrients, which may come from natural processes or from fertilizers applied to farmland. Excessive nutrient levels in lakes stimulate the growth of algae and plants. This can accelerate a process that eventually leads to the early death of the lake. Similar processes can occur in coastal bays and other aquatic habitats.

Controlling Erosion Although we cannot eliminate soil erosion, we can significantly slow the process by using soil conservation measures. You have seen how a misunderstanding of the composition of rain forest soil has led to the destruction of millions of acres and left behind unproductive land depleted of soluble nutrients. Conservation measures include steps taken to preserve environments and protect the land, such as planting rows of trees called windbreaks, terracing hillsides, plowing along the contours of hills, and rotating crops. Preserving fertile soil is essential to feeding the world's rapidly growing population.

5.2 Assessment

Review Key Concepts

1. List the four major components of soil.

2. How does climate affect soil formation?

3. Describe the contents of the three soil horizons found in most mature soils.

4. What climates are usually associated with pedalfer, pedocal, and laterite?

5. How can an activity such as road construction affect the rate of soil erosion?

Think Critically

6. Relate Cause and Effect A gardener notices that rain showers usually produce long-lasting puddles on the soil in her garden. Is it more likely that the soil contains too much sand or too much clay? Explain.

7. Predict Which activity would cause more sediment to be deposited in a river that flows through a gently sloping valley—cultivating the valley or cultivating the hills that surround the valley? Explain.

BIGIDEA
WEATHERING AND EROSION

8. Explain Using what you learned about chemical weathering in Lesson 5.1, explain why the soils formed in hot, wet climates have different characteristics than soils formed in cold, dry climates.

4. pedalfer—temperate climate with more than 63 cm of rain per year; pedocal—dry climate; laterite—hot, wet tropical climate

5. Such activities may accelerate erosion by removing natural vegetation, allowing soil to be carried away more easily by wind and water.

6. too much clay, because sandy soils drain quickly, while clay-rich soils drain slowly

7. cultivating the hills that surround the valley, because erosion is accelerated on slopes, and erosion leads to sediment deposition

8. A hot, wet climate favors chemical weathering, which hastens soil formation. Therefore, the soil that forms in this climate is usually thick. There is little chemical weathering in a cold, dry climate, so soil forms slowly and is usually thin, consisting mostly of mechanically weathered debris.

5.3 Mass Movements

EARTH'S LAND SURFACE consists of slopes. Some slopes are steep, while others are so gradual they appear flat to the naked eye. Although most slopes appear stable, they are always changing. Gravity causes material to move downslope. **The transfer of rock and soil downslope due to gravity is called mass movement.** Some types of mass movement are so slow that you cannot see or perceive their effects. Others, such as the landslide illustrated in **Figure 20,** are very sudden and catastrophic.

The combined actions of weathering and mass movement produce most landforms. Once weathering weakens and breaks rock apart, mass movement sends the debris downslope, where a stream may carry the debris away. Stream valleys are the most common of Earth's landforms, but many of them are so gradual and subtle that you may not think of them as valleys at all.

Key Questions

🔑 *What is mass movement?*

🔑 *What factors trigger mass movements?*

🔑 *How do geologists classify mass movements?*

Vocabulary

- mass movement • rockfall
- rockslide • slump
- mudflow • earthflow
- creep

Reading Strategy

Preview Copy the table. Before you read the lesson, rewrite the orange topic headings as questions that start with the word *what*. As you read, write an answer to each question.

Question	Answer
a. ___?___	b. ___?___
c. ___?___	d. ___?___

FIGURE 20 Landslide This home in Pacific Palisades, California, was destroyed by a landslide triggered by the January 1994 Northridge earthquake.

■ FOCUS

Lesson Objectives

5.8 **Define** mass movement.
5.9 **Identify** the factors that trigger mass movements.
5.10 **Classify** mass movements.

Build Vocabulary 〔L2〕

Venn Diagrams Have students construct Venn diagrams showing the differences and similarities between mudflows and earthflows. The diagrams should consist of two overlapping circles. One circle should be labeled Mudflow; the other should be labeled Earthflow. Similarities between the two types of mass movements should be listed in the middle, or overlapping, part of the circles. Differences should be listed in those parts of the circles that do not overlap. Students can construct other Venn diagrams to compare and contrast rockfalls and rockslides, and slump and creep.

Reading Strategy 〔L2〕

a. What triggers mass movements?
b. saturation of surface materials with water, oversteepening of slopes, removal of vegetation, and earthquakes
c. What are the types of mass movements?
d. rockfalls, slides (or rockslides), slumps, flows (or mudflows and earthflows), and creep

■ INSTRUCT

Use Visuals 〔L1〕

Figure 20 Tell students that in some cases, damages from earthquake-induced mass movements are greater than damages caused directly by an earthquake's ground vibrations. After students have examined the photograph, ask them to explain why the term *mass movement* is appropriate for this type of natural hazard. *(A large amount of mass in the form of rock and soil moves downslope.)*
Visual

LESSON 5.3

OVERSTEEPENED SLOPES　L2

Purpose Students will observe how the angle of a slope contributes to mass movements.

Materials bag of potting soil, water, cardboard box, plastic knife

Procedure Use the soil to create a gently sloping hillside in the cardboard box. Add water, if necessary, to help the hill maintain its form. Gently shake the box and have students observe the effects on the soil. Recreate the hill. This time, however, use the knife to cut away a good portion of one slope so that it is sharply steepened. Again, shake the box and have students observe the effects on the soil.

Expected Outcomes Some erosion and movement will occur during both trials. However, students will note that mass movements were more severe on the steepened slope.
Visual

FIGURE 21 Mudflow In October 1998, heavy rains from Hurricane Mitch led to massive mudflows in Central America.
Form a Hypothesis *What human activities before the rains might have contributed to the mudflows?*

INQUIRY
APPLY IT!

Q: *Are snow avalanches a type of mass movement?*

A: Yes. These thundering downslope movements of snow and ice can also transport large quantities of rock, soil, and trees. About 10,000 snow avalanches occur each year in the mountainous western United States. Besides damaging buildings and roads at the bottom of slopes, they are especially dangerous to skiers. In an average year, snow avalanches claim between 15 and 25 lives in the United States and Canada. Snow avalanches are a growing problem as more people participate in winter sports and recreation.

Triggers of Mass Movements

Gravity is the force behind mass movements. Several factors make slopes more susceptible to the pull of gravity. **Among the factors that commonly trigger mass movements are saturation of surface materials with water, oversteepening of slopes, removal of vegetation, and earthquakes.**

Water Heavy rains and rapid melting of snow can trigger mass movement by saturating surface materials with water. This was the case when torrential downpours associated with Hurricane Mitch caused devastating mudflows, as shown in **Figure 21.** When the pores in sediment become filled with water, the particles slide past one another more easily. You can demonstrate this effect with sand. If you add water until the sand becomes slightly moist, the sand grains will stick together. However, if you add enough water to fill all the pores between the sand grains, the sand-water mixture will ooze downhill. Clay also becomes very slick when it is wet.

Oversteepened Slopes Loose soil particles can maintain a relatively stable slope up to a certain angle. That angle ranges from about 25 to 40 degrees, depending on the size and shape of the particles. If the steepness of a slope exceeds the stable angle, mass movements become more likely. Such slopes are said to be oversteepened. An oversteepened slope can result when a stream undercuts a valley wall or waves pound against the base of a cliff. People may also create oversteepened slopes by excavating during the construction of roads and buildings.

☑ **Reading Checkpoint** *How do oversteepened slopes trigger mass movements?*

Differentiated Instruction

ENGLISH LANGUAGE LEARNERS Have students work in pairs to think of possible interactions among the factors that trigger mass movements. For example, students might note that slopes are sometimes steepened during road construction. The steepening of slopes often involves the removal of vegetation. Following a heavy rain, a mass movement might occur on the barren, steepened slope. Strengthen discussion skills by having students share their examples with the class. Encourage students to refer to the text on pp. 144–145 as they brainstorm ideas.

Removal of Vegetation Plants make slopes more stable because their root systems bind soil and regolith together. When plants are removed by forest fires or by human activities such as logging or farming, the likelihood of mass movement increases. An example that illustrates the stabilizing effect of plants occurred several decades ago on steep slopes near Menton, France. Farmers replaced olive trees, which have deep roots, with carnations, a profitable but shallow-rooted crop. Planting carnations made the slopes less stable. A landslide on one of the slopes killed 11 people.

Earthquakes Earthquakes are one of the most dramatic triggers of mass movements. An earthquake and its aftershocks can dislodge enormous amounts of rock and unconsolidated material, causing catastrophic damage.

Types of Mass Movements

Geologists classify mass movements based on the kind of material that moves, how it moves, and the speed of movement. We'll consider five basic types of mass movement: rockfalls, slides, slumps, flows, and creep.

Rockfalls A **rockfall** occurs when rocks or rock fragments fall freely through the air. This type of mass movement is common on slopes that are too steep for loose material to remain on the surface. Many rockfalls result from the mechanical weathering of rock caused by freeze-thaw cycles or plant roots. Rockfalls sometimes trigger other mass movements.

Slides In a slide, a block of material moves suddenly along a flat, inclined surface. Slides that include segments of bedrock are called **rockslides.** They often occur in high mountain areas such as the Andes, Alps, and Canadian Rockies. Rockslides are among the fastest mass movements, reaching speeds of over 200 km per hour. Some rockslides, such as the one shown in **Figure 22,** are triggered by rain, melting snow, or glacial collapse.

FIGURE 22 Rockslide A huge rockslide blocked this coastal highway in British Columbia, Canada, in 2008.

Weathering, Soil, and Mass Movements **145**

Refer to **p. 64D** in **Chapter 3,** which provides the guidelines for a DRTA strategy.

Directed Reading/Thinking Activity (DRTA) Have students read the first paragraph under the heading Types of Mass Movements. List the five basic types of mass movements on the board. Point out that each term is very descriptive. Based on the terms alone, have students predict the following for each mass movement: the kind of material that moves, how it moves, and the speed of the movement. For example, students will likely predict that rockfalls involve rocks, and that the rocks fall at a fast speed. Record all ideas on the board. Then, have students read each subsection under the heading. After they have finished reading a subsection, pause to review their predictions, and make any necessary modifications. Repeat until the entire passage has been read. Conclude by having students confirm which of their predictions were correct.
Verbal

Answers

Figure 21 *activities that remove natural vegetation, such as farming, logging, and construction*

☑ **Reading Checkpoint** *Loose soil particles can maintain a relatively stable slope up to a certain angle. If the steepness of a slope exceeds that angle, mass movements become more likely.*

Build Science Skills L2

Pose Questions After students have read the text on pp. 145–147, ask if they have any questions about types of mass movements. List the questions on the board. Assign small groups a question to research. Have students present their answers to the class.
Verbal, Group

Use Visuals L1

Figure 24 Have students compare and contrast Figures 23 and 24. **Ask:** How are slumps and earthflows similar? How are they different? *(Both move at a relatively slow rate. A slump refers to a block of material that moves along a curved surface. An earthflow refers to material that moves downslope as a thick fluid.)*
Visual

FIGURE 23 Slump Heavy rains triggered this slump in Santa Barbara, California. Notice the crescent-shaped cliff just above the slump.

PLANET DIARY

For links on **Mass Movements,** visit PlanetDiary.com/HSES.

Slumps A **slump** is the downward movement of a block of material along a curved surface. The material in a slump usually does not travel very fast or very far. As the block moves, its upper surface may tilt backward. Slumps leave a crescent-shaped cliff just above the slump, as shown in **Figure 23.** They are common on oversteepened slopes where the soil contains thick accumulations of clay.

Flows Flows are mass movements of material containing a large amount of water, which move downslope as a thick fluid. Flows that move quickly, called **mudflows,** are common in semiarid mountainous regions, such as parts of southern California. In these regions, protective vegetation is sparse. A heavy downpour or rapid snowmelt can flood canyons with a mixture of soil, rock, and water the consistency of wet concrete. It follows the contours of the canyon, taking large boulders and trees along with it. As you saw in Figure 21, mudflows in populated areas are very destructive.

Earthflows are flows that move relatively slowly—from about a millimeter per day to several meters per day. Their movement may continue for years. Earthflows occur most often on hillsides in wet regions. When water saturates the soil and regolith on a hillside, the material breaks away, forming a tongue-shaped mass like the one shown in **Figure 24.** Earthflows range in size from a few meters long and less than a meter deep to over 1 km long and more than 10 m deep.

☑ **Reading Checkpoint** *How do mudflows differ from earthflows?*

FIGURE 24 Earthflow This small, tongue-shaped mass movement occurred on a newly formed slope along a recently built highway.
Compare and Contrast *Which other type of mass movement looks most similar to an earthflow?*

Facts and Figures

Landslides threaten lives and property in all 50 states. To reduce the risk from active landslides, the U.S. Geologic Survey (USGS) uses real-time landslide monitoring systems. Data from a variety of sensors installed at active landslides are transmitted by radio to USGS computers. The monitoring systems focus on detecting precipitation and groundwater conditions that could destabilize a hill slope. They also record the acceleration of slide movement and ground vibrations associated with this movement.

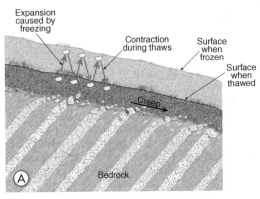

Expansion caused by freezing

Contraction during thaws

Surface when frozen

Surface when thawed

Creep

Bedrock

A

B

FIGURE 25 Creep
A Repeated expansion and contraction of the soil on a slope results in a gradual downhill movement of the soil.
Infer In which direction is creep occurring in this photograph?

B Years of creep have caused these gravestones to tilt.

Creep The slowest type of mass movement is **creep,** which usually travels only a few millimeters or centimeters per year. One factor that contributes to creep is alternating between freezing and thawing, as **Figure 25A** shows. Freezing expands the water in soil, lifting soil particles at right angles to the slope. Thawing causes contraction, which allows the particles to fall back to a slightly lower level. Each freeze-thaw cycle moves the particles a short distance downhill.

Because creep is so slow, you cannot observe it directly as it happens. However, the effects of creep are easy to recognize. As **Figure 25B** shows, creep causes structures that were once vertical to tilt downhill. Creep can also displace fences and crack walls and underground pipes.

5.3 Assessment

Review Key Concepts

1. What is mass movement?

2. How does water trigger mass movements?

3. How does a rockfall differ from a rockslide?

4. What is the slowest type of mass movement?

Think Critically

5. **Apply Concepts** When highway engineers build a road in a mountainous area, they insert drainage pipes into the slopes alongside the road. Explain why.

6. **Form an Opinion** Which mass movement—a slump, a mudflow, or an earthflow—poses the greatest risk to human life? Explain your reasoning.

WRITING IN SCIENCE

7. **Explain** Explain how people can make mass movements more likely. Include two examples in your explanatory paragraph.

Weathering, Soil, and Mass Movements **147**

Weathering, Soil, and Mass Movements **147**

How Earth Works

1 FOCUS

Objectives

In this feature, students will
- describe how soil is formed.
- identify the qualities of different kinds of soil.
- explain how soil supports various kinds of life.

Build Vocabulary   L2

Define Terms Write the words *mature* and *immature* on the board. Have students look up the meaning of *mature* in a dictionary. Then underline the prefix *im-* and tell them that it means "not." Explain that by adding the prefix *im-*, writers turn words into their opposites. Have students practice forming opposites by adding *im-* to the following words: *possible, probable, polite.*

2 INSTRUCT

Use Visuals   L1

Have students study the diagram that shows how soil is formed. Ask them to define *regolith. (weathered rock)* Then **ask:** What is the difference between mature soil and immature soil? *(Mature soil has more humus and supports a wide variety of plants and animals.)*
Visual

How Earth Works

Soil

On the surface of Earth, **soil** is the thin layer of loose material in which plants grow. Soil consists partly of mineral particles, and partly of **organic matter** derived from living organisms and their remains. Other key components of soil are water and air. Complex natural processes build soil over many thousands of years. The process begins when rock is broken down by weathering. Next, plants take root in the weathered rock. Then, organic material in the soil, called **humus,** is formed from decaying organisms. Different types of soil occur because of variations in climate, types of vegetation, and types and quantities of bedrock.

1. Regolith
Moss and lichen
Rock fragments
Bedrock

2. Immature soil
A layer of organic material begins to form

3. Mature soil
Decaying organisms form humus
Worms improve the soil texture
Root system

Grasses and small plants

Burrowing animals break up the soil

SOIL FORMATION
Typically, the first step in soil building is the development of **regolith,** or weathered rock. Next, immature soil is formed as organic material begins to decay. Finally, mature soil supports abundant life both above and below the surface.

◄**SOIL HORIZONS**
As soil develops, distinct layers, called **soil horizons,** appear. The A horizon is topsoil that is rich in minerals and organic matter. The B horizon is poorer in humus but rich in minerals washed down from above by rainwater soaking through the soil. Further below lie the C horizon of weathered rock and, below that, unweathered bedrock.

A horizon Topsoil
B horizon Subsoil
C horizon Rock fragments
Bedrock

SOILS AND FARMING
Mature soils that are rich in organic matter support agriculture. Decaying organic matter releases nutrients including potassium, nitrogen, and phosphorus that are vital for all plants.

148 Chapter 5

Differentiated Instruction

GIFTED Have students plan a memorial garden to honor someone. Have them decide the size and location of the garden. Then have them use the library or Internet to find out what plants grow best in their climate and what kind of soil is best for the plants. Students should present a diagram of their garden along with text to describe it.

Clay soil

◀ **SOIL TEXTURE**
Soil texture depends on the size and nature of soil particles. Clay soils have the smallest grains, silty soils have medium-sized grains, and sandy soils have the largest grains. **Loam,** a mixture of clay, silt, and sand, is the best soil for agriculture.

Silty soil   *Sandy soil*

← smallest grain size   largest grain size →

This sandy soil is found in northern coniferous forests.

Desert soils such as this have high concentrations of salts.

▲ **SOIL CLASSIFICATION**
Some experts recognize thousands of different soil types. The U.S. Department of Agriculture has devised a comprehensive soil classification system for categorizing soils. Each type of soil can be identified by the characteristics of its horizons.

Wildflowers   *Grass*   *Snail*
Slug   *Decomposing leaf*
Loam   *Roots*

▲ **LIFE IN THE SOIL**
Soil is home to a vast array of life, including microorganisms, ants, termites, worms, and rodents. Fungi and bacteria convert dead plant and animal matter into chemicals that enrich the soil. Burrowing creatures improve the soil by mixing it.

Highly alkaline   *Highly acidic*   *stomach acid*
ammonia   *coffee*
pH 1–14 full range
seawater   *Neutral*

▲ **SOIL pH**
The pH scale measures acidity or alkalinity on a scale of 0 to 14. When a chemical solution called an indicator is added to a soil sample, the indicator changes color, showing the soil's pH. Most plants thrive only in soils with a pH between 5 and 9.

Assessment

1. **Key Terms** Define **(a)** soil, **(b)** organic matter, **(c)** humus, **(d)** regolith, **(e)** soil horizon, **(f)** indicator, **(g)** loam.

2. **Physical Processes** Describe the three stages of soil formation.

3. **Physical Characteristics** How do various types of soil differ from one another?

4. **Natural Resources** What soil characteristics are most beneficial for agriculture?

5. **Critical Thinking Making Comparisons** Study the cross-sections of soils that form in coniferous forests and desert soils. **(a)** How are they alike? **(b)** How do they differ? **(c)** Do research to learn more about their different characteristics.

149

Assessment Answers

1. **(a)** the thin layer of loose material in which plants grow; **(b)** material derived from living plants and animals and their remains; **(c)** organic material formed from decaying vegetation and animals; **(d)** weathered rock; **(e)** distinct soil layer; **(f)** a chemical solution that shows pH by changing color; **(g)** soil made up of clay, silt, and sand

2. First is the development of weathered rock. Then organic material begins to decay and form immature soil. At last mature soil forms when more decaying plants and animals form humus.

3. Soils differ in their depth, level of acidity or alkalinity, texture or size, and nature of soil particles.

4. Loam (soil that includes sandy, silty, and clay-sized particles) with a pH between 5 and 9 that contains large amounts of organic matter is best for agriculture.

5. **(a)** Both have different horizons. **(b)** The desert soil contains a lot of salt in its upper soil horizons, while the coniferous forest soil does not. **(c)** Sample answer: Coniferous forest soils are acidic with lots of humus; desert soils have salt layers with accumulations of lime or gypsum.

EFFECT OF TEMPERATURE ON CHEMICAL WEATHERING `L2`

Objective
In this activity, students will determine the relationship between temperature and chemical weathering.

Skills Analyze Data, Draw Conclusions, Formulate Hypotheses, Design Experiments, Predict, Infer

Prep Time 10 minutes

Class Time 45 minutes

Teaching Tips Have students work in small groups to complete the activity. Assign each group member a task, such as recording water temperature or calculating average temperatures.

Be sure to review the ingredients list on the container of antacid tablets. In order for this experiment to work appropriately, the tablets must contain calcium carbonate.

Questioning Strategies Ask: What two climatic factors affect rates of chemical weathering? *(temperature and moisture)* Which type of climate experiences the highest rates of chemical weathering? *(hot and wet climates)*

Expected Outcome Students will observe that the antacid tablets dissolve most rapidly at high temperatures. They will recognize that rates of chemical weathering increase as temperature increases.

Effect of Temperature on Chemical Weathering

Problem How does temperature affect the rate of chemical weathering?

Materials 250-mL beaker, thermometer, hot water (40–50°C), ice, 5 antacid tablets, stopwatch, graph paper

Skills Measure, Use Tables and Graphs, Draw Conclusions, Infer

Connect to the `Big idea` Water is the most important agent of chemical weathering. One way water promotes chemical weathering is by reacting with the minerals in rocks. In this lab, you will model the effect of temperature on chemical weathering by measuring the rate at which antacid tablets dissolve in water at different temperatures. These tablets contain calcium carbonate, the mineral found in rocks such as limestone and marble.

Procedure

1. On a sheet of paper, copy the data table.

2. Add a mixture of hot water and ice to the beaker. Use the thermometer to measure the temperature of the mixture. Add either more hot water or more ice until the temperature is between 0°C and 10°C. The total volume of the mixture should be about 200 mL.

3. When the temperature is within the correct range, remove any remaining ice from the beaker. Record the starting temperature of the water in your data table. Remove the thermometer from the beaker.

4. Drop an antacid tablet into the beaker. Start the stopwatch as soon as the tablet enters the water. Stop the stopwatch when the tablet has completely dissolved and no traces of the tablet are visible. (Don't wait for the bubbling to stop.) Record the time in your data table.

5. Place the thermometer in the beaker and wait for the temperature of the water to stabilize. Record the final temperature of the water in your data table.

6. Calculate the average temperature by adding the starting and final temperatures and dividing by 2. Record the result in your data table.

7. Repeat Steps 2 through 6 four more times, once at each of the following temperature ranges: 10–20°C, 20–30°C, 30–40°C, and 40–50°C. Adjust the relative amounts of hot water and ice to produce the correct water temperatures. The total volume of water and ice should always be about 200 mL.

8. On graph paper, make a graph with average temperature on the *x*-axis and dissolving time on the *y*-axis. Plot your data on the graph. Draw a smooth curve through the data points.

Data Table			
Starting Temperature (°C)	Dissolving Time(s)	Final Temperature (°C)	Average Temperature (°C)

150 Chapter 5

Analyze and Conclude

1. **Analyze Data** At which temperature did the antacid tablet dissolve most rapidly?

2. **Analyze Data** At which temperature did the antacid tablet dissolve most slowly?

3. **Draw Conclusions** What is the relationship between temperature and the rate at which antacid tablets react with water?

4. **Form a Hypothesis** Based on your observations, form a hypothesis about the relationship between temperature and the rate of chemical weathering.

5. **Design an Experiment** How could you test your hypothesis?

6. **Predict** What would your results have been if you had ground each tablet into a fine powder before dropping it into the water? Would your conclusion be the same or different? Explain.

7. **Infer** Would a limestone building weather more rapidly in Homer, Alaska, or in Honolulu, Hawaii? (Both cities receive about the same amount of precipitation in an average year.) Explain your reasoning.

8. **Communicate** Write a lab report in which you explain your procedures in this lab and discuss whether or not your data supported your hypothesis. In your report, identify the manipulated variable and the responding variable in this experiment.

GO FURTHER Look for signs of chemical weathering on old stone buildings in your community. Consult your local library or historical society to find out when the buildings were constructed and what type of stone they are made of.

Sample Data See sample answers in the data table on the student page.

Analyze and Conclude

1. the highest temperature
2. the lowest temperature
3. Antacid tablets react more rapidly in water as the temperature increases.
4. As temperature increases, the rate of chemical weathering increases.
5. Sample answer: perform a similar experiment using rock that is sensitive to chemical weathering, such as limestone. Test the water for the presence of calcium or carbonate ions.
6. The dissolving times would have been shorter because grinding increases the surface area exposed to water. The conclusion would be the same because increasing surface area would speed the rate of reaction at each temperature.
7. Honolulu; Hawaii is much closer to the equator than Alaska is, so the average temperature in Honolulu is greater than that in Homer. The higher temperature promotes faster chemical weathering.
8. Answers will vary. The manipulated variable is temperature. The responding variable is dissolving time.

GO FURTHER

Look for student examples that show an understanding of the process of weathering, such as smooth corners, worn away letters, etc.
Kinesthetic, Portfolio

Make a List
Suggest that students make a list of everything they need to review for a test a day or two before the test. Creating the list is a thorough review in itself. Students can study the list on their way to and from school, during lunch, and between classes.

21st Century Learning

Self-Direction

How is your town weathering?
Weathering and erosion happen everywhere. As a class, brainstorm a list of examples of weathering and erosion in your community. Encourage students to visit those places, or organize a field trip. Students should take photographs and write descriptions of what they see. Then, encourage students to research possible causes of erosion and to develop a multimedia presentation that summarizes what they learn.

Homework Guide

Lesson	Questions
1	1–3, 11–14, 25–28, 33, 34
2	4–7, 15–19, 29–32, 35
3	8–10, 20–24, 36, 37

5 Study Guide

Big idea ▶ **Weathering and Erosion**

5.1 Weathering

🔑 Mechanical weathering occurs when physical forces break rock into smaller pieces without changing the rock's mineral composition.

🔑 In nature, three physical processes are especially important causes of mechanical weathering: frost wedging, unloading, and biological activity.

🔑 Chemical weathering is the transformation of rock into one or more new compounds.

🔑 Two factors that affect the rate of weathering are rock characteristics and climate.

mechanical weathering (126)
frost wedging (127)
talus (127)
exfoliation (128)
chemical weathering (129)

5.2 Soil

🔑 Soil is the part of the regolith that supports the growth of plants.

🔑 Soil has four major components: mineral matter, or broken down rock; organic matter, or humus, which is the decayed remains of organisms; water; and air.

🔑 The most important factors in soil formation are parent material, time, climate, organisms, and slope.

🔑 Soil varies in composition, texture, structure, and color at different depths.

🔑 Three common types of soil are pedalfer, pedocal, and laterite.

🔑 Human activities that remove natural vegetation, such as farming, logging, and construction, have greatly accelerated erosion.

regolith (133)   pedalfer (139)
soil (133)   pedocal (139)
soil horizon (138)   laterite (139)
soil profile (138)

5.3 Mass Movements

🔑 The transfer of rock and soil downslope due to gravity is called mass movement.

🔑 Among the factors that commonly trigger mass movements are saturation of surface materials with water, oversteepening of slopes, removal of vegetation, and earthquakes.

🔑 Geologists classify mass movements based on the kind of material that moves, how it moves, and the speed of movement.

mass movement (143)   mudflow (146)
rockfall (145)   earthflow (146)
rockslide (145)   creep (147)
slump (146)

Assessment Answers

Review Content

1. c	**2.** a	**3.** d
4. b	**5.** d	**6.** b
7. c	**8.** a	**9.** c
10. b		

Understand Concepts

11. The total surface area increases. The process represents mechanical weathering.
12. Exfoliation is a process in which unloading causes slabs of outer rock to separate and break loose. Examples include Stone Mountain in Georgia and Half Dome in Yosemite National Park.
13. By breaking rocks into smaller pieces, mechanical weathering increases the surface area of exposed rock.

5 Assessment

Review Content

Choose the letter that best answers the question or completes the statement.

1. The breaking down and changing of rocks at or near Earth's surface is called
   a. mass movement. c. weathering.
   b. sheet erosion.   d. uplift.

2. Which of the following is NOT a cause of mechanical weathering?
   a. dissolving   c. unloading
   b. frost wedging   d. burrowing

3. In which type of climate does chemical weathering occur most rapidly?
   a. cold, dry   c. warm, dry
   b. cold, wet   d. warm, wet

4. Organic matter in soil is also called
   a. regolith.   c. talus.
   b. humus.   d. loam.

5. A soil's texture is determined by its
   a. water content.   c. thickness.
   b. mineral composition. d. particle sizes.

6. In soils with distinct soil horizons, the topmost zone is the
   a. parent material. c. B horizon.
   b. A horizon.   d. C horizon.

7. Human activities that remove plants covering the soil cause soil erosion to
   a. decrease.
   b. stay the same.
   c. increase.
   d. increase briefly, then stop.

8. Which of the following does NOT usually trigger mass movements?
   a. growth of native vegetation on slopes
   b. formation of oversteepened slopes
   c. saturation of surface materials with water
   d. vibration of the ground during an earthquake

9. When a block of material moves downward along a curved surface, the process is called
   a. a rockslide.   c. a slump.
   b. a rockfall.   d. an earthflow.

10. Which of the following best describes a mudflow?
    a. movement too slow to be observed directly
    b. material moving downslope as a thick fluid
    c. material falling freely through the air
    d. sudden movement along a flat, inclined surface

Understand Concepts

11. What happens to the total surface area of the cubes in the process shown below? What type of weathering does this process represent?

12. What is exfoliation? Give an example of a feature produced by exfoliation.

13. How does mechanical weathering promote chemical weathering?

14. How is carbonic acid formed in nature? What happens when this acid reacts with feldspar?

15. Which factor has the greatest effect on soil formation? Explain.

16. How does slope affect the formation of soil?

17. Describe the major characteristics of A, B, and C horizons.

18. Distinguish between pedalfer and pedocal.

19. List three negative effects of soil erosion.

20. Explain how weathering and mass movement together produce most landforms.

21. What is the force behind mass movements? What other factors can trigger mass movements?

22. Distinguish between rockfalls and rockslides.

23. Distinguish between mudflows and earthflows.

24. How do freezing and thawing contribute to creep?

18. Pedalfer usually forms in temperate areas with an annual rainfall greater than 63 cm. It is present in much of the eastern half of the United States, most often in forested areas. It contains large amounts of iron oxide and aluminum-rich clays and is brown to red-brown in color. Pedocal is found in the drier western United States in areas that have grasses and brush vegetation. It generally contains less clay than pedalfer does. Pedocal is rich in calcite and is typically light gray-brown in color.

19. Possible answers include those related to loss of cropland (lowering farm productivity, reducing crop quality, and threatening the world food supply) or sediment deposition (hindering shipping on rivers, reducing the effectiveness of reservoirs, endangering organisms through pesticide contamination, and causing the early death of lakes).

20. Once weathering weakens and breaks rock apart, mass movement moves the debris downslope, where a stream usually carries it away.

21. Gravity is the force behind mass movements. Other factors that can trigger mass movements include saturation of surface materials with water, oversteepening of slopes, removal of vegetation, and earthquakes.

22. A rockfall occurs when rocks or rock fragments fall freely through the air. A rockslide occurs when a block of material that includes segments of bedrock moves suddenly along a flat, inclined surface.

23. Mudflows are flows that move quickly, typically in semiarid mountainous regions, following a heavy downpour or rapid snowmelt. Earthflows are flows that move relatively slowly, most often in wet regions when water saturates the soil and regolith.

24. Freezing expands the water in soil, lifting soil particles at right angles to the slope. Thawing causes contraction, which allows the particles to fall back to a slightly lower level. Each freeze-thaw cycle moves the particles a short distance downhill.

14. Carbonic acid forms when carbon dioxide reacts with water. It converts feldspar mostly to clay minerals.

15. Climate has the greatest effect. It influences the rate, depth, and type of weathering, the rate at which nutrients are removed from soil, and the types of organisms that live on and in the soil.

16. On steep slopes, erosion is accelerated, so soils are usually thin or nonexistent. In flat areas, there is little erosion, so soils are typically thick.

17. The A horizon contains a mixture of mineral matter and organic matter and is teeming with insects, fungi, and microorganisms. The B horizon contains fine clay particles washed out of the A horizon; the clay sometimes forms a compact, impenetrable layer called hardpan. The B horizon is the lower limit of most plant roots and burrowing animals. The C horizon contains partially weathered parent material.

ASSESSMENT

Think Critically

25. In northern states, there is more freezing and thawing during the winter, so frost wedging causes more severe weathering of roads.

26. Mechanical weathering produces smaller pieces of the same rock, while chemical weathering produces new compounds from the rock.

27. Marble will weather more rapidly. Hot, wet climates favor chemical weathering, which acts more rapidly on marble than on granite.

28. The most important agent of chemical weathering is water, which is scarce in a desert.

29. Soil erosion is not artificial. It is a natural part of the constant recycling of Earth materials known as the rock cycle. However, humans can accelerate erosion through activities that remove natural vegetation, such as farming, logging, and construction.

Analyze Data

30. A: thin or nonexistent; B: thick
31. B: transported soil; C: residual soil
32. The slope in area D is greater than that in area C. Because the rate of erosion is greater on steeper slopes, the soil is thinner in area D.

Concepts in Action

33. The water expanded as it froze, exerting pressure on the jar and cracking the glass. A similar process occurs during the type of mechanical weathering called frost wedging, in which water enters cracks in rock, expands during freezing, and enlarges the cracks.

34. It would be better to use the whole block as a single memorial. Smaller blocks would have a greater total surface area exposed to chemical weathering, which is accelerated in areas that have a warm, wet climate.

35. Examine a sample of the soil to determine how much clay, silt, and sand it contains. Then use the diagram in Figure 11 to classify soil texture.

36. No, removing all vegetation would promote erosion and increase the chance of mudflows. It would be safer to trim the vegetation, leaving it alive with its roots intact.

37. Students should focus their paragraph on one of the mass movements discussed in Section 5.3. Encourage students to gather information for their paragraphs from library or Internet resources.

Think Critically

25. Infer Roads in northern states such as Maine and Michigan need to be repaired more often than roads in southern states such as Florida and Louisiana. What form of mechanical weathering could account for this?

26. Compare and Contrast How do the effects of mechanical weathering on rock differ from the effects of chemical weathering?

27. Predict Granite and marble are exposed at the surface in a hot, wet region. Which of the rocks will weather more rapidly? Explain.

28. Apply Concepts Heat speeds up most chemical reactions. Why then does chemical weathering happen slowly in a hot desert?

29. Form an Opinion Do you think that soil erosion is a byproduct of careless land use by humans? Explain.

Analyze Data

Use the diagram below to answer Questions 30–32.

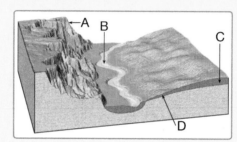

30. Compare and Contrast Compare the thickness of the soil in the areas labeled A and B.

31. Interpret Diagrams What name is given to the soil that develops in the area labeled B? In the area labeled C?

32. Infer Why is the soil in the area labeled D thinner than the soil in the area labeled C?

Concepts in Action

33. Use Analogies Explain how the following scenario is analogous to weathering: One evening you place a sealed jar full of water in a freezer. The next morning, the water has turned to ice and the jar is cracked.

34. Apply Concepts A committee has been established to design a stone memorial commemorating 100 soldiers who died in battle. The committee decides to use a large block of marble for the memorial. Considering only the memorial's durability, would it be better to use the whole block as a single memorial for all 100 soldiers or to divide it into 100 blocks of equal size, one for each soldier?

35. Classify How would you determine the texture of the soil in your area?

36. Form an Opinion Should a homeowner in a dry, mountainous area remove all vegetation from surrounding slopes to reduce fire danger? Explain your answer.

37. Communicate Write a paragraph describing one type of mass movement. Include a specific example of a time when such a mass movement made the news.

Performance-Based Assessment

Observe Look for places in your community where people have taken specific actions to reduce erosion. Such places may include sites where buildings are being constructed or roads are being built or repaired. Make a list of each action and explain how it is intended to reduce erosion.

Performance-Based Assessment

Examples may include setting up soil-catching barriers around building sites, covering exposed slopes along roads with straw or netting, and terracing sloped planting areas.

Standardized Test Prep

Choose the letter that *best* answers the question or completes the statement.

1. Which of the following *best* describes regolith?
   - **A** a soil that contains large amounts of iron oxide and aluminum-rich clays
   - **B** a mixture of mineral matter, organic matter, water, and air
   - **C** a large pile of rock fragments at the base of a steep cliff
   - **D** the layer of rock and mineral fragments that covers nearly all of Earth's land surface

2. In which mass movement do rock fragments fall freely through the air?
   - **F** rockslide
   - **G** rockfall
   - **H** slump
   - **J** earthflow

Use the diagram below to answer Questions 3 and 4.

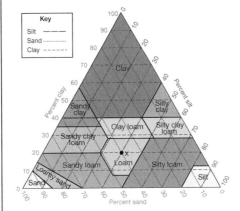

3. What are the percentages of clay, silt, and sand in the soil at the point labeled X?
   - **A** 60 percent clay, 80 percent silt, and 60 percent sand
   - **B** 0 percent clay, 40 percent silt, and 60 percent sand
   - **C** 20 percent clay, 40 percent silt, and 40 percent sand
   - **D** 50 percent clay, 40 percent silt, and 10 percent sand

4. The name given to soil that contains 60 percent clay, 20 percent silt, and 20 percent sand is—
   - **F** clay
   - **G** loam
   - **H** silty clay loam
   - **J** sandy loam

5. Which of the following statements is true?
   - **A** Increasing the surface area of an exposed rock increases the rate of weathering.
   - **B** Decreasing the surface area of an exposed rock increases the rate of weathering.
   - **C** Increasing the surface area of an exposed rock decreases the rate of weathering.
   - **D** The surface area of an exposed rock has no effect on the rate of weathering.

If You Have Trouble With . . .					
Question	1	2	3	4	5
See Lesson	5.2	5.3	5.2	5.2	5.1

Weathering, Soil, and Mass Movements **155**

6 Running Water and Groundwater Planning Guide

BIGIDEA: WEATHERING AND EROSION

Lesson Objectives		Activities
6.1 Running Water, pp. 158–163 6.1 **Explain** how the water cycle circulates Earth's water supply in an unending cycle. 6.2 **Explain** how the water cycle is kept in balance. 6.3 **Describe** the ability of a stream to erode and transport material. 6.4 **Compare and contrast** the changes in gradient and discharge between a stream's headwaters and mouth. 6.5 **Define** base level.		TE Build Science Skills, p. 159 L2 TE Teacher Demo: The Ability to Erode, p. 160 L2
6.2 The Work of Streams, pp. 164–170 6.6 **Explain** how streams erode their channels and transport sediments. 6.7 **Explain** how stream deposition occurs. 6.8 **Identify** the two general types of stream valleys. 6.9 **Predict** the causes of floods and **describe** major flood control measures. 6.10 **Explain** the relationship between streams and drainage basins.		TE Teacher Demo: Alluvium, p. 166 L2 TE Build Science Skills, p. 167 L2 SE Map It: Mississippi Delta Region, p. 166 L2 SE Map It: Mississippi River Flooding, p. 168 L2
6.3 Water Beneath the Surface, pp. 171–179 6.11 **Describe** the movement and location of groundwater. 6.12 **Describe** the formation of a spring. 6.13 **Explain** environmental threats to water supplies. 6.14 **Describe** the formation of caverns. 6.15 **Describe** landforms in karst areas.		TE Teacher Demo: Water Table, p. 172 L2
Chapter Features and Labs		
Try It How Do Local Bodies of Water Affect Your Community? p. 157		LM Rivers That Shape the Land L2
Earth & Its Resources The Ogalla Aquifer—How Long Will the Water Last, p. 180		LM Modeling Cavern Formation L1
Exploration Lab Investigating the Permeability of Soils, p. 181		

Ability Levels	Components	
L1 For students who need additional help	**SE** Student Edition	**LP** Lesson Plans
L2 For all students	**TE** Teacher's Edition	**AA** Active Art
L3 For students who need to be challenged	**LM** Laboratory Manual	**PD** Planet Diary
	CT Chapter Tests	**GEODe** Geode CD-ROM
	GRSW Guided Reading & Study Workbook	**eText**
	CTB Computer Test Bank	

Resources	Lesson Assessment
GRSW Lesson 6.1 **LP** Lesson Planning 6.1 **AA** Water Cycle Activity **GEODe** Sculpturing Earth's Surface: Hydrologic Cycle	**SE** Lesson 6.1 Assessment, p. 163 **eText** Lesson 6.1
GRSW Lesson 6.2 **LP** Lesson Planning 6.2 **PD** Links on Floods **GEODe** Sculpturing Earth's Surface: Running Water	**SE** Lesson 6.2 Assessment, p. 170 **eText** Lesson 6.2
GRSW Lesson 6.3 **LP** Lesson Planning 6.3 **GEODe** Sculpturing Earth's Surface: Groundwater	**SE** Lesson 6.3 Assessment, p. 179 **eText** Lesson 6.3

Materials for Activities and Labs

Quantities for each group

STUDENT EDITION

Exploration Lab, p. 181
100-mL graduated cylinder; beaker; small funnel; 3 pieces of cotton; samples of coarse sand, fine sand, and soil; clock or watch with a second hand

TEACHER'S EDITION

Build Science Skills, p. 159
shoe boxes, cardboard, aluminum foil, cotton balls, clay

Teacher Demo, p. 160
stream table, soil, short length of hose, bucket, access to sink or running water

Teacher Demo, p. 166
mixed sediment (pebbles, sand, silt, and clay-sized particles), clear glass jar with lid, water

Build Science Skills, p. 167
sloped paint trays, sand, water source

Teacher Demo, p. 172
large clear plastic cup; clean, dry sand; water

Assessment

CHAPTER ASSESSMENT
SE Assessment, pp. 183–184
CT Chapter 6 Test
CTB Chapter 6
eText Chapter 6

21st Century Learning

Health Literacy: How safe is your water?, TE p. 182

Before You Teach
Running Water and Groundwater

Michael Wysession
Washington University

Common Themes

The water cycle is a defining feature of Earth's surface. The water cycle, involving the evaporation, precipitation, stream runoff, and ground infiltration of water, shapes and changes continental surfaces.

Space and Time Oceans contain 97.2 percent of Earth's surface water, with most of the rest in glaciers and groundwater. Though only a tiny amount of water exists in streams and the atmosphere, huge amounts of water pass through them. Networks of streams form drainage basins that allow rain to eventually drain back to the oceans. Groundwater, though hidden from our sight, is vitally important to humans. In the United States, it supplies drinking water for 50 percent of the population and supports 40 percent of agriculture. Groundwater is retrieved from aquifers that have high porosity and permeability. Caverns form underground in rocks below the water table, but develop familiar cave formations when they are above the water table.

Forces and Motion Streams erode or deposit sediment, depending upon their velocity and sediment load. Stream velocity depends upon discharge and slope gradient. Stream valleys tend to be narrow and V-shaped at their steep headwaters, and wider along flatter gradients, forming floodplains. Most of the erosion and transportation of sediment occurs during times of stream flooding.

Matter and Energy The surface part of the water cycle, and therefore of the rock cycle as well, is ultimately powered by the sun through evaporation and the movement of air.

Earth as a System After rocks are weathered to form sediment, the sediments are transported by flowing water. The sediment grains are picked up and suspended when water flows rapidly. When flowing water slows, sediments are deposited, forming deltas, alluvial fans, and levees.

EARTH SCIENCE REFRESHER

Deep-Earth Water Cycle

We are most familiar with the surface water cycle involving evaporation, precipitation, and streams, but there is another, even larger water cycle involving the deep Earth. The rock of the mantle contains a huge amount of water, estimated to be up to five times the amount of water in the ocean. This water has a lubricating effect on the mantle rock, allowing it to flow and to melt much more easily that it would if it were dry.

This water in the deep Earth interacts with the surface water through the process of plate tectonics—at subduction zones and volcanoes. When the giant sheets of the ocean seafloor subduct beneath other plates and sink into the mantle, they carry water with them. This water seeps into the ocean crust during the tens to hundreds of millions of years that the crust lies beneath the oceans.

Most of this water leaves the subducting lithosphere and rises back to the surface within magma. Most of the gas that accompanies the eruption of subduction zone volcanoes is water vapor. Some of the water gets carried deeper into the mantle, perhaps eventually to accompany erupting magma at mid-ocean ridge volcanoes. There is more water involved with the deep Earth water cycle than the surface water cycle, but because of the very slow rates of plate tectonics water moves through it at a much slower rate.

> **Address Misconceptions**
>
> *Some students may think that a "100-year flood" only occurs every 100 years.* This is not true. The probability is that it will only happen every 100 years but it could happen during any year. For a strategy that helps to overcome this misconception, see **Address Misconceptions** on **TE p. 169.**

The Changing Shapes of Streams

Streams naturally change their course. Meanders continually cross a floodplain over time, and stream deltas jump around when the stream mouth gets clogged with sediment. However, most people don't like rivers suddenly cutting through their farms, houses, and towns, so artificial levees are built to keep the rivers in their present course. The buildup of sediment in streams forces the levees to be built higher and higher. One of the world's largest engineering construction projects is the United States Army Corps of Engineers' attempt to keep the Mississippi River from changing its course. In fact, the Mississippi River flows past New Orleans about 5 m higher than the level of the city, kept in place by high levees. People look up to see ships pass.

As can be seen in Figure 9 on p. 166, however, this situation is not stable. Notice how the Atchafalaya River presents a much shorter path to the Gulf of Mexico. The Mississippi would naturally switch to this course, as it has done in the past, if it were not for the artificial levees. It almost did in 1973. During the great flood of that year, rushing waters almost undermined the concrete structures to flood gates that opened into the Atchafalaya. Had the great Mississippi River jumped course, there would have been no way of ever getting it back, and New Orleans would have been left dry. Even though the floodgates have been repaired, there is still a chance that a large enough flood could make the Mississippi jump its tracks for good.

BUILD READING LITERACY
Reciprocal Teaching

Modeling Strategies in Combination

Strategy Help students learn to apply the strategies of predict, question, clarify, and summarize. Teaching this strategy should take place over several days, beginning with the teacher modeling and leading students in discussion. The teacher gradually turns leadership over to students and becomes a facilitator, intervening only as needed. Prepare for the reading by choosing a passage of several paragraphs from Chapter 6. Make a copy of the paragraphs and note appropriate places to model the strategies for students.

Example

1. Read a few paragraphs aloud or have one student read aloud as other students follow along silently.

2. Discuss appropriate strategies for clarifying meaning and getting past trouble spots in the passage. Engage the group in discussing ways to apply each of the following strategies:

• Predicting what will come next in the text. Remind students to use what they already know about a topic to make connections that will help them understand what comes next.

• Asking "teacher-like questions" to check understanding and to think about what they need to find out.

• Clarifying the meaning of unfamiliar words or concepts.

• Summarizing what has been read.

3. Reread the paragraphs, modeling all four strategies.

4. Continue reading a few paragraphs at a time, discussing and modeling.

5. Repeat the process with different passages over a few days, gradually turning over the leadership role to students by having them lead the discussion of portions of the text.

6. When students are comfortable with the strategies, they can lead the entire discussion. Intervene only to get students back on track or to jump-start a discussion.

See TE p. 159 for a script on how to use this strategy with students. For additional strategies, see TE pp. 161, 162, 164, 173, and 177.

CHAPTER 6

ASSESS PRIOR KNOWLEDGE

Use the Chapter Pretest below to assess students' prior knowledge. As needed, review these concepts.

Review Science Concepts

Lesson 6.1 Students would benefit from a brief discussion on cloud formation and water in the atmosphere. This would allow them to become familiar with the behavior of moisture in the atmosphere as it relates to the water cycle.

Lesson 6.2 Review with students the concept of velocity. This will make the discussion of streams easier for them to understand.

Lesson 6.3 Reviewing erosion and weathering will provide students with the background to discuss the formation of groundwater features as well as the work that a stream can do. Also, a quick look at some major rock types, especially limestone, will provide students with the background into karst regions and less resistant rock.

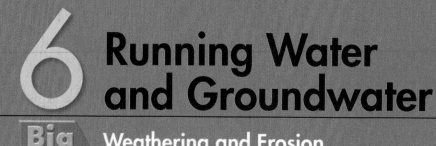

6 Running Water and Groundwater

Big idea Weathering and Erosion

Q: How does water shape Earth's surface?

156

Chapter Pretest

1. True or False: A nonrenewable resource will be replenished within your lifetime? *(False)*

2. Briefly discuss the connection between weathering and erosion. *(Erosion is the moving of weathered material.)*

3. What type of rock reacts in weak acid? *(c)*
   a. granite   **b.** shale
   c. limestone   **d.** gneiss

4. True or False: There can be more moisture in warm air than in cool air. *(True)*

5. Velocity is equal to *(a)*
   a. distance/time
   b. time × length
   c. distance × distance
   d. distance × depth

INSIDE:

This photograph shows the narrow canyon of Huka Falls on the Waikato River in New Zealand.

INQUIRY
TRY IT!

HOW DO LOCAL BODIES OF WATER AFFECT YOUR COMMUNITY?

Procedure

1. Identify an important body of water in or near your community. It could be a river, lake, dam reservoir, stream, ocean, or estuary.
2. List the ways the people of your community use this body of water.
3. Observe and record the ways this body of water has affected (or still affects) the local landscape.

Think About It

1. **Classify** Is the body of water used for recreation (boating, swimming, fishing), for industry and business (transportation or waste disposal for factories and power plants), for drinking water, or a combination of these purposes?
2. **Infer** If your community uses this body of water as a source of drinking water, how might that affect other possible uses of the water?
3. **Draw Conclusions** Has this body of water shaped the landscape in the area? How?

157

ENGAGE/EXPLORE

INQUIRY
TRY IT!

HOW DO LOCAL BODIES OF WATER AFFECT YOUR COMMUNITY? L2

Purpose In this activity, students will identify an important body of water in their community. They will explore how people use the body of water and how it affects the community.

Skills Classify, Infer, Draw Conclusions

Prep Time none

Materials paper, pencil, computer and other research sources

Class Time 50 minutes

Expected Outcome Students will understand the effect an important body of water has had and continues to have on their community.

Think About It

1. Answers will vary according to the body of water chosen.
2. The body of water could only be used in ways that would carefully monitor pollutants that go into the water.
3. Answers will vary according to the body of water chosen.

6.1 Running Water

1 FOCUS

Lesson Objectives

6.1 **Explain** how the water cycle circulates Earth's water supply in an unending cycle.

6.2 **Explain** how the water cycle is kept in balance.

6.3 **Describe** the ability of a stream to erode and transport material.

6.4 **Compare and contrast** the changes in gradient and discharge between a stream's headwaters and mouth.

6.5 **Define** base level.

Build Vocabulary L2

Cycle Diagram Have students create a cycle diagram of the water cycle. Instruct students to place the terms in ovals and connect the ovals with lines.

Reading Strategy L2

Water cycle—unending circulation of Earth's water supply

Infiltration—movement of surface water through cracks and pore spaces

Gradient—the slope or steepness of a stream channel

2 INSTRUCT

Use Visuals L1

Figure 1 Direct student's attention to the pie graph of the distribution of Earth's water. **Ask:** What percent of Earth's water is in freshwater lakes and streams combined? *(0.0091 percent)*
Visual

Key Questions

 What is the water cycle?

What does it mean to say Earth's water cycle is balanced?

What is the most important factor in determining the power of a stream to erode and transport material?

How do gradient and discharge change between a stream's source and its mouth?

What is a stream's base level?

Vocabulary

- water cycle
- infiltration
- stream channel
- gradient
- discharge
- tributary
- meander

Reading Strategy

Build Vocabulary Copy the table. As you read the lesson, define in your own words each vocabulary term listed in the table.

Vocabulary Term	Definition
Water cycle	?
Infiltration	?
Gradient	?

WATER IS EVERYWHERE on Earth—oceans, glaciers, rivers, lakes, air, and soil. All of these reservoirs make up Earth's hydrosphere. Most of Earth's water—about 97.2 percent—is stored in oceans, as **Figure 1** shows. Ice sheets and glaciers account for another 2.15 percent, leaving only 0.65 percent to be divided among lakes, streams, groundwater, and the atmosphere. The water found in glaciers, ice sheets, lakes, streams, groundwater, and the atmosphere may seem like a tiny percent of Earth's water, but the actual quantities are great.

FIGURE 1 Distribution of Earth's Water
Interpret Graphs What percentage of Earth's water is not held in its oceans?

Freshwater lakes 0.009%
Saline lakes and inland seas 0.008%
Soil moisture 0.005%
Stream channels 0.0001%
Atmosphere 0.001%
Oceans 97.2%
2.8%
Glaciers 2.15%
Hydrosphere
Nonocean Component (% of total hydrosphere)
Groundwater 0.62%

The Water Cycle

Water constantly moves among the oceans, the atmosphere, the geosphere, and the biosphere. This unending circulation of Earth's water supply is the water cycle. This cycle is possible because water readily changes from one state of matter to another at temperatures and pressures common on Earth's surface.

The water cycle, shown in **Figure 2**, is a worldwide system powered by energy from the sun and by gravity. Water evaporates into the atmosphere from the ocean, and to a lesser extent from the continents. Winds transport this moisture-rich air until conditions cause the moisture to condense into clouds. Precipitation—rain and snow—then falls to the surface of Earth, from which it will eventually evaporate again.

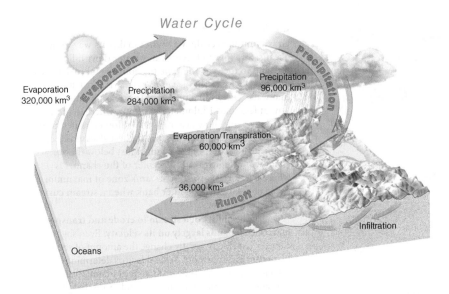

Water Cycle

Evaporation
320,000 km³

Precipitation
284,000 km³

Precipitation
96,000 km³

Evaporation/Transpiration
60,000 km³

36,000 km³

Infiltration

Oceans

FIGURE 2 The Water Cycle The many processes of the water cycle maintain Earth's overall water balance.
Interpret Diagrams *In which three ways does precipitation return to oceans?*

What happens to precipitation that falls on land? Some of it slowly soaks into the ground through infiltration. **Infiltration** is the movement of surface water into rock or soil through cracks and pore spaces. The water gradually moves through the land and actually seeps into lakes, streams, or the ocean. When the rate of rainfall exceeds Earth's ability to absorb it, the excess water flows over the surface into lakes and streams in a process called *runoff*. Much of that runoff returns to the atmosphere through evaporation from the soil, lakes, and streams. Plants also absorb water and release it into the atmosphere through *transpiration*.

When precipitation falls in very cold areas—at high elevations or high latitudes—the water may not immediately soak in, run off, or evaporate. Instead, it may become part of a glacier. Glaciers store large amounts of water on land. If present-day glaciers were to melt and release all their water, ocean levels would rise by several dozen meters. Even with all these processes occurring, Earth's water cycle is balanced.

Balance in the water cycle means the average annual precipitation over Earth equals the amount of water that evaporates and transpires. The amounts of water shown in Figure 2 reflect this overall balance, but Figure 2 also shows that there are local imbalances. For example, precipitation exceeds evaporation and transpiration over continents. Over oceans, evaporation exceeds precipitation. In general, the balance between precipitation and evaporation and transpiration keeps the level of the world oceans consistent.

☑ **Reading Checkpoint** *What is infiltration?*

Student Activity: Use Models Have students make their own three-dimensional model of the water cycle. Provide them with material, including shoe boxes, cardboard, aluminum foil, cotton balls, and clay. Their model should represent the major processes at work in the water cycle. Display the models around the classroom for other students to compare.
Kinesthetic, Visual

Build Reading Literacy L1

Refer to **p. 156D** in this chapter, which provides the guidelines for reciprocal teaching.

Reciprocal Teaching Have students read about the water cycle with a partner. One partner reads the lesson out loud. The other partner draws a diagram that explains what is being read. The partners then switch roles. The second partner re-reads the lesson, while the other partner fills in any gaps in the water cycle diagram.
Intrapersonal

Answers

Figure 1 *2.8 percent*

Figure 2 *Precipitation returns to oceans as rain or snow, as runoff, and through infiltration.*

☑ **Reading Checkpoint** *Infiltration is the movement of surface water into rock or soil through cracks and pore spaces.*

LESSON 6.1

Teacher **Demo**

THE ABILITY TO ERODE　**L2**

Purpose Students are provided with a visual representation of the impact that gradient and discharge have on the ability of a stream to erode and transport material.

Materials stream table, soil, short length of hose, bucket, access to sink or running water

Procedure Fill the stream table with dry soil. Set the stream table at a slight angle (less than 45 degrees). Position the hose at one end of the stream table. Turn on the water, releasing a small but steady stream into the hose. Have students observe the resulting erosion and sediment transported into the bucket at the other end of the stream table. Turn off the water and spread the soil out again to form a continuous cover of soil. Perform the demonstration several more times, using different variables. For example, increase the discharge of the stream by turning the water up so a more forceful stream is created. Increase the gradient of the stream by raising and lowering the stream table. Have students predict what will happen in each scenario before turning on the water. Discuss the impact the variables will have on the area surrounding the stream as well as the areas downstream.

Expected Outcomes Students will understand how streams can erode soil and transport materials.

FIGURE 3 Stream Velocity
A Along straight stretches, stream velocity is highest at the center of the channel. **B** When a stream curves, its zone of maximum speed shifts toward the outer bank.
Interpret Diagrams *How does velocity change with depth in the middle of the stream?*

FIGURE 4 Stream Gradient
This cross section along the length of a stream shows a steeper gradient upstream, and a gentler gradient downstream.

Streamflow

Gravity influences the way water makes its way to the oceans. Streams and rivers carry water downhill from the land to the sea. The time this journey takes depends on the velocity of the stream. Velocity is the distance that water travels in a period of time. Some slow streams flow at less than 1 kilometer per hour, whereas a few rapid ones may flow faster than 30 kilometers per hour.

Along straight stretches, the highest stream velocities are near the center of the channel just below the surface, as shown in **Figure 3A.** The center of the channel is where friction is lowest. A stream's zone of maximum speed shifts toward its outer bank when a stream curves, as **Figure 3B** shows.

The ability of a stream to erode and transport materials depends largely on its velocity. Even slight changes in velocity greatly change the amount of sediment that water can transport. Several factors determine the velocity of a stream. They include its gradient; the shape, size, and roughness of its channel; and its discharge.

Gradient A **stream channel** is the course the water in a stream follows. **Gradient** is the slope or steepness of a stream channel. Gradient is usually expressed as the vertical drop of a stream over a certain distance. Portions of the lower Mississippi River have very low gradients of 10 centimeters per kilometer or less. By contrast, some mountain streams tumble downhill at a gradient of 40 meters per kilometer. The gradient of such mountain streams is 400 times steeper than that of the lower Mississippi. Gradient varies over a stream's length and between streams. The steeper the gradient, the more energy the stream has as it flows downhill. Compare the steep and gentle gradients in **Figure 4.**

Channel Characteristics As the water in a stream flows, it encounters friction from the sides and the bottom of its channel. This friction slows the forward movement of the water. The shape, size, and roughness of the channel affect the amount of friction.

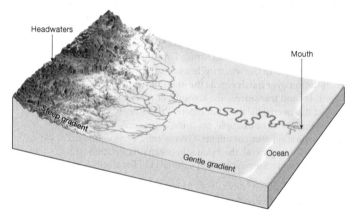

Differentiated Instruction

SPECIAL NEEDS Make concept maps for each lesson and cover them with clear contact paper. Then, cut the concept maps into puzzle pieces. Provide students with the pieces and have them put the puzzle together. After students complete the puzzle, have them make flashcards of concept connections and added notes.

Students may have flashcards with the factors determining the velocity of a stream. They may also have flashcards with an important word missing. Example: **The _____ of a stream is the volume of water flowing past a specific point in a specific amount of time.** On the back of the card, the answer *discharge* is written.

Table 1 World's Largest Rivers Ranked by Discharge			
Rank	River	Country	Average Discharge m³/s
1	Amazon	Brazil	212,400
2	Congo	Zaire	39,650
3	Yangtze	China	21,800
4	Brahmaputra	Bangladesh	19,800
5	Ganges	India	18,700
6	Yenisei	Russia	17,400
7	Mississippi	United States	17,300
8	Orinoco	Venezuela	17,000
9	Lena	Russia	15,500
10	Parana	Argentina	14,900

For example, an irregular channel filled with boulders creates enough turbulence to slow the stream significantly. Water in a smooth channel flows more easily. Larger channels also have more efficient water flow because a smaller proportion of water is in contact with the channel surfaces.

Discharge The **discharge** of a stream is the volume of water flowing past a certain point in a given unit of time. Discharge is usually measured in cubic meters per second. **Table 1** lists the world's largest rivers in terms of discharge. The discharges of most rivers change with rainfall and snowmelt. The size and velocity of the stream also changes when discharge changes. The stream channel widens and deepens to handle additional water. As the size of the channel increases, there is less friction and the water flows more swiftly.

The construction of urban centers around a stream channel affects discharge. For example, streets, parking lots, and buildings cover soil that once soaked up water. Less water soaks into the ground and runoff increases, especially at times of heavy rainfall. As a result, the magnitude and frequency of floods can increase. Also, because less water soaks into the ground, the dry season flow of streams is reduced.

☑ **Reading Checkpoint** What determines the velocity of a stream?

Changes From Upstream to Downstream

One useful way to study a stream is to look at its profile. A *stream profile* is a cross-sectional view of a stream from its source, or headwaters, to its mouth—the point downstream where the river empties into another body of water. In Figure 4, you can see that the most obvious feature of a typical stream profile is a decreasing gradient or slope from its headwaters to its mouth.

Running Water and Groundwater **161**

Refer to **p. 446D** in **Chapter 16,** which provides guidelines for sequencing.

Build Reading Literacy   L1

Sequence Have students make a flowchart that follows the stream in Figure 4 from its headwaters to the mouth. In the flowchart, students should describe how the velocity, gradient, and discharge of the stream changes as it flows.
Verbal

Integrate Math   L2

Visualize Gradient If students have difficulty understanding the expression of gradient as a vertical drop over a certain distance, tell them to visualize a right-angled triangle. The vertical side corresponds to the vertical drop, the base side represents the "certain distance," and the hypotenuse represents the gradient, or slope. With this model in mind, it should be easy for students to recognize that a gradient of 40 m/km is much steeper than one of 10 cm/km. To further illustrate this concept, divide students into groups and have them make three-dimensional models using a table top (or flat surface), a meter stick, and several books. Have students stack one book on top of the other with the ruler running from the top of each book to the table. Ask them to describe how the gradient changes as they stack more books.

You can also illustrate how a larger gradient yields a faster velocity by placing a ramp or a wooden board instead of a ruler on top of the books. Let a marble roll down the ramp each time you add a book to the stack. Ask students to describe how the velocity of the marble changes each time you add a book to the stack.
Visual, Kinesthetic

Answers

Figure 3 *Velocity generally decreases with depth.*

☑ **Reading Checkpoint** *Gradient, channel characteristics, and discharge determine the velocity of a stream.*

Facts and Figures

The Missouri River is the longest river in the United States. Its headwaters are in Three Forks, Montana, and it flows to near St. Louis, Missouri—a distance of 4087 km. The Mississippi River, which flows from Lake Itasca, Minnesota to the Gulf of Mexico, is 3765 km long.

However, the Mississippi and Missouri rivers together form the third longest river in the world. Only the Nile and the Amazon rivers are longer. The actual length of the Mississippi River varies by 48 to 80 km each year and has shortened by several hundred kilometers since the 1800s. Most of the changes in length are due to efforts to reduce flood damage.

LESSON 6.1

Use Visuals · L1

Figure 5 Have students study the diagram in Figure 5. **Ask:** Compare the way the stream looks on the steep gradient with the shape the stream makes on the gentle gradient. *(The stream is branched and fairly straight on the steep gradient. It is very curvy on the gentle gradient. Tributaries join the main stream on the steep gradient. On the gentler gradient, just the main stream travels to the sea. The curvy appearance is due to the fact that the stream is close to base level.)*
Visual

Build Reading Literacy · L1

Refer to **p. 186D** in **Chapter 7,** which provides the guidelines for this strategy.

Relate Text and Visuals Photocopy and distribute Figure 5 or ask students to sketch the picture on a sheet of paper. Ask them to label a meander, a tributary, and the mouth of the stream. They should also include an arrow indicating the direction in which the headwaters would be located.
Visual

Integrate Health · L2

Mercury in the Environment Mercury is produced naturally at very low and usually harmless levels. But larger amounts can cause health problems. Coal burning industries, mining, and waste dumps tend to release mercury. Mercury vapor released into the atmosphere can fall to Earth's surface in rain and mercury can dissolve in water on Earth's surface and groundwater. In 1989, studies done by several government agencies showed high levels of mercury in bass in the Everglades. By 1999, experts projected that bass in about two thirds of Florida's lakes and streams were probably affected by high levels of mercury. Beginning in the late 1980s, Florida responded to the growing mercury problem with a number of laws and regulations that reduced mercury in waste and resulted in tighter standards for emissions. Researchers at the University of Florida found that the levels of mercury in the Everglades have fallen significantly since the 1990s.

Research Encourage students to find out whether there is a mercury problem in your state. If so, have students find out what your state is doing to solve the problem. Then have students summarize their findings in a written report.
Verbal

 While gradient decreases between a stream's headwaters and mouth, discharge increases. The amount of discharge increases because more and more tributaries enter the main channel as it moves downstream. A **tributary** is a stream that empties into another stream. In most humid regions, the groundwater supply adds even more water. As the river moves downstream, its width, depth, and velocity change with the increased volume of water.

The observed increase in the average velocity of the water downstream contradicts what people may think about mountain streams. Most people believe that mountain streams are swift and lowland rivers are slow. Although a mountain stream may look like a violent, gushing flow of water, its average velocity is often less than the average velocity of a river near its mouth.

The difference in velocity is mostly due to the great efficiency of the larger downstream channel. In the headwaters area where the gradient may be steep, water often flows in a small channel over many boulders. The small channel and rough bed increase friction. This increase in friction scatters the water and slows its movement. However, downstream the channel is usually smoother so that it offers less resistance to flow. The width and depth of the channel also increase toward the mouth to handle the greater discharge.

☑ **Reading Checkpoint** *What is a stream profile?*

Base Level

There is a lower limit to how deep a stream can erode its channel. **Base level is the lowest point to which a stream can erode its channel.** The *base level* is the level at which the mouth of a stream enters the ocean, a lake, or another stream.

There are two types of base level—ultimate base level and temporary base level. As **Figure 5** shows, sea level is the ultimate base level because it's the lowest level that stream erosion can lower the land. Temporary base levels include lakes, resistant layers of rock, and main streams that act as base level for their tributaries. For example, when a stream enters a lake, its velocity quickly approaches zero. Its ability to erode ceases. The lake prevents the stream from eroding below its level at any point upstream from the lake. However, because the outlet of the lake can cut downward and drain the lake, the lake is only a temporary obstacle to the stream's ability to erode its channel.

FIGURE 5 Base Level Sea level is the ultimate base level of any stream.

FIGURE 6 **Meanders** A river in a broad, flat-floored valley near base level often has a channel with many meanders.
Infer **Is the river in this picture close to or high above its base level?**

FIGURE 7 **Downcutting** When land is gradually uplifted, a meandering river adjusts to being higher above base level by downcutting. The result can be a winding river in a steep, narrow valley such as this one in Utah's Canyonlands National Park.

A stream in a broad, flat-bottomed valley that is near its base level often develops a course with many bends called **meanders,** as shown in **Figure 6.** If base level dropped or the land was uplifted, the river would be considerably higher than base level. The river would have excess energy and flow faster as a result. The river could then downcut its channel. Downcutting occurs when a stream erodes the bottom of its channel resulting in a deepening of the channel. A river that winds through a steep, narrow valley, as shown in **Figure 7,** is one outcome of downcutting.

6.1 Assessment

Review Key Concepts
1. What is the water cycle?
2. How is Earth's water cycle balanced?
3. Where is most of Earth's water located?
4. What part does infiltration play in the water cycle?
5. What factor most influences the power of a stream to erode and transport material?
6. How do gradient and discharge change between a stream's headwaters and its mouth?
7. How might lowering of the base level affect stream erosion?

Think Critically
8. **Relate Cause and Effect** What would happen if evaporation exceeded precipitation over the continents and oceans?
9. **Compare and Contrast** How does the development of urban areas along streams and rivers affect discharge during heavy rainfall?

MATH PRACTICE

10. **Calculate** A stream that is 27 kilometers long drops 90 meters in elevation from its headwaters to its mouth. What is the stream's gradient?

Running Water and Groundwater **163**

Build Science Skills [L2]

Predict Have students study the photo of a meander in Figure 6. Ask them to predict what may happen to the meander if the river suddenly flooded. Have students write their answer in their notebooks. When students read the section on flooding on p. 168, allow them to return to their original answer and make any necessary corrections.
Verbal

3 ASSESS

Evaluate Understanding [L2]

To assess students' knowledge of lesson content, have them write two questions about stream flow. Review the questions for accuracy, and then have students form groups and ask each other their approved questions.

Reteach [L1]

Use Figure 2 to summarize the main concepts about the water cycle. Use Figure 4 to review the characteristics of a stream near its headwaters and its mouth.

Answers

Figure 6 *The flat landscape and meanders indicate it's close to base level.*

☑ **Reading Checkpoint** *A stream profile is a cross-section view of a stream from its headwaters to its mouth.*

Assessment Answers

1. The water cycle is the unending circulation of the water supply on Earth.
2. The average annual precipitation over Earth equals the amount of water that evaporates and transpires.
3. oceans
4. Infiltration is the movement of surface water into rock or soil through cracks and pore spaces.

5. The stream's velocity is the most influencing factor.
6. While gradient decreases between a stream's headwaters and mouth, discharge increases.
7. Lowering base level could result in downcutting.
8. The Earth's surface and oceans would start to dry up.

9. It can increase the magnitude and frequency of floods.
10. 90 meters per 27 kilometers
90 m/27 km = 3.33 m/km

1 FOCUS

Lesson Objectives

6.6 **Explain** how streams erode their channels and transport sediment.

6.7 **Explain** how stream deposition occurs.

6.8 **Identify** the two general types of stream valleys.

6.9 **Predict** the causes of floods and **describe** major flood control measures.

6.10 **Explain** the relationship between streams and drainage basins.

Build Vocabulary L2

Paraphrase Ask students to write the vocabulary terms on a sheet of paper. Instruct students to write a definition, in their own words, for each term as they encounter the term in the lesson. After writing their own definition, encourage students to write the term in a complete sentence.

Reading Strategy L2

Answers will vary. Sample answer: What I Expect to Learn—how erosion happens and what features it can form What I Learned—Erosion occurs when fast-moving water lifts loose particles by abrasion, grinding, and by dissolving soluble material. Pebbles caught in swirling stream currents can bore circular "potholes" into the channel floor.

2 INSTRUCT

Build Reading Literacy L1

Refer to **p. 334D**, in **Chapter 12**, which provides guidelines for outlining.

Outline Have students outline the lesson, leaving room for notes. Then have students scan through each heading and find the main idea. Allow students to refer to their outlines when answering the questions in Lesson 6.2 Assessment.
Logical, Verbal

6.2 The Work of Streams

Key Questions

How do streams erode their channels and transport sediment?

How does stream deposition occur?

What are the two types of stream valleys?

What causes floods, and what are the major flood control measures?

What is the relationship between a stream and a drainage basin?

Vocabulary

- bed load • capacity
- delta • natural levee
- floodplain • flood
- drainage basin
- divide

Reading Strategy

Monitor Your Understanding
Preview the Key Concepts, topic headings, vocabulary, and figures in this lesson. List two things you expect to learn about each. After reading, state what you learned about each item you listed.

What I Expect to Learn	What I Learned

STREAMS ARE EARTH'S most important agents of erosion. They can downcut or erode their channels. They can also transport enormous amounts of sediment. Most of the sediment a stream carries comes from weathering. Weathering produces huge amounts of material that are delivered to streams by sheet flow, mass movements, and groundwater. As streams drop much of this material, they create many different depositional features.

Erosion

Streams generally erode their channels by lifting loose particles, by abrasion and grinding, and by dissolving soluble material. When the flow of water is turbulent enough, it can dislodge loose particles from the channel and lift them into the moving water. In this manner, the force of running water rapidly erodes some streambeds and banks. The stronger the current is, the more erosional power it has and the more effectively the water will pick up particles.

Sand and gravel carried in a stream can erode solid rock channels like sandpaper grinds down wood. Moreover, pebbles caught in swirling stream currents can act like cutting tools and bore circular "potholes" into the channel floor.

☑ **Reading Checkpoint** What are three ways that streams erode their channels?

Sediment Transport

Streams transport sediment in three ways:
(1) in solution (dissolved load),
(2) in suspension (suspended load), and
(3) bouncing or rolling along the bottom (bed load).

Dissolved Load Most of the dissolved load enters streams through groundwater. Dissolving rock also contributes dissolved load along the stream's course. The amount of material the stream carries in solution changes depending on climate and the geologic setting. Usually the dissolved load is expressed as parts of dissolved minerals per million parts of water (parts per million, or ppm). Some rivers may have a dissolved load of 1000 ppm or more. However, the average figure for the world's rivers is estimated to be between 115 and 120 ppm. Streams supply almost 4 billion metric tons of dissolved minerals to the oceans each year.

FIGURE 8 Suspended Load
During this 2011 flood, the suspended load in the muddy Ohio River is clearly visible. The greatest erosion and sediment transport occur during floods.
Apply Concepts Why does the suspended load in water increase during a flood?

Suspended Load Most streams carry the largest part of their load in suspension. The visible cloud of sediment suspended in the water is the most obvious portion of a stream's load. Streams usually carry only sand, silt, and clay this way. However, streams also transport larger particles during a flood because water velocity increases. The total amount of material a stream carries in suspension increases during floods, as shown by the muddy water in **Figure 8.**

Bed Load The part of a stream's load of solid material that is made up of sediment too large to be carried in suspension is called **bed load.** These larger, coarser particles move along the bottom, or bed, of the stream channel. The suspended and dissolved loads are always moving. But the bed load moves only when the force of the water is great enough to move the larger particles. The grinding action of the bed load is very important in eroding the stream channel.

Competence and Capacity The ability of streams to carry a load is determined by two factors: the stream's competence and its capacity. Competence of a stream measures the largest particles it can transport. A stream's competence increases with its velocity. In fact, the competence of a stream increases four times when the velocity doubles. The competence increases nine times when the velocity triples, and so forth. Thus, large boulders that seem immovable can be transported during exceptional floods because of the stream's increased competence.

The **capacity** of a stream is the maximum load it can carry. Capacity is directly related to a stream's discharge. The greater the volume of water in a stream, the greater its capacity for carrying sediment. As a result, large rivers with high velocities have large capacities.

Integrate Chemistry

Solutions and Suspensions Streams transport sediment in solution and in suspension. In chemistry, a solution is a homogeneous mixture of dissolved substances. A suspension is a heterogeneous mixture that separates into layers over time. Ask students to write a paragraph explaining how streams are both solutions and suspensions. *(Streams are composed, in part, of groundwater that contains dissolved substances, and in this way streams are solutions. Streams also transport fine sand, silt, and clay that are not dissolved, but rather suspended in moving water. In this way, streams are suspensions.)*
Verbal

Build Science Skills

Use Models Some students will have difficulty comprehending the tiny scale of one part per million. To help build number sense and awareness of how small a part per million is, ask students to imagine they have a budget of one million dollars, and have them think of the cost of their lunch in terms of parts per million. A four-dollar lunch would be equal to 4 ppm. This represents only a tiny fraction of their total budget.
Logical

Answers

Figure 8 *During a flood, the velocity of a stream or river increases. Therefore, streams carry larger particles in suspension during a flood.*

 Reading Checkpoint *Streams erode their channels lifting loose particles by abrasion, grinding, and by dissolving soluble material.*

Differentiated Instruction

ENGLISH LANGUAGE LEARNERS Students who are learning English can benefit from real-life examples that relate to science content. Encourage students to think of actual flooding events that may have occurred in your area or that they have heard about on the news. Have them research the floods and find photos of rescues or flooded neighborhoods. Encourage students to work together to write captions that describe what is occurring in the photos.

ALLUVIUM   L2

Purpose Students learn how deposition occurs in a stream.

Materials mixed sediment (pebbles, sand, silt, and clay-sized particles), clear glass jar with lid, water

Procedure Fill the jar about one-third full with the mixed sediment. Pour water into the jar and tightly close the lid. Shake the jar and allow sediment to settle out.

Expected Outcomes Sediment should settle out in layers, with pebbles on the bottom and clay-sized particles at the top. As the energy from the shaking dissipates, the heavier material drops out sequentially. If this is not apparent, try using a larger jar, which will allow more room for the materials to settle out.

Answers

MAP IT! The Mississippi River has built its delta to the southeast. New Orleans gets farther from the mouth as the delta is built.

Deposition

Whenever a stream slows down, its competence decreases because sediment begins to drop out, largest particles first. Each particle size has a critical settling velocity. **Deposition occurs as streamflow drops below the critical settling velocity of a certain particle size. The sediment in that category begins to settle out.** Stream transport separates solid particles of various sizes, large to small. This process, called sorting, explains why particles of similar size are deposited together.

The sorted material deposited by a stream is called *alluvium*. Many different depositional features are made of alluvium. Some occur within stream channels. Some occur on the valley floor next to the channel. And others occur at the mouth of a stream.

Deltas When a stream enters the relatively slow-moving water of an ocean or a lake, its velocity drops. As a result, the stream deposits sediment and forms a delta. A **delta** is an accumulation of sediment formed where a stream enters a lake or ocean. As a delta grows outward, the stream's gradient lessens and the water slows down. The channel becomes choked with sediment settling out of the slow-moving water. As a result, the river changes direction in route to base level. The main channel often divides into several smaller channels called distributaries as shown in sub-delta 7 in **Figure 9.** These shifting channels act in the opposite way of tributaries.

FIGURE 9 Mississippi Delta Region

MAP IT!
ACTIVITY

The map in **Figure 9** shows the growth of the Mississippi River delta over the past 5000 to 6000 years. As you can see, the river has built a series of sub-deltas, one after the other. The numbers indicate the order in which they were deposited.

Interpret Maps In which overall direction has the Mississippi River built its delta over the past few thousand years?

Interpret Maps How has the growth of the delta changed the location of the mouth of the Mississippi River in relation to New Orleans?

Facts and Figures

The city of New Orleans, Louisiana, is built on a delta at the mouth of the Mississippi River. As is expected, the water table in this area is very high due to the fact that the delta is built right into the ocean. This high water table leaves New Orleans with a troubling problem—how do they bury their dead?

Early settlers were forced to bury their dead in shallow graves due to the high water table.

If they dug down only a few feet, the grave filled with water and caused the casket to float.

Finally, settlers adopted another method of burial. They built above-ground vaults. Today many of the cemeteries in New Orleans have tombs arranged in a street-like fashion. In fact, the cemeteries are often referred to as "cities of the dead."

Rather than carrying water into the main channel like tributaries, distributaries carry water away. After many shifts of the channel, a delta may grow into a triangular shape, like the Greek letter delta (Δ). However, not all deltas have this idealized shape. Differences in the shapes of shorelines and variations in the strength of waves and currents result in different shapes of deltas.

Natural Levees Some rivers occupy valleys with broad, flat floors. Successive floods over many years can build natural levees along them. A **natural levee** is a ridge made up mostly of coarse sediments that parallels some streams. A natural levee forms when a stream repeatedly overflows its banks. Its velocity rapidly decreases, and it leaves coarse sediment deposits in strips that border the channel. As the water spreads out over the valley, less sediment is deposited. This uneven distribution of material produces the gentle slope of the natural levee.

Stream Valleys

Streams are constantly changing the valleys through which they flow. A *stream valley* consists of the channel and the surrounding land that contributes water to the stream. Stream valleys range in size from narrow, steep-sided valleys to those that are wide and flat.

Narrow Valleys The Yellowstone River, shown in **Figure 10,** is an excellent example of a narrow valley. **A narrow V-shaped valley shows that the stream's primary work has been downcutting toward base level.** Rapids and waterfalls are the most prominent features of a narrow valley. Both rapids and waterfalls occur where the stream profile drops rapidly. The variations in the erosion of the underlying bedrock cause these rapid drops.

Wide Valleys Once a stream has cut its channel closer to base level, downcutting becomes less dominant. More of the stream's energy is directed from side to side. The result is a widening of the valley as the river cuts away first at one bank and then at the other. The side-to-side cutting of a stream eventually produces a flat valley floor, or **floodplain.** A floodplain is appropriately named because during a flood the river overflows its banks and floods the plain.

Streams that flow on floodplains move in meanders. Once a bend in a channel begins to form, it grows larger. Most of the erosion occurs on the outside of the meander—often called the cut bank—where velocity and turbulence are greatest. Much of the debris the stream removes at the cut bank moves downstream where it is deposited as point bars. Point bars form in zones of decreased velocity on the insides of meanders. In this way, meanders move side to side by eroding the outside of bends and depositing on the inside.

FIGURE 10 Narrow Valleys The Yellowstone River is an example of a V-shaped valley. The rapids and waterfall show that the river is vigorously downcutting the channel.

Running Water and Groundwater **167**

FIGURE 11 Formation of an Oxbow Lake
A. One meander has overtaken the next, forming a ring of water on the floodplain.

B. After deposits of sediment cut off the ring, an oxbow lake forms.

LESSON 6.2

Build Science Skills [L2]

Infer Draw on the board a cross section of a river valley. *(a broad relatively flat-bottomed shape, similar to a horizontal bracket)* Then have students draw cross sections representing at least three earlier stages in the development of the valley. Tell them the first stage should be of a time when waterfalls and rapids were common along the river's course. *(Cross sections should show the valley getting narrower with each earlier stage of development. The earliest cross section should show a V-shaped valley.)*
Logical

Use Visuals [L1]

Figure 11 Have students study the streams shown in the diagrams. **Ask:** Are other oxbow lakes shown on these diagrams? *(Yes, the remnants of two other crescent-shaped lakes are shown.)* What does this show you about the river? *(The oxbow lakes indicate previous positions of the river.)* Where might the next oxbow lake form along this section of river? *(It will most likely form along the course at the lower part of the diagrams, where a neck is forming at the base of a meander that loops to the left. Some students might think the course of the river at the top of the diagrams represents an even narrower neck that is not shown but would pinch off the large meander to the right, forming an oxbow lake.)*
Visual, Logical

Answers

MAP IT! The second satellite image shows the rivers during flood stage. You can tell the rivers are at flood stage because the area covered by water is much wider.

Erosion is more effective on the outside edge of a meander because of the slope of the channel. The bends gradually travel down the valley. Sometimes the downstream movement of a meander slows when it reaches a more resistant portion of the floodplain. This resistance allows the next meander upstream to overtake it, as shown in **Figure 11**. Gradually the neck of land between the meanders is narrowed. Eventually the river may erode through the narrow neck of land to the next loop. The new, shorter channel segment is called a cutoff and, because of its shape, the abandoned bend is called an *oxbow lake*. Such a situation is shown in the bottom portion of Figure 6 in Lesson 1.

Floods and Flood Control

A **flood** occurs when the discharge of a stream becomes so great that it exceeds the capacity of its channel and overflows its banks. Floods are the most common and most destructive of all natural geologic hazards. **Most floods are caused by rapid spring snow melt or storms that bring heavy rains over a large region.** Heavy rains caused the devastating floods in the upper Mississippi River Valley during the summer of 1993, as shown in **Figure 12.**

MAP IT!
ACTIVITY

The satellite images in **Figure 12** show the Missouri and Mississippi rivers. The satellite image on the left shows the rivers during normal flow.
Interpret Photographs What does the satellite image on the right show? How do you know?

FIGURE 12
Mississippi River Flooding

Facts and Figures

On May 31, 1889, residents of Johnstown, Pennsylvania, heard what sounded like a roar of thunder. Their worst fears were realized. The South Fork Dam, located 22.4 km upstream along the Little Conemaugh River, broke after a night of heavy rain. Twenty million tons of water crashed down the river valley made narrower by the growing community. More than 2200 people died as a result of the flood and the aftermath of fires that followed.

Unlike far-reaching regional floods, flash floods are more limited in extent. However, flash floods occur with little warning, and they can be deadly as walls of water sweep through river valleys. Several factors influence flash floods: rainfall intensity and duration, surface conditions, and topography. As you have learned, urban areas are susceptible to flash floods. Mountainous areas are also susceptible because steep slopes can send runoff into narrow canyons.

Human interference with the stream system can worsen or cause floods. A prime example is the failure of a dam or an artificial levee. These structures are designed to contain floods of a certain size. If that size is exceeded, water can then spill over or break through a dam or levee and rush downstream causing a disastrous flood.

There are several flood control strategies. **Measures to control flooding include artificial levees, flood control dams, and placing limits on floodplain development.**

Artificial Levees Artificial levees are earthen mounds built on the banks of a river. These levees increase the volume of water a channel can hold. When levees confine a river during periods of high water, the river often deposits material in its channel as the discharge diminishes. This discharge is sediment that would have been dropped on the floodplain. Because the stream cannot deposit material outside of its channel the bottom of the channel is gradually built up. When the channel is built up, it takes less water to overflow the levee. As a result, people may have to raise the height of the levee periodically to protect the floodplain behind it. Moreover, many artificial levees are not built to withstand periods of extreme flooding. For example, in August of 2005, the flooding rains and strong winds of Hurricane Katrina damaged the levees separating New Orleans from Lake Pontchartrain. As a result, much of the city was flooded for many weeks.

Flood-Control Dam Flood-control dams store floodwater and then let it out slowly. Since the 1920s, thousands of dams have been built on nearly every major river in the United States. Many dams have other non-flood related functions, such as providing water for irrigation and for hydroelectric power generation.

Although dams may reduce flooding and provide other benefits, building dams has consequences. For example, dams trap sediment. Deltas and floodplains downstream can erode because transported sediment no longer replenishes them during floods. Built up sediment behind a dam means the volume of the stored water will gradually diminish. This build-up reduces the effectiveness of the dam for flood control. Large dams also cause ecological damage to river environments.

Limiting Development Today many scientists and engineers advocate sound floodplain management instead of building structures. That often means preserving floodplains in their natural state. Minimizing development on floodplains allows them to absorb floodwaters with little harm to homes and businesses.

INQUIRY APPLY IT!

Q: *Sometimes a major flood is described as a 100-year flood. What does that mean?*

A: The phrase "100-year flood" is misleading because it makes people believe that such an event happens only once every 100 years. In truth, a huge flood can happen any year. The phrase "100-year flood" is really a statistical designation. It indicates that there is a 1-in-100 chance that a flood this size will happen during any year. Perhaps a better term would be the "1-in-100 chance flood."

PLANET DIARY

For links on **Floods**, visit PlanetDiary.com/HSES.

Some students may have heard the term "100-year flood" and assume that this means that floods only occur in the area every 100 years. This is not true and is often misleading. A major flood can occur along a river during any year. What the term does suggest, however, is that statistically speaking there is a 1 in 100 chance that in any given year, a major flood will occur. The chances of flooding along any stream are reevaluated periodically. It has been found that the flooding likelihood changes and that major flooding may occur more frequently than every 100 years. Ask students to predict what sort of human activity may increase the likelihood of flooding. *(Urban development, cutting down trees, and the building of dams may increase the amount of serious flooding in an area.)*
Logical

LESSON 6.2

Use Visuals L1

Figure 13 Point out the Mississippi River drainage basin. **Ask:** Do other drainage basins exist within this one? *(Yes, every stream, regardless of size, has its own drainage basin. A larger river, such as the Mississippi, will have a drainage basin that includes those of all of its tributaries.)* The Continental Divide separates waters that flow into the Atlantic Ocean or Gulf of Mexico from those that flow into the Pacific Ocean. **Ask:** Is the eastern or western portion of the Mississippi River drainage basin divide the continental divide? *(The western portion of the Mississippi River drainage basin divide that runs through the Rocky Mountains is the continental divide.)*

Use Community Resources L2

Drainage Basins Invite a hydrologist to speak to the class about a drainage basin in your area. Have students trace out the drainage basin of a local stream or river and discuss their findings with the scientist. **Interpersonal**

3 ASSESS

Evaluate Understanding L2

To assess students' knowledge of lesson content, have them develop a visual showing a narrow and a wide stream valley.

Reteach L1

Have students make a chart summarizing the differences between erosion and deposition.

Drainage Basins

Every stream has a drainage basin, also called a watershed. **A drainage basin is the land area that contributes water to a stream.** An imaginary line called a **divide** separates the drainage basins of one stream from another. Divides range in scale from a ridge separating two small gullies on a hillside to a continental divide, which splits continents into enormous drainage basins. The Mississippi River, shown in **Figure 13**, has the largest drainage basin in North America. The river and its tributaries collect water from an area of more than 3.2 million square kilometers.

FIGURE 13 Mississippi River Drainage Basin Divides are the boundaries that separate drainage basins from each other.

6.2 Assessment

Review Key Concepts

1. How do streams erode their channels?

2. What causes floods?

3. What is the relationship between a stream and a drainage basin?

4. How do streams transport sediments?

Think Critically

5. **Apply Concepts** How does urban development interfere with the natural function of floodplains?

6. **Relate Cause and Effect** Explain the formation of one of the landforms that streams create by deposition.

WRITING IN SCIENCE

7. **Descriptive Paragraph** Use library sources or the Internet to research the causes of a recent major flood. Write a paragraph that tells the name of the flood, when it happened, where it happened, and the conditions that led to the flood itself.

170 Chapter 6 • Lesson 2

Assessment Answers

1. Streams erode their channels by lifting loose particles by abrasion, grinding, and by dissolving soluble material.
2. Floods occur when the discharge of a stream exceeds the capacity of the channel. Most floods are caused by rapid spring snow melt and storms.
3. A drainage basin is the land area that contributes water to a stream.

4. Streams transport sediment in solution, in suspension, and by rolling along the bottom.
5. Urban development can decrease the effectiveness of floodplains by replacing water-absorbing vegetation with concrete and asphalt and increasing flooding.
6. Sample answer: Deltas are formed as accumulating sediment is deposited where a stream or river enters a lake or ocean.

7. Student paragraphs should describe accurately researched floods and their causes and effects.

6.3 Water Beneath the Surface

THE GROUND BENEATH your feet isn't as solid as you might think. It includes countless tiny pore spaces between grains of soil and sediment. It also contains narrow joints and fractures in bedrock. Together these spaces add up to an immense volume of tiny openings where water collects underground and moves.

Underground water in wells and springs provides water for cities, crops, livestock, and industry. In the United States, it is the drinking water for more than 50 percent of the population. It also provides 40 percent of the irrigation water and more than 25 percent of industry's needs.

Movement and Distribution of Water Underground

When it rains, some of the water runs off, some evaporates, some transpires, and the rest soaks into the ground to become subsurface water. The amount of water that ends up underground in an area depends on the steepness of slopes, the nature of surface materials, the intensity of rainfall, and the type and amount of vegetation.

Movement The flow and storage of groundwater depends on the porosity and permeability of the subsurface material. **Porosity** is the percentage of the total volume of rock or sediment that consists of pore spaces. Pore spaces are openings in bedrock, sediment, and soil. These openings are similar to those of a sponge.

Rock or sediment may be very porous and still block water's movement. The **permeability** of a material is its ability to transmit a fluid. Groundwater moves by twisting and turning through interconnected small openings. The groundwater moves more slowly when the pore spaces are smaller. If the spaces between particles are too small, water cannot move at all. For example, clay has high porosity. But clay is impermeable because its pore spaces are so small that water can't move through them at all.

Impermeable layers that prevent water movement are *aquitards*. Larger particles, such as sand, have larger pore spaces between them. Water moves through them easily. Permeable rock layers or sediments that transmit groundwater freely are **aquifers.** Aquifers are important because they are the source of well water.

Key Questions

- How does groundwater move and where is it located?
- How do springs form?
- What are some environmental threats to groundwater supplies?
- How and where do most caverns form?
- What landforms are common in an area of karst topography?

Vocabulary

- porosity • permeability
- aquifer • zone of saturation
- groundwater • water table
- spring • geyser • well
- artesian well
- cavern • travertine
- karst topography • sinkhole

Reading Strategy

Preview Copy the table below. Before you read the section, rewrite the orange topic headings as how, why, and what questions. As you read, write an answer to each question.

Question	Answer
How does water move underground?	

1 FOCUS

Lesson Objectives

- **6.11** **Describe** the movement and location of groundwater.
- **6.12** **Describe** the formation of a spring.
- **6.13** **Explain** environmental threats to water supplies.
- **6.14** **Describe** the formation of caverns.
- **6.15** **Describe** landforms in karst areas.

Build Vocabulary

Paraphrase Students may find terms such as *porosity, permeability, aquifer,* and *artesian* unfamiliar. Encourage students to write definitions for these terms in their own words to help them remember their meaning.

Reading Strategy L2
Sample answers

Question	Answer
How does water move underground?	by twisting and turning through interconnected small openings
How does a spring form?	when the water table intersects the ground surface
What is a well?	a hole bored into the zone of saturation
What are some environmental problems associated with groundwater?	overuse and contamination
What kind of terrain do Karst areas have?	irregular terrain with many sinkholes

2 INSTRUCT

Build Science Skills

Infer After students read p. 171, **ask:** On sloping land, which would likely result in more groundwater: a quick thunderstorm or the same volume of water from a longer, gentle rain? Why? *(the gentle rain because the water would have more time to soak into the ground rather than run off the land)*
Logical

WATER TABLE `L2`

Purpose Students visually see the boundary between the zone of saturation and the zone of aeration.

Materials large clear plastic cup; clean, dry sand; water

Procedure Fill the cup about two-thirds full with the clean sand. Slowly pour the water on top of the sand and allow it to filter down to the bottom. Add enough water so that the cup is approximately half full of water.

Expected Outcomes Students should be able to clearly see the separation between the sand that contains water and the sand that has very little water in its pore space. Identify this boundary for them as the water table. Students can then infer what would happen to the water table in times of drought or excessive rainfall.

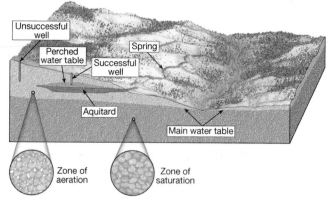

FIGURE 14 Distribution of Groundwater This diagram shows the relative positions of many features associated with subsurface water.

Apply Concepts *What is the source of the spring in the center of the illustration?*

Distribution The water that soaks into the ground does not travel far. Molecular attraction holds it in place as a surface film on soil particles. This near-surface zone is called the belt of soil moisture. Roots, voids left by decayed roots, and animal and worm burrows criss-cross this zone. These features help rainwater seep into soil.

Much of the water in soil seeps downward until it reaches the zone of saturation. The **zone of saturation** is the area where water fills all of the pore spaces in sediment and rock. **Groundwater** is the water within this zone. The upper limit of the zone of saturation is the **water table,** as you can see in **Figure 14.** The area above the water table where the soil, sediment, and rock are not saturated is the *zone of aeration*. Wells cannot pump water from this zone. The water clings too tightly to the rocks and soil. Only below the water table—where water pressure is great enough to allow water to enter wells—can water be pumped.

Springs

A spring forms whenever the water table intersects the ground surface. A **spring** is a flow of groundwater that emerges naturally at the ground surface, as shown in **Figure 15.** Springs form when an aquitard blocks downward movement of groundwater and forces it to move laterally.

Hot Springs A hot spring is 6°C to 9°C warmer than the mean annual air temperature where the spring occurs. There are more than 1000 hot springs in the United States. Approximately 95 percent of these hot springs are in the west.

Temperatures in deep mines and oil wells usually rise with an increase in depth at an average of 2°C per 100 meters. So when groundwater circulates at great depths, it becomes heated. If it rises to the surface, the water may emerge as a hot spring. This process heats many hot springs in the eastern United States.

FIGURE 15 Spring A spring flows from a valley wall into a stream.

172 Chapter 6 • Lesson 3

Differentiated Instruction

ENGLISH LANGUAGE LEARNERS Have students work in pairs to think of ways that groundwater can be conserved. Examples include shutting off the faucet when brushing your teeth, taking shorter showers, and running the dishwasher only when full. Strengthen discussion skills by having students share their examples with the class.

The source of heat for most of the hot springs in the western United States is cooling igneous rock. In some places, hot acidic groundwater mixes with minerals from adjacent rock to form thick, bubbling mineral springs called mudpots.

Geysers A **geyser** is an intermittent hot spring or fountain in which a column of water shoots up with great force at various intervals. Geysers often shoot up columns of water 30 to 60 meters. After the jet of water stops, a column of steam rushes out—usually with a thundering roar. Perhaps the most famous geyser in the world is Old Faithful in Yellowstone National Park. It erupts about once each hour.

Geysers occur where extensive underground chambers exist within hot igneous rocks. Follow the geyser eruption cycle in **Figure 16.** As relatively cool groundwater enters the chambers, the surrounding rock heats it. The weight of the overlying water creates great pressure at the bottom of the chamber. This pressure prevents the water from boiling at the normal surface boiling temperature of 100°C. However, the heat makes the water expand, and it forces some of the water out at the surface. This loss of water reduces the pressure in the chamber. The boiling point drops. Some of the water deep within the chamber then turns to steam and makes the geyser erupt. Following the eruption, cool groundwater again seeps into the chamber. Then the cycle begins again.

☑ **Reading Checkpoint** *What is a geyser?*

Wells

A **well** is a hole bored into the zone of saturation. Irrigation for agriculture is by far the single greatest use of well water in the United States—more than 65 percent of groundwater used annually. Industrial uses of groundwater rank a distant second, followed by the amount used by homes.

The level of the water table may change considerably during a year. The level can drop during the dry season and rise following periods of rain. To ensure a continuous water supply, a well must penetrate far below the water table. The water table around the well drops whenever a substantial amount of water is withdrawn from a well. This effect is called drawdown, and it decreases with an increase in distance from the well.

GEYSER ERUPTION CYCLE
FIGURE 16

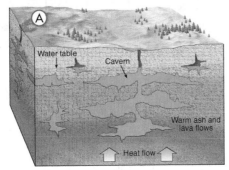

A Groundwater enters underground caverns and fractures in hot igneous rock where it is heated to near its boiling point.

B Heating causes the water to expand, with some being forced out at the surface. The loss of water reduces the pressure on the remaining water, thus reducing its boiling temperature. Some of the water flashes to steam.

C The rapidly expanding steam forces the hot water out of the chambers to produce a geyser. The empty chambers fill again, and the cycle starts anew.

Running Water and Groundwater **173**

Facts and Figures

Yellowstone National Park is home to approximately two thirds of the geysers on Earth. Included in these is one of the most famous geysers, Old Faithful. Despite its name, Old Faithful can be rather unpredictable. It usually erupts every 76 minutes but it can range from 35 minutes to 2 hours. The time between eruptions depends upon the length of the previous eruption.

Old Faithful can shoot up water to 60 m. This is not the largest geyser, however. Steamboat Geyser, also located in Yellowstone, is the largest geyser in the world. It can shoot water 90 m into the air.

Use Visuals L1

Use Visuals L1

Figure 17 Ask students to compare the wells in both diagrams in Figure 17. **Ask:** As you can see in the diagrams, two of the wells went dry as a result of heavy pumping and one well stayed productive. What rule of well digging can you deduce from this example? *(When digging a well, be sure to sink it well below the average water table.)*
Visual, Logical

Use Community Resources L2

Invite a hydrologist or water conservationist to speak to the class on ways to conserve the use of groundwater. The Soil and Water Conservation Society can provide a list of local chapters and resources. To prepare for the presentation, have students research current positions on water conservation. They can develop a list of questions to ask the speaker.
Interpersonal, Verbal

FIGURE 17 Well A cone of depression in the water table often forms around a pumping well. If heavy pumping lowers the water table, some wells may be left dry.

INQUIRY
APPLY IT!

Q: *I have heard people say that supplies of groundwater can be located using a forked stick. Can this actually be done?*

A: What you describe is a practice called "water dowsing." In the classic method, a person holding a forked stick walks back and forth over an area. When water is detected, the bottom of the "Y" is supposed to be attracted downward.

Geologists and engineers are extremely doubtful, to say the least. Case histories and demonstrations may seem convincing, but when dowsing is exposed to scientific scrutiny, it fails. Most "successful" examples of water dowsing occur in places where water would be hard to miss. In a region of adequate rainfall and favorable geology, it is difficult to drill and *not* find water!

The result of a drawdown is a cone of depression in the water table, such as the one shown in **Figure 17.** For most small domestic wells, the cone of depression is tiny. However, when wells are used for irrigation or industry, a very wide and steep cone of depression can result.

Water must be pumped out of most wells. However, water rises on its own in some wells, sometimes overflowing the surface. In an **artesian well,** groundwater rises on its own under pressure. For such a situation to occur, two conditions must exist. First, water must be in an aquifer that is tilted so that one end is exposed at the surface, where it can receive water. Second, there must be aquitards both above and below the aquifer to stop the water from escaping. The pressure created by the weight of the water above forces the water to rise when a well taps the aquifer.

☑ **Reading Checkpoint** *How does an artesian well differ from most wells?*

Environmental Problems Associated With Groundwater

As with many valuable natural resources, groundwater is being threatened at an increasing rate. 💧 **Contamination and overuse threaten groundwater supplies in some areas.**

Groundwater Contamination The pollution of groundwater is a serious matter, particularly in areas where aquifers provide much of the water supply. Major sources of groundwater pollution are sewage from septic tanks, farm wastes, and inadequate or broken sewers.

If sewage water that is contaminated with harmful bacteria enters the groundwater system, it may become purified through natural processes. The bacteria can be destroyed by chemical oxidation.

174 Chapter 6 • Lesson 3

FIGURE 18 Purification of Contaminated Groundwater
FIGURE 18 Purification of Contaminated Groundwater A Although the contaminated water has traveled more than 100 meters before reaching Well 1, the water moves too quickly through the cavernous limestone to be purified. **B** As the discharge from the septic tank percolates through the permeable sandstone, it is purified in a short distance.

It can be mechanically filtered by the sediment through which the water passes or assimilated by organisms. For purification to occur, however, the aquifer must be of the correct composition.

For example, extremely permeable aquifers have such large openings that contaminated groundwater may travel long distances without being cleansed. In this case, the water flows too quickly and is not in contact with the surrounding material long enough for purification to occur. This is the problem at Well 1 in **Figure 18A.**

However, when the aquifer is composed of sand or permeable sandstone, the water can sometimes be purified after traveling through it for only a few dozen meters. The openings between sand grains are large enough to permit water movement, yet the movement of the water is slow enough to allow enough time for its purification. This is the case at Well 2 in **Figure 18B.**

Other sources and types of contamination also threaten supplies, as you can see in **Figures 19** and **20.** These include fertilizers that are spread across the land, pesticides, and highway salt. In addition, chemicals and industrial materials—some hazardous—may leak from pipelines, storage tanks, landfills, and holding ponds. As rainwater oozes through the refuse, it may dissolve contaminants. If this material reaches the water table, it will mix with and contaminate groundwater. In coastal areas, heavy use can deplete aquifers, causing underground salt water to enter wells.

Once the source of the contamination has been identified and eliminated, the most common practice is to abandon the water supply. Abandoning the water supply allows the pollutants to flush out gradually. It's the least costly and easiest solution, but the aquifer must stay unused for years.

FIGURE 19 Fertilizers and Pesticides Agricultural chemicals sprayed on farm fields can seep into soil and contaminate underground water supplies.

FIGURE 20 Landfill If landfills leak, harmful waste buried in them can escape into groundwater.

Running Water and Groundwater **175**

Integrate Health L2

Groundwater Contamination Arsenic contamination of groundwater is a common problem. Arsenic is a known carcinogen. It was once an ingredient in pesticides used on apple orchards. Many communities now are testing old apple orchards and finding that there are significant amounts of arsenic in their soil, which seeps into the groundwater. The Environmental Protection Agency (EPA) recently revised the standard for safe levels of arsenic in drinking water. Prior to January 22, 2001, the acceptable level was 50 parts per billion. As of January 23, 2006, public water systems must comply with the new acceptable level of 10 parts per billion. This serves as a further level of protection of groundwater resources. Ask students to research other types of groundwater contamination and steps that have been taken to prevent or eliminate it. Pairs of students can present short reports to the class.
Interpersonal, Verbal

Build Science Skills L2

Student Activity: Analyze Data In 1986, researchers found data that lead them to discover an impact crater along Virginia's coastal plains. Have students conduct library or Internet research about the discovery of this crater. In a presentation or poster, students should explain how the crater was discovered and how the crater is related to salt-water contamination of groundwater in eastern Virginia.
Verbal

Answers

☑ **Reading Checkpoint** *In an artesian well, water rises on its own, instead of being pumped.*

Facts and Figures

Drilling a well can be a daunting task. Not only do you have to locate the source of water on your property and determine how much water is available, you have to estimate the amount of water that you, your family, and possibly your business will need. The following are estimates that can be used to determine the peak demand that will be placed on a well.

For a single family home, assume 190 to 285 liters of water a day per person.

Maintenance of an average lawn and garden requires 190 to 3800 liters per day. Farmers are faced with a more challenging estimate. For example, dairy cattle require 133 liters per day per animal for drinking water. A goat requires 7.6 liters per day; each pig requires 15.2 liters, a horse 45.6 liters per day. A flock of 100 chickens requires 19 to 38 liters of drinking water per day and a flock of 100 turkeys needs 38 to 68 liters per day.

LESSON 6.3

Build Science Skills L2

Apply Concepts After students read the section on Groundwater Contamination, present them with the following problem. Imagine you are an environmental scientist and have been called in to solve a groundwater contamination problem. Some people have noticed that their well water has a funny smell and taste and they think that the contamination is coming from a farmer who lives upstream. The farmer insists that he is not contaminating the water supply and suggests instead that a large chemical factory farther upstream is to blame. How can you determine the origin of the contamination? *(Answers will vary but students may recognize a few places to start. For example, they should suggest determining the type of contamination. Is the water supply being contaminated by fertilizer, for example? Identifying the contaminant will help in pinpointing the source. They also may recognize that by testing the groundwater upstream and downstream from the farmer, they may be able to identify if the contamination is occurring upstream or downstream of the farm.)*

Logical, Intrapersonal

FIGURE 21 Land Subsidence
The marks on the utility pole indicate the level of the surrounding land in years past. Between 1925 and 1975 this part of the San Joaquin Valley sank almost 9 meters because of the withdrawal of groundwater and the resulting compaction of sediments.

To speed up this process, engineers sometimes pump out and treat polluted water. The aquifer then recharges naturally, or the treated water is pumped back in. This process can be risky, because there is no way to be sure that treatment has removed all the pollution. Prevention remains the most effective solution to groundwater contamination.

Some substances in groundwater are natural. Ions of substances (from adjacent rock) such as calcium and iron make some water "hard." Hard water forms scum with soap instead of suds. It can also deposit residue that clogs pipes. But hard water is generally not a health risk.

Treating Groundwater as a Nonrenewable Resource
Groundwater seems like an endlessly renewable resource. However, supplies are finite. In some regions, the amount of water available to recharge an aquifer is much less than the amount being withdrawn.

The High Plains, a relatively dry region that extends from South Dakota to western Texas, provides one example of severe groundwater depletion. In some parts of the region, intense irrigation has gone on for a long time. Even if pumping were to stop now, it could take thousands of years for the groundwater to be fully replenished.

The ground may sink when water is pumped from wells faster than natural processes can replace it. As water is withdrawn, the ground subsides as the weight of the overburden packs relatively loose sediment grains more tightly together.

This type of subsidence is extreme in the San Joaquin Valley of California, as shown in **Figure 21.** Land subsidence due to groundwater withdrawal for irrigation began there in the mid-1920s. It exceeded eight meters by 1970. During a drought in 1976 and 1977, heavy groundwater pumping led the ground to sink even more. Land subsidence affected more than 13,400 square kilometers of irrigable land—one half the entire valley. To slow subsidence, the San Joaquin Valley now imports water from the Sacramento-San Joaquin River Delta. The imported water reduces the need for groundwater withdrawal.

☑ **Reading Checkpoint** *What are some common sources of groundwater pollution?*

Caverns

The most spectacular results of groundwater's ability to weather and erode rock are limestone caverns. Soluble rocks, especially limestone, underlie millions of square kilometers of Earth's surface. Limestone is nearly insoluble in pure water. But water containing small quantities of carbonic acid dissolves it easily. Most natural water contains the weak acid because rainwater dissolves carbon dioxide from the air and decaying plants. Therefore, when groundwater comes in contact with limestone, the carbonic acid reacts with calcite in the rocks, and calcium bicarbonate forms.

Facts and Figures

The Environmental Protection Agency (EPA) recognizes that groundwater needs to be treated as a nonrenewable resource. They have strict regulations on public water supplies but have no control over private wells and water sources. They do, however, have some suggestions for homeowners with private wells to ensure that this vital resource remains protected. They advise homeowners to

- inspect exposed portions of the well for settling or damaged well casings periodically.

- build a slope in the area around the well to drain runoff away from the well.
- have the well tested each year for bacteria and nitrates and other possible contaminants.
- avoid using pesticides, herbicides, fuels, and other contaminants near the well.
- inspect septic systems regularly.
- refrain from disposing of hazardous material in septic systems or abandoned wells.

FIGURE 22 **Cavern** The dissolving action of groundwater creates caverns. These dripstone features are in Three Fingers Cave in New Mexico.

As groundwater carries away the calcium bicarbonate in solution, it slowly erodes rock, and a cavern forms. A **cavern** is a naturally formed underground chamber, such as the one you see in **Figure 22.**

There are thousands of caverns in the United States. Most are fairly small, but some have spectacular dimensions. Carlsbad Caverns in southeastern New Mexico is a famous example. One chamber has an area equivalent to 14 football fields, and it is high enough to fit the U.S. Capitol building inside it.

Erosion forms most caverns at or below the water table in the zone of saturation. Here, acidic groundwater follows lines of weakness in the rock, such as joints and bedding planes. As time passes, the dissolving process slowly creates cavities and enlarges them into caverns. Material the groundwater dissolves eventually flows into streams and then the ocean.

The features that produce the greatest curiosity for most cavern visitors are depositional stone formations. These formations give some caverns a wonderland appearance. They form from seemingly endless dripping of water over great spans of time. The calcium carbonate that is left behind produces the limestone we call **travertine.** These cave deposits are commonly called *dripstone.*

Although the formation of caverns takes place in the zone of saturation, the deposition of dripstone is not possible until the caverns are above the water table in the zone of aeration. The formation of caverns in the zone of aeration commonly occurs as nearby streams cut their valleys deeper. As the elevation of the stream drops, the water table also lowers, leaving the caverns high and largely dry.

Running Water and Groundwater **177**

Use Visuals

Figure 22 Challenge students to imagine themselves as the spelunker (cave explorer) in the photograph. **Ask:** What would the overall climate be in the Three Fingers Cave? *(Climate would be cool and very damp.)*
Visual

Build Reading Literacy L2

Refer to **p. 474D** in **Chapter 17,** which provides guidelines for the monitor your understanding strategy.

Monitor Your Understanding Have students read the section on caverns. When they are finished, ask them to write the main ideas of that section. Have students ask themselves, "Did I have any trouble reading this section? If so, why?" Invite students to come up with their own strategies to improve their understanding of cavern formation and features. Have students use their own strategies as they continue reading.
Intrapersonal, Verbal

Answers

☑ **Reading Checkpoint** *Common sources of groundwater pollution are sewage from septic tanks, farm wastes, and inadequate or broken sewers.*

Differentiated Instruction

HEARING IMPAIRED Reinforce the lesson's content by providing a variety of visual examples. Be sure to spend time on all the visual examples provided in the text. In addition, you may wish to demonstrate how limestone can be dissolved in a dilute acid. Wear safety goggles and use a dropper to place several drops of hydrochloric acid on a sample of limestone. Do not touch the acid. Students will observe a bubbling action. Challenge students to imagine how this action could, over a long period of time, form an underground cavern.

LESSON 6.3

Build Science Skills

Infer Describe for students the characteristics of "hard" water. Water containing a lot of dissolved minerals can decrease the effectiveness of soap and leave a residue behind on fixtures and shower curtains. Ask students if they think the water may be hard in a karst region, and if so, what mineral is most likely dissolved in the groundwater? *(The water is hard in a karst region due to the calcium dissolved in the water from the erosion of the limestone underground.)*
Logical

Integrate Chemistry

Acid Rain on Karst Topography
Explain to students that chemical and power plants release sulfur dioxide and nitrogen monoxide into the air. These chemicals combine with precipitation to become acid rain. Acid rain harms plants, animals, and soil. It also affects karst topography because limestone is vulnerable to the effects of acid. Have students research the effects of acid rain on karst topography. Ask each student to prepare a presentation that includes a graph or chart of data collected.
Verbal, Logical

FIGURE 23 Dripstone Feature
These soda straw stalactites formed in Great Basin National Park's Lehman Caves.
Relate Cause and Effect *What part do these drops of water play in the formation of the stalactites?*

Dripstone Features Perhaps the most familiar dripstone features are *stalactites*. Stalactites are icicle-like stone pendants that hang from the ceiling of a cavern. They form when water seeps through cracks in the cavern ceiling. When water reaches air in the cave, some of the dissolved carbon dioxide escapes from the drop and calcite begins to separate out. Deposition occurs as a ring around the edge of the water drops. As drops fall, each one leaves a tiny trace of calcite behind. This calcite creates a hollow limestone tube called a soda straw, as shown in **Figure 23.** Often the hollow tube becomes plugged or its supply of water increases. When a stalactite becomes plugged or the water supply increases, the water flows and deposits along the outside of the tube. As deposition continues, the stalactite takes on the more common conical shape.

Stalagmites are formations that develop on the floor of a cavern and reach up toward the ceiling. The water supplying the calcite for stalagmite growth falls from the ceiling and splatters over the surface of the cavern floor. As a result, stalagmites do not have a central tube. They are usually more massive and more rounded on their upper ends than stalactites. Given enough time, a downward-growing stalactite and an upward-growing stalagmite may join to form a column.

☑ **Reading Checkpoint** *What is a dripstone feature?*

Karst Topography

Many areas of the world have landscapes that have been shaped by the dissolving power of groundwater. These areas are said to have **karst topography.** This term comes from the Krs region of Slovenia, where such topography is strikingly developed. In the United States, karst landscapes occur in many areas that are underlain by limestone. These areas include parts of Kentucky, Tennessee, Alabama, southern Indiana, and central northern Florida.

Karst areas typically have irregular terrain, with many depressions called sinkholes. A **sinkhole** is a depression produced in a region where groundwater has removed soluble rock. In the limestone areas of Florida, Kentucky, and southern Indiana, there are tens of thousands of these depressions. They vary in depth from just a meter or two to more than 50 meters.

Sinkholes commonly form in one of two ways. Some develop gradually over many years without any physical disturbance to the rock. In these situations, downward-seeping rainwater containing carbon dioxide dissolves limestone below the soil. These depressions are fairly shallow and have gentle slopes. Sinkholes can also form suddenly when the roof of a cavern collapses forming depressions that are steep-sided and deep. When they form in populated areas, they may be a serious geologic hazard, as shown in **Figure 24.**

FIGURE 24 **Sinkhole** This small sinkhole formed suddenly when the roof of a cavern collapsed. It destroyed this home in Frostproof, Florida.

In addition to a surface pockmarked by sinkholes, karst regions usually show a striking lack of surface drainage (streams). Following a rainfall, runoff is quickly funneled below ground through sinkholes. It then flows through caverns until it finally reaches the water table. Where streams do exist at the surface, their paths are usually short. The names of such streams often give a clue to their fate. In the Mammoth Cave area of Kentucky, for example, there is Sinking Creek, Little Sinking Creek, and Sinking Branch. Some sinkholes become plugged with clay and debris, creating small lakes or ponds.

6.3 Assessment

Review Key Concepts

1. Where is groundwater located under the surface?

2. How does water move underground?

3. What are some environmental threats to groundwater supplies?

4. How and where do most caverns form?

5. What landforms are common in an area of karst topography?

Think Critically

6. **Compare and Contrast** What is the difference between stalactites and stalagmites?

7. **Analyze Concepts** How is groundwater a nonrenewable resource?

8. **Analyze Concepts** Explain why caverns form in the zone of saturation, while dripstone features form in the zone of aeration.

9. **Relate Cause and Effect** Write a paragraph that connects these three concepts: land subsidence, extensive farming in dry regions, and water conservation.

BIGIDEA WEATHERING AND EROSION

10. Describe how weathering and erosion forms caverns and sinkholes.

Running Water and Groundwater **179**

3 ASSESS

Evaluate Understanding L2

To assess students' knowledge of lesson content, have them create a visual of the inside of a cavern. Encourage students to include and label as many features as possible.

Reteach L1

Use Figure 24 to discuss the hazards of living in a region with karst topography.

Answers

Figure 23 *The water in each drop that drips down a stalactite contains dissolved minerals. Each water drop that evaporates leaves a small deposit at the end of the stalactite.*

☑ **Reading Checkpoint** *Dripstone features, such as stalactites and stalagmites, are depositional stone formations that form as dripstone is deposited inside caverns.*

Assessment Answers

1. in the zone of saturation
2. Groundwater moves by twisting and turning through interconnected small openings.
3. overuse and contamination
4. Most caverns form by erosion at or below the water table in the zone of saturation.
5. depressions and sinkholes
6. Stalactites are dripstone features that cling to the ceiling of a cavern. Stalagmites are dripstone features that build upward from a cavern floor.

7. Groundwater is becoming a nonrenewable resource in some areas due to overuse and contamination.
8. The deposition of dripstone is not possible until the caverns are above the water table.
9. Student paragraphs should accurately describe cause-and-effect relationships among land subsidence, extensive farming in dry regions, and water conservation.

10. Chemical weathering occurs when the carbonic acid in groundwater reacts with the calcite in limestone forming calcium bicarbonate. As groundwater carries away calcium carbonate in solution, it slowly erodes rock to produce a cavern. Chemical weathering can also gradually produce sinkholes when downward-seeping rainwater containing carbon dioxide dissolves limestone below the soil.

The Ogallala Aquifer—How Long Will the Water Last?

The Ogallala Aquifer— How Long Will the Water Last?

L2

Background

- Dry-land farming is a system of producing crops without irrigation in semi-arid regions. These regions often receive less than 50 cm of rainfall per year. Dry-land farmers usually rebuild soil moisture by allowing the land to be unplanted or mulched in alternate years.
- In May, 2003, the United States government provided $53 million to aid Western farmers and ranchers impacted by drought. About half of this funding went to farmers and ranchers in the High Plains. The funds helped implement technologies and practices to conserve water to relieve the long-term impact of drought on the region.

Teaching Tips

- Ask students to research dry-land farming and other methods that reduce agricultural dependence upon irrigation. Have them create a presentation with visuals that would educate people about these methods and the importance of finding a solution to the decline in the High Plains water table.
- Have students find out about regions in the world where there are large supplies of groundwater. Ask students to address these questions: What is the source of the groundwater? How is groundwater used by people in the region? How are they accessing it? Is the water table in danger of becoming low? If so, what are plans to help remedy the situation?

Visual

The High Plains extend from the western Dakotas south to Texas. Despite being a land of little rain, this is one of the most important agricultural regions in the United States. The reason is a vast supply of groundwater that makes irrigation possible throughout most of the region. The source of most of this water is the Ogallala Formation. The largest aquifer in the United States, the Ogallala Formation averages 60 meters thick. However, in some places it is as thick as 180 meters.

The Ogallala Formation is made up of sandy and gravelly rock layers that contain groundwater in their pore spaces. This formation was produced by compaction and cementation of sediments that were carried eastward by streams from the Rocky Mountains, as shown in **Figure 25.**

Groundwater in the aquifer came from melting glaciers in the Rocky Mountains between 10,000 and 25,000 years ago.

The groundwater traveled downslope from high in the Rocky Mountains and was joined with small amounts of surface precipitation that soaked into the ground over thousands of years.

Because of its high porosity and great size, the Ogallala Formation accumulated a large amount of groundwater—enough to fill Lake Huron! Today, with the connection between the aquifer and the Rockies gone (erosion has removed much of the formation in eastern Colorado), all of the Ogallala's recharge must come from the meager rainfall of the Plains.

In the late 1800s, people first started to use the Ogallala for irrigation. However, the capacity of pumps available at the time limited water withdrawal. Then in the 1920s, large-capacity irrigation pumps were invented. High Plains' farmers began tapping the Ogallala for irrigation. Today, there are nearly 170,000 wells irrigating more than 65,000 square kilometers of land.

The increase in irrigation has caused a drastic drop in the Ogallala's water table, especially in the High Plains. Declines in the water table of 3 to 15 meters are common. In places, however, the water table is now 60 meters below its original level.

Although the decline in the water table has slowed in parts of the southern High Plains, substantial pumping continues—often in excess of recharge. The future of irrigated farming here is clearly in jeopardy.

The southern High Plains will return sooner or later to dry-land farming. The transition will come sooner and with fewer ecological and economic crises if the agricultural industry is weaned gradually from its dependence on groundwater irrigation. If nothing is done until all the accessible water in the Ogallala aquifer has been removed, the transition will be ecologically dangerous and economically dreadful.*

*National Research Council. *Solid-Earth Sciences and Society.* Washington, DC: National Academy Press, 1993, p. 148.

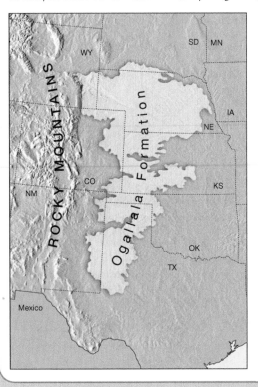

FIGURE 25 Ogallala Formation The Ogallala Formation underlies about 450,000 square kilometers of the High Plains, making it the largest aquifer in the United States.

Investigating the Permeability of Soils

Problem How does the permeability of soil affect its ability to move water?

Materials 100 mL graduated cylinder, beaker, small funnel, 3 pieces of cotton, samples of coarse sand, fine sand, and soil, clock or watch with a second hand

Skills Observe, Measure, Compare and Contrast, Analyze Data

Connect to the Big idea The permeability of soils affects the way groundwater moves—or if it moves at all. Some soils are highly permeable, while others are not. In this lab, you will determine the permeability of various soils, and draw conclusions about their effect on the movement of water underground.

Procedure

1. Place a small, clean piece of cotton in the neck of the funnel. Fill the funnel above the cotton with coarse sand. Fill the funnel about two-thirds of the way.
2. **Measure** Pour water into the graduated cylinder until it reaches the 50 mL mark.
3. With the bottom of the funnel over the beaker, pour the water from the graduated cylinder slowly into the sand in the funnel.
4. **Measure** In a data table like the one shown, keep track of the time from the second you start to pour the water into the funnel. Measure the amount of time that it takes the water to drain through the funnel filled with coarse sand. Using the graduated cylinder, measure the amount of water recovered in the beaker.
5. Record in the data table the time it takes for the water to drain through the coarse sand.
6. Empty and clean the measuring cylinder, funnel, and beaker.
7. Repeat Steps 1 through 6, first using fine sand and then using soil.

Analyze and Conclude

1. **Compare and Contrast** Of the three materials you tested, which has the greatest permeability? The least permeability?
2. **Analyze Data** Why were different amounts of water recovered in the beaker for each material tested?
3. **Analyze Data** What effect would the differences you observed in this lab have on the movement of groundwater through different soils?
4. **Control Variables** What factors might affect the accuracy of your results in this experiment? How would repeating each test several times affect your measurements?

Data Table

	Time Needed for Water to Drain Through Funnel	Water Collected in Beaker (mL)
Coarse Sand		
Fine Sand		
Soil		

 ES.1 The student will plan and conduct investigations in which **a.** volume, area, mass, elapsed time, direction, temperature, pressure, distance, density, and changes in elevation/depth are calculated utilizing the most appropriate tools; and **e.** variables are manipulated with repeated trials.

INVESTIGATING THE PERMEABILITY OF SOILS `L2`

Objective In this activity, students will explain how the permeability of soil affects its ability to move water.

Skills **Observe, Measure, Compare and Contrast, Analyze Data, Interpret Data**

Prep Time 10 minutes

Advance Prep If time is limited, set up the apparatus for the students ahead of time.

Class Time 40 minutes

Teaching Tip If the time needed for the water to seep through the cotton proves to be too long, line the funnel with a coffee filter instead.

Expected Outcome Students should find that it takes the longest time for the water to filter through the fine sand. The length of time for the water to filter through the soil depends on the composition of the soil, but it is most likely that the quickest filtering time is through the coarse sand.

Analyze and Conclude

1. The coarse sand has the greatest permeability. The fine sand has the least permeability.
2. Some of the water was left behind in the sample. For example, the soil sample trapped water in the organic material and finer grained sediment.
3. In general, the soils with coarser grain would move water faster.
4. Factors that might affect the results include accuracy in measuring the volume of water and judgement about the point at which all the water has drained through. Also, if the positioning of the cotton in the funnel is not consistent, that may affect the observed results.

Assuming that the procedure was carried out consistently, repeating the test would permit the calculation of an average permeability for the different samples.
Logical

STUDY GUIDE

Study Tip

Organize New Information
This chapter contains many new words and much new information. Tell students to create outlines, charts, flashcards, timelines, and concept maps to help them visualize relationships. Have students create a vocabulary list with definitions for all of the vocabulary terms in their own words.

21st Century Learning

Health Literacy

How safe is your water?
Clean drinking water is key to good health. Ask students to work in small groups to research the drinking water in your community. They should try to answer the following questions: (1) What is the source of the drinking water in our community? (2) What treatment process is used? (3) What tests are completed before water reaches the tap?

Then, ask each group to find a news story about an illness related to drinking water. Encourage groups to determine what measures could have been taken to prevent the outbreak and to present their findings to the class. Remind students to cite their sources.

Homework Guide

Lesson	Questions
1	1–4, 12, 22, 27–30
2	5–7, 13–16, 23, 24, 32–34
3	8–11, 17–21, 25, 26, 31

6 Study Guide

Big idea Weathering and Erosion

6.1 Running Water

Water constantly moves among the oceans, the atmosphere, the geosphere, and the biosphere. This unending circulation of Earth's water supply is the water cycle.

Balance in the water cycle means the average annual precipitation over Earth equals the amount of water that evaporates and transpires.

The ability of a stream to erode and transport materials depends largely on its velocity.

While gradient decreases between a stream's headwaters and mouth, discharge increases.

Base level is the lowest point to which a stream can erode its channel.

water cycle (158)   discharge (161)
infiltration (159)   tributary (162)
stream channel (160)   meander (163)
gradient (160)

6.2 The Work of Streams

Streams generally erode their channels by lifting loose particles, by abrasion and grinding, and by dissolving soluble material.

Streams transport their load of sediment in three ways: (1) in solution (dissolved load), (2) in suspension (suspended load), and (3) bouncing or rolling along the bottom (bed load).

Deposition occurs as streamflow drops below the critical settling velocity of a certain particle size. The sediment in that catetory begins to settle out.

A narrow V-shaped valley shows that the stream's primary work has been downcutting toward base level.

Most floods are caused by rapid spring snow melt or storms that bring heavy rains over a large region.

Measures to control flooding include artificial levees, flood control dams, and placing limits on floodplain development.

A drainage basin is the land area that contributes water to a stream.

bed load (165)   floodplain (167)
capacity (165)   flood (168)
delta (166)   drainage basin (170)
natural levee (167)   divide (170)

6.3 Water Beneath the Surface

Groundwater moves by twisting and turning through interconnected small openings. The groundwater moves more slowly when the pore spaces are smaller.

Much of the water in soil seeps downward until it reaches the zone of saturation. The zone of saturation is the area where water fills all of the pore spaces in sediment and rock. Groundwater is the water within this zone.

A spring forms whenever the water table intersects the ground surface.

Contamination and overuse threaten groundwater supplies in some areas.

Erosion forms most caverns at or below the water table in the zone of saturation.

Karst areas typically have irregular terrain, with many depressions called sinkholes.

porosity (171)   geyser (173)
permeability (171)   well (173)
aquifer (171)   artesian well (174)
zone of saturation (172)   cavern (177)
groundwater (172)   travertine (177)
water table (172)   karst topography (178)
spring (172)   sinkhole (178)

Assessment Answers

Review Content

1. b	**2.** c	**3.** d
4. c	**5.** a	**6.** a
7. a	**8.** c	**9.** b
10. a	**11.** c	

Understand Concepts

12. (1) Winds transport moisture-rich air. (2) Conditions cause the moisture to condense into clouds. (3) Precipitation fall to Earth. (4) Water evaporates from oceans and begins the cycle again.
13. Velocity increases as gradient increases.
14. A stream downcuts its channel until it reaches its base level.
15. a V-shaped valley

6 Assessment

Review Content

Choose the letter that best answers the question or completes the statement.

1. The energy for the water cycle comes from the
   - **a.** ocean.
   - **b.** sun.
   - **c.** atmosphere.
   - **d.** soil.

2. How does water move from plants to the atmosphere?
   - **a.** infiltration
   - **b.** precipitation
   - **c.** transpiration
   - **d.** condensation

3. By what process do streams and rivers move material?
   - **a.** weathering
   - **b.** infiltration
   - **c.** mass wasting
   - **d.** erosion

4. A river's discharge is generally greatest
   - **a.** at its source.
   - **b.** on its floodplain.
   - **c.** at its mouth.
   - **d.** at the sides of its channel.

5. When do streams and rivers deposit sediment?
   - **a.** when their velocity decreases
   - **b.** when they are in the midst of flooding
   - **c.** when their velocity increases
   - **d.** when they plunge over waterfalls

6. A stream's drainage basin (or watershed) is all the water that
   - **a.** flows into it.
   - **b.** infiltrates from it into the ground.
   - **c.** is removed from it for drinking water.
   - **d.** is within 100 kilometers of its channel.

7. What is a stream's bed load?
   - **a.** sediment that moves along its bottom
   - **b.** sediment that is carried in solution
   - **c.** sediment that floats on its surface
   - **d.** sediment that is carried in suspension

8. Where is groundwater located?
   - **a.** zone of aeration
   - **b.** zone of reduction
   - **c.** zone of saturation
   - **d.** zone of distribution

9. Water in an artesian well
   - **a.** dries up after a short amount of time.
   - **b.** rises on its own under pressure.
   - **c.** has been contaminated by saltwater.
   - **d.** is heated by cooling igneous rocks.

10. Caverns form when rocks such as limestone are dissolved by a mixture of water and
    - **a.** carbonic acid.
    - **b.** sulfur dioxide.
    - **c.** nitrogen.
    - **d.** ammonia.

11. Which of these landforms is characteristic of an area with karst topography?
    - **a.** mountains
    - **b.** canyons
    - **c.** sinkholes
    - **d.** drumlins

Understand Concepts

12. Write a list of numbered statements that summarize the major steps in the water cycle.

13. How does a stream's gradient affect its velocity?

14. Why does a stream's base level affect how it downcuts its channel?

15. Which type of stream valley is formed primarily by downcutting?

16. What are the main causes of floods?

17. What is the relationship between a spring and the water table?

18. Why are leaking landfills and septic tanks of concern to people who use groundwater?

19. How do stalactites form?

20. What type of rock is often associated with the formation of caverns and karst topography?

21. How do dripstone columns form?

---

21. Dripstone columns form when downward-growing stalactites join with upward-growing stalagmites.

16. rapid spring snowmelt and/or storms that bring heavy rain over a large region
17. Springs can form where the water table meets the ground surface.
18. Contaminants from leaking landfills and septic tanks can enter soil and eventually leak into and pollute groundwater supplies.

19. Stalactites form as water containing dissolved minerals drips from the ceiling of a cavern. The water evaporates and leaves a deposit of calcite behind. Over a long period of time, these deposits lengthen into icicle-like formations that hang from the ceiling.
20. limestone

ASSESSMENT

Think Critically

22. There must be as much water leaving Earth's surface as returning to it overall, or the system would break down. The breakdown would occur because too much water would be accumulating on Earth's surface and not enough would be evaporating, or too much would be evaporating, causing Earth's surface to become drier.

23. The velocity would increase.

24. The stream's capacity would decrease.

25. Some porous materials soak up liquids in their pore spaces. These pore spaces are small and not well connected. So the liquid can't easily move through the material.

26. It is unlikely that the area has a karst landscape. Karst landscapes form in regions where water (containing acids) dissolves certain types of rock (often limestone) underground. A dry area with resistant rock doesn't have the needed characteristics.

Analyze Data

27. ice sheets and glaciers

28. Add the percents for "Lakes and reservoirs" and "River water" to get 0.553 percent.

29. Take the percentage of water not in "ice sheets and glaciers" (about 15 percent) and find what percentage that is of Earth's fresh water (3 percent), or 15 percent of 3 percent, which is 0.45 percent.

30. Earth's freshwater supply is a small percentage of the whole—less than 1 percent. It's nonrenewable, and it's crucial for life on Earth. So Earth's fresh water is a precious resource that must be protected.

Concepts in Action

31. The well isn't deep enough and is probably above the water table. The well must be dug deeper until it is beneath the water table in the zone of saturation to produce water.

32. Velocity and competence would be most affected. Velocity would increase because there is less friction in the streambed. With increased velocity, the stream's competence, or ability to carry larger particles, would also increase. The size of the pebbles on the streambed wouldn't necessarily change its discharge.

33. Deltas and natural levees are both depositional figures. They form when a stream's velocity decreases and it deposits sediment. However, deltas form at the mouths of streams, while natural levees form along the sides of their channels.

---

22. Apply Concepts Why must Earth's water cycle be balanced in order for the system to work?

23. Relate Cause and Effect How would a reduction in friction in a stream channel affect the stream's velocity?

24. Apply Concepts A stream's discharge decreases. Explain how this affects the stream's capacity.

25. Explain Briefly explain how a material can be porous but also impermeable.

26. Draw Conclusions The bedrock under a region is primarily a very hard rock that doesn't easily erode. The area is also very arid. Is it likely that this area has karst topography? Explain your answer.

Analyze Data

Use the graph below to answer Questions 27–30.

Lakes and reservoirs 0.549%
Soil moisture 0.294%
Water vapor in the atmosphere 0.049%
River water 0.004%

Ice sheets and glaciers 84.945%

Groundwater 14.158%

27. Interpret Graphs Where is the greatest percentage of Earth's fresh water located?

28. Calculate What percentage of Earth's fresh water is held in rivers, lakes, and reservoirs?

29. Calculate Oceans hold about 97 percent of Earth's water. The rest of the water is fresh. What percentage of Earth's water is fresh water that people can use for drinking, cooking, and growing crops?

---

30. Draw Conclusions Taking into account your answer to Question 29, explain why many people think of Earth's supply of fresh water as a resource that must be protected.

Concepts in Action

31. Apply Concepts A person drills a well into an area where there is a known aquifer underground. But the well doesn't produce water. What might be the cause of the problem? What does this person need to know about the water table in this area to solve the problem?

32. Predict Erosion reduces the size of pebbles on the bottom of a stream channel. Which of the following would be most affected: the stream's competence, velocity, or discharge? Explain your answer.

33. Connect Concepts Explain what deltas and natural levees have in common.

34. Writing in Science Imagine you live in a town that floods often. The people in your community want to take measures to decrease the amount of flooding and property damage. The community has identified three choices: a set of artificial levees, a flood control dam, or clearing development from the river floodplain. Write a letter to the editor supporting one of these choices.

Performance-Based Assessment

35. Explain Draw a graphic organizer that shows the major steps of the water cycle. Label each step.

---

34. Students can choose any method, but must demonstrate their knowledge of its benefits for flood control.

Performance-Based Assessment

35. Graphic organizers should include at least these features arranged cyclically: evaporation, cloud formation, precipitation, runoff and infiltration, then back to evaporation.

Standardized Test Prep

Standardized Test Prep
1 C
2 H
3 D
4 H
5 A
6 A

Tips for Success

Evaluating and Revising Frequently, a scientifically accurate answer choice may not answer the question that is being asked. Keep these tips in mind.

• Verify what the question is asking.

• Determine if an answer choice is a true statement or not.

• Determine if a true answer choice actually answers the question.

• Be cautious with inserted or deleted words that make a false statement seem accurate.

Practice using these tips in Question 3.

Choose the letter that best answers the question or completes the statement.

1 Which of these processes of the water cycle is a direct effect of the sun's energy?
  A formation of precipitation
  B runoff of water over soil
  C evaporation
  D seeping of water into soil

2 Which factor is most important in determining the erosive power of a stream?
  F stream discharge
  G dissolved load
  H stream velocity
  J channel width

3 If land was uplifted, streams will downcut their channels because—
  A the stream's greatest velocity is at its bottom
  B the stream's bed load helps erode the stream's bottom
  C natural levees restrict the lateral movement of stream waters
  D the streams have a new base level

4 When a soil is impermeable, it—
  F allows water to flow freely through it
  G has no water in it at all
  H does not allow water to pass through it
  J has large pore spaces

5 Which of these features is a landform associated with karst topography?
  A sinkholes
  B streams
  C natural levees
  D deltas

6 Which of the following drawings shows a delta?

If You Have Trouble With . . .

Question	1	2	3	4	5	6
See Lesson	6.1	6.2	6.1	6.2	6.3	6.2

7 Glaciers, Deserts, and Wind Planning Guide

BIGIDEA: WEATHERING AND EROSION

Lesson Objectives		Activities
7.1 Glaciers, pp. 188–198		TE Teacher Demo: Glacial Erosion, p. 192 L2
7.1 **Describe** the different types of glaciers and where each type is found.		TE Build Science Skills, p. 195 L2
7.2 **Explain** how glaciers move and **describe** the different types of glacial drift.		
7.3 **Identify** the landscape features that glaciers form.		
7.4 **Explain** the causes of the most recent ice age.		
7.2 Deserts, pp. 199–202		TE Teacher Demo: Desert Water Erosion, p. 201 L2
7.5 **Explain** the roles mechanical and chemical weathering play in deserts.		
7.6 **Describe** how running water affects deserts.		
7.3 Landscapes Shaped by Wind, pp. 203–207		TE Teacher Demo: Wind Erosion, p. 205 L2
7.7 **Describe** two ways that wind can cause erosion.		
7.8 **Identify** types of landforms that are deposited by the wind.		
7.9 **Identify** the factors that determine the shape of a sand dune.		
Chapter Features and Labs		
Try It How Does Pressure Affect Ice Crystals? p. 187		LM Continental Glaciers Change Earth's Topography L2
How Earth Works Erosion, p. 208		
Exploration Lab Interpreting a Glacial Landscape, p. 210		

Resources	Lesson Assessment
GRSW Lesson 7.1 **LP** Lesson Planning 7.1 **PD** Links on Glaciers **GEODe** Sculpturing Earth's Surface: Glaciers	**SE** Lesson 7.1 Assessment, p. 198 **eText** Lesson 7.1
GRSW Lesson 7.2 **LP** Lesson Planning 7.2 **GEODe** Sculpturing Earth's Surface: Deserts	**SE** Lesson 7.2 Assessment, p. 202 **eText** Lesson 7.2
GRSW Lesson 7.3 **LP** Lesson Planning 7.3	**SE** Lesson 7.3 Assessment, p. 207 **eText** Lesson 7.3

Materials for Activities and Labs

Quantities for each group

STUDENT EDITION

Try It, p. 187
ice crystals or snow, beaker, table knife, magnifying glass

Exploration Lab, pp. 210–211
topographic map

TEACHER'S EDITION

Teacher Demo, p. 192
sand, soap, ice cube

Build Science Skills, p. 195
freezer, sand, ice cube trays, water, sloping paint tray

Teacher Demo, p. 201
sharpened pencil, paper cup, scissors, 1/2 of a drinking straw, modeling clay, cookie sheet, ruler, large beaker, water, soil, two 2″ × 4″ boards about 15 cm long

Teacher Demo, p. 205
sand, large piece of cardboard, water

Assessment

CHAPTER ASSESSMENT

SE Assessment, pp. 213–214
CT Chapter 7 Test
CTB Chapter 7
eText Chapter 7

21st Century Learning

Information and Media Literacy: Are melting glaciers due to climate change?, TE p. 212

Before You Teach
Glaciers, Deserts, and Wind

Michael Wysession
Washington University

Common Themes

While flowing water is the primary agent of erosion and deposition, in certain environments ice and wind also play important roles.

Space and Time Glaciers occur in two forms: valley glaciers (cold because of altitude) and continental glaciers (cold because of latitude). Glacial ice accumulates through snowfall, and wastes through melting, calving, and sublimation. During ice ages, large portions of continents are covered with a thick sheet of ice. The major cause of ice ages is likely changes in Earth's orbital parameters, called Milankovitch cycles.

Forces and Motion Glaciers flow by plastic flow and basal slip, and erode through plucking and abrasion. Erosional features include U-shaped valleys, hanging valleys, cirques, arêtes, and horns. Depositional glacial features include moraines, kettles, drumlins, and outwash plains. In deserts, wind erodes by deflation and abrasion, forming desert pavements. Wind deposits sediments in the form of dunes and layers of loess. Different wind patterns form different kinds of dunes.

Matter and Energy In deserts mostly, weathering occurs mechanically through running water, even though most streams are intermittent.

Earth as a System No two geological environments are the same, so the relative importances of flowing water, ice, and wind as agents of the rock cycle are different in every location.

EARTH SCIENCE REFRESHER

Ice Ages of the Past

The recent ice age created a dramatic change on Earth's surface. Present-day Chicago was under a few kilometers of ice. When the ice melted, bursting glacial lakes eroded giant valleys in a matter of days, leaving ripple marks a hundred meters apart! Mammals evolved thick coats of fur to survive, and the lowered sea level allowed many different life-forms (including humans) to settle across previously unconnected continents. But this was not the only ice age, nor was it the most severe.

About 280 million years ago, just before the mass extinction of life at the end of the Paleozoic era, there was a period of extreme glaciation. In fact, this may be one of the factors that led to extinctions. The continents were in different places, and the existence of glaciation in places like India and Australia from this era was used as evidence of continental drift by Alfred Wegener.

There were several periods of even more extreme glaciation that may have occurred about 750–580 million years ago. Geological data suggest that, at several points during this time period, Earth was almost totally covered by ice, a scenario referred to as "Snowball Earth." The climate would have been so cold that even the surfaces of the oceans would have been frozen. Life, which was still only single-celled at this point, would have had to survive around volcanoes, at mid-ocean ridges, or cracks in the sea ice. During the periods of extreme glaciation, carbon dioxide would have built up beneath the ice to the extent that when it was released, Earth's climate would have rapidly swung to very hot conditions involving a rampant greenhouse effect. As carbon dioxide began to be removed from the atmosphere and deposited in ocean sediments, the climate would swing back toward a Snowball Earth condition.

Students may have the misconception that glaciers cannot form in the tropics. Glaciers form wherever there are low temperatures and adequate supplies of snow. Because the temperatures drop with an increase altitude, glaciers can occur in the tropics at high elevations. Even near the equator, glaciers form at elevations above 5000 m. For a strategy that helps to overcome this misconception, see **Address Misconceptions** *on* **TE p. 189.**

"Snowball Earth" never happened again after the evolution of multicellular life, and it is likely that we have worms to thank for this. Ocean worms continually churn up sediments through the construction of their burrows, and it is possible that this activity prevented too much carbon dioxide from being stored in ocean sediments, and so prevented any more extreme ice ages.

Interestingly, it is through the other life-forms that we know the history of Earth's climate. The shells of marine animals are made of calcium carbonate, which is a combination of calcium, carbon, and oxygen. Most oxygen atoms are $^{16}_{8}O$ isotopes, but a small number are $^{18}_{8}O$ isotopes. Marine shells form with either isotope indiscriminately. Water that evaporates from the ocean and falls as ice or snow, however, is almost entirely made of $^{16}_{8}O$ isotopes because the $^{18}_{8}O$ isotopes require much more energy to evaporate. That means that when there is a lot of glacial ice on land (which is all made with $^{16}_{8}O$), the ocean water is enriched in $^{18}_{8}O$. By looking at the ratio of the two oxygen isotopes in marine shells, geologists can determine if they formed during periods of glaciation.

BUILD READING LITERACY
Relate Text and Visuals

Use Graphic Elements to Clarify and Extend

Strategy Help students relate visuals to text, in order to clarify difficult concepts in the text or to understand information beyond that stated in the text. This strategy enables students to focus on their own thought processes as they actively make use of photos and illustrations as tools to support comprehension. Before students begin, choose a section in Chapter 7, such as Section 7.3, Types of Sand Dunes, pp. 206–207.

Example

1. Have students keep their book closed as you read a few paragraphs aloud, including text that refers to a figure. You may want to think aloud as you read, saying, for example, "I wonder what that would look like?"

2. Then, have students open their book to the passage that you read. Tell them to reread it and then study the figure and its caption carefully. Ask what parts of the passage make more sense when students look at the figure.

3. Point out that visuals also sometimes communicate information that is not in the text. Have students identify any new information that can be learned from the figure.

4. Have students work in pairs, with one reading aloud through the text reference to a figure, and then both working together to discuss how the figure helps them understand the passage or provides additional information.

See TE p. 189 for a script on how to use this strategy with students. For additional strategies, see TE pp. 200 and 204.

CHAPTER 7

ASSESS PRIOR KNOWLEDGE

ASSESS PRIOR KNOWLEDGE

Use the Chapter Pretest below to assess students' prior knowledge. As needed, review these concepts.

Review Science Concepts

Lesson 7.1 Reviewing the concept of erosion ensures that students will understand the impact that glaciers have on the landscape.

Lesson 7.2 Reviewing chemical and mechanical weathering will help students understand the geological processes that occur in desert climates.

Lesson 7.3 Reviewing the concepts of soil erosion will help students understand the significance of erosion by wind.

7 Glaciers, Deserts, and Wind

Big idea

Weathering and Erosion

Q: What surface features do ice, water, and wind form?

A glacier slowly advances down a valley in Alaska's Glacier Bay National Park.

Chapter Pretest

1. What are two types of weathering? *(chemical and mechanical)*

2. What happens to a rock during weathering? *(It is broken into smaller pieces and converted into new minerals.)*

3. What are two erosional forces that move soil from one place to another? *(wind, ice, and water)*

4. What is mechanical weathering? *(physical forces that break rock into smaller and smaller pieces without changing the rock's composition)*

5. Soil erosion is a natural process that is part of which cycle? *(c)*
  a. carbon
  b. phosphorus
  c. rock
  d. water

6. True or False: Plants stabilize soil and prevent erosion. *(True)*

7. True or False: Glaciers, groundwater, waves, and wind are insignificant causes of landform changes. *(False)*

8. What is the most important agent in chemical weathering? *(c)*
  a. erosion
  b. climate
  c. water
  d. wind

INSIDE:

INQUIRY ?
TRY IT!

HOW DOES PRESSURE AFFECT ICE CRYSTALS?

Procedure

1. Obtain a beaker full of ice crystals, either by collecting snow outside or by scraping ice crystals from the inside surfaces of a freezer. Use a hand lens to observe the loose crystals. Sketch their appearance in your science notebook.
2. Use your hands to mold a snowball from the crystals. Then squeeze the snowball as hard as you can, making the snowball compact.
3. Use a table knife to cut the snowball in half. Observe the compressed crystals with your hand lens and sketch them.

Think About It

1. **Draw Conclusions** How did the ice crystals change after you squeezed them? Describe how pressure seems to affect ice crystals.
2. **Predict** The raw material for glaciers is snow. Predict how snowflakes will change under the increasing pressure of overlying snow.

187

ENGAGE/EXPLORE

HOW DOES PRESSURE AFFECT ICE CRYSTALS?   L2

Purpose In this activity, students will observe the effect of pressure on ice crystals.

Skills Observe, Draw Conclusions, Predict

Prep Time 20 minutes

Materials ice crystals or snow, beaker, table knife, magnifying glass

Advance Prep Fill beakers with ice crystals or snow in advance. Store the beakers in a freezer until you are ready to use them.

Class Time 20 minutes

Expected Outcome Students will observe open spaces in individual ice crystals before pressure is applied. After pressure is applied, the individual ice crystals are compacted and the open spaces are no longer visible.

Think About It

1. The ice crystals appear to fuse and grow larger. Pressure appears to cause ice crystals to fuse and transform to solid ice.
2. As snow piles up on top of snowflakes, they will be subject to increasing pressure. The pressure will cause the flakes to fuse and become ice.

1 FOCUS

Lesson Objectives

7.1 **Describe** the different types of glaciers and where each type is found.

7.2 **Explain** how glaciers move and **describe** the different types of glacial drift.

7.3 **Identify** the landscape features that glaciers form.

7.4 **Explain** the causes of the most recent ice age.

Build Vocabulary [L2]

Concept Map Have students construct a concept map using as many vocabulary terms as possible and the following landform features: hanging valleys, cirques arêtes, and horns. Students should place the main concept (Glaciers) in the center oval and use descriptive linking phrases to connect the terms. Instruct students to place the terms in ovals and connect the ovals with lines on which linking words are placed.

Reading Strategy [L2]

a. Ice age—a period of time when much of Earth's land is covered in glaciers.

b. Glacier—a thick ice mass that moves slowly over the land surface.

c. Ice sheet—an enormous ice mass that flows in all directions from one or more centers and covers everything but the highest land

d. Snowline—the lowest elevation in an area that remains covered in snow all year.

7.1 Glaciers

Key Questions

⊂⊃ **What are the two types of glaciers?**

⊂⊃ **How do glaciers move?**

⊂⊃ **What distinguishes the various types of glacial drift?**

⊂⊃ **What landscape features do glaciers form?**

⊂⊃ **Describe the causes of the most recent ice age.**

Vocabulary

- ice age • glacier
- snowline • valley glacier
- abrasion • till
- moraine • drumlin
- esker

Reading Strategy

Build Vocabulary Draw a table similar to the one below that includes all the vocabulary terms listed for the section. As you read the section, define each vocabulary term in your own words.

Vocabulary Term	Definition
Glacier	a. _____?_____
Snowline	b. _____?_____
Moraine	c. _____?_____
Till	d. _____?_____

CLIMATE IS a major factor in the processes that shape Earth's surface. In this lesson, you will learn about the strong link between climate and geology in studying how glaciers shape the land.

Types of Glaciers

As recently as 15,000 years ago, Earth was coming out of an ice age. An **ice age** is a period of time when much of Earth's land is covered in glaciers. A **glacier** is a thick ice mass that moves slowly over the land surface. About 15,000 years ago, up to 30 percent of Earth's land was covered by glaciers. In some areas, the glaciers were thousands of meters thick and covered entire continents. These massive glaciers shaped places such as Cape Cod, Long Island, and the Great Lakes. Today glaciers still cover nearly 10 percent of Earth's land area. In these regions, they continue to sculpt the landscape.

FIGURE 1 **Valley Glacier** A glacier in Alaska's Chugach Mountains slowly advances down this valley.

Glaciers originate on land in places where more snow falls than melts. The **snowline** is the lowest elevation in a particular area that remains covered in snow all year. At the poles, the snowline occurs at sea level. Closer to the equator, the snowline is near the top of tall mountains. Instead of completely melting away, snow above the snowline accumulates and compacts. The compressed snow first recrystallizes into coarse grains of ice. Further pressure from added snow above changes the coarse grains into interlocking crystals of glacial ice.

A glacier appears to be motionless, but it's not. Sit beside a glacier for an hour and you may hear a sporadic chorus of creaks, cracks, and groans as gravity pulls the mass of ice slowly downhill. Just like running water, groundwater, wind, and waves, glaciers are dynamic agents of erosion. They accumulate, transport, and deposit sediment. Thus, glaciers are an important part of the rock cycle.

🔑 **There are two main types of glaciers: valley glaciers and ice sheets**.

Valley Glaciers Thousands of small glaciers exist in high mountains worldwide. These glaciers advance anywhere from a few centimeters to a few meters each day. **Valley glaciers** are ice masses that slowly advance down valleys that were originally occupied by streams. Valley glaciers flow between steep rock walls from the top of mountain valleys. Like rivers, valley glaciers can be long or short, wide or narrow, single or with branching tributaries. **Figure 1** shows a valley glacier in Alaska.

Ice Sheets In contrast to valley glaciers, *ice sheets* are enormous ice masses that flow in all directions from one or more centers and cover everything but the highest land. Ice sheets are sometimes called continental glaciers because they cover large regions, such as Antarctica and Greenland. They are huge compared to valley glaciers. Ice sheets covered much of North America during the recent ice age. **Figure 2** shows the two remaining ice sheets, which combined cover almost 10 percent of Earth's land area. One ice sheet covers about 80 percent of Greenland. It averages nearly 1500 meters thick, and in places it rises to 3000 meters above sea level.

The huge Antarctic Ice Sheet in the Southern Hemisphere is nearly 4300 meters thick in places. This glacier accounts for 90 percent of the world's ice, and it holds nearly two-thirds of Earth's fresh water. If it melted, sea level could rise 60 to 70 meters and many coastal cities would flood.

☑ **Reading Checkpoint** *Where do ice sheets exist on Earth today?*

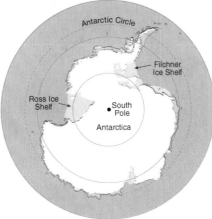

FIGURE 2 Ice Sheets The only present-day ice sheets are those covering Greenland and Antarctica.

Glaciers, Deserts, and Wind **189**

❷ INSTRUCT

Build Reading Literacy

Refer to **p. 186D**, which provides the guidelines for relating text and visuals.

Relate Text and Visuals Have students read pp. 188–189. Have students use Figures 1 and 2 to distinguish between valley glaciers and ice sheets. *(Valley glaciers are ice masses that slowly advance down valleys originally occupied by streams. Ice sheets are enormous ice masses that flow in all directions from one or more centers and cover everything but the highest land.)*
Visual, Logical

(Address **Misconceptions**)

Students may have the misconception that glaciers cannot form in the tropics. Glaciers form whenever there are low temperatures and adequate supplies of snow. Because temperatures drop with an increase in altitude, glaciers can occur in the tropics at high elevations. Even near the equator, glaciers form at elevations above 5000 m. Examples of equatorial glaciers include those atop Mt. Kenya and Mt. Kilimanjaro in East Africa. Have students use a map or an atlas to find these mountains and the distance to the equator.
Verbal, Visual

Build Science Skills

Compare and Contrast Have students read the text on valley glaciers and ice sheets.
Ask: How are these two types of glaciers similar? *(Both types of glaciers are composed of ice.)* How do they differ? *(Valley glaciers are smaller and advance slowly down valleys. Ice sheets cover everything except the highest land in some areas.)*
Verbal

Answers

☑ **Reading Checkpoint** *Greenland, Antarctica*

Differentiated Instruction

ENGLISH LANGUAGE LEARNERS Have students develop an illustrated science glossary using the vocabulary terms and additional terms that are unfamiliar. Students should write the definition of the term in their own words. Then, students should draw a diagram illustrating the meaning of the term.

Figure 4 Have students look at the illustration. **Ask:** What is the zone of accumulation? *(the region of the glacier where snow accumulates and ice forms)* What is the zone of wastage? *(the foot of the glacier where it loses ice and snow)* What must happen for a glacier to advance? *(The glacier must accumulate more ice and snow than is lost by melting at the foot.)* What must happen for a glacier to retreat? *(The glacier must lose more snow and ice through melting than it accumulates at the head.)*
Verbal

Most glaciers are blue, unless they contain a large amount of eroded sediment at the surface. Invite students to search the Internet or printed reference sources to find photographs of blue glaciers. Explain that glacial ice absorbs the longer red wavelengths of visible white light while reflecting and scattering shorter blue wavelengths. **Ask:** What is another real-world example of something that reflects short wavelengths to cause a blue appearance? *(the sky)*
Verbal, Logical

FIGURE 3 Zone of Fracture
Crevasses, such as this one in Pakistan, can extend 50 meters into the brittle, top layer of a glacier known as the zone of fracture.

How Glaciers Move

You might wonder how a glacier, which is solid, can move. **The movement of glaciers is referred to as flow. Glacial flow happens in two ways: plastic flow and basal slip.** Plastic flow involves movement within the ice. Under high enough pressure, the normally brittle ice begins to distort and change shape—a property known as *plasticity*. The weight of overlying ice exerts pressure on the ice below, causing it to flow. Plastic flow begins at about 50 meters below the glacier surface. Basal slip is the second cause of glacial movement. In basal slip, liquid water and mud at the bottom of the glacier reduce the friction between the glacier and the ground. The reduced friction and gravity cause the entire ice mass to slip and slide downhill.

The upper 50 meters of a glacier is not under enough pressure to have plastic flow. This layer of a glacier, called the *zone of fracture*, is brittle. The zone of fracture rides on the flowing ice below and experiences tension when the glacier moves over irregular terrain. This tension results in gaping cracks called *crevasses*, as shown in **Figure 3**. Crevasses are often hidden by snow and make travel across glaciers dangerous.

Rates of Glacial Movement Different glaciers move at different speeds. Some flow so slowly that trees and other vegetation grow in the debris on their surface. Other glaciers can advance several meters per day. Some glaciers alternate between periods of rapid movement and periods of relatively little movement.

Budget of a Glacier Glaciers constantly gain and lose ice. Glaciers gain ice when snow accumulates and becomes ice at the head of the glacier in the *zone of accumulation*, shown in **Figure 4.** Here new snowfall thickens the glacier and promotes movement downhill. The area of the glacier below the snowline is called the *zone of wastage*. Here, the glacier loses mass as ice and any new snow melts away.

FIGURE 4 Glacial Budget
Whether the foot of a glacier advances, retreats, or remains stationary depends on the balance or lack of balance between accumulation and wastage.

Facts and Figures

Oxygen, water, and carbon are all fundamental cycles in the Earth system. In the water cycle, water constantly travels among the oceans, the atmosphere, the geosphere, and the biosphere. For example, water that evaporates from oceans will fall back to Earth's surface as precipitation. If precipitation ends up on land, rivers and underground streams may carry it back to the ocean. However, when precipitation falls at high elevations or high latitudes, water may not immediately travel back to the ocean. Instead, it may become part of a glacier. Although the ice will eventually melt and travel back to the ocean, it may be stored as glacial ice for tens, hundreds, or even thousands of years.

FIGURE 5 **Calving A** Ice calves from the front of the Perito Moreno Glacier in Patagonia, Argentina. **B** Only 10 percent of an iceberg's mass is visible above the surface.

Whether the foot of a glacier advances, retreats, or stays in place depends on the glacier's budget. The glacial budget is the balance or lack of balance between accumulation at the head of a glacier and loss, or wastage, at the foot. If more ice builds up in the zone of accumulation than is lost from the zone of wastage, then the glacier advances. The glacier retreats when it loses ice faster than it gains ice. If a glacier gains ice at the same rate as it loses ice, the foot of the glacier remains stationary. Whether the foot of a glacier advances, retreats, or remains stationary, the ice within the glacier continues to flow downhill. In the case of a retreating glacier, the ice still flows downhill, but not rapidly enough to offset wastage.

In addition to melting, a glacier loses ice when large pieces break off at its foot. This process is called *calving*. Calving occurs where glaciers meet the ocean, as shown in **Figure 5A**. The pieces that break off into the ocean are called *icebergs*. Because icebergs are just slightly less dense than seawater, they float low in the water. Only about 10 percent of their mass is visible above the surface, as shown in **Figure 5B**. The Greenland Ice Sheet calves thousands of icebergs each year. Many drift southward into the North Atlantic where they are hazardous to ships.

☑ **Reading Checkpoint** *What causes a glacier to retreat?*

Glaciers, Deserts, and Wind **191**

PLANET DIARY

For links about **Glaciers,**
go to PlanetDiary.com/HSES

LESSON 7.1

GLACIAL EROSION `L2`

Purpose Students will observe how rocks and sand incorporated into glaciers form striations.

Materials sand, soap, ice cube

Procedure Place the ice cube in the sand. Sand will stick to the ice cube. The sand represents the rocks and debris that glaciers pick up as they move. Then, scrape the ice cube across the bar of soap. The scratches in the soap represent the striations carved into the surrounding rock by a moving glacier. Also note how some of the sand becomes stuck in the soap.

Expected Outcome Students will see how easily the sand carves grooves into the soap. Students may also note that sand is more likely to become stuck in the soap as the ice begins to melt. The same processes occur between glaciers and surfaces such as bedrock and valley walls that surround a glacier.

Visual, Logical

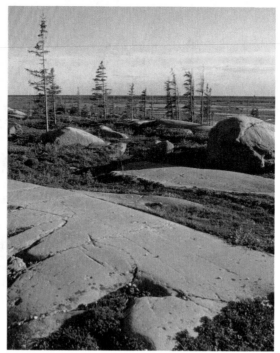

FIGURE 6 Glacial Abrasion
A glacier smoothed and polished these rock surfaces in Canada's Hudson Bay. Rock fragments embedded in the glacier carved the scratches and grooves.

Glacial Erosion

Glaciers are nature's bulldozers. Their ice scrapes, scours, and tears rock from valley floors and walls. Glaciers then carry the rock fragments down the valley. They can carry rocks as big as buses over long distances. Some of these rock fragments become embedded in the bedrock under the weight of the glacier. The rest of the rock fragments drop at the glacier's foot.

Today's glaciers have limited importance as erosional agents as compared to the glaciers of the most recent ice age. ⟲ **Many landscapes were changed by the widespread glaciers of the recent ice age.** These landscapes show the erosional power of ice.

How Glaciers Erode Glaciers mainly erode the land in two ways: *plucking* and *abrasion*. Plucking occurs when rocks and sediments from the bedrock become embedded in the ice as the glacier flows past them. Some of these rocks are plucked from the bedrock once they have been loosened by repeated cycles of water melting and freezing. When water freezes in cracks in the bedrock, it expands and pries the rock apart.

Abrasion is the second method of erosion. **Abrasion** occurs as the glacial ice and its load of rock fragments slide over bedrock. The fragments act like sandpaper to smooth and polish the rock surface below. Some of the bedrock and some of the rock carried by the glacier are crushed into finely grained rock particles, called rock flour. So much rock flour may be produced that streams of meltwater leaving the glacier often have the grayish appearance of skim milk. When the bottom of a glacier contains large rock fragments, long scratches and grooves may be gouged in the bedrock, as shown in **Figure 6.** These grooves, or striations, provide valuable clues to the direction of past glacial movement. By mapping the striations over large areas, geologists often can reconstruct the direction in which the ice flowed.

As is the case with other erosional agents, the rate of glacial erosion varies. Four factors determine the rate of glacial erosion: 1) rate of glacial movement; 2) thickness of the ice; 3) shape, amount, and hardness of the rock fragments in the ice at the bottom of the glacier; and 4) the type of surface below the glacier. The highest rates of erosion occur when glaciers that are very thick flow quickly, carrying lots of hard rocks over a much softer bedrock.

☑ **Reading Checkpoint** *How do glaciers cause erosion?*

Facts and Figures

In addition to valley and continental glaciers, other types of glaciers also exist. Covering some uplands and plateaus are masses of glacial ice called ice caps. Like ice sheets, ice caps completely bury the underlying landscape but are much smaller. Ice caps occur in Iceland and many other places. Another type of glacier, known as piedmont glaciers, occupies broad lowlands at the bases of steep mountains and forms when one or more valley glaciers emerge into the lowland area. The advancing ice spreads out to form a large sheet. The size of individual piedmont glaciers varies greatly. The largest piedmont glacier in North America is the Malaspina Glacier in southeastern Alaska.

Landforms Formed by Glacial Erosion

Erosion by valley glaciers produces many spectacular features in mountainous areas.

🔑 **Glaciers produce a variety of erosional landscape features, such as glacial troughs, hanging valleys, cirques, arêtes, and horns.** Compare and contrast the topography of the mountain setting in **Figure 7** before, during, and after glaciation. *Glaciation* is a period of time within an ice age that is marked by colder temperatures and glacier advances.

Glaciated Valleys Before glaciation, alpine valleys are usually V-shaped as a result of erosion by mountain streams. However, in mountain regions that have been glaciated, the valleys are no longer narrow. As a glacier moves down a valley once occupied by a stream, the glacier widens, deepens, and straightens the valley. The once narrow V-shaped valley is changed into a U-shaped valley, which is also called a *glacial trough*.

The amount of glacial erosion depends on the thickness of the ice flowing through a valley. For example, the amount of ice flowing through a main valley can be much greater than the amount advancing down smaller, side valleys that join the main valley. As a result, the main valley is eroded deeper than the smaller valleys, forming a glacial trough that is also deeper. When the ice retreats, the side valleys are left standing higher than the main valley. These higher valleys are called *hanging valleys*. Rivers flowing from hanging valleys sometimes produce spectacular waterfalls, such as those in Yosemite National Park, California.

☑ **Reading Checkpoint** *What is a glacial trough?*

VISUAL SUMMARY

FORMATION OF LANDFORMS BY VALLEY GLACIERS

FIGURE 7 1. Before glaciation, stream erosion formed a network of V-shaped valleys. **2.** The valley glacier erodes the mountainous region during glaciation. **3.** After glaciation, the landscape contains several erosional features.

Predict *What will happen to the glacial trough as the stream continues to flow through it?*

① Unglaciated topography

② Region during period of maximum glaciation

③ Glaciated topography

Glaciers, Deserts, and Wind **193**

Use Visuals L1

Figure 7 Have students look carefully at Parts 1 and 2 of Figure 7. **Ask:** How would you describe a cirque? *(a bowl-shaped depression that is surrounded on three sides by steep rock walls)* How did the arête form? *(Cirques on opposite sides of a rock wall grew and the rock wall became a sharp ridge as it was eroded.)* How did the horn form? *(Several cirques surrounded a single high mountain. As the cirques grew and the rock walls between them were eroded, a single horn emerged.)*
Visual, Verbal

Build Science Skills L2

Use Analogies Ask students: What does the bottom of the bath tub look like after you let dirty water drain out? *(All of the dirt settles to the bottom of the tub.)* Explain that this is similar to the way a glacier deposits its load of debris. As the ice melts from the glacier, the debris falls to the terrain just as the suspended dirt falls to the bottom of the tub.
Verbal

Answers

Figure 7 *The stream will start to cut a V-shaped valley into the bottom of the glacial trough.*

☑ **Reading Checkpoint** *Glaciers erode by plucking and abrasion.*

☑ **Reading Checkpoint** *a once narrow V-shaped valley that changes into a U-shape after a glacier moves down the valley*

FIGURE 8 Cirque The plucking action of ice in a glacier's zone of accumulation produced this cirque in Canada's Yukon Territory.

FIGURE 9 Glacial Till This unsorted mixture of many different sediment sizes is glacial till. The inset photo shows the scratches a rock likely got from being dragged along by a glacier.

Cirques A *cirque* is a bowl-shaped depression at the head of a glacial valley that is surrounded on three sides by steep rock walls, as shown in **Figure 8.** Cirques begin as irregularities in the mountainside. Glaciers carve cirques by plucking rock from along the sides and the bottom. The glaciers then act as conveyor belts that carry away the debris. Sometimes the melting glacier leaves a small lake, called a *cirque lake*, in the cirque basin.

Arêtes and Horns Valley glaciers also create snaking, sharp-edged ridges called *arêtes* and sharp, pyramid-like peaks called *horns*. Both of these features form because glacial erosion causes cirques to get bigger. Arêtes form where cirques occur on opposite sides of a divide. As the cirques get bigger, the divide separating them is reduced to a narrow, sharp ridge. Horns such as the Matterhorn in the Swiss Alps form when several cirques surround a single, high mountain. As the cirques get bigger, an isolated horn is produced.

Glacial Deposition

Glaciers transport huge loads of debris as they slowly advance across the land and deposit their loads where they melt. For example, in many areas once covered by the ice sheets of the recent ice age, the bedrock is rarely exposed because glacial deposits that are dozens— or even hundreds—of meters thick completely cover the terrain. Rocky pastures in New England, wheat fields in the Dakota plains, and rolling Midwest farmland are all landscapes resulting from glacial deposition. The term *glacial drift* applies to all of the rock debris of glacial origin, no matter how, where, or in what form it was deposited. There are two types of glacial drift: till and stratified drift.

Till is material deposited directly by the glacier. It is deposited as the glacier melts and drops its load of rock debris. Rock debris does not sort in moving ice as it does in moving water and wind. Therefore, till deposits are usually mixtures of many particle sizes. Notice the unsorted till in **Figure 9.**

Stratified drift is rock debris laid down by glacial meltwater. Stratified drift contains particles that are sorted according to size and mass. Sand and gravel often make up stratified drift because finer sediments remain suspended and are carried far from the glacier.

Rocks that are transported by a glacier and that differ from the underlying bedrock are called *erratics*. Erratics can range in size from small pebbles to huge boulders. Geologists can sometimes reconstruct the path of a long-gone glacier by tracing erractics back to their source.

☑ **Reading Checkpoint** *What is glacial drift?*

FIGURE 10 **Medial Moraines**
The dark stripes running down
the length of this glacier are
medial moraines. They formed
when valley glaciers merged
and flowed together.

Moraines, Outwash Plains, and Kettles

🔑 **Glaciers are responsible for a variety of depositional features, including moraines, outwash plains, kettles, drumlins, and eskers.** When glaciers melt, they leave layers or ridges of till called **moraines.** These widespread glacial features come in several varieties.

Lateral and Medial Moraines The sides of a valley glacier gather large amounts of debris from the valley walls. *Lateral moraines* are ridges that form along the sides of glacial valleys from rock fragments that fall from the valley walls along the edge of the glacier. *Medial moraines* form when two valley glaciers join to form a single ice stream. The till that was once carried along the edges of each glacier joins to form a dark stripe of debris within the newly enlarged glacier as shown in **Figure 10.**

End Moraines and Ground Moraines Although the ice within a glacier continues to flow downhill, the foot of a glacier can remain stationary for long periods of time. This occurs when snow and ice build up in the zone of accumulation at the same rate that snow and ice melt in the zone of wastage. A glacier acts as a conveyor belt to carry rock debris to the foot of the glacier. When the ice there melts, it deposits the debris and forms a ridge called an *end moraine.* The longer the glacier's foot remains stationary, the larger the end moraine will get.

Ground moraines form when glaciers begin to retreat. The glacier foot continues to deliver and deposit rock debris as the ice melts away. However, instead of forming a ridge, the retreating glacier forms a rock-strewn, gently rolling plain. This ground moraine fills in low spots and clogs old stream channels. Ground moraines can thus result in poorly drained swamp lands.

LESSON 7.1

Compare and Contrast Have students read the text on pp. 196–197 about outwash plains, kettles, drumlins, and eskers. **Ask:** What do outwash plains, kettles, drumlins, and eskers have in common? *(All are landscape features formed by glaciers.)* How do they differ? *(An outwash plain is a deposit of rock debris left by the glacial meltwater. A kettle forms when blocks of stagnant ice become buried and eventually melt. This melting leaves pits in the glacial rock material. Drumlins are parallel hills composed of till. The steep side of a drumlin faces the direction the ice came from, and the gentler slope points in the direction the ice moved. Eskers are snake-like ridges composed of sand and gravel that were deposited by streams once flowing in tunnels beneath the glaciers.)*
Verbal

End Moraines A glacier can cycle many times between being stationary or in retreat before the glacier melts completely. A glacier forms a new end moraine during a stationary period, then another ground moraine during a retreat. The end moraines that form when the glacier is temporarily stationary are *recessional moraines.* The farthest end moraine is the *terminal moraine.* The only difference between recessional and terminal moraines is their relative positions.

FIGURE 11 Ice Sheet Moraines Long Island, Cape Cod, Martha's Vineyard, and Nantucket are remnants of end moraines deposited by ice sheets.

End moraines that formed in the recent ice age are prominent in the landscapes of the Midwest and Northeast. New York's Long Island is part of a series of end moraines stretching from eastern Pennsylvania to Cape Cod, Massachusetts. **Figure 11** shows the locations of these end moraines that form part of the Northeast coast.

Outwash Plains An outwash plain begins to form as streams of fast-moving meltwater emerge from the foot of a glacier. This water is often so choked with rock flour that it looks like milk. Once it leaves the glacier, the water slows and drops the rock debris in a broad, ramplike deposit downstream from the end moraine. This wide, gently sloping apron of rock debris is called an *outwash plain.*

Kettles and Kettle Lakes You can often find depressions and small lakes within end moraines and outwash plains. *Kettles* form when blocks of ice become buried in drift and eventually melt. This melting leaves pits, or kettles, in the glacial rock material. If these kettles fill up with water, they are known as *kettle lakes.* Walden Pond in Concord, Massachusetts, shown in **Figure 12,** is a well-known example of a kettle lake. Thousands of kettle lakes dot the landscape of the Upper Midwest in Wisconsin and Minnesota.

Drumlins Moraines are not the only landforms deposited by glaciers. Some landscapes have many elongated parallel hills made of till, called **drumlins.** Drumlins are taller and steeper on one end, and they range in height from 15 to 60 meters and average 0.4 to 0.8 kilometer long. The steep side of the hill faces the direction the ice came from, and the gentler slope points in the direction the ice moved. In areas covered by ice sheets during the recent ice age, drumlins can occur in clusters called *drumlin fields.* Near Rochester, New York, one cluster contains nearly 10,000 drumlins. Their distinctive shapes show that they were molded by active glaciers.

Eskers Other areas have narrow, winding ridges made mainly of stratified drift, called **eskers.** Eskers are snakelike ridges composed of sand and gravel that were deposited by streams once flowing in tunnels beneath glaciers. They can be several meters high and many kilometers long. Many eskers are mined for their sand and gravel.

FIGURE 12 A Kettle Lake Walden Pond, in Concord, Massachusetts, is a well-known example of a kettle lake. The writer, Henry David Thoreau, lived on the shores of the pond for two years starting in 1845.

196 Chapter 7 • Lesson 1

Differentiated Instruction

SPECIAL NEEDS You can modify the procedure described in "Design Experiments" on p. 195 to help struggling students understand the formation of the depositional features caused by glaciers. For example, you could provide each group of students with the materials, and have them discuss how the materials could be used in the experiment. Then, on a whiteboard or chalkboard, write the names of the materials. Ask students to identify what each material represents in a model of the formation of depositional features caused by glaciers. Then have students work in groups to write a step-by-step procedure for the experiment.

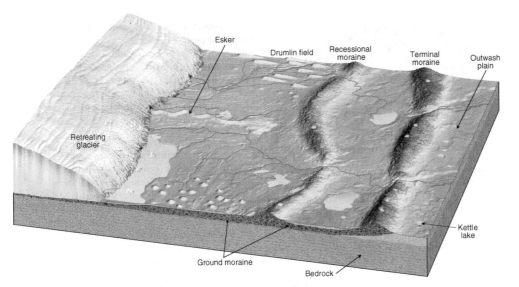

FIGURE 13 **Glacial Deposition** The terminal moraine marks the farthest extent of the glacier. Recessional moraines occur where a retreating glacier temporarily becomes stationary. Infer *If the glacier were completely melted away, how would you be able to tell in which direction the glacier retreated?*

If you know what to look for, the signs of a once-glaciated landscape are unmistakable—especially from an airplane. **Figure 13** shows the depositional features of a glaciated landscape.

☑ **Reading Checkpoint** *What depositional features do glaciers form?*

Glaciers of the Ice Age

Thousands of years ago, continental ice sheets and valley glaciers covered a lot more land than they do today. People once thought that glacial deposits had drifted in on icebergs or that they swept across the landscape in a catastrophic flood. However, scientific field investigations during the nineteenth century provided convincing evidence that an extensive ice age caused these deposits and many other features.

The most recent ice age is actually a series of glacial advances and retreats, which began two to three million years ago. **Continental glaciers repeatedly formed, spread, and melted as Earth's climate cooled and warmed. Each cycle of glaciation, or glacial period, lasted about 100,000 years.** Many of the glacial periods occurred while wooly mammoths and saber-toothed cats roamed the landscape.

Integrate Biology

Change in Sea Level A far-reaching effect of the most recent ice age was the worldwide change in sea level that accompanied each advance and retreat of the ice sheets. The snow that forms glaciers ultimately comes from moisture evaporated from the oceans. Therefore, when the ice sheets increased in size, sea level fell and the shorelines shifted seaward. Estimates suggest that sea level was as much as 100 m lower than today. Land that is presently flooded by the oceans was dry. The Atlantic Coast of the United States lay more than 100 km to the east of New York City. France and Britain were joined where the English Channel is today. Alaska and Siberia were connected across the Bering Strait. Southeast Asia was tied by dry land to the islands of Indonesia. **Ask:** If Siberia and Alaska were connected by a land bridge, would biologists find evidence of this? Explain. *(Yes, biologists should find evidence such as fossil remains of the same animals in both locations. In fact, fossil remains suggest that there was a migration of mammoths across the Bering Strait from Asia into North America.)*
Verbal, Logical

Answers

Figure 13 *The gentler slope of drumlins points in the direction the ice moved.*

☑ **Reading Checkpoint** *moraines, outwash plains, drumlins, eskers*

LESSON 7.1

Evaluate Understanding L2

Divide the class into six groups. Have each group write three questions about the material covered in one of the following headings: Types of Glaciers; How Glaciers Move; Glacial Erosion; Landforms Formed by Glacial Erosion; Glacial Deposition; Moraines, Outwash Plains, and Kettles; and Glaciers of the Ice Age. Invite students to take turns asking one question of the class.

Reteach L1

Use Figures 4 and 7 to review information about glaciers.

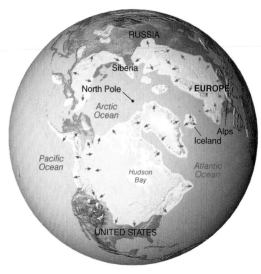

FIGURE 14 **Ice Age** During the ice age, ice sheets covered large areas in the Northern Hemisphere. So much ice formed that sea level was more than 100 meters lower than it is today. (The map shows modern coastlines.)

Although the glaciers are in retreat right now, at the peak of this ice age, glaciers covered almost 30 percent of Earth's land. Glaciers covered large portions of North America, Europe, and Siberia, as shown in **Figure 14.** The Northern Hemisphere had twice as much ice as did the Southern Hemisphere, where glaciation was mostly confined to Antarctica.

Ice Age Effects on Drainage The ice sheets greatly affected the drainage patterns over large regions. For example, before glaciation, the Missouri River flowed through central Illinois northward toward Hudson Bay in Canada. Furthermore, the Great Lakes did not exist. Their locations were marked by lowlands with rivers that flowed toward the east. During the recent ice age, glacial erosion transformed these lowlands into wide, deep basins that filled with water and eventually became the Great Lakes.

The formation and growth of ice sheets triggered changes in climates beyond the glacial margins. This change in climate resulted in the formation of lakes in such areas as the Basin and Range region of Nevada and Utah. One of these lakes was ancient Lake Bonneville, which covered much of western Utah. The Great Salt Lake is all that remains of this glacial lake.

7.1 Assessment

Review Key Concepts 🔑

1. What are the two basic types of glaciers? Where is each type found?

2. Describe how glaciers move. Which property or properties of ice allow this movement?

3. How does glacial till differ from stratified drift? Describe one glacial feature made of each type of glacial drift.

4. Name three glacial features formed by erosion and three that are formed by deposition. What does each feature look like?

Think Critically

5. Compare and Contrast Compare and contrast advancing and retreating glaciers.

6. Infer The snowline at the poles is sea level. Close to the equator, the snowline occurs high up on the tallest mountains. What is the relationship between the distance from the equator and the snowline?

MATH PRACTICE

7. Calculate A glacier advances 20 meters over a period of about two months. What is its approximate rate of advance per day?

198 Chapter 7 • Lesson 1

Assessment Answers

1. Valley glaciers look like streams of ice flowing between steep rock walls. They exist in high mountains. Ice sheets are enormous ice masses that cover everything but the highest land in some areas. The biggest ones are in Greenland and Antarctica.

2. Glaciers slip downhill due to gravity as well as flowing due to actual movement within the ice. The property known as plasticity allows for this.

3. Glacial till is an unsorted mixture of rock debris of many different sizes. Moraines, which are ridges formed from material dropped by glaciers, are made of till. Stratified drift contains particles sorted by size and mass of the debris. Outwash plains, which are rock debris ramps that extend downstream of an end moraine, are composed of stratified drift.

4. Erosion: cirque—a bowl-shaped depression at the head of a glacial valley; arête—snaking, sharp-edged ridge; horn—pyramid-shaped peak. Deposition: end moraine—debris dropped in a ridge at the face of a stationary glacier; ground moraine—a rock-strewn, gently rolling plain formed from sediments dropped by a retreating glacier; drumlins—parallel hills made of glacial till

5. Both types flow and carry debris. Advancing glaciers accumulate ice faster than ice melts; retreating glaciers melt faster than ice accumulates.

6. The farther away from the equator you travel, the lower the snowline is.

7. 20 m/60 days = 0.33 m/day

7.2 Deserts

IF YOU LIVE in a humid region and visit an arid region, or desert, it might seem as if you are going to another planet. In humid regions, the hills are rounded and the slopes are curved. By contrast, deserts often have angular rocks and surfaces covered in pebbles or sand, as shown in **Figure 15.**

To a visitor from a humid region, it may seem as though different forces act to shape the desert landscape. However, the processes of weathering and erosion shape both arid and wet regions. The differences merely reveal the effects of the same processes acting under different climatic conditions.

Weathering in Deserts

In humid regions, well-developed soils support an almost continuous cover of vegetation. Here slopes and rock edges are rounded. Such a landscape is due to the strong influence of chemical weathering. In contrast, the angular edges of rocks and slopes in deserts are a result of mechanical weathering. **Although chemical weathering occurs in deserts, mechanical weathering is far more dominant in shaping desert landscapes.** The lack of well-developed soils and abundant plant life allows mechanical weathering agents to break down and transport rocks in deserts.

FIGURE 15 A Desert Landscape Desert landscapes, such as California's Death Valley, have relatively few plants when compared to more humid climates.

Key Questions

What roles do mechanical and chemical weathering play in deserts?

How does running water affect deserts?

Vocabulary
- alluvial fan
- playa lake

Reading Strategy

Summarize Write each blue heading in the section on a sheet of paper. Write a brief summary of the text for each heading.

Desert Streams
?
?
Interior Drainage
?
?

LESSON 7.2

1 FOCUS

Lesson Objectives
7.5 **Explain** the roles that mechanical and chemical weathering play in deserts.

7.6 **Describe** how running water affects deserts.

Build Vocabulary L2
Paraphrase Have students write the definition of each vocabulary term in their own words.

Reading Strategy L2
Weathering in Deserts Sample answer: Mechanical weathering is dominant in the desert. Chemical weathering does occur, but the process is very slow.

Water in Deserts Sample answer: Although it doesn't rain often in the desert, the erosional effects of rain are significant.

2 INSTRUCT

Build Science Skills L2

Observe Have students look closely at Figure 15. Ask: If someone showed you this photograph, what are three features that would lead you to conclude that this was a desert climate? *(Sample answers: sparse vegetation; only small, shrub-like vegetation present; lots of exposed soil and gravel)*
Visual, Logical

Build Reading Literacy L1

Refer to **p. 586D** in **Chapter 21,** which provides the guidelines for SQ3R (Survey, Question, Read, Recite, Review).

SQ3R Teach this independent-study skill as a whole-class exercise. Direct students to survey the lesson and write headings such as Weathering in Deserts. As they survey, ask students to write one question for each heading, such as "What type of weathering occurs in a desert?" Then, have students write answers to the questions as they read the lesson. After students finish reading, demonstrate how to recite the questions and answers. Explain that vocalizing your questions and answers helps you retain what you have learned. Finally, have students review their notes the next day.
Verbal

Use Visuals L1

Figure 17 Have students look carefully at Figure 17. **Ask:** When rain falls at the top of these barren mountains, what will the water look like when it reaches the bottom? *(The water will be dirty because it will contain a lot of sediment that it has picked up as it flowed down the mountainside.)* What happens to the sediment when the water reaches the gentle slopes in the foreground of this picture? *(The rain water loses speed and dumps its load of sediment on the gentle slopes.)*
Verbal

Chemical weathering is not completely lacking in deserts, however. Chemical weathering can create clays and thin soils over long time spans. Many iron-bearing silicate minerals oxidize, producing the rust-colored stain that tints some desert landscapes. But a combination of a lack of moisture, fewer plants, and the resulting scarcity of organic acids from decaying plants means that the minerals in the rock debris remain unchanged.

☑ **Reading Checkpoint** *Why do deserts experience less chemical weathering than humid regions?*

Water in Deserts

Water is a powerful erosive agent in deserts, partially because the sands are loose and exposed due to a lack of vegetation. Although scarce in deserts, water can rapidly change and shape the landscape, especially after it rains. **In deserts, water collects in streams and rivers that can erode mountains, deposit alluvial fans, and form playa lakes.**

Desert Streams In a desert, there are bridges with no water beneath them and dips in the road crossing empty stream channels. Deserts receive very little rain during the year. As a result, most desert streams are not permanent. In some years, stream channels may remain completely dry as shown in **Figure 16A.** But after a rain, streams may carry water for a few hours or a few days.

Desert streams are known for dangerous flash flooding after heavy rains. Heavy showers can release so much rain that the soil cannot absorb it, as shown in **Figure 16B.** Without vegetation, water quickly runs off the land. The floods end almost as quickly as they start, but the amount of erosion caused during a single, short-lived rain event is impressive. By contrast, in humid regions, a flood on a river such as the Mississippi can take days to reach its crest and days to subside.

☑ **Reading Checkpoint** *How do floods differ between deserts and humid regions?*

FIGURE 16 Desert Streams
A Most of the time, stream channels in deserts remain dry.
B This is the same stream channel shortly after a heavy rain shower. Desert streams can cause a large amount of erosion in a short time. **Predict** *How long will the water flow in this stream?*

Differentiated Instruction

SPECIAL NEEDS For students with difficulty reading and writing, customize item 7 in the Lesson Assessment on p. 202 to allow students to make a multimedia presentation instead of a written report.

Interior Drainage Most desert streams do not reach the ocean. As a result, most deserts have interior drainage. In the United States, the evolution of the landscape in the dry Basin and Range region is an excellent example of interior drainage. The region includes southern Oregon, Nevada, western Utah, southeastern California, southern Arizona and New Mexico, and far west Texas.

The early stages of this landscape evolution occurred during and following the uplift of mountains. Running water began eroding the mountains and depositing large quantities of debris in the basin. Sporadic, heavy rains caused large amounts of water heavily loaded with sediment to move down the mountain canyons. Emerging from the confines of the canyon, the runoff spread over the gentler slopes at the base of the mountains and quickly lost speed. Consequently, most of its load was dumped within a short distance. The result was a cone of debris known as an **alluvial fan,** which forms at the mouth of a canyon. Over the years, the alluvial fans enlarged and merged with fans from adjacent canyons to produce an apron of sediment along the mountain front, as shown in **Figure 17.**

During the early stages of landscape evolution, elevation differences are the greatest. As erosion lowers the mountains, elevation differences diminish. By the late stages of landscape evolution, erosion has reduced the mountain areas to a few large bedrock knobs called *inselbergs.*

Each of the stages of landscape evolution can be observed in the Basin and Range region. Southern Oregon and northern Nevada contain recently, uplifted mountains in an early stage of erosion. Death Valley, California, and southern Nevada fit into the more advanced middle stage, whereas the late stage, with its inselbergs, can be seen in southern Arizona.

FIGURE 17 Alluvial Fans Over the years, alluvial fans enlarge and merge with fans from adjacent canyons to produce an apron of sediment along the mountain front. These features are common in mountainous deserts, such as in Death Valley, California.

Facts and Figures

Many of the world's deserts are located in two belts. One belt is located along the Tropic of Cancer in the Northern Hemisphere. The deserts located in this belt are the deserts in southwestern North America, the Sahara in North Africa, the Arabian and Iranian deserts in the Middle East, the Thar in India, and the Gobi in China. The second belt is located along the Tropic of Capricorn in the Southern Hemisphere. These deserts include the Patagonia in Argentina, the Kalahari in southern Africa, and the Great Victoria and Great Sandy deserts of Australia. These belts are formed when hot, moist air at the equator rises, cools, and loses its moisture. Then, the air descends, picking up moisture and drying out the land, creating these desert regions along the tropics.

❸ ASSESS

Evaluate Understanding L2

Have students write three review questions for the lesson. Invite students to take turns asking questions to the class.

Reteach L1

Use Figures 15, 16, 17, and 18 to review the main ideas in this lesson.

FIGURE 18 Playa Lakes and Playas A The water in playa lakes may be less than a meter deep and very rich in minerals. **B** Playas can be identified by their cracked lake bed surface and salt crusts left behind by the evaporated water.

INQUIRY
APPLY IT!

Q: *I heard that deserts are expanding. Is that true?*

A: Yes. The problem is called desertification, and it refers to the alteration of land to desertlike conditions as the result of human activities. It commonly takes place on the margins of deserts. It occurs when the modest natural vegetation in these marginal areas is removed by plowing or grazing. When droughts occur, the lack of vegetation allows heavy soil erosion to remove any remnants of fertile soil. Desertification is particularly serious in the region south of the Sahara Desert known as the Sahel.

Playa Lakes and Playas On the rare occasions of abundant rainfall, or snowmelt in the mountains, streams may flow across the alluvial fans to the center of the basin, converting the basin floor into a shallow **playa lake,** as shown in **Figure 18A.** Playa lakes last only a few days or weeks, before evaporation and infiltration remove the water. The dry, flat lake bed that remains is called a *playa*.

Permanent Streams Some permanent streams do manage to cross arid regions. The Colorado and Nile Rivers begin in well-watered mountains with huge water supplies. The rivers are full enough at the beginning to survive their desert crossings. The Nile River, for example, leaves the lakes and mountains of central Africa and covers almost 3000 kilometers of the Sahara without a single tributary adding to its flow. In contrast, rivers in humid regions generally gain water from both incoming tributaries and groundwater.

7.2 Assessment

Review Key Concepts

1. How do weathering processes affect deserts?

2. How are desert streams different from streams in humid locations?

3. Why is erosion by running water important in deserts?

4. How does a river survive crossing an arid region?

Think Critically

5. Compare and Contrast Compare and contrast the Nile River with the Mississippi River. Which factor is most responsible for their differences?

6. Apply Concepts Explain how evaporation and infiltration affect drainage systems in desert areas.

BIGIDEA WEATHERING AND EROSION

7. Describe how a desert stream might start to flow and the features its waters may create in the desert. Make sure to use the terms learned in this section.

202 Chapter 7 • Lesson 2

Assessment Answers

1. Water can cause mechanical weathering and produce angular rocks, sheer canyon walls, and pebble-covered surfaces.
2. Desert streams are typically not permanent but have the ability to produce flash floods, which cause substantial erosion.
3. Because there are fewer plants in deserts to anchor the soil, there can be a great amount of erosion caused during a single short-lived rain event.

4. It must be full enough at the beginning to survive the soil infiltration and evaporation that occur in the desert.
5. Both carry water. The Nile has few tributaries. The Mississippi takes longer to crest and subside. Climate is the factor most responsible for the rivers' differences.
6. Streams in desert areas lack extensively branched drainage systems. They do not flow out of the desert to oceans, and instead have interior drainage, helping evaporation to dry up desert streams.

7. A desert stream will start to flow as a result of a sudden rush of water from a rainstorm. The stream will flow for a few hours or days causing much erosion. When a desert stream moves down a mountain canyon, it erodes the sides of the canyon carrying sediment as it travels. As the stream loses speed at the bottom of the mountain, it drops this sediment forming a cone of debris known as an alluvial fan.

7.3 Landscapes Shaped by Wind

COMPARED WITH running water, wind does not do nearly as much erosional work on the land even in deserts. But wind is still an important force. Farmers of the Great Plains experienced the power of wind erosion during the 1930s. After they plowed the natural vegetation from this semiarid region, a severe drought set in. The land was left exposed to wind erosion. Vast dust storms swept away the exposed, fertile topsoil. The area became known as the *Dust Bowl*.

Wind Erosion

As the drought in the 1930s shows, the wind can be very erosive to exposed sands and soils. Strong winds pick up, transport, and deposit great quantities of fine sediment. In deserts, the soils are drier and generally have less vegetation to hold soil in place. Therefore, wind does its most effective erosional work in deserts. But wind can be very erosive to exposed sands and soils in any climate. **Wind erodes land surfaces in two ways: deflation and abrasion.**

Deflation When the wind lifts and removes loose particles such as clay and silt, **deflation** occurs. Coarser sand particles roll or skip along the surface in a process called *saltation*. In the Dust Bowl, deflation lowered the land by a meter or more in only a few years, as shown in **Figure 19.**

Deflation also results in shallow depressions called *blowouts*. Thousands of blowouts dot the Great Plains. They range from small dimples less than 1 meter deep and 3 meters wide to depressions more than 45 meters deep and several kilometers across.

FIGURE 19 Wind Erosion The photo shows soil loss in the Dust Bowl. The mounds are the level of the land before deflation removed the topsoil. The mounds are 1.2 meters tall and are anchored by vegetation.
Apply Concepts *How did farmers contribute to ruining the land during the Dust Bowl?*

Glaciers, Deserts, and Wind **203**

Key Questions

 What are two ways in which wind causes erosion?

What types of landforms are deposited by wind?

What factors determine the shape of a sand dune?

Vocabulary
- deflation • desert pavement
- loess • dune

Reading Strategy

Outline Before you read, make an outline of this lesson. Use the orange headings as the main topics and the blue headings as subtopics. As you read, add supporting details.

Landscapes Shaped by Wind
I. Wind Erosion
A. Deflation
B. Abrasion
II. _____?_____
A. _____?_____

LESSON 7.3

1 FOCUS

Lesson Objectives
7.7 **Describe** two ways that wind can cause erosion.
7.8 **Identify** types of landforms that are deposited by the wind.
7.9 **Identify** the factors that determine the shape of a sand dune.

Build Vocabulary　L2
Concept Map Have students construct a concept map using all of the vocabulary terms. Students should place the main concept (Landscapes Shaped by Wind) in the center oval and use descriptive linking phrases to connect the terms. Instruct students to place the terms in ovals and connect the ovals with lines on which linking words are placed.

Reading Strategy　L2
II. Wind Deposits; **A.** Loess; **B.** Sand Dunes; **III.** Types of Sand Dunes; **A.** Barchan Dunes; **B.** Transverse Dunes; **C.** Barchanoid Dunes; **D.** Longitudinal Dunes; **E.** Parabolic Dunes; **F.** Star Dunes

2 INSTRUCT

(Address **Misconceptions**)　L2

Students may think that an area shrouded in mist cannot be a desert. This is not true. Deserts shrouded in mist form along some coastlines. Cold waters from the Arctic and Antarctic regions and cold water that rises up from ocean depths and moves toward the equator cool the air currents above them. This cool air carries fog and mist, but little rain. These misty air currents flow across the coastal regions of southern California, Baja California, southwest Africa, and Chile where only desert communities survive.

Answers

Figure 19 *Because they removed the natural vegetation from the area, the soil was left exposed to wind erosion, which stripped the area of its fertile soil.*

Use Visuals L1

Figure 20 Have students look closely at Figure 20A. **Ask:** What is occurring in the first picture of Figure 20A? *(Deflation of the desert surface begins. Fine sediment is removed from the surface of the desert floor.)* What is occurring in the second picture of Figure 20A? *(Deflation continues as fine sediment is removed, leaving only coarse particles.)* What is occurring in the third picture of Figure 20A? *(All fine particles are removed. The remaining coarse particles have been compressed into desert pavement.)*
Visual, Verbal

Build Reading Literacy L1

Refer to **p. 392D** in **Chapter 14,** which provides the guidelines for preview.

Preview Have students read the bold subheads and examine the figures in the lesson. Then, ask students to list the important concepts they learned or will learn in the lesson. *(how landscapes are shaped by wind and what wind erosion and wind deposits can do)*
Visual, Verbal

Integrate Language Arts L2

Dust Bowl Literature John Steinbeck's novel *The Grapes of Wrath* is about an Oklahoma farming family who are forced to leave their home and move to California in a desperate attempt to survive during the Dust Bowl and the Depression. Select a passage from this novel to share with the class.
Verbal

FIGURE 20 Deflation A These cross sections show how deflation removes the sand and silt of the desert surface until only coarser particles remain. These coarser particles concentrate into a tightly packed layer called desert pavement.
Predict *What will happen if a vehicle disturbs this desert pavement?*

B Desert pavement such as this in southern Africa protects the surface from further deflation.

In portions of many deserts, the surface is characterized by a layer of coarse pebbles and cobbles that are too large to be moved by the wind. Deflation creates this kind of stony surface layer, called **desert pavement,** when it removes all the sand and silt and leaves only coarser particles as **Figure 20** shows. The remaining surface of coarse pebbles and cobbles protects the soils and sands below it from further deflation—unless vehicles or animals break it up. If something does disturb the surface, the wind is able to erode the unprotected soils and sands again.

Abrasion The second form of wind erosion is abrasion. Abrasion happens when windblown sand cuts and polishes exposed rock surfaces. Blowing sand can grind away at boulders and smaller rocks, sometimes sandblasting them into odd shapes. Abrasion is often credited for features such as balanced rocks that stand high atop narrow pedestals or the detailing on tall pinnacles. However, these features are not the results of abrasion. Sand rarely travels more than a meter above the surface, so sandblasting by wind is not typically seen above this height. However, in some areas, telephone poles have been cut through near the base.

☑ **Reading Checkpoint** *What is deflation?*

FIGURE 21 Loess This vertical deposit of loess near the Mississippi River in southern Illinois is about 3 meters high.

Wind Deposits

Although wind does not produce many landforms through erosion, it does produce significant landforms by deposition. ▭ **Wind produces loess and sand dunes when it deposits its sediments.** Loess and sand dunes are common in deserts and along coasts.

Loess Thick deposits of wind-blown silt are called **loess.** Dust storms deposit loess over thousands of years. When streams or roads cut through loess, it maintains vertical cliffs and lacks any visible layers, as you can see in **Figure 21.** The thickest and most extensive deposits of loess on Earth occur in western and northern China, where the wind transported the silt from nearby deserts. This fine, buff-colored sediment gives the Yellow River its name.

204 Chapter 7 • Lesson 3

Differentiated Instruction

ENGLISH LANGUAGE LEARNERS Help beginning language learners by using a Cloze strategy to extract key information from the text about wind deposits. After reading the section Wind Deposits, have students fill in the blanks in the following sentences: **The wind can create landforms when it deposits its _____, especially in deserts and along _____. Both** layers of loess and _____ _____ are landscape features deposited by the _____. Unlike deposits of _____, which form blanket-like layers over broad areas, winds commonly deposit _____ in mounds or ridges called _____.
(sediments, coasts, sand dunes, wind, loess, sand, dunes)

FIGURE 22 **Sand Dunes** Wind blows sand up the windward side of a dune in New Mexico's White Sands National Monument and drops it on the leeward side. Sand sliding down the leeward side results in the dune moving in the same direction the wind blows.

FIGURE 23 **Cross Beds** These cross beds are found in Utah.

Teacher **Demo**

WIND EROSION

Purpose Students will observe how wind erodes the landscape.

Materials sand, large piece of cardboard, water

Procedure Make two mounds of sand on the cardboard. Sprinkle water over one and leave the other one dry. Blow across the wet sand. Then, blow across the dry sand.

Expected Outcomes Students will observe the wet sand does not move. They will also observe that the dry sand is blown away by the movement of air just as wind moves the sand in a desert or in a dry region.
Visual, Logical

In the United States, you can find loess in South Dakota, Nebraska, Iowa, Missouri, and Illinois, as well as portions of the Columbia Plateau in the Pacific Northwest. Unlike the deposits in China, the source of the loess in the United States and Europe is deposits of stratified drift. During the retreat of the ice sheets, many river valleys were filled with sediment deposited by meltwater. Strong westerly winds picked up the finer sediment and dropped it as a blanket on the eastern sides of valleys.

Sand Dunes Sand particles fall to the ground when wind speed lessens and the energy available for transport diminishes, as happens at an obstruction. Sand deposits in mounds or ridges are called **dunes.** Dunes can begin near obstructions as small as a clump of vegetation or a rock. Once the sand starts to mound, it serves as its own obstruction and traps more sand. With enough sand and long periods of steady wind, the mound of sand becomes a dune.

Dunes often are steeper on the leeward side and slope more gently on the windward side. Wind blows sand grains up the windward side. Once the sand blows over the crest of the dune, the wind slows and the sand drops out. The leeward side of the dune becomes steeper, and the sand eventually slides down the slope, as shown in **Figure 22.** In this way, the dune tends to move in the same direction as the wind blows.

As sand is deposited on the leeward side of the dune, it forms layers that slope in the same direction in which the wind blows. These sloping layers are called *cross beds*. When the dunes are eventually buried under other layers of sediment and become sedimentary rock, the cross beds remain as a record of their origin, as shown in **Figure 23.**

☑ **Reading Checkpoint** *How do obstructions help to form dunes?*

Glaciers, Deserts, and Wind **205**

Answers

Figure 20 *Further deflation will remove more sand and silt.*

☑ **Reading Checkpoint** *Deflation occurs when wind lifts and removes loose particles such as clay and silt.*

☑ **Reading Checkpoint** *Obstructions reduce wind speed and cause sand particles to drop to the ground.*

Facts and Figures

What caused the Dust Bowl? Clearly, the fact that portions of the Great Plains experienced some of North America's strongest winds is important. However, it was the huge expansion of agriculture that set the stage for this disastrous period of soil erosion. Mechanization allowed the rapid transformation of the grass-covered prairies of this semiarid region into farms. Between 1870 and 1930, the area of cultivation in the region expanded nearly tenfold, from about 10 million acres to more than 100 million acres. As long as precipitation was adequate, there were enough plants and moisture to help hold the soil in place. However, when a prolonged drought struck in the 1930s, the crops failed, leaving the dry soils exposed to heavy wind erosion. These factors contributed to further economic hardship.

Interpret Diagrams Have students study Figure 24. **Ask:** Which sand dunes form from wind that blows in a single direction? *(barchan, transverse, barchanoid, and parabolic)* Which sand dunes form from wind that blows in multiple directions? *(longitudinal and star)*
Verbal, Logical

Integrate Language Arts   L2

Word Roots Tell students that one of the meanings of the Latin root *trans-* is "across." Ask students to discuss why *transverse* is an appropriate name for this type of dune. *(The wind blows across the dune.)*
Verbal

Types of Sand Dunes

Dunes occur in a variety of consistent forms worldwide. **The shape of a sand dune depends on the wind direction and speed, how much sand is available, and the amount of vegetation.** Figure 24 shows six different types of dunes.

Barchan Dunes Isolated sand dunes shaped like crescents are called *barchan dunes*. These form on flat, hard ground where vegetation and the supply of sand are limited. Barchan dunes move slowly and only reach heights of about 30 meters. If the wind direction is constant, barchan dunes remain symmetrical. One tip of the dune can grow larger than the other if the wind direction varies somewhat.

VISUAL SUMMARY

TYPES OF SAND DUNES

FIGURE 24 The speed and direction of wind, the supply of sand, and vegetation cover determine the formation of sand dunes. *Classify* **Which type of sand dune forms in coastal areas with some vegetation and strong onshore winds?**

A. Barchan
B. Transverse
C. Barchanoid
D. Longitudinal
E. Parabolic
F. Star

Differentiated Instruction

VISUALLY IMPAIRED Use dampened sand to create models of each type of sand dune pictured in Figure 24 for students with visual impairments.

Transverse Dunes If prevailing winds are steady, sand is plentiful, and vegetation is sparse, dunes form in a series of long ridges. They are called *transverse dunes* because these ridges are perpendicular to the direction of the wind. Transverse dunes are typical in many coastal areas. They also comprise the "sand seas" found in parts of the Sahara and Arabian deserts. Transverse dunes in both of these deserts reach heights of 200 meters, measure 1 to 3 kilometers across, and extend for distances of 100 kilometers or more.

Barchanoid Dunes A common dune form that is intermediate between a barchan and transverse dune is the *barchanoid dune*. These rows of sand form at right angles to the wind. The rows resemble a series of barchans that have been positioned side by side. You can see them in White Sands National Monument in New Mexico.

Longitudinal Dunes *Longitudinal dunes* are long ridges of sand that form parallel to the prevailing wind. These dunes occur where sand supplies are moderate and the prevailing wind direction varies slightly. In portions of North Africa, Arabia, and central Australia, longitudinal dunes can reach nearly 100 meters high and extend for more than 100 kilometers.

Parabolic Dunes *Parabolic dunes* look like backward barchans. Their tips point into the wind instead of away from it. They form where some vegetation covers the sand. Parabolic dunes often form along the coast where strong onshore winds and abundant sand are available.

Star Dunes *Star dunes* are isolated hills of sand mostly found in parts of the Sahara and Arabian deserts. Their bases resemble stars and they usually have three or four sharp ridges that meet in the middle. Star dunes develop in areas of variable wind direction, and they sometimes reach heights of 90 meters.

INQUIRY APPLY IT!

Q: *Aren't deserts mostly covered with sand dunes?*

A: Many people think a desert is covered in drifting sand dunes. Some deserts do have striking sand dunes. But sand dunes worldwide represent only a small percentage of the total desert area. Dunes cover only one-tenth of the world's largest desert, the Sahara and only one-third of the Arabian, the world's sandiest desert, is covered in dunes.

7.3 Assessment

Review Key Concepts

1. How does deflation lower the surface of the desert?

2. What would you expect to see in areas subject to abrasion?

3. What was the Dust Bowl? Why did it occur?

4. How does a dune help itself to grow?

5. What factors determine the shape of sand dunes?

Think Critically

6. **Compare and Contrast** Compare and contrast loess and sand dunes.

7. **Design an Experiment** Describe how you would conduct an experiment to determine the wind speed necessary to suspend sand, silt, and clay particles.

CONNECTING CONCEPTS

8. **Explain** Which dune type would you expect to travel the least? Explain your answer.

Glaciers, Deserts, and Wind **207**

Assessment Answers

1. Wind removes the loose clay and silt particles from the surface.
2. polished rock surfaces; oddly shaped rocks
3. a vast area of the Great Plains where wind erosion occurred in the 1930s; because a drought and lack of plant cover made the plowed ground vulnerable to wind erosion
4. It serves as its own wind obstruction, causing the wind to slow and sand to drop out.

5. wind direction and speed, how much sand is available, amount of vegetation
6. Both are wind-blown deposits. Loess is made of silt; dunes are made of sand.
7. Answers should include a reasonable way to alter and measure the wind speed, as well as to collect particles.

8. Star dunes would travel the least, because variable winds will move the dunes back and forth rather than in a single direction.

How Earth Works

How Earth Works

Erosion

Erosion is the process by which weathered sediment is picked up and carried away. Sediment can be moved by streams and rivers, ocean waves, glacial ice, gravity, or wind. The amount of sediment that is moved and the distance that it travels depend on the size and mass of the particles and the speed at which the eroding agent is moving. Erosion affects the landscapes of all the regions of the world.

1. Before glaciation A narrow, V-shaped river valley is surrounded by rounded mountains.

2. During glaciation Moving ice erodes mountaintops and carves wider valleys.

3. After glaciation The result is a U-shaped valley with rugged, sharp peaks above.

EROSION BY GLACIAL ICE ▶
Huge masses of ice that move downhill are called **glaciers.** Over thousands or millions of years, they can scour mountainsides and dramatically change the shapes of valleys.

Sand dunes

Rock arch

Wash

Sediments collect in wash

SAND DUNES
A dune begins to form where a plant or other obstacle slows the wind, which drops its load of sand. As the sand piles up, it creates an ever-growing barrier to the wind, causing more sand to be dropped. Eventually the dune crest may collapse like an ocean wave.

▲ EROSION IN ARID LANDS
When rare torrential rain comes to arid areas, entire mountainsides may be swept clean of boulders, rock fragments, sand, and clay. Flash floods move sediment down washes—the valleys of streams that are usually dry.

SEAS OF SAND
The huge amounts of sand that make up some deserts started out as rock that was weathered to form fine particles. The finer the particle, the farther it can be transported by agents of erosion.

FOCUS

Objectives
In this feature, students will
- define erosion and identify its agents.
- describe the effects of erosion on different landforms.

Build Vocabulary **L2**
Define Terms Write the word *erosion* on the board. Have students define it. Have students brainstorm a list of places that show the effects of erosion in your region. Remind them of beaches, canyons, and other appropriate places.

2 INSTRUCT

Bellringer **L2**
Ask students if they have ever collected rocks from a river or ocean. **Ask:** What was the texture of the rocks you collected? *(Most of them are smooth.)* **Ask:** What would account for the smoothness of these rocks? *(The constant motion of the water on the rocks wears down rough points and makes the surface smooth.)* Discuss how running water affects hard objects and land over time.
Logical

Use Visuals **L1**
Have students study the pictures and diagrams on this page and the next. **Ask:** Are the effects of erosion obvious from year to year? Why or why not? *(In most cases, the effects are not obvious because erosion is a gradual process. In the case of erosion due to desert storms, the effects are more immediately obvious.)*
Visual

Differentiated Instruction

GIFTED Have students research ways to minimize erosion at the library or on the Internet. Ask them to create a flowchart or diagram that shows what people can do to minimize erosion. Students can present their diagrams to the class and explain them.

WATER FLOWING
As water flows from highlands to the sea, sharp descents result in rapids and waterfalls. Flowing water is an important agent of erosion.▼

STREAM EROSION▲
Streams erode their banks and beds, continually widening and deepening them. In some cases, a canyon may result. A **canyon**, such as this one in Utah, is a deep valley with steep sides that have been eroded by river water.

WAVE ACTION
Coastlines are constantly eroded by waves. Waves are formed by winds blowing over water. Cracked and soft rocks are eroded away first, forming arches. If the arch roof collapses, a **sea stack** results.▼

Sea stack off the British Isles

1. *Headlands cause waves to curve.*
2. *An arch forms.*
3. *When the top of the arch is eroded by gravity and falls into the ocean, a sea stack results.*

Assessment

1. **Key Terms** Define the following, using your own words: (a) erosion, (b) wash, (c) glacier, (d) canyon, (e) sea stack.

2. **Environmental Change** How does water gradually reshape the land?

3. **Physical Characteristics** What are some major physical characteristics of an arid landscape eroded by wind and rain?

4. **Physical Processes** Analyze the three diagrams of glacial erosion. How does the shape of an unglaciated valley compare to the shape of a valley that's been eroded by glaciers?

5. **Critical Thinking Analyze Cause and Effect** How can erosion on farmlands cause a reduction in agricultural production?

209

❸ ASSESS

Evaluate Understanding   L2

Have students write sentences using the key terms from this feature. Remind them that the sentences should include the definition of each term. Encourage students to use more than one key term per sentence when possible.

Reteach   L1

Draw a two-column chart on the board. Label the columns *Eroding Agent* and *Effects*. Have students use information from the text to describe how streams, waves, glaciers, and other eroding agents change the landscape.

Assessment Answers

1. (a) the transport of weathered sediment; (b) a valley of a usually dry stream; (c) a huge mass of ice that moves downhill; (d) a deep valley with steep sides that have been eroded by river water; (e) an isolated column of eroded coastline that resulted from the collapse of a sea arch.

2. Moving water in the form of waterfalls, rivers, waves, or rain breaks up and moves rocks and other loose material.

3. Sample answer: sand dunes formed and changed by wind, washes created during flash floods, weathering of rocks into sediment.

4. An unglaciated valley is V-shaped and surrounded by rounded mountains. A glaciated valley is U-shaped and surrounded by rugged mountains.

5. The fertile topsoils wash or blow away, making the land less productive.

INTERPRETING A GLACIAL LANDSCAPE

L2

Objectives

In this activity, students will:

- use a topographic map to identify geographic features formed by glaciers.
- infer how geographic features were formed.

Skills Interpret Maps, Infer, Draw Conclusion

Prep Time 10 minutes to copy map

Class Time 45 minutes

Expected Outcome Many geographic features on a topographical map are easily identified and their origin is easily inferred.

INQUIRY ?
EXPLORATION LAB

Interpreting a Glacial Landscape

Problem How can a topographic map allow you to interpret a glacially formed landscape?

Materials topographic map, piece of blank paper, pencil

Skills Interpret Maps, Infer, Draw Conclusions

Connect to the Big idea Topographic maps are valuable tools geologists use to interpret landscapes. Especially in the field—when your view can be limited—these maps not only help you determine your location, they can offer a bigger landscape picture than what is actually visible. See how well you can do at identifying glacial features on the map and interpreting them to reconstruct geologic history.

Procedure

1. Following line A on the map, sketch a topographic profile of the Lake Fork Valley onto the grid below.
2. Place the straight edge of your blank paper along the line and mark in pencil where it meets every fifth contour line (the darker guide contours).
3. Be sure to write the elevation of every fifth contour line along the *y*-axis of the profile grid.

Analyze and Conclude

1. **Analyze Data** How can you tell from your profile that the valley was formed by a glacier?
2. **Draw Conclusions** Use the map to help you describe the direction the glacier flowed through this valley. How can you tell?
3. **Interpret Maps** Which letter arrow points to cirques? You can refer to Figure 7 in your textbook for help.
4. **Interpret Maps** Which letter arrows point to hanging valleys?
5. **Interpret Maps** Which letter arrows point to arêtes?
6. **Interpret Maps** Name a peak on the map that is a horn.
7. **Infer** Feature E on the map is composed of glacial till. What type of glacial feature is E, and how did it form?
8. **Apply Concepts** Explain how Turquoise Lake formed.

GO FURTHER Use library or Internet sources to research a glacier of interest. Find out whether it is growing or shrinking and how the glacier is used by people and other organisms. Give a short presentation on your findings to the class. Include visual aids to help make your points.

210 Chapter 7

Answers to Procedure Questions

1–3. Student profiles should show a U-shaped valley.

Answers to Analyze and Conclude Questions

1. because it is U-shaped

2. west to east because the direction is downhill.

3. D

4. B

5. C

6. Galena Mountain

7. It is an end moraine made of debris deposited by stationary face of the valley glacier. Water backed up behind the end moraine as the glacier retreated.

8. A glacier carved out of a U-shaped valley that ran west-east between the Galena Mountain region to the north and the Sugar Loaf and Bald Eagle Mountain region to the south. The glacier moved down slope, accumulating mass where topography leveled off, carving a deep enough basin for Turquoise Lake to form from melted ice and runoff.

Visual, Logical

GO FURTHER

Students should be able to answer each of the questions provided in the task thoughtfully and accurately. They may choose to create a poster showing the glacier and how it is used. You can ask them to provide you with a list of their sources to help them learn this research skill.

Visual, Kinesthetic

Study Tip

Review Daily

Encourage students to set a time each day to review their science notes and text. This is an easier, more effective, and less stressful way to prepare for quizzes and tests, as compared to cramming all of the studying in a day or two before an exam. Even spending as little time as 15–20 minutes per day reviewing information recently covered in class can help students improve performance by monitoring their understanding before the class moves on to new concepts. Encourage students to write down any questions that come up during this daily study routine and bring them to class so that you can answer them.

21st Century Learning

Information and Media Literacy

Are melting glaciers due to climate change?

Scientists think that one sign of climate change is that many glaciers are retreating. Ask students to search the Web for three articles about the retreat of a glacier. One article should be a news article, the second should be from a popular science magazine, and the third should be from a scientific journal. Instruct students to write a report comparing and contrasting the articles. Students should determine each article's target audience and purpose. They should also describe what information or "spin" each article has that the others do not.

Homework Guide

Lesson	Questions
1	1, 3, 4, 6, 10–15, 17, 21–28, 30, 31
2	5, 9, 18, 20, 24, 30
3	2, 7, 8, 16, 19, 24, 29–31

Big idea ▶ **Weathering and Erosion**

7.1 Glaciers

🔑 There are two main types of glaciers: valley glaciers and ice sheets.

🔑 The movement of glaciers is referred to as flow. Glacial flow happens in two ways: plastic flow and basal slip.

🔑 Whether the foot of a glacier advances, retreats, or stays in place depends on the glacier's budget. The glacial budget is the balance or lack of balance between accumulation at the head of a glacier and loss, or wastage, at the foot.

🔑 Many landscapes were changed by the widespread glaciers of the recent ice age.

🔑 Glaciers produce a variety of erosional landscape features, such as glacial troughs, hanging valleys, cirques, arêtes, and horns.

🔑 The term *glacial drift* applies to all of the rock debris of glacial origin, no matter how, where, or in what form it was deposited. There are two types of glacial drift: till and stratified drift.

🔑 Glaciers are responsible for a variety of depositional landscape features, including moraines, outwash plains, kettles, drumlins, and eskers.

🔑 Continental glaciers repeatedly formed, spread, and melted as Earth's climate cooled and warmed. Each cycle of glaciation, or glacial period, lasted about 100,000 years.

ice age (188)
glacier (188)
snowline (189)
valley glacier (189)
abrasion (192)
till (194)
moraine (195)
drumlin (196)
esker (196)

7.2 Deserts

🔑 Although chemical weathering occurs in deserts, mechanical weathering is far more dominant in shaping desert landscapes.

🔑 In deserts, water collects in streams and rivers that can erode mountains, deposit alluvial fans, and form playa lakes.

alluvial fan (201)
playa lake (202)

7.3 Landscapes Shaped by Wind

🔑 Wind erodes land surfaces in two ways: deflation and abrasion.

🔑 Wind produces loess and sand dunes when it deposits its sediments.

🔑 The shape of a sand dune depends on the wind direction and speed, how much sand is available, and the amount of vegetation.

deflation (203)
desert pavement (204)
loess (204)
dune (205)

Assessment Answers

Review Content

1. c	2. b	3. c
4. b	5. b	6. a
7. b	8. c	9. d
10. c		

Understand Concepts

11. The ice is brittle, and there isn't enough pressure for plastic flow; deep cracks form as the glacier moves over rough terrain.

12. In plucking, meltwater beneath the glacier seeps into rock cracks, refreezes, pries rock apart, and carries fragments along with the glacial ice. In abrasion, rock fragments on the underside of a glacier smooth rock beneath the moving glacier.

7 Assessment

Review Content

Choose the letter that best answers the question or completes the statement.

1. Icebergs are produced when large pieces of ice break from the foot of a glacier during a process called
   a. plucking.   c. calving.
   b. deflation.   d. abrasion.

2. Which type of dune forms at right angles to the wind when there is abundant sand, a lack of vegetation, and a constant wind direction?
   a. barchan
   b. transverse
   c. longitudinal
   d. parabolic

3. Which area was NOT covered in ice sheets at the peak of the most recent ice age?
   a. Siberia   c. North Africa
   b. Europe   d. Antarctica

4. All rock debris of glacial origin is called
   a. till.
   b. glacial drift.
   c. stratified drift.
   d. outwash.

5. Which term is used to describe a dry channel in a desert?
   a. playa lake
   b. wash
   c. alluvial fan
   d. playa

6. The two major ways that glaciers erode land are abrasion and
   a. plucking.   c. deflation.
   b. tension.   d. slipping.

7. The most noticeable result of deflation in some places are shallow depressions called
   a. sinkholes.   c. loess.
   b. blowouts.   d. kettles.

8. In which of these places do extensive yellow loess deposits occur?
   a. Canada   c. China
   b. Cambodia   d. Australia

9. Which of the following is NOT a feature associated with valley glaciers?
   a. horn   c. arête
   b. cirque   d. loess

10. A broad, ramp-like surface of stratified drift built downstream from an end moraine is a(n)
    a. kettle.
    b. drumlin.
    c. outwash plain.
    d. terminal moraine.

Understand Concepts

11. Why is the uppermost 50 m of a glacier called the zone of fracture?

12. How do the erosional processes of plucking and abrasion work?

Use the diagram below to answer Question 13.

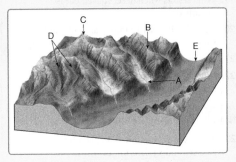

13. The area in the diagram was eroded by valley glaciers. For each feature listed below, write the letter of that feature in the diagram.
    a. cirque
    b. glacial trough
    c. hanging valley
    d. horn
    e. arête

14. Describe each type of moraine.
    a. end moraine
    b. lateral moraine
    c. ground moraine

17. Glaciers hold onto their sediment over long distances until they melt. Water drops sediments once velocity decreases.

18. Desert streams only flow in response to rainfall. They produce flash floods. They usually dry up before reaching the ocean.

19. Deflation begins again, removing sediments formerly protected by the rocks and cobbles of the pavement. Blowouts can also occur.

20. Although both are important, water is a stronger agent of erosion in deserts than is wind.

21. Under the great pressure of overlying snow and ice, the normally brittle material becomes plastic, so it can deform and flow.

22. Cracks only form where the ice is brittle. Below 50 m, the ice exhibits plasticity due to pressure.

---

13. a) D
    b) E
    c) A
    d) C
    e) B

14. a) forms at the foot of a stationary glacier
    b) forms at the sides of a glacier where it scours valley walls
    c) scatters glacial drift over the ground as a glacier recedes

15. a) A
    b) G
    c) C
    d) B

16. Wind blows sand up the gentler slope to its crest. The sand drops down the steeper slope. Eventually, the steeper slope slides and moves the crest in the same direction as the wind blows.

ASSESSMENT

Think Critically

23. If accumulation is greater than melting, the glacier advances. If accumulation is less than melting, the glacier retreats. If accumulation equals melting, the glacier remains stationary.

24. All three help to break up rock and transport sediments. Wind is the weakest factor because it does a poor job at carrying rock debris. Water carries and sorts rock debris. Glaciers break up and remove rock and carry it over long distances, but glaciers usually deposit the debris unsorted.

25. Glacial erratics are derived from bedrock that occurred some distance away, where the erratic was plucked by the glacier.

Analyze Data

26. just over 5000 m
27. 25 percent
28. The farther away from the equator you travel, the closer to sea level the snowline becomes.

Concepts in Action

29. The fan would model the wind, and the playing cards would model the protective cover of vegetation. Students would need to vary the factors of wind direction, wind speed, amount of sand, and amount of protective cover to model each type of sand dune.

30. erosion: arête, cirque, desert pavement, hanging valley, horn; deposition: alluvial fan, dune, moraine, drumlin, esker, erratic, kettle, outwash plain

31. Climate determines whether an area will be glaciated, arid, windy, dry, or wet. Glaciers, water, and wind are Earth's primary agents of erosion. Earth's glaciated areas are those most transformed by erosion, followed by those areas subject to running water, and then by those affected by wind. Deserts are more affected by wind than any other area, but are still more affected by running water.

15. For each feature listed below, write the letter of that feature in the diagram.

   a. drumlin
   b. outwash plain
   c. esker
   d. end moraine

16. Describe how sand dunes move.

17. How does the transport of sediment by glaciers differ from transport by water?

18. How do desert streams differ from those in humid regions?

19. What results when desert pavement is disturbed?

20. Describe the relative importance of wind and running water in eroding the desert landscape.

21. How is it possible for ice to flow?

22. Why do crevasses only extend 50 meters or so beneath the surface of a glacier?

Think Critically

23. Relate Cause and Effect Explain how a glacier's budget determines whether it advances, retreats, or remains stationary.

24. Compare and Contrast In what ways are the erosional actions of wind, water, and glaciers similar? How are they different?

25. Infer Explain why glacial erratics will usually be made of rocks that differ from the bedrock in the area where they are found.

Analyze Data

Use the graph below to answer Questions 26–28.

26. Interpret Graphs What is the minimum elevation required for year-round snow on a mountain located on the equator?

27. Infer Suppose a 2000-meter tall mountain was located at 75 degrees north of the equator. What percentage of its height would have year-round snow?

28. Draw Conclusions Write a statement that summarizes the information in the graph.

Concepts in Action

29. Use Models Explain how you would model each type of sand dune using a fan, a pan full of sand, and some playing cards.

30. Classify Which types of landscape features described in this chapter resulted from erosion? Which types resulted from deposition?

31. Writing in Science Write a paragraph that summarizes the role of climate in the development of the landscapes discussed in this chapter.

Performance-Based Assessment

32. Research Eskers are one glacial feature that people have transformed into a resource. Find out why glacial sediments are useful, who mines them, how they mine them, and the extent of their commercial value. Explain whether glacial deposits are considered renewable or nonrenewable resources.

Performance-Based Assessment

32. Student answers will vary but should accurately reflect their research. Sample answer: Sand and gravel are used in road building and as surface aquifiers for drinking water wells. Students should indicate that glacial deposits are considered nonrenewable.

Standardized Test Prep

Choose the letter that best answers the question.

1 **Which of the following statements about ice sheets is *not* true?**
   A They cover 30 percent of Earth's land surface.
   B They form where more snow accumulates than melts.
   C They are also called continental glaciers.
   D They can flow.

2 **Which is *not* true of loess?**
   F Loess is a blanket of silt covering the landscape.
   G The Yellow River in China is named for the loess that it transports.
   H Wind carries and deposits the sediments that comprise loess.
   J There are no loess deposits in the United States.

3 **Under which of the following conditions will star dunes form?**
   A in areas where the direction of the wind changes
   B in areas where the wind direction changes slightly and the sand supplies are moderate
   C in areas with steady winds, and limited vegetation and supplies of sand
   D along shores with strong onshore winds, lots of sand, and some vegetation

4 **When a stream emerges from a mountain canyon, the stream slope is greatly reduced. As a result the sediment is deposited within a short distance and forms a (an)—**
   F playa lake
   G alluvial fan
   H sinkhole
   J arête

5 **Are glaciers a part of Earth's lithosphere or hydrosphere? Explain.**
   A lithosphere; When water falls to Earth's surface, it enters the lithosphere.
   B lithosphere; Earth's lithosphere contains all solid objects on Earth's surface, including ice.
   C hydrosphere; When glaciers melt, they enter the water cycle.
   D hydrosphere; Earth's hydrosphere contains all of Earth's water, including ice.

If You Have Trouble With . . .

Question	1	2	3	4	5
See Lesson	7.1	7.3	7.3	7.2	7.1

Standardized Test Prep

1 A
2 J
3 A
4 G
5 D

8 Earthquakes and Earth's Interior Planning Guide

BIGIDEA: DYNAMIC EARTH

Lesson Objectives		Activities
8.1 What Is an Earthquake?, pp. 218–221 8.1 **Compare and contrast** the epicenter and focus of an earthquake. 8.2 **Identity** the cause of earthquakes. 8.3 **Compare and contrast** aftershocks and foreshocks.		TE Build Science Skills, p. 219 L2 TE Teacher Demo: Sweet Stress, p. 219 L2
8.2 Measuring Earthquakes, pp. 222–227 8.4 **Identify** th e three types of seismic waves. 8.5 **Describe** how seismic waves are recorded. 8.6 **Describe** the different ways earthquakes are measured. 8.7 **Explain** how to locate the epicenter of an earthquake.		TE Teacher Demo: Seismic Waves, p. 223 L2
8.3 Earthquake Hazards, pp. 228–232 8.8 **Identify** the major hazards associated with earthquakes. 8.9 **Describe** how earthquake damage can be reduced.		TE Build Science Skills, pp. 229, 231 L2
8.4 Earth's Layered Structure, pp. 233–237 8.10 **List** the layers of Earth based on composition and physical properties. 8.11 **Describe** the composition of each layer of Earth. 8.12 **Explain** how scientists determined Earth's structure and composition.		TE Teacher Demo: Floating Crackers, p. 234 L2
Chapter Features and Labs		
Try It How Can Buildings Be Made Earthquake-Safe? p. 217		LM Design and Build a Simple Seismograph L3
How Earth Works Effects of Earthquakes, p. 238		
Exploration Lab Locating an Earthquake, p. 240–241		

Ability Levels	Components			
L1 For students who need additional help	**SE**	Student Edition	**LP**	Lesson Plans
L2 For all students	**TE**	Teacher's Edition	**AA**	Active Art
L3 For students who need to be challenged	**LM**	Laboratory Manual	**PD**	Planet Diary
	CT	Chapter Tests	**GEODe**	Geode CD-ROM
	GRSW	Guided Reading & Study Workbook	**eText**	
	CTB	Computer Test Bank		

Resources	Lesson Assessment
GRSW Lesson 8.1 **LP** Lesson Planning 8.1 **GEODe** Forces Within: Earthquakes	**SE** Lesson 8.1 Assessment, p. 221 **eText** Lesson 8.1
GRSW Lesson 8.2 **LP** Lesson Planning 8.2 **AA** Seismic Waves Activity	**SE** Lesson 8.2 Assessment, p. 227 **eText** Lesson 8.2
GRSW Lesson 8.3 **LP** Lesson Planning 8.3	**SE** Lesson 8.3 Assessment, p. 232 **eText** Lesson 8.3
GRSW Lesson 8.4 **LP** Lesson Planning 8.4	**SE** Lesson 8.4 Assessment, p. 237 **eText** Lesson 8.4

Materials for Activities and Labs

Quantities for each group

STUDENT EDITION

Try It, p. 217
cardboard (thin), sugar cubes, frosting, large book, window screen (or wire meshing), scissors or wire cutters to cut screen

Exploration Lab, pp. 240–241
pencil, drawing compass, world map or atlas, photocopy of map on p. 241

TEACHER'S EDITION

Build Science Skills, p. 219
flexible metric ruler

Teacher Demo, p. 219
chocolate-covered candy bar with nougat center

Teacher Demo, p. 223
coiled spring toy

Build Science Skills, p. 229
sand, potting soil, thin tray, wire netting, water, craft sticks for model house

Teacher Demo, p. 234
shallow baking pan, package of pudding, 2 cups of milk, several animal crackers

Assessment

CHAPTER ASSESSMENT
SE Assessment, pp. 243–244
CT Chapter 8 Test
CTB Chapter 8
eText Chapter 8

21st Century Learning

Communication Skills: What can you find out about earthquakes?

Before You Teach
Earthquakes and Earth's Interior

Michael Wysession
Washington University

Common Themes

Earthquakes are the rupture of rock within Earth. The result of the rupture is a fault. Earthquakes are important because they are significant natural hazards, with the capability of destroying cities. They are also important because the waves they create are used to investigate the structure of Earth's interior

Space and Time Earthquakes can occur anywhere near Earth's surface, but mostly occur in narrow bands that turn out to be the boundaries between pieces of lithosphere. About 200,000 earthquakes are located each year. An earthquake usually lasts for only seconds, and there may be a wait of years to hundreds of years between large earthquakes on a given fault. Despite a tremendous amount of research, efforts to predict earthquakes have been unsuccessful, and it may turn out that earthquakes cannot be predicted.

Forces and Motion Earthquakes occur because bending stresses within the rock exceeds the strength of the rock. The rupture causes seismic waves to propagate through Earth (P and S waves) and along its surface (surface waves).

Matter and Energy Seismic waves, as with most waves, are a propagation of energy, not matter. Seismic waves are recorded on seismographs, and the amplitudes of the waves are used to determine the magnitude of the earthquake. The biggest earthquakes release more energy than the world's entire nuclear arsenal.

Earth as a System Seismic waves are used to make images of Earth's layering, which is based on density, with the light rock of the crust overlying the heavier rock of the mantle, which overlies the dense iron/nickel core. Though high pressures keep most of Earth's interior solid, the high temperatures cause some of it to be molten.

EARTH SCIENCE REFRESHER

The Start of Seismology

Interestingly, much of our understanding of seismology, and therefore of Earth's interior structure, is the result of politics. The seismic waves from an earthquake are similar to, but distinctly different from, those of an underground nuclear bomb. Therefore, since the early 1960s, the United States has helped to install worldwide networks of seismographs for the purpose of monitoring nuclear testing, initially in the Soviet Union, and now elsewhere. With these seismographs, we have always known of the nuclear capabilities of other countries. The seismic data, however, have also allowed us to make detailed images of Earth's interior.

How Earthquakes Are Located

In this chapter is an example of how an earthquake could be located using P and S waves from three seismographs. In actual use, however, an earthquake is located using thousands of seismographs. These seismographs record the seismic waves digitally, and in many cases broadcast out the data in real-time through the Internet or via satellite. Computer programs analyze

---

Address Misconceptions

Many students may think that small-to medium-sized earthquakes in an area will decrease the chances of a major earthquake in the same region because the smaller earthquakes will release all of the built-up energy. Explain that this is not true. The amount of energy released in a major earthquake is much greater than can be released in a series of smaller earthquakes. For a strategy that helps to overcome this misconception, see **Address Misconceptions** *on TE p. 225.*

the seismograms automatically, and determine the best location, magnitude, and fault orientation that matches the observed seismograms. In this way, information about an earthquake can be available minutes after it occurred, allowing for fast hazard assessment such as whether or not a tsunami warning should be announced.

Earth's Layering

Seismic waves travel at different speeds depending upon the property of the materials. Seismic waves also reflect off of boundaries between different materials. These are the main ways by which we have identified the different layers within Earth. The layers can be a result of changes in composition, stiffness, or mineral structure.

The composition between the crust and mantle (and mantle and core) is different, so waves bounce off of these boundaries and can be detected. Within the mantle, however, there are other layers that are observed. The asthenosphere is a region where the temperature within Earth is very close to the melting point of mantle rock. This makes the rock relatively soft and causes seismic waves to travel more slowly through it. The stiffer mantle rock beneath the asthenosphere is often called the mesosphere, and seismic waves travel through it faster because it is *not* close to melting.

There are other layers, however, that result from mineral phase changes. At a depth of about 410 km, the olivine we know at the surface becomes unstable, and its atoms rearrange into a denser structure called β-olivine. This creates a boundary seen by reflecting seismic waves. Around a depth of 520 km, this β-olivine becomes unstable, and changes to spinel. At about 660 km, the spinel becomes unstable and changes to a much denser and stiffer material called perovskite. This is a major boundary, and is used to separate the upper and lower mantles, discussed more in the next chapter. Because the lower mantle comprises most of Earth, and because most of the lower mantle is perovskite, the single most abundant material within Earth is perovskite, which is made of iron, magnesium, silicon, and oxygen.

Earthquake Hazards: Present Everywhere

The most seismically active regions of the United States are along the plate boundaries of the western coast (California, Oregon, Washington, and Alaska). However, it turns out that there are seismic hazards in all states. Our continent is old and filled with faults, and stresses within the rock can cause earthquakes anywhere. Some states not on the West Coast have had magnitude 6 (or greater) earthquakes in recorded time. There is an active field of engineering research that is working to design buildings, bridges, and other structures that can withstand the shaking from earthquakes.

BUILD READING LITERACY
Compare and Contrast
Identify Similarities and Differences

Strategy Help students read and understand material that discusses two or more related topics or concepts. This strategy helps students identify similarities and differences, thus enabling them to link prior knowledge with new information. Before students begin, assign a section in Chapter 8 for them to read, such as Section 8.2, pp. 222–227.

Example

1. Have students compare two or more topics or concepts under a section heading. Tell them that when they compare, they should focus on both similarities and differences. Remind them to look for these signal words:

• Similarities: *similar, similarly, also, just as, like, likewise, in the same way*

• Differences: *but, however, although, whereas, on the other hand, different, unlike*

2. Have students contrast two or more topics or concepts. Remind students that when they contrast, they should focus only on differences.

3. Have students create a chart or diagram comparing or contrasting two or more topics or concepts they read about in the section. Suggest that they create either a compare/contrast table or a Venn diagram to present their information.

See TE pp. 221 and 223 for a script on how to use this strategy with students. For additional strategies, see TE pp. 229, 230, 234, and 236.

CHAPTER 8

ASSESS PRIOR KNOWLEDGE

Use the Chapter Pretest below to assess students' prior knowledge. As needed, review these concepts.

Review Science Concepts

Lesson 8.1 Reviewing the concept of potential energy will help students to understand the elastic rebound hypothesis. An overview of waves and wave propagation will allow students to visualize the movement of waves from the focus of an earthquake.

Lesson 8.2 Students should review different types of waves in order to better understand the movement of seismic waves through Earth. Reviewing the different types of rocks and discussing their density will help students understand the movement of seismic waves through different rock types.

Lesson 8.3 A review of tidal waves will emphasize that tsunamis and tidal waves are actually distinct and different types of waves. A discussion of weathering and mass wasting will refresh students' general understanding of the dangers and mechanics of landslides, in a general sense.

Lesson 8.4 Review with students the basic characteristics of minerals and rocks. This will make the discussion of the composition of the layers of Earth more meaningful and successful.

8 Earthquakes and Earth's Interior

Big idea > **Dynamic Earth**

Q: What is an earthquake?

Thousands of homes were destroyed in the town of Ofunato, Iwate Prefecture, Japan after a major earthquake triggered a tsunami on March 26, 2011.

216

Chapter Pretest

1. Potential energy is *(b)*
 a. energy of motion.
 b. stored energy.
 c. used energy.

2. True or False: Granite is denser than basalt. *(False)*

3. The average continental crust is composed of _____. *(granite)*

4. The main force driving landslides is *(a)*
 a. gravity.
 b. time.
 c. water.

5. True or False: A wave is a disturbance involving the transfer to energy from place to place. *(True)*

INQUIRY
TRY IT!

HOW CAN BUILDINGS BE MADE EARTHQUAKE-SAFE?

Procedure

1. Construct a model of a one-story brick building using two thin pieces of cardboard as the floor and roof. Use sugar cubes as bricks and frosting, or two-sided tape, to hold the bricks together.
2. Construct a second building. Make this building a two-story structure.
3. To test how well your buildings stand up to a simulated earthquake, place each building on a table or desk. Then gently shake the edge of the table. Record your observations.
4. Construct another one-story building using pieces of window screen as reinforcement. Spread a thin layer of frosting on the inside walls and carefully attach the screens. Use extra frosting to reinforce the inside corners.
5. Repeat Step 3 with the reinforced building. Record your observations.

Think About It

1. **Observe** What happened to each building during the simulated earthquakes?
2. **Use Models** Compare the amount of earthquake damage in the three model buildings.

217

ENGAGE/EXPLORE

INQUIRY
TRY IT!

HOW CAN BUILDINGS BE MADE EARTHQUAKE-SAFE? **L2**

Purpose Students will design, construct, and test model buildings to simulate how different building designs resist earthquake damage.

(Address **Misconceptions**)

Students may not know what it means for a building to be considered "earthquake-safe." Explain that while it is impossible to completely protect buildings from earthquake damage, reinforcements and crossbars can be used to strengthen buildings, and certain construction materials, such wood or steel, are preferable over concrete or brick because they allow for greater flexibility.

Skills Model, Observe, Compare and Contrast

Prep Time 10 minutes

Materials cardboard (thin), sugar cubes, frosting, large book, window screen (or wire meshing), scissors or wire cutters to cut screen

Class Time 20 minutes

Safety Monitor students using scissors and/or wire cutters.

Teaching Tips To conserve materials, and keep students from using scissors, pre-cut the screens and direct students to build their walls to the correct dimensions. Also direct students to use the same force when testing their models.

Expected Outcome The two-story model should collapse, the one-story model without screening may or may not collapse, and the one-story model with screening should not collapse.

Think About It

1. Students should observe that the one-story, screen-reinforced model is the most stable. The two-story model is the least stable.
2. Damage should be minimal on the one-story model with screening, and most extreme on the two-story model.

LESSON 8.1

① FOCUS

Lesson Objectives

8.1 **Compare and contrast** the epicenter and focus of an earthquake.

8.2 **Identify** the cause of earthquakes.

8.3 **Compare and contrast** aftershocks and foreshocks.

Build Vocabulary L2

Word Parts Tell students that the prefix *epi-* is from the Greek word for "on" or "above." Ask them to guess what the word *epicenter* means based on this *(above the center)*. What other words can students come up with that have the same prefix? *(epidermis, epidemic)*

Reading Strategy L2

a. vibration of Earth due to the rapid release of energy within the lithosphere
b. fracture in Earth's lithosphere
c. location inside Earth where an earthquake starts
d. waves that travel through Earth carrying the energy released by an earthquake

② INSTRUCT

Use Visuals L1

Figure 1 Direct student's attention to the arrows and circles labeled "wave fronts" in the diagram. **Ask:** What do the arrows and circles in the diagram represent? *(the fact that seismic waves move outward in all directions from the focus, carrying the energy released in the earthquake)*
Visual

8.1 What Is an Earthquake?

Key Questions

🔑 **What is a fault?**

🔑 **What is the cause of earthquakes?**

Vocabulary
- earthquake • fault • focus
- seismic waves • epicenter
- elastic rebound • aftershock

Reading Strategy

Build Vocabulary Copy the table below. Then as you read the section, write a definition for each vocabulary term in your own words.

Vocabulary	Definition
earthquake	a. _____ ?
fault	b. _____ ?
focus	c. _____ ?
seismic waves	d. _____ ?

THOUSANDS OF earthquakes occur around the world every day. Fortunately, most of these earthquakes are so small that only sensitive instruments can detect them. About 75 strong earthquakes occur each year, and many of them occur in remote regions. Occasionally, a strong earthquake occurs near a major population center. As you will learn, such events are among the most destructive natural forces on Earth.

Earthquakes

An **earthquake** is the vibration of Earth produced by the rapid release of energy within the lithosphere. Earthquakes are caused by slippage along a break in the lithosphere, called a **fault.** 🔑 **Faults are fractures in Earth where movement has occurred.**

Focus and Epicenter The point within Earth where an earthquake starts is called the **focus.** The focus of an earthquake is located along a fault beneath the surface. The energy released by the earthquake travels in all directions from the focus in the form of **seismic waves.** These waves are similar to the waves produced when a stone is dropped into a calm pond. Just as the impact of the stone causes waves to travel outward in all directions from the point of impact, seismic waves travel outward in all directions from the focus.

When you see a news report about an earthquake, the reporter always mentions the place on Earth's surface where the earthquake was centered. The **epicenter** is the location on the surface directly above the focus, as shown in **Figure 1.**

FIGURE 1 Earthquake The focus of an earthquake is the place within Earth where the earthquake starts. The surface location directly above the focus is called the epicenter. **Predict** *Where do you think the damage from an earthquake is usually greatest?*

Faults and Change to Earth's Surface The movement that occurs along faults during earthquakes is a major factor in changing Earth's surface. The land along a fault can shift up to tens of meters in just one earthquake. Over time, this movement can push up coastlines, mountains, and plateaus.

The crust can move vertically or horizontally as a result of fault movements. If the crust moves up vertically, geologists say that it has been uplifted. Vertical movement can produce a sharp-edged ridge called a *fault scarp*. If the crust moves horizontally, geologists say it has been *offset* or displaced. **Figure 2** shows the effect of horizontal displacement in a spring onion field. In the middle of the photograph, you can see where offset caused a shift in the crop rows.

The San Andreas Fault The San Andreas fault system in California is one of the most studied in the world. The fault extends about 1300 kilometers through the state and into the Pacific Ocean. Studies have shown that displacement has often occurred along segments of the fault that are 100 to 200 kilometers long. Each fault segment behaves a bit differently than the others. Some parts of the fault show a slow, gradual movement known as *fault creep*. Other segments regularly slip and produce small earthquakes. However, some segments stay locked for hundreds of years before they break and cause great earthquakes.

One great earthquake on the San Andreas fault was the 1906 San Francisco earthquake. During this earthquake, the land on the western side of the fault moved as much as 4.7 meters relative to the land on the eastern side of the fault.

☑ **Reading Checkpoint** *What fault was involved in the 1906 San Francisco earthquake?*

FIGURE 2 Offset An earthquake caused the offset in this spring onion field. The offset occurred as a result of the 1995 Kobe earthquake in western Japan.

The Cause of Earthquakes

Before the great San Francisco earthquake, scientists did not understand what causes earthquakes. Measurements and studies after the 1906 earthquake led to the development of a hypothesis that explains how earthquakes occur. **According to the elastic rebound hypothesis, most earthquakes are produced by the rapid release of energy stored in rock that has been subjected to great forces. When the strength of the rock is exceeded, it suddenly breaks, releasing some of its stored energy as seismic waves.** Earthquakes occur when the frictional forces on the fault surfaces are overcome.

Earthquakes and Earth's Interior **219**

Build Science Skills
L2

Student Activity: Use Models Have students use a plastic, flexible ruler to model the vibrations that cause earthquakes. Students should place the ruler on the edge of their desk, with approximately half of the ruler hanging off the edge. Tightly holding the other half to the desk, they should bend the ruler down. Releasing the ruler will model the release of energy along a fault. Students will be able to visualize the waves generated along the fault as the energy is released.
Kinesthetic, Visual

(Teacher **Demo**)

SWEET STRESS
L2

Purpose Students witness the buildup of stress and the release of energy in an earthquake through the use of a candy bar as a model.

Materials chocolate-covered candy bar with nougat center (such as Three Musketeers)

Procedure Unwrap the candy bar and ask students to describe the surface of the chocolate coating. Grab both ends of the candy bar and slowly begin to bend the ends down. Ask students to observe the cracks on the surface as the stress is built up. Keep bending the candy bar until it breaks or snaps. Ask students to describe the surface of the candy bar right before, during, and after the bar broke.
Visual, Logical

Answers

Figure 1 *at the epicenter*

☑ **Reading Checkpoint** *the San Andreas fault*

Facts and Figures

The 1906 earthquake in San Francisco was one of the most devastating in the United States. The earthquake and resulting fires caused an estimated 3,000 deaths and $524 million in property loss. Damage in San Francisco alone was estimated at $20 million; outside the city, it was estimated at $4 million. The duration of the shaking in San Francisco was about 1 minute.

The earthquake damaged buildings and structures in all parts of the city and county of San Francisco. On the San Andreas fault, buildings were completely destroyed or torn apart; trees fell to the ground. The surface of the ground was torn and heaved into furrow-like ridges. Roads crossing the fault line were impassable. Pipelines were broken, shutting off the water supply to the city. The fires that ignited soon after the earthquake quickly raged through the city because of the lack of water to control them.

LESSON 8.1

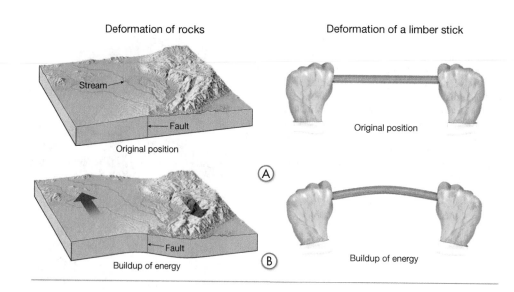

Deformation of rocks   Deformation of a limber stick

Stream

Fault

Original position

Original position

Fault

Buildup of energy

Buildup of energy

Ⓐ

Ⓑ

Use Community Resources   L2

Have students research their town's geologic history. They should make a list of any earthquakes or notable seismic activity in the area. They should investigate any major events further. They can consult reference and online sources, or gather firsthand knowledge by interviewing people who experienced the events. They should find out whether there is any remaining property damage or rock deformation, such as in Figure 2. If so, they should take photographs.

If information on local geologic events is not available, have students visit the U.S. Geological Survey's Web site to search for recent earthquakes. Then have groups look at online articles from newspapers in the area of a recent earthquake.

Use Visuals   L1

Figure 3 Ask: What evidence of deformation is present in part D? *(Each stream has been divided in two.)*

Integrate Physics   L2

Potential Energy Read the first paragraph of the section Elastic Rebound aloud. Ask students to identify the words that relate to energy. *(stored energy and elastic energy)* Explain that stored energy is potential energy, and that elastic energy is a type of potential energy.

VISUAL SUMMARY

ELASTIC REBOUND

FIGURE 3 A Rock does not change shape until enough force is applied. **B** Rock bends as it is stressed, storing elastic potential energy. **C** Once the rock is strained beyond its breaking point, it ruptures. **D** Stored energy is released in the form of seismic waves. Predict *How do you think the temperature of rock would affect its ability to bend or break?*

Deformation of Rocks Forces inside Earth slowly deform the rock that makes up Earth's crust, causing the rock to change its shape, or bend. As rocks bend, they store elastic energy, just as a wooden stick does when it is bent. *Elastic energy* is the energy associated with objects that can be stretched or compressed. Elastic energy is stored when you stretch a rubber band or compress a spring.

Elastic Rebound What happens to the elastic energy stored in rock? Again, think about bending a wooden stick. If you let go of one end, the stick springs back to its original shape. At the same time, the stick's stored elastic energy is released. But if you continue to apply force to the stick, it eventually snaps, also releasing the stored energy.

    Something similar to bending a stick happens in the rock along a fault. Stored elastic energy builds up as the rock is deformed as shown in **Figure 3B.** Then, suddenly, the resistance caused by internal friction that holds the rocks together is overcome. The rocks slip at their weakest point—the focus of an earthquake. This movement exerts force farther along the fault, where additional slippage occurs until most of the elastic energy is released as shown in **Figures 3C** and **3D.** The tendency for the deformed rock along a fault to spring back after an earthquake is called **elastic rebound.** Elastic rebound is similar to what happens when you release a stretched rubber band. But most of the energy released as a result of elastic rebound causes the movement along a fault that takes place during an earthquake.

☑ **Reading Checkpoint** *What is elastic rebound?*

Facts and Figures

EARTH'S FUNDAMENTAL NOTE When a large earthquake occurs, seismic waves can circle the globe for many months. Constructive interference among the waves sets the whole Earth vibrating like a gong. These vibrations are called *modes of oscillation.* The size, shape, and composition of a gong determine its pitch (dominant note) and texture (mixture of harmonic overtones). In the same way, the frequencies of the different overtones of Earth's modes of oscillation give seismologists information about the composition of Earth's deep interior. The lowest note of Earth's modes has a period of about 54 minutes (corresponding to the surface going up for 27 minutes, then down for 27 minutes), which corresponds to the note of an E, twenty octaves below a middle E on the piano. Johannes Kepler wrote about the "music of the spheres," but he was referring to the Earth's revolution around the sun, which, at 365.25 days, would correspond to a C#, thirty-three octaves below middle C#.

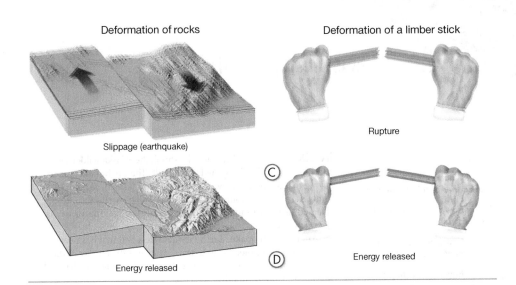

Deformation of rocks

Slippage (earthquake)

Energy released

Deformation of a limber stick

Rupture

Energy released

Aftershocks and Foreshocks Even a strong earthquake such as the 1906 San Francisco earthquake usually does not release all the elastic energy stored in the rock along a fault. Aftershocks and foreshocks also release some of a fault's stored elastic energy. An **aftershock** is an earthquake that occurs sometime soon after a major earthquake. Aftershocks may occur hours or even weeks after the major earthquake. Although usually much weaker than the main earthquake, an aftershock can still damage structures already weakened by the main quake. Small earthquakes called *foreshocks* sometimes come before a major earthquake. Foreshocks can happen days or even years before the major quake.

8.1 Assessment

Review Key Concepts

1. What is a fault?

2. Describe the cause of earthquakes.

3. What is an earthquake?

4. What are two ways in which deformation affects rock?

5. What are foreshocks and aftershocks?

Think Critically

6. Draw Conclusions How are an earthquake's fault, focus, and epicenter related?

7. Explain What is meant by elastic rebound?

8. Make Judgments Why do most earthquakes cause little damage and loss of life?

MATH PRACTICE

9. Calculate In 25 years, how much movement will result from a fault that slowly slips 1.5 centimeters per year?

Earthquakes and Earth's Interior **221**

Build Reading Literacy   L1

Refer to **p. 216D,** which provides the guidelines for compare and contrast.

Compare and Contrast Have students review the section on aftershocks and foreshocks. Ask them to complete a Venn diagram.
Verbal

3 ASSESS

Evaluate Understanding   L2

Have students draw a diagram that shows the difference between the focus and the epicenter of an earthquake.

Reteach   L1

Ask students to use Figure 3 to explain how deformation can occur in rocks. Provide them with a popsicle stick so they can reproduce the phenomena.

Answers

Figure 3 *Rocks at higher temperatures would bend more before breaking.*

☑ **Reading Checkpoint** *Elastic rebound is the tendency for deformed rock along a fault to spring back to its original shape after an earthquake.*

Assessment Answers

1. A fault is a fracture in Earth where movement has occurred.
2. Earthquakes are caused by the rapid release of elastic energy stored in rock that has been subjected to great forces. When the strength of the rock is exceeded, it suddenly breaks, releasing some of its stored energy as seismic waves.
3. An earthquake is the vibration of Earth produced by the rapid release of energy within the lithosphere.

4. Deformation affects rock by causing it to bend. At the same time, elastic energy is stored in the rock.
5. Aftershocks are smaller, weaker earthquakes that occur after the main earthquake. Foreshocks are small earthquakes that come before a major earthquake.
6. The focus of an earthquake is the place within Earth where the earthquake begins. The spot on the surface directly above the focus is the epicenter. Most earthquakes are usually

associated with fractures in the crust known as faults.
7. Elastic rebound is the process in which deformed rocks first bend and then break, releasing energy.
8. Most earthquakes do little damage because they are either weak or occur in areas that are not populated.
9. 25 yr × 1.5 cm/yr = 37.5 cm

Earthquakes and Earth's Interior **221**

1 FOCUS

Lesson Objectives

8.4 **Identify** the three types of seismic waves.

8.5 **Describe** how seismic waves are recorded.

8.6 **Describe** the different ways earthquakes are measured.

8.7 **Explain** how to locate the epicenter of an earthquake.

Build Vocabulary L2

Word Parts Tell students that the prefix *seismo-* is Greek for "shaking." Ask them to infer what a seismograph and a seismogram are. Challenge them to come up with other terms that begin with the prefix *seismo-* (*seismology, seismologist*).

Reading Strategy L2

I. Seismic Waves
  A. P Waves
  B. S Waves
  C. Surface Waves
II. Recording Seismic Waves
III. Measuring Earthquakes
  A. Richter Scale
  B. Moment Magnitude
  C. Modified Mercalli Scale
IV. Locating an Earthquake

8.2 Measuring Earthquakes

Key Questions

 What are the two categories of seismic waves?

 How are seismic waves recorded?

 How is the size of an earthquake measured?

 How is an earthquake epicenter located?

Vocabulary

- P wave • S wave
- surface wave
- seismograph • seismogram
- moment magnitude

Reading Strategy

Outline As you read, make an outline of the important ideas in this section. Use the orange headings as the main topics and the blue headings as subtopics.

Measuring Earthquakes
I. Seismic Waves
A. P Waves
B. _____?_____
C. _____?_____
II. _____?_____

IN 2003, a powerful earthquake shook the Alaska wilderness south of Fairbanks along the Denali fault. The earthquake was so strong that it rippled the water in ponds and lakes thousands of kilometers away in Louisiana and Texas. What carries the energy released in an earthquake over such vast distances? The answer is seismic waves.

After an earthquake, Earth vibrates like a bell that has been struck with a hammer. Seismic waves transmit the energy of these vibrations from particle to particle through the materials that make up the lithosphere, mantle, and core.

Seismic Waves

 Earthquakes produce two main types of seismic waves—body waves and surface waves. These seismic waves differ in their type of wave motion, their behavior as they travel through Earth, and their speed. Body waves travel through Earth's interior to the surface. Surface waves only travel at the surface. There are two types of body waves: P waves and S waves.

P Waves **P waves** compress, or push, and expand, or pull particles in the direction the waves travel. P waves are also known as *compressional waves*. The motion of P waves can be illustrated by attaching one end of a spring toy to a wall and pushing and pulling on the other end as shown in **Figure 4A.** P waves cause material to compress and then spring back once the force is removed. Since solids, liquids, and gases all have the ability to alternatively compress and expand in response to a force, P waves can travel through all three states of matter. The back-and-forth motion of P waves causes the ground to buckle and fracture as shown in **Figure 4B.**

S Waves **S waves** shake particles at right angles to the direction that the waves travel. S waves are also called *transverse waves*. Their motion can be illustrated by attaching one end of a rope to a wall and shaking the other end up-and-down, as shown in **Figure 4C.** S waves temporarily change the shape of the material that transmits them. Since liquids and gases will not return to their shape once a force is removed, they will not transmit S waves. Solids, on the other hand, do resist changes in their shape, so they will transmit S waves. As **Figure 4D** shows, S waves cause the ground to shake sideways and up-and-down. S waves travel more slowly than P waves.

SEISMIC WAVES

FIGURE 4 A P waves are made in a spring toy by pushing and pulling on one end while the other end is fixed to a wall. **B** The ground moves back-and-forth as a result of P waves. **C** S waves are made in a rope by moving one end up-and-down while the other end is fixed to a wall. **D** The ground moves up-and-down and sideways as a result of S waves. **E** Surface waves can move the ground from side to side, and **F** in an elliptical motion.

Ⓐ

P waves are compressional waves that alternately compress and expand the material through which they pass.

Ⓑ

The back-and-forth motions produced as P waves travel along the surface can cause the ground to buckle and fracture.

Ⓒ

S waves are transverse waves which cause material to shake at right angles to the direction of wave motion.

Ⓓ

S waves cause the ground to shake up-and-down and sideways.

Ⓔ

One type of surface wave moves the ground from side to side and can damage the foundations of buildings.

Ⓕ

Another type of surface wave travels along Earth's surface much like rolling ocean waves.

Surface Waves When body waves reach the surface, they produce **surface waves.** Surface waves travel more slowly than body waves. As shown in **Figures 4E** and **4F,** surface waves can move the ground up-and-down as well as side to side. Surface waves are usually much larger than body waves. As a result, surface waves are the most destructive seismic waves.

Earthquakes and Earth's Interior **223**

Teacher **Demo**

SEISMIC WAVES

Purpose Students will use a coiled spring toy to see the ways that the three different seismic waves move though substances.

Materials coiled spring toy

Procedure Have a student hold one end of the spring toy. Hold the other end of the toy and step away from the student to stretch the spring out. Gather approximately one fifth of the spring in your hand. Keep holding onto the end of the spring, but release the gathered coils. Ask students to explain what they observed as the bunch of coils moves down the extending spring. Explain to students that this is how a P wave travels through a medium. Again, with the spring stretched out, gently move the toy from side to side in a snake-like motion. Students should observe how the toy moves as a result of such motion. Explain that this is how an S wave moves. Finally, move your end of the toy in a rolling motion (like winding a fishing reel) to model surface waves.
Kinesthetic, Visual

Build Reading Literacy

Refer to **p. 216D** which provides the guidelines for this reading strategy.

Compare and Contrast Ask students to use the visuals and the captions in Figure 4 to describe how the three types of waves are different. *(P waves compress and expand material in the same horizontal direction as the waves' energy. S waves are transverse waves that cause the ground to shake up and down, perpendicular to the waves' direction. Surface waves travel along the outer layer and can move in both up-and-down motions and side-to-side motions.)*

Differentiated Instruction

SPECIAL NEEDS Ask students to simulate P waves and S waves with a coiled spring toy and jump rope. If they need help getting started, instruct them to recreate the scenarios pictured in Figures 4A and 4C.

Build Reading Literacy L1

Build Reading Literacy L1

Refer to **p. 156D** in **Chapter 6,** which provides the guidelines for reciprocal teaching.

Reciprocal Teaching Have students read the lesson with a partner. One partner should read a paragraph out loud. Then the other partner should summarize the paragraph's contents and explain the main concepts. Instruct partners to switch roles with each new paragraph until they have finished the lesson.
Intrapersonal

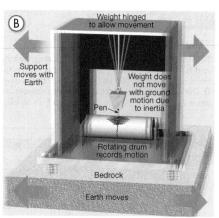

FIGURE 5 Seismograph
A A seismograph is attached to bedrock so that it can record ground motion. **B** One type of seismograph uses a pen and a rotating drum to record Earth's movement relative to a nearly stationary weight.

Recording Seismic Waves

🔑 **An instrument that records seismic waves is called a seismograph.** The word seismograph comes from the Greek words *seismos,* meaning "shake" and *graph,* meaning "write."

As shown in **Figure 5B,** a seismograph can consist of a weight suspended from a support attached to bedrock. When seismic waves reach the seismograph, the inertia of the weight keeps it almost stationary while Earth and the support vibrate. Because the weight stays almost motionless, it provides a reference point for measuring the amount of ground movement caused by seismic waves. In older seismographs a pen records the movement of Earth relative to the stationary weight on a rotating drum. Modern seismographs amplify and record ground motion electronically.

A seismograph produces a time record of ground motion during an earthquake called a **seismogram.** A seismogram shows all three types of seismic waves. The stronger the earthquake, the larger the waves on the seismogram. By reading a typical seismogram, as shown in **Figure 6,** you can see that P waves arrive first at the seismograph, followed by S waves, and then surface waves.

☑ **Reading Checkpoint** *What is a seismogram?*

FIGURE 6 Typical Seismogram
The first wave to arrive is the P wave, followed later by S waves. The last waves recorded are the surface waves.
Measure *What is the time interval in minutes between the arrival of the first P wave and the arrival of the first S wave?*

Differentiated Instruction

SPECIAL NEEDS Place the palms of your hands together and slide one quickly against the other. This movement represents two rock surfaces slipping against each other. The fingertips of the hand that moves forward are like the rock that moves forward. This is called a "push wave" or P wave. The wave travels at about 8 km/s.

Earthquakes also send out a second kind of wave. This time, put your hands together

with a pencil between them. Slide one hand forward to represent the slipping rock surfaces. The pencil rotates, or twists, as you move your palm. In the same way, rocks twist between slipping surfaces. The twisting rocks send a "twist wave," or S wave, throughout Earth. A twist wave travels more slowly than a push wave, moving through Earth at about 5 km/s.

Measuring Earthquakes

Intensity is a measure of the amount of earthquake shaking at a given location based on the amount of damage. *Magnitude* (abbreviated as "M") is a measure of the size of seismic waves or the amount of energy released at the source of the earthquake. 🔑 **The Richter scale and the moment magnitude scale measure earthquake magnitude. The Modified Mercalli scale is based on earthquake intensity.**

Richter Scale A familiar but outdated scale for measuring the magnitude of earthquakes is the Richter scale. The Richter scale is based on the height of the largest seismic wave (P, S, or surface wave) recorded on a seismogram. A tenfold increase in wave height equals an increase of 1 on the magnitude scale. For example, the amount of ground shaking for a M5.0 earthquake is 10 times greater than the shaking produced by an earthquake of M4.0 on the Richter scale.

Seismic waves weaken as the distance between the earthquake focus and the seismograph increases. The Richter scale is only useful for small, shallow earthquakes within about 500 kilometers of the epicenter. News reports often use the Richter scale in reporting earthquake magnitudes. Scientists, however, no longer use it routinely.

Moment Magnitude Scientists today use a more precise means of measuring earthquakes. It is called the moment magnitude scale. The **moment magnitude** is derived from the amount of displacement that occurs along a fault. Moment magnitude is the most widely used measurement for earthquakes because it is the only magnitude scale that estimates the energy released by earthquakes. The moment magnitude is calculated using several factors in addition to seismographic data. These factors include the average amount of movement along the fault, the area of the surface break, and the strength of the broken rock. Together these factors provide a measure of how much energy rock can store before it suddenly slips and releases this energy during an earthquake.

Table 1 describes the incidence of earthquakes of different magnitudes. During the last 100 years, there were only a few earthquakes with magnitudes of 9.0 or greater. These rare but extremely powerful earthquakes all occurred on faults located around or near the Pacific basin.

☑ **Reading Checkpoint** *What is moment magnitude?*

Table 1 Earthquake Magnitudes		
Moment Magnitudes	Effects Near Epicenter	Number per Year
< 2.0	Generally not felt	Not available
2.0–2.9	Potentially perceptible	≈1,300,000
3.0–3.9	Rarely felt	≈130,000
4.0–4.9	Can be strongly felt	≈13,000
5.0–5.9	Can be damaging shocks	1319
6.0–6.9	Destructive in built-up areas	134
7.0–7.9	Major earthquakes; serious damage	15
8.0 and above	Great earthquakes; destroy communities near epicenter	1

Source: United States Geological Survey

Answers

Figure 6 *about 5 minutes*

☑ **Reading Checkpoint** *a graphic record of an earthquake's seismic waves*

☑ **Reading Checkpoint** *a more precise measure of earthquake magnitude than the Richter scale, which is derived from the amount of displacement that occurs along a fault zone and estimates the energy released by an earthquake*

Facts and Figures

LOCATING EARTHQUAKES While the method discussed on p. 227 is an effective way to locate an earthquake, it is no longer the predominant way to locate an earthquake. Instead, all available arrival times of P and S waves (mostly P waves, because they occur first, and are more easily recognized) are entered into a computer program to find the location. For large earthquakes, this can involve thousands of arrival times. A mathematical algorithm called an inversion is used to find the epicenter, depth, and origin time that do the best job of simultaneously matching all of the observed data.

Integrate Math L2

The epicenter of an earthquake is located using information on the arrival times of the P and S waves at three seismograph stations. **Ask:** Why must three seismograph stations be used? Why aren't two enough to locate the epicenter? *(The intersection of three circles will yield a more exact location. If only two stations were used, these two circles would most likely intersect at two points. This would give two possible locations for the same earthquake.)*
Logical, Visual

Use Visuals L1

Figure 8 Make sure students understand how to read the travel-time graph. Explain that distance is expressed in both kilometers (bottom) and miles (top), and tell them that one kilometer equals approximately 0.6 mile. **Ask:** If a station records 2 minutes elapsed time between the arrival of the first P wave and the arrival of the first S wave, how far in kilometers is that station from the epicenter? *(about 1000 km)* A good way to help students comprehend all the information compiled in a travel-time graph is to draw one on the board. Plot data points to simulate how seismic recordings are used to make P and S wave curves.

FIGURE 7 Modified Mercalli Scale
The magnitude-6.9 Loma Prieta earthquake struck the northern San Andreas fault near Santa Cruz, California, in 1989.

0   40   80 km

Modified Mercalli Scale

Intensity	I	II-III	IV	V	VI	VII	VIII	IX	X+
Shaking	Not felt	Weak	Light	Moderate	Strong	Very strong	Severe	Violent	Extreme
Damage	none	none	none	Very light (some windows break)	Light (some plaster falls)	Moderate (chimneys break)	Moderate to Heavy (chimneys and walls fall)	Heavy (buildings shift off foundations; ground cracks)	Very Heavy (most structures get destroyed; rails bend)

Modified Mercalli Scale Another scale used to rate earthquakes is the Modified Mercalli scale. This scale rates an earthquake's intensity in terms of the earthquake's effects at different locations. The scale has up to 12 steps, expressed as Roman numerals. An earthquake that can be barely felt is rated I. An earthquake that causes near total destruction is rated XII. The same earthquake can receive different Mercalli scale ratings at different locations. For example, an earthquake might be rated VIII (severe damage) near the epicenter, but only IV (light damage) 50 kilometers away. The map in **Figure 7** uses the Mercalli scale to show areas affected by different levels of shaking from a major California earthquake.

Locating an Earthquake

The difference in speeds of P and S waves provides a way to locate the epicenter. The movement of these two types of seismic waves is like a race between two cars. The winning car is faster than the losing car. The P wave always wins the race, arriving ahead of the S wave. The longer the race, the greater the difference will be between the arrival times of the P and S waves at the finish line (the seismic station). The greater the interval between the arrival of the first P wave and the first S wave, the greater the distance to the earthquake epicenter. The difference in arrival times of P waves and S waves can be shown on a travel-time graph like the one in **Figure 8A.**

Differentiated Instruction

ENGLISH LANGUAGE LEARNERS Tell students that, after a significant earthquake, the United States Geologic Survey (USGS) sends out questionnaires to people in the area affected by the quake. The questionnaire asks them to use the modified Mercalli scale to rate the shaking and damage experienced in their area. Explain that, in this activity, they will use the Mercalli scale to describe the effects of an earthquake.

Have students work in pairs. Each pair should pick one of the locations on the map in Figure 7 above. Referring to the Mercalli scale in the figure, each pair of students should write a sentence describing how the Loma Prieta earthquake might have affected that location. Students should then read their sentences aloud to the class.

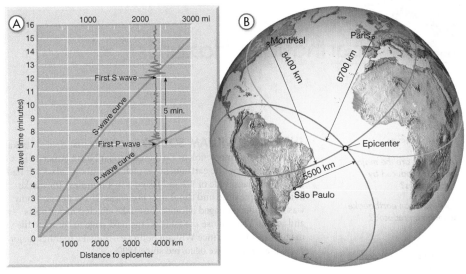

FIGURE 8 **Locating an Earthquake A** The difference in arrival times of the first P wave and the first S wave on the travel-time graph is 5 minutes. So the epicenter is roughly 3800 kilometers away.

B Once scientists determine the distance from three or more seismic stations to the epicenter, they can draw circles to determine the location of the epicenter. The epicenter is the point where the circles intersect.

Read Graphs *What is the difference in arrival times between P waves and S waves for a seismic station that is 2000 km from an epicenter?*

🔑 **You can use a travel-time graph, data from seismograms at three or more locations, and a globe to determine an earthquake's epicenter.** First you use the travel-time graph to determine the distance from each seismic station to the epicenter. Then, on a globe showing each seismic station, as in **Figure 8B**, you draw circles at the correct scale for the distance from each station to the epicenter. The radius of each circle equals the distance to the epicenter from that station. The point where all three circles intersect is the epicenter.

8.2 Assessment

Review Key Concepts 🔑

1. List the two categories of seismic waves.

2. Describe how scientists detect and record seismic waves.

3. Describe the three different ways to measure the size of an earthquake.

4. Briefly describe how the epicenter of an earthquake is located.

Think Critically

5. Compare and Contrast Describe the differences in speed and mode of travel between P waves and S waves.

6. Apply Concepts How does a seismograph measure an earthquake?

7. Draw Conclusions Describe what would occur in an earthquake with a moment magnitude of 6.0.

Earthquakes and Earth's Interior **227**

Assessment Answers

1. body waves (P and S) and surface waves
2. The graphic record produced by a seismograph, called a seismogram, shows when the different types of seismic waves arrived at the seismograph.
3. Scientists use the Richter scale and the moment magnitude scale to measure earthquake magnitude. They use the Modified Mercalli scale to measure earthquake intensity.
4. The epicenter of an earthquake is located using data taken from at least three different

seismograph stations. The difference between the time that the first S wave and the first P wave arrives is converted into the distance from the epicenter to the station. A circle is drawn around each seismograph station and the circles meet where the earthquake epicenter is likely to be found.
5. P waves push and pull rocks in the direction of travel. Their velocity is greater than the velocity of S waves. S waves shake the

3 ASSESS

Evaluate Understanding L2

Have students write three review questions for this lesson. Students should then break into groups of three or four and ask each other their questions.

Reteach L1

Review the types of seismic waves from earthquakes by asking students to explain what they see in Figure 6.

Answers

Figure 8 *about 3.5 minutes*

particles of material at right angles to their direction of travel.
6. In concept, a seismograph has a weight which is suspended from a support that is attached to bedrock. When the bedrock shakes, the weight remains almost stationary. The movement of Earth can then be compared to the weight and recorded on a rotating drum.
7. An earthquake measuring a moment magnitude of 6 could prove to be potentially devastating to structures not built to new earthquake standards. Poorly built structures would suffer significant damage. However, structures that were constructed with earthquake safety in mind would most likely fare well.

Earthquakes and Earth's Interior **227**

8.3 Earthquake Hazards

Lesson Objectives

8.8 **Identify** the major hazards associated with earthquakes.

8.9 **Describe** how earthquake damage can be reduced.

Build Vocabulary   L2

Paraphrase Ask students to write the vocabulary words on a sheet of paper. Instruct students to write a definition, in their own words, for each term as they encounter the term while going through the chapter. After writing their own definition, they should also write a complete sentence with the term.

Reading Strategy   L2

Sample answers:

a. how seismic vibrations can cause damage

b. Damage depends on the building design, intensity and length of time of the vibrations, and the material that the building was constructed on.

c. dangers associated with earthquakes

d. These include tsunamis, landslides, and fire.

2 INSTRUCT

Reading Strategy   L2

Invite a structural engineer to speak to the class about the construction of earthquake-safe buildings. Have students ask about specific regulations for building codes in your area.

Interpersonal

Key Questions

⌐ **What are the major hazards produced by earthquakes?**

⌐ **How can earthquake damage be reduced?**

Vocabulary

• liquefaction • tsunami
• seismic gap

Reading Strategy

Monitor Your Understanding Preview the Key Concepts, topic headings, vocabulary, and figures in this section. List two things you expect to learn. After reading, state what you learned about each item you listed.

What I Expect To Learn	What I Learned
a. ___?___	b. ___?___
c. ___?___	d. ___?___

THE PRINCE WILLIAM SOUND earthquake that struck Alaska in 1964 was the most violent earthquake to jar North America in the 20th century. The earthquake was felt throughout Alaska. It had a moment magnitude of 9.2 and lasted 3 to 4 minutes. The quake left 131 people dead and thousands homeless. The state's economy was also badly damaged because the quake affected major ports and towns. You can use the table on the next page to compare the magnitude of the Prince William Sound earthquake to other major earthquakes that have occurred since 1900.

Causes of Earthquake Damage

An earthquake as powerful as the 1964 Alaska earthquake can cause catastrophic damage. But even less powerful earthquakes also pose serious hazards. ⌐ **Earthquake-related hazards include seismic shaking, liquefaction, landslides and mudflows, and tsunamis.**

Seismic Shaking The ground vibrations caused by seismic waves, called seismic shaking, are the most obvious earthquake hazard. Seismic waves interact to jolt and twist structures. Buildings made of unreinforced brick may collapse. Wood-frame buildings may remain intact, but still can be jolted off their foundations.

Seismic shaking is generally strongest close to an epicenter. Yet strong seismic shaking can occur in areas of loose soil or filled land relatively far from an epicenter. The filled soil magnifies the effects of seismic waves. Structures in such areas can experience severe damage as shown in **Figure 9A**.

FIGURE 9 Earthquake Damage A magnitude-7.6 earthquake in northern Pakistan in 2005 destroyed mountain villages and killed more than 70,000 people.

Differentiated Instruction

GIFTED When we consider how many earthquakes there are in one year, the number of earthquakes that cause terrible damage is actually very small. The amount of damage an earthquake causes depends on many conditions. For example, if a building is well constructed and built on solid ground, it may survive an earthquake. Most injuries and deaths during earthquakes are because of poor construction or substandard building sites. Another serious problem is not knowing how to respond to an earthquake. When people panic and rush out of buildings there is a danger of being trampled, suffocated, or injured by falling debris. Go to the Red Cross website at http://www.redcross.org and read about earthquake safety.

FIGURE 10 Liquefaction and Landslides
A During a 1985 earthquake in Mexico, the soil beneath this toppled building liquified.
B A landslide triggered by an earthquake in 2001 buried this neighborhood in El Salvador.

Liquefaction In areas where soil and rock are saturated with water, earthquakes can cause a process called **liquefaction**. When liquefaction occurs, what had been stable soil suddenly turns into liquid. The liquid cannot support buildings or other structures. Buildings and bridges may settle and collapse as shown in **Figure 10A.** Underground storage tanks and sewer lines may float toward the surface. During the 1989 Loma Prieta earthquake in San Francisco's Marina District, foundations failed and geysers of sand and water shot from the ground, indicating that liquefaction had occurred.

Landslides and Mudflows Earthquakes can trigger different types of mass movement. These destructive events can quickly bury entire towns under millions of tons of debris.

Earthquakes often cause loose rock and soil on slopes to move. The result is a *landslide*, as shown in **Figure 10B.** Most landslides occur on steep slopes where sediment is loose or where the rocks are highly fractured. During the 1964 Alaska earthquake, much of the damage in the city of Anchorage was a result of landslides. Homes were lost when more than 200 acres of land slid toward the ocean.

In areas where the water content of soil is high, an earthquake can start a *mudflow*. During a mudflow, a mixture of soil and water slides rapidly downhill.

☑ **Reading Checkpoint** What is liquefaction?

Major Earthquakes Since 1900		
Year	Location	Magnitude†
1906	San Francisco, California	7.8
1923	Tokyo, Japan	7.9
1960	Southern Chile	9.5
1964	Alaska	9.2
1971	San Fernando, California	6.5
1985	Mexico City	8.1
1989	Loma Prieta, California	6.9
1994	Northridge, California	6.7
1999	Izmit, Turkey	7.4
1999	Chi Chi, Taiwan	7.6
2004	Indian Ocean near Indonesia	9.3
2005	Pakistan/Kashmir	7.6
2008	Sichuan, China	7.9
2010	Port-au-Prince, Haiti	7.0
2010	Maule, Chile	8.8
2011	Sendai, Japan	9.0

† Widely differing magnitudes have been estimated for some earthquakes. When available, moment magnitudes are used.

LESSON 8.3

Build Science Skills L2

Observe Have pairs of students investigate recent or historically significant tsunamis. (They may use library resources or conduct an Internet search.) After students have had time to obtain information, have them compare their findings with another group.
Interpersonal, Verbal

Build Reading Literacy L1

Refer to **p. 334D** in **Chapter 12** for guidelines on outlining content.

Outline Have students read the lesson. Then have students use the headings as major divisions in an outline. Allow students to refer to their outlines when answering the questions in the Lesson 8.3 Assessment.
Visual

Build Science Skills

Research Ask small groups to research online or in the library about tectonic activity along the East and West Coast of the United States. Ask students to develop a presentation that describes recent earthquakes and that summarizes the earthquake risks in each area.
Interpersonal, Verbal

FIGURE 11 Indian Ocean Tsunami, 2004 A surge of water rushes inland as a tsunami strikes the coast of Thailand. On average, only one or two destructive tsunamis occur worldwide every year. Only about one tsunami in every 10 years causes major damage and loss of life.

PLANET DIARY

For links about **Earthquakes**, visit PlanetDiary.com/HSES.

FIGURE 12 How a Tsunami Forms Movement of the ocean floor causes a tsunami. The speed of a tsunami is related to the ocean depth. As waves slow down in shallow water, they can grow in height until they topple and hit shore with tremendous force.

Tsunamis A **tsunami** is a series of waves formed when the ocean floor shifts suddenly during an earthquake. For example, in 2004 a magnitude- 9.3 earthquake west of the island of Sumatra in the Indian Ocean produced devastating tsunamis. Without warning, huge waves such as the one shown in **Figure 11** struck coastal areas of Indonesia, Sri Lanka, Thailand, and several other countries killing over 230,000 people.

A tsunami can occur when an earthquake pushes up a slab of ocean floor along a fault. An underwater landslide or volcanic eruption can also trigger a tsunami. Once formed, a tsunami resembles the ripples created when you drop a pebble in a pond. Surprisingly, a tsunami on the open ocean is usually less than 1 meter high. This wave races across the ocean at hundreds of kilometers per hour. However, as the wave enters shallower water near shore, the wave slows down and water begins to pile up. As you can see in **Figure 12**, a tsunami can strike the shore as a huge wave that sweeps inland causing great destruction. Tsunamis range from a few meters to more than 30 meters high.

A tsunami warning system alerts people in coastal areas around the Pacific Ocean. After the deadly 2004 tsunami, a similar system was established for areas around the Indian ocean. A system is planned for the Atlantic Ocean. Scientists use devices that measure wave height to detect a tsunami. Tsunami warnings allow sufficient time to evacuate all but the area closest to the epicenter.

Tsunami speed: 835 km/hr   Tsunami speed: 340 km/hr   Tsunami speed: 50 km/hr

Sea level

Water depth: 5500 meters   Water depth: 900 meters   Water depth: 20 meters

Subducting plate   Displacement

230 Chapter 8 • Lesson 3

Facts and Figures

TSUNAMI DISPERSION Something very dangerous happens when a tsunami travels across the ocean. It breaks up into several different waves, a process called *dispersion*. This occurs because the waves of different wavelengths travel at different speeds. Students may be most familiar with dispersion from the way that different colors of light (which also have different wavelengths) refract differently through a prism, causing the colors to separate. Tsunami waves with longer periods travel faster and arrive first. However, this means that the tsunami hazard is not over after the first wave hits. In fact, the largest and most destructive waves often arrive after the first wave hits.

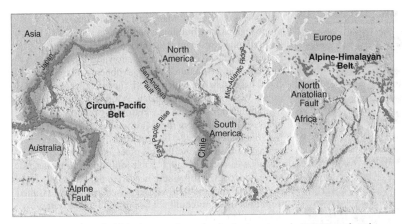

FIGURE 13 Earthquake Risk The map shows the distribution of nearly 15,000 earthquakes with magnitudes equal to or greater than 5 for a 10-year period. **Interpret Maps** *Where do you find most of the earthquakes—in the interiors of the continents or at the edges?*

Reducing Earthquake Damage

Earthquake damage depends on several factors. Two important factors are the strength and duration of seismic shaking and the materials and design of structures. 🔑 **Earthquake damage and loss of life can be reduced by determining the earthquake risk for an area, building earthquake-resistant structures, and following earthquake safety precautions.**

Assessing Earthquake Risk How can people reduce damage from earthquakes? First, it is important to know the risk of earthquakes in a region. As you can see in **Figure 13,** the distribution of earthquakes forms a pattern. Scientists have found that earthquakes are most frequent along the boundaries of Earth's tectonic plates.

Scientists use several methods to determine earthquake risk. They study historical records of earthquakes. They use devices to measure uplift, subsidence, and strain in the rocks near active faults. They also study "seismic gaps." A **seismic gap** is an area along a fault where there has not been any earthquake activity for a long period of time. Scientists hypothesize that the buildup of strain along a seismic gap will eventually lead to an earthquake. Considering all these data, scientists are studying ways to estimate the probability that an earthquake will occur in an area within the next 30 to 100 years.

Scientists also look for warning signs that an earthquake is about to strike. In addition to monitoring fault movements, they measure water levels and pressure in wells, radon gas emissions, and changes in the electromagnetic properties of rocks. But efforts at short-term prediction of earthquakes have not generally been successful.

☑ **Reading Checkpoint** *How do scientists assess earthquake risk?*

Earthquakes and Earth's Interior **231**

LESSON 8.3

3 ASSESS

Evaluate Understanding L2

Have students work in groups to develop a short public service announcement on the other dangers facing areas that have experienced an earthquake.

Reteach L1

Ask students to use Figure 12 to explain how tsunamis are generated and how they move to shore.

(Address Misconceptions) L2

Many students may have heard that the safest place in a house during an earthquake is in a doorway. Challenge this misconception by pointing out that modern doorways are no stronger than other sections of a house and usually have doors that could swing and injure someone. Encourage students to come up with another plan for earthquake safety. This should involve ducking under a sturdy table or desk, holding onto the table or desk and staying clear of objects that could tip over, such as file cabinets and bookcases.

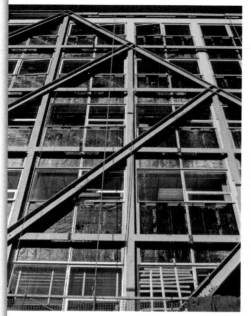

FIGURE 14 Cross Braces
Strong, diagonal beams called cross-braces have been installed in this building to improve the structure's ability to withstand seismic waves.

Seismic-Safe Design Many cities in earthquake-prone regions have building codes that set standards for earthquake-resistant structures. Steel frames can be reinforced with cross-braces as shown in **Figure 14.** Buildings can be mounted on large rubber and steel pads, called base-isolators, which absorb the energy of seismic waves. Wood-frame homes can be reinforced and bolted to their foundations. People can "retrofit" or reinforce older buildings to make them more earthquake resistant.

Utility lines must also be protected. To prevent fires or explosions in gas mains, flexible pipes and automatic shut-off valves can be installed. Flexible joints in water mains can prevent loss of water pressure needed to fight fires. Much of the damage after the 1906 San Francisco earthquake resulted from fires. The fires could not be put out because water mains had broken.

Earthquake Safety Knowing what to do during an earthquake can reduce your risk of injury. The basic rule is to "drop, cover, and hold." Indoors, crouch beneath a sturdy table or desk and hold onto it. If no desk or table is nearby, crouch against an inner wall away from the outside of a building. Cover your head and neck with your arms. Avoid windows, mirrors, and furniture that might topple.

If you are outdoors when an earthquake strikes, move to an open area. Avoid vehicles, power lines, trees, and buildings. Sit down to avoid being thrown down. The danger does not end once an earthquake has stopped because an aftershock could cause weakened structures to collapse.

8.3 Assessment

Review Key Concepts

1. Describe five hazards caused by earthquakes.

2. Explain how earthquake-related damage can be reduced.

3. What is a tsunami?

4. What is a seismic gap?

Think Critically

5. **Predict** In an earthquake-prone area, it has been many years since the last earthquake along a fault. Should residents be concerned about a future earthquake? Explain.

6. **Propose a Solution** A builder in Alaska has a choice of two sites for a building: one is on filled land next to the ocean, and the other is inland on solid ground. Both sites are the same distance from an active fault. Which site should the builder choose? Explain.

7. **Explain** Why is it possible to issue a tsunami warning but not provide a warning for an earthquake? Describe a scenario where a tsunami warning would be of little value.

BIGIDEA DYNAMIC EARTH

8. **Predict** In Lesson 8.1, you learned about the elastic energy stored in rocks before an earthquake and the elastic rebound hypothesis. How could this information be used to try to predict earthquakes?

Assessment Answers

1. Seismic shaking, liquefaction, landslides, mudflows, tsunamis
2. Ways of reducing earthquake damage include determining the level of earthquake risk for the area, constructing earthquake-safe buildings, and taking steps for earthquake safety.
3. A tsunami is a series of waves created by an underwater earthquake or volcanic eruption, or a landslide under the ocean floor generated by an earthquake.
4. A seismic gap is an area along a fault that has not had any earthquake activity for a long period of time.

5. Yes. Stress may have been building up along the fault, making an earthquake more likely.
6. The builder should choose the inland site on solid ground. If an earthquake occurred, the other site would be in danger from tsunamis and liquefaction.
7. Scientists are not yet able to predict when an earthquake is going to happen. Scientists know that a tsunami is likely to occur if the epicenter of an earthquake is on the ocean floor. A tsunami warning would be of little

value if the earthquake epicenter was very close to the shore as people would not have enough time to evacuate.
8. If there were some way to measure the amount of energy stored in rocks, this might lead to the prediction of earthquakes. If scientists could observe and measure the buildup of stress within rocks, they might be able to determine the amount of stress the rocks could withstand before the energy needed to be released. This could provide an estimate of time for an earthquake.

8.4 Earth's Layered Structure

COMPARED TO THE planets we see in the night sky, Earth's interior is close by. But we can't reach it. The deepest well has drilled only 12 kilometers into Earth's crust. With such limited access, how do we know what Earth's interior is like? Most knowledge of the interior comes from the study of seismic waves that travel through Earth.

Layers Defined by Composition

If Earth's materials had the same chemical composition, or makeup, throughout seismic waves would travel in straight lines at constant speed. However, this is not the case. Seismic waves reaching seismographs located farther from an earthquake travel at faster average speeds than those recorded at locations closer to the event. As the speed of seismic waves increase, the waves *refract*, or bend as shown in **Figure 15**. Scientists study the speed and paths of seismic waves to determine the chemical composition of rocks inside Earth. Scientists used this information to define layers of Earth.

Earth's interior consists of three major layers defined by their chemical composition—the crust, mantle, and core.

Crust The **crust**—the thin, rocky outer layer of Earth—is divided into oceanic and continental crust. The oceanic crust is roughly 7 kilometers thick and composed of the igneous rocks basalt and gabbro. The continental crust is 8–75 kilometers thick, but averages a thickness of 40 kilometers. It consists of many rock types, but the most common rock found there is a granitic rock called granodiorite. The rocks of the continental crust have an average density of about 2.7 g/cm³ and some are over 4 billion years old. The rocks of the oceanic crust are younger (180 million years or less) and have an average density of about 3.0 g/cm³.

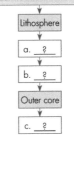

FIGURE 15 Paths of Seismic Waves The arrows show a few possible paths that seismic waves may travel. Infer *What causes the wave paths to change?*

Key Questions

🔑 **What are Earth's layers based on chemical composition?**

🔑 **What are Earth's layers based on physical properties?**

🔑 **How did scientists determine Earth's structure and composition?**

Vocabulary

- crust • mantle
- lithosphere
- asthenosphere
- outer core • inner core
- Moho

Reading Strategy

Sequence Copy the flowchart. After you read, complete the sequence of Earth's layers defined by physical properties.

Earth's Internal Structure
Lithosphere
a. ?
b. ?
Outer core
c. ?

1 FOCUS

Lesson Objectives
8.10 **List** the layers of Earth based on composition and physical properties.
8.11 **Describe** the composition of each layer of Earth.
8.12 **Explain** how scientists determined Earth's structure and composition.

Build Vocabulary
LINCS Have students: List the parts of the vocabulary that they know, such as *core*, *sphere*, and *litho-*. Imagine what the interior of Earth might look like and how the terms might fit together. Note a reminding, sound-alike term, such as apple core or atmosphere. Connect the terms, perhaps in a long sentence or as labels on a diagram. Self-test.

Reading Strategy L2
a. asthenosphere
b. lower mantle
c. inner core

2 INSTRUCT

Use Visuals L2

Figure 15 Have students look at the model of Earth and seismic waves in the diagram. **Ask:** One seismic wave travels straight through the center of Earth. Considering that a portion of Earth's center contains fluid, do you think that this wave is a P wave or an S wave? *(P wave)*
Visual

Answers

Figure 15 *Seismic waves change direction because their speed changes as they move through Earth.*

Facts and Figures

CORE-MANTLE BOUNDARY One of the strangest regions within Earth is the boundary between the rocky mantle and liquid iron outer core. Here, upside-down mountains of rock stick into the flowing ocean of liquid iron, getting eroded and then redeposited in upside-down "ocean" basins at the bottom of the mantle. The Core-Mantle Boundary Region (CMBR) is an important gateway between the core and mantle. Heat flowing out of the core heats the base of the mantle, providing the thermal source of major hot spots like Hawaii. Meanwhile, sinking pieces of cold ocean lithosphere pile up at the bottom of the mantle, cooling off the core and affecting Earth's magnetic field by changing the flow patterns of the outer core's liquid iron.

LESSON 8.4

Build Reading Literacy   L2

Refer to **p. 502D** in **Chapter 18,** which provides the guidelines for using visualization.

Visualize Have students keep their books closed. Tell them to listen carefully while you read the paragraphs about defining the layers of Earth based on physical properties. Ask students to describe how they visualize the interior of Earth. Then, ask students to work in pairs and discuss how they visualized the process.
Visual

(Teacher **Demo**)

FLOATING CRACKERS   L2

Purpose To model for students the characteristics and behavior of the lithosphere and asthenosphere.

Materials shallow baking pan, package of chocolate pudding, 2 cups of milk, several animal crackers

Procedure Review with students the general characteristics and thicknesses of the lithosphere and asthenosphere. You may want to introduce the idea of the lithosphere being broken into smaller pieces called plates. These plates move about on top of the asthenosphere. Then make the pudding and pour it into the shallow baking pan. This will model the asthenosphere. Once the pudding has set, place the animal crackers on top of the asthenosphere to represent the lithosphere.

Expected Outcomes Students should see that the lithospheric plates are relatively thin compared to the asthenosphere. They also can see how the lithosphere "floats" on top of the asthenosphere, without sinking into it. The asthenosphere has a solid consistency yet has some ability to move.
Logical, Visual

FIGURE 16 Earth's Layered Structure Based on chemical composition, Earth is made up of the crust, mantle, and core. Based on physical properties, Earth is made up of the lithosphere, asthenosphere, lower mantle, outer core, and inner core. The block diagram shows the relationship between the crust, lithosphere, and asthenosphere.
Infer *Which part of Earth has the highest density? Explain.*

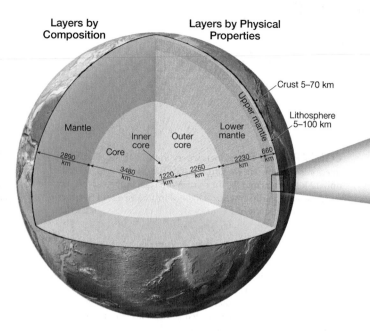

Mantle Over 82 percent of Earth's volume is contained in the **mantle**—a solid, rocky shell that extends to a depth of 2890 kilometers. The boundary between the crust and mantle represents a change in chemical composition. A common rock type in the uppermost mantle is peridotite, which has a density of 3.4 g/cm³.

Core The core is a sphere composed mostly of an iron-nickel alloy. At the extreme pressures found in the center of the core, the average density of the iron-rich material is 13 g/cm³ (13 times denser than water). **Figure 16** shows Earth's layered structure.

Layers Defined by Physical Properties

The physical properties of temperature, pressure, and density increase with depth in Earth. When a substance is heated, the transfer of energy increases the vibrations of particles. If the temperature exceeds the melting point, the forces between particles are overcome and melting begins.

If temperature were the only factor that determined whether a substance melted, our planet would be a molten ball covered with a thin, solid outer shell. Fortunately, pressure also increases with depth and increases rock strength. Depending on the temperature and pressure of the physical environment, rock may behave like a brittle solid, a putty, or a liquid. 🔑 **Earth can be divided into layers based on physical properties—the lithosphere, the asthenosphere, lower mantle, the outer core, and the inner core.**

Differentiated Instruction

ENGLISH LANGUAGE LEARNERS Use the following analogy to help students understand Earth's layers.

Imagine that Earth was a ball. If you could cut it in half, you would see that Earth is made up of layers. The deepest layer is a solid core of metal, which is surrounded by a core of liquid metal. The liquid metal spins as Earth rotates. These two parts are thick and extremely hot. The next layer is called the mantle.

The mantle is much cooler than the core, but it is still so hot that some of the rock is completely liquid. A brittle crust of solid rock covers the mantle.

Ask students to imagine that they are taking a trip through Earth. Ask them to write and illustrate a journal entry for the trip. Interested students may then share their journal entry with the class.

Lithosphere and Asthenosphere

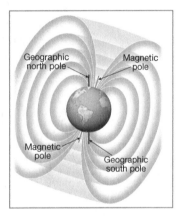

Oceanic crust
Continental crust
Lithosphere (sphere of rock)
Asthenosphere (weak sphere)
Upper mantle
Depth (km)
100
200
300
400
660

Lithosphere Earth's outermost layer consists of the crust and uppermost mantle and forms a relatively cool, rigid shell called the **lithosphere.** This layer averages about 100 kilometers in thickness as shown in Figure 16.

Athenosphere Beneath the lithosphere lies a soft, comparatively weak layer known as the **asthenosphere.** Within the asthenosphere, the rocks are close enough to their melting temperatures that they are easily deformed. Thus, the asthenosphere is weak because it is near its melting point, just as hot wax is weaker than cold wax. The lower lithosphere and asthenosphere are both part of the upper mantle.

Lower Mantle From a depth of about 660 kilometers down to near the base of the mantle lies a more rigid layer called the lower mantle. Despite their strength, the rocks of the lower mantle are still very hot and capable of gradual flow.

Inner and Outer Core The core, which is composed mostly of an iron-nickel alloy, is divided into two regions with different physical properties. The **outer core** is a liquid layer 2260 kilometers thick. The flow of metallic iron within this layer generates Earth's magnetic field. Just as there is a magnetic field around a bar magnet, an immense magnetic field surrounds Earth, as shown in **Figure 17.** The poles of the magnetized needle on a compass align themselves with Earth's magnetic field.

The **inner core** is a sphere having a radius of 1220 kilometers. Despite its higher temperatures, the materials in the inner core are compressed into a solid state by the immense pressure.

☑ **Reading Checkpoint** *Why is the inner core solid?*

Geographic north pole
Magnetic pole
Magnetic pole
Geographic south pole

FIGURE 17 Earth's Magnetic Field Movements in Earth's liquid outer core produce the planet's magnetic field. As a result, a compass needle points to one of the magnetic poles.

Earthquakes and Earth's Interior **235**

Facts and Figures

WATER IN THE MANTLE When people talk about the water cycle, they usually refer to the cycle of evaporation and precipitation on Earth's surface, but there are more parts to the water cycle. Rocks in the oceanic lithosphere can trap water. As the rocks sink into the mantle, most of this water comes back up beneath the stratovolcanoes at subduction zones. But some water makes it much deeper, eventually coming back up at mid-ocean ridges or hot-spot volcanoes, like those in Iceland. By some estimates, there could be many oceans worth of water within the rock of the mantle. Water weakens rock and makes it melt and flow more easily, so mantle water could affect the vigorousness of mantle convection, the rate at which Earth's tectonic plates move, the formation of some hot-spot volcanoes, and even the breakup of supercontinents.

Physical and Chemical Properties
Have students read the caption for Figure 18. Then ask students for examples of physical and chemical properties. Make a two-column chart on the board and compile a list of physical and chemical properties. *(Examples of physical properties: conductivity, hardness, melting point, density, pressure. Examples of chemical properties: flammability, reactivity.)* **Ask:** What physical properties change between the mantle and outer core? *(hardness, density, pressure, state; outer core is liquid, mantle is solid)*

Refer to **p. 186D** in **Chapter 7,** which provides guidelines for relating text and visuals.

Relate Text and Visuals Instruct students to look at Figure 18. Refer them to the key and point out that P waves and S waves are different colors in the picture. **Ask:** What happens when P waves hit the mantle-core boundary? *(They bend around the core, or go through the core.)* What sentences in the text support this observation? *("It was observed that P waves were bent around the liquid outer core. . . P waves that travel through the core. . . ")* What happens when S waves meet the boundary? *(They stop traveling.)* What sentence in the text supports this? *("S waves could not travel through the outer core.")*

Discovering Earth's Layers

Recall that seismic waves bend as they travel through Earth and that this information helped scientists to infer the planet's layered structure. 🔑 **During the twentieth century, studies of the paths of P and S waves through Earth helped scientists identify the boundaries of Earth's layers and determine that the outer core is liquid.**

In 1909, a Croatian seismologist, Andrija Mohorovičić, presented the first evidence of layering within Earth's mantle. By studying seismic records, he found that the velocity of seismic waves increased abruptly about 50 kilometers below eastern Europe. This boundary separates the crust from the underlying mantle and is now known as the Mohorovičić discontinuity. The name of the boundary is usually shortened to **Moho.**

Another boundary had been discovered in 1906 between the mantle and outer core. Seismic waves from even small earthquakes can travel around the world. This is why a seismograph in Antarctica can record earthquakes in California or Italy. However, it was observed that P waves bend around the liquid outer core beyond about 100 degrees away from an earthquake's epicenter. This region, where bent P waves arrive, is sometimes called the *shadow zone*. You can see the shadow zone in **Figure 18.** It is the area of Earth from approximately 100 degrees to 140 degrees from the earthquake's epicenter. The outer core also causes P waves that travel through the core to arrive several minutes later than expected.

The reason the wave paths bend is due to the differences in the composition of the core and the overlying mantle. The P waves bend around the core in a way similar to how sound waves bend around the corner of a building. For example, you can hear people talking around a corner even though you cannot see them. In this way, rather than stopping in the shadow zone, P waves bend around the outer core. It was further shown that S waves could not travel through the outer core. Therefore, geologists concluded that this layer is liquid.

FIGURE 18 Earth's Interior Showing P and S Wave Paths P waves either bend around or travel through the liquid outer core while S waves stop at the mantle-core boundary.

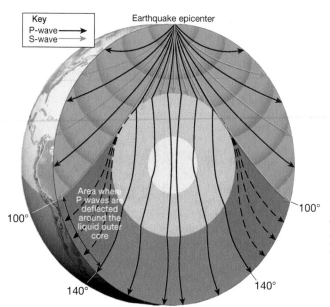

Key
P-wave ⟶
S-wave ⟶

Earthquake epicenter

Area where P waves are deflected around the liquid outer core

100°   100°

140°   140°

Facts and Figures

MINERAL PHYSICS Scientists can interpret seismic properties of particular rock types by performing high-pressure experiments. Small samples of rock and metal are squeezed and heated to the same conditions found in Earth's deep interior, and the speed of P and S waves traveling through the samples are measured. One of the most effective ways of doing this is to put a tiny rock sample between two large diamonds with flat surfaces. Diamond is the hardest naturally occurring substance, and can usually withstand the high pressures without shattering. Diamonds are also transparent, so the rock sample can be heated by a laser shone through the diamond. Scientists used this method to determine that the most abundant rock within Earth is perovskite, which makes up most of the lower mantle.

Discovering Earth's Composition

🔑 **To determine the composition of Earth's layers, scientists studied seismic data and rock samples from the crust, mantle, and meteorites. They also performed high-pressure experiments on Earth materials.** Scientists obtain data on the seismic properties of rocks by performing experiments at high pressures. Small samples of rock and metal are squeezed and heated to the same conditions found in Earth's deep interior. Scientists then measure the speeds of P and S waves through the samples.

Seismic data and rock samples from drilling indicate that the continental crust is mostly made of low-density granitic rocks. Until the late 1960s, scientists had only seismic evidence they could use to determine the composition of oceanic crust. The development of deep-sea drilling technology made it possible to obtain rock samples from the ocean floor. The crust of the ocean floor has a basaltic composition.

The composition of the rocks of the mantle and core is known from more indirect data. Some of the lava that reaches Earth's surface comes from the partially melted asthenosphere within the mantle. In the laboratory, experiments show that partially melting the rock called peridotite produces a substance that is similar to the lava that erupts during volcanic activity of islands such as Hawaii.

Surprisingly, meteorites that collide with Earth provide evidence of Earth's inner composition. Meteorites are assumed to be composed of the original material from which Earth was formed. Their composition ranges from metallic meteorites made of iron and nickel to stony meteorites composed of dense rock similar to peridotite. Because Earth's crust contains a smaller percentage of iron than do meteorites, geologists believe that dense metals, such as iron, sank toward Earth's center during the planet's formation.

☑ **Reading Checkpoint** *Why did scientists conduct experiments at high-pressures to learn about the seismic properties of rocks?*

8.4 Assessment

Review Key Concepts 🔑

1. Describe Earth's layers based on composition.

2. List Earth's layers based on physical properties, and their characteristics, in order from Earth's center to the surface.

3. What evidence led scientists to conclude that Earth's outer core is liquid? Explain.

Think Critically

4. **Compare and Contrast** Compare the physical properties of the asthenosphere and the lithosphere.

5. **Infer** Why are meteorites considered important clues to the composition of Earth's interior?

WRITING IN SCIENCE

6. **Creative Writing** Write a short fictional story about a trip to Earth's core. Make sure the details about the layers of Earth's interior are scientifically accurate.

Earthquakes and Earth's Interior **237**

Assessment Answers

1. Based on composition, Earth is made up of the rocky crust, the mantle (made of rock-forming materials), and the metallic, iron-nickel core.

2. inner core, outer core, lower mantle, asthenosphere, lithosphere (upper mantle)

3. Scientists studied the different paths that P waves and S waves take inside Earth to determine the nature of Earth's core. P waves bent in a pattern indicating the existence of a boundary between the core and the mantle. The fact that S waves did not travel through the outer core indicated that the outer core is liquid.

4. The lithosphere is a cool, rigid shell formed from the crust and upper mantle. On average it is 100 km thick. The asthenosphere is a soft, weak layer that experiences the conditions needed to produce a small amount of melting.

5. Meteorites are thought to be made of the same material from which Earth was formed. Therefore, when they are found, they can give us an indication of the composition of the interior of Earth.

6. Stories will vary but students should include accurate information on the lithosphere, upper mantle, lower mantle, as well as the inner and outer core.

How Earth Works

How Earth Works

1 FOCUS

Objectives

In this feature, students will
- explain what causes an earthquake.
- describe the possible physical effects of an earthquake.

Build Vocabulary   L2

Key Terms Write the key terms on the board. Ask volunteers to write definitions beside them. Then have the class work together to use the words in sentences that describe the causes and effects of earthquakes.

2 INSTRUCT

Bellringer   L1

Ask students what comes to mind when they think of earthquakes. Discuss earthquake experiences they may have had or heard about.
Verbal

Use Visuals   L1

Have students read and examine the photographs on this page and the next.
Ask: What do you suppose people in these regions had to do after the earthquake? *(They had to find people who were trapped under snow and rubble, rebuild buildings, and fix streets.)*
Visual

Effects of Earthquakes

As Earth's asthenosphere sluggishly flows, the overlying tectonic plates of the lithosphere are dragged along with it. Sometimes these tectonic plates collide head-on, while at other times they grind past one another. No matter how the tectonic plates collide, very strong forces build up between them as they are propelled by the motion of the asthenosphere. These forces get larger and larger until suddenly, the plates shift their positions. This releases a shock wave of energy that travels through Earth, causing ground shaking and deformation. This is called an **earthquake.** Most earthquakes last less than one minute. Even so, the effects of an earthquake can be devastating and long-lasting.

TSUNAMI ▶
In 1755, an earthquake in Lisbon, Portugal, caused a tsunami, as illustrated in this painting. A **tsunami** is a huge sea wave that is set off by an undersea earthquake or volcanic eruption. When tsunamis break on shore, they often devastate coastal areas. Tsunamis can race at speeds of about 720 km/h (450 mph) and may reach heights of about 30.5 meters (100 feet).

THE BIG ONE
On December 26, 2004, a massive undersea earthquake struck Indonesia, caused by the unprecedented rupture of a 1500 kilometer (900 mile) long fault zone in Earth's crust. The tsunami produced by this earthquake inundated coastlines around the Indian Ocean and killed over 230,000 people in 14 countries, making this event one of the deadliest natural disasters in modern history.

LANDSLIDE
In January 2001, an earthquake struck El Salvador. It caused the landslide that left these Salvadoran women homeless. A **landslide** is a sudden drop of a mass of land down a mountainside or hillside. Emergency relief workers from around the world often rush to the site of an earthquake disaster like the one that occurred in El Salvador. ▼

238 Chapter 8

Differentiated Instruction

GIFTED Ask students to research a historic earthquake, like the one that hit Lisbon in 1755. Have them imagine that they survived it and are writing a story about it for a foreign newspaper. Encourage them to use factual details and fictional interviews in their stories. Before they begin, remind them that the first paragraph should answer these questions: *Who? What? Where? When?* and *Why?*

▲ INFRASTRUCTURE DAMAGE
When an earthquake occurred in Los Angeles in 1994, underground gas and water lines burst, causing fires and floods. Earthquakes often cause tremendous damage to the **infrastructure**—the network of services that supports a community. Infrastructure includes power utilities, water supplies, and transportation and communication facilities.

AVALANCHE ▶
Earthquakes may trigger an **avalanche**—a sudden fall of a mass of ice and snow. In 1970, a severe earthquake off the coast of Peru caused a disastrous slide of snow and rock that killed some 18,000 people in the valley below.

▲ WHEN THE EARTH CRACKS
Most people killed or injured by an earthquake are hit by debris from buildings. Additional damage can be caused by **aftershocks**—tremors that can occur hours, days, or even months after an earthquake. The scene above shows the city of Anchorage, Alaska, after a major earthquake in 1964. Extensive ground tremors caused the street to break up as the soil below it collapsed. Buildings and cars were dropped more than 10 feet (3 m) below street level.

When two tectonic plates suddenly move past each other, waves of stored energy are released.

Epicenter

As seismic waves travel away from the epicenter, the destruction caused by the earthquake decreases.

Seismic waves travel outward from the focus, or hypocenter.

Focus, or hypocenter

▲ SEISMIC WAVES
As tectonic forces build, rocks on both sides of the fault deform in response, and stress levels increase. The fault ruptures when the tectonic forces overcome the forces holding the rocks together along the fault. The tectonic plates suddenly move, causing **seismic waves** to travel through the ground. The waves travel outward from an underground area called the focus, or hypocenter. Damage is usually greatest near the **epicenter**, the point on the surface directly above the focus.

Assessment

1. **Key Terms** Define **(a)** earthquake, **(b)** tsunami, **(c)** landslide, **(d)** infrastructure, **(e)** avalanche, **(f)** aftershock, **(g)** seismic wave, **(h)** epicenter.

2. **Physical Processes** Explain how the buildup of tectonic forces along faults causes earthquakes.

3. **Environmental Change** List and describe the types of damage a region may suffer if it experiences an earthquake.

4. **Natural Hazards** How does an earthquake damage the services that communities need to survive?

5. **Critical Thinking Solve Problems** What can a community do to reduce the amount of earthquake damage that might occur in the future?

239

3 ASSESS

Evaluate Understanding L2

Work with students to model how an earthquake happens. Encourage them to build models using everyday classroom materials, such as books for tectonic plates and paper strips for seismic waves.

Reteach L1

Group students in groups of four or five. Tell students to find out the recommended ways to protect themselves during an earthquake. Have them develop a pamphlet that explains and illustrates safety instructions. Each group should have researchers, an editor to compile the instructions, and an illustrator to draw the pictures. Post the completed pamphlets on a bulletin board.

Assessment Answers

1. (a) a shaking of the ground caused by sudden movements in Earth's lithosphere; **(b)** a sea wave that is set off by an undersea earthquake or volcanic eruption; **(c)** a sudden drop of a mass of land down a mountainside or hillside; **(d)** the network of services that supports a community; **(e)** a sudden fall of a mass of ice and snow; **(f)** tremors that can occur days, or even months, after an earthquake; **(g)** waves that travel through the ground as a result of an earthquake; **(h)** the location on the surface directly above the focus

2. As tectonic plates grind past each other, they get "stuck", causing large forces to accumulate between them. When these large forces overcome the forces holding the rocks together along the fault, an earthquake occurs.

3. Earthquakes can destroy buildings, cause tsunamis that flood coastal regions, disrupt electrical and gas lines (causing fires), and cause avalanches in snowy mountainous regions.

4. Earthquakes can make buildings uninhabitable, disrupt gas, electrical, and water lines, and make roads impassible for cars and other vehicles. Earthquakes can also damage telephone land lines and cell phone towers, hindering communications.

5. Sample answers: Design buildings and water, electrical, and gas lines to withstand the shock of an earthquake. Build villages, towns, and cities far from fault lines.

LOCATING AN EARTHQUAKE **L2**

Objective
Students should be able to determine the location of an earthquake epicenter.

Skills Measure, Interpret Maps, Interpret Graphs

Prep Time 15 minutes

Advance Prep Photocopy the map on p. 241 for each student.

Class Time 45 minute

Safety Students should use caution when using the drawing compasses. The ends are sharp.

Teaching Tips

- Encourage students to be very neat and precise in their measurements. It is important that the circles they draw be as accurate as possible in order to achieve the most accurate epicenter location. You may want to encourage them to place the map on top of their notebooks when they draw the circles with the compass, giving the tip of the compass something to dig into.

- Also, students should realize that they may not get an exact point for their epicenter location. It is possible that they will draw a small triangle at the junction of their circles. This is acceptable, but the triangle should be small.

- Too big an area indicates that either the calculations were incorrect or the circles were not precise enough.

Locating an Earthquake

Problem How can you determine the location of an earthquake's epicenter?

Materials pencil, drawing compass, world map or atlas, photocopy of the map on next page

Skills Measure, Interpret Maps, Interpret Graphs

Connect to the Big idea To locate an epicenter, records from three different seismographs are needed. Ideally, this activity should be done using a globe. When projected onto a flat map, the circles showing distances to the epicenter become distorted. For this reason, the method used here is an approximation.

Procedure

1. These three seismograms recorded the same earthquake, in New York City, Seattle, and Mexico City. Use the travel-time graph to determine the distance that each station is from the epicenter. Record your answers in a data table like the one shown.

2. Refer to a world map or atlas for the locations of the three seismic stations. Place a small dot showing the location of each of the three stations on the photocopy of the map on the next page. Neatly label each city on the map.

New York, NY

(Time marks in minutes)

9:00 UTC

Seattle, WA

9:00 UTC

Mexico City, Mexico

9:00 UTC

Data Table			
	New York	Seattle	Mexico City
Elapsed time between first P and first S waves			
Distance from epicenter in miles			

3. On the map, use a drawing compass to draw a circle around each of the three stations. The radius of the circle, in miles, should be equal to each station's distance from the epicenter. Use the scale on the map to set the distance on the drawing compass for each station. **CAUTION:** *Use care when handling the drawing compass.*

Analyze and Conclude

1. Interpret Graphs How far from the epicenter are the three cities located?

2. Calculate What would the distances from the epicenter to the cities be in kilometers?

3. Interpret Maps What is the approximate latitude and longitude of the epicenter of the earthquake that was recorded by the three stations?

4. Draw Conclusions On the New York seismogram the first P wave was recorded at 9:01 UTC. UTC is the international standard on which most countries base their time. At what time (UTC) did the earthquake actually occur? Explain.

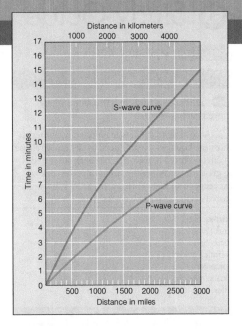

GO FURTHER Use the Internet or the library to find the locations of recent earthquake epicenters. Make a data table displaying the location, date, and magnitude of ten recent earthquakes. Report your findings to the class.

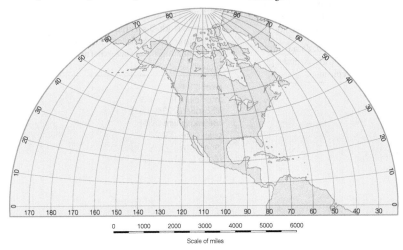

Expected Outcome Students should find a unique point or location for the epicenter of the earthquake.

Analyze and Conclude

1. NY—approximately 2400 miles; Seattle—approximately 1400 miles; Mexico City—approximately 1200 miles

2. NY—approximately 3864 km; Seattle—approximately 2254 km; Mexico City—approximately 1932 km

3. 28°N latitude and 112°30′W longitude

4. 8:54 UTC; There is 7 minutes difference between the actual time of the earthquake and when it was recorded in New York.

GO FURTHER

Answers will vary, but students' data tables should neatly show the dates, locations, and magnitudes of ten recent earthquakes.
Visual, Logical

21st Century Learning

Communication Skills

What can you find out about earthquakes?

Geologists present earthquake data on the United States Geological Survey's (USGS) Web site. Have students visit the site and find the map with recent earthquakes. Have them choose an earthquake and read the description. Ask them to determine which pieces of information are intended for the general public and which are for scientists. Then, they should write a brief report explaining how they made decisions in categorizing the information.

Homework Guide

Lesson	Questions
1	1, 2, 7, 13
2	4, 9–12, 18, 19, 22, 24–27, 31
3	5, 8, 14, 15, 17, 20, 21, 28–30
4	3, 6, 16, 23

8 Study Guide

Big idea ▸ Dynamic Earth

8.1 What Is an Earthquake?

Faults are fractures in Earth along where movement has occurred.

According to the elastic rebound hypothesis, most earthquakes are produced by the rapid release of energy stored in rock that has been subjected to great forces. When the strength of the rock is exceeded, it suddenly breaks, releasing some of its stored energy as seismic waves.

earthquake (218)
fault (218)
focus (218)
seismic waves (218)
epicenter (218)
elastic rebound (220)
aftershock (221)

8.2 Measuring Earthquakes

Earthquakes produce two main types of seismic waves—body waves and surface waves.

An instrument that records seismic waves is called the seismograph.

The Richter scale and the moment magnitude scale measure earthquake magnitude. The Modified Mercalli scale is based on earthquake intensity.

You can use a travel-time graph, data from seismograms at three or more locations, and a globe to determine an earthquake's epicenter.

P wave (222)
S wave (222)
surface wave (223)
seismograph (224)
seismogram (224)
moment magnitude (225)

8.3 Earthquake Hazards

Earthquake-related hazards include: seismic shaking, liquefaction, landslides and mudflows, and tsunamis.

Earthquake damage and loss of life can be reduced by determining the earthquake risk for an area, building earthquake-resistant structures, and following earthquake safety precautions.

liquefaction (229)
tsunami (230)
seismic gap (231)

8.4 Earth's Layered Structure

Earth's interior consists of three major layers defined by their chemical composition—the crust, the mantle, and the core.

Earth can be divided into layers based on physical properties—the lithosphere, the asthenosphere, lower mantle, the outer core, and the inner core.

During the twentieth century, studies of the paths of P waves and S waves through Earth helped scientists establish the boundaries of Earth's layers and determine that the outer core is liquid.

To determine the composition of Earth's layers, scientists studied seismic data and rock samples from the crust, mantle, and meteorites. They also performed high-pressure experiments on Earth materials.

crust (233)
mantle (234)
lithosphere (235)
asthenosphere (235)
outer core (235)
inner core (235)
Moho (236)

Assessment Answers

Review Content

1. d	**2.** a	**3.** c
4. d	**5.** b	**6.** d
7. c	**8.** b	**9.** a
10. b		

Understand Concepts

11. seismogram

12. A: P waves
   B: S waves
   C: surface waves

13. According to the elastic rebound hypothesis, an earthquake occurs when rock subjected to stress finally breaks, releasing stored elastic energy.

14. surface waves

15. fire, landslides, and tsunamis

8 Assessment

Review Content

Choose the letter that best answers the question or completes the statement.

1. Approximately how many earthquakes are strong enough to be felt each year worldwide?
   a. 500
   b. 1000
   c. 10,000
   d. 30,000

2. What is the location on the surface directly above the earthquake focus called?
   a. epicenter
   b. fault
   c. magnitude
   d. Moho

3. The rigid layer of Earth that includes the entire crust and the uppermost part of the mantle is called the
   a. asthenosphere.
   b. mesosphere.
   c. lithosphere.
   d. Moho.

4. The instrument that records earthquakes is called
   a. a seismogram.
   b. a seismologist.
   c. seismology.
   d. a seismograph.

5. Look at the map of earthquake activity in Lesson 3. Which region has the most earthquake activity?
   a. central Europe
   b. the edge of the Pacific Ocean
   c. eastern North America
   d. central Africa

6. What material do scientists believe makes up a large part of the upper mantle?
   a. basalt
   b. granite
   c. iron
   d. peridotite

7. The point at which an earthquake begins is called
   a. a foreshock.
   b. the epicenter.
   c. the focus.
   d. the Moho.

8. In areas where soil is saturated with water, earthquakes can turn stable soil into a fluid during a process called
   a. faulting.
   b. liquefaction.
   c. tsunamis.
   d. subsidence.

9. To find the epicenter of an earthquake, what is the minimum number of seismic stations that are needed?
   a. three
   b. nine
   c. five
   d. two

10. What scale do scientists today most often use to express the magnitude of an earthquake?
    a. Richter scale
    b. moment magnitude
    c. tsunami scale
    d. Moho scale

Understand Concepts

Use the diagram below to answer Questions 11 and 12.

11. The diagram shows a typical recording of an earthquake. What is the record called?

12. Identify the waves recorded at A, B, and C on the diagram.

13. What is the elastic rebound hypothesis?

14. What type of seismic wave causes the greatest destruction to buildings?

15. In addition to the damage caused directly by seismic shaking, list four other types of destructive events that can be triggered by earthquakes.

16. Describe the composition and physical properties of the crust.

17. What is liquefaction and how can earthquakes cause liquefaction to occur?

18. List the major differences between P waves and S waves.

19. How much more ground shaking occurs in an earthquake that measures 4.2 on the Richter scale compared with an earthquake that measures 6.2 on the Richter scale?

16. The crust is the thin, rocky outer layer of Earth. The oceanic crust is composed of basalt and gabbro. The continental crust is largely composed of granite.

17. Liquefaction is when stable soil turns to a liquid that is unable to support buildings. This happens when soil saturated with water is shaken during an earthquake.

18. P waves travel faster than S waves. P waves are push-and-pull waves while S waves shake the particles at right angles to the direction of travel. P waves can travel through solids and liquids while S waves can only travel through solids.

19. 100 times

ASSESSMENT

20. Answer should include two of the following: intensity and duration of earthquake, nature of material the structure is built on, and design of structure.

Think Critically

21. if a moderate earthquake occurs in a more densely populated area than an earthquake with a higher magnitude; or if the moderate earthquake occurs in an area that lacks earthquake-safe building stands; or if the moderate earthquake triggers landslides, fires, or tsunamis

22. The Richter scale is based on the height of the largest seismic wave, and so depends on ground motion as recorded by a seismograph. Conversely, the moment magnitude scale estimates the amount of energy released by earthquakes; it is a calculation based on the average amount of movement along the fault, the area of the surface break, and the strength of the broken rock.

23. by looking at the behavior of seismic waves as they travel through the different layers of Earth

Analyze Data

24. approximately 1500 km

25. The first P wave will arrive 5 minutes after the earthquake. The first S wave will arrive 9 minutes after the earthquake.

26. approximately 2 minutes

Concepts in Action

27. The moment magnitude scale is the most frequently used because it is the only scale that measures the energy released by an earthquake.

28. A tsunami begins when an earthquake or underwater landslide causes movement of the ocean floor, pushing up a mass of water and forming a wave. The wave races across the open ocean, but it is less than 1 m high. As the wave nears a coastline, the wave gets higher in shallow water. When it reaches the shore, a tsunami can be up to 30 m high and can cause great destruction.

29. The intensity of the earthquake may have been greater farther from the epicenter because of soft, unstable soil or the presence of filled land, both of which can increase the effects of seismic waves.

30. Answers will vary. Accept reasonable answers.

---

20. What are two factors that can determine the amount of destruction that results from an earthquake?

Think Critically

21. Apply Concepts Give two reasons why an earthquake with a moderate magnitude might cause more extensive damage than an earthquake with a high magnitude.

22. Compare and Contrast How are the moment magnitude scale and the Richter scale different?

23. Infer How did scientists determine the structure and composition of Earth's interior?

Analyze Data

Use the diagram below to answer Questions 24–26.

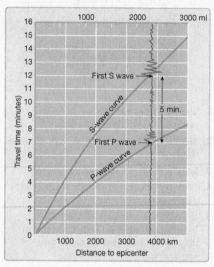

24. Interpret Graphs Determine the distance between an earthquake and seismic station if the first S wave arrives three minutes after the first P wave.

---

25. Interpret Graphs If a seismic station is 2500 kilometers from the earthquake's epicenter, approximately when will the first P wave be received? When will the first S wave be received?

26. Calculate What is the difference in the travel-times of the first P wave and the first S wave if the seismic station is 1000 kilometers from the earthquake epicenter?

Concepts in Action

27. Apply Concepts Why is the moment magnitude the most commonly used scale by scientists for measuring earthquakes?

28. Relate Cause and Effect Describe a tsunami from the event that produces it to the time that it reaches a coastline.

29. Infer A magnitude 6 earthquake has an intensity of V on the Mercalli scale 10 km from the epicenter. But the same earthquake has an intensity of VII on the Mercalli scale 25 km from the epicenter. What might explain this difference?

30. Writing in Science Research a recent earthquake and write about the earthquake damage in the style of a newspaper article.

Performance-Based Assessment

31. Design an Experiment Design a model seismograph to record simulated earthquakes. When your model is completed, test it for the class. Then determine how your seismograph design could be improved or changed if it doesn't work well.

Performance-Based Assessment

31. Sample answer: Students may design a seismograph with a pen hanging on a string above a paper towel roll.

Standardized Test Prep

Choose the letter that best answers the question.

1 What property that is different for P and S waves provides a method for locating the epicenter of an earthquake?
  A magnitude
  B foci
  C modes of travel
  D speed

2 Movements that follow a major earthquake often generate smaller earthquakes called—
  F aftershocks
  G foreshocks
  H surface waves
  J landslides

3 An earthquake in the ocean floor can cause a destructive sea wave called a—
  A P wave
  B S wave
  C Moho
  D tsunami

Use the diagram below to answer Question 4.

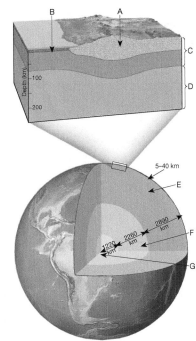

4 In the diagram, which letters would indicate layers that form the lithosphere?
  F A, B, C
  G C, D, E
  H D, E
  J F, G

If You Have Trouble With . . .			
Question	1	2	3	4
See Lesson	8.2	8.1	8.3	8.4

9 Plate Tectonics Planning Guide

Lesson Objectives		Activities
9.1 Continental Drift, pp. 248–253 9.1 **Describe** the hypothesis of continental drift. 9.2 **Evaluate** the evidence in support of continental drift. 9.3 **Identify** the main objections to Wegener's hypothesis of continental drift.		TE Teacher Demo: Evidence: Matching Fossils, p. 249 **L2** TE Build Science Skills, p. 250 **L2** SE Quick Lab: Charting the Age of the Atlantic Ocean, p. 251 **L2**
9.2 Sea-Floor Spreading, pp. 254–260 9.4 **Identify** mid-ocean ridges and deep-ocean trenches. 9.5 **Explain** the processes of sea-floor spreading and subduction. 9.6 **Explain** the evidence for sea-floor spreading, including paleomagnetism and magnetic reversals, earthquake patterns, and the age of the ocean floor.		TE Build Science Skills, p. 255 **L2** TE Build Science Skills, p. 257 **L2** TE Teacher Demo: Testing Minerals for Magnetism, p. 258 **L1**
9.3 Theory of Plate Tectonics, pp. 261–268 9.7 **Explain** the theory of plate tectonics. 9.8 **Describe** lithospheric plates. 9.9 **Identify** the three types of plate boundaries.		TE Build Science Skills, p. 261 **L2** TE Teacher Demo: A Convergent Model, p. 262 **L2** SE Map It: Earth's Tectonic Plates, p. 262 **L2** TE Teacher Demo: Creating a Continental Rift, p. 264 **L2**
9.4 Mechanisms of Plate Motions, pp. 270–271 9.10 **Relate** the unequal distribution of heat in Earth and the mechanism of mantle convection to the movement of tectonic plates. 9.11 **Compare** the mechanisms of slab-pull and ridge-push as contributing to plate motion.		TE Reteach, p. 277 **L1** TE Build Science Skills, p. 270 **L2** SE Map It: Future Continent Positions, p. 269 **L2**
Chapter Features and Labs		
Try It How Do the Continents Fit Together? p. 247		LM Modeling a Plate Boundary **L2**
Exploration Lab Paleomagnetism and the Ocean Floor, pp. 272–273		
Earth & Its Systems Plate Tectonics into the Future, p. 269		

Ability Levels

L1 For students who need additional help
L2 For all students
L3 For students who need to be challenged

Components

SE	Student Edition	LP	Lesson Plans
TE	Teacher's Edition	AA	Active Art
LM	Laboratory Manual	PD	Planet Diary
CT	Chapter Tests	GEODe	Geode CD-ROM
GRSW	Guided Reading & Study Workbook	eText	
CTB	Computer Test Bank		

Resources	Lesson Assessment
GRSW Lesson 9.1 **LP** Lesson Planning 9.1 **AA** Continental Drift	**SE** Lesson 9.1 Assessment, p. 252 **eText** Lesson 9.1
GRSW Lesson 9.2 **LP** Lesson Planning 9.2 **PD** Mid-Ocean Ridges	**SE** Lesson 9.2 Assessment, p. 260 **eText** Lesson 9.2
GRSW Lesson 9.3 **LP** Lesson Planning 9.3 **GEODe** Forces Within: Plate Tectonics	**SE** Lesson 9.3 Assessment, p. 268 **eText** Lesson 9.3
GRSW Lesson 9.4 **LP** Lesson Planning 9.4	**SE** Lesson 9.4 Assessment, p. 271 **eText** Lesson 9.4

Materials for Activities and Labs

Quantities for each group

STUDENT EDITION

Try It, p. 247
atlas or world map, paper, scissors

Quick Lab, p. 251
calculator

Exploration Lab, pp. 272–273
pencil, metric ruler, calculator

TEACHER'S EDITION

Teacher Demo, p. 249
2 groups of photographs or samples of fossils, including at least one type of fossil found in both groups

Build Science Skills, p. 250
child's jigsaw puzzle, 2 pieces of cardboard the size of the puzzle or larger, pencil or marker

Build Science Skills, p. 257
2 colors of modeling clay

Teacher Demo, p. 258
magnet, minerals (include at least one sample of a mineral that contains iron or cobalt), compass

Build Science Skills, p. 261
hard-boiled egg

Teacher Demo, p. 262
two slabs of modeling clay, wax paper

Teacher Demo, p. 264
2 slices of individually wrapped American cheese, dull knife or fingernail, metric ruler

Reteach, 271
beaker, water, hot plate, ice cube, food coloring

Assessment

CHAPTER ASSESSMENT
SE Assessment, pp. 275–276
CT Chapter 9 Test
CTB Chapter 9
eText Chapter 9

21st Century **Learning**

Critical Thinking and Systems Thinking: What observations led to the theory of plate tectonics? TE p. 274

Common Themes

Earth's lithosphere is broken into about a dozen major pieces and many other smaller pieces. These "plates" move about Earth's surface in a process called plate tectonics, which is the unifying framework within which all of modern geology is understood. Plate tectonics explains the existence of earthquakes, volcanoes, mountains, oceans, and many other things.

Michael Wysession
Washington University

Space and Time Earth's plates have been moving around, changing and reforming, for at least 4 billion years. The moving plates drag the continents around with them, sometimes bringing them together to form supercontinents, the last of which was Pangaea.

Forces and Motion Plates move slowly but steadily, and interesting geology occurs when they collide, separate, or move past each other. Plates that are subducting into the mantle tend to move fast, pulled by the slab-pull force and pushed by the ridge-push force. Plates that contain continents tend to move slowly.

Matter and Energy Plate tectonics is the surface expression of a global cycle of mantle convection. Oceanic lithosphere forms at mid-ocean ridges, cool, and sink back into the mantle at subduction zones. The decay of radioactive isotopes is the source of heat that drives mantle convection.

Earth as a System Plate tectonics has profoundly affected the history of Earth's life: volcanic eruptions affect the atmosphere, the positions of continents affect ocean circulation, and plate collisions have created the continents and their unique distributions of minerals, metals, and other resources.

EARTH SCIENCE REFRESHER

Why do we have plate tectonics?

Plate tectonics, and all of the exciting geology associated with it, is the result of Earth's attempt to cool down. It is the result of the second law of thermodynamics, which implies that heat tends to flow from hotter regions to cooler regions. Earth, as well as all other planets, was very hot when it formed. Earth's center is still hotter than 5000 K. This heat will try to make its way to the surface and out into space in the fastest way possible. The situation is complicated because heat is still being generated by the decay of radioactive isotopes, the four most important of which are uranium-235, uranium-238, thorium-232, and potassium-40. There were many other short-lived radioactive isotopes providing heat early in Earth's history.

Planets cool down by a combination of radiation, conduction, and convection. Once the heat gets out to Earth's surface, it radiates out into space, but it gets to the surface by conduction and convection.

> **Address Misconceptions**
>
> *Students often think that the movement of lithospheric plates causes Earth's surface area to become either larger or smaller (depending on which way the plates move.) Explain that if surface area decreased, the interior would become compressed and internal pressure would increase. If surface area increased, either the interior would expand or the lithosphere would separate from the mantle. For a strategy that helps to overcome this misconception, see* **Address Misconceptions** *on TE p. 263.*

Some students may think that the continents have remained in approximately the same positions since the breakup of Pangaea. In reality, the locations of continents have continued to shift. For a strategy that helps to overcome this misconception, see **Address Misconceptions** on **TE p. 252**.

When rock is stiff, like with the lithosphere, or where there are compositional boundaries, like between the core and mantle, heat must conduct. This is a slow process, which is why rock-like materials such as ceramic are used for coffee mugs. Throughout most of the Earth, however, heat moves by convection, by which it is carried along with the moving material. This occurs in the core and across most of the mantle.

This cycle of convection, not unlike a pot of boiling soup, involves hot rock rising, forming plates of oceanic lithosphere cooling off by heating the ocean, and sinking back down into the mantle. The cycle may take, on average, about a half-billion years. Because it moves slowly, the Earth is cooling slowly, and plate tectonics will continue throughout Earth's lifetime.

It is interesting to note that no other planets in our solar system have Earth-like plate tectonics. There are many factors needed for plate tectonics to occur. The existence of an asthenosphere layer is vital, as this soft layer allows the overlying plates to move horizontally more easily than they otherwise would. Water plays a vital role, as the existence of the asthenosphere is due to the large amount of water (perhaps more than five oceanfuls!) that exists in the mantle, making the mantle rock softer and lowering its melting point.

BUILD READING LITERACY
Relate Cause and Effect

Understanding How and Why Things Occur

Strategy Help students read and understand relationships between events. Cause-effect relationships are integral to science, so it is very important that students understand the cause-effect relationships developed in the text. Before students begin, assign a passage in Chapter 9 for them to read, such as pp. 265–267 in Lesson 9.3.

Example

1. Remind students that a cause is what makes something happen and the effect is what happens as a result. Point out that in science, many actions cause other actions to occur.

2. Have students identify cause-effect relationships in the passage. Remind them that the text does not always directly state the cause-effect relationship, but in many cases clue words or phrases do point out such a connection: *because, so, since, results, therefore, cause, lead to.* For example, "Rain is always slightly acidic because carbon dioxide dissolves in water droplets and forms carbonic acid."

3. Then, explain that causes and effects often occur in chains, with effects becoming causes of later effects. Have students find a cause-effect chain and show it in the form of a flowchart. For example, insufficient oxygen for complete combustion → carbon monoxide produced → inhaled and absorbed by blood → hemoglobin cannot carry oxygen to cells.

See TE p. 250 for a script on how to use this strategy with students. For additional strategies, see TE pp. 260 and 265.

CHAPTER 9

ASSESS PRIOR KNOWLEDGE

Use the Chapter Pretest below to assess students' prior knowledge. As needed, review these concepts.

Review Science Concepts

Lesson 9.1 Reviewing fossil formation and rock types ensures that students will understand the concepts of matching fossils and rock types and formations as evidence for continental drift. An understanding of erosion and deposition leads to an understanding of the gaps and overlaps between continents.

Lesson 9.2 A knowledge of Earth's structure will help students understand sea-floor spreading.

Lesson 9.3 Reviewing the causes of earthquakes and the structure of Earth's interior will help students understand the evidence supporting the theory of plate tectonics.

Lesson 9.4 A knowledge of the convection process and how radioactive decay produces heat is essential for an understanding of the causes of plate motions.

9 Plate Tectonics

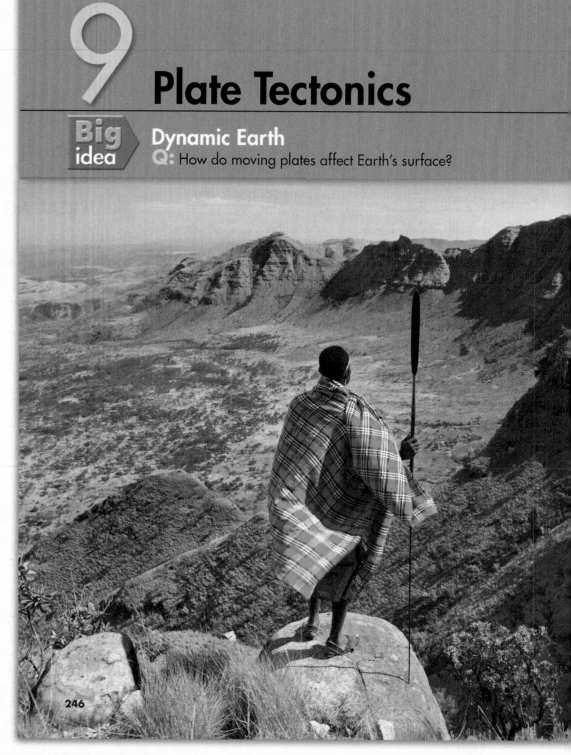

Big idea Dynamic Earth

Q: How do moving plates affect Earth's surface?

246

Chapter Pretest

1. What kind of rock forms when magma or lava cools? *(Igneous rock)*

2. What is the outer portion of solid Earth containing the crust and uppermost mantle? *(b)*
   a. outer core   **b.** lithosphere
   c. hydrosphere   **d.** atmosphere

3. How does igneous rock form sedimentary rock? *(Igneous rock at Earth's surface is exposed to chemical and physical weathering. These rocks are broken down to form sediment. Eventually, sediment is lithified, forming layers of sedimentary rock.)*

4. Explain how features of sedimentary rock can provide clues about how, when or where the rock formed. *(Each layer of a sedimentary rock records a period of deposition. Ripple marks indicate that a rock bed formed in water. Mud cracks indicate that sediments were drying out when the rock formed. Fossils can be used to match up rocks of the same age found in different places.)*

5. Why is there such a large diversity in the chemical composition of igneous rocks? *(The chemical composition depends on the composition of the magma from which the rock crystallized. During stages of crystallization, the solid and liquid components of magma separate to form many different minerals.)*

6. Name two sources of sedimentary rocks. *(solid particles from weathered rocks and soluble material from chemical weathering)*

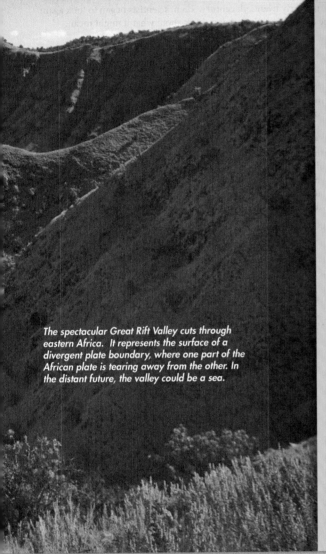

The spectacular Great Rift Valley cuts through eastern Africa. It represents the surface of a divergent plate boundary, where one part of the African plate is tearing away from the other. In the distant future, the valley could be a sea.

INQUIRY ?
TRY IT!

HOW DO THE CONTINENTS FIT TOGETHER?

Procedure

1. Get a copy of a world map from your teacher. Cut out the continents along their coastlines. **CAUTION:** *Be careful when using scissors.*

2. Try to fit together the pieces into one large landmass. Look for a "best-fit" configuration.

3. Compare your large landmass with those of other students. Did anyone come up with a landmass that was very different from the others?

Think About It

1. **Observe** From your continental reconstruction, where did the continents fit together well? Where did problems occur?

2. **Form a Hypothesis** Use your observations to develop a hypothesis on how to get a better fit of the continents. How could the overlaps and large gaps be explained? (*Hint:* What if the outline of the coasts is not the same as the boundaries of the continents themselves?)

247

ENGAGE/EXPLORE

HOW DO THE CONTINENTS FIT TOGETHER?   L2

Purpose In this activity, students begin to recognize the shapes of the continents and fit together cutouts of the continents to form one large landmass.

Address Misconceptions

Students may think that some pieces of the continents have sunk into the oceans, causing them not to fit together well. Explain that overlaps occur because of sedimentation at river deltas and deformation of the plates.

Skills Observe, Develop, Hypothesize

Prep Time 5 minutes

Materials world map or atlas, paper, scissors

Advance Prep 20 minutes to copy maps

Class Time 10 minutes

Safety Remind students to handle scissors carefully.

Teaching Tips It may be helpful to students, especially tactile learners, if you paste the maps onto cardboard, card stock, or sand paper. The backing material should be thin enough that students can easily cut it with scissors.

A Robinson Projection Map would be most useful in this activity. These maps show most distances, sizes, and shapes accurately.

Expected Outcome Africa and South America fit together well. Other continents will fit together with areas of overlap and gaps.

Think About It

1. Students should find that Africa and South America fit together well. Other continental pieces will fit together with many areas of overlap and large gaps.

2. If the continental shelves are used as the outer edges of the continents, the fit will be better in many areas. Students may hypothesize that the outlines of the continents have been modified by depositional and stretching processes that make the reconstruction difficult. Students also may hypothesize (incorrectly) that some pieces of the continents have sunk into the oceans.

1 FOCUS

Lesson Objectives

9.1 **Describe** the hypothesis of continental drift.

9.2 **Evaluate** the evidence in support of continental drift.

9.3 **Identify** the main objections to Wegener's hypothesis of continental drift.

Build Vocabulary L2

Word Forms Before students read this lesson, ask them to write a sentence or two describing the meaning of the word *drift*. Then have them predict the meaning of *continental drift*. After students read the lesson, have them examine their predictions and discuss whether their predictions must be changed.

Reading Strategy L2

a. continental puzzle
b. matching fossils
c. matching rocks and structures
d. ancient climates

2 INSTRUCT

Use Visuals L1

Figure 1 Point out the small areas of brown and light blue between Africa and South America. **Ask:** What could cause the brown-shaded regions of overlap? *(accumulation of sediments deposited by rivers and stretching of the plates)* What do you think the light blue areas represent? *(the continental shelf)*

Visual

Key Questions

 What is the hypothesis of continental drift?

 What evidence supported continental drift?

 Why was Wegener's hypothesis rejected?

Vocabulary

• continental drift
• Pangaea

Reading Strategy

Summarize Copy the table. Fill it in as you read to summarize the evidence of continental drift.

Hypothesis	Evidence
Continental Drift	a. continental puzzle
	b. ___?___
	c. ___?___
	d. ___?___

MORE THAN 300 years ago, mapmakers produced world maps that accurately showed the shapes of the continents. Looking at these maps, people noticed that some continents fit together like pieces of a jigsaw puzzle. Few people thought much about this observation until the early twentieth century. Then, scientists began to look again at the fit of the continents and think about what it might mean.

The Continental Puzzle

A German scientist, Alfred Wegener, also noticed the similarity between the coastlines on opposite sides of the South Atlantic Ocean. As you can see in **Figure 1,** the shapes of South America and Africa are an approximate fit with each other. In 1915, Wegener proposed his radical hypothesis of **continental drift.** **According to Wegener's hypothesis of continental drift, the continents had once been joined to form a single supercontinent.** He called this supercontinent **Pangaea,** meaning "all land."

Wegener also hypothesized that about 200 million years ago Pangaea began breaking into smaller continents. The continents then drifted slowly to their present positions.

FIGURE 1 A Curious Fit
This map shows the best fit of South America and Africa at a depth of about 900 meters. Areas of overlap appear in brown.

Evidence for Continental Drift

Wegener presented a variety of evidence to support the hypothesis of continental drift. His evidence included similar fossils, types of rock, and traces of glaciation on widely separated landmasses.

Matching Fossils 🔊 **Fossil evidence for continental drift includes several fossil organisms found on different landmasses.** Wegener reasoned that these organisms could not have crossed the vast oceans presently separating the continents. An example is *Mesosaurus*, a reptile whose fossil remains are limited to eastern South America and southern Africa, as shown in **Figure 2.** Scientists think that *Mesosaurus* lived in freshwater lakes and shallow bays. It could not have swum across a vast, salty ocean such as the Atlantic. Therefore, Wegener argued, South America and Africa must have been joined when *Mesosaurus* lived.

The distribution of other types of fossils also supported Wegener's hypothesis. For example, fossils of *Glossopteris*, a small plant, are found today in South America, southern Africa, India, Antarctica, and Australia. Yet the characteristics of *Glossopteris* seeds make it very unlikely that the seeds could have blown or floated long distances across the oceans. Fossils of the land reptile *Lystrosaurus* show a similar pattern of distribution across landmasses that are now far apart from each other.

In Wegener's time, the idea of land bridges was the accepted explanation for similar fossils being found on different landmasses. However, if land bridges did exist between South America and Africa, their remnants should still lie below sea level. But no signs of such land bridges have ever been found in the Atlantic Ocean.

☑ **Reading Checkpoint** *How does the distribution of Mesosaurus fossils provide evidence for continental drift?*

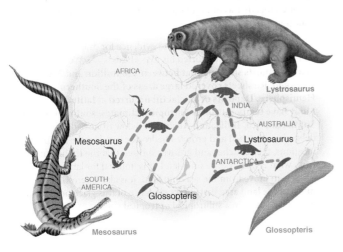

FIGURE 2 Fossil Evidence
Fossils of *Mesosaurus* have been found on both sides of the South Atlantic and nowhere else in the world. Fossil remains of this and other organisms on the continents of Africa and South America appear to link these landmasses at some time in Earth's history.

Plate Tectonics **249**

Student Activity: Use Models Have students use a child's jigsaw puzzle with several large pieces to demonstrate matching rock types and mountain belts as follows. Students should put the puzzle together on a piece of cardboard. After putting it together, the puzzle should be covered with another piece of cardboard and flipped over. On the back of the puzzle, students should draw lines representing a mountain belt that extends across several puzzle pieces. Students will understand when the puzzle is put together how mountain chains form continuous belts across land masses.
Kinesthetic, Visual

Refer to **p. 246D** in this chapter, which provides the guidelines for relating cause and effect.

Relate Cause and Effect Have students read the section on pp. 250–251 about ancient climates as evidence for continental drift. **Ask:** Why did Wegener think that the existence of glaciers in tropical regions of the Southern Hemisphere was evidence of continental drift rather than of climatic change? *(The Northern Hemisphere was once tropical, as evidenced by coal deposits that were formed from tropical plants. If the Northern Hemisphere had once been closer to the equator, the Southern Hemisphere probably had also been further south, closer to the South Pole. It was not likely that such a large change in climate could have taken place without continental drift.)*
Logical

FIGURE 3 Matching Mountain Ranges
A The Appalachian Mountains run along the eastern side of North America and end off the coast of Newfoundland. Mountains that are similar in age and structure are found in the British Isles and Scandinavia.

B When these landmasses were united as Pangaea, these ancient mountain chains formed a nearly continuous belt.

Rock Types Anyone who has worked a jigsaw puzzle knows that the pieces must fit together to form a complete picture. The picture in the continental drift puzzle is one of matching rock types and mountain belts. If the continents were once part of Pangaea, the rocks found in a particular region on one continent should closely match in age and type those in adjacent positions on the adjoining continent.

 Matching types of rock in several mountain belts that today are separated by oceans provide evidence for continental drift. For example, the Appalachian mountain belt in eastern North America ends off the coast of Newfoundland, as shown in **Figure 3A.** Mountains of the same age with similar rocks and structures are found in the British Isles and Scandinavia. When these landmasses are fitted together as in **Figure 3B,** the mountain chains form a nearly continuous belt.

Ancient Climates Wegener found evidence for dramatic global climate changes that supported his hypothesis. **Wegener found glacial deposits showing that between 220 million and 300 million years ago, ice sheets covered large areas of the Southern Hemisphere. Deposits of glacial till occurred at latitudes that today have temperate or even tropical climates: southern Africa, South America, India, and Australia.** Below these beds of glacial debris lay scratched and grooved bedrock carved by the ice. In some locations, the scratches and grooves showed that the ice had moved from what is now the sea onto land. It is unusual for large continental glaciers to move from the sea onto land. It is also interesting that much of the land area that shows evidence of this glaciation now lies near the equator in a subtropical or tropical climate.

Facts and Figures

Scientists think that 200 million years ago, what is now Pennsylvania was located farther south, near the equator. Fossils from coal fields in Pennsylvania show that the plants from which the coal formed had large leaf-like structures that are typical of tropical plants. The trunks of the plants had no growth rings, also typical of tropical plants because there is little seasonal temperature fluctuation to produce the rings. Scientists believe that these fossils are evidence that Pennsylvania once had a tropical climate and was located closer to the equator.

Could Earth have been cold enough to allow the formation of continental glaciers in what is now a tropical region? Wegener rejected this idea because, during this same time period, large tropical swamps existed in the Northern Hemisphere. The lush vegetation of these swamps eventually became the major coal fields of the eastern United States, Europe, and Siberia.

Wegener thought there was a better explanation for the ancient climate evidence he observed. Thinking of the landmasses as a supercontinent, with South Africa centered over the South Pole, would create the conditions necessary to form large areas of glacial ice over much of the Southern Hemisphere. The supercontinent idea would also place the northern landmasses nearer the tropics and account for their vast coal deposits, as shown in **Figure 4**.

☑ **Reading Checkpoint** *Summarize the climate evidence for continental drift.*

FIGURE 4 Glacier Evidence
A The area of Pangaea covered by glacial ice 300 million years ago. **B** The continents as they are today. The white areas indicate where evidence of the old ice sheets exists.
Interpret Diagrams *Where were the continents located when the glaciers formed?*

CHARTING THE AGE OF THE ATLANTIC OCEAN

Procedure

1. The distance between two locations across the Atlantic Ocean, one in South America and one in Africa, is 4300 km.

2. Assume that these two locations were once joined as part of Pangaea.

Analyze and Conclude

1. Calculate If the landmasses moved apart at a rate of 3.3 cm per year, how long did it take to arrive at their current positions?

CHARTING THE AGE OF THE ATLANTIC OCEAN L2

Objective
After completing this activity, students will be able to calculate the length of time it takes two land masses to separate, given the rate of spreading.

Skills Calculate, Infer

Prep Time none

Class Time 10 minutes

Teaching Tips You might want to review conversion factors with students.

Expected Outcome The two continents took more than 130 million years to separate.

Analyze and Conclude
1. 130.3 million years
Logical

For Enrichment L3

Have students research the following question: Pangaea began to break up and South America and Africa began to separate 200 million years ago. What types of living organisms were found on Earth when the two continents reached their current positions?

Answers

Figure 4 *The continents were near the South Pole when the glaciers formed.*

☑ Reading Checkpoint *Glaciers in southern South America, southern Africa, India, and Australia are found in areas that now have tropical climates. There is also evidence for tropical climates and coal swamps in areas that are now at higher latitudes, such as northern Europe and the northeastern United States.*

LESSON 9.1

Use Visuals

Figure 5 Have students study the maps showing the breakup of Pangaea. **Ask:** In the breakup of Pangaea, what continents appear to have separated first? *(North America and Africa)* What ocean began to form when North America and Africa separated? *(Atlantic Ocean)* How was India formed? *(India broke away from Gondwanaland. It moved north and eventually collided with Asia.)*
Visual, Logical

Address **Misconceptions**   L2

Some students may think that the continents have remained in approximately the same positions since the breakup of Pangaea. Make transparencies of the five parts of Figure 5. Superimpose the transparencies two at a time to show students the changes. Ask students to come up to the projection to point out changes in the location of continents from one transparency to another. Ask which continent has moved the farthest. *(Asia)*
Visual, Logical

BREAKUP OF PANGAEA

FIGURE 5 Pangaea broke up gradually over a period of 200 million years.

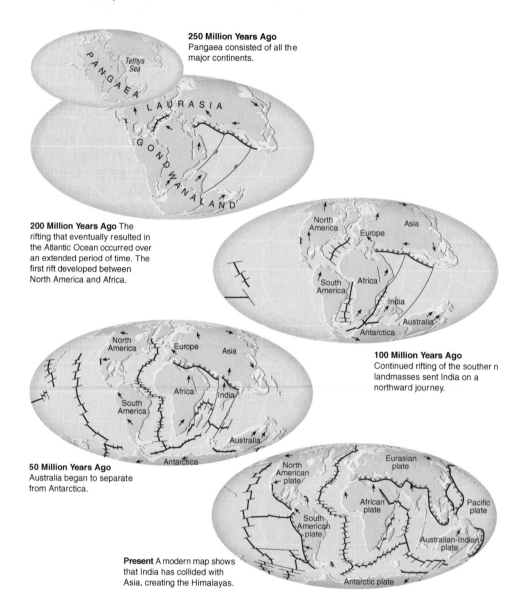

250 Million Years Ago
Pangaea consisted of all the major continents.

200 Million Years Ago The rifting that eventually resulted in the Atlantic Ocean occurred over an extended period of time. The first rift developed between North America and Africa.

100 Million Years Ago Continued rifting of the southern landmasses sent India on a northward journey.

50 Million Years Ago Australia began to separate from Antarctica.

Present A modern map shows that India has collided with Asia, creating the Himalayas.

Rejection of Wegener's Hypothesis

Wegener's hypothesis faced a great deal of criticism from other scientists. **The main objection to Wegener's hypothesis was that he could not describe a mechanism capable of moving the continents.** Wegener proposed that the tidal influence of the Moon was strong enough to give the continents a westward motion. However, physicists quickly responded that tidal friction great enough to move the continents would stop Earth's rotation.

Wegener also proposed that the larger and sturdier continents broke through the oceanic crust, much like ice-breakers cut through ice. However, there was no evidence to suggest that the ocean floor was weak enough to permit passage of the continents without the ocean floors being broken and deformed in the process.

Most scientists in Wegener's day rejected his hypothesis. However, a few geologists continued to search for evidence of continental drift.

During the years that followed Wegener's hypothesis, major strides in technology enabled scientists to map the ocean floor. Extensive data on earthquake activity and Earth's magnetic field also became available. By 1967, these findings led to a new theory, known as plate tectonics. The theory of plate tectonics proved that Wegener was correct—the continents move. The theory also provided the framework for understanding many other geologic processes, such as the formation of the mountains shown in **Figure 6.**

FIGURE 6 Mountain Origins Today, scientists know that plate movements pushed up mountain ranges such as the Canadian Rockies in Alberta, Canada.

9.1 Assessment

Review Key Concepts

1. What is the hypothesis of continental drift?
2. List the evidence that supported the hypothesis of continental drift.
3. Why did scientists reject Wegener's continental drift hypothesis?
4. What was Pangaea?

Think Critically

5. **Apply Concepts** How does the occurrence of the same plant fossils in South America and Africa support continental drift? Explain.
6. **Draw Conclusions** How did Wegener explain the existence of glaciers in the southern landmasses, and the lush tropical swamps in North America, Europe, and Siberia?
7. **Review** Write a paragraph describing Pangaea. Include the location and climate of Pangaea. Use the equator as your reference for position.

Plate Tectonics **253**

Assessment Answers

1. a hypothesis that proposes that the continents where once joined to form one supercontinent
2. matching continental outlines, matching fossils, matching rocks and structures, ancient climates
3. He could not provide a mechanism to explain the movement of the continents.
4. the supercontinent proposed by Wegener's hypothesis of continental drift
5. A land plant most likely could not travel across a large ocean such as the Atlantic. If

the plant is found in both Africa and South America, those areas had to have been joined when the plant was growing.
6. It is difficult to imagine that Earth had cooled enough to form glaciers in tropical latitudes, so in order to explain the glaciers, those areas had to have been closer to the poles than in the present day. Also, the glacial grooves indicate the ice was coming from an area that at present is ocean. Large continental glaciers form only on land, so that area had to be land.

7. Pangaea was a supercontinent made up of all the major land areas joined together. It began breaking into smaller continents about 200 million years ago. Pangaea was located near the South Pole. The southern part of Pangaea, made up of South America, Africa, India, Australia, and Antarctica, had a cold climate with large continental glaciers.

Lesson Objectives
9.4 **Identify** mid-ocean ridges and deep-ocean trenches.

9.5 **Explain** the processes of sea-floor spreading and subduction.

9.6 **Explain** the evidence for sea-floor spreading, including paleomagnetism and magnetic reversals, earthquake patterns, and the age of the ocean floor.

Build Vocabulary **L2**
Word Parts Have students break the word *subduction* into roots, prefixes, or suffixes. They may need to use a dictionary to find the meaning of some parts. *(Subduction comes from the Latin prefix sub-, meaning "below" and the Latin root word ducere, meaning "to draw or pull." Thus, subduction means to draw or pull below.)*

Reading Strategy **L2**
a. magnetic strips in ocean-floor rock
b. earthquake patterns in subduction zones
c. age of the ocean floor

9.2 Sea-Floor Spreading

Key Questions
 What are mid-ocean ridges and deep-ocean trenches?

 What occurs during sea-floor spreading?

 What is the evidence for sea-floor spreading?

Vocabulary
- sonar • deep-ocean trench
- mid-ocean ridge
- rift valley
- sea-floor spreading
- subduction
- paleomagnetism

Reading Strategy
Identify Supporting Evidence Copy the graphic organizer. After you read, complete it to show the evidence that supported the hypothesis of sea-floor spreading.

Evidence	Hypothesis
a. ?	
b. ?	Sea-floor spreading
c. ?	

FIGURE 7 Sea-Floor Vents These worms live next to hydrothermal vents on the ocean floor. The vents are found around mid-ocean ridges and other areas where super-heated water, gases, and other materials emerge from below.

WEGENER PUBLISHED his book *On the Origin of Continents and Oceans* in 1915. During the decades that followed, very few scientists studied continental drift. But discoveries in other branches of Earth science eventually led to new interest in Wegener's hypothesis. Surprisingly, important new data came from one of the least-known parts of Earth—the ocean floor.

Exploring the Ocean Floor
During the mid 1800s, several nations sent ships on scientific expeditions to gather data about the oceans. Scientists wanted to know more about the topography of the ocean floor. They measured ocean depths in many areas. Data from the middle of the Atlantic Ocean, where scientists expected the water to be very deep, revealed large undersea mountains. This discovery helped to fuel interest in mapping the ocean floor.

During the early 1900s, a new technology made it easier to map the ocean floor. **Sonar,** which stands for **so**und **na**vigation and **r**anging, is a system that uses sound waves to calculate the distance to an object. The sonar equipment on a ship sends out pulses of sound that bounce off the ocean floor. The equipment then measures how quickly the sound waves return to the ship. The deeper the water, the longer it takes the sound waves to return to the ship.

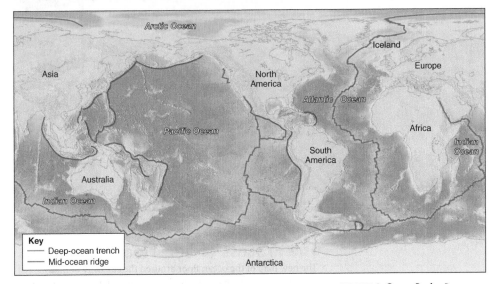

FIGURE 8 **Ocean Basins** Deep trenches and mountainous mid-ocean ridges are major features of Earth's ocean basins.
Observe *Which ocean has the most trenches?*

Deep-Ocean Trenches As scientists mapped the ocean floor, they found long, steep valleys called **deep-ocean trenches.** Trenches form the deepest parts of Earth's oceans. For example, the Mariana Trench in the Pacific Ocean is over 11 kilometers deep. Most trenches occur around the edges of the Pacific Ocean, although others occur in the Indian and Atlantic oceans.

Mid-Ocean Ridges By the late 1950s, scientists had constructed a more complete map of the ocean floor. The map showed that the mountain range in the middle of the Atlantic Ocean was not an isolated feature. Instead, it formed a **mid-ocean ridge,** a long chain of mountains extending throughout all the oceans. 🔑 **Earth's mid-ocean ridge system forms the longest feature on Earth's surface.** The system winds more than 70,000 kilometers across the sea floors of every ocean basin, like the seam on a baseball. The term *ridge* may be misleading, because it is not narrow like the ridges that hikers find on mountains. It ranges from 1,000 to 4,000 kilometers wide. In a few places, such as Iceland, the mid-ocean ridge rises above the ocean surface.

Often, a deep, central valley runs down the center of a ridge. Called a **rift valley,** the central valley of a mid-ocean ridge resembles a long canyon. Some parts of the ridge system lack a rift valley.

☑ **Reading Checkpoint** *What are mid-ocean ridges?*

Composition of the Ocean Floor Earth's ocean floors are made of igneous rocks of basaltic composition. Recall that basalt forms when magma reaches the surface and hardens to form solid rock. Most of the ocean floor is covered with a thick layer of sediment. Scientists found that the sediment layer is progressively thinner to mid-ocean ridges, and that along the ridge there was no sediment.

Plate Tectonics **255**

PLANET DIARY

For an activity on **Mid-Ocean Ridges**, visit PlanetDiary.com/HSES.

---

② INSTRUCT

Use Visuals L1

Figure 8 Have students study the map in Figure 8 showing Earth's ocean floor. **Ask:** Where are most trenches found? *(Around the edges of ocean basins)* Where are most mid-ocean ridges found? *(Toward the centers of ocean basins)* When students have read The Process of Sea-Floor Spreading on pp. 256–257, have them revisit Figure 8 and discuss the distribution of mid-ocean ridges and trenches in relation to what they have learned about sea-floor spreading.
Visual, Verbal

Build Science Skills L2

Ocean Cross Section Using a world atlas or the Internet, find data on ocean depths along a line drawn across the Atlantic Ocean. Use these data to construct a graph that shows how depth changes across the ocean floor. Ask students to label features of the ocean floor, such as the mid-ocean ridge, that appear on the cross section.
Logical, Visual

Answers

Figure 8 *the Pacific Ocean*

☑ **Reading Checkpoint** *long chains of mountains that wind across the floors of the oceans*

Facts and Figures

Until the nineteenth century, the ocean floors were considered to be flat, featureless plains. Early attempts to map the ocean floors used soundings taken with weighted lines from ships. This method was slow and inaccurate. In 1855, U.S. Navy Lieutenant Matthew Maury published a bathymetric chart, that showed an underwater mountain range in the middle of the Atlantic Ocean.

In the twentieth century, the use of sonar greatly accelerated sea-floor mapping.

Based on these data, Bruce Heezen and Marie Tharp of Columbia University's Lamont Doherty Earth Observatory began compiling detailed maps of the ocean floor in the 1950s and 1960s. The work of Heezen and Tharp revealed the extent and structure of mid-ocean ridges and trenches and provided evidence in support of sea-floor spreading and plate tectonics. Their 1978 map, World Ocean Floor, was the first complete map of Earth's ocean floor.

LESSON 9.2

L2

Integrate Oceanography

Explore Ridges and Trenches
Explain that oceanographers have used small submarines called submersibles to explore features of the ocean floor. Have groups of students use library or Internet resources to research the use of submersibles to explore the geology and biology of mid-ocean ridges and deep-ocean trenches. Have each group prepare a poster on their findings and present them to the class.
Verbal, Visual

Build Math Skills

L1

Conversion Factors Remind students to label the units of each factor when solving the following problem. Doing this ensures that all the conversion factors are included and the answer has the correct units. Tell students that sea-floor spreading occurs at an average rate of 5 cm per year. At this rate, how long would it take for a narrow sea that is 1 km wide to form? *(about 20,000 years)*
Logical

Integrate History

L3

Harry Hess Have interested students research the contribution of Harry Hess and other scientists to the scientific revolution that led to the modern theory of plate tectonics. Ask them to summarize their findings in a short essay that explains how understanding of the ocean floor changed as a result of this scientific revolution.
Verbal

FIGURE 9 Widening Sea
A spreading center in the Red Sea is slowly causing the sea to become wider.

The Process of Sea-Floor Spreading

The new map of the ocean floor aroused the curiosity of many scientists. One geologist, Harry Hess, thought that the mid-ocean ridges and deep-ocean trenches might help to explain how the ocean floor was formed. In 1963, Hess published his hypothesis of sea-floor spreading. **In the process of sea-floor spreading, new ocean floor forms along Earth's mid-ocean ridges and slowly moves outward across ocean basins.** During sea-floor spreading, new oceanic lithosphere is formed, and the floor of a particular ocean basin can become wider. Today, the Atlantic Ocean is thousands of kilometers wide. Millions of years ago, the Atlantic would have been a narrow sea, like the Red Sea, shown in **Figure 9.**

Eruptions Along Mid-Ocean Ridges How did the mid-ocean ridges form? Scientists found evidence that the mid-ocean ridges formed as the result of volcanic activity. As shown in **Figure 10,** fractures along the central valley of a mid-ocean ridge fill with magma that wells up from the hot mantle below. (Recall that magma is molten rock that forms in the upper mantle and rises through the crust.) Spreading and upwelling of magma continuously adds new ocean floor.

The process can also begin on land when a rift valley forms and splits a continental landmass. Over millions of years, the rift valley widens to form a new ocean basin like the Red Sea, shown in Figure 9.

Movement of the Ocean Floor As new ocean floor is added along mid-ocean ridges, the older ocean floor moves outward and away from the ridge on both sides. Rates of sea-floor spreading average about 5 centimeters per year. These rates are slow on a human time scale. But they are fast enough that all of Earth's ocean basins could have been formed within the last 200 million years. This further supports the theory of plate tectonics.

Facts and Figures

WORLD WAR II AND PLATE TECTONICS Much of the evidence for plate tectonics comes from the structure of the ocean sea floor, and its discovery is largely due to submarines. A submarine can avoid hitting the ocean floor by using sonar. However, sonar signals can be detected by other vessels, so using sonar would give away a submarine's location. As a result, the U.S. sponsored a large research effort to map the bathymetry, gravity, and magnetism of the oceans so that submarines could know the depth to the sea floor at a given location without using sonar. The discoveries about the sea floor amazed the Navy researchers. In fact, one U.S. Navy submarine captain, Harry Hess, went on to become a geophysics professor at Princeton University, and was one of the founding discoverers of plate tectonics.

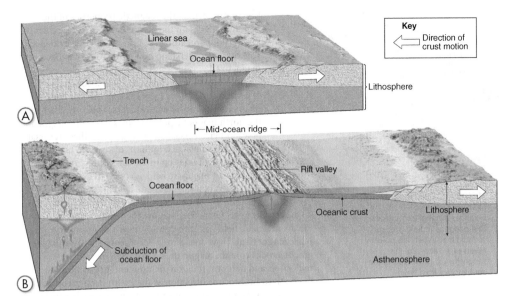

Use Visuals   L1

Figure 10 Point out the rising magma in each of the diagrams. **Ask:** What happens to the rising magma in the diagram? *(It fills the cracks formed by sea-floor spreading.)* Why is this process called sea-floor spreading? Does the sea-floor actually get thinner and spread out? *(The sea-floor does not get thinner. Rather, the sea-floor spreads apart and new rock is constantly added to the ridge.)*
Visual

Build Science Skills   L1

Student Activity: Use Models Give students two colors of modeling clay (one color for the magma and the other color for the crust) and have them model sea-floor spreading, from a mid-ocean ridge to subduction beneath a trench.
Kinesthetic, Visual

FIGURE 10 Sea-Floor Spreading and Subduction The process of sea-floor spreading produces the ocean floor. **A** A linear sea forms along a spreading center. **B** Over millions of years a mid-ocean ridge develops, and the ocean basin becomes wider. Overall, the addition of new crust at mid-ocean ridges is counteracted by subduction of old crust at deep-ocean trenches.
Relate Cause and Effect *What process adds new material to the ocean floor?*

Subduction at Deep-Ocean Trenches Although new ocean floor is constantly being added at the mid-ocean ridges, our planet is not growing larger. Earth's total surface area remains the same. How can that be? To accommodate newly created lithosphere, older portions of the ocean floor return to the mantle. In the process of **subduction,** ocean floor returns to the mantle as it sinks beneath a deep ocean trench. The areas where subduction occurs, shown in Figure 10, are called subduction zones.

☑ **Reading Checkpoint** *What happens during subduction?*

Evidence for Sea-Floor Spreading

Hess's hypothesis got the attention of geologists. Sea-floor spreading explained the formation and destruction of ocean floor and how ocean basins could grow wider or close up. But what evidence was there to support Hess's hypothesis? 🔷 **Evidence for sea-floor spreading included magnetic strips in ocean-floor rock, earthquake patterns, and measurements of the ages of ocean floor rocks.**

Plate Tectonics **257**

Facts and Figures

LAKES AND OCEANS The term *bathymetry* refers to measurements of depth in the oceans. The bathymetry of oceans is the opposite of what you might expect. If you look at a lake, the shallowest parts are usually around the edges, and the deepest parts are usually in the middle. Oceans are just the opposite. Deep-ocean trenches, like the Marianas Trench, Puerto Rico Trench, and

Peru-Chile Trench, are at the edges of the oceans, often adjacent to continents. In the middle of oceans are often found the elevated mountain ranges of mid-ocean ridges like the Mid-Atlantic Ridge. This backward nature of sea-floor bathymetry was an early clue to geoscientists that the oceans were not just large lakes.

TESTING MINERALS FOR MAGNETISM `L1`

Purpose Students test various minerals with a magnet to determine whether they have magnetic properties.

Materials magnet, minerals (include at least one sample of magnetite or hematite), compass

Procedure Have students test the mineral samples with the magnet to see if they are attracted by it. Have students place the compass near each mineral sample to see if the needle moves. If it does, the material is magnetic.

Expected Outcomes Minerals that contain iron have magnetic properties. Some meteorites also have magnetic properties.
Kinesthetic, Visual

Use Visuals `L1`

Figure 12 Have students study the figure. **Ask:** Could the rocks in a strip possessing reverse polarity ever possess normal polarity? *(No, once the rocks solidify, their polarity is permanently set.)* How do you think the width of a strip relates to the sea-floor spreading rate? *(The faster the spreading rate is, the wider the strip will be.)*
Visual, Logical

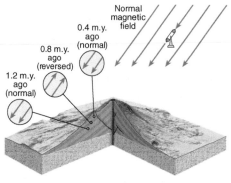

FIGURE 11 Paleomagnetism in Lava As lava cools, it becomes magnetized parallel to the magnetic field present at that time. When the polarity reverses, a record of the magnetism is preserved in the sequence of lava flows.

Magnetic Strips The magnetic properties of the rock that makes up the ocean floor provided evidence for sea-floor spreading. To understand this evidence, you need to understand how some rocks can become magnetized.

Recall that Earth's magnetic field is much like that of a bar magnet. Geophysicists learned that Earth's magnetic field occasionally reverses *polarity*. That is, the north magnetic pole becomes the south magnetic pole, and vice versa. Scientists graphed these reversals of polarity going back millions of years. When Earth's magnetic field lines up in the same direction as the present magnetic field, it is said to have *normal polarity*. When the magnetic field lines up in the opposite direction, it is said to have *reverse polarity*.

As certain rocks form, they acquire the polarity that Earth's magnetic field has at the time. These rocks possess **paleomagnetism.** How does a rock become magnetized? Many igneous rocks contain magnetite, an iron-rich mineral. As the rock cools and hardens, the iron-rich mineral grains become magnetized in the same direction as the existing magnetic field. You can see this process in **Figure 11.** Once the rock has formed, its polarity remains frozen unless the rock is reheated above a certain temperature. But what if the rock is moved or if the magnetic pole changes its position? The rock's paleomagnetism does not change.

Scientists collected data on the paleomagnetism of the rock that makes up the ocean floor. Ships towed instruments called magnetometers across the ocean floor. The data revealed a pattern of alternating strips of magnetized rock. Strips of rock with normal polarity alternated with strips of rock having reverse polarity. Scientists inferred that as new oceanic lithosphere forms along the mid-ocean ridges, it becomes magnetized according to the polarity of Earth's magnetic field at the time. The matching pattern of strips on both sides of a ridge, shown in **Figure 12,** is evidence that sea-floor spreading occurs.

☑ **Reading Checkpoint** *What is paleomagnetism?*

FIGURE 12 Polarity Reversals

1. Period of Normal Polarity

Magma

1 As new material is added to the ocean floor at the oceanic ridges, it is magnetized according to Earth's existing magnetic field.

2. Period of Reverse Polarity

Magma

2 A period of reverse polarity is recorded in the same way.

Differentiated Instruction

ENGLISH LANGUAGE LEARNERS Explain to students that there are many uses of the term *polar*, both in science and in everyday usage. For example, in magnetism, polarity refers to the magnetic poles. In chemistry, polar molecules are molecules in which one side of the molecule has a partial negative charge and the opposite side has a partial positive charge. Polar also means diametrically opposite. Have students look up the various meanings of the term polar and use each meaning in a sentence.

FIGURE 13 Distribution of Earthquake Foci Note that intermediate- and deep-focus earthquakes occur only within the sinking slab of oceanic lithosphere.

Earthquake Patterns More evidence for sea-floor spreading came from studies of the depth at which certain earthquakes occur. Scientists knew that there were many earthquakes in subduction zones. Two scientists, Kiyoo Wadati and Hugo Benioff, found a pattern when they plotted the depth of earthquakes in relation to their distance from deep-ocean trenches.

Shallow-focus earthquakes occur in and around a trench. Wadati and Benioff observed that intermediate-focus and deep-focus earthquakes occur in a belt about 50 kilometers thick. This belt extends through the lithosphere and deep into the asthenosphere. As you can see in **Figure 13,** the deeper the earthquake, the farther away its focus is from the deep-ocean trench. No earthquakes have been recorded below about 700 kilometers. At this depth the subducting slab of ocean floor has been heated enough to soften.

Scientists considered the pattern of earthquakes in Wadati-Benioff zones in relation to sea-floor spreading. The pattern was what scientists expected would result from subduction of the ocean floor. These data convinced scientists that slabs of ocean floor return to the mantle in subduction zones.

3. Period of Normal Polarity

3 Note that the pattern of magnetism is captured on both sides of the ridge.
Apply Concepts *Why are the magnetized strips about equal width on either side of the ridge?*

Plate Tectonics **259**

LESSON 9.2

Build Reading Literacy L1

Refer to **p. 530D** in **Chapter 19**, which provides the guidelines for making inferences.

Make Inferences Have students read the lesson about the age of the ocean floor on this page. **Ask:** What can you infer about the age of the ocean floor based on its distance from a mid-ocean ridge? *(You can infer that the age of the sea floor increases with increasing distance from the spreading center at an ocean ridge. The theory of sea-floor spreading states that new ocean lithosphere is created at ocean ridges, so the ocean floor should be younger closer to the ridges and older farther from the ridges.)*
Verbal, Intrapersonal

3 ASSESS

Evaluate Understanding L2

To assess students' knowledge of lesson content, have them make flashcards for the vocabulary terms and the four lines of evidence supporting the plate tectonic theory. For each vocabulary term, the card should include a definition and an example, where applicable. For each line of evidence, the card should give an explanation of why it supports the theory and include an example. Students can use the cards to quiz one another.

Reteach L1

Have students explain in their own words why data produced by drilling into ocean-floor sediment provides evidence for sea-floor spreading.

Assessment Answers

1. Mid-ocean ridges are part of a large, volcanic mountain range that winds through Earth's oceans; deep-ocean trenches are deep canyons in the ocean floor beneath which oceanic lithosphere sinks into the mantle through subduction.
2. During sea-floor spreading, magma erupts along a mid-ocean ridge to form new oceanic lithosphere. The ocean floor then moves away from the ridge, often toward a trench at the edge of the ocean basin.
3. magnetic strips in ocean floor rock, earthquake patterns in subduction zones, and the fact that the age of the ocean floor increases with distance from mid-ocean ridges
4. A Wadati-Benioff zone is the belt in which earthquakes occur along a slab of subducting ocean floor.

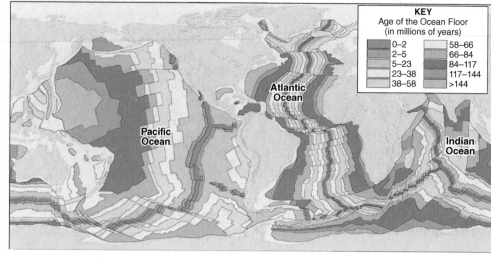

KEY
Age of the Ocean Floor
(in millions of years)

0–2	58–66
2–5	66–84
5–23	84–117
23–38	117–144
38–58	>144

Pacific Ocean Atlantic Ocean Indian Ocean

FIGURE 14 Sea-Floor Ages
As the map shows, the youngest parts of the ocean floor lie along the mid-ocean ridges. The oldest parts of the ocean floor are found along the outer edges of ocean basins.

The Age of the Ocean Floor Drilling into sediment on the ocean floor and the crust beneath it provided some of the best evidence for sea-floor spreading. Beginning in 1968, the drilling ship *Glomar Challenger* collected data on both sides of mid-ocean ridges.

The data confirmed what the sea-floor spreading hypothesis predicted. The ocean floor is youngest along the central valley of the mid-ocean ridge, as shown in **Figure 14.** The ocean floor is oldest in subduction zones or near the edges of continents far from the ridge. The data also confirmed that none of the ocean floor is more than about 180 million years old. Older oceanic rock would have returned to the mantle through subduction.

9.2 Assessment

Review Key Concepts 🔑

1. Describe mid-ocean ridges and deep-ocean trenches.

2. Explain what occurs during sea-floor spreading.

3. List the evidence for sea-floor spreading.

4. What is a Wadati-Benioff zone?

Think Critically

5. Infer Why are the oldest parts of the ocean floor less than 200 million years old?

6. Apply Concepts How do strips of magnetized rock on the ocean floor provide evidence of sea-floor spreading?

7. Relate Cause and Effect Do earthquakes occur at a depth of more than 700 kilometers? Explain your answer.

WRITING IN SCIENCE

8. Explain Write a paragraph explaining how scientists learned the age of the ocean floor and how these data supported sea-floor spreading.

5. The ocean floor is less than 200 million years old because that is the maximum amount of time it takes sea-floor spreading to move oceanic lithosphere from the mid-ocean ridges where it forms to the trenches where it is subducted.
6. Strips of ocean-floor basalt record the polarity of Earth's magnetic field at the time the rock formed. These strips form a pattern that is the same on both sides of the mid-ocean ridge. The pattern shows that ocean floor forms along mid-ocean ridges and then moves away from the ridge.

7. Earthquakes do not occur below 700 km because at that depth mantle rock is too soft and hot to store the elastic energy needed to cause an earthquake.
8. Students' paragraphs should explain that scientists drilled into the ocean floor in many locations to obtain rock samples that could be dated. The samples showed that the age of the ocean floor increases with distance from the mid-ocean ridges.

9.3 Theory of Plate Tectonics

DURING the 1960s, scientists realized that sea-floor spreading explained part of Alfred Wegener's idea of continental drift. Namely, it explained how ocean basins could open and close. Canadian geologist J. Tuzo Wilson combined the evidence for sea-floor spreading with other observations. Wilson and other scientists soon developed a new theory that led to a revolution in geology.

Earth's Moving Plates

Wilson suggested that the lithosphere is broken into several huge pieces, called **plates.** Deep faults, like cracks in the shell of a hard-boiled egg, separate the different plates. **In the theory of plate tectonics, Earth's lithospheric plates move slowly relative to each other, driven by convection currents in the mantle.** The plates, shown in **Figure 15** on the following pages, generally are made up of both oceanic lithosphere and continental lithosphere. Some plates may contain no continents and just a small number of landmasses.

Causes of Plate Motion Recall that Wegener had failed to explain how the lithosphere could move. The theory of plate tectonics identified a force that could set Earth's outer shell in motion. According to J. Tuzo Wilson, convection currents within Earth drive plate motion. Hot material deep in the mantle moves upward by convection. At the same time, cooler, denser slabs of oceanic lithosphere sink into the mantle.

Effects of Plate Motion Lithospheric plate motion averages about 5 centimeters per year. That's about as fast as your fingernails grow. The results of plate motion include earthquakes, volcanoes, and mountain building, which are some of the most powerful and violent forces on Earth.

Key Questions

What is the theory of plate tectonics?

What are the three types of plate boundaries?

Vocabulary

- plate • plate tectonics
- divergent boundary
- convergent boundary
- transform fault boundary
- continental volcanic arc
- volcanic island arc

Reading Strategy

Compare and Contrast Copy the table. After you read, compare the three types of plate boundaries by completing the table.

Boundary Type	Relative Plate Motion
convergent	a. ___?___
divergent	b. ___?___
transform fault	c. ___?___

1 FOCUS

Lesson Objectives
9.7 **Explain** the theory of plate tectonics.
9.8 **Describe** lithospheric plates.
9.9 **Identify** the three types of plate boundaries.

Build Vocabulary   L2
Concept Map Have students make a concept map using the term *plate tectonics* as the starting point. All the vocabulary terms in this lesson should be used.

Reading Strategy   L2
a. plates move together
b. plates move apart
c. plates slide past each other

2 INSTRUCT

Build Science Skills   L2
Student Activity: Use Analogies Crack the shell of a hard-boiled egg, but do not remove the shell. Ask students if the egg reminds them of anything. The egg can be used as a tiny model of Earth. The thin eggshell is analogous to Earth's crust, divided into plates. Within the shell is the firm mantle. Have students move the pieces of shell around. They should notice how the shell buckles in some places and exposes "mantle" in other places. This movement is analogous to the movement of Earth's crust. However, Earth's movement results in the formation of mountains, earthquakes, and new ocean floor.
Kinesthetic, Visual

Plate Tectonics **261**

Use Visuals L1

Figure 15 Have students examine the figure. They may need help from an atlas or a globe to locate the features in the questions. **Ask:** How do you think the Andes Mountains were formed? *(The Nazca plate collided with the South American plate.)* How do you think the Red Sea was formed? *(The African plate and the Arabian plate moved apart, forming a rift that became the Red Sea.)* Which plate is the largest? Where is it located? *(The Pacific plate; it is mostly within the Pacific Ocean.)* Encourage students to examine each plate boundary. Show them how to use the key to determine the type of boundary and the direction of plate motion. As a class, compare and contrast the motion at each boundary.
Visual

Teacher **Demo**

A CONVERGENT MODEL L2

Purpose Students will observe what happens when two plates collide in a model of a convergent boundary.

Materials two slabs of modeling clay, wax paper

Procedure Place the slabs of clay on the wax paper on a table so they will slide easily. Push the two slabs of clay together to model a collision of two plates.

Expected Outcome The clay slabs will buckle up to create folds and breaks that resemble mountains.
Kinesthetic, Visual

MAP IT!
ACTIVITY

As shown in **Figure 15**, most of the Earth's plates are made up of both oceanic and continental lithosphere.
Identify Find a major plate that includes an entire continent plus a large area of ocean floor. Then locate two examples of a divergent boundary, a convergent boundary, and a transform fault boundary.

FIGURE 15 Earth's Tectonic Plates

Types of Plate Boundaries Interactions among individual plates occur along plate boundaries. The three types of plate boundaries are convergent, divergent, and transform fault boundaries. Most plates feature a combination of each of the three types.

Divergent boundaries are found where two of Earth's plates move apart. Oceanic lithosphere is created at divergent boundaries—think of how sea-floor spreading adds rock to the ocean floor.

Convergent boundaries form where two plates move together. Lithosphere can be destroyed at convergent boundaries—think about how oceanic lithosphere sinks into the mantle during subduction.

262 Chapter 9 • Lesson 3

Differentiated Instruction

SPECIAL NEEDS Students will benefit by having globes in the classroom. You might want to mark the major plates on a globe so students can better visualize how Earth's lithosphere is divided into tectonic plates.

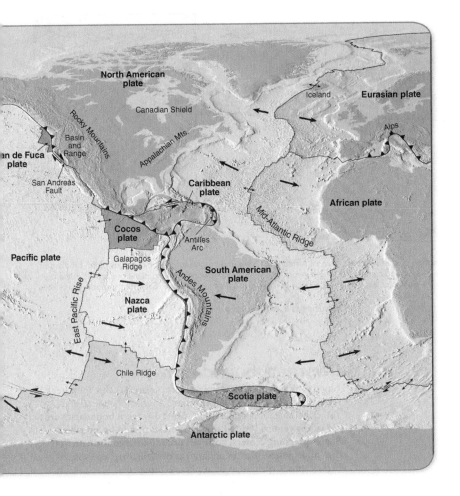

North American plate
Iceland
Eurasian plate
Canadian Shield
Rocky Mountains
Appalachian Mts.
Alps
Basin and Range
an de Fuca plate
San Andreas Fault
Caribbean plate
Mid-Atlantic Ridge
African plate
Cocos plate
Antilles Arc
Pacific plate
Galapagos Ridge
South American plate
East Pacific Rise
Andes Mountains
Nazca plate
Chile Ridge
Scotia plate
Antarctic plate

Transform fault boundaries occur where two plates grind past each other. Along transform boundaries, lithosphere is neither created nor destroyed.

Transform fault boundaries occur where two plates grind past each other. Along transform boundaries, lithosphere is neither created nor destroyed.

Plates may shrink or grow in area, depending on the locations of convergent and divergent boundaries. For example, you can see in Figure 15 that the Philippine plate is subducting beneath Asia, but has no ridges as boundaries to create new lithosphere. As a result, the plate is getting smaller because of subduction.

☑ **Reading Checkpoint** *What is a transform fault boundary?*

Plate Tectonics **263**

Facts and Figures

WIDE PLATE BOUNDARIES Earth is always more complicated than a book can describe. The boundaries between plates are rarely the sharp lines that are shown in maps and figures. Significant deformation occurs where two plates interact. For instance, the entire Himalayas and much of southern China is actually part of the India/Asia plate boundary, actively deforming from the collision. Much of the western United States,

like the Basin and Range region, is actually a "plate boundary" area and is internally deforming. The San Andreas fault is part of a wide system of faults and deformation many hundreds of kilometers across. In fact, about 15% of Earth's surface can be considered plate boundary areas. This is half as much area as the amount of land at Earth's surface (30%).

LESSON 9.3

CREATING A CONTINENTAL RIFT **L2**

Purpose Students will observe how fractures grow to form a continental rift as a result of the stretching of the lithosphere.

Materials 2 slices of individually wrapped American cheese, dull knife or fingernail, metric ruler

Procedure Using your fingernail or a dull knife, make a small cut in the center of a cheese slice parallel to one edge. Pull on the two cheese edges parallel to the cut. You will be pulling perpendicular to the direction of the cut. Observe how the small defect (the cut) concentrates the tearing. Observe the shape of the fracture that forms, especially the pointed tips where the tearing is taking place, and how the fracture tips move faster as the fracture gets bigger.

Now, make a cut near the center of the second piece of cheese. Make a second parallel cut about 2 cm below and 2 cm to the right of the first cut. Pull on the cheese as before. Fractures will begin to form from each of the cuts. As the tips of these fractures begin to move past each other, they will begin to curve toward each other and eventually link up into a single fracture.

Safety Do not allow students to eat the cheese.

Expected Outcome Students should infer that the fractures in the cheese are analogous to the formation of faults that result in the development of a rift valley. Visual, Logical

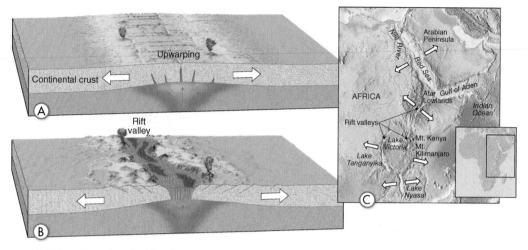

FIGURE 16 Formation of a Rift Valley The East African rift valleys may represent the initial stages of the breakup of a continent along a spreading center. **A** Rising hot rock forces the crust upward, causing numerous cracks in the rigid lithosphere. **B** As the crust is pulled apart, large slabs of rock sink, causing a rift zone. **C** Further spreading produces a narrow sea like the Red Sea.
Relate Cause and Effect *What causes the continental crust to stretch and break?*

Divergent Boundaries

Along divergent boundaries, plates move apart. Because they are the areas where sea-floor spreading begins, divergent boundaries are also called spreading centers. **Most divergent boundaries are spreading centers located along the crests of mid-ocean ridges. Some spreading centers, however, occur on the continents.** You can think of these plate boundaries as *constructive* plate margins because this is where new lithosphere is produced.

When a spreading center forms on land, the process can literally split a continent apart. As shown in **Figure 16A,** the process begins when the forces of plate motion begin to stretch an area of the lithosphere. Plumes of hot rock rise from the mantle. In a process called upwarping, the rising plumes bend the crust upward, fracturing it. The fractures allow magma to reach the surface. The result is the floor of a new rift valley, as shown in **Figure 16B.**

Examples of active rift valleys include the Rhine Valley in northwestern Europe and the Great Rift Valley, a series of connected rifts in eastern Africa, as shown in **Figure 16C.** The Great Rift Valley, which is also seen at the opening of this chapter, may represent the first stage in the breakup of the African continent. If the sides of the rift valley continue to move apart, the rift could eventually become a narrow sea similar to the Red Sea.

☑ **Reading Checkpoint** *How do rift valleys begin to form?*

Facts and Figures

The first rift that developed as Pangaea began to break apart 200 million years ago resulted in the separation of North America and Africa. Large quantities of basalts were produced. These basalts can be found today as weathered rock beds along the eastern seaboard of the United States. They are buried beneath rocks that form the continental shelf and have been radiometrically dated as being between 200 million and 165 million years old. The rifting eventually formed the Atlantic Ocean basin.

Convergent Boundaries

🔑 **At convergent boundaries, plates collide and interact, producing features including trenches, volcanoes, and mountain ranges.** Along convergent boundaries, old portions of oceanic lithosphere return to the mantle. As a result, Earth's total surface area can remain the same, even though new lithosphere is constantly being added at mid-ocean ridges. Because lithosphere is "destroyed" at convergent boundaries, they are sometimes called *destructive* plate margins.

The type of lithosphere involved and the forces acting upon it determine what happens at convergent boundaries. Convergent boundaries can form between plate edges made of oceanic lithosphere, between oceanic lithosphere and continental lithosphere, or between plate edges made of continental lithosphere.

Oceanic-Continental When continental lithosphere converges with oceanic lithosphere, the less dense continental lithosphere continues to float. The denser oceanic lithosphere sinks into the asthenosphere. When a descending, or subducting, plate reaches a depth of about 100 to 150 kilometers, some of the asthenosphere above the subducting plate melts. The newly formed magma, being less dense than the rock of the mantle, rises. Eventually, some of this magma may reach the surface and cause volcanic eruptions.

A **continental volcanic arc** is a range of volcanic mountains within a continent produced in part by the subduction of oceanic lithosphere, as shown in **Figure 17**. The volcanoes of the Andes in South America are the product of magma formed during subduction of the Nazca plate.

FIGURE 17 Oceanic-Continental Convergent Boundary
Oceanic lithosphere is subducted beneath a continental plate.
Infer *Why doesn't volcanic activity occur closer to the trench?*

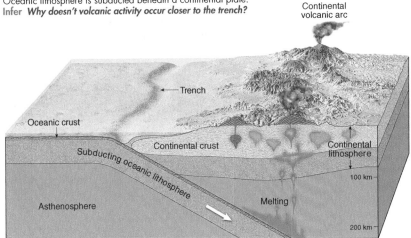

Continental volcanic arc

Trench

Oceanic crust

Continental crust

Subducting oceanic lithosphere

Continental lithosphere

100 km

Asthenosphere

Melting

200 km

Plate Tectonics **265**

LESSON 9.3

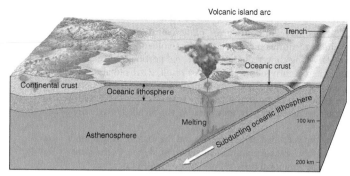

FIGURE 18 Oceanic-Oceanic Convergent Boundary One oceanic plate is subducted beneath another oceanic plate, forming a volcanic island arc.
Predict *What would happen to the volcanic activity if the subduction stopped?*

Oceanic-Oceanic When two oceanic slabs converge, one descends beneath the other. This causes volcanic activity similar to what occurs at an oceanic-continental boundary. However, the volcanoes form on the ocean floor instead of on a continent, as shown in **Figure 18.** If this activity continues, it will eventually build a chain of volcanic structures that become islands. This newly formed land consisting of an arc-shaped chain of small volcanic islands is called a **volcanic island arc.** The islands of Java and Sumatra in the Indian Ocean are an example of a volcanic island arc. Next to these islands is the Java trench, where one of the most powerful earthquakes ever recorded occurred in 2004.

Continental-Continental When oceanic lithosphere is subducted beneath continental lithosphere, a continental volcanic arc develops along the margin of the continent. However, if the subducting plate also contains continental lithosphere, the subduction eventually brings the two continents together, as shown in **Figure 19.** Because continental lithosphere is less dense than oceanic lithosphere, it is not subducted. Instead, the result is a collision between the two continents and the formation of complex mountains.

**FIGURE 19
Continental-Continental Convergent Boundary** Continental lithosphere cannot be fully subducted, because it isn't very dense. The collision of two continents forms mountain ranges. The suture (red line) represents the zone where the two plates meet.

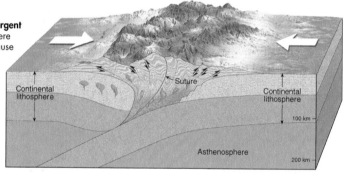

Facts and Figures

Only two volcanic island arcs are located in the Atlantic Ocean—the Lesser Antilles adjacent to the Caribbean Sea and the Sandwich Islands in the South Atlantic. There have been many volcanic eruptions in the Lesser Antilles. In 1902 on the island of Martinique, Mount Pelé erupted, killing 28,000 people and destroying the town of St. Pierre. More recently, the Soufriere Hills Volcano on the island of Montserrat erupted from 1995 until 1997. Although volcanic activity has since decreased, seismic activity has increased. There were several earthquakes on Montserrat in early 2004.

Before continents collide, they are separated by an ocean basin. As the continents move toward each other, the ocean floor between them is subducted beneath one of the plates. When the continents collide, the collision folds and deforms the sediments along the margin as if they were placed in a giant vise. A new mountain range forms that is composed of deformed and metamorphosed sedimentary rocks, fragments of the volcanic arc, and possibly slivers of oceanic crust.

This kind of collision occurred when the subcontinent of India rammed into Asia and produced the Himalayas, as shown in **Figure 20.** During this collision, the continental crust buckled and fractured. Several other major mountain systems, including the Alps, Appalachians, and Urals, were also formed by this process.

☑ **Reading Checkpoint** *What caused the Himalayas to form?*

FIGURE 20 Collision of India and Asia A The leading edge of the plate carrying India is subducted beneath the Eurasian plate. **B** The landmasses collide and push up the crust. **C** India's collision with Asia continues today.

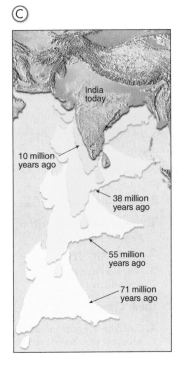

Build Science Skills L2

Use Analogies The discussion on this page uses an analogy of a giant vise to help students visualize and understand what happens to the lithosphere during a continental-continental collision. Be sure students understand what a vise is. *(a tool that holds an object by squeezing two plates together, usually by turning a large screw)* If they are not familiar with the term, have them look it up in a dictionary, or have another student describe it. Revisit the text and discuss why the analogy is useful. *(A squeezing vise could fold and deform material as colliding continents fold and deform rock)* **Ask:** What other analogies might be used to describe continental-continental collisions? *(Sample answers: small entry rug crumpling as it gets caught between an opening door and a wall, two cars colliding)*
Intrapersonal, Logical

Answers

Figure 18 *If the subduction stopped, the volcanic activity would probably also soon stop because the source of new magma is the continuing subduction of the oceanic plate.*

☑ **Reading Checkpoint** *The collision of two continental plates*

Facts and Figures

The Himalayas include the highest mountains on Earth. When India and Asia collided, the leading edge of the Indian plate was forced partially under Asia, generating an unusually great thickness of continental lithosphere.

This accumulation accounts in part for the high elevation of the Himalayas and may also explain the elevated Tibetan Plateau to the north.

LESSON 9.3

Build Science Skills   L2

Relate Cause and Effect Remind students that plates in a transform fault boundary move past each other without production or destruction of lithosphere. **Ask:** Why does this movement cause earthquakes? *(The tremendous friction caused by two plates grinding past each other causes earthquakes.)*
Logical

3 ASSESS

Evaluate Understanding   L2

To assess students' knowledge of lesson content, have them write three short paragraphs describing the three convergent boundaries and what results when they converge.

Reteach   L1

Have students demonstrate the action of the three convergent boundaries by using their hands to represent the converging plates.

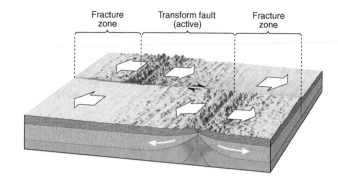

FIGURE 21 Transform Faults
A transform fault boundary offsets segments of a divergent boundary at an oceanic ridge.

Fracture zone   Transform fault (active)   Fracture zone

Transform Fault Boundaries

The third type of plate boundary is the transform fault boundary, where pieces of lithosphere move past each other. **At a transform fault boundary, plates grind past each other without destroying the lithosphere.** Most transform faults join two parallel segments of a mid-ocean ridge, as shown in **Figure 21.** These faults occur about every 100 kilometers along the ridge axis. Active transform faults lie between the two offset ridge segments. These are considered active because the parallel segments of young ocean floor are moving in opposite directions and grinding past each other.

Although most transform faults are located within the ocean basins, a few cut through continental lithosphere. One example is the San Andreas fault in California, where the Pacific plate is moving past the North American plate. If this movement continues, that part of California west of the fault will become an island off the West Coast. However, a more immediate concern is the earthquake activity triggered by movements along this fault system.

9.3 Assessment

Review Key Concepts

1. In your own words, briefly explain the theory of plate tectonics.

2. List the three types of plate boundaries.

3. Why is a divergent boundary considered a constructive plate margin?

Think Critically

4. **Calculate** If a plate moves at a rate of 10 cm per year, how far will the plate move in 20,000,000 years? Give your answer in kilometers.

5. **Predict** Suppose you could view the Great Rift Valley in Africa millions of years from now. How might the region have changed?

6. **Relate Cause and Effect** What forms when oceanic lithosphere collides with continental lithosphere at a convergent boundary? Explain.

WRITING IN SCIENCE

7. **Predict** A series of deep-ocean trenches rings the Pacific Ocean. Write a paragraph that describes how the Pacific Ocean might change over millions of years, based on the theory of plate tectonics.

268 Chapter 9 • Lesson 3

Assessment Answers

1. According to the theory of plate tectonics, large pieces of Earth's lithosphere, called plates, move slowly over Earth's surface driven by convection currents in the mantle. Plates can include oceanic and/or continental lithosphere. Plate interactions help cause earthquakes, volcanoes, and mountain building.
2. convergent boundaries, divergent boundaries, and transform boundaries

3. because volcanic activity along divergent boundaries produces new oceanic lithosphere
4. 2000 km
5. After millions of years, the Great Rift Valley could widen and form a new ocean basin similar to the Red Sea.
6. Because the oceanic lithosphere is denser than the continental lithosphere, a trench forms, and the oceanic lithosphere is subducted beneath the less dense continental lithosphere.

7. Students' paragraphs should make the point that the Pacific Ocean should get smaller as ocean floor is subducted beneath the trenches around the margins of the ocean.

Plate Tectonics into the Future

Two geologists, Robert Dietz and John Holden, used present-day plate movements to predict the locations of landmasses in the future. The map below shows where they predict Earth's landmasses will be 50 million years from now if plate movements continue at their present rates.

FIGURE 22 Future Continent Positions

MAP IT!
ACTIVITY

As shown in **Figure 22**, the world may look quite different 50 million years from now.
Interpret Maps What effect will the movement of the North American and South American plates have on the Atlantic Ocean?

L.A. on the Move

In North America, the Baja Peninsula and the portion of southern California that lies west of the San Andreas fault will have slid past the North American plate. If this northward motion takes place, Los Angeles and San Francisco will pass each other in about 12 million years.

New Sea in Africa

Major changes are seen in Africa, where a new sea will emerge as eastern Africa is ripped away from the mainland. In addition, the African plate will collide with the Eurasian plate, perhaps triggering the next major mountain-building phase. Meanwhile, the Arabian Peninsula will move away from Africa, causing the Red Sea to widen.

Atlantic Ocean Grows

In other parts of the world, Australia will straddle the equator and, along with New Guinea, will be on a collision course with Asia. Meanwhile, North and South America will begin to separate, while the Atlantic and Indian oceans will continue to grow as the Pacific Ocean shrinks.

These projections, although interesting, must be viewed critically. Many assumptions must be correct for these events to occur. We can be sure that large changes in the shapes and positions of continents will occur for millions of years to come, but directions and rates of plate movement could change.

Plate Tectonics **269**

PLATE TECTONICS INTO THE FUTURE   L2

Background
Robert Dietz began his career as a marine geologist. He was an early proponent of continental drift and of sea-floor spreading, which he named. Much of his early work was conducted in submersibles off the coast of California. John Holden was Dietz's colleague and his illustrator.

Teaching Tip Have students cut out outlines of the continents and place them on a piece of white poster paper in their current locations. As students read each paragraph of the feature, they should move the continents to their predicted location. When they finish reading the feature, ask students to write a short paragraph describing how plant and animal life would be different on the continents in their new positions. For example, tropical vegetation in southern California would be replaced with plant life that could exist in an Arctic climate.
Verbal, Kinesthetic

Answers

MAP IT!   As the North American and South American plates move west, the Atlantic Ocean will grow wider.

Facts and Figures

SLAB SUCTION Though subducting lithosphere often goes into the mantle at an angle close to 45°, gravity is pulling it straight down, with the result that the location of the trench often moves away from the overlying plate in a process called trench roll-back. This trench roll-back creates a large force called *slab suction* that pulls the overlying plate toward the trench. Slab suction is a large force and has important consequences. Slab suction is responsible for the formation of back-arc basins that are rifting and opening up behind volcanic arcs, as the arcs are pulled away from the rest of the continent. The Japan Sea, between Japan and China, formed this way. Slab suction may also be the cause of the breakup of supercontinents like Pangaea. A supercontinent has subduction occurring all around its edges. The combined slab suction forces from all this subduction may be what finally pulls the supercontinent apart.

9.4 Mechanisms of Plate Motion

Lesson Objectives

9.10 **Relate** the unequal distribution of heat in Earth and the mechanism of mantle convection to the movement of tectonic plates.

9.11 **Compare** the mechanisms of slab-pull and ridge-push as contributing to plate motion.

Build Vocabulary ![L2]

Paraphrase Have students explain, in their own words, the meaning of the new vocabulary terms in this lesson. Because each term contains an "action-type" word *(pull, push, plume, convection)*, students should be able to form mental images to help with their explanations.

Reading Strategy ![L2]

a. the major mechanism of plate motion as the upward flow of hot, less dense mantle material and the downward flow of cold, dense material drives plate tectonics
b. mechanism of plate motion in which the descending slab pulls on the plate
c. mechanism of plate motion in which the force of new crust formed at the high ridges pushes on the plate

2 INSTRUCT

Build Science Skills ![L2]

Use Models Challenge students to use their hands, phone books, or other objects to model slab-pull and ridge-push. Have them explain the processes as they manipulate the model.
Verbal, Kinesthetic

Key Questions

🔑 *What causes plate motions?*

🔑 *What are the mechanisms of plate motions?*

Vocabulary
- convection current
- slab-pull
- ridge-push
- mantle plume

Reading Strategy

Review Copy the table. As you read, write the main ideas for each topic.

Topic	Main Idea
Mantle convection	a. ____ ?
Slab pull	b. ____ ?
Ridge push	c. ____ ?

YOU MAY have watched bits of vegetables rising and sinking in a pot of soup on the stove. This rising and sinking is an example of a convection current. A **convection current** is the continuous, circular flow that occurs in a fluid because of differences in density. Warm material is less dense, so it rises. Cool material is denser, so it sinks. Some convection currents, such as the hypothetical pot of soup on a stove, are driven by heat.

What Causes Plate Motions?

The convection currents in a pot of soup can serve as a model for the causes of plate motion. 🔑 **Convection currents in the mantle provide the basic driving forces for plate motions.** The hot, but solid, rock of the mantle behaves in a plastic way over geologic time—that is, it can flow slowly. The main heat source for mantle convection is energy released by radioactive isotopes in the mantle, such as uranium, thorium, and potassium. Another source is heat from the core. Since most of the heat comes from within the mantle, a bowl of soup in a microwave oven may be a better analogy for this process than a pot on a stove.

But how does mantle convection produce plate motions? The plates are simply the top part of mantle convection currents. The weakness of the asthenosphere allows the stiff lithosphere above to slide across it. The relatively new oceanic lithosphere at the top of the convection current cools and becomes denser than the mantle rock beneath it. As a result, a plate edge of oceanic lithosphere will eventually subduct beneath another plate. The density of the oceanic lithosphere causes it to sink down toward the base of the mantle. Meanwhile, material from the lower mantle rises up to the upper mantle. It reaches the surface at mid-ocean ridges. Where it emerges, new lithosphere is formed. This cyclic flow of material from the mantle to the surface and back again, which may take a half-billion years, is called whole-mantle convection, shown in **Figure 23.**

Plate Motion Mechanisms

Density plays a major role in sending lithosphere back into the mantle. **The sinking of dense oceanic lithosphere directly drives the motions of mantle convection through slab-pull and ridge-push.** In **slab-pull,** gravity pulls dense oceanic lithosphere down into the deep mantle. In **ridge-push,** the oceanic lithosphere slides down the asthenosphere that is elevated near mid-ocean ridges. Acting together, ridge-push and slab-pull take oceanic lithosphere from mid-ocean ridges toward subduction zones and back to the mantle.

Because Earth is not growing or shrinking in size, the downward flow of subducted oceanic lithosphere must equal the upward flow of rock back toward the surface. Scientists are debating how this happens. Some scientists think that most upwelling of mantle rock occurs in the form of hot-spot **mantle plumes,** which are rising columns of hot mantle rock. Other scientists disagree. They think that rock replaces sinking oceanic lithosphere through a slow, broad rise of rock throughout the mantle. Most scientists think both processes are involved.

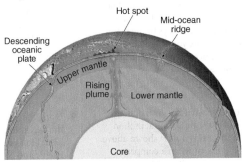

FIGURE 23 Whole-Mantle Convection In the whole-mantle convection model, cold oceanic lithosphere descends into the mantle. Hot mantle plumes transfer heat toward the surface.

9.4 Assessment

Review Key Concepts

1. How are plate motions connected with motions within the rest of Earth's mantle?

2. How are the forces of slab-pull and ridge-push related to plate motions?

3. What is the ultimate source of heat that moves the plates?

Think Critically

4. Predict If Earth did not form with very much uranium, thorium, or potassium, how might it have been different than it is today?

5. Infer What characteristic of old, oceanic lithosphere in a subduction zone contributes to slab-pull? Explain.

BIGIDEA DYNAMIC EARTH

6. Explain Review Lesson 9.2. Use what you learned about sea-floor spreading and about the role of convection currents in plate tectonics to write the "life story" of a plate made of oceanic lithosphere.

Plate Tectonics **271**

Use Visuals L1

Figure 23 Have students study the figure. **Ask:** At what type of boundary does upward convective movement occur? *(divergent)* At what type of boundary does downward convective movement occur? *(convergent)*

3 ASSESS

Evaluate Understanding L2

To assess students' knowledge of lesson content, have them write a short paragraph explaining convection. Paragraphs should include the cause of convection currents and the movements that occur.

Reteach L1

Demonstrate convection as follows: Heat a beaker of water on a hot plate. When the water is hot, add an ice cube to the water near the edge of the beaker. Drop a few drops of food coloring next to the ice cube. Students will be able to watch the food coloring move through the water by convection.

Assessment Answers

1. Convection currents in the mantle provide the forces that drive plate motions in the lithosphere.

2. In slab-pull, gravity pulls cool, dense oceanic lithosphere down into the mantle. In ridge-push, gravity causes stiff oceanic lithosphere to slide down the asthenosphere, which is elevated near mid-ocean ridges. Both slab-pull and ridge-push contribute to the movement of oceanic lithosphere.

3. Heat from the core and heat from radioactive isotopes such as uranium, thorium, and potassium

4. Without radioactive elements, Earth's interior would be cooler. This would slow or perhaps stop the convection currents that cause plate motions. As a result, Earth might lack many of the geologic features, such as mountains and volcanoes, produced by plate tectonics.

5. Old oceanic lithosphere in a subduction zone is cooler and denser than oceanic lithosphere near a mid-ocean ridge. As a result, it can more easily be subducted beneath continental lithosphere or younger, less dense oceanic lithosphere.

6. Student answers should mention that new ocean floor forms during sea-floor spreading and that convection currents drive plate movement.

Plate Tectonics **271**

PALEOMAGNETISM AND THE OCEAN FLOOR L2

Objectives
In this activity, students will
- interpret diagrams of sea-floor sections with respect to paleomagnetism.
- measure the distance that different ocean basins have opened.
- calculate the rate of sea-floor spreading in different ocean basins based on magnetic polarity reversals.

(Address Misconceptions)

Students may think that the rocks on the ocean floor change their polarity every time Earth's polarity reverses. Remind students that magnetic polarity cannot be changed after rock material crystallizes. **Ask:** What causes a substance to be magnetic? *(The molecules in the substance are all aligned in the same direction.)* Tell students that once the substance solidifies, its molecules are held in a rigid lattice and cannot change their alignment.

Skills Observe, Compare and Contrast, Infer, Calculate, Measure, Interpret Diagrams

Prep Time 20 minutes to copy diagrams

Advance Prep Copy the diagrams on p. 273 and distribute them to students.

Class Time 30 minutes

Teaching Tips
- Copying and handing out the diagrams in this lab will ensure that students will not write in their textbooks.
- Have students review the material on paleomagnetism before they begin the lab.

Expected Outcome Students will find that the left side of the Pacific basin has moved about 80 km in 2 million years, whereas the left side of the North Atlantic basin has moved only 37 km during the same time period. During this time period, the ocean basins spread by the following distances: Pacific—approximately 160 km; North Atlantic—approximately 74 km; South Atlantic—approximately 78 km

---

Paleomagnetism and the Ocean Floor

Problem How are the paleomagnetic patterns on the ocean floor used to determine the rate of sea-floor spreading?

Materials pencil, metric ruler, calculator, photocopy of diagrams on next page

Skills Measure, Interpret Diagrams, Calculate

Connect to the [Big idea] When Wegener proposed his hypothesis of continental drift, little was known about the ocean floor. He thought that the continents plowed through the ocean floor like icebreaking ships plowing through ice. Later studies of the oceans provided one of the keys to the plate tectonic hypothesis. In this lab, you will observe how the magnetic rocks on the ocean floor can be used to understand plate tectonics.

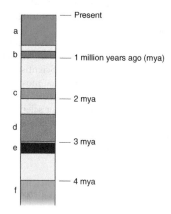

Procedure

1. Scientists have reconstructed Earth's magnetic polarity reversals over the past several million years. A record of these reversals is shown above. Periods of normal polarity, when a compass would have pointed north as it does today, are shown in color. Periods of reverse polarity are shown in white. Record the number of times Earth's magnetic field has had reversed polarity in the last 4 million years.

2. The three diagrams on the next page illustrate the magnetic polarity reversals across sections of the mid-ocean ridges in the Pacific, South Atlantic, and North Atlantic oceans. Periods of normal polarity are shown in color and match the colors in the illustration above. Observe that the patterns of polarity in the rock match on either side of the ridge for each ocean basin.

3. On the photocopy of the three ocean-floor diagrams, identify and mark the periods of normal polarity with the letters *a–f*. Begin at the rift valley and label along both sides of each ridge. (*Hint:* The left side of the South Atlantic has already been done and can act as a guide.)

4. Using the South Atlantic as an example, label the beginning of the normal polarity period c, "2 million years ago," on the left sides of the Pacific and North Atlantic diagrams.

5. Using the distance scale shown with the ocean floor diagrams, determine which ocean basin has spread the greatest distance during the last 2 million years. (Measure from the center of the rift valley.)

6. Refer to the distance scale. Notice that the left side of the South Atlantic basin has moved approximately 39 kilometers from the center of the rift valley in 2 million years.

Analyze and Conclude

1. **Analyze Data** How many kilometers has the left side of the Pacific basin moved in 2 million years?

2. **Analyze Data** How many kilometers has the left side of the North Atlantic basin moved in 2 million years?

3. **Infer** By how many kilometers has each ocean basin spread in the past 2 million years?

4. Calculate If both the distance that each ocean basin has spread and the time it took to do so are known, the rate of sea-floor spreading can be calculated. Determine the rate of sea-floor spreading for the South Atlantic Ocean basin in centimeters per year. (*Hint:* To determine the rate of spreading in centimeters per year for each ocean basin, first convert the distance from kilometers to centimeters and then divide this distance by the time, 2 million years.)

5. Calculate Determine the rate of sea-floor spreading for the North Atlantic and Pacific Ocean basins.

6. Draw Conclusions Which ocean basin is spreading the fastest? The slowest?

7. Infer Do ocean basins spread uniformly over the entire basin? Explain.

GO FURTHER Use the library or the Internet to research the spreading rates for other divergent plate boundaries on Earth. Where is the fastest spreading rate? The slowest spreading rate?

Pacific Ocean

Ridge crest

Ocean floor crust

South Atlantic Ocean

f   e   d   c   b   a   ← 39 km →   Magnetic polarity record
2 million years

North Atlantic Ocean

0   20   40 km
Scale

Plate Tectonics **273**

Answers to Procedure Questions
1. five times
5. The Pacific Ocean basin has moved the greatest distance.

Analyze and Conclude
1. approximately 80 km
2. approximately 37 km
3. Pacific: approximately 160 km; North Atlantic: approximately 74 km; South Atlantic: approximately 78 km
4. The South Atlantic Ocean basin spreading rate is 3.9 cm/yr.
5. The Pacific Ocean basin's spreading rate is 8.0 cm/yr. The North Atlantic Ocean basin's spreading rate is 3.7 cm/yr.
6. Fastest: Pacific; slowest: North Atlantic
7. No, large basins such as the Pacific Ocean basin are spreading at various rates along their spreading ridges.

GO FURTHER

The fastest spreading rate is the northern part of the Pacific plate, which is spreading at approximately 15.6 cm/yr. The slowest spreading rate is the Southwest Indian Ridge, between the African plate and the Antarctic plate, which is spreading at 1.4–1.5 cm/yr.
Visual, Logical

Organize New Information

Have students make vocabulary flashcards by writing a vocabulary word on one side of a card and its definition on the other side. Students can also give an example or draw a simple diagram of the term's meaning. Have students quiz each other by using the cards.

21st Century | Learning

Critical Thinking and Systems Thinking

What observations led to the theory of plate tectonics?

It took a lot of evidence for Wegener's hypothesis of continental drift to become the theory of plate tectonics. Encourage students to research the history of the theory of plate tectonics. Then, ask them to develop a concept map that details the evidence that led to the theory. Tell them to include the names of any relevant scientists in the concept map.

Homework Guide

Lesson	Questions
1	2, 3, 10, 19, 21
2	4, 9, 11, 13, 17, 18, 20, 25, 26
3	1, 5–8, 12, 14–16, 22, 23, 27, 28–30
4	24

9 Study Guide

Big idea ▸ Dynamic Earth

9.1 Continental Drift

🔑 According to Wegener's hypothesis of continental drift, the continents were once joined to form a single supercontinent.

🔑 Fossil evidence for continental drift includes several fossil organisms found on different landmasses.

🔑 Matching types of rock in several mountain belts that today are separated by oceans provide evidence for continental drift.

🔑 Wegener found glacial deposits showing that between 220 million and 300 million years ago, ice sheets covered large areas of the Southern Hemisphere. Deposits of glacial till occurred at latitudes that today have temperate or even tropical climates: southern Africa, South America, India, and Australia.

🔑 The main objection to Wegener's hypothesis was that he could not describe a mechanism capable of moving the continents.

continental drift (248)
Pangaea (248)

9.2 Sea-Floor Spreading

🔑 Earth's mid-ocean ridge system forms the longest feature on Earth's surface.

🔑 In the process of sea-floor spreading, new ocean floor forms along Earth's mid-ocean ridges and slowly moves outward across ocean basins.

🔑 Evidence for sea-floor spreading included magnetic strips in ocean-floor rock, earthquake patterns, and measurements of the age of the ocean floor.

sonar (254)	sea-floor spreading (256)
deep-ocean trench (255)	subduction (257)
mid-ocean ridge (255)	paleomagnetism (258)
rift valley (255)	

9.3 Theory of Plate Tectonics

🔑 In the theory of plate tectonics, Earth's lithospheric plates move slowly relative to each other, driven by convection currents in the mantle.

🔑 Most divergent boundaries are spreading centers located along the crests of mid-ocean ridges. Some spreading centers, however, occur on the continents.

🔑 At convergent boundaries, plates collide and interact, producing features including trenches, volcanoes, and mountain ranges.

🔑 At a transform fault boundary, plates grind past each other without destroying the lithosphere.

plate (261)
plate tectonics (261)
divergent boundary (262)
convergent boundary (262)
transform fault boundary (263)
continental volcanic arc (265)
volcanic island arc (266)

9.4 Mechanisms of Plate Motion

🔑 Convection currents in the mantle provide the basic driving forces for plate motions.

🔑 The sinking of dense oceanic lithosphere directly drives the motions of mantle convection through slab-pull and ridge-push.

convection current (270)
slab-pull (271)
ridge-push (271)
mantle plume (271)

Assessment Answers

Review Content

1. b	**2.** c	**3.** c
4. b	**5.** c	**6.** d
7. d	**8.** a	**9.** b
10. c		

Understand Concepts

11. During sea-floor spreading, new oceanic lithosphere forms along mid-ocean ridges. It then cools and moves across ocean basins as a result of ridge push and slab pull. Finally, it sinks into the mantle through subduction beneath a trench.

9 Assessment

Choose the letter that best answers the question or completes the statement.

1. What is the weaker, hotter zone beneath the lithosphere that allows for motion of Earth's rigid outer shell?
   a. crust
   b. asthenosphere
   c. outer core
   d. inner core

2. Alfred Wegener is best known for what hypothesis?
   a. plate tectonics
   b. sea-floor spreading
   c. continental drift
   d. subduction

3. What is the name given by Wegener to the supercontinent he proposed existed before the current continents?
   a. Euroamerica
   b. Atlantis
   c. Pangaea
   d. Panamerica

4. Support for Harry Hess's hypothesis of sea-floor spreading did NOT include
   a. magnetic stripes in ocean floor rock.
   b. granitic rock in the ocean floor.
   c. earthquake patterns in subduction zones.
   d. the age of the ocean floor rock.

5. Most of Earth's earthquakes, volcanoes, and mountain building occur
   a. in the center of continents.
   b. in the Himalayas.
   c. at plate boundaries.
   d. at volcanic island arcs.

6. Complex mountain systems such as the Himalayas are the result of
   a. oceanic-oceanic convergence.
   b. oceanic-continental convergence.
   c. continental volcanic arcs.
   d. continental-continental convergence.

7. Which of the following mountain ranges was NOT the result of continental-continental convergence?
   a. Himalayas
   b. Alps
   c. Appalachians
   d. Andes

8. What is the type of plate boundary where two plates move together, causing one of the slabs of lithosphere to descend into the mantle beneath an overriding plate?
   a. oceanic-continental convergent
   b. divergent
   c. transform fault
   d. continental-continental convergent

9. Most deep-focus earthquakes occur near
   a. rift valleys.
   b. trenches.
   c. mid-ocean ridges.
   d. transform fault boundaries.

10. One of the main objections to Wegener's hypothesis of continental drift was that he was unable to provide an acceptable
   a. rate of continental drift.
   b. date of continental drift.
   c. mechanism for continental drift.
   d. direction of continental drift.

11. Describe the process of sea-floor spreading.

12. What are the three types of convergent plate boundaries?

13. How were earthquake patterns used to provide evidence of sea-floor spreading?

14. Briefly explain the theory of plate tectonics.

15. What type of plate boundary is shown? What types of lithosphere are involved?

16. At what location is most lithosphere created? At what location is most lithosphere destroyed?

17. At what types of plate boundaries do subduction zones form?

Plate Tectonics **275**

---

12. oceanic-oceanic, oceanic-continental, and continental-continental

13. Earthquake patterns are used to show plate boundaries and to trace how the slabs descend into the mantle.

14. The theory of plate tectonics states that Earth's rigid outer shell consists of rigid slabs called plates that are in continuous slow motion relative to each other. This interaction of plates causes most volcanoes, earthquakes, and mountains.

15. divergent boundary, with oceanic lithosphere on both sides

16. Lithosphere is created at divergent boundaries at ocean ridges. It is destroyed at convergent boundaries in subduction zones.

17. Subduction zones form at oceanic-oceanic convergent and oceanic-continental convergent boundaries.

ASSESSMENT

Think Critically

18. at the continental margins

19. The evidence that supported continental drift included the fact that the continents, especially South America and Africa, looked like they could fit together. Similar rock types and structures such as mountain ranges match up on different continents now separated by oceans. Similar fossils are found on different continents. Climate data supports continental drift because glacial deposits occur in areas that now have more tropical climates.

20. Scientists mapped the magnetic polarity of ocean floor on both sides of the ridge. They found that the pattern of strips of rock with the same polarity matched on both sides of the ridge. This showed that the ocean floor moves away from mid-ocean ridges as new rock forms.

21. If *Mesosaurus* were able to swim well enough to cross the Atlantic Ocean, its remains should be found over a wider area on other continents. Since its remains are not found, the two continents were together.

22. The collision of oceanic lithosphere with continental lithosphere produces a subduction zone and the formation of a deep-ocean trench and a continental volcanic arc. No subduction zone, trench, or volcanic arc is produced during the collision of two plates of continental lithosphere. Instead, the collision produces a major mountain range.

Analyze Data

23. The boundary is an oceanic-continental convergent boundary. The plate on the left is made up of oceanic lithosphere, and the plate on the right is made up of continental lithosphere.

24. As the slab of oceanic lithosphere descends, some of the asthenosphere above it melts. This magma rises. When the magma reaches the surface, volcanic activity results. The volcanoes that form are called a continental volcanic arc.

25. The earthquake foci would be shallow along and within the slab as it begins to descend beneath the continental plate. As the plate descends deeper, the earthquake foci will also be deeper within the slab.

Concepts in Action

26. Because of sea-floor spreading, the age of the rock sample from near a mid-ocean ridge would be much younger than the age of a sample from near a trench.

27. A transform fault boundary is formed. Examples include the San Andreas fault in California and many faults along ocean ridges.

Think Critically

18. Draw Conclusions In the Atlantic Ocean basin, where is the oldest oceanic lithosphere found?

19. Review Describe the evidence that supported the hypothesis of continental drift.

20. Relate Cause and Effect Explain how changes in the polarity of Earth's magnetic field provided one type of evidence for the hypothesis of sea-floor spreading.

21. Infer Why did the discovery of *Mesosaurus*, in both South America and Africa but nowhere else, support the hypothesis of continental drift?

22. Compare and Contrast What is the difference between the collision of oceanic lithosphere with continental lithosphere and the collision of two plates of continental lithosphere?

Analyze Data

Use the diagram below to answer Questions 23–25.

23. Interpret Diagrams What type of boundary is shown? What types of lithosphere are involved?

24. Infer What process occurs as the slab of oceanic lithosphere descends beneath the other plate?

25. Apply Concepts What pattern would the foci of earthquakes form if they were plotted in the diagram?

Concepts in Action

26. Predict How would the age of a rock sample obtained by drilling in the ocean floor near a mid-ocean ridge compare with the age of a rock sample from the ocean floor near a trench? Explain.

27. Classify What type of plate boundary is formed when two plates grind past each other? Give an example of this type of boundary.

28. Form a Hypothesis Form a hypothesis to explain what you think would happen if the direction of motion between India and Asia changed and India began to move in a southward direction.

29. Calculate How much wider would the Atlantic Ocean become in 10 million years if the spreading rate at the Mid-Atlantic Ridge were 2.5 cm/yr? Give your answer in kilometers.

30. Explain Write a paragraph explaining why earthquakes are less likely in the middle of the North American plate than they are along the edges of the plate.

Performance-Based Assessment

Classify Use a world map to choose ten different locations around the world. Then use Figure 15 on pages 262–263 to find the plate boundary nearest each location. Classify each boundary.

28. If the motion of India changed to a southward direction, the boundary would change from a continental-continental convergent boundary to a divergent boundary. As India moved away from Asia, rifting would occur between them, and a new ocean might form.

29. The Atlantic Ocean would grow 250 km in 10 million years at a spreading rate of 2.5 cm/yr.

30. Along plate boundaries, enormous stress in the crust deforms and fractures rock. This produces the active faults where earthquakes occur. Areas near the center of a continental plate are far away from these stresses, and therefore they have fewer earthquake-producing active faults.

Performance-Based Assessment

Student answers will vary but should accurately reflect the information presented in Figure 15. An example would be as follows: The boundary between India and Asia is a continental-continental convergent boundary.

Standardized Test Prep

Standardized Test Prep
1 B
2 F
3 C
4 J
5 A

Tips for Success

Eliminating Unreasonable Answers When you answer a multiple-choice question, you can often eliminate at least one answer choice because it is clearly incorrect. If you eliminate one or more choices, you increase your odds of choosing the correct answer.

In the question below, you can immediately eliminate choice B because the outer core is located deep in Earth's interior. The mantle, answer choice A, is another layer that is found in Earth's interior. So you can eliminate A. You have narrowed your choices down to either C, the lithosphere, or D, the asthenosphere. The asthenosphere is not rigid. It is a weak layer over which the plates move. The remaining choice, C, must be the correct answer.

What is Earth's strong, rigid outer layer called?

  A the mantle
  B the outer core
  C the lithosphere
  D the asthenosphere

(Answer: C)

Choose the letter that best answers the question.

1 Which one of the following was *not* used as support of Wegener's continental drift hypothesis?
  A fossil evidence
  B paleomagnetism
  C the fit of South America and Africa
  D ancient climates

2 At what type of plate boundary do plates move apart, resulting in the upwelling of material from the mantle to create new seafloor?
  F divergent
  G convergent
  H transform fault
  J subduction

If You Have Trouble With . . .

Question	1	2	3	4	5
See Lesson	9.1	9.2	9.3	9.3	9.4

Use the diagram below to answer Questions 3–5.

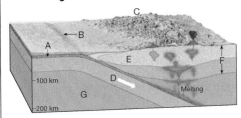

3 What feature is labeled F?
  A a continental volcanic arc
  B a subduction zone
  C continental lithosphere
  D an ocean ridge

4 The process occurring at the location labeled D is—
  F the creation of oceanic lithosphere
  G the creation of continental lithosphere
  H a continental-continental collision
  J the subduction of oceanic lithosphere

5 What characteristic of the lithosphere contributes to the process occurring at the location labeled D?
  A The oceanic lithosphere is denser than the continental lithosphere.
  B The continental lithosphere is denser than the oceanic lithosphere.
  C The older continental lithosphere is denser than the newly formed continental lithosphere.
  D The newly formed continental lithosphere is denser than the older continental lithosphere.

10 Volcanoes and Other Igneous Activity Planning Guide

BIGIDEA: DYNAMIC EARTH

Lesson Objectives		Activities
10.1 Volcanoes and Plate Tectonics, pp. 280–285 10.1 **Describe** the origin of magma. 10.2 **Explain** the relationship between plate tectonics and volcanism, including intraplate volcanism.		TE Teacher Demo: Observing Plate Movement, p. 284 L2 SE Map It: Three Types of Volcanism, pp. 282–283 L2
10.2 The Nature of Volcanic Eruptions, pp. 286–294 10.3 **Explain** the factors that determine the type of volcanic eruptions that occur. 10.4 **Describe** the various types of volcanic materials that are ejected from volcanoes. 10.5 **List** the three main types of volcanoes. 10.6 **Distinguish** how the different types of volcanic landforms form.		SE Quick Lab: Why are some volcanoes explosive? p. 287 L2 TE Teacher Demo: Observing Viscosity, p. 288 L2 TE Teacher Demo: Observing an Explosive Eruption, p. 291 L2
10.3 Intrusive Igneous Activity, pp. 295–297 10.7 **Describe** the major intrusive igneous features, such as dikes, sills, and laccoliths, and how they form. 10.8 **Describe** batholiths and how they form.		
Chapter Features and Labs		
Try It Where Are Volcanoes Located? p. 279		
How Earth Works Effects of Volcanoes, pp. 298–299		
Exploration Lab Melting Temperatures of Rocks, pp. 300–301		

Ability Levels

L1	For students who need additional help
L2	For all students
L3	For students who need to be challenged

Components

SE	Student Edition	LP	Lesson Plans
TE	Teacher's Edition	AA	Active Art
LM	Laboratory Manual	PD	Planet Diary
CT	Chapter Tests	GEODe	Geode CD-ROM
GRSW	Guided Reading & Study Workbook	eText	
CTB	Computer Test Bank		

Resources	Lesson Assessment
GRSW Lesson 10.1 **LP** Lesson Planning 10.1 **PD** Volcanoes	**SE** Lesson 10.1 Assessment, p. 285 **eText** Lesson 10.1
GRSW Lesson 10.2 **LP** Lesson Planning 10.2 **AA** Composite Volcano Eruption **GEODe** Forces Within: Igneous Activity	**SE** Lesson 10.2 Assessment, p. 294 **eText** Lesson 10.2
GRSW Lesson 10.3 **LP** Lesson Planning 10.3	**SE** Lesson 10.3 Assessment, p. 297 **eText** Lesson 10.3

Materials for Activities and Labs

Quantities for each group

STUDENT EDITION

Try It, p. 279
Internet and library resources, world map copy or overlay for world atlas, permanent marker

Quick Lab, p. 287
2 bottles of noncarbonated water, 2 bottles of club soda, paper towels

Exploration Lab, pp. 300–301
photocopy of Temperature Curves graph, colored pencils (3 different colors), ruler

TEACHER'S EDITION

Teacher Demo, p. 284
9 student textbooks, 2 pieces of poster board, thin cardboard or 1-cm stack of notebook paper

Teacher Demo, p. 288
2 large beakers, hot plate, water, 2 large test tubes, test-tube clamp, ice, corn syrup

Teacher Demo, p. 291
2-L soda bottle, rubber stopper, white vinegar, baking soda, paper towel, rubber band, thin bath or kitchen towel, scissors

Assessment

CHAPTER ASSESSMENT
SE Assessment, pp. 303–304
CT Chapter 10 Test
CTB Chapter 10
eText Chapter 10

21st Century Learning

Civic Literacy: What are the best ways to evacuate from a volcano?, TE p. 302

Common Themes

Volcanic activity leads to the formation of igneous rock, and so is the foundation of the rock cycle. Volcanoes are a continual reminder of how geologically active Earth's interior is.

Michael Wysession
Washington University

Space and Time Volcanoes come in many different forms, the most common of which are shield volcanoes, cinder cones, and composite cones. Magma comes up through a conduit which ends with a vent. The top of a volcano often forms a depression called a crater. Magma that cools underground produces a variety of forms that include sills, laccoliths, dikes, and batholiths.

Forces and Motion Volcanic eruptions take the form of lava flows, gases (mostly water vapor and carbon dioxide), and pyroclastic material (such as ash and bombs). Volcanic eruptions can pose significant hazards in the form of pyroclastic flows, ash falls, and lahars (mudflows). Volcanism occurs at divergent margins, such as mid-ocean ridges, through the mechanism of pressure release, and at convergent margins (subduction zones) through the subduction of water, which lowers the melting point of rock. Intraplate volcanism can occur from the eruption of hot plumes of mantle rock called hot spots.

Matter and Energy The style of volcanic eruption is determined by the magma's viscosity, which is due to factors that include the magma's temperature and composition (amount of silica and dissolved gases). Large amounts of dissolved gases often result in explosive eruptions.

Earth as a System Volcanoes are the most dramatic examples of the connection between Earth's surface and interior systems. Volcanic eruptions were largely responsible for forming Earth's early oceans, and still greatly affect global climate.

EARTH SCIENCE REFRESHER

Not All Hot Spots Are Equal

An exciting new area of geophysical research involves the discovery of several different reasons why rock melts to cause intraplate volcanism. Three-dimensional images of Earth's interior structure made using seismic waves (a process called seismic tomography) have verified that there are indeed giant mantle plumes of hot rock that extend from the bottom to the top of the mantle and erupt as hot spot volcanoes. However, many more sites of intraplate volcanism that were traditionally considered hot spots are now found to originate closer to the surface and to occur for other reasons. Earth is a fascinating and complex planet, and it is often not possible to explain its geology with a single simple model.

Hawaii is the classic example of a hot spot mantle plume. Seismic tomography shows the presence of hot rock extending from the base of the mantle up to Hawaii. The rock is heated at the bottom of the mantle by heat from the outer core that conducts across the core-mantle boundary. The added heat makes the rock expand and become buoyant, and it pushes slowly upward, reaching the surface after tens of millions of years.

Address Misconceptions

Students may have the misconception that earthquakes shaking the region around the volcano are the only reason for volcanic eruptions. Earthquakes are common triggers of volcanic eruptions, but are not the only factors involved. For a strategy that helps to overcome this misconception, see **Address Misconceptions** on TE p. 288.

Address **Misconceptions**

Some students may have the misconception that all mountains are volcanoes (either extinct, dormant, or active). Actually most mountains are the result of crustal deformation. Mountain building is discussed in the next chapter. For a strategy that helps to overcome this misconception, see **Address Misconceptions** on **TE p. 283**.

Iceland's large volume of lava, however, may have a different origin. When North America collided with Europe more than 400 million years ago, basaltic ocean crust of the Iapetus Ocean (the previous Atlantic Ocean) was subducted into the mantle. Now that North America and Europe are moving apart to form a new Atlantic Ocean, it seems some of this old basaltic crust is being pulled toward the mid-Atlantic ridge to fill the void created. Because the basalt melts more easily than mantle rock, it is creating a greater volume of magma that has become the island of Iceland, one of the few places where a mid-ocean ridge occurs above sea level. Another cause of volcanism at Iceland and other "hot spots" may be a larger amount of water in the mantle, which lowers the melting temperature of rock and so causes more melting. Such volcanoes would be the result of "wet spots" and not "hot spots."

The volcanism at Yellowstone has long been attributed to a hot spot, but here seismic tomography shows that the source of the magma is very shallow, so it clearly cannot be a true mantle plume hot spot. Several explanations are currently being examined for the cause of Yellowstone volcanism, including small-scale convection beneath the lithosphere and a propagating rift. Whatever the cause, it is worth noting that Yellowstone poses one of the greatest seismic hazards on this continent, and though it doesn't erupt often, it can do so dramatically. An eruption at Yellowstone 630,000 years ago covered the continent with ash, ejecting about 1000 cubic km of pyroclastic material. In comparison, Mt. St. Helens only erupted about 1 cubic km of ash in its big 1980 eruption. Many scientists are concerned that Yellowstone has shown a recent increase in thermal activity associated with rising temperatures, because when Yellowstone erupts, it does so extremely explosively.

BUILD READING LITERACY
Identify Main Idea/Details

Locating Topic Sentences in Paragraphs

Strategy Help students understand and remember the most important information about a topic. This strategy can be applied to short segments of text, such as a single paragraph or a subsection, to find the main idea and details that support the topic. Assign students a short passage to read, such as Anatomy of a Volcano on p. 289.

Example

1. Tell students that many paragraphs have a topic sentence that expresses the paragraph's main idea. Topic sentences are often the first or second sentence in the paragraph. Sometimes, however, they are the last sentence, or even a sentence in the middle of the paragraph.

2. Then, explain that the rest of the paragraph contains details, or additional facts and examples about the main idea.

3. Direct students' attention to a paragraph with a clearly stated topic sentence, and ask students which sentence best states the main idea of the paragraph.

4. Next, help students find sentences with details that explain more about the main idea.

5. Have students organize the main idea and details visually in a web format.

6. Have students work in pairs to identify the main idea and details in another passage and organize them in a web.

See TE p. 289 for a script on how to use this strategy with students. For additional strategies, see TE pp. 285 and 296.

CHAPTER 10

ASSESS PRIOR KNOWLEDGE

Use the Chapter Pretest below to assess students' prior knowledge. As needed, review these concepts.

Review Science Concepts

Lesson 10.1 Have students review the theory of plate tectonics.

Lesson 10.2 Review the composition and nature of the formation of basaltic, andesitic, and rhyolitic rocks with students.

Lesson 10.3 Review sedimentary rock composition and formation with students.

10 Volcanoes and Other Igneous Activity

Big idea Dynamic Earth

Q: Where does new lithosphere come from?

Molten lava pours over the edge of the big island of Hawaii and into the sea, producing clouds of steam. The eruption of deep-ocean volcanoes is what produced these islands.

Chapter Pretest

1. Rhyolite is composed of which of the following? *(a)*
   a. light-colored silicates
   b. dark-colored silicates
   c. a high percentage of iron and magnesium

2. True or False: Basalt is the most common type of extrusive igneous rock. *(True)*

3. True or False: Andesitic rocks contain at least 75 percent dark silicate minerals. *(False)*

4. Identify the type of rock formed by the settling of solid material from a fluid. *(sedimentary rock)*

5. What is the name of the most recent supercontinent in the plate tectonics theory? *(Pangaea)*

6. How do scientists explain the evidence of glacial features in present-day Africa, Australia, South America, and India? *(These areas were once joined into a single continent and located at latitudes farther south than they are today.)*

7. What types of activity can be found along plate boundaries? *(volcanoes, earthquakes, mountain building)*

INQUIRY
TRY IT!

WHERE ARE VOLCANOES LOCATED?

Procedure

1. Use the Internet and library resources to locate at least 15 active volcanoes and 10 historical volcanic eruptions.
2. Plot the locations of these volcanoes on a copy of a world map or on an overlay for a world atlas.
3. Neatly label the volcanoes on the map or overlay.
4. Compare your volcano map with the map of the worldwide distribution of earthquakes on page 231 and the map of plate boundaries on pages 262–263.

Think About It

1. **Observe** What is the relationship between the locations of the volcanoes you plotted and the earthquake epicenters and plate boundaries on the maps?
2. **Infer** If there have been numerous volcanic eruptions in an area, would the area be a likely place for earthquakes to occur? Explain your answer.
3. **Predict** Use your volcano map to predict if a volcanic eruption would be likely or not likely in each of the following areas: eastern coast of North America, Spain, eastern coast of South America, Italy, and Japan.

279

ENGAGE/EXPLORE

INQUIRY
TRY IT!

WHERE ARE VOLCANOES LOCATED? L2

Purpose In this activity, students will observe the locations of volcanic activity in the world.

Skills Observe, Infer, Predict, Interpret Diagrams and Photographs

Prep Time 5 minutes

Materials Internet access, library resource materials, world map copy or overlay for world atlas, permanent marker

Advance Prep Find Web sites and library sources in advance to reduce the time it takes for students to complete the activity. Have copies of world maps or overlays readily available for students to use.

Class Time 30 minutes

Teaching Tip The U.S. Geological Society (USGS) maintains several web sites that may be useful for this activity. In addition, Oregon State University has a program called "Volcano World." This title is a useful search term in most Internet search engines.

Expected Outcome Students will observe a pattern in the locations of volcanic activity, earthquake epicenters, and plate boundaries.

Think About It

1. Volcanoes and earthquake epicenters both occur along plate boundaries for the most part. Only a few volcanoes occur within plates, such as the Hawaiian volcanoes.

2. yes; both volcanoes and earthquake epicenters occur mostly along plate boundaries.

3. eastern coast of North America: no; Spain: no; eastern coast of South America: no; Italy: yes; Japan: yes.

10.1 Volcanoes and Plate Tectonics

Lesson Objectives

10.1 **Describe** the origin of magma.

10.2 **Explain** the relationship between plate tectonics and volcanism, including intraplate volcanism.

Build Vocabulary `L2`

Definitions Have students write a definition for *continental volcanic arc* and *intraplate volcanism* in their own words. After students read the lesson, ask them to draw a diagram that illustrates the definitions.

Reading Strategy `L2`

I. Origin of Magma
   A. Heat
   B. Pressure
   C. Water Content
II. Volcanoes and Plate Boundaries
   A. Divergent Boundary Volcanism
   B. Convergent Boundary Volcanism
   C. Intraplate Volcanism

❷ INSTRUCT

Build Science Skills `L2`

Interpret Photographs Tell students that Tungurahua volcano in Figure 1 formed where two of Earth's plates, the Nazca plate and the South American plate, come together. Have students find these plates on a map of Earth's plates. **Ask:** What type of plate boundary lies between the two plates? *(a convergent boundary)* What is the origin of the magma that forms a volcano like Tungurahua? *(As one plate is subducted beneath the other, magma forms in the mantle rock above the subducting plate.)* Explain that in this lesson, students will learn that heat, pressure, and the water content of mantle rock are factors that affect the melting point of rock and magma formation.

Key Questions

 How does magma form?

What is the relationship between plate boundaries and volcanic activity?

Vocabulary

- decompression melting
- Ring of Fire
- intraplate volcanism
- hot spot

Reading Strategy

Outline After you read, make an outline of the most important ideas in the section.

Volcanoes and Plate Tectonics
I. Origin of Magma
A. Heat
B. _____ ?
II. _____ ?

FIGURE 1 Eruption
Tungurahua volcano in Ecuador erupted violently in 2006.

STARTING IN 1999, the 5000-meter-high Tungurahua volcano in Ecuador began to erupt. It spewed glowing chunks of lava, volcanic ash, and gases into the sky. In August 2006, streams of hot gas and rock exploded down the volcano's sides. Villagers fled as ash blanketed their farms and homes.

Tungurahua volcano is one of more than 800 active volcanoes on Earth. The process leading to a volcanic eruption begins deep beneath the surface where magma forms.

Origin of Magma

Recall that magma is molten rock beneath Earth's surface. Magma is a complex mixture that contains partly melted mineral crystals, dissolved gases, and water. **Magma forms in the crust and upper mantle when solid rock partially melts. The formation of magma depends on several factors, including heat, pressure, and water content.**

Heat What source of heat is sufficient to melt rock? At a depth of 100 kilometers, the temperature of the mantle ranges from 1400°C to 1600°C. At these temperatures, the solid rock of the lower crust and upper mantle is near, but not quite at, its melting point. The additional heat needed to produce magma comes from three sources. First, friction generates heat as huge slabs of lithosphere slide past each other in subduction zones. Second, the mantle itself heats these subducting slabs. Third, hot mantle rock can rise and intrude into the cooler lithosphere, heating it.

Pressure You have learned that pressure increases with depth inside Earth. Increasing pressure raises the melting point of rock deep beneath the surface. Decreasing pressure, in contrast, lowers rock's melting point. **Decompression melting** occurs when rock rises and melts due to reduced pressure. This process typically takes place as hot yet solid mantle rock rises because it is less dense than the surrounding rock. As the rock rises, pressure on the rock decreases. As you can see in **Figure 2,** this decrease in pressure lowers the rock's melting point, forming pockets of magma.

FIGURE 2 Decompression Melting For granite and basalt that are "dry" (have low water content), decompression melting occurs as pressure decreases near the surface.
Interpret Graphs What is basalt's melting temperature at a depth of 7 km?

Water Content Increasing water content of rock also lowers the rock's melting temperature. Because of this, "wet" rock deep beneath the surface melts at a much lower temperature than does "dry" rock of the same composition and under the same pressure. Laboratory studies have shown that the melting point of basalt can be lowered by up to 100°C when basalt's water content is increased from zero to 0.1 percent.

☑ Reading Checkpoint *How does higher water content affect rock's melting point?*

Volcanoes and Plate Boundaries

Fortunately, magma only reaches the surface in certain areas. What determines where volcanoes form? **Most volcanoes form along divergent and convergent plate boundaries. Some volcanoes form far from plate boundaries above "hot spots" in the crust.** You can see different types of volcanic activity associated with plate boundaries in **Figure 3**, which begins on the next page.

Divergent Boundary Volcanism At divergent boundaries, volcanic activity occurs where the plates pull apart. Mantle rock rises to fill the gap between the plates. As the rock rises, decompression melting occurs. This forms magma, which erupts through a spreading center.

Although most spreading centers are located along mid-ocean ridges, some are not. The Great Rift Valley in eastern Africa is an area where continental crust is being pulled apart along a divergent boundary. Mount Kilimanjaro in Tanzania is one of many volcanoes that have formed near the rift valley.

Volcanoes and Other Igneous Activity **281**

Build Math Skills L2

Read Graphs Help students read the graph showing the melting points of "dry" granitic and "dry" basaltic magma in Figure 2. Ask volunteers to explain the values represented on the x- and y-axes of the graph. Then ask students to use the graph to determine the melting points of the two different types of magma at specific depths. Finally, ask students to state in their own words what general statement they can make about the melting point of magma based on the graph.

Answers

Figure 2 *about 1200°C*

☑ Reading Checkpoint *Water lowers the rock's melting point.*

Facts and Figures

Volcanoes in California The chain of volcanoes that exist in the Pacific Northwest, like Mount St. Helens and Mount Ranier, used to extend all the way down through California, connecting with the volcanoes in Mexico. This is because a huge oceanic plate in the Pacific Ocean, known as the Farrallon plate, used to subduct beneath most of North America. Our continent has been moving westward, riding over the Farrallon plate, for a long time. The plate is entirely gone in the region of south and central California, leaving two small pieces of the Farrallon plate remaining: the Juan de Fuca plate (subducting beneath the Pacific Northwest) and the Cocos plate (subducting beneath Mexico and Central America.) Soon North America will override the Juan de Fuca plate, and there will be no more subduction zone volcanoes in the continental United States.

LESSON 10.1

Build Science Skills L2

Compare and Contrast Have students read the section on Volcanoes and Plate Boundaries and study the different types of volcanism shown in Figure 3 on pp. 282–283. **Ask:** What do volcanoes at divergent and convergent boundaries have in common? *(At both, lava erupts at the surface, forming volcanic mountains.)* **Ask:** How are the two types of volcanoes different? *(Students will respond that the two types differ in important ways, including the way in which their magma forms and the type of geologic features formed along the plate boundaries. For example, along a divergent boundary, magma forms within rising plumes of hot mantle rock, producing volcanic mountains on the ocean floor or along a rift valley on land. Along convergent boundaries, magma forms when mantle rock in a subduction zone partially melts, producing volcanic island arcs or a continental volcanic arc.)*

Verbal, Logical

FIGURE 3 Three Types of Volcanism

A. Convergent plate volcanism
(Island arc)

Volcanic island arc
Trench
Marginal sea
Oceanic crust
Continental crust
Mantle rock melts
Water driven from plate
Asthenosphere
Subducting oceanic lithosphere

C. Intraplate volcanism
(Oceanic)

Oceanic crust
Hot spot
Hawaii
Decompression melting
Rising mantle plume

North America
Hawaii
South America

Continental volcanic arc
Trench
Oceanic crust
Continental crust
Subducting oceanic lithosphere
Mantle rock melts
Water driven from plate

E. Convergent plate volcanism
(Continental volcanic arc)

282 Chapter 10 • Lesson 1

Facts and Figures

Volcanism and Short-Term Climate Change When volcanoes erupt, they eject ash and aerosols into the atmosphere that can block out incoming sunlight and lower temperatures for years. This happened significantly in 1815 with the eruption of the Indonesian volcano Tambora, which is the largest eruption in the past two centuries. Global temperatures dropped, and 1816 was called "the year without a summer," as it snowed in New England during the summer.

Events like this can shape the history of countries. During the 1780s there was a lot of active volcanism in Japan (Asama volcano) and Iceland (Hekla volcano), making the winter of 1789 the coldest of the century in Europe. Benjamin Franklin, living in France at the time, noted that the sun shown faintly, as if through a haze, and speculated that this might be due to the eruption of the Iceland volcano. Crops failed across Europe, causing severe starvation and political unrest.

B. Divergent plate volcanism
(Oceanic ridge)

Oceanic crust

Magma chamber

Decompression melting

Asthenosphere

Mid-Atlantic Rift

Africa

Deccan Plateau ☐

East Africa Rift Valley ☐

Hot spot

Flood basalts

Continental crust

Decompression melting

Rising mantle plume

D. Intraplate volcanism
(Continental)

Rift valley

Continental crust

Decompression melting

F. Divergent plate volcanism
(Continental rifting)

Volcanoes and Other Igneous Activity **283**

MAP IT!
ACTIVITY

The three types of volcanism are convergent plate volcanism, divergent plate volcanism, and intraplate volcanism. Each type is shown in two different real-world examples in **Figure 3.**

Classify Which type of volcanism involves the destruction of slabs of lithosphere? Explain.

LESSON 10.1

OBSERVING PLATE MOVEMENT L2

Purpose Students will observe convergent plate movements.

Materials 9 student textbooks, 2 pieces of poster board, thin cardboard or 1-cm stack of notebook paper

Procedure Stack eight textbooks in two equal stacks. Leave about 5 cm between the textbook stacks. The remaining textbook will represent a continental crustal plate. The poster board will represent the subducting oceanic lithosphere. Give the poster board a slight curve so that it will subduct downward. Place the textbook on one of the stacks and the poster board on the other stack. **Ask:** What do you predict will happen when these two plates collide? *(The less rigid plate will subduct under the rigid plate.)* Start moving the "plates" toward each other. The oceanic lithosphere should subduct under the continental plate. Repeat this procedure using two pieces of poster board. Before moving the plates together, **ask:** What do you predict will happen when these two plates collide? *(The two slabs of crust will form a trench as they descend into the mantle.)* One piece of poster board needs to be curved so it will form a trench as it subducts.

Expected Outcomes Students will observe how the oceanic lithosphere subducts under the crustal plate and how two oceanic plates form a trench.
Visual, Kinesthetic

Answers

MAP IT! These volcanoes occur where plates diverge at the mid-ocean ridge in the Atlantic Ocean.

FIGURE 4 Major Volcanoes

MAP IT!
ACTIVITY

In **Figure 4**, note the volcanoes encircling the Pacific basin, known as the "Ring of Fire."
Infer How are the volcanoes in the middle of the Atlantic Ocean related to a plate boundary?

PLANET DIARY

For links about **Volcanoes**, visit PlanetDiary.com/HSES.

Convergent Boundary Volcanism Volcanoes form at convergent plate boundaries where slabs of oceanic crust subduct into the mantle. As a slab sinks deeper into the mantle, the increase in temperature and pressure drives water from the oceanic lithosphere. Once the sinking slab reaches a depth of about 100 to 150 kilometers, this water reduces the melting point of hot mantle rock low enough for melting to begin. Magma migrates upward through the overlying plate, forming volcanoes.

If the affected part of the overlying plate is made of oceanic lithosphere, the process produces a chain of volcanoes on the ocean floor. Eventually, these volcanic mountains may grow large enough to rise above the surface. If that happens, the volcanoes are called a *volcanic island arc*. Numerous volcanic island arcs, such as the Mariana islands, are found near subduction zones of the Pacific Ocean. Together with other volcanoes bordering the Pacific, they form the Ring of Fire, shown in **Figure 4**. The **Ring of Fire** is the long belt of volcanoes that circles much of the Pacific Ocean.

Volcanism may also occur at convergent plate boundaries where a slab of oceanic lithosphere is subducted under continental lithosphere. The result is a *continental volcanic arc*. The process is basically the same as for an island arc. Tungurahua and the other volcanoes of the Andes in South America form a continental volcanic arc. These volcanoes formed as the Nazca plate was subducted beneath the South American plate.

☑ **Reading Checkpoint** What process formed the volcanoes of the Andes?

Differentiated Instruction

ENGLISH LANGUAGE LEARNERS Select and copy an appropriate paragraph from one of the sections, such as the first paragraph on p. 284. For the first three sentences, replace several key words with blanks. For example, leave blanks for *convergent* in the first sentence of this paragraph, *mantle* in the second sentence, and the last use of *melting* in the third sentence. Have students read the paragraph and fill in the blanks with the appropriate words.

Intraplate Volcanism Hawaii's Mount Kilauea is Earth's most active volcano. But Kilauea is in the middle of the Pacific plate, thousands of kilometers from a plate boundary and the Ring of Fire. Another volcanic region, centered on the hot springs and geysers of the Yellowstone National Park, is in the middle of the North American plate. Both Kilauea and Yellowstone are examples of **intraplate volcanism**—volcanic activity that occurs within a plate.

Most intraplate volcanism occurs where a mass of hotter-than-normal mantle material, called a mantle plume, rises toward the surface. As the plume nears the top of the mantle, decompression melting forms magma. The result may be a small volcanic region a few hundred kilometers across called a **hot spot.** More than 40 hot spots are known. Most of these hot spots have lasted for millions of years.

The volcanic mountains that make up the Hawaiian Islands have formed as the Pacific plate moves over a hot spot. As shown in **Figure 5**, the age of each volcano indicates the time when it was over the hot spot. Kauai is the oldest of the major islands in the Hawaiian chain. Its volcanoes are not likely to erupt again. The more recently formed island of Hawaii has two active volcanoes—Mauna Loa and Kilauea.

FIGURE 5 Intraplate Volcano
The Hawaiian hot spot activity is currently centered beneath Kilauea and is an example of intraplate volcanic activity.

Build Reading Literacy L1

Refer to **p. 186D** in **Chapter 7,** which provides the guidelines for relating text and visuals.

Relate Text and Visuals Have students compare the diagram of intraplate volcanism in Figure 5 to the text explanation.
Visual

3 ASSESS

Evaluate Understanding L2

Have students create a ten-question crossword puzzle or word scramble using the concepts from this lesson. Have students exchange papers and work the puzzles.

Reteach L1

Use Figure 3 on pp. 282–283 to reteach the concepts in this lesson.

10.1 Assessment

Review Key Concepts

1. What three factors affect how magma forms?

2. How are the locations of volcanoes related to plate boundaries?

3. What causes intraplate volcanism?

4. What is the Ring of Fire?

5. How is magma formed through decompression melting?

Think Critically

6. Review Describe how an island arc forms at a convergent boundary.

7. Infer Geologists have found ancient deposits of lava and volcanic ash extending southwest from the Yellowstone hot spot to Nevada. What can you infer from this observation?

WRITING IN SCIENCE

8. Explain Recall what you learned about convection currents in Chapter 9. Explain how convection currents could affect the depth at which molten rocks are found.

Answers

☑ **Reading Checkpoint** *subduction of the Nazca plate beneath the South American plate at a convergent boundary*

Assessment Answers

1. Heat, pressure, and water content
2. Most volcanoes are located at either divergent or convergent plate boundaries, where plate motions provide the mechanisms to form magma.
3. hot mantle plumes rising up from the core-mantle boundary, causing decompression melting and forming small areas of volcanic activity on the surface
4. a chain of volcanoes that are located around the edge of the Pacific Basin

5. Decreasing pressure lowers a rock's melting point. As hot rock rises through the lithosphere, the pressure on it gradually decreases. When the pressure on the rock has fallen enough, decompression melting occurs.
6. A volcanic island arc is formed when two oceanic plates converge and form a subduction zone. A continental volcanic arc is formed by subduction of an ocean plate beneath a continental plate.

7. A mantle plume, or hot spot, probably caused the volcanic activity. The hot spot remained stationary as the North American plate moved over it, producing the trail of volcanic deposits extending southwest from Yellowstone.
8. Magma can form by decompression melting if the rock begins to rise and the pressure decreases. This causes the melting point to decrease. If water is added, the rock's melting point decreases. A body of hotter rock may rise and trigger melting in the crust.

1 FOCUS

Lesson Objectives

10.3 **Explain** the factors that determine the type of volcanic eruptions that occur.

10.4 **Describe** the various types of volcanic materials that are ejected from volcanoes.

10.5 **List** the three main types of volcanoes.

10.6 **Distinguish** how the different types of volcanic landforms form.

Build Vocabulary   `L2`

Word Parts Explain to students that the prefix *pyro-* is Latin and Greek for "fire" or "heat." *Clastic* means "made from fragments of preexisting rocks." Pyroclastic materials are hot fragments of preexisting rocks that are blown from the vent of a volcano.

Reading Strategy   `L2`

a. viscosity and dissolved gases
b. What are the types of volcanic materials? lava flows; pyroclastic material, such as ash; volcanic gases
c. What are the types of volcanoes? shield volcanoes, cinder cones, composite cones
d. What are some other volcanic landforms? calderas, pipes, lava plateaus

2 INSTRUCT

Use Visuals   `L1`

Figure 6 During the eruption of Mount St. Helens, the height of the volcano was lowered by 400 meters. **Ask:** What would have caused this damage? *(Force built up within the volcano and blew the top off.)* Infer where the debris from this blast went. *(Some of the fine debris particles remained in the air for a time before settling; some of the material flowed down the side of the volcano in the form of mud; some of the material simply tumbled down the side of the volcano.)*
Verbal

10.2 The Nature of Volcanic Eruptions

Key Questions

 What determines the type of volcanic eruption?

 What materials are ejected from volcanoes?

What are the three main types of volcanoes?

What other landforms are associated with eruptions?

Vocabulary

- viscosity • vent
- pyroclastic material
- volcano • crater
- shield volcano
- cinder cone
- composite cone
- caldera • volcanic neck
- lava plateau • lahar

Reading Strategy

Preview Copy the table. Before reading the section, rewrite the orange topic headings as questions. As you read, answer the questions.

The Nature of Volcanic Eruptions	
What factors affect an eruption?	a. ____?____

ON MAY 18, 1980, Mount St. Helens erupted with tremendous force. The blast blew out the entire north side of the volcano. The eruption ejected nearly a cubic kilometer of ash and other debris, producing a dramatic change in scenery captured in **Figure 6**.

Factors Affecting Eruptions

Why did Mount St. Helens erupt explosively, while others, such as Kilauea, erupt slowly and more quietly? **The primary factors that determine whether a volcano erupts explosively or quietly include characteristics of the magma and the amount of dissolved gases in the magma.**

Viscosity Magma's viscosity—whether the magma is thick and sticky or thin and runny—affects the type of eruption that occurs. **Viscosity** is a substance's resistance to flow. For example, maple syrup is more viscous than water, so it flows more slowly. Magma from an explosive eruption may be thousands of times more viscous than magma that erupts quietly. The temperature and chemical composition of magma determine the magma's viscosity. The same is true for *lava*, which is magma that has reached the surface.

If you heat maple syrup, it becomes more fluid and less viscous. In the same way, the viscosity of magma and lava are strongly affected by temperature. As lava flow cools and hardens, its viscosity increases. The lava flow slows, halts, and eventually becomes rock.

Chemical composition is the more important factor in determining type of eruption. In general, the more silica in magma, the greater its viscosity. Because of their high silica content, granitic lavas are very viscous and will erupt explosively. Basaltic lavas, which contain less silica, are less viscous and tend to erupt quietly.

FIGURE 6 Mount St. Helens
A Mount St. Helens before the May 18, 1980, eruption.
B After the eruption, Spirit Lake filled with debris.

286 Chapter 10 • Lesson 2

Table 1 Magma Composition

Composition	Silica Content	Viscosity	Gas Content	Tendency to Form Pyroclastics (ejected rock fragments)	Volcanic Landform
Basaltic	Least (about 50%)	Least	Least (1–2%)	Least	Shield volcanoes Basalt plateaus Cinder cones
Andesitic	Intermediate (about 60%)	Intermediate	Intermediate (3–4%)	Intermediate	Composite cones
Granitic	Most (about 70%)	Greatest	Most (4–6%)	Greatest	Pyroclastic flows Volcanic domes

Dissolved Gases During explosive eruptions, the gases trapped in magma provide the force to propel lava out of the **vent,** which is a volcano's opening at the surface. As magma approaches the surface, the pressure is greatly reduced, allowing dissolved gases such as water vapor and carbon dioxide to be released explosively. Basaltic magma allows gases to bubble upward and escape relatively easily. Therefore, eruptions of fluid basaltic lava are relatively quiet. Granitic magma is slow to release expanding gases. The gases collect in bubbles and pockets that increase in size until they explode from a vent. The characteristics of basaltic, andesitic, and granitic magma are summarized in **Table 1**. As you will learn on the following pages, the different types of magma build different types of volcanic landforms.

☑ **Reading Checkpoint** *What causes the dissolved gases in magma to be released?*

WHY ARE SOME VOLCANOES EXPLOSIVE?

Procedure

1. Obtain two bottles of noncarbonated water and two bottles of club soda.
2. Open one bottle of the noncarbonated water and one bottle of the club soda. Record your observations.
3. Gently shake each of the remaining unopened bottles. **CAUTION:** *Wear safety goggles and point the bottles away from everyone.*
4. Carefully open each bottle over a sink or outside. Record your observations.

Analyze and Conclude

1. **Observe** What happened when the bottles were opened?
2. **Infer** Which bottle represents lava with the most dissolved gas?

WHY ARE SOME VOLCANOES EXPLOSIVE? L2

Objective
After completing this activity, students will be able to explain why trapped gases cause explosive reactions in volcanoes.

Skills Observe, Infer, Predict

Prep Time 5 minutes

Materials 2 bottles of noncarbonated water, 2 bottles of club soda, paper towels

Class Time 20 minutes

Safety Be sure that students wear goggles throughout the activity and point the open bottles away from everyone.

Teaching Tip Have paper towels available for students to clean up after the lab.

Expected Outcome Students will observe dissolved gases and fluid "explode" from the bottle of carbonated liquid.
Kinesthetic, Logical

Analyze and Conclude
1. Answers may vary but should state that the bottles with non-carbonated water opened without any escaping gases or fizzing. The bottles of club soda, when opened, fizzed with the escaping carbon dioxide. After the club soda was shaken, the gases escaped more explosively.
2. the shaken bottle of club soda

For Enrichment L3

Have students research the violent eruption of Krakatau in 1883. Have students prepare a newspaper article detailing the events surrounding the eruption of this volcano. The article should be written as if the volcano had erupted recently.

Answers

☑ **Reading Checkpoint** *Reduced pressure as magma nears the surface allows the gases to bubble out.*

Facts and Figures

Volcanoseismology Seismometers tell us a great deal about the process of volcanism. Magma has to crack its way through the crust to get to the surface, and this causes huge numbers of small earthquakes along the way. When Mount St. Helens had an episode of volcanism in 2005, the network of seismometers around the volcano could track the movement of magma by locating the many thousands of small earthquakes that resulted. Ironically, though earthquakes themselves cannot be predicted at this time, earthquakes beneath volcanoes can be used to help predict volcanic eruptions, reducing the risks of living near volcanoes.

LESSON 10.2

Address Misconceptions   L2

Students may have the misconception that earthquakes shaking the region around the volcano are the only reason for volcanic eruptions. Earthquakes are common triggers of volcanic eruptions, but are not the only factors involved. Explain to students that volcanoes can erupt whenever magma builds up enough force to erupt from underground to the surface. The factors that determine the violence of the eruption are magma composition, magma temperature, and the amount of dissolved gases the magma contains.
Verbal

Use Visuals   L1

Figure 7 Have students look closely at these photographs. **Ask:** How can you tell the aa flow is slow moving? *(It is rough and jagged rather than smooth.)*
Visual

Teacher Demo

OBSERVING VISCOSITY   L2

Purpose Students will observe fluids that have different viscosities.

Materials 2 large beakers, hot plate, water, 2 large test tubes, test-tube clamp, ice, corn syrup

Procedure Pour corn syrup into the two large test tubes in advance. Put one test tube into a large beaker filled with ice. Put the other test tube into a large beaker half filled with water on a hot plate. Heat the syrup in a hot-water bath until it is very hot. Boiling the syrup is not necessary. Slowly pour the contents of each test tube into another beaker one at a time to demonstrate the nature of fluids with differing viscosities.

Expected Outcome Students will observe that the cold syrup is very viscous and flows very slowly—similar to silica-rich lava. The hot syrup is not viscous and flows very fast—similar to silica-poor lava.
Visual, Verbal

Volcanic Material

Lava may appear to be the main material produced by a volcano, but this is not always the case. Just as often, explosive eruptions eject huge quantities of broken rock, lava bombs, fine ash, and dust. **Depending on the type of eruption, volcanoes may produce lava flows or eject pyroclastic materials, or both. All volcanic eruptions also emit large amounts of gases.**

Lava Flows As with magma, silica content and temperature affect the characteristics of lava flows. Hot basaltic lavas are usually very fluid because of their low silica content. Flow rates between 10 and 300 meters per hour are common. In contrast, the flow of silica-rich, granitic lava is often too slow to be visible.

Temperature differences produce two types of basaltic lava: *pahoehoe* and *aa*. Pahoehoe (pah hoh ay HOH ay) is hotter, fast-moving basaltic lava. Pahoehoe forms a relatively smooth, blue-black skin that wrinkles as the still-molten subsurface lava continues to flow. **Figure 7A** shows that pahoehoe resembles the braids in twisted ropes. Aa (AH ah) is cooler, slower-moving basaltic lava, which forms a surface of rough, jagged blocks with sharp, spiny projections, as shown in **Figure 7B**.

Gases Magmas and lavas contain varied amounts of dissolved gases held under pressure in the molten rock, just as carbon dioxide is held in soft drinks. As with soft drinks, as soon as the pressure is reduced, the gases begin to escape. The gaseous portion of most lavas is only about 1 to 6 percent of the total weight. The percentage may be small, but the actual quantity of emitted gas can exceed thousands of tons each day. Gas samples collected during a Hawaiian eruption consisted of about 70 percent water vapor, 15 percent carbon dioxide, 5 percent nitrogen, 5 percent sulfur, and lesser percentages of chlorine, hydrogen, and argon. Sulfur compounds are easily recognized because they smell like rotten eggs and readily form sulfuric acid, a natural source of air pollution.

FIGURE 7 Lava Flows, Mount Kilauea, Hawaii Pahoehoe (**A**) is hotter and faster moving than aa (**B**).
Draw Conclusions *Which type of lava is more viscous?*

Differentiated Instruction

ENGLISH LANGUAGE LEARNERS Have students work in pairs to make a chart showing the facts about factors affecting eruptions, volcanic material, types of volcanoes, and other volcanic landforms.

Students may want to illustrate their facts with drawings to further their understanding of the concepts. Students can use this chart as a study aid for quizzes and tests.

Pyroclastic Materials Particles produced in volcanic eruptions are called **pyroclastic materials.** When basaltic lava is extruded, dissolved gases propel blobs of lava to great heights. Some of this ejected material may land near the vent. As it cools and hardens over time, the ejected material builds a cone-shaped structure. The wind will carry smaller particles great distances. Viscous granitic magmas are highly charged with gases. As the gases expand, pulverized rock and lava fragments are blown from the vent.

The fragments ejected during eruptions range in size from very fine dust and volcanic ash (less than 2 millimeters) to pieces that weigh several tons. Particles that range in size from small beads to walnuts (2–64 millimeters) are called *lapilli*, or cinders. Particles larger than 64 millimeters in diameter are called *blocks* when they are made of hardened lava and *bombs* when they are ejected as glowing lava.

☑ **Reading Checkpoint** *What is a volcanic bomb?*

Types of Volcanoes

Volcanic landforms come in a wide variety of shapes and sizes. Each structure has a unique eruptive history. 🔑 **The three main volcanic types are shield volcanoes, cinder cones, and composite cones.**

Anatomy of a Volcano Volcanic activity often begins when a fissure, or crack, develops in the crust as magma is forced toward the surface. The magma collects in a pocket beneath the surface called the magma chamber. The gas-rich magma rises from the magma chamber, travels through a circular pipe, and reaches the surface at a vent, as shown in **Figure 8.** Repeated eruptions of lava or pyroclastic material eventually build a mountain called a **volcano.** Located at the summit of many volcanoes is a steep-walled depression called a **crater.**

The form of a volcano is largely determined by the composition of the magma. As you will see, fluid lavas tend to produce broad structures with gentle slopes. More viscous, silica-rich lavas produce cones with moderate to steep slopes.

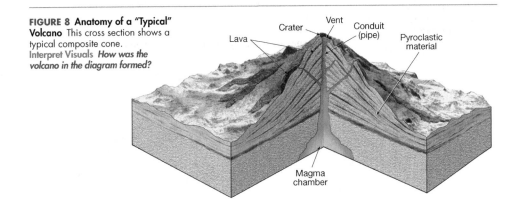

FIGURE 8 Anatomy of a "Typical" Volcano This cross section shows a typical composite cone.
Interpret Visuals How was the volcano in the diagram formed?

Lava · Crater · Vent · Conduit (pipe) · Pyroclastic material · Magma chamber

Volcanoes and Other Igneous Activity **289**

Geothermal Energy Hot magma near the surface of Earth can be beneficial. Geothermal energy takes advantage of Earth's internal energy and uses it as an energy source. Have students research this renewable source of energy. Students should prepare a short report about this natural energy source. The report should include an illustration showing an example of how geothermal energy can be used in a specific application.
Verbal

Use Visuals L1

Figure 9 Have students compare the photograph in this figure to the profile of a shield volcano in Figure 11. **Ask:** Why might photographs of shield volcanoes make them look not as tall as they really are? *(Because shield volcanoes are so broad, they often give the impression of being lower than they are.)* How would you describe the viscosity of the lava at a shield volcano? *(low viscosity)* What is the origin of the other islands in the diagram? What do you think they would look like under the sea level? *(They are shield volcanoes, or parts of shield volcanoes. Beneath the surface, the rocky formations likely flare outward either as individual shield volcanoes or as portions of a volcano shared by one or more of the other islands.)*

FIGURE 9 Shield Volcanoes
Shield volcanoes like Mauna Loa and Mauna Kea in Hawaii are built mainly of fluid basaltic lava flows. These broad, slightly domed structures are the largest volcanoes on Earth.

Shield Volcanoes **Shield volcanoes** are produced by the accumulation of fluid basaltic lavas. Shield volcanoes have the shape of a broad, slightly domed structure that resembles a warrior's shield, as shown in **Figure 9.** Most shield volcanoes have grown up from the deep-ocean floor to form islands. Examples of shield volcanoes include those in the Hawaiian Islands and Iceland.

Cinder Cones Ejected lava fragments that harden in the air and fall around a vent can build a **cinder cone.** The fragments consist mostly of lapilli. Cinder cones are usually a product of relatively gas-rich basaltic or granitic magma. The shape of a cinder cone is determined by the steep-sided slope that forms as loose pyroclastic material builds up around the vent. Cinder cones are usually the product of a single eruption that sometimes lasts only a few weeks and rarely more than a few years. Once the eruption ends, the magma in the pipe connecting the vent to the magma chamber solidifies, and the volcano never erupts again. As shown in **Figure 11,** cinder cones are relatively small compared to other volcanoes.

FIGURE 10 Cinder Cones
A A typical cinder cone has steep slopes of 30–40 degrees. **B** Many cinder cones, like this one near Flagstaff, Arizona, are located in volcanic fields. Others form on the sides of larger volcanoes.
Infer *What feature is shown in the lower part of the photograph?*

Facts and Figures

Parícutin is an active volcano in Mexico. It is one of the youngest volcanoes on Earth. On February 20, 1943, Parícutin began erupting from a fissure in a cornfield. By the end of the first year, the cone had reached an elevation of 450 m. Volcanic eruptions finally ended in 1952.

The resulting fire, ash, and lava destroyed two villages. In one of the villages, a local church is still standing at the edge of the lava flow. The top of the church and the bell tower are visible, but the lower portions of the church are buried in lava.

FIGURE 11 Comparing Volcanic Landforms Cinder cones and composite cones are small in comparison with a large shield volcano such as Mauna Loa in Hawaii.

Sea level

Ⓐ Mauna Loa, Hawaii, a large shield volcano

0   10   20 km

4 km

Ⓑ Mount Rainier, Washington, a large composite cone

Ⓒ Sunset Crater, Arizona, a large cinder cone

Composite Cones Earth's most dangerous volcanoes are composite cones, or *stratovolcanoes*. A **composite cone** is a large, nearly symmetrical volcanic mountain composed of layers of both lava and pyroclastic deposits. For the most part, composite cones are the product of gas-rich magma having an andesitic composition. The silica-rich magmas typical of composite cones generate viscous lavas that can travel only short distances. Composite cones generate explosive eruptions, ejecting huge quantities of pyroclastic material.

Most composite cones are located in a relatively narrow zone that rims the Pacific Ocean, called the Ring of Fire. The Ring of Fire includes the large cones of the Andes in South America and the Cascade Range of the western United States and Canada. The Cascade Range includes Mount St. Helens, Mount Rainier, and Mount Shasta, shown in **Figure 12**. The most active regions in the Ring of Fire are located along volcanic island arcs next to deep ocean trenches. This nearly continuous chain of volcanoes stretches from the Aleutian Islands to Japan, the Philippines, and New Zealand.

FIGURE 12 Composite Cone Mount Shasta, California, is one of the largest composite cones in the Cascade Range. Shastina is the smaller cone that formed on the left flank of Mt. Shasta.

Volcanoes and Other Igneous Activity **291**

Teacher **Demo**

OBSERVING AN EXPLOSIVE ERUPTION

L2

Purpose Students will observe the explosive nature of gases trapped in an enclosed container.

Materials 2-L soda bottle, rubber stopper, white vinegar, baking soda, paper towel, rubber band, thin bath or kitchen towel, scissors

Procedure Pour 150 mL of vinegar into the empty soda bottle. For safety, fold the towel around the bottle. Secure the towel at the neck of the bottle with a rubber band. Cut an 8-cm square piece of paper towel. Put about 5 mL of baking soda in the center of the paper towel. Fold the paper towel around the baking soda to make a packet. Drop the packet into the bottle. Put the stopper into the bottle. Do not put the stopper in too tight. Have everyone stand a safe distance away from the bottle.

Expected Outcome Students will observe the explosive forces that are created when trapped gases are released. Point out to students that this is similar to gases trapped inside an active volcano. When enough force is built up, trapped gases can blow the top off of the volcano. Gases, magma, and pyroclastic materials then flow from the volcano through the new opening.
Visual

Answers

Figure 10 *a lava flow*

Differentiated Instruction

ENGLISH LANGUAGE LEARNERS Living in the shadow of a composite cone can be dangerous. In 1902, Mount Pelée erupted in a fiery pyroclastic flow that destroyed the port town of St. Pierre on the Caribbean island of Martinique. The destruction happened in moments. All of the 28,000 inhabitants of the town were killed with the exception of one person who was being held in a dungeon on the outskirts of town. A few people on ships in the harbor also were spared.

Have students use the Internet to research this volcanic eruption and prepare an eyewitness account of it as seen from one of the ships in the harbor. The account should describe the scene before, during, and after the eruption. Students should then present their account to the class.

Volcanoes and Other Igneous Activity   **291**

VISUAL SUMMARY

CALDERA FORMATION

FIGURE 13 Crater Lake in Oregon occupies a caldera about 10 kilometers in diameter that formed about 7000 years ago.

Eruption of
Mount Mazama

A

Partially emptied
magma chamber

B

Collapse of
Mount Mazama

C

Formation of Crater Lake and Wizard Island

D

E

Other Volcanic Landforms

Volcanic mountains are not the only landforms that result from volcanic activity. **Volcanic landforms also include calderas, volcanic necks, and lava plateaus.** Each of these features forms in a different way. Long after eruptions have ended, these landforms can provide evidence of volcanic activity.

Calderas One spectacular reminder of what can happen when a volcano's activity ends is the caldera. A **caldera** is a depression in a volcanic mountain. Most calderas form in one of two ways: by the collapse of the top of a composite volcano after an explosive eruption, or from the collapse of the top of a shield volcano after the magma chamber is drained.

Crater Lake in Oregon occupies a caldera. This caldera formed about 7000 years ago when a composite cone, Mount Mazama, erupted violently, as shown in **Figure 13**. The eruption of Mount Mazama partly emptied the magma chamber. The roof of the magma chamber collapsed, forming a huge depression that became Crater Lake. A later eruption produced Wizard Island, the small cinder cone in the lake.

There are several other large calderas in the United States. In Hawaii, the vast "crater" atop Mount Haleakala on the island of Maui is, in fact, a caldera. In the Yellowstone caldera in Wyoming and the Valles caldera in northern New Mexico, hot springs are evidence of past, and perhaps future, volcanic activity.

Facts and Figures

The five deadliest volcanic eruptions known are (1) Tambora, Indonesia, which occurred in 1815. There were 92,000 deaths, primarily the result of starvation. (2) Krakatau, Indonesia, which occurred in 1883. There were 36,000 deaths, primarily the result of a tsunami. (3) Mount Pelée, Martinique, which occurred in 1902. There were 28,000 deaths, primarily the result of pyroclastic flows. (4) Nevado del Ruiz, Colombia, which occurred in 1985. There were 25,000 deaths, primarily the result of mudflows. (5) Unzen, Japan, which occurred in 1792. There were 14,000 deaths, primarily the result of a volcano collapse and a tsunami.

Volcanic Necks Another volcanic landform that provides evidence of past volcanic activity is the volcanic neck. A **volcanic neck** is a landform made of magma that hardened in a volcano's conduit, or pipe, and later was exposed by erosion. Recall that a volcano's pipe connects the magma chamber with the surface. When a volcano's activity ends, magma remaining in the pipe hardens to form igneous rock.

Weathering and erosion act constantly to wear away volcanoes. For example, cinder cones are easily eroded because they are made up of loose materials. But the rock in a volcano's pipe is more resistant to erosion, so it stands alone above the surrounding land after the cone has been eroded. Ship Rock, shown in **Figure 14,** is a volcanic neck in New Mexico.

FIGURE 14 Volcanic Neck Ship Rock, New Mexico, is a volcanic neck. Ship Rock consists of igneous rock that crystallized in the pipe of a volcano that then was eroded away.

☑ **Reading Checkpoint** *What is a volcanic neck?*

Lava Plateaus If you visited the Columbia River gorge in Washington state, you would see huge cliffs made up of layers of dark, volcanic rock. These layers of rock are part of the Columbia plateau, a huge lava plateau that covers parts of Washington, Oregon, and Idaho. A **lava plateau** is a volcanic landform produced by repeated eruptions of very fluid, basaltic lava. As shown in **Figure 15,** the lava that forms a lava plateau erupts through long cracks called fissures. Instead of building a cone, the lava spreads out over a wide area.

The Columbia plateau is nearly 1.6 kilometers thick. The plateau formed over hundreds of thousands of years as a series of lava flows, some 50 meters thick, buried the landscape. Another major lava plateau is the Deccan plateau in India.

FIGURE 15 Lava Plateau Lava erupting from a fissure forms fluid lava flows called flood basalts that build up in layers to form a lava plateau. These dark-colored basalt flows are near Idaho Falls, Idaho.

Lava fountaining

Basaltic lava flows

Fissure

Use Visuals L1

Figure 14 Have students study Figure 14. **Ask:** Infer why the volcanic neck is still in place while the surrounding terrain has eroded away. *(The rock in the volcanic neck is more resistant to erosion than the surrounding terrain.)* **Verbal, Logical**

Use Community Resources L2

Many U.S. Geological Survey (USGS) offices have educational outreach staff and programs. Contact your regional office and ask a USGS scientist to speak to your class about plate tectonics and volcanic activity. **Interpersonal**

Answers

☑ **Reading Checkpoint** *A volcanic neck is the remains of a volcanic pipe left standing above the surface after erosion has removed the softer rock around it.*

Facts and Figures

Floor Basalts and Hot Spots Giant outpourings of basaltic lava known as flood basalts seem to be related to hot spots. Many hot spot tracks trace back to a flood basalt. For instance, the Reunion Island hot spot is the last of a series of volcanoes that trace back to the Deccan Traps flood basalt in India that erupted 65 million years ago. The Tristan hot spot in the Atlantic Ocean traces back to the Karoo flood basalt in South America and the Etandeka flood basalt in Africa, at a time when the two continents were connected. The Yellowstone hot spot traces back to the Columbia River flood basalt. One hypothesis is that the head of a rising mantle plume erupts as the flood basalt and the magma coming up the tail of the plume forms the succeeding hot spot volcanoes.

LESSON 10.2

Build Science Skills

Use the Internet Students may think of volcanoes as a danger that is far removed from everyday life. **Ask:** What parts of the U.S. are potentially at risk from volcanic eruptions? *(Several states, including California, Oregon, Washington, Alaska, and Hawaii, have active volcanoes that are potentially dangerous.)* **Ask:** Is the danger from a volcano limited to the area near the volcano? *(No. Lahars and lava flows can travel tens of kilometers, and winds can carry volcanic ash hundreds of kilometers through the atmosphere.)* The United States Geologic Survey (USGS) maintains a number of Web sites that describe volcanic activity and hazards in the United States. Ask students to use these Web sites to research volcano hazards in different parts of the U.S. and report their findings to the class.

3 ASSESS

Evaluate Understanding L2

Have students play a quiz game to review the material in this lesson. Ask each student to write three questions on three separate sheets of paper. Collect the questions. Divide the class into two teams. To play the game, alternate giving a member of each team a question from the collected papers. Give each team a point for each correct response. The team with the most points wins the game.

Reteach L1

Set aside any questions that are answered incorrectly from the quiz game above. After the game, give each team the stack of missed questions. Let the entire team work together to give the correct response to the questions.

Volcanic Hazards

Throughout history, people often have settled near volcanoes because rich volcanic soils are good for farming. They may not realize that an active or dormant volcano can erupt at any time, even centuries after the last eruption. ▭ **Volcanic hazards include lava flows, volcanic ash, pyroclastic flows, and mudflows.**

Lava flows are a major volcanic hazard. For example, the frequent lava flows from Mount Kilauea in Hawaii sometimes destroy homes and other structures in their path.

Active composite volcanoes, such as those in the Cascade Range of the Pacific Northwest, are among the most dangerous volcanoes. A composite volcano can eject huge quantities of volcanic ash, burying widespread areas under thick ash deposits. In the year 79, ash from the eruption of Italy's Mount Vesuvius completely buried Pompeii.

An explosive eruption can also release a *pyroclastic flow,* a scorching mixture of glowing volcanic particles and gases that sweeps rapidly down a volcano's flanks. In 1902, a pyroclastic flow from Mount Pelée on the the island of Martinique in the Caribbean killed 29,000 people. Volcanoes may emit poisonous gases such as hydrochloric acid and hydrogen sulfide.

Composite volcanoes may also produce mudflows called lahars. A **lahar** occurs when water-soaked volcanic ash and rock slide rapidly downhill. Ice and snow melted by an eruption or by heavy rains can trigger a lahar. In 1985, a lahar caused by the eruption of Nevada del Ruiz in Colombia killed 23,000 people.

Volcanoes usually give some warning that an eruption is near. For example, seismographs can detect the small earthquakes caused by movement of magma beneath the surface. Gases and ash released by a volcano may also signal an approaching eruption.

10.2 Assessment

Review Key Concepts ▭

1. What factors determine the type of volcanic eruption?

2. List the materials ejected from volcanoes.

3. Describe the three main types of volcanoes.

4. List three volcanic landforms.

Think Critically

5. **Relate Cause and Effect** What propels magma out of a volcano during an eruption?

6. **Compare and Contrast** Compare and contrast the magma that forms a shield volcano with the magma that forms a composite cone.

7. **Explain** Explain how a caldera forms.

8. **Form an Opinion** Should a resort hotel be built on the side of an active composite volcano? Explain.

BIGIDEA DYNAMIC EARTH

9. **Communicate** Research a volcanic eruption. Write a paragraph describing the eruption. Make sure to classify the type of volcano that erupted and identify the plate boundary or hot spot associated with the volcano.

Assessment Answers

1. Magma composition, magma temperature, and amount of dissolved gases
2. Lava, gases, and pyroclastic materials, such as ash, dust, cinders, volcanic blocks, and volcanic bomb
3. Cinder cones are small, steep cones, made of loose cinders. Shield volcanoes are large, gently sloping volcanoes made of layers of mainly quiet lava flows.

Composite cones are large, steep cones, made of lava flows and pyroclastic material.
4. Caldera, volcanic neck, lava plateau
5. Expanding gases dissolved in the magma
6. Shield volcanoes have fluid basaltic magma. Composite cones generally have more viscous, andesitic magma.
7. A caldera may form when the top of a composite cone shatters in an explosive eruption or when the magma chamber of a shield volcano empties and collapses.

8. No—the hotel would be in danger from volcanic ash, lava flows, and pyroclastic flows if the volcano became active.
9. Answers will vary, but should accurately classify the volcano and give a clear description of the eruption and the volcano's origin in terms of plate tectonics or hot spot activity.

10.3 Intrusive Igneous Activity

VOLCANIC ROCK made of hardened lava covers large parts of Earth's surface. But you may be surprised to learn that most magma cools and hardens deep within Earth. This magma forms the roots of mountain ranges and a variety of landscape features.

Recall that magma rises through the crust toward the surface. As it rises, the magma may rise through fractures in the rock or force its way between rock layers. The magma may form thin sheets a few centimeters thick or collect in vast pools that can be many kilometers wide and several kilometers thick.

Classifying Plutons

The structures that result from the cooling and hardening of magma beneath Earth's surface are called **plutons.** The word *pluton* is derived from *Pluto,* the name of the mythological Roman god of the underworld. Plutons form in continental crust wherever magma slowly crystallizes and forms intrusive igneous rock. Over millions of years, uplift and erosion can expose plutons at the surface.

There are several types of plutons. **Types of plutons include sills, laccoliths, and dikes. Geologists classify plutons and other bodies of intrusive igneous rock according to their size, shape, and relationship to surrounding rock layers.**

Key Questions

 What are the different types of plutons, and how are they classified?

 What is a batholith?

Vocabulary

- pluton • sill
- laccolith • dike
- batholith

Reading Strategy

Compare and Contrast After you read, compare the types of intrusive igneous features by completing the table.

Types of Intrusive Igneous Features	Description
Sill	a. ____?____
Laccolith	b. ____?____
Dike	c. ____?____

FIGURE 16 Dike This dike in the Grand Canyon in Arizona is a pluton that cuts across layers of sandstone.

LESSON 10.3

Build Reading Literacy **L1**

Refer to **p. 474D** in **Chapter 17,** which provides guidelines for monitoring your understanding.

Monitor Your Understanding As soon as students have read the lesson, ask them to write down the main ideas in the passages. Have them ask themselves, "Did I have any trouble reading this lesson? If so, why?" Then, have them come up with their own strategies to improve their understanding.
Interpersonal, Verbal

Integrate Social Studies **L2**

The Henry Mountains These mountains, located in southeastern Utah, are largely composed of several laccoliths thought to be fed by a much larger magma body nearby. The mountain range is named for Joseph Henry, an American scientist. Henry was the first Secretary of the Smithsonian Institution. Have students find the Henry Mountains on a map or an atlas.
Verbal

FIGURE 17 Sills, Laccoliths, and Dikes
A Plutons form as magma intrudes into cracks in rock or between rock layers.
B Erosion later exposes the plutons. A sill forms a horizontal band, laccoliths push overlying layers upward, and dikes cut across rock layers.
Infer How could you determine if a horizontal igneous rock layer was a lava flow or a sill?

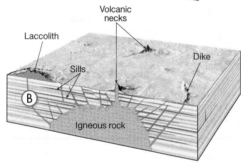

Sills and Laccoliths Sills and laccoliths are plutons that form when magma intrudes between rock layers close to the surface. Sills and laccoliths differ in shape and often differ in composition. A **sill** is a pluton that forms where magma flows between parallel layers of sedimentary rock. Horizontal sills, like the one shown in **Figure 17,** are the most common.

Sills form only at shallow depths, where the pressure exerted by the weight of overlying rock layers is low. Why is this? For a sill to form, the magma must lift the overlying rock to a height equal to the thickness of the sill. You might think that this would require a great deal of energy. But forcing the magma between rock layers often requires less energy than forcing the magma up to the surface.

A **laccolith** is a lens-shaped pluton that has pushed the overlying rock layers upward. As with sills, laccoliths form when magma intrudes between sedimentary rock layers close to the surface. But the magma that forms laccoliths has higher viscosity than the magma that forms sills. For this reason, the magma collects in a mass that bulges upward instead of spreading out in an even layer.

Dikes Some plutons form when magma from a large magma chamber moves into fractures in the surrounding rocks. A **dike** is a pluton that forms when magma moves into fractures that cut across rock layers. Dikes are sheetlike structures that can range in thickness from less than a centimeter to more than a kilometer. Most dikes are a few meters thick and extend laterally for no more than a few kilometers.

☑ **Reading Checkpoint** *What is a laccolith?*

Differentiated Instruction

SPECIAL NEEDS Make concept maps for each section and cover them with clear contact paper. Then, cut the maps into puzzle pieces. Provide students with the pieces and have them put the puzzle together. After students complete the puzzle, have them make flashcards with concept connections and added notes. For example, students may have cards with the names of plutons on one side and a definition or example on the other. Students also may have key concept cards with an important word missing. For example, **A _____ is a pluton formed when magma is injected along sedimentary bedding surfaces, parallel to the bedding planes.** *(sill)*

Batholiths

Batholiths are the largest bodies of intrusive igneous rocks. **A batholith is a body of intrusive igneous rock that has a surface exposure of more than 100 square kilometers.** Much larger than a pluton, a batholith can be hundreds of kilometers long and tens of kilometers across. Gravity studies and seismic evidence indicate that batholiths are also very thick, possibly extending dozens of kilometers into the crust. A body of igneous rock similar to a batholith, but having an area of less than 100 square kilometers, is called a *stock*.

How are batholiths formed? Batholiths are made of many individual plutons that begin as blobs of magma deep beneath the surface. The plutons slowly rise through the crust. They clump together, forming a huge irregular mass. But this mass of magma never erupts to the surface. Instead, it cools slowly deep underground, forming granitic rock. Over millions of years, uplift and erosion gradually expose the batholith at the surface. Weathering gradually shapes the batholith into distinct mountains.

Batholiths form the core of many of Earth's great mountain ranges. For example, the Idaho batholith forms part of the northern Rocky Mountains. This batholith has an area of more than 40,000 square kilometers. The Sierra Nevada in California, shown in **Figure 18**, is also formed from a huge batholith. An even larger batholith makes up the coastal mountains of British Columbia in Canada.

FIGURE 18 Batholiths Mount Whitney in California makes up just a tiny portion of the Sierra Nevada batholith, a huge structure that extends for approximately 400 kilometers.

Build Science Skills L1

Use Models Challenge groups of students to brainstorm ways of modeling the formation of a batholith and make sketches of their models. Have each group submit their model designs with a list of materials needed to construct the models. The groups may then build their own models, using safe, approved materials, and present them to the class.
Interpersonal, kinesthetic

3 ASSESS

Evaluate Understanding L2

Have students write three review questions from the chapter. Then have students work with a partner to ask each other their questions.

Reteach L1

Use Figures 16, 17, and 18 to review the different types of igneous plutons and compare them with batholiths.

10.3 Assessment

Review Key Concepts

1. List three different types of plutons.

2. How are plutons classified?

3. Write a definition of *batholith* in your own words.

4. Explain how a laccolith forms.

Think Critically

5. Compare and Contrast Describe the difference between a sill and a dike.

6. Infer What can you infer about the origin of mountain ranges made of granitic rock, such as the Sierra Nevada? Explain.

CONNECTING CONCEPTS

7. Predict Recall what you learned about the texture of igneous rocks in Chapter 3. Predict how the texture of the rock in a batholith would compare with the texture of the rock in a sill. Explain.

Volcanoes and Other Igneous Activity **297**

Answers

Figure 17 *Accept all reasonable responses. The rocks above and below a sill might be very similar in composition, while the rocks above a lava flow might be quite different than those below the flow. The crystals in the rock of a sill, which cooled relatively slowly, might be larger than the crystals of a lava flow that hardened quickly at the surface.*

☑ **Reading Checkpoint** *A lens-shaped pluton*

Assessment Answers

1. sills, laccoliths, and dikes
2. Plutons are classified by their shape, size, and relationship to the surrounding rock layers.
3. A batholith is a large mass of igneous rock that cooled and hardened below the surface, then was uplifted and exposed at the surface by erosion.
4. A laccolith forms when viscous magma collects between rock layers and hardens into igneous rock. Because the magma is viscous (thick), it doesn't spread out in thin layers, as in a sill. Instead, it causes the rock above to bulge upward.
5. A sill is a pluton that forms when magma is injected along bedding surfaces and parallel to the bedding planes. A dike is a pluton that forms when magma is injected into fractures, cutting across preexisting rock layers.

6. A mountain range like the Sierra Nevada is made up of a large batholith that was uplifted and eroded to form the mountain range.
7. Sample answer: Convection currents within the mantle bring hot mantle material closer to the surface.

How Earth Works

1 FOCUS

Objectives
In this feature, students will
- explain what a volcano is.
- describe the immediate effects of a volcanic eruption.
- identify some long-term effects of a volcanic eruption.

Build Vocabulary   L2
Classify Terms Draw a four-column chart on the board. Label the columns as follows: *Volcanic Effect, Definition of Effect, Immediate or Long-Term Effect,* and *Local or Worldwide Effect.* Have students use information on these two pages to complete the chart.

2 INSTRUCT

Use Visuals   L2
Ask students to read the captions on this page and the next. Have them make a list of places in the United States and in other countries where volcanoes are or have been active.
Visual

Bellringer   L2
Have students list ten effects of a volcanic eruption. Examples may include clouds of smoke, lava trails, and a scorched landscape.
Logical

How Earth Works
Effects of Volcanoes

A **volcano** is an opening in Earth's crust from which **lava**, or molten rock, escapes to the surface. Some volcanoes erupt dramatically, flinging hot rocks in all directions and releasing huge clouds of scorching ash and gases. Other volcanoes release lava and gases in a smooth steady flow. No matter how they erupt, all volcanoes have both immediate and long-lasting effects on the landscape and even the weather. Soil may become more fertile when enriched with nutrients from volcanic ash. Islands, mountains, and other landforms may be created from the material emitted by volcanoes.

The Giant's Causeway in Northern Ireland

◄**DRAMATIC ROCK FORMATIONS**
Molten rock can create amazing rock formations. When molten rock cools, contracts, and hardens, sometimes **columnar rocks** are produced. The Devil's Tower in Wyoming (below) is one example of a columnar rock that formed when magma gradually cooled underground. The columnar rocks of Giant's Causeway (left) in Northern Ireland are the result of a lava flow that erupted millions of years ago. ▼

DUST AND GAS ▶
Composite cones, such as Mount St. Helens in Washington (right), spit clouds of ash and fumes into the sky. The debris can completely cover human communities. Another hazard is that volcanic gases may be deadly poisons.

The Devil's Tower in Wyoming

◄**ERUPTING LAVA**
Red-hot lava is hurled into the air during an eruption of a volcano on Stromboli, an island off the coast of southern Italy. The Stromboli volcano is one of only a few volcanoes to display continuous eruptive activity over a period of more than a few years.

Facts and Figures

The ancient Roman city of Pompeii was encased in lava when Mount Vesuvius erupted in A.D. 79. The volcano destroyed the city, and most people were buried in ash and lava. Rain hardened the ash, forming perfect molds of people and preserving articles of everyday life. Pompeii's ruins were first discovered in the late sixteenth century.

Since 1748, archaeologists have excavated materials that provide a detailed picture of life in a busy Roman port town. In addition to houses, bakeries, restaurants, and factories, scholars have uncovered inscriptions on buildings, tombs, and statues. Even the graffiti on Pompeii's walls gives us clues about the values and concerns of this ancient society.

A CRATER LAKE ▶
A **crater lake** is a body of water that occupies a bowl-shaped depression around the opening of a dormant volcano. A future eruption could hurl the water out of the crater. The water could then mix with hot rock and debris and race downhill in a deadly mudslide.

A crater lake in Iceland

A STRING OF ISLANDS ▶
The Hawaiian Islands are the tops of volcanic mountains. They have developed over millions of years above a hot spot in Earth's mantle and have erupted great amounts of lava. As the Pacific plate moves over the stationary plume, it carries older islands in the chain to the northwest. Today, active volcanoes are found on the island of Hawaii and the newly forming island of Loihi.

Kauai *Oahu* *Maui* *Hawaii*

Volcanic pipe

Magma chamber

Stationary plume

Plate moving across plume

A satellite image shows the global spread of emissions from the 1991 eruptions of Mount Pinatubo in the Philippines. (Volcanic emissions over land are not shown in this satellite image.)

▲ AFFECTING THE WORLD'S WEATHER
Powerful eruptions emit gas and dust that can rise high into the atmosphere and travel around the world. Volcanic material can reduce average temperatures in parts of the world by filtering out some of the sunlight that warms Earth.

A few lichens find a home on the lava.

Plants take root in the beginnings of topsoil.

▲ LIFE AFTER LAVA
In time, plant life grows on hardened lava. Lichen and moss often appear first. Grass and larger plants slowly follow. The upper surface of the rock is gradually weathered by physical and biological processes to form soil. One example of a biological process is when plant roots grow into tiny cracks of the rock, breaking it apart. After many generations, the land may become lush and fertile again.

Assessment

1. **Key Terms** Define **(a)** volcano, **(b)** lava, **(c)** columnar rock, **(d)** plume, **(e)** crater lake.

2. **Natural Resources** How can soil become more fertile as a result of volcanic eruptions?

3. **Environmental Change (a)** How can volcanic activity create new landforms? **(b)** How can explosive volcanic eruptions affect the atmosphere and weather around the world?

4. **Natural Hazards** What are some of the ways in which a volcanic eruption can devastate nearby human settlements?

5. **Critical Thinking Sequencing** Study the diagram of the Hawaiian Islands and the caption that accompanies it. **(a)** Which island on the diagram is probably the oldest? Why do you think so? **(b)** What will happen to the volcanoes on the island of Hawaii as a result of plate movement?

299

Assessment Answers

1. (a) an opening in Earth's crust from which lava escapes to the surface; (b) molten rock; (c) volcanic rocks that split into columns as the lava cools; (d) a very hot spot in Earth's mantle; (e) a body of water that occupies a bowl-shaped depression around the opening of an extinct or dormant volcano

2. Soil becomes enriched with nutrients from volcanic ash.

3. (a) Underwater plumes erupt great amounts of lava over millions of years, building the tops of underwater volcanic mountains.
(b) Gas and dust from an eruption may rise high into the atmosphere, travel around the world, and filter out sunlight.

4. Volcanic debris can completely cover human communities, and volcanic gases are deadly poisons.

5. (a) Kauai is the oldest island because of the direction in which the plate is moving.
(b) The volcanoes on the island of Hawaii will become extinct as plate movement causes the island to move away from the stationary plume.

MELTING TEMPERATURE OF ROCKS `L2`

Objectives
After completing this activity, students will be able to
- describe the temperature gradient for Earth's interior.
- explain the relationship between depth and the melting temperatures of granite and basalt rocks.

Skills **Use Tables and Graphs, Analyze Data, Draw Conclusions**

Prep Time 5 minutes

Class Time 45 minutes

Teaching Tip Closely monitor students who may have difficulty constructing graphs or assign these students a partner to help them construct their graphs. These students may need extra time to complete this lab.

Expected Outcome Students will observe the relationships between depth and melting temperature of basalt and granite rocks. Students will observe that basalt rock melts at higher temperatures than granite at all depths.

Sample Data

Melting Temperatures of Rocks

Problem How can rocks melt to form magma in the crust and uppermost mantle?

Materials photocopy of Temperature Curves graph, colored pencils (three different colors), ruler

Skills Analyze Data, Graph, Calculate

Connect to the **Big idea** Measurements of temperatures in wells and mines have shown that Earth's internal temperatures increase with depth. Recall that this rate of temperature increase is called the geothermal gradient. Although the geothermal gradient varies from place to place, it is possible to calculate an average. In this lab, you will investigate Earth's internal temperatures and the temperatures at which rocks melt. You will also investigate the effect of water on the melting temperatures of rock.

Procedure

1. Obtain a photocopy of the unfilled Temperature Curves graph on page 301. Use it to plot the average temperature gradient for Earth's interior. Use the photocopied graph, or make your own version on a sheet of graph paper or by using graphing software.

2. Plot the temperature values from **Table 1** on your graph. Then draw a single best-fit line through the points with a colored pencil. Extend your line from the surface (0) to 200 kilometers. Label the line "Temperature Gradient."

3. The melting temperature of a rock changes as pressure increases deeper within Earth. The approximate melting points of the igneous rocks, granite and basalt, under various pressures (depths) have been determined in the laboratory and are shown in **Table 2**. Granite and basalt were used because they are common materials in the upper layer of Earth. Plot the melting temperatures from Table 2 on the same graph you made above. Use a different colored pencil to plot each set of points and draw the best-fit lines.

4. Label the two lines "Melting Curve for Wet Granite" and "Melting Curve for Basalt."

Table 1 Idealized Internal Temperatures of Earth

Depth (kilometers)	Temperature (°C)
0	20
25	600
50	1000
75	1250
100	1400
150	1700
200	1800

Table 2 Melting Temperatures of Granite (with water) and Basalt at Various Depths Within Earth

Granite (with water)		Basalt	
Depth (km)	Melting Temperature (°C)	Depth (km)	Melting Temperature (°C)
0	950	0	1100
5	700	25	1160
10	660	50	1250
20	625	100	1400
40	600	150	1600

300 Chapter 10

Analyze and Conclude

1. **Interpret Graphs** Does the rate of increase of Earth's internal temperature stay the same or change with increasing depth?

2. **Interpret Graphs** Is the rate of temperature increase greater from the surface to a depth of 100 kilometers or below 100 kilometers?

3. **Interpret Graphs** What is the temperature at 100 kilometers below the surface?

4. **Calculate** Use the data and your graph to calculate the average temperature gradient for the upper 100 kilometers of Earth in °C/100 kilometers and in °C/kilometer.

5. **Draw Conclusions** Based on your data, at approximately what depth within Earth would wet granite reach its melting temperature and begin to form magma? Explain.

6. **Draw Conclusions** Based on your data, at what depth will basalt have reached its melting temperature and begin to form magma?

GO FURTHER What is the name of the layer within Earth's upper mantle that is below about 100 kilometers? Why do scientists theorize that this zone is capable of "flowing" more easily than other mantle rock, allowing the lithosphere to move across it?

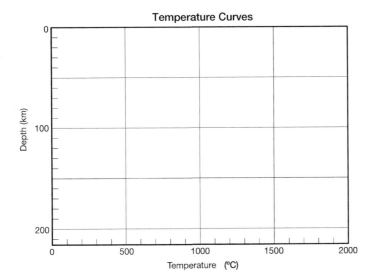

Temperature Curves

Analyze and Conclude

1. change with increasing depth
2. greater from the surface to 100 km
3. 1400°C
4. 1400°C/100 km; 14°C/km
5. approximately 25 km; at this depth, the internal temperature of Earth is approximately the same as the melting temperature for wet granite. (The two curves intersect.)
6. Basalt will reach its melting temperature at approximately 100 km in depth.

GO FURTHER

asthenosphere; one model proposed by scientists states that because the asthenosphere is partially molten, heat from within Earth may cause convection currents to form more easily in this layer. These convection cells within the asthenosphere act like conveyor belts that allow the lithosphere to move horizontally.
Verbal, Logical

STUDY GUIDE

Study Tip

Flashcards

Making flashcards is a good way to organize new or hard-to-learn information. Encourage students to review their notes every evening and make flashcards for the material covered that day. Students can review the flashcards alone or with a study partner.

Think Visually

a. shield volcanoes
b. composite cones
c. divergent plate volcanism
d. intraplate volcanism
e. magma composition
f. gas content (or amount of dissolved gases)

21st Century Learning

Civic Literacy

What are the best ways to evacuate from a volcano?

Scientists are trying to figure out how to predict a volcanic eruption far enough in advance to evacuate an area before it becomes endangered. Tell students to search the Web for articles about five recent evacuations due to volcanic eruptions. Ask students to use the articles to build a database on evacuations. They should then develop a table that has the date, the volcano's name, the number of people evacuated, the number of deaths, and any other relevant information. Finally, ask students to summarize the difficulties the local authorities encountered while evacuating people and to present their data to the class. Students should be prepared to answer questions during their presentation.

Homework Guide

Lesson	Questions
1	10, 12, 13, 14, 15, 18
2	2–9, 11, 16, 17, 19, 21, 24–35
3	1, 22, 23

---

10 Study Guide

Big idea Dynamic Earth

10.1 Volcanoes and Plate Tectonics

🔑 Magma forms in the crust and upper mantle when solid rock partially melts. The formation of magma depends on several factors, including heat, pressure, and water content.

🔑 Most volcanoes form along divergent and convergent plate boundaries. Some volcanoes form far from plate boundaries above "hot spots" in the crust.

decompression melting (280)
Ring of Fire (284)
intraplate volcanism (285)
hot spot (285)

10.2 The Nature of Volcanic Eruptions

🔑 The primary factors that determine whether a volcano erupts explosively or quietly include characteristics of the magma and the amount of dissolved gases in the magma.

🔑 Depending on the type of eruption, volcanoes may produce lava flows or eject pyroclastic materials, or both. All volcanic eruptions also emit large amounts of gases.

🔑 The three main volcanic types are shield volcanoes, cinder cones, and composite cones.

🔑 Volcanic landforms also include calderas, volcanic necks, and lava plateaus.

🔑 Volcanic hazards include lava flows, volcanic ash and gases, pyroclastic flows, and mudflows.

viscosity (286)	cinder cone (290)
vent (287)	composite cone (291)
pyroclastic material (289)	caldera (292)
volcano (289)	volcanic neck (293)
crater (289)	lava plateau (293)
shield volcano (290)	lahar (294)

10.3 Intrusive Igneous Activity

🔑 Types of plutons include sills, laccoliths, and dikes. Geologists classify plutons and other bodies of intrusive igneous rock according to their size, shape, and relationship to surrounding rock layers.

🔑 A batholith is a body of intrusive igneous rock that has a surface exposure of more than 100 square kilometers.

pluton (295)
sill (296)
laccolith (296)
dike (296)
batholith (297)

Think Visually

Review Copy the web diagram below and use information from the chapter to complete it.

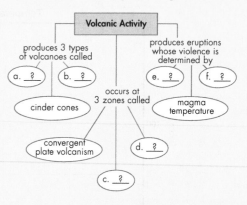

Assessment Answers

Review Content

1. b	**2.** c	**3.** c
4. d	**5.** d	**6.** a
7. b	**8.** d	**9.** d
10. a		

Understand Concepts

11. A volcanic neck is the rock in a volcanic pipe that is more resistant to erosion and remains standing after the surrounding volcanic cone has been eroded.

12. It is the name for the volcanoes that are located around the margins of the Pacific basin.

13. intraplate volcanism

14. a continental volcanic arc; composite cone

10 Assessment

Choose the letter that best answers the question or completes the statement.

1. Underground igneous rock bodies are called
   a. lava flows.   c. volcanoes.
   b. plutons.   d. calderas.

2. The greatest volume of volcanic material is produced by
   a. eruptions of cinder cones.
   b. eruptions of composite cones.
   c. eruptions along ocean ridges.
   d. eruptions of shield volcanoes.

3. The most explosive type of volcanic activity is associated with
   a. cinder cones.   c. composite cones.
   b. sills.   d. shield volcanoes.

4. A magma's viscosity is directly related to its
   a. depth.   c. color.
   b. age.   d. silica content.

5. What are the pulverized rock, lava, ash, and other fragments ejected from the vent of a volcano called?
   a. sills   c. pahoehoes
   b. craters   d. pyroclastic material

6. Which type of volcano consists of layers of lava flows and pyroclastic material?
   a. composite cone   c. shield volcano
   b. cinder cone   d. laccolith

7. The hotter of two types of basaltic lava commonly forms
   a. aa flows.   c. pyroclastic flows.
   b. pahoehoe flows. d. lapilli flows.

8. What is the very large depression at the top of some volcanoes called?
   a. a vent   c. a volcanic neck
   b. a lava plateau   d. a caldera

9. When silica-rich magma is extruded, ash, hot gases, and larger fragments propelled from the vent at high speeds may produce which of the following?
   a. a lava plateau   c. a pahoehoe flow
   b. a lahar   d. a pyroclastic flow

10. What feature may form in an intraplate area over a rising plume of hot mantle material?
    a. a hot spot   c. a subduction zone
    b. a dike   d. an ocean ridge

Understand Concepts

11. What is a volcanic neck, and how does it form?

12. Describe the Ring of Fire.

13. The Hawaiian Islands and Yellowstone National Park are associated with which of the three types of volcanism?

14. What is the chain of volcanoes called that forms at a convergent boundary between a subducting oceanic plate and a continental plate? What type of volcano commonly forms?

15. Explain how scientists think most magma is formed.

Use the diagram below to answer Questions 16 and 17.

16. Identify the type of volcano shown in the diagram.

17. What types of eruptions are commonly associated with this type of volcano?

18. How do hot spots form?

19. How are pyroclastic materials classified?

20. What is viscosity, and how does it affect volcanic eruptions?

21. Give an example of each of the three types of volcanoes.

22. How do dikes form?

21. Answers will vary. Sample answer: cinder cone—small cones on the side of shield volcanoes, SP Crater in Arizona, Sunset Crater in Arizona, Parícutin; composite cones—Fujiyama, Mount St. Helens, Mount Rainier, Mount Shasta; shield volcanoes—Kilauea, Mauna Loa, Mauna Kea

22. Dikes form when magma from a magma chamber intrudes into fractures in the surrounding rock and cuts across the preexisting rock layers.

15. Most magma originates by the partial melting of rock in the crust and upper mantle, either when heat is added by hot, deeper mantle material intruding into the lithosphere, by a decrease in pressure as the rock rises into the crust, or by the addition of water to lower the melting point.

16. shield volcano

17. quiet eruptions of basaltic lava, forming mainly pahoehoe lava flows

18. A plume of hot mantle material produced at the core-mantle boundary rises to the surface and causes volcanic activity at the surface.

19. by size and shape

20. Viscosity is resistance to flow of a substance. The more viscous the magma or lava, the more explosive the volcanic eruption will be.

ASSESSMENT

Think Critically

23. Laccoliths are intruded at shallow depths and often push up the overlying rock layers to form a lens-shaped structure. This structure may be detected before the laccolith itself is exposed by erosion.

24. When magma moves close to the surface, the gases dissolved in the magma begin to rise and expand. The viscosity of the magma determines how easily the gases can escape. Highly viscous magma prevents the gases from escaping easily, so they can accumulate and cause a violent eruption.

25. Pahoehoe lava flows have smooth, ropy surfaces and are formed from very fluid basaltic lava. Aa lava flows have sharp, jagged surfaces and are formed when more viscous lava cools.

26. A lahar is a mudflow on the slopes of a volcano. Lahars can be triggered by heavy rainfall saturating the loose, weathered volcanic deposits on the steep slopes of a volcano without an eruption occurring.

27. Cinder cones commonly erupt once for a short time. When the eruption ends, the magma in the pipe solidifies and the volcano doesn't erupt again. Because cinder cones erupt only once for a short time, they don't build large cones.

Analyze Data

28. Toba

29. over 7 times greater (7.14 times)

30. Vesuvius erupted in a.d. 79 before much was known about volcanic eruptions, while Pinatubo erupted more recently and people were warned and evacuated. Most likely more people were killed by the Vesuvius eruption because more people lived closer to Vesuvius than near Pinatubo.

31. 44 km − 19 km = 25 km higher and 19/44 × 100 = 43.2% higher

Concepts in Action

32. An eruption of a composite cone is more likely to affect global climate because these volcanoes have the most explosive eruptions due to the amount of gases and high viscosity of their magmas.

33. either a recent lava flow or a lahar (mudflow)

34. You would probably be safer near a cinder cone in Arizona. Composite cones in the Andes Mountains erupt more violently, and the snow could melt to form a lahar.

35. Answers will vary, but should be scientifically accurate as to the types of pyroclastic material ejected, and other possible features associated with eruptions of composite cones.

Think Critically

23. Apply Concepts How might a laccolith be detected at Earth's surface before being exposed by erosion?

24. Infer Why is a volcano fed by a highly viscous magma likely to be a greater threat to people than a volcano fed by very fluid magma?

25. Compare and Contrast Compare pahoehoe lava flows and aa lava flows.

26. Relate Cause and Effect What is a lahar? Explain why a lahar can occur on a volcano without an eruption.

27. Draw Conclusions Why are cinder cones usually small?

Analyze Data

Use the data table below to answer Questions 28–31.

Notable Volcanic Eruptions			
Volcano	Date	Volume Ejected	Height of Plume
Toba	74,000 years ago	2800 km³	50–80 km
Vesuvius	A.D. 79	4 km³	32 km
Tambora	1815	150 km³	44 km
Krakatau	1883	21 km³	36 km
Mount St. Helens	1980	1 km³	19 km
Mount Pinatubo	1991	5 km³	35 km

28. Interpret Tables Which volcanic eruption listed in the data table ejected the greatest volume of pyroclastic material?

29. Calculate How many times larger than the volume of material ejected by the eruption of Krakatau was the volume of material ejected by the eruption of Tambora?

---

30. Form a Hypothesis Develop a hypothesis to explain why the eruption of Mount Vesuvius in A.D. 79 was more deadly than the eruption of Mount Pinatubo in 1991, even though the eruptions were approximately the same size.

31. Calculate Calculate how much higher the plume of volcanic debris during the eruption of Tambora in 1815 was than the plume from the 1980 eruption of Mount St. Helens. Calculate the difference in kilometers and as a percent.

Concepts in Action

32. Form a Hypothesis Large volcanic eruptions eject large amounts of gas, dust, and ash into the atmosphere. This volcanic material can affect the world's climate by blocking incoming solar radiation. An eruption from what type of volcano is most likely to cause global climate changes? Explain your answer.

33. Classify On the side of a composite cone you see a large area where there are no trees, and the ground surface looks disturbed. What possible volcanic feature or event could have caused this?

34. Apply Concepts Would you be safer from a violent, explosive eruption while vacationing in Arizona near a cinder cone or while skiing in the Andes Mountains of South America? Explain.

35. Review Write a paragraph describing what an eruption of a nearby composite cone might be like.

Performance-Based Assessment

Communicate Make a poster illustrating the internal and external features that are typical of a composite cone. Include on your poster copies of photographs of some classic composite cones. Also explain some of the possible dangers associated with living near a composite cone.

Performance-Based Assessment

Posters should be scientifically accurate, neatly labeled, and clearly explain the potential dangers, such as pyroclastic flows and lahars.

Standardized Test Prep

Choose the letter that best answers the question.

1 Which of the following is *not* a factor that determines if a volcano erupts explosively or quietly?
A temperature of the magma
B size of the volcanic cone
C the magma's composition
D amount of dissolved gases in the magma

2 How does an increase in pressure affect a rock's melting temperature?
F The melting temperature increases.
G The melting temperature decreases.
H The melting temperature is stabilized.
J It has no effect on the melting temperature.

Use the diagram below to answer Questions 3 and 4.

3 What intrusive igneous feature in the diagram is labeled C?
A a dike
B a sill
C a batholith
D a laccolith

4 If the feature labeled E extended for over 100 square kilometers after being exposed by erosion, what would it be classified as?
F a dike
G a stock
H a laccolith
J a batholith

Standardized Test Prep

1 B
2 F
3 B
4 J

If You Have Trouble With . . .				
Question	1	2	3	4
See Lesson	10.2	10.1	10.3	10.3

11 Mountain Building Planning Guide

BIGIDEA: DYNAMIC EARTH

Lesson Objectives		Activities
11.1 Forces in Earth's Crust, pp. 308–311 11.1 **Identify** the factors that determine the strength of a rock and explain how rocks permanently deform. 11.2 **Distinguish** among the types of stresses that affect rocks. 11.3 **Explain** how isostatic adjustment is involved in mountain formation.		TE Build Science Skills, p. 309 L2 TE Teacher Demo: Modeling Isostasy, p. 310 L2
11.2 Folds, Faults, and Mountains, pp. 312–319 11.4 **List** the three main types of folds. 11.5 **Identify** the main types of faults. 11.6 **Describe** folded mountains and fault-block mountains and explain how they form. 11.7 **Describe** plateaus, domes, and basins and explain how they form.		TE Teacher Demo: Making an Anticline, p. 313 L2 TE Build Science Skills, p. 314 L2 TE Build Science Skills, p. 317 L2 SE Map It: Regions, p. 318 L2
11.3 Mountains and Plates, pp. 320–325 11.8 **Identify** the type of mountains associated with the different types of convergent plate boundaries. 11.9 **Identify** the type of mountains associated with divergent plate boundaries. 11.10 **Describe** the role of accretion in the formation of continents and mountain building.		TE Teacher Demo: Partial Melting, p. 321 L2 SE Quick Lab: Rates of Mountain Building, p. 323 L2
Chapter Features and Labs		
Try It Can You Model How Rocks Deform? p. 307		LM Interpreting a Geologic Map L1
Earth & Its Systems Mountain Building Away from Plate Margins, pp. 326–327		
Exploration Lab Investigating Anticlines and Synclines, pp. 328–329		

Ability Levels

L1 For students who need additional help
L2 For all students
L3 For students who need to be challenged

Components

SE	Student Edition	LP	Lesson Plans
TE	Teacher's Edition	AA	Active Art
LM	Laboratory Manual	PD	Planet Diary
CT	Chapter Tests	GEODe	Geode CD-ROM
GRSW	Guided Reading & Study Workbook	eText	
CTB	Computer Test Bank		

Resources	Lesson Assessment
GRSW Lesson 11.1 **LP** Lesson Planning 11.1	**SE** Lesson 11.1 Assessment, p. 311 **eText** Lesson 11.1
GRSW Lesson 11.2 **LP** Lesson Planning 11.2	**SE** Lesson 11.2 Assessment, p. 319 **eText** Lesson 11.2
GRSW Lesson 11.3 **LP** Lesson Planning 11.3 **PD** Himalayas **GEODe** Forces Within: Igneous Activity	**SE** Lesson 11.3 Assessment, p. 325 **eText** Lesson 11.3

Materials for Activities and Labs

Quantities for each group

STUDENT EDITION

Try It, p. 307
large, thick rubber band; plastic putty; straight, thin wooden stick about 25 cm long

Exploration Lab, pp. 328–329
pencil, protractor, tracing paper

TEACHER'S EDITION

Build Science Skills, p. 309
marshmallow or piece of foam rubber

Teacher Demo, p. 310
large plastic container, water, balance, metric ruler, several blocks of varying sizes and kinds of wood

Teacher Demo, p. 313
stack of construction paper sheets in several colors

Build Science Skills, p. 314
2 wooden blocks, small towel or piece of fabric

Build Science Skills, p. 317
3 wooden blocks

Teacher Demo, p. 321
can of frozen grape juice concentrate (inexpensive brands work best), can opener, plastic tub, rubber gloves, apron, water, plastic pitcher, paper towels for clean-up

Assessment

CHAPTER ASSESSMENT
SE Assessment, pp. 331–332
CT Chapter 11 Test
CTB Chapter 11
eText Chapter 11

21st Century Learning

Communication Skills: How were the Rocky Mountains formed?, TE p. 330

Common Themes

Michael Wysession
Washington University

Mountains provide evidence of enormous tectonic forces within Earth, which are usually associated with the boundaries between lithospheric plates.

Space and Time Mountains primarily form by folding and faulting rock at compressional plate boundaries, by faulting rock at tensional plate boundaries, by uplifting the lithosphere, and through volcanism.

Forces and Motion Rock deforms in an elastic, brittle, or ductile manner, depending upon the type and amount of stress, the applied temperature and pressure, the type of rock, and the amount of time it is stressed. Stress can be tensional, compressional, or shear. Folds, such as anticlines and synclines, occur when rock strains in a ductile manner. Faults, in the form of normal, reverse, and strike-slip, occur when rock deforms in a brittle manner.

Matter and Energy The world's longest mountain chain is of volcanoes along the interconnected divergent plate boundaries of the mid-ocean ridges. At ocean-ocean convergent plate boundaries, volcanic mountains form an island arc. At an ocean-continent convergent boundary, mountains form from composite volcanoes and accreted sediments. At continent-continent boundaries, mountains form from folded continental crust and the accretion of sediments, island arcs, continental fragments, and slivers of ocean crust.

Earth as a System Because of isostasy, mountains have deep crustal roots, and buoy upward when the tops are eroded. Continents like North America have grown in size through the accretion of land at their edges during plate collisions.

EARTH SCIENCE REFRESHER

How Do Continents Grow?

There is currently a debate within geology as to how continents grow over time. One point of view is that continents began as small fragments of continental crust, and have grown to their current size over time as a result of major plate collisions. Continents now cover about 39 percent of Earth's surface (including the continental shelves that are under water). North America would seem to fit this model well. Our continent contains pieces of crust that are about 4 billion years old. Called cratons, or shields, or platforms, these pieces of old crust located in Canada seem to have been sutured together by younger rock when they collided about 2 billion years ago. As you go from Canada to Florida, however, you pass across terranes of successively younger ages that were added onto North America when it collided with other continents and island arcs. The rock of Missouri is about 1.7 billion years old, but the rock of Florida is only a few hundred million years old.

However, another point of view is that there has always been about the same amount of continental crust, but it has continually been altered and reworked, so there is very little in its original form. Continental crust is

---

Address Misconceptions

Students may have the common misconception that southern California is going to slide into the Pacific Ocean due to movement of the San Andreas Fault. Explain that the San Andreas Fault is a strike-slip fault that runs northwest. The Pacific Ocean is due west. Movement of the crust is north and not west toward the ocean. For a strategy that helps to overcome this misconception, see **Address Misconceptions** on TE p. 315.

Address Misconceptions

Students may have the misconception that mountain-building processes are no longer taking place on Earth. Using Mount Everest as an example, students will learn that recent data show that the Indian and Eurasian plates are still pushing against each other and causing movement. For a strategy that helps to overcome this misconception, see **Address Misconceptions on TE p. 322.**

continually changing. Continents can grow by accretion of added terranes. They also grow by volcanism and platform deposition. Most volcanoes add rock to the edges of continents, but some add to the middle. Platform deposition is the addition of sedimentary rocks like limestone, shale, and sandstone, to the surface of continents when they are flooded by oceans.

At the same time, however, continents shrink by lateral accretion and erosion. Lateral accretion is the horizontal shortening of continents that occurs during plate collisions. The rock gets narrower but taller, as mountains form. Mountains erode quickly, however, so rock gets removed from continents quickly this way. The Appalachian Mountains used to be about 10 km taller than they are now. Much of that rock is now on the ocean seafloor.

This continental rock, in the form of ocean sediments, gets returned to continents, however. When the ocean seafloor subducts beneath a continent, much of the sediment get scraped off and added to the edge of the continent in the form of an accretionary wedge. And much of the sediment that does get subducted likely comes back up to the surface with the water-rich magma that erupts as volcanoes like Mt. St. Helens. This is the essence of part of the rock cycle. So it is possible that most of the continental rock has been around for 4 billion years, but has traveled through the rock cycle enough times that only a few pieces, like the Canadian cratons, are still in their original form.

Address Misconceptions

Students may confuse the words terrane *and* terrain. Using a dictionary will help students distinguish between the two words. For a strategy that helps to overcome this misconception, see **Address Misconceptions on TE p. 324**

BUILD READING LITERACY

KWL (Know-Want to Know-Learned)

Know/Want to Know/Learned

Strategy Help students access prior knowledge, set a purpose for reading, recall what has been read, and link new information to prior knowledge. The KWL strategy has students create and complete a three-column chart similar to the one below. Before reading, students write what they already Know about the topic, and what they Want to Know. As students read, they complete the Learned column.

Know	Want to Know	Learned

Assign a section in Chapter 11, such as Folds, pp. 312–313, for students to read. Before they begin, have them create and complete the first two columns of the KWL chart.

Example

1. Draw a three-column KWL chart on the board for students to copy.

2. Have students complete the Know column with facts, examples, and other information they already know about the topic.

3. Tell students to complete the Want to Know column with questions about the topic that they want answers to. Students may scan the section to help them generate questions.

4. Have students read the section to learn more about the topic and determine answers to their questions. As they read, have them note answers in the Learned column, along with other facts, examples, and details they learned.

See TE p. 309 for a script on how to use this strategy with students. For additional strategies, see TE pp. 312, 315, and 323.

Use the Chapter Pretest below to assess students' prior knowledge. As needed, review these concepts.

Review Science Concepts

Lesson 11.1 Review the structure of different types of rock and minerals to help students understand why different rock types deform in predictable ways. A review of faults and the movements that take place along faults will be necessary for students to learn how stress is involved in deformation.

Lesson 11.2 The material on mountain types in this section follows directly from the discussion of rock deformation in Lesson 11.1. Be sure students have mastered the concepts involved in rock folding and faulting.

Lesson 11.3 Review the theory of plate tectonics and the interactions at plate boundaries to give students a starting point for understanding how mountains are formed at different boundaries.

11 Mountain Building

Big idea **Dynamic Earth**
Q: How are mountains built?

306

Chapter Pretest

1. What plate is subducted in an ocean-continental convergent boundary? *(The oceanic plate is subducted.)*

2. Which rock is formed when shale is subjected to stress? *(c)*
  a. granite
  b. sandstone
  c. slate

3. True or False: Most earthquakes occur along faults in Earth's crust and mantle. *(True)*

4. Which of the following is a result of ocean-continental convergence? *(b)*
  a. Volcanoes form on the ocean floor.
  b. Volcanoes form on a continent.
  c. A narrow linear sea forms.

5. When is a rift valley formed? *(It forms when two continental plates diverge.)*

6. Why does the oceanic lithosphere sink during oceanic-continental convergence? *(The oceanic lithosphere is more dense than the continental lithosphere, so it sinks.)*

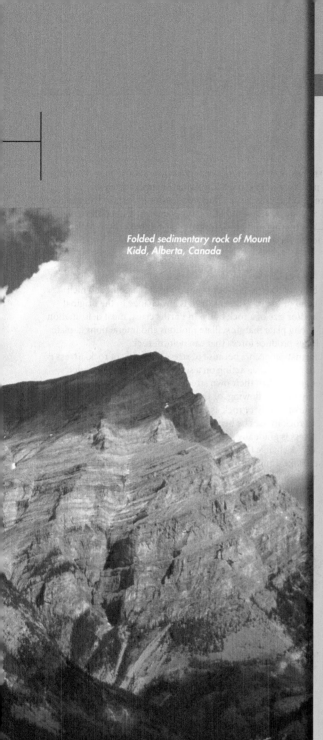

Folded sedimentary rock of Mount Kidd, Alberta, Canada

CAN YOU MODEL HOW ROCKS DEFORM?

Procedure

1. Take a large, thick rubber band and stretch it out a few centimeters. Then let it relax. **CAUTION:** *Put on your safety goggles. Hold both ends of the band.* Record your observations.

2. Take a chunk of plastic putty. Pull on the ends of the piece of putty rapidly. Record your observations.

3. Now take the chunk of plastic putty, and work it gently until it is warm and flexible. Slowly stretch it. Record your observations.

4. Take a straight, thin wooden stick about 25 centimeters long. Gently bend the ends of the stick until it breaks. Record your observations.

Think About It

1. **Observe** Describe how the rubber band, plastic putty, and wooden stick behaved.

2. **Observe** Which items returned to the original shape and size after the force was removed?

3. **Draw Conclusions** Which item was the easiest to deform? The hardest to deform?

4. **Infer** Under what conditions do you think rocks are easier to bend? Under what conditions to you think rocks will break?

307

ENGAGE/EXPLORE

CAN YOU MODEL HOW ROCKS DEFORM?

L2

Purpose In this activity, students model the various ways rocks can deform.

Skills Observe, Infer, Draw Conclusions

Prep Time 10 minutes

Materials large, thick rubber band; plastic putty; straight, thin wooden stick about 25 cm long

Advance Prep Purchase plastic putty. Gather sticks.

Class Time 10 minutes

Teaching Tips Use a thin, relatively flexible stick that is not too thick or dry and that will bend quite a bit before it breaks. Twigs from bushes work well.

Expected Outcome The rubber band stretches when pulled and then returns to the same size and shape when released. The cool putty stretches somewhat and then breaks into two pieces when stretched rapidly. The warm putty pulls into a long, thin strip when stretched, before pulling apart. The stick bends quite a bit before breaking.

Think About It

1. The rubber band stretched when pulled, then returned to the same size and shape when released. The cooler piece of plastic putty stretched a small amount, and then broke into two pieces when stretched rapidly. The warmer piece of putty slowly pulled into a long, thin strip before pulling apart. The stick bent quite a bit before breaking.

2. Only the rubber band returned to its original size and shape.

3. The warm plastic putty was the easiest to deform, and the stick was the hardest to deform.

4. Rocks probably will bend more easily when they are warmer and are deformed slowly. Rocks will probably break when they are cool and deform rapidly.

LESSON 11.1

1 FOCUS

Lesson Objectives

11.1 **Identify** the factors that determine the strength of a rock and explain how rocks permanently deform.

11.2 **Distinguish** among the types of stresses that affect rocks.

11.3 **Explain** how isostatic adjustment is involved in mountain formation.

Build Vocabulary   L2

Word Parts The term *isostasy* is made up of two Greek root words: *iso-* meaning "equal" and *-stasis* meaning "standing." The term refers to the tendency of different parts of the lithosphere to move toward gravitational balance, or equilibrium, as the lithosphere thickens during mountain building or gets thinner as mountains erode. If plate motions, earthquakes, and volcanic eruptions stopped, mountain building would end and the lithosphere would eventually erode to an equal thickness and "float" at a uniform depth on the mantle below.

Reading Strategy   L2

Sample Answers:

a. stress in Earth's crust

b. What are the types of stress?

c. tensional stress, compressional stress, and shear stress

d. What is the principle of isostasy?

e. The thicker the crust is, the higher it "floats" on the mantle below.

2 INSTRUCT

Integrate Physics   L2

Force Remind students that force is defined as a push or pull exerted on an object. A force has magnitude; for example, you can push hard or gently on an object. Force also has direction; you can push on an object to the left, to the right, up, or down.

Logical

Key Questions

 What factors affect the deformation of a rock?

 What are the types of stresses that affect rocks?

 How does isostasy affect Earth's crust?

Vocabulary

- deformation • stress
- strain • isostasy
- isostatic adjustment

Reading Strategy

Preview Copy the table below. Before you read, rewrite the orange topic headings as how, why, or what questions. As you read, write an answer to each question.

Forces in Earth's Crust	
What causes deformation of rock?	a. _____ ?

EARTH has only 14 mountains higher than 8000 meters. Four of these peaks are in Pakistan's Karakoram Range, shown in **Figure 1.** What causes such huge mountains to form? Over millions of years, plate motions and other forces deform and uplift the crust. Weathering and erosion shape the uplifted crustal rock into spectacular mountain peaks.

Deformation of Rock

Every body of rock, no matter how strong, has a point at which it will bend or break. **Deformation** is any change in the original shape and/or size of a rock body. In Earth's crust, most deformation occurs along plate margins. Plate motions and interactions at plate boundaries produce forces that can deform rock.

Deformation occurs because of stress in a body of rock. **Stress** is the force per unit area acting on a solid. When rocks are under stresses greater than their own strength, they begin to deform, usually by folding, flowing, or fracturing. The change in shape or volume of a body of rock as a result of stress is called **strain.** How can rock masses be bent into folds without being broken? When stress is gradually applied, rocks first respond by deforming elastically. A change that results from elastic deformation can be reversed. Like a rubber band, the rock will return to almost its original size and shape once the force is removed. Once the elastic limit or strength of a rock is surpassed, it either flows or fractures. **The factors that affect the deformation of rock include temperature, pressure, rock type, and time.**

FIGURE 1 Mountain Ranges This peak is in the Karakoram Range in Pakistan, part of the Himalayas.

Temperature and Pressure Rocks deform permanently in two ways: brittle deformation and ductile deformation. Rocks near the surface, where temperatures and pressures are low, usually behave like brittle solids and fracture once their strength is exceeded. This type of deformation is called brittle failure or *brittle deformation*. You know that glass objects, wooden pencils, china plates, and even our bones show brittle failure once their strength is exceeded.

At depth, where temperatures and pressures are high, rocks become ductile. *Ductile deformation* is a type of solid-state flow that produces a change in the size and shape of an object without fracturing the object. Ductile materials include modeling clay, bee's wax, caramel candy, and most metals. For example, a copper penny placed on a railroad track will be flattened and deformed without breaking by the force and heat applied by a passing train. Ductile deformation of a rock is somewhat similar to the deformation of a flattened penny.

Rock Type The mineral composition and texture of a rock also greatly affect how it will deform. Rocks such as granite and basalt that are composed of minerals with strong internal molecular bonds usually fail by brittle fracture. Sedimentary rocks that are weakly cemented or metamorphic rocks that contain zones of weakness—such as foliation—are more likely to deform by ductile flow. Rocks that are weak and ductile when under stress include rock salt, gypsum, and shale. Limestone, schist, and marble are of intermediate strength and may also become ductile.

Time Small stresses applied over long time spans eventually cause the deformation of rock. You can see the effects of time on deformation in everyday settings. For example, marble benches have been known to sag under their own weight over a span of a hundred years or so. Forces that cannot deform rock when first applied may cause rock to flow if the force is maintained over time.

☑ **Reading Checkpoint** *What is brittle deformation?*

Types of Stress

Plate motions cause different types of stress in the rocks of the lithosphere. 🔑 **The three types of stress that cause deformation of rocks are tensional stress, compressional stress, and shear stress.** These stresses are summarized in **Figure 2.** When rocks are squeezed or shortened the stress is compressional. Tensional stress is caused by rocks being pulled in opposite directions. Shear stress causes a body of rock to be distorted.

TYPES OF STRESS

FIGURE 2 Undeformed material is changed as it undergoes different types of stress. The arrows show the direction of maximum stress. **A** Tensional stress causes a material to be stretched or to undergo extension. **B** Compressional stress causes a material to shorten. **C** Shear stress causes a material to be distorted with no change in volume.

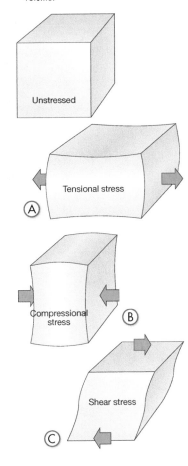

Unstressed

Tensional stress (A)

Compressional stress (B)

Shear stress (C)

LESSON 11.1

MODELING ISOSTASY   L2

Purpose Students model the principle of isostasy by measuring how high blocks of varying density float in water.

Materials large plastic container, water, balance, metric ruler, several blocks of varying sizes and kinds of wood

Procedure Wear apron and goggles. Fill a large plastic container approximately half full with water. Determine the mass and volume of each of the wooden blocks. Calculate the density of each. Place each block in the water. Use a ruler to measure how much of each block is supported above the water. Stack two or more blocks on top of the other blocks in the water. Measure how much of the blocks are supported above the water.

Expected Outcomes The thicker blocks floated higher than the thinner blocks. The blocks that had lower densities also floated higher than the denser blocks.
Visual, Kinesthetic

FIGURE 3 Isostasy This drawing illustrates how wooden blocks of different thicknesses float in water. In a similar manner, thick sections of crustal material float higher than thinner crustal slabs. Infer *Would a denser wooden block float at a higher or lower level?*

Principle of Isostasy

In addition to the horizontal movements of lithospheric plates, there are also gradual up-and-down motions of the crust. Much of this vertical movement occurs along plate margins and is linked to mountain building. But, the up-and-down motions also occur in the interiors of continents far from plate boundaries.

What Is Isostasy? Earth's crust floats on top of the denser and more flexible mantle. The concept of a floating crust in gravitational balance is called **isostasy** (*iso* = equal; *stasis* = standing). Visualize a series of wooden blocks of different thicknesses floating in water, as shown in **Figure 3.** The thicker wooden blocks float higher than the thinner blocks. In a similar way, many mountain belts tower high above the surface because they have "roots" that extend deep into the mantle. The denser mantle supports the mountains from below.

What would happen if another small block of wood were placed on top of one of the blocks in Figure 3? The thickened block would sink until a new gravitational balance was reached. However, the top of the thickened block would actually be higher than before, and the bottom would be lower. This process of establishing a new level of gravitational balance is called **isostatic adjustment.**

☑ **Reading Checkpoint** *What is isostatic adjustment?*

Isostatic Adjustment for Mountains Applying the concept of isostasy, we should expect that when weight is added to the crust, the crust responds by subsiding. Likewise, when weight is removed, the crust will rebound. Evidence of crustal subsidence followed by crustal rebound was provided by the continental ice sheets that covered parts of North America during the ice age. The added weight of a 3-kilometer-thick mass of ice depressed Earth's crust by hundreds of meters. In the 8000 years since the last ice sheet melted, uplift of 330 meters has occurred in Canada's Hudson Bay region, where the ice was thickest.

Most mountain building thickens and shortens the sections of the crust involved. **Because of isostasy, deformed and thickened crust will undergo regional uplift during mountain building and for a long period afterward.** As the crust rises, the processes of erosion increase, and the deformed rock layers are carved into a mountainous landscape.

Facts and Figures

Growing Mountain Roots Students are often puzzled as to how the deep crustal roots of mountains come about. The crustal roots grow simultaneously with the growth of the mountains. In that sense the mountains behave in a fluid manner—the isostasy keeps up with the growth of the mountains. The crustal roots of mountains also deflate simultaneously with the erosion of the tops of the mountain—as the surface erodes, the whole mountain continuously rises.

ISOSTATIC ADJUSTMENT IN MOUNTAINS

FIGURE 4 This sequence illustrates how the combined effect of erosion and isostatic adjustment results in a thinning of the crust in mountainous regions.

1 When mountains are young, the continental crust is thickest.

2 As erosion lowers the mountains, the crust rises in response to the reduced load.

3 Erosion and uplift continue until the mountains reach "normal" crustal thickness.

As erosion lowers the summits of mountains, the crust will rise in response to the reduced load, as shown in **Figure 4**. The processes of uplifting and erosion will continue until the mountain block reaches "normal" crustal thickness. When this occurs, the mountains will be eroded to near sea level, and the once deeply buried interior of the mountain will be exposed at the surface. This process allows igneous batholiths, which form within the cores of mountains, to eventually be exposed at the surface. Meanwhile, the deposition of eroded sediment can produce a heavier load on low-lying portions of crust, causing sinking, or subsidence.

 Assessment

Review Key Concepts 🔑

1. List four factors that affect how a rock deforms.

2. Describe the different types of stress.

3. Explain the role of isostasy in vertical movements of the crust.

Think Critically

4. Apply Concepts What is the difference between brittle deformation and ductile deformation? Use examples of brittle and ductile materials in your answer.

5. Predict Would rock in the lower mantle undergo brittle deformation or ductile deformation? Explain.

6. Relate Cause and Effect Geologists find an area in which the crust has been stretched and thinned. Which type of stress produced this effect? Explain.

7. Interpret Diagrams In Figure 4.2 above, what process leads to uplift due to isostatic adjustment? Explain.

CONNECTING CONCEPTS

8. Infer Review the types of plate boundaries in Chapter 9. At which type of boundary would compressional stress be the dominant force?

Mountain Building **311**

Predict When you place a block of wood in a pail of water, the block displaces some of the water, and the water level rises. **Ask:** If you could measure the mass of the water that the block displaces, what would you find? *(The mass of the water equals the mass of the block.)* If 1 million kg of ice were added to a land mass, how much mantle would be displaced? *(1 million kg)* **Logical**

3 ASSESS

Evaluate Understanding [L2]

Ask students to describe two events that would cause crust to subside. *(Accept any event that increases the mass of the crust, such as formation of large ice sheets, accumulation of large amounts of sediments, or formation of volcanic mountains.)*

Reteach [L1]

Have students design an experiment that models the formation of an uplifted mountain. Students may use a bicycle pump, balloon, fabric, and any other materials they choose when designing their model.

Answers

Figure 3 *At a lower level*

☑ **Reading Checkpoint** *Vertical movement of the crust, resulting from changes in its thickness, to bring the crust into gravitational balance*

Assessment Answers

1. temperature, pressure, type of rock, time
2. Tensional stress: rock stretched; compressional stress: rock squeezed or shortened; shearing stress: rock shape distorted without a change in volume
3. As the crust is thickened due to mountain building, the lithosphere will sink deeper into the mantle. But the lithosphere is less dense than the mantle, so the lithosphere will stand higher. To balance the added thickness, the crust will rise as a new level of gravitational equilibrium is reached.

4. In brittle deformation, a rock or brittle object such as a wooden pencil breaks once its strength is exceeded. In ductile deformation, a rock or ductile material such as a copper wire bends when a force is applied to it.
5. Rock in the lower mantle would undergo ductile deformation because high temperatures and pressures in the lower mantle cause rock to become ductile.

6. Tensional stress stretches the crust. For example, plate motions that pull a piece of crust in opposite directions would cause it to stretch or become thinner.
7. As erosion removes material from the mountains, the crust rises due to isostatic adjustment. Overall, though, the crust will be thinner and will float lower than it did before the erosion.
8. A convergent boundary

11.2 Folds, Faults, and Mountains

Lesson Objectives

11.4 **List** the three main types of folds.
11.5 **Identify** the main types of faults.
11.6 **Describe** folded mountains and fault-block mountains and explain how they form.
11.7 **Describe** plateaus, domes, and basins and explain how they form.

Build Vocabulary ☐L2

Related Terms Ask students to identify two related sets of vocabulary terms in this lesson other than the types of faults. *(Anticline, syncline, and monocline and horst, graben, and fault-block mountain)* Then ask students to pick one set of terms and write a definition of each term in their own words. The definitions should state how the terms are related to each other.

Reading Strategy ☐L2

a. formed by tensional forces; hanging wall moves down relative to footwall
b. reverse fault
c. formed by compressional forces; footwall moves up relative to hanging wall
d. thrust fault
e. a reverse fault with a dip of less than 45°
f. strike-slip fault
g. formed by shearing forces; the two sides of the fault slip past each other horizontally

❷ INSTRUCT

Build Reading Literacy ☐L1

Refer to **p. 186D** in **Chapter 7,** which provides the guidelines for relating text and figures.

Relate Text and Figures Have students read the section on Folds on pp. 312–313. Have them draw a diagram of an anticline and a syncline. **Ask:** What are three types of folds? *(anticlines, synclines, and monoclines)* What types of folds can you see in the photograph in Figure 5? *(anticlines and synclines)*
Logical, Visual

Key Questions

 What are the different types of folds?

▭ **What are the major types of faults?**

▭ **What are the major types of mountains?**

▭ **How are landforms such as domes, basins, and plateaus formed?**

Vocabulary

- anticline • syncline
- monocline • normal fault
- reverse fault • thrust fault
- strike-slip fault • orogenesis
- folded mountain
- fault-block mountain
- graben • horst

Reading Strategy

Compare and Contrast
After you read the section, compare types of faults by completing the table below.

Type of Fault	Description
Normal Fault	a. _____?_____
b. _____?_____	c. _____?_____
d. _____?_____	e. _____?_____
f. _____?_____	g. _____?_____

FIGURE 5 Folded Mountains
Folded sedimentary layers are exposed in the northern Rocky Mountains on the face of Mount Kidd, Alberta, Canada.

HOW CAN ROCK bend like a piece of ribbon or a soft, cooked noodle? Over millions of years, stress forces can cause rock to fold. You can clearly see the results in Mount Kidd in the Canadian Rockies, shown in **Figure 5.** Before Mount Kidd formed, its rock consisted of flat, sedimentary layers on the bottom of a shallow sea. Stress slowly folded the layers into dramatic zigzags of solid rock.

Folds

During mountain building, compressional stresses often bend flat-lying sedimentary and volcanic rocks into wavelike ripples called *folds*. Folds in sedimentary strata are much like those that would form if you were to hold the ends of a sheet of paper and then push them together. Folds in rock come in a wide variety of sizes and shapes. ▭ **The three main types of folds are anticlines, synclines, and monoclines.**

Anticlines and Synclines The two most common types of folds are anticlines and synclines. An **anticline** is usually formed by the upfolding, or arching, of rock layers, as shown in **Figure 6.** Often found in association with anticlines are downfolds, or troughs, called **synclines.** Notice in Figure 6 that the *limb,* or side, of an anticline is also a limb of the adjacent syncline.

The angle that a fold or fault makes with the horizontal plane is called the *dip*. (Flat rock layers would have a dip of 0°. A vertical fold or fault would have a dip of 90°.) In the symmetrical fold shown in Figure 6, both limbs of the anticline have the same, low-angle dip. In the asymmetrical fold, one limb has a much steeper dip than the other. In the overturned fold, one limb has been tilted beyond the vertical. This is called an *overturned limb*.

Monoclines In general, folds are closely associated with faults. Examples of this close association are broad, regional features called monoclines. **Monoclines** are large, steplike folds in otherwise horizontal sedimentary strata. Monoclines seem to occur as sedimentary layers are folded over a large faulted block of underlying rock. Monoclines are prominent features of the Colorado Plateau, featured in **Figure 7,** which overlaps areas of Colorado, New Mexico, Utah, and Arizona.

☑ **Reading Checkpoint** What is a syncline?

FIGURE 6 Anticlines and Synclines The upfolded or arched structures are anticlines. The downfolds or troughs are synclines. Notice that the limb of an anticline is also the limb of the adjacent syncline.

FIGURE 7 Monocline A Monocline located near Mexican Hat, Utah. **B** This monocline consists of bent sedimentary beds that were deformed by faulting in the bedrock below.

Mountain Building **313**

Facts and Figures

The Colorado Plateau is a high, sparsely vegetated region of deep canyons, mesas, and plateaus. It encompasses almost 363,000 sq km at the four corners—the area where Utah, Colorado, Arizona, and New Mexico come together. The Colorado Plateau includes the Colorado River and its tributaries. The high Sierra Nevada mountain range located to the west of the Plateau prevents moisture-laden air masses from reaching the region. This rain shadow effect causes the region to be very dry; the average precipitation is about 25 cm per year. Because plant cover is so sparse, the area has been eroded by fast-moving streams, which has exposed the bare rocks that contribute to the area's beauty.

LESSON 11.2

Build Science Skills　L2

Student Activity: Use Models Have students model the formation of a monocline by holding two wooden blocks together so the "fault" between them runs at a 60° angle. Have another student carefully drape the towel or fabric over the wooden blocks. The student holding the blocks should slide them along the "fault" until the towel forms a fold. **Ask:** What does the towel represent? *(sedimentary rock layers)* What do the wooden blocks represent? *(rock blocks)*
Kinesthetic, Logical

Use Visuals　L1

Figure 8 Have students examine the photograph of a normal fault. **Ask:** Which side of the fault is the footwall? *(the right side)* How can you tell which side is the footwall? *(A normal fault occurs when the hanging wall block moves down relative to the footwall. In the picture, the right side is higher than the left side, so it must be the footwall.)* Can you tell from the photo which side of the fault has moved? *(No, there is no way to tell. The two sides of the fault have moved relative to each other but it is impossible to know whether one side has moved up or the other side has moved down.)*
Visual, Logical

Faults

Recall that faults are fractures in the crust along which movement has taken place. Small faults can be recognized in road cuts where sedimentary beds have been offset a few meters, as shown in **Figure 8.**

The rock surface that is immediately above the fault is called the *hanging wall*, and the rock surface below the fault is called the *footwall.* **The major types of faults are normal faults, reverse faults, thrust faults, and strike-slip faults.** Faults are classified according to the type of movement that occurs along the fault.

Normal Faults Normal faults occur due to tensional stress. A **normal fault** occurs when the hanging wall block moves down relative to the footwall block, as shown in **Figure 8.** Most normal faults have steep dips of about 60°, as shown in **Figure 9A.** These dips often flatten out with depth. The movement in normal faults is mainly in a vertical direction, with some horizontal movement. Because of the drop of the hanging wall block, normal faults result in the lengthening, or extension, of the crust.

Reverse Faults and Thrust Faults Both reverse and thrust faults result from compressional stress. A **reverse fault** is a fault in which the hanging wall block moves up relative to the footwall block. Reverse faults are high-angle faults with dips greater than 45°. **Thrust faults** are reverse faults with dips of less than 45°. Because the hanging wall block moves up and over the footwall block, reverse and thrust faults result in a shortening of the crust, as shown in **Figures 9B** and **9C.**

Most high-angle reverse faults are small. They cause only local displacements in regions dominated by other types of faulting. Thrust faults, on the other hand, exist at all scales. In the Alps, northern Rockies, Himalayas, and Appalachians, thrust faults have displaced rock layers as far as 50 kilometers. The result of this large-scale movement is that older rocks end up on top of younger rocks.

FIGURE 8 Normal Fault
Faulting caused the vertical displacement of these beds located near Kanab, Utah. Arrows show the relative motion of rock units.
Observe *Which side of the fault is the hanging wall?*

314 Chapter 11 • Lesson 2

Facts and Figures

The terms *hanging wall* and *footwall* were coined by prospectors and miners who excavated shafts and tunnels along fault zones because these are frequent sites of ore deposits. In these tunnels, the miners would walk on the rocks below the mineralized fault zone (the footwall) and hang their lanterns on the rocks above (the hanging wall).

Types of Mountains

Folding and faulting produce many, but not all of Earth's mountains. In general, mountains are classified by the processes that formed them. 🔑 **The major types of mountains include volcanic mountains, folded mountains, fault-block mountains, and dome mountains.** Geologists refer to the collection of processes involved in mountain building as **orogenesis.** The term is derived from the Greek *oros* meaning "mountain" and -*geny* meaning "born."

Earth's mountains do not appear randomly. Several mountains of similar shape, age, and structure form a group called a *mountain range*. For example, the Sangre de Cristo range extends from north to south in Colorado and New Mexico. A group of different mountain ranges in the same region form a *mountain system*. The Sangre de Cristo and West Elk ranges are both part of the Rocky Mountains system.

Mountain ranges and systems occur in long mountain belts that stretch along the edges of continents. The Rocky Mountains and the Andes are part of a mountain belt that extends along the western sides of North and South America.

Folded Mountains Mountains that are formed primarily by folding are called **folded mountains.** Compressional stress is the major factor that forms folded mountains. In **Figure 10,** you can see how compressional stresses helped to form the Alps in Europe.

Thrust faulting is also important in the formation of folded mountains, which are often called *fold-and-thrust belts*. Folded mountains often contain numerous stacked thrust faults that have displaced the folded rock layers many kilometers horizontally. The Appalachian Mountains, the northern Rocky Mountains, and the Alps in Europe are examples of folded mountain ranges.

FIGURE 10 Folded Mountains
Folded mountains, such as the Alps, shown here, form where compressional forces squeeze the crust.

Fold

Key
Compressional stress

Facts and Figures

Making the Appalachians The Appalachian Mountains and the rest of the eastern United States formed through a long and complex sequence of mountain-building events, or orogenies. Between 1.2 and 1.0 billion years ago, a collision along the eastern coast of early North America associated with the formation of the supercontinent Rodinia formed the Grenville orogeny. Half a billion years later the Iapetus ocean (proto-Atlantic) closed up in a series of orogenic events.

During the Penobscottian (520–490 million years ago) and Taconic (470–440 million years ago) orogenies North America collided with oceanic island arcs. During the Acadian orogeny (370 million years ago) North America collided with a continental fragment called the Avalon terrane. The supercontinent Pangaea came together during 400–350 million years ago as part of the Alleghenian orogeny (sometimes called the Appalachian orogeny).

Volcanic Mountains Recall from Chapter 10 that volcanic mountains form along plate boundaries and at hot spots. In addition, igneous activity forms rock deep in the crust that can be uplifted as a result of plate motions and isostatic adjustment.

Fault-Block Mountains Another type of mountain forms as the result of movement along normal faults. Most normal faults are small and have displacements of only a meter or so. Others extend for tens of kilometers where they may outline the boundary of a mountain front. Large-scale normal faults are associated with fault-block mountains. **Fault-block mountains** form as large blocks of crust are uplifted and tilted along normal faults.

Normal faulting occurs where tensional stresses cause the crust to be stretched or extended. As the crust is stretched, a block called a **graben,** which is bounded by normal faults, drops down. *Graben* is the German word for ditch or trench. Grabens produce an elongated valley bordered by relatively uplifted structures called **horsts.** The Basin and Range region of Nevada, Utah, and California, shown in **Figure 11,** is made of elongated grabens. Above the grabens, tilted fault-blocks or horsts produce parallel rows of fault-block mountains.

In the western United States, other examples of fault-block mountains include the Teton Range of Wyoming and the Sierra Nevada of California. Both are faulted along their eastern flanks, which were uplifted as the blocks tilted downward to the west. These steep mountain fronts were produced over a period of 5 million to 10 million years by many episodes of faulting. Each faulting event produced just a few meters of displacement.

☑ **Reading Checkpoint** *What is a horst?*

FIGURE 11 **Fault-Block Mountains A** Part of the Basin and Range region of Nevada, California, and Utah **B** Here, tensional stresses have elongated and fractured the crust into numerous blocks. Movement along these fractures has tilted the blocks producing parallel mountain ranges called fault-block mountains.

Horst
Horst (Fault-block mountain)
Graben
Normal faults

Mountain Building **317**

Facts and Figures

African Rift Valley Grabens Some of the best examples of continental grabens are found in the Great Rift Valley of Africa, which stretches more than 6000 km from Jordan through Ethiopia, Kenya, and Tanzania all the way to Mozambique. They occur because the continent of Africa is rifting apart into two separate plates, the Somalian and Nubian plates. Where they are separating along the rift valleys, the crust is stretched and thinned, and blocks of crusts have dropped down more than a kilometer to form long, linear grabens that are often more than 50 kilometers wide. These grabens are fertile regions that might have supported the first human beings nearly 200,000 years ago.

LESSON 11.2

Use Visuals

Figure 13 Have students examine the map and cross-section of the Michigan basin. **Ask:** Which color on the map represents the youngest rocks? *(yellow)* The oldest rocks? *(light orange)* Then **ask:** Where in the Michigan basin do you find the youngest rocks? *(in the center of the Michigan peninsula)* Point out to students that the layers of sedimentary rock in the basin are also thickest in the center.

Answers

MAP IT! The granite core, consisting of the oldest rocks, is found in the center or core of the Black Hills in the area labeled "Central crystalline area."

Figure 13 *The Michigan basin is a syncline because it is made up of downfolded rock and occupies a trough.*

☑ **Reading Checkpoint** *A dome is a roughly circular structure formed by the upwarping of sedimentary rock layers.*

Plateaus, Domes, and Basins

Mountains are not the only landforms that result from forces in Earth's crust. 🔑 **Up-and-down movements of the crust can produce a variety of landforms, including plateaus, domes, and basins.**

Many of the factors that contribute to the development of mountains also help to create these landforms. Within the crust, these factors include plate motions, folding and faulting, igneous activity, and isostatic adjustment. Other factors work on the surface. Weather and climate affect the rates of weathering and erosion and the production of sediment. Because of isostasy, the weight of sediment added to or eroded from an area contributes to vertical movement of the crust.

The overall effect of these factors is that certain areas of crust may rise or sink relative to other areas. Where the crust bends downward, geologists say that the crust has been *downwarped.* Where the crust bows upward, they say it has been *upwarped.*

Plateaus A plateau is a landform with a relatively high elevation and more-or-less level surface. To form a plateau, a broad area of the crust is uplifted vertically. The Colorado Plateau in the southwestern United States is made up of sandstone and other sedimentary rocks. These rocks were laid down in horizontal layers hundreds of millions of years ago. Before being uplifted more than 2 kilometers, the area was covered by a shallow sea. Geologists are still trying to determine what caused the uplift of the Colorado Plateau. One hypothesis is that a subducting plate, sliding from west to east beneath the North American plate, scraped off the bottom of the lithosphere. This allowed the overlying rock to rise, forming the Colorado Plateau.

Domes Broad upwarping in the rock underlying an area may deform the overlying sedimentary layers. When upwarping produces a roughly circular structure, the feature is called a *dome.* Domes, such as the one in **Figure 12,** often have the shape of an elongated oval. You can think of the upwarped layers that make up a dome as a large fold. Look at the cross section in Figure 12. You can see that the layers that make up the sides of the dome bend upward as in an anticline.

The Black Hills of western South Dakota are a well-known example of a dome. Geologists think that the Black Hills began to form about 60 million years ago when tectonic forces caused upwarping of the North American plate in the region. Uplift and erosion stripped away layers of sedimentary rock. This exposed crystalline igneous and metamorphic rocks that today form the core of the Black Hills. As you can see in Figure 12, the younger sedimentary layers form rings around the older rocks near the center of the Black Hills.

☑ **Reading Checkpoint** *What is a dome?*

FIGURE 12 Domed Mountains

MAP IT!
ACTIVITY

The Black Hills of South Dakota is a large, domed structure, exposing resistant igneous and metamorphic rocks in the center as shown in **Figure 12.**

Identify Locate the schist and granite core of the Black Hills, shown on the cross section.

Basins Downwarped structures that have a roughly circular shape are called *basins*. The central United States contains a number of basins, including the Michigan basin, shown in **Figure 13.** Basins can form in several ways. During mountain building, plate motions can cause the crust to bend downward and form a basin. If the basin sinks below sea level, it may become a shallow sea. Over time, sediments such as sand and the skeletons of marine organisms are laid down, forming layers of sedimentary rock.

Basins may also form along the edges of continents where thick layers of sediment build up. The weight of the sediment downwarps the crust to form a basin.

When forces in the crust uplift the sedimentary layers, the rock that fills the basin is exposed at the surface. As you can see in Figure 13, a geologic map of a basin looks somewhat like a dart board. The oldest rocks are around the edges of the basin and the youngest rocks are near the center.

The plate motions that help to form basins can also destroy them. For example, when two continental plates collide, the ocean basin between them closes up. Sedimentary rock in the basin becomes part of the landmass formed by the collision.

FIGURE 13 Basin Erosion has exposed the layers of sedimentary rock deposited in the bowl-shaped Michigan basin.
Apply Concepts *Should the Michigan basin be described as an anticline or a syncline? Explain.*

11.2 Assessment

Review Key Concepts

1. List the three main types of folds.

2. Describe the four main types of faults in terms of the motion along each type.

3. List the major types of mountains.

4. Define plateau, dome, and basin in your own words.

5. What is a graben? In what type of mountains are grabens most commonly found?

Think Critically

6. **Apply Concepts** How would you classify a mountain range made up of numerous thrust faults?

7. **Compare and Contrast** Compare domes and basins.

WRITING IN SCIENCE

8. **Communicate** Write a paragraph describing a trip across a fault-block mountain. Describe the types of rocks and structures you might observe.

Assessment Answers

1. anticlines, synclines, monoclines
2. normal fault: hanging wall moves down relative to footwall; reverse fault: footwall moves up relative to hanging wall; thrust fault: a reverse fault with a dip of less than 45°; strike-slip fault: a fault in which the two sides are vertical and move past each other horizontally
3. folded mountains, fault-block mountains, and uplifted or domed mountains

4. plateau: area of land with a high elevation and relatively level surface; dome: roughly circular structure that forms when sedimentary layers are uplifted; basin: roughly circular structure formed when sedimentary layers are downwarped
5. A graben is a block bounded by normal faults that has been down-dropped. Grabens are most commonly found in fault-block mountains.

6. Most likely, it is a folded mountain range.
7. Domes form where sedimentary layers are uplifted, while basins form where they are downwarped. In a dome, the oldest rock layers are exposed in the center. In a basin, the oldest rock layers are exposed around the basin's edges.
8. Answers will vary but should accurately reflect the structures and rocks commonly found in fault-block mountains.

LESSON 11.3

1 FOCUS

Lesson Objectives

11.8 **Identify** the type of mountains associated with the different types of convergent plate boundaries.

11.9 **Identify** the type of mountains associated with divergent plate boundaries.

11.10 **Describe** the role of accretion in the formation of continents and mountain building.

Build Vocabulary L2

Paraphrase After students have read the definition of *accretionary wedge* on p. 321, but before they have learned the definition of *accretion* on p. 324, have them write a short paragraph describing in their own words the process of accretion. After they have read the definition of *accretion,* ask if they would change their definitions.

Reading Strategy L2

I. Mountains and Plates
  A. Convergent Boundary Mountains
    1. Ocean-Ocean Convergence
    2. Ocean-Continent Convergence
    3. Continent-Continent Convergence
  B. Divergent Boundary Mountains
  C. Non-Boundary Mountains
  D. Continental Accretion
    1. Terranes
    2. Mountains from Accretion

Key Questions

🔑 *What types of mountains form along convergent plate boundaries?*

🔑 *What types of mountains form along divergent plate boundaries?*

🔑 *How do mountains form away from plate boundaries?*

🔑 *How does accretion affect continents and mountain building?*

Vocabulary

• accretionary wedge
• accretion • terrane

Reading Strategy

Outline As you read, make an outline of the important ideas in this section. Use the orange topic headings as the main topics and the blue headings as subtopics.

I. Mountains and Plates
  A. Convergent Boundary Mountains
    1. Oceanic-Oceanic Convergence
    2. a. _____?_____
    3. b. _____?_____
  B. Divergent Boundary Mountains

MOUNTAIN BUILDING is still occurring in many places worldwide. For example, the jagged spires of the Teton Range in Wyoming began to form about a million years ago and are still rising. In contrast, older mountain ranges, such as the Appalachians in the eastern United States, are deeply eroded.

Many hypotheses have been proposed to explain mountain formation. One early proposal incorrectly suggested that mountains are wrinkles in Earth's crust, produced as the planet cooled from a semi-molten state.

Convergent Boundary Mountains

With the development of the theory of plate tectonics, a widely accepted model for mountain building became available. Most mountain building occurs at convergent plate boundaries. Colliding plates produce the compressional forces that fold, fault, and metamorphose the thick layers of rock and sediment at the edges of landmasses. At convergent plate boundaries where subduction occurs, volcanic activity triggered by the sinking and melting of lithosphere into the mantle can produce new volcanic mountains on the overlying plate. This can occur when the overlying plate is made of oceanic lithosphere or continental lithosphere.

FIGURE 14 Young Mountains The Teton Range in Wyoming is an example of a relatively young mountain range.

Oceanic-Oceanic Convergence The convergence of two plate edges of oceanic lithosphere mainly produces volcanic mountains. Recall from Chapter 10 that this process occurs where plates made of oceanic lithosphere converge in a subduction zone, as shown in **Figure 15.** The result of this collision is the formation of an arc of volcanoes on the ocean floor. If the volcanoes rise above the sea surface, the arc is called a *volcanic island arc.*

Oceanic-Continental Convergence The convergence of an oceanic plate edge and a continental plate edge can produce volcanic mountains and folded mountains. As shown in Figure 16, these mountains develop in two belts that are roughly parallel to the edge of a continent.

Recall from Chapter 10 that a continental volcanic arc forms when a slab of oceanic lithosphere is subducted beneath a plate edge of continental lithosphere. The belt of mountains that results is made of volcanoes and intrusive igneous rocks mixed with metamorphic rocks. One example is the Andes of South America. The Andes formed through the subduction of the Nazca plate beneath the South American plate.

Another process forms a belt of coastal mountains made up of folded and faulted rocks. How do these mountains form? During subduction, sediment is eroded from the land and scraped from the subducting plate. This sediment becomes stuck, or *accreted*, to the overlying plate. The scraps of oceanic crust and sediment form an **accretionary wedge.** A long period of subduction can build an accretionary wedge that stands above sea level. California's Coast Ranges formed by this process.

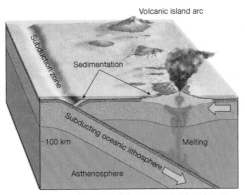

FIGURE 15 Oceanic-Oceanic Convergence Subduction along a convergent boundary results in the development of volcanic mountains.

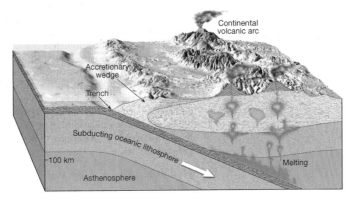

FIGURE 16 Oceanic-Continental Convergence Plate convergence produces a subduction zone and a continental volcanic arc. Continued convergence and igneous activity further deform the crust and form a roughly parallel folded mountain belt.
Observe *What type of mountains result from the partial melting?*

Mountain Building **321**

Use Visuals `L1`

Figure 17 Have students examine the diagram of continental-continental convergence. **Ask:** Why are there sedimentary rocks and oceanic crust high above sea level in the Himalayas? *(They come from sediment and bits of crust that were scraped off an oceanic slab as it subducted under India. When India and Asia collided, this material was uplifted.)* What caused the formation of a continental volcanic arc in the Himalayas? *(partial melting of the overlying mantle rocks triggered by the subducting oceanic slab)* **Visual, Logical**

Address Misconceptions `L2`

Ask students if Mount Everest will always be the highest mountain on Earth. If they say yes, they may think that mountain-building processes are no longer taking place and that mountains will remain the same size as they are now. Because the Indian and Eurasian plates continue to push against each other—at a rate of about 2 cm a year—the Himalayas are continuing to grow. According to data from recent GPS experiments, the Himalayas are growing at a rate of 5 mm a year. **Ask:** What process could prevent the Himalayas from growing? *(erosion)* What would happen if the Indian and Eurasian plates stop moving? *(The Himalayas will stop growing and will decrease in height due to erosion.)* **Logical**

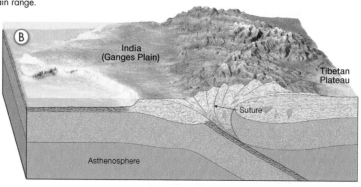

FIGURE 17 Continental-Continental Convergence The collision of India and Asia started about 45 million years ago and produced the Himalayas. **A** Converging plates collided at a subduction zone, producing a continental volcanic arc. **B** The two landmasses collided, deforming and elevating the mountain range.

PLANET DIARY

For links about the **Himalayas,** go to PlanetDiary.com/HSES

Continental-Continental Convergence 🔊 **A collision between two continental plate edges will form folded mountains.** The reason for this is that continental lithosphere is not dense enough, compared with the denser rock of the mantle, to be subducted. An example of such a collision began about 45 million years ago when India collided with the Eurasian plate, as shown in **Figure 17.** Before this event, India was part of Antarctica. It slowly moved a few thousand kilometers due north. The result of the collision was the formation of the Himalaya Mountains and the Tibetan Plateau. Most of the oceanic lithosphere that separated these landmasses before the collision was subducted, but some was caught up in the collision zone, along with the sediment along the shoreline. Today these sedimentary rocks and slivers of lithosphere are elevated high above sea level. The closing up of the ocean between India and the Eurasian plate is an example of how plate motions can destroy a sedimentary basin.

☑ **Reading Checkpoint** *Why can't continental lithosphere be subducted?*

322 Chapter 11 • Lesson 3

Facts and Figures

Numerous earthquakes recorded off the southern coast of India indicate that a new subduction zone may be forming. If formed, it would provide a subduction site for the floor of the Indian Ocean, which is continually being produced at a spreading center located to the southwest. Should this occur, India's northward journey, relative to Asia, would come to an end, and the growth of the Himalayas would cease.

Divergent Boundary Mountains

Most mountains are formed at convergent boundaries, but some are formed at divergent boundaries, usually on the ocean floor. These mountains form a chain that curves along the ocean floor at the ocean ridges. This mountain chain is more than 70,000 kilometers long and rises up to 3000 meters above the ocean floor. **The mountains that form along ocean ridges at divergent plate boundaries are fault-block mountains made of volcanic rock.** Rock at the ridge is hotter and less dense, so it rises higher than older, colder oceanic lithosphere.

Non-Boundary Mountains

Some mountains form well away from plate boundaries. **Volcanic mountains at hot spots, as well as some upwarped mountains and fault-block mountains, can form far from plate boundaries.** The Hawaiian Islands are a well-known example of volcanic mountains at a hot spot. Mountains formed by upwarping and faulting include the southern Rocky Mountains and the mountains of the Basin and Range region.

The southern Rockies began to form about 60 million years ago with the subduction of oceanic lithosphere at least 1600 kilometers away. At first, compressional forces deformed the crust. Then the subducting plate separated from the lithosphere above. This allowed hot rock to upwell from the mantle, pushing up the crust and forming the southern Rockies. As the crust bent upward, tensional forces stretched and fractured it, forming the fault-block mountains of the Basin and Range region, as shown in Figure 20 on page 326.

INQUIRY QUICK LAB

RATES OF MOUNTAIN BUILDING

The mighty Himalayas between India and Tibet are the tallest mountains on Earth, rising to more than 8 kilometers. These mountains are still rising at a rate of about 1 centimeter per year. Mount Everest is the tallest peak with an elevation of 8848 meters above sea level. The Himalayas formed as a result of India colliding with the Eurasian plate.

1. **Calculate** If you assume that the Himalayas will continue to be uplifted at the current rate of 1 centimeter per year, how long will it take the mountains to rise another 500 meters?

2. **Calculate** Assuming a rate of uplift of 1 centimeter per year, how much higher could the Himalayas be in one million years?

3. **Apply Concepts** If the convergence of tectonic plates is causing the Himalayas to rise in elevation, what common surface processes are working to decrease their elevations?

4. **Predict** Will the Himalayas continue to rise in elevation indefinitely? Explain your answer.

Facts and Figures

For years, scientists thought that the elevation of Mount Everest was 8848 m above sea level. A number of attempts over several years were made to set up Global Position System (GPS) equipment so the mountain could be measured using satellite-based technology. A team of seven climbers successfully measured the mountain from the summit on May 5, 1999. The data were collected from various GPS satellite receivers, one of which had to be placed in bedrock, at the top of Mount Everest. Using GPS technology, Mount Everest finally was re-measured and was found to be 8850 m above sea level.

LESSON 11.3

Address Misconceptions ▢ L2

Students often confuse a *terrane* with a *terrain*. The term *terrane* is used to designate a distinct and recognizable series of rock formations that has been transported by plate tectonic processes. Because geologists who mapped these rocks were unsure where they came from, these rocks were sometimes called "exotic," "suspect," "accreted," or "foreign" terranes. The term *terrain* describes the shape of the surface topography or "lay of the land." Have students use the two terms in sentences so that their meanings are clear.
Verbal

Use Visuals ▢ L1

Figure 18 Have students examine the map showing terranes added to western North America. **Ask:** What mechanism of plate tectonics might have caused the addition of so many terranes to the West Coast? *(The North American plate could have moved westward, overriding the Pacific Basin and picking up crustal fragments as it moved.)* What was the origin of the Baja Peninsula? *(It was originally an island arc.)* What does this map imply about the number of times crustal material has been added to the West Coast? *(Based on the many sources of crustal material, it is likely that material has been added many times.)*
Visual, Logical

FIGURE 18 Accretion in Western North America
These terranes are thought to have been added to western North America during the past 200 million years.
Interpret Maps *What do the areas in blue represent?*

Map legend:
Accreted Terranes
- Island arc
- Submarine deposits
- Ancient ocean floor
- Displaced continental fragments

Map labels: Wrangellia Terrane, Sonoma Terrane, Canada / United States, United States / Mexico, 0 — 600 km

Continental Accretion

You may be surprised to learn that the size and shape of a continent changes over time. Some of these changes occur when continents collide or split apart. Geologists have studied another process in which smaller fragments of crust collide and merge with continents. **The process of accretion enlarges continental landmasses and forms mountains along the edges of continents.** When fragments of crust collide with a continental plate, they become stuck to or embedded into the continent through accretion. Many of the mountainous regions rimming the Pacific have been produced through collision and accretion.

Terranes Geologists refer to accreted crustal blocks as terranes. A **terrane** is any crustal fragment that has a geologic history distinct from that of the adjoining terranes. Terranes come in many shapes and sizes. Some are no larger than volcanic islands, while others are immense, such as the one making up the entire Indian subcontinent. Before their accretion to a continental block, some of the fragments may have been microcontinents similar to the present-day island of Madagascar, located in the Indian Ocean east of Africa. Many others were island arcs similar to Japan and the Philippines. As you can see in **Figure 18**, much of western North America is made up of terranes added to the continent by accretion.

How does the process of accretion work? As plates made mostly of oceanic lithosphere move, they carry the embedded volcanic island arcs and microcontinents along with them. Eventually, a collision with a continent occurs. The features carried by the subducting plate are peeled off and accreted to the continent similar to how snow and ice are shoveled from a sidewalk. This newly added material increases the width and thickness of the continent. A terrane may end up far inland after subsequent accretions add even more material to the continent.

☑ **Reading Checkpoint** *What is a terrane?*

Facts and Figures

Imagine finding 45-million-year-old tree stumps next to glaciers. These ancient trees resembled the giant redwoods that grow today in northern California. Fossils of palm trees and tropical rain forest plants have all been found in Alaska within 800 km of the North Pole. Not only is the present climate too cold to support these organisms, but they would not be able to live in a region that has limited sunlight five months of the year. Either the climate of Earth was different when the palms grew 45 million years ago or the rocks in which the fossils occur moved in from someplace else. Most paleontologists think the rocks were once part of terranes that were added to the Pacific coast of North America.

MOUNTAIN BUILDING BY CONTINENTAL ACCRETION

FIGURE 19 This sequence illustrates the collision of an inactive volcanic island arc with the margin of a continental plate edge. The island arc becomes accreted onto the continent.

① ② ③

Mountains From Accretion The accretion of larger crustal fragments, such as a mature island arc, may result in a mountain range, though such a range is smaller than mountain ranges produced by continental–continental convergence. Because of its thickness and low density, an island arc will not subduct beneath a continental plate edge. Instead, it will plow into the continent and deform both blocks, as shown in **Figure 19.**

11.3 Assessment

Review Key Concepts 🔑

1. What types of mountains are associated with convergent plate boundaries?

2. What types of mountains are associated with divergent plate boundaries?

3. List three types of mountains that can form far from a plate boundary.

4. Describe the process that can enlarge a continent and form mountains along the continent's edge.

Think Critically

5. Compare and Contrast Compare mountain building along an oceanic-continental convergent boundary and a continental-continental convergent boundary.

6. Draw Conclusions How does the theory of plate tectonics help explain the existence of marine fossils in sedimentary rocks on top of the Himalayas?

7. Infer A geologist collects rock samples as she travels inland from the coast of Alaska. First, she finds rock from an island arc, then rock from oceanic crust, then rock from a microcontinent. What can she infer about the origin of the land in this area? Explain.

BIGIDEA DYNAMIC EARTH

8. Communicate Describe a trip through a mountain range like the Andes that has formed at an oceanic-continental convergent boundary.

Mountain Building **325**

Mountain Building Away From Plate Margins

EARTH & ITS SYSTEMS

Mountain Building Away From Plate Margins

L2

Background

The mountain ranges generated during the Laramide Orogeny include Colorado's Front Range, the Sangre de Cristo of New Mexico and Colorado, and Wyoming's Bighorns.

The rugged topography of the Rocky Mountains and the Basin and Range Province, as shown in **Figure 20,** includes lofty peaks and elevated plateaus typical of the Southwest.

But, how did such mountainous topography form, far from a convergent plate boundary? The key to understanding how these landforms came about lies in their geologic history.

FIGURE 20 Topography of the Western United States

The Laramide Orogeny

The portion of the Rocky Mountains that runs from southern Montana to New Mexico was produced about 60 million years ago by a period of uplift known as the Laramide Orogeny.

The Laramide Orogeny started with the nearly horizontal subduction of the Farallon plate eastward beneath North America, shown in **Figure 21A.** The subducted slab scraped beneath the continent at a shallow angle.

The resulting compressional forces produced steep mountains. By about 65 million years ago, the Farallon plate had completely subducted under the North American plate. At that time, the mid-ocean ridge that had separated the Pacific plate and the Farallon plate now lay between the Pacific plate and the North American plate. The northwest motion of the Pacific plate changed this plate boundary from a ridge to a transform fault, giving birth to the San Andreas Fault, as shown in Figure **21B.**

Facts and Figures

Lithosphere Delamination When two continents collide, the continental crust is too buoyant to sink, so it thickens into a large mountain like the Himalayas. In the case of the Himalayas, the Indian crust is actually sliding under the Asian crust. But what happens to the rest of the lithosphere? The bottom part of the continental lithosphere, beneath the crust, is mantle rock, and it is dense enough to sink. Geologists think that during continental collisions the mantle part of the lithosphere peels off from the crust and sinks. This makes way for hot asthenosphere rock to come up and fill the space left by the delaminated lithosphere. This hot asthenosphere provides buoyancy that additionally lifts the mountains.

Basin and Range

About 50 million years ago, as the completely subducted Farallon plate gradually broke off from the lithosphere and sank into the asthenosphere, it was replaced by hot rock that upwelled from the asthenosphere. This hot, buoyant asthenospheric rock lifted the southern Rockies, as well as the Colorado Plateau. The melting of the Farallon plate slab also produced volcanoes in the overlying North American plate.

To the west, the buoyancy of the warm material caused upwarping and rifting that elongated the overlying crust by 200 to 300 kilometers, forming the Basin and Range Province. Extension and faulting shifted individual blocks of the crust. The high portions of these tilted blocks make up the mountain ranges of the Basin and Range. Low areas form the basins, now partially filled with sediment.

FIGURE 21 Shaping the Southwest

Ⓐ

70 million years ago, crustal shortening in the Southwest formed the Rocky Mountains (Laramide Orogeny). As compression formed and activated reverse faults in the North American plate, the crust thickened, narrowing the Southwest.

Ⓑ

50 million years ago, crustal extension in the Southwest formed the Basin and Range Province. As hot mantle material welled upward, the crust rose, extended, and became thinner. This pulling apart of Earth's crust formed normal faults, dropping some blocks of the crust relative to others. Note that the marked points (black arrowheads) are much further apart after crustal extension, indicating the widening of the Southwest.

- Be sure students understand that the processes described and illustrated represent one possible mechanism for the uplift that led to the formation of the southern Rockies, Colorado Plateau, and Basin and Range Province. Other mechanisms may be possible.
- Refer students back to p. 315 for more on the formation of the fault-block mountains that make up the Basin and Range Province.
- Point out that the structural geology of a mountain range, or any other geologic feature, is not always evident from looking at the topography. For example, to the casual observer, a mountain range produced primarily by folding may look like a mountain range produced primarily by faulting. Ask students why this is the case. *(Erosion and deposition shape the landscape and often obscure the structural geology of the area.)* Discuss how geologists learn about the structural geology of an area. *(by making observations of the entire area; identifying and mapping the rock, faults, folds, and other geologic features in the area; correlating this information with that from adjacent areas; and putting all the information together to get an accurate picture of an area's geology)*

Logical

INVESTIGATING ANTICLINES AND SYNCLINES L2

Objective In this activity, students will:
- measure the angles of rock layers in diagrams of an anticline and a syncline.
- determine whether a fold is an anticline or a syncline.
- visualize how rocks are oriented in anticlines and synclines.
- make a block diagram to show the appearance of an eroded fold.

Skills Observe, Measure, Classify, Interpret Diagrams

Prep Time none

Class Time 30 minutes

Teaching Tips
- You may have to remind students how to measure angles with a protractor.
- Have students review the material about folds, domes, and basins in the text before doing this lab.
- Students may have trouble visualizing the three-dimensional structure of an eroded fold when drawing the diagram in step 5. Making a model of the fold out of different-colored layers of clay and then cutting off the top of the model to represent erosion will help them to draw the diagram.

Expected Outcome In Fold A, an anticline, the left limb dips at about 50°, and the right limb dips at 80°. In Fold B, a syncline, both limbs dip at about 45°.

Investigating Anticlines and Synclines

Problem How are rocks oriented in anticlines and synclines?

Materials pencil, protractor, tracing paper

Skills Observe, Measure, Classify, Interpret Diagrams

Connect to the Big idea The *axial plane* of a fold is an imaginary plane drawn through the long axis of a fold. The axial plane divides the fold into two limbs, as shown in **Figure 1**. In a symmetrical fold, the limbs are mirror images of each other and move away, or *dip*, at the same angle. In an asymmetrical fold, the limbs dip at different angles. Folds do not continue forever. Where the fold axis drops and is no longer horizontal, the fold is said to be *plunging*, as shown in **Figure 2**. A geologic principle known as the *principle of superposition* states that in most situations with layered rocks, the oldest rocks are at the bottom of the sequence.

FIGURE 1
Horizontal Fold Axis

FIGURE 2
Plunging Fold Axis

328 Chapter 11

Procedure

1. Study the two diagrams, labeled Fold A and Fold B in **Figures 3** and **4**.

2. Use a protractor to measure the angles of the rock layers in both limbs of Fold A. Repeat your measurements for both limbs of Fold B. For consistency, measure the angles on both folds at the surface between layers 3 and 4.

3. Use Figures 3 and 4 and Figure 6 on page 313 to determine what types of folds are shown by Fold A and Fold B.

4. Anticlines and synclines are linear features caused by compressional stresses. Two other types of folds—domes and basins—can be nearly circular and are caused by vertical displacement. Uplift produces domes. Downwarping produces basins.

5. Use tracing paper to make a copy of the blank block diagram shown below. Draw shaded rock layers and surface structures to show an eroded fold consistent with the rock layer shown on the right side of the block.

FIGURE 3 Fold A

Analyze and Conclude

1. **Interpret Diagrams** What type of fold is shown by Fold A? In what direction do the limbs dip or tilt from the axial plane?

2. **Interpret Diagrams** What type of fold is shown by Fold B? In what direction do the limbs dip or tilt from the axial plane?

3. **Draw Conclusions** In Fold A, which rock layer is the oldest shown? Which rock layer is the youngest shown?

4. **Measure** In Fold A, at what angle are the rock layers in both limbs dipping or tilted?

5. **Draw Conclusions** In Fold B, which rock layer is the oldest shown? Which rock layer is the youngest shown?

6. **Measure** In Fold B, at what angle are the rock layers in both limbs dipping or tilted?

FIGURE 4 Fold B

7. **Classify** What type of fold did you draw in the blank block diagram on your tracing paper?

8. **Observe** Is Fold A symmetrical or asymmetrical? Is Fold B symmetrical or asymmetrical?

9. **Observe** Is Fold A plunging or nonplunging? Is Fold B plunging or nonplunging?

10. **Apply Concepts** If you walk away from the axis on an eroded anticline, do the rocks get older or younger? How do the ages of the rocks change as you walk away from the axis in a syncline?

GO FURTHER Use library or Internet sources to research the geologic terms "strike" and "dip." Draw a block diagram showing rocks layers that illustrate these terms. Give a presentation to the class, and explain the terms using your diagram as a visual aid.

Analyze and Conclude

1. an anticline; away from the axial plane
2. a syncline; towards the axial plane
3. In Fold A, the oldest rock layer shown is #1; the youngest is #6.
4. In Fold A the left limb dips at about 50°, and the right limb dips at 80°.
5. In Fold B, the oldest rock layer shown is #1; the youngest is #5.
6. In Fold B, both limbs dip at about 45°.
7. The completed block diagram should show a basin with the rock layers dipping or tilted towards the center. The older rocks should be indicated as occurring toward the outside of the basin, with younger rocks in the center. Diagrams should show the basin from all three sides (top, front, and side)
8. Fold A is asymmetrical; Fold B is symmetrical.
9. Both Fold A and Fold B are nonplunging folds.
10. On an eroded anticline, the rock layers get younger as you walk away from the axial plane. On an eroded syncline, the rock layers get older as you walk away from the axial plane.

GO FURTHER

Strike is the direction or trend of a bedding or fault plane as it intersects the horizontal. Dip is the angle that a bedding or fault plane makes with the horizontal, measured perpendicular to the strike of the planar surface. Student diagrams should clearly illustrate these concepts. Student presentations should clearly explain strike and dip and be organized and scientifically accurate.
Visual, Kinesthetic

Study Tip

Organize New Information

Have students make a glossary for the chapter vocabulary terms using their own words for the definitions. Many of the vocabulary terms can be described visually. Encourage students to use illustrations or mnemonics in their glossary to help them remember meanings.

Think Visually

a. ocean-ocean
b. continent-continent
c. volcanic island arc on the ocean floor and volcanic mountains
d. folded mountains

21st Century Learning

Communication Skills

How were the Rocky Mountains formed?

Ask students to research the formation of the Rocky Mountains and to identify the key dates and processes in the development of the range. Each student should prepare an explanation and diagrams describing how the Rocky Mountains were formed. Instruct students to assume that their readers know as much about geology as they do, and remind them to include relevant technical terms. Students may share their findings in a report or through a Web page.

Homework Guide

Lesson	Questions
1	1, 4, 10–12, 26, 35
2	2, 3, 5, 6, 8, 13–18, 22, 24, 27, 29, 30, 31–34
3	7, 9, 19–21, 23, 25, 28, 36, 37

11 Study Guide

Big idea ▶ Dynamic Earth

11.1 Forces in Earth's Crust

🔑 The factors that affect the deformation of rock include temperature, pressure, rock type, and time.

🔑 The three types of stress that cause deformation of rocks are tensional stress, compressional stress, and shear stress.

🔑 Because of isostasy, deformed and thickened crust will undergo regional uplift during mountain building and for a long period afterward.

deformation (308)
stress (308)
strain (308)
isostasy (310)
isostatic adjustment (310)

11.2 Folds, Faults, and Mountains

🔑 The three main types of folds are anticlines, synclines, and monoclines.

🔑 The major types of faults are normal faults, reverse faults, thrust faults, and strike-slip faults.

🔑 The major types of mountains include volcanic mountains, folded mountains, fault-block mountains, and dome mountains.

🔑 Up-and-down movements of the crust can produce a variety of landforms, including plateaus, domes, and basins.

anticline (312)
syncline (312)
monocline (313)
normal fault (314)
reverse fault (314)
thrust fault (314)

strike-slip fault (315)
orogenesis (316)
folded mountains (316)
fault-block mountain (317)
graben (317)
horst (317)

11.3 Mountains and Plates

🔑 The convergence of two plate edges of oceanic lithosphere mainly produces volcanic mountains.

🔑 The convergence of an oceanic plate edge and a continental plate edge can produce volcanic mountains and folded mountains.

🔑 A collision between two continental plate edges will form folded mountains.

🔑 The mountains that form along ocean ridges at divergent plate boundaries are fault-block mountains made of volcanic rock.

🔑 Volcanic mountains at hot spots, as well as some upwarped mountains and fault-block mountains, can form far from plate boundaries.

🔑 The process of accretion enlarges continental landmasses and forms mountains along the edges of continents.

accretionary wedge (321)
accretion (324)
terrane (324)

Think Visually

Copy the concept map onto a sheet of paper. Use information from the chapter to complete it.

Assessment Answers

Review Content

1. d	**2.** a	**3.** c
4. b	**5.** c	**6.** b
7. c	**8.** b	**9.** a
10. c		

Understand Concepts

11. Tensional stress pulls a body of rock apart or stretches it.

12. It is a type of deformation that occurs in a solid state and produces a change in size and shape of an object without fracturing.

13. Both are types of folds with two limbs. The limbs of an anticline dip or tilt in towards the fold axis. The limbs of a syncline dip or tilt away from the fold axis. The oldest rocks are in the axis of an anticline. A syncline has younger rocks in the axis.

11 Assessment

Review Content

Choose the letter that best answers the question or completes the statement.

1. Which one of the following is NOT a form of rock deformation?
   a. elastic deformation
   b. ductile deformation
   c. brittle deformation
   d. oblique deformation

2. The two most common types of folds are
   a. anticlines and synclines.
   b. basins and terranes.
   c. fault-blocks and synclines.
   d. thrusts and anticlines.

3. Orogenesis refers to those processes that produce
   a. spreading centers.
   b. earthquakes.
   c. mountains.
   d. subduction zones.

4. Which one of the following is NOT a factor that affects how a rock deforms?
   a. time
   b. age of the rock
   c. rock type
   d. temperature

5. The rock surface immediately above a fault surface is commonly called the
   a. anticline.   c. hanging wall.
   b. footwall.   d. syncline.

6. Folding is usually the result of what type of stress?
   a. tensional stress
   b. compressional stress
   c. shear stress
   d. faulting

7. The collision and joining of crustal fragments to a continent is called
   a. subduction.   c. accretion.
   b. isostasy.   d. extension.

8. The San Andreas fault is a
   a. normal fault.
   b. strike-slip fault.
   c. reverse fault.
   d. thrust fault.

9. What type of mountains form at convergent boundaries where two oceanic plates meet?
   a. volcanic mountains
   b. upwarped mountains
   c. folded mountains
   d. fault-block mountains

10. Because of isostasy, the erosion of rock from a mountain range would at first cause the mountains to
    a. sink lower.
    b. maintain the same elevation.
    c. float higher on the mantle below.
    d. develop normal faults.

Understand Concepts

11. How does tensional stress deform a body of rock?

12. What is ductile deformation?

13. How is a syncline different from an anticline?

14. What types of faults are most commonly associated with fault-block mountains?

15. Define *graben*.

16. What types of faults are most commonly formed by compressional stress?

Use the diagram below to answer Questions 17 and 18.

17. What type of fault is shown in the diagram?

18. What type of stress formed the fault shown in the diagram?

22. Folded mountains are formed from compressional stresses. Folds and thrust faults are the primary structures found in folded mountains. The Alps, northern Rocky Mountains, and the Appalachians are examples of folded mountains.

23. Volcanic mountains can form at mantle hot spots. The volcanoes in the Hawaiian Islands are examples.

24. The rocks are oldest near the center of the dome and get younger towards the outside of the dome.

25. Tensional stress is most common at divergent boundaries. Fault-block mountains most commonly form at divergent boundaries. The Mid-Atlantic Ridge is an example.

---

14. normal faults

15. A graben is a fault-bounded block that has been down-dropped to form a valley or depression.

16. reverse faults and thrusts faults

17. a strike-slip fault

18. shear stress

19. Mountain building is most directly associated with convergent plate boundaries.

20. As a subducting plate bends and begins to descend into the mantle, most sediments are scraped off the oceanic crust and from along the shoreline. These sediments are deposited in a wedge along the edge of the continental plate. This wedge of rock is deformed, faulted, and folded as subduction continues.

21. A terrane refers to an area that has different rocks, fossils, and structures from the surrounding areas.

ASSESSMENT

Think Critically

26. The erosion would remove rock from the mountain range, which would thin the crust. As the crust is thinned, it will rise because the load on the crust is reduced. In this way, the "roots" of the mountain range will rise to balance the crustal load lost to erosion.

27. Normal faults and reverse faults are both relatively high-angle faults. Normal faults are caused by tensional stress, while reverse faults are caused by compressional stress. In a normal fault, the hanging wall moves down relative to the footwall. In a reverse fault, the hanging wall moves up relative to the footwall.

28. The continental fragment would not be subducted because it is too buoyant. The fragment would be accreted onto the edge of the continent. The collision would probably cause deformation and mountain building.

29. Over time, erosion often levels the surface expression of anticlines, leaving only the upfolded rock layers below the surface.

30. Both a dome and basin are circular in shape and are caused by warping. A dome is caused by broad upwarping in basement rock by the pushing up of the crust during the intrusion of a laccolith. Basins are caused by downwarping. In basins, the youngest rocks are found near the center. In a dome, the oldest rocks form the core.

Analyze Data

31. the hanging wall
32. The hanging wall has moved up relative to the footwall.
33. a reverse fault
34. compressional stress

Concepts in Action

35. Students could use wooden blocks or books stacked on a surface that can be depressed by the weight, such as a blanket or rubber sheet stretched between tables. The surface must be able to "give" under the weight, but it cannot break or slide completely down, so it needs to be secured in some way.

36. The Himalayas were formed by a collision between India and the Eurasian plate. A slice of ocean crust that occurred in the ocean between India and the Eurasian plate before the collision could have been incorporated into the accretionary wedge along the edge of the Eurasian plate and then become thrust-faulted, folded, or uplifted up onto the peaks of the mountains after the continental collision.

19. In the theory of plate tectonics, what type of plate boundary is associated with the formation of the Himalayas and Appalachians?

20. What is an accretionary wedge? Briefly describe its formation.

21. Define terrane.

22. Describe folded mountains. Give an example of folded mountains.

23. How do volcanic mountains form at locations that are not near plate boundaries? Give an example.

24. How do the ages of rock layers change as you go outward from the center of an eroded dome?

25. What type of stress is most common at divergent boundaries? What type of mountains are most often found at this type of boundary? Give an example.

Think Critically

26. Apply Concepts How would a period of major erosion affect the isostatic adjustment of a mountain range?

27. Compare and Contrast Compare normal faults and reverse faults.

28. Predict What would most likely happen if a continental fragment the size of Greenland was carried by oceanic lithosphere into a subduction zone along the margin of a continent?

29. Infer Why don't anticlines always appear as hills, even though the rocks beneath the surface are folded upward?

30. Compare and Contrast How are a dome and a basin similar? How are they different?

Analyze Data

Use the diagram below to answer Questions 31–34.

31. Infer What is the block on the right side of the fault called?

32. Observe Describe the movement along the fault.

33. Interpret Diagrams What type of fault is shown in the diagram?

34. Draw Conclusions What type of stress was responsible for forming this fault?

Concepts in Action

35. Design an Experiment Put together an experiment that models the isostatic adjustment that results from a continent-continent collision and the erosion that takes place on the resulting mountain range.

36. Form a Hypothesis Explain how a slice of ocean crust could be found on top of a peak in the Himalayas.

37. Communicate Write a paragraph briefly describing the development of volcanic mountains at an oceanic-oceanic convergent boundary.

Performance-Based Assessment

Classify Use a world map or an atlas and Figure 15 in Chapter 9 to classify the following mountains or mountain ranges: Mount Baker in Washington State, the Zagros Mountains in Iran, Mount Fuji in Japan, and the mountains in western Egypt.

37. A volcanic island arc occurs where two plate edges made of oceanic lithosphere converge and one is subducted beneath the other. The interaction of the two plates results in partial melting of the mantle above the subducting plate. The magma slowly · rises, creating volcanoes on the seafloor that eventually grow into volcanic mountains.

Performance-Based Assessment

volcanic mountain; folded mountains; volcanic mountain; fault-block mountains

Standardized Test Prep

Choose the letter that best answers the question.

1 A fracture with horizontal displacement parallel to its surface trend is called a—
   A joint
   B normal fault
   C strike-slip fault
   D reverse fault

2 Compared to the elevation of a thin piece of continental crust in isostatic balance, the highest elevation of a thick piece of crust will be—
   F the same
   G higher
   H lower
   J older

3 The removal of material by erosion will cause the crust to—
   A subduct
   B fold
   C rise
   D subside

4 Which of the following are *not* generally associated with convergent boundaries?
   F volcanic mountains
   G folded mountains
   H thrust faulted mountains
   J fault-block mountains

Use the diagram below to answer Questions 5 and 6.

5 What feature is illustrated at the area labeled D in the diagram?
   A accretionary wedge
   B subducting continental lithosphere
   C ocean trench
   D continental volcanic arc

6 What types of mountains can form at the type of plate boundary illustrated in the diagram?
   F dome mountains and volcanic mountains
   G volcanic mountains and fault-block mountains
   H volcanic mountains and folded mountains
   J folded mountains and upwarped mountains

If You Have Trouble With . . .

Question	1	2	3	4	5	6
See Lesson	11.2	11.1	11.1	11.2	11.3	11.3

12 Geologic Time Planning Guide

BIGIDEA: EARTH HISTORY

Lesson Objectives		Activities
12.1 Discovering Earth's History, pp. 336–341 **12.1 Explain** the principle of uniformitarianism. **12.2 Describe** how geologists use relative dating principles, inclusions, and unconformities to help them understand Earth's history. **12.3 Describe** how geologists use correlation of rock layers to interpret the rock record.		**TE** Teacher Demo: Cross-Cutting Relationships, p. 339 · L2 **TE** Evaluate Understanding, p. 341 · L2
12.2 Fossils: Evidence of Past Life, pp. 342–346 **12.4 Describe** the different types of fossils and how they form. **12.5 Identify** the factors that determine if an organism will become a fossil. **12.6 Explain** how fossils are used to correlate rock layers, to infer past environments, and as evidence for evolution. **12.7 Explain** the theory of natural selection.		**TE** Teacher Demo: Charcoal and Fossil Fuels, p. 343 · L2 **TE** Build Science Skills, p. 344 · L2
12.3 Dating with Radioactivity, pp. 347–351 **12.8 Define** radioactivity and half-life. **12.9 Explain** radiometric dating. **12.10 Describe** how carbon-14 is used in radiometric dating. **12.11 Explain** how radiometric dating of igneous rock layers can help date sedimentary rock layers indirectly.		**TE** Teacher Demo: Modeling Half-Lives, p. 349 · L2 **TE** Reteach, p. 351 · L2
12.4 The Geologic Time Scale, pp. 353–355 **12.12 Describe** the geologic time scale. **12.13 Explain** how the geologic time scale is organized.		

Chapter Features and Labs

Try It What Can Become a Fossil? p. 335		**LM** Modeling Radioactive Decay · L1
Earth & History Dating With Tree Rings, p. 352		
Exploration Lab Fossil Occurrence and the Age of Rocks, pp. 356–357		

Ability Levels		Components			
L1	For students who need additional help	SE	Student Edition	LP	Lesson Plans
L2	For all students	TE	Teacher's Edition	AA	Active Art
L3	For students who need to be challenged	LM	Laboratory Manual	PD	Planet Diary
		CT	Chapter Tests	GEODe	Geode CD-ROM
		GRSW	Guided Reading & Study Workbook	eText	
		CTB	Computer Test Bank		

Resources	Lesson Assessment
GRSW Lesson 12.1 **LP** Lesson Planning 12.1 **GEODe** Geologic Time: Relative Dating	**SE** Lesson 12.1 Assessment, p. 341 **eText** Lesson 12.1
GRSW Lesson 12.2 **LP** Lesson Planning 12.2 **PD** Fossils **AA** Index Fossils	**SE** Lesson 12.2 Assessment, p. 346 **eText** Lesson 12.2
GRSW Lesson 12.3 **LP** Lesson Planning 12.3 **GEODe** Geologic Time: Radiometric Dating	**SE** Lesson 12.3 Assessment, p. 351 **eText** Lesson 12.3
GRSW Lesson 12.4 **LP** Lesson Planning 12.4 **GEODe** Geologic Time: Geologic Time Scale	**SE** Lesson 12.4 Assessment, p. 355 **eText** Lesson 12.4

Materials for Activities and Labs

Quantities for each group

STUDENT EDITION

Try It, p. 335
raisin, seashell, small bone, small tooth, insect wing, hair, leaf, stick, apple slice with seeds, orange seed, magnifying glass, microscope

Exploration Lab, pp. 356–357
geologic time scale, graph paper

TEACHER'S EDITION

Teacher Demo, p. 339
wooden stick, piece of foam

Evaluate Understanding, p. 341
clay

Teacher Demo, p. 343
wooden splints, Bunsen burner, test tube, test tube stand

Build Science Skills, p. 344
clay, plastic container, beaker, plaster of Paris, water

Teacher Demo, p. 349
scissors, adding machine tape, metric ruler

Reteach, p. 351
different-colored jelly beans

Assessment

CHAPTER ASSESSMENT
SE Assessment, pp. 359–360
CT Chapter 12 Test
CTB Chapter 12
eText Chapter 12

21st Century Learning

Self Direction: How old are the rocks where you live?
TE p. 358

Common Themes

Michael Wysession
Washington University

Few aspects of geology have had a more profound impact than the discovery that the Earth is exceedingly old—4.56 billion years old. An important concept in geology is uniformitarianism—the idea that geologic processes operating today have been slowly at work through much of Earth's history.

Space and Time The geologic time scale was created in order to establish correlations in space and time between rocks layers found in different locations. Divisions in the geologic time scale were largely determined by periods of mass extinctions and major changes in the evolution of life.

Forces and Motion Relative geologic dating was determined through an understanding of the sequence of geologic events, and relies upon the principles of superposition, original horizontality, cross-cutting, index fossils, and the presence of unconformities between rock layers.

Matter and Energy Absolute dates were assigned to the time divisions of the geologic time scale using radiometric dating, which relies upon the radioactive decay of unstable isotopes. Because different radioactive isotopes have different half-lives, different parent-daughter pairs are used to date objects of different ages. For example, the short half-life of carbon-14 makes it useful for dating more recent objects.

Earth as a System A record of the history of biological evolution exists in the form of fossils, which can be found as unaltered remains, altered remains (like molds, casts, and compressions), indirect evidence (like tracks, burrows, and dung), and conditions (hard parts, rapid burial). Fossils are also important indicators of the paleoenvironments in which they formed.

EARTH SCIENCE REFRESHER

Determining the Age of Earth

In today's age it is hard to get a feeling for just how revolutionary the discovery of radioactivity was for the determination of Earth's age. Scientists and theologians had spent centuries trying to quantify the age of the planet through a variety of means. At times, the topic was at the center of a struggle between science and religion, and between the opposing philosophies of uniformitarianism and catastrophism. Radiometric dating, however, laid all of these debates to rest.

Some of the early attempts of determining Earth's age were very clever. The ancient Greek, Xenophanes of Colophon (570–470 B.C.), realized that fossils were the ancient remains of life and that Earth was therefore extremely old. Another Greek, Herodotus (about 450 B.C.) used sediments from the Nile River. The Nile floods each year, depositing an additional layer of sediment. Herodotus dug into the river bank and counted the layers, determining that Earth was at least many thousands of years old.

In 1779, the Count de Buffon compared Earth to a ball of cooling iron, and came up with an age of 75,000 years.

> **Address Misconceptions**
>
> *Some students mistakenly think that when theories gain enough supporting evidence, they automatically become laws. In reality, a theory never becomes a law. A scientific law simply describes the behavior of an event or process in nature. A theory attempts to explain this behavior. For a strategy that helps to overcome this misconception, see* **Address Misconceptions** *on* **TE p. 337**.

Several scientists tried to use the saltiness of the ocean to determine Earth's age. In 1899, John Joly compared the ocean's salinity to the amount of salt entering the ocean from rivers, and concluded that Earth was 90 million years old. His calculations were wrong because salt precipitates out when the ocean becomes supersaturated with it.

The most significant determination of Earth's age was by William Thompson, also known as Lord Kelvin, who held Newton's chair at the Royal Astronomical Society in London. Thompson used the best understanding of the physical property of heat conduction, combined with actual measurements of the rate of heat flow out of Earth's surface, and concluded, in 1897, that Earth was no older than 20 to 40 million years. As Thompson was considered the leading physicist in Europe, his calculation was a blow to geologists and evolutionary biologists, who were sure Earth had to be older in order to explain the rock and fossil records. Charles Darwin wrote that he would die an unhappy man if Thompson was right, because his work would then be wrong.

Radioactivity proved that Darwin was correct, of course. Radioactivity not only provides the means of determining Earth's age, but it provides the necessary heat to keep Earth warm and prevent if from cooling down. Thompson did the best job he could, but he did not know about radioactivity, which was first explained at the start of the twentieth century by Ernest Rutherford, and not fully understood until much later.

BUILD READING LITERACY

Outline

Understanding Text Structure

Strategy Help students focus on the text and not simply skim it. Outlining is a good strategy to apply to an entire section, if it is not excessively long, using the headings as major divisions. Outlining is best applied to sections in which the headings are parallel, and in which there are main headings and subheadings. Before you begin, choose a section for students to read and outline, such as Lesson 12.3, pp. 347–351.

Example

1. Before students read, have them preview the section's title and headings. Demonstrate and display how to make a skeleton outline for the section. Have students list the section title as the top level, the main headings as major divisions, and the subheadings as the next level.

  I. Lesson Title
    A. Main Heading
      1. Subheading
        a. detail
        b. detail
        c. detail

2. Have students copy the skeleton outline as they read, filling in details under each subheading of the outline.

3. Tell students not to outline sections that focus on the details of cycles or processes. Students can represent these by diagrams and flowcharts rather than outlining.

4. After reading, have students review the entire section and their outlines to make sure they have included all vocabulary definitions and key concepts as main ideas or details under the appropriate levels of their outlines.

See TE p. 344 for a script on how to use this strategy with students. For additional strategies, see TE pp. 338, 340, 350, and 351.

CHAPTER 12

ASSESS PRIOR KNOWLEDGE

Use the Chapter Pretest below to assess students' prior knowledge. As needed, review these concepts.

Review Science Concepts

Lesson 12.1, Lesson 12.2 Review how igneous, metamorphic, and sedimentary rocks form. Discuss igneous features, such as dikes and sills, and the process of deposition.

Lesson 12.3 Have students recall the basic structure and properties of an atom. They should be able to define nucleus, proton, neutron, electron, mass number, and atomic number. Briefly review the periodic table of elements.

Lesson 12.4 Remind students that Earth is about 4.5 billion years old, and that the physical features and environmental conditions for any particular area have changed over time.

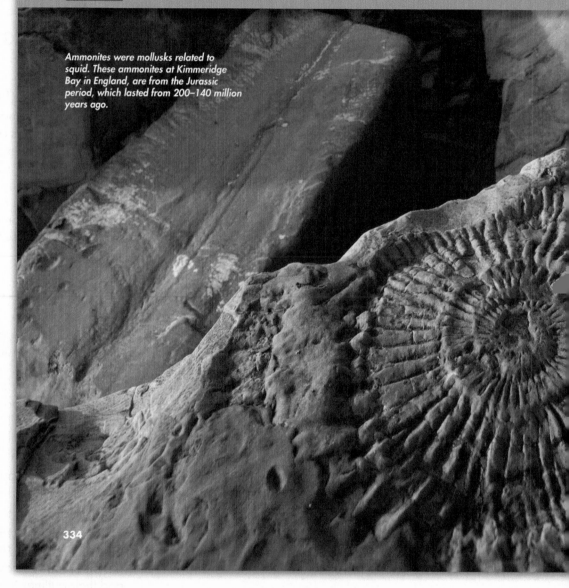

12 Geologic Time

Big idea **Earth History**

Q: How do geologists reconstruct Earth's past?

Ammonites were mollusks related to squid. These ammonites at Kimmeridge Bay in England, are from the Jurassic period, which lasted from 200–140 million years ago.

334

Chapter Pretest

1. Describe the formation of igneous, metamorphic, and sedimentary rocks. *(Igneous rocks form from cooled magma or lava. Metamorphic rocks form when pre-existing rocks are altered by heat, pressure, and/or fluids. Sedimentary rocks form by compaction and cementation.)*

2. How is a dike formed? *(A dike is formed when magma is injected into fractures in rock.)*

3. True or False: Sediments are deposited through the process of weathering. *(False)*

4. Which atomic particles orbit the nucleus? *(c)*
   a. protons
   b. neutrons
   c. electrons
   d. elements

5. Which atomic particles have a positive electrical charge? *(a)*
   a. protons
   b. neutrons
   c. electrons
   d. all of the above

6. How old is Earth? *(about 4.5 billion years)*

INQUIRY
TRY IT!

WHAT CAN BECOME A FOSSIL?

Procedure

1. Your teacher will give you some samples of different organic materials. Organic material comes from a living thing.
2. Using a hand lens and microscope, examine each sample carefully.
3. Separate those items that you think have a good chance of becoming a fossil.

Think About It

1. **Observe** What characteristics do the samples have that led you to select them as possible candidates for fossilization?
2. **Form a Hypothesis** What do you think needs to happen to these samples in order for them to become fossilized?
3. **Design an Experiment** Outline an experiment to test your answers to Questions 1 and 2.

335

ENGAGE/EXPLORE

WHAT CAN BECOME A FOSSIL? L2

Purpose Students will infer what types of organic materials may become fossils.

Skills Observe, Infer, Hypothesize, Design Experiments

Prep Time 10 minutes

Materials raisin, seashell, small bone, small tooth, insect wing, hair, leaf, stick, apple slice with seeds, orange seed, magnifying glass, microscope

Class Time 15 minutes

Teaching Tips

- Remind students that it takes a long time for fossils to form. Tell them to consider what might happen to organic matter such as apples and raisins over a long period of time. *(They decompose.)*
- Have students make a two-column table to classify the samples as "Potential Fossil" or "Non-Fossil."

Expected Outcome Students will recognize that hard materials, such as teeth, are more suitable to fossilization than soft materials, such as raisins.

Think About It

1. Sample answer: They all had hard parts.
2. Sample answer: They need to be buried quickly so as to protect them from decay and scavengers.
3. Sample answer: Bury the items in dirt or sand, weigh down the dirt with a heavy object, then observe the materials after one month or more.

■ FOCUS

Lesson Objectives

12.1 **Explain** the principle of uniformitarianism.

12.2 **Describe** how geologists use relative dating principles, inclusions, and unconformities to help them understand Earth's history.

12.3 **Describe** how geologists use correlation of rock layers to interpret the rock record.

Build Vocabulary [L2]

Word Forms Point out that the word *uniform* is closely tied to this lesson's vocabulary term *uniformitarianism*. Ask students to state the meaning of *uniform* in their own words. *(Sample answer: always the same)* Tell them that the meaning of *uniform* can help them to remember the meaning of *uniformitarianism*, which refers to processes that have operated in a similar manner throughout Earth's history.

Reading Strategy [L2]

Sample answers: **a.** rock record; **b.** clues to geological events and changing life forms; **c.** uniformitarianism; **d.** today's processes mimic those of the past; **e.** Earth's age; **f.** Earth is very old and has changed over time.

■ INSTRUCT

Build Science Skills [L2]

Use Analogies Have students develop analogies that describe the following key concept: "Rocks record geological events and changing life forms of the past." A sample analogy might be that rocks are like a long and complicated well-worn novel. Even though some of the pages might be missing or torn, enough of the book remains for the story to be understood.
Verbal

Key Questions

📖 **What is the principle of uniformitarianism?**

📖 **What are the key principles of relative dating?**

📖 **How do geologists interpret the rock record?**

Vocabulary

- uniformitarianism
- relative dating
- law of superposition
- principle of original horizontality
- principle of cross-cutting relationships
- unconformity
- correlation

Reading Strategy

Identify Main Ideas Copy the table below, leaving room for notes. As you read, fill in the first column with a main idea and add details that support it in the second column.

Main Idea	Details
1. ___a. ?___	___b. ?___
2. ___c. ?___	___d. ?___
3. ___e. ?___	___f. ?___

LIKE PAGES in a long and complicated history book, rocks record the geological events and changing life forms of the past. The book, however, is not complete. Many pages, especially in the early chapters, are missing. Others are tattered, torn, or smudged. Yet enough of the book remains to allow much of the story to be deciphered. Interpreting Earth history is a prime goal of the science of geology. The Grand Canyon, seen in **Figure 1,** is an example of just how beautiful the book of Earth's history can be.

Uniformitarianism

Scientists in Europe and the British Isles began developing the basic principles of modern geology during the 1700s by observing the landscapes around them. James Hutton, a Scottish physician and farmer, published *Theory of the Earth* in 1795. In this work, Hutton argued that Earth's varied landscape, from towering mountains to deep valleys, is the result of weak, slow-acting processes acting over long spans of time. Hutton's work was expanded upon by other geologists and was the foundation for the principle of uniformitarianism. 📖 **Uniformitarianism is the idea that the physical, chemical, and biological laws that operate today also operated in the past.** Thus, to understand ancient rocks, we must first understand present-day processes and their results. The principle of uniformitarianism is commonly expressed by saying "The present is the key to the past."

Acceptance of uniformitarianism requires acceptance of a very long history for Earth. If Earth were just a few thousand years old, there would not be enough time for slow-acting processes to form the geologic features we see today. To address this need, Hutton introduced a concept called *deep time*, which proposed that Earth had an indefinitely long history. As we will see, scientists were eventually able to determine that the absolute age of Earth is approximately 4.5 billion years.

Today, scientists understand that geological processes may not always have had the same relative importance. Nor have they always operated at precisely the same rate. Moreover, some important geologic processes are not currently observable, but evidence that they occur is well established. For example, we know that large meteorites have hit Earth, changed its climate, and caused extinctions even though we have no human witnesses.

FIGURE 1 Layers of History
Trained geologists read and interpret layers of rock in the Grand Canyon as a historian might read and interpret pages in a book.

Despite these complications, the principle of uniformitarianism is an extremely important idea in modern geology. Hutton and other early geologists gave us the knowledge and framework for understanding the rock record. Their work established that Earth is very old and has changed over geologic time, and that processes observed on Earth in the present also acted in the past.

☑ **Reading Checkpoint** *What is deep time?*

Relative Dating

By studying layers of rock exposed at the surface, such as those visible in the Grand Canyon, scientists can infer the order in which the layers formed. The method that geologists use to place rocks in chronological order is called **relative dating.** Relative dating identifies which rock units formed first, second, third, and so on. 🗝 **The law of superposition, the principle of original horizontality, the principle of cross-cutting relationships, unconformities, and inclusions all help determine the relative ages of rock layers.** As important as relative dating is, it can only provide information about the sequence in which events occurred. It does not tell us how long ago the events occurred.

Law of Superposition Nicolaus Steno, a Danish anatomist, geologist, and priest (1636–1686), made observations that are the basis of relative dating. Based on his observations, Steno developed the law of superposition. The **law of superposition** states that in an undeformed sequence of sedimentary rocks, each layer is older than the one above it and younger than the one below it. Although it may seem obvious that a rock layer could not be deposited unless it had something older beneath it for support, it was not until 1669 that Steno stated the principle. This rule also applies to other surface-deposited materials, such as lava flows and layers of ash from volcanic eruptions.

Geologic Time **337**

Use Community Resources   L2

Arrange for students to visit a local museum or historical society to view artifacts that relate to important events in your community's geologic history.
Kinesthetic

(Address **Misconceptions**)   L2

As students read about the law of superposition, make sure they clearly distinguish between theories and laws. Some students mistakenly think that when theories gain enough supporting evidence, they automatically become laws. In reality, a theory never becomes a law. A scientific law simply describes the behavior of an event or process in nature. A theory attempts to explain this behavior.
Verbal

Answers

☑ **Reading Checkpoint** *The idea that Earth has an indefinitely long history*

Differentiated Instruction

ENGLISH LANGUAGE LEARNERS Use a cloze strategy to extract information from the text about the key principles of relative time. For example, after reading pp. 336–337, have ELL students fill in the blanks in the following paragraph: **Rocks record _____ events and changing _____ of the past.**

Uniformitarianism means that the _____ and processes that operate _____ have been at work for a very long time. *(geological, life forms, forces, today)* Use student answers to pinpoint misunderstandings and clarify key concepts.

LESSON 12.1

Build Reading Literacy   **L1**

Refer to **p. 1D** in **Chapter 1,** which provides the guidelines for an anticipation guide.

Anticipation Guide Before students read about the principle of cross-cutting relationships and unconformities, have them review the law of superposition. Point out that this law pertains only to an undisturbed sequence of sedimentary rocks. **Ask:** What might happen if the rocks were disturbed? *(Sample answer: The youngest rocks might not necessarily be on top.)* Have students read the text on pp. 339–341 to see if their predictions were correct.
Verbal, Logical

Build Science Skills   **L2**

Hypotheses, Laws, and Theories

Reinforce the distinction among laws, hypotheses, and theories. Ask volunteers to define each term. *(A scientific law describes the behavior of an event or process in nature. A scientific theory attempts to explain the behavior. A scientific hypothesis is a prediction based on prior knowledge and observations.)* Review the relationship between hypotheses and theories. *(Several closely related hypotheses may be supported by many experiments. This evidence can be used to develop a theory.)* Ask students to read the paragraph describing the law of superposition. Lead a discussion about the relationship between the law of superposition and the theory of plate tectonics.

FIGURE 2 Disturbed Rock Layers Rock layers that are folded or tilted must have been moved into that position by crustal disturbances after their deposition. These folded layers are exposed in the Namib Desert (southwestern Africa).

Principle of Original Horizontality Steno also developed the important **principle of original horizontality,** which states that sediment is generally deposited in flat, horizontal layers. Many layers of the Grand Canyon are horizontal. We can therefore infer that they are in their original undisturbed position. However, the rock layers shown in **Figure 2** have been tilted and bent. According to the principle of original horizontality, these rocks formed in flat layers. So whatever bent and tilted the layers must have done so after the rock layers had formed.

Principle of Cross-Cutting Relationships Later geologists developed another principle used in relative dating. This principle, called the **principle of cross-cutting relationships,** states that a fault or intrusion must be younger than any geologic formation through which it cuts. For example, in **Figure 3** you can see that Fault A occurred after the sandstone was deposited because Fault A "broke" the sandstone layer. However, Fault A occurred before the conglomerate was laid down, because that layer is unbroken by the fault. Using the same principle, Intrusion A must be younger than Fault A and the conglomerate layer because it crosses both of them.

☑ **Reading Checkpoint** *To what type of rock can the law of superposition and the principle of original horizontality be best applied?*

FIGURE 3 Principle of Cross-cutting Relationships An intrusive rock body is younger than the rocks it intrudes. A fault is younger than the rock layers it cuts.
Interpret Diagrams *What are the relative ages of Fault B, Intrusion B, and Intrusion C?*

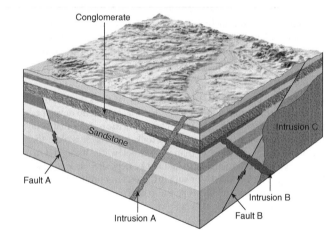

Facts and Figures

The work of Swiss scientist Louis Agassiz provides an excellent example of the application of the principle of uniformitarianism. In 1821, Agassiz heard another scientist present a paper stating that glacial features occurred in places that were far from existing glaciers in the Alps. The hypothesis implied that these glaciers had once been much larger in size. Agassiz doubted the hypothesis and set out to prove it wrong. Ironically, he was the one who was wrong. In the Alps, Agassiz found the same unique deposits and features that could be seen forming with active glaciers far beyond the limits of the ice in the Alps. Subsequent work led Agassiz to hypothesize that a great ice age had occurred in response to a period of worldwide climate change. Agassiz's ideas eventually developed into our present-day glacial theory.

Unconformities Throughout Earth's history, the deposition of sediment has been interrupted again and again. Nowhere is Earth's rock record complete. A surface that represents a break in the rock record is termed an **unconformity.** An unconformity indicates a long period during which deposition stopped, erosion removed previously formed rocks, and then deposition resumed. Unconformities help geologists identify what intervals of time are not represented in the rock record. There are three basic types of unconformities: angular unconformities, disconformities, and nonconformities. **Figure 5** shows examples of each type of unconformity in the Grand Canyon.

▶ *Angular Unconformity* In an angular unconformity, layers of sedimentary rock form over older sedimentary rock layers that are tilted or folded. **Figure 4** shows this process.

▶ *Disconformity* In a disconformity, two sedimentary rock layers are separated by an erosional surface. Because the rocks on both sides of the unconformity are of the same type, disconformities can be difficult to recognize.

▶ *Nonconformity* In a nonconformity, an erosional surface separates older metamorphic or igneous rocks from younger sedimentary rocks.

FIGURE 4 Formation of an Angular Unconformity An angular unconformity represents an extended period during which deformation and erosion occurred.

① Deposition

② Folding and uplifting

③ Erosion

④ Subsidence and renewed deposition

FIGURE 5 Unconformities This cross section through the Grand Canyon illustrates the three basic types of unconformities. All layers, except for the labeled granite and schist, are sedimentary.

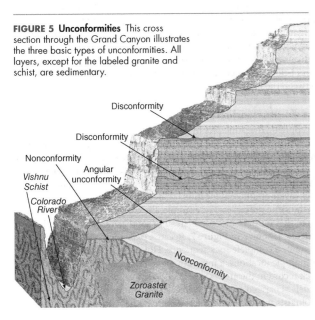

Disconformity

Disconformity

Nonconformity

Angular unconformity

Vishnu Schist

Colorado River

Nonconformity

Zoroaster Granite

Geologic Time **339**

CROSS-CUTTING RELATIONSHIPS L2

Purpose Students will observe how cross-cutting relationships can be used in relative dating.

Materials wooden stick, piece of foam

Procedure To represent a dike, insert a wooden stick into a corner of the foam from underneath. Then break off that corner and realign the pieces so that the foam and stick are close to their original positions. Ask students to explain what each element represents, and the relative ages of those elements.

Expected Outcomes Students will recognize that the foam represents the oldest layer of rock. The wooden stick represents a younger intrusion. The broken foam represents a fault; it is the youngest element. **Visual**

Answers

Figure 3 *Fault B is the oldest, then intrusion C. Intrusion B is the youngest.*

☑ **Reading Checkpoint** *undisturbed sedimentary rocks*

Facts and Figures

HUTTON'S UNCONFORMITY James Hutton got some of his ideas about uniformitarianism from looking at an angular unconformity at Jedburgh, Scotland. He noticed that the underlying layers were tilted and eroded, and reconstructed the geologic history from them. Old sedimentary rock must have been made from shorelines advancing back and forth over the land many times, stacking up the sediments. The land was then lifted, rotated, eroded, and put back under water to receive more sediments that became the horizontal sedimentary rocks on top of the unconformity. Now the land is above water again, and eroding back down to the depth of the unconformity. Hutton surmised that this cyclic process of erosion and deposition had gone on countless times before, and would continue to do so in the future.

Build Reading Literacy [L1]

Refer to **p. 530D** in **Chapter 19,** which provides the guidelines for making inferences.

Make Inferences Have students draw on their prior knowledge to infer why sedimentary rocks in particular help scientists learn about Earth's past. **Ask:** How would heat, pressure, and melting affect fossils? *(They would destroy fossils.)* What type of rock likely contains most fossils? Explain your answer. *(Sedimentary rock likely contains most fossils because it has not been affected by melting, heat, or pressure.)* **Verbal, Logical**

Use Visuals

Figure 7 Use Figure 7 to clarify the idea of horizontality. Students may be confused by the fact that horizontal layers appear far from current shorelines. Point out that, because sea level goes up and down significantly with changes in climate (as ice caps freeze and then melt) and the continents are mostly low and flat, shorelines go back and forth great distances. For instance, the fact that the many different sedimentary layers shown in Figure 7 reach from the Grand Canyon in Arizona to the canyons of Utah means that the ocean shoreline passed back and forth over these locations many, many times.

FIGURE 6 Inclusions
Inclusions are pieces of an older rock unit found within a younger rock unit.

Inclusions Sometimes the study of inclusions can help the relative dating process. *Inclusions* are pieces of one rock unit that are contained within another rock unit. We know that the rock unit containing the inclusions must have formed after the layer that provided the fragments. Therefore, the rock unit containing inclusions is the younger of the two. **Figure 6** shows inclusions of igneous rock within a layer of sedimentary rock. The inclusions indicate that the sedimentary layer was deposited on top of a layer of igneous rock. The sedimentary layer must be younger than the igneous rock because the sedimentary layer contains pieces of the igneous rock. We know the layer was not intruded upon by magma from below that later hardened, because there is a nonconformity between the layers.

Correlation

By applying the principles of relative dating, geologists can interpret the history of an area. But what if the goal is to interpret the history of an entire region? **Scientists correlate rock layers at different locations to piece together a more complete interpretation of the rock record.** In geology, **correlation** is the process of matching rock layers at different locations that formed at the same time and by the same processes. For example, the correlation of rock layers at three sites on the Colorado Plateau in southern Utah and northern Arizona is shown in **Figure 7.** Because of erosion, neither location contains a complete rock sequence. However, by correlating layers at multiple locations, a more complete picture of the sedimentary rock record in the area is revealed. When correlation between widely separated areas or between continents is the goal, however, geologists must rely on something else to help them—fossils.

340 Chapter 12 • Lesson 1

Facts and Figures

Although Earth processes vary in intensity, they still take a very long time to create or destroy major landscape features. For example, geologists have established that mountains once existed in portions of present-day Minnesota, Wisconsin, and Michigan.

Today the region consists of low hills and plains. Erosion gradually wore down these peaks. Scientists estimate that the North American continent is eroding at a rate of about 3 cm every 1000 years.

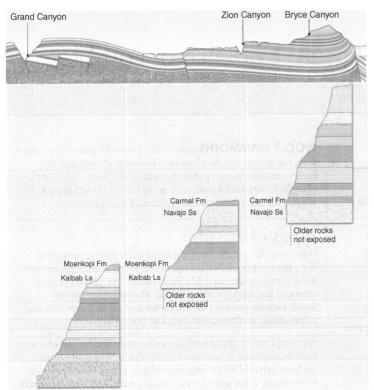

Grand Canyon   Zion Canyon   Bryce Canyon

Carmel Fm
Navajo Ss

Carmel Fm
Navajo Ss

Older rocks
not exposed

Moenkopi Fm
Kaibab Ls

Moenkopi Fm
Kaibab Ls

Older rocks
not exposed

FIGURE 7 A More Complete Record Correlation of rock layers at three locations on the Colorado Plateau—the Grand Canyon, Zion Canyon, and Bryce Canyon—provides a more complete geologic history for the area than any one site could provide. **Interpret Diagrams** *Which rock layers are found in both the Grand Canyon and Zion Canyon?*

Apply Concepts Review Steno's principles. Then **ask:** Why must the rock layers be undisturbed in order to apply them? *(Sample answer: Folding can cause entire sequences of rock to be overturned, in which case the oldest layers would be on the top.)*
Logical

3 ASSESS

Evaluate Understanding L2

Have students use clay to model the three basic types of unconformities.

Reteach L1

Have students summarize how our views of Earth's age have changed over time. *(People once thought that Earth was only a few thousand years old. Scientists now think that Earth is more than 4.5 billion years old.)*

12.1 Assessment

Review Key Concepts

1. Explain the following statement: "The present is the key to the past."

2. List and briefly describe Steno's principles.

3. In your own words, write definitions for the terms *inclusion, unconformity,* and *correlation.*

4. Why do geologists correlate rock layers?

Think Critically

5. **Apply Concepts** How did the acceptance of uniformitarianism change the way scientists viewed Earth?

6. **Infer** What can you infer about the age of sedimentary rock layers relative to the age of a sill intruded into those layers?

7. **Classify** A geologist finds layers of sedimentary rocks immediately above an eroded anticline. What type of unconformity is this? Explain.

8. **Relate Cause and Effect** Why is Earth's rock record for any given location incomplete?

WRITING IN SCIENCE

9. **Describe** Imagine that you are hiking in the Grand Canyon. Using Steno's principles, write a paragraph describing what you see, how old the layers are, and how they were deposited.

Geologic Time **341**

Answers

Figure 7 *The Moenkopi formation and Kaibab limestone are exposed in both canyons.*

---

the processes they observed had also been at work in the past.
6. The sedimentary rock layers are older than the sill.
7. Angular unconformity; sedimentary rock layers overlie the eroded surface of tilted sedimentary layers in the anticline
8. Erosion leads to the formation of unconformities representing breaks in the rock record.
9. A sample paragraph might use the law of superposition to describe the layers from bottom to top; the principle of original horizontality to describe the rock layers on either side of the canyon and how they match up; and the principle of cross-cutting relationships to explain the relative ages of the dikes toward the bottom of the canyon.

Geologic Time **341**

Assessment Answers

1. The same processes that operated in the past still operate today. By understanding these processes, you can interpret Earth's history.
2. The law of superposition states that in a sequence of undisturbed rock layers, the oldest layer is on the bottom; the upper layers are progressively younger. The principle of original horizontality states that sedimentary rocks are generally deposited horizontally. The principle of cross-cutting relationships states that features

such as faults and intrusions are younger than the features they cut across.
3. Inclusion: piece of one kind of rock contained in another rock; unconformity: surface that represents a break in the rock record; correlation: way of determining that two separated rock units are the same
4. To gain a more complete picture of the geologic history of an area
5. They learned that Earth was very old, that Earth's landscape is always changing, and that

1 FOCUS

Lesson Objectives

12.4 **Describe** the different types of fossils and how they form.

12.5 **Identify** the factors that determine if an organism will become a fossil.

12.6 **Explain** how fossils are used to correlate rock layers, to infer past environments, and as evidence for evolution.

12.7 **Explain** the theory of natural selection.

Build Vocabulary `L2`

Compare/Contrast Tables Have students make tables that compare and contrast the different types of fossils, such as molds and casts, compressions, impressions, and trace fossils. Students can list each type of fossil at the top of a column, and add details in the rows below.

Reading Strategy `L2`

Possible answers include:
a. Fossils are traces or remains of organisms preserved from the geologic past. **b.** Fossils can form by freezing, burial and replacement with minerals, formation of a carbon film, preservation in amber or tar, and formation of trace fossils. **c.** Fossils are used to correlate rock layers, show changes in life forms through time, and provide information on ancient environments.

2 INSTRUCT

Integrate Biology `L2`

Woolly Mammoth The remains of the mammoth found in Siberia are estimated to be about 20,000 years old. The mammoth died relatively young—no more than 49 years. Japanese scientists have announced their plans to clone a woolly mammoth by 2016. The team will attempt to transfer recovered mammoth DNA to enucleated elephant eggs. Have students share their thoughts regarding this idea.
Verbal

12.2 Fossils: Evidence of Past Life

Key Questions

🔑 What are the different types of fossils?

🔑 What conditions help a fossil to form?

🔑 Why are fossils important?

🔑 What is natural selection?

Vocabulary

- extinct • fossil
- principle of fossil succession
- index fossil
- evolution
- natural selection
- adaptation

Reading Strategy

Monitor Your Understanding Draw and complete a chart like the one below. After you finish this section, correct or add details as needed.

Fossils	How Fossils Form	How Fossils are Used
a. _?_	b. _?_	c. _?_

WOOLY MAMMOTHS once roamed the cold plains of northern Asia, North America, and Europe. Thousands of years ago, they became **extinct,** meaning they died out. In the Arctic, scientists often find mammoth fossils, such as the huge tusks in **Figure 8.** A **fossil** is the preserved remains or traces of an organism.

Types of Fossils

When you think of the word *fossil*, you likely picture something like a dinosaur bone. But the bones you see on display in a natural history museum are more like rocks than bones. Moreover, they represent just one type of fossil. 🔑 **The different types of fossils include petrified fossils, molds and casts, compressions, impressions, unaltered remains, and trace fossils.**

Petrified Fossils If you were allowed to pick up a dinosaur bone, you'd be surprised at how heavy it felt. That is because the bone has been petrified, or literally "turned into stone." In this process, mineral-rich water soaks into the small cavities and pores of organic tissue such as shell, bone, or even wood, as shown in **Figure 9A.** As minerals precipitate, they fill the spaces and replace dissolving tissue. In this way, petrification preserves the detailed structure of the original organism.

Molds and Casts A fossil mold is created when a shell or other organic structure is buried in sediment and then dissolved by underground water. The mold reflects only the shape and surface markings of the organism. It doesn't reveal any information about its internal anatomy. Cast fossils (**Figure 9B**) are created if the hollow spaces of a mold are later filled with minerals.

FIGURE 8 Frozen in Time The permafrost in Siberia preserved the frozen remains of this mammoth for thousands of years. Permafrost is a layer of ice that forms under land in the Arctic.

FIGURE 9 Types of Fossils A Petrified fossil of wood in Petrified Forest National Park, Arizona **B** Natural casts of shelled organisms called ammonites **C** Compression fossil of bee, preserved as a thin film of carbon **D** Impression fossil of two ancient fish **E** Unaltered remains of an insect in amber **F** Trace fossil of dinosaur footprints found in fine-grained limestone near Tuba City, Arizona

Compression Fossils Compression fossils are two-dimensional organic remains. Compression fossils form when pressure squeezes out liquids and gases from a buried organism, leaving behind only a delicate, thin film of carbon. Most impression fossils are of plants, though there are some of animals, as shown in **Figure 9C.**

Impression Fossils Impression fossils, like compression fossils, are two dimensional. Unlike compression fossils, impression fossils do not contain any organic matter. However, impression fossils, like those of the fish in **Figure 9D,** may still show fine details of an organism's external structure.

Unaltered Remains Sometimes, fossilization preserves all or part of an organism with relatively little change. The mammoth frozen in permafrost is one example. **Figure 9E** shows another example. The fly seen in the figure has been preserved in amber—the hardened resin, or sap, of ancient trees.

Trace Fossils Trace fossils are indirect evidence of prehistoric life. Tracks, like those in **Figure 9F,** form when footprints are covered with sediment before they can be washed away. Other types of trace fossils include burrows, coprolites, and gastroliths. Burrows are holes made by an animal that were later filled with minerals and preserved. Coprolites and gastroliths provide useful information about the eating habits of organisms. Coprolites are fossils of dung and stomach contents and gastroliths are highly polished stomach stones used by some extinct reptiles to grind food.

☑ **Reading Checkpoint** *What is a trace fossil?*

PLANET DIARY

For links about **Fossils,** visit PlanetDiary.com/HSES.

Geologic Time **343**

The Fossil Record

All the fossils that geologists have found, arranged by their relative ages, make up the fossil record. But the fossil record includes only a fraction of the different kinds of organisms that have lived on Earth. Why? Some organisms are more likely than others to be preserved as fossils. **Two conditions that favor preservation of an organism as a fossil are rapid burial and the possession of hard parts.** Rapid burial protects an organism from being eaten by scavengers or decomposed by bacteria. Once buried, organisms also have a better chance of being preserved if they have hard parts such as shells, bones, and teeth. Hard parts are tougher than soft parts and more likely to remain intact long enough to become fossilized.

Even if an organism becomes fossilized, it is no guarantee that it will one day be found. If the rock layer that surrounds it is melted or metamorphosed, the fossil will be lost. And if the rock layer remains buried, the fossils it contains will likely never be discovered. Despite their incomplete record, however, scientists have learned a tremendous amount from fossils. **Fossils enable scientists to correlate rock layers and infer past environments, and they provide evidence for evolution.**

Fossil Succession The **principle of fossil succession** states that fossil organisms tend to be found in the same general order at different locations. This principle was developed by William Smith, an English engineer. While digging and planning canal routes, Smith noted that the fossils he encountered weren't randomly distributed through rock layers. Instead, each layer contained a distinct assortment of fossils that did not occur in the layers above or below it. In **Figure 10,** for example, Rock unit A has a different collection of fossils from Rock Unit B. Many geologists who followed Smith confirmed his observations.

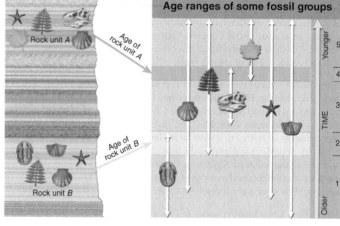

FIGURE 10 Correlating With Fossils Overlapping ranges of fossils help date rocks more exactly than using a single fossil. The fossils contained in Rock Unit A all have overlapping age ranges in time 4. The fossils in Rock Unit B have overlapping age ranges in time 2. Therefore, Rock Unit A was deposited in time 4, and Rock Unit B was deposited in time 2.

344 Chapter 12 • Lesson 2

Facts and Figures

Early attempts to determine Earth's age included a method based on the deposition of sediment. Some scientists thought that if they could determine both the rate of sediment accumulation and the total thickness of sedimentary rock that had been deposited throughout Earth's history, they could estimate the length of geologic time. To do this, scientists divided the rate of sediment accumulation into the total thickness of the sedimentary rock. However, estimates of Earth's age varied each time the method was attempted. The calculated age of Earth ranged from 3 million to 1.5 billion years.

Fossils and Correlation The principle of fossil succession enables geologists to correlate rock layers based on the fossils they contain. The best type of fossils to use for correlation are called index fossils. An **index fossil** is a fossil that is both geographically widespread and abundant in the fossil record, but that existed for only a limited span of time. The presence of an index fossil in rock layers at different locations means that the layers are of roughly the same age. Rock layers, however, do not always contain a specific index fossil. In this case, geologists can use groups of fossils to establish the relative age of the rock, as shown in Figure 10.

Fossils and Past Environments Fossils can help build detailed pictures of past environments. Suppose, for example, that geologists working far from shore find fossil clam shells in limestone. From this, they can infer that the region was once covered with seawater. The geologists might also be able to conclude the approximate position of the ancient shoreline by observing the types and locations of fossils and comparing them to modern forms. For example, living organisms that live near shore tend to have thick shells that can withstand powerful waves. So, if the fossil clams had thick shells, a scientist could infer that the ancient shoreline was once located nearby.

Fossils can also provide information about the temperature of water in the past. Certain present-day corals, for example, require warm and shallow tropical seas—similar to those around Florida and the Bahamas today. When similar corals are found in ancient limestone, such as those in **Figure 11,** they indicate that a Florida-like marine environment must have existed when the corals were alive.

FIGURE 11 Evidence of a Past Environment Fossil corals found in Texas limestone indicate the area was covered by a warm, tropical sea about 300 million years ago.

Fossils and Evolution Geologists had noticed that fossils from older rock layers were very different from the fossils in younger layers. This had, by the mid-nineteenth century, convinced most scientists that life on Earth had undergone **evolution,** or changed over time. However, there was not a scientifically accepted explanation for *how* life evolved until English naturalist Charles Darwin came along. In 1859, Darwin proposed the theory of natural selection. 🔑 **According to the theory of natural selection, traits that improve an individual's chance for survival and reproduction will be passed on more frequently to future generations than traits that do not.** These beneficial traits are called **adaptations.** Natural selection is among the most well-tested and accepted theories in science. It provides a framework by which scientists study and interpret the history of life.

☑ **Reading Checkpoint** *What is an adaptation?*

Integrate Biology L3

Paleontology and Biogeography Tell students that there are two scientific fields that combine the study of Earth's geologic history with the study of how Earth's life forms evolved. Most students will know something about paleontology. Paleontologists study the evolution of life forms as preserved in the fossil record. Few students will have heard of biogeography. Biogeographers study how changes in Earth's landmasses have affected evolution over geologic time. For example, biogeographers study the colonization of volcanic islands by life forms that subsequently evolve into new species. They also study how continental drift has affected evolution. One famous example of the latter is called "The Great Faunal Exchange." This refers to the movement of animal species (such as the mountain lion and armadillo) between North America and South America when the two continents became joined a few million years ago. Ask for volunteers to research the relationship between biogeography and evolution on the Internet and report their findings to the class.

Answers

☑ **Reading Checkpoint** *A trait that improves an organism's chance to survive and reproduce*

Facts and Figures

LIVING FOSSILS Relative dating using fossils works best with organisms that go extinct quickly, living for a very limited amount of time. However, there are some organisms that have managed to remain on Earth for extremely long periods of time, largely unchanged. They have survived and thrived through different climates and different populations of predators and competitors. Examples of these "living fossils" include the gingko tree, platypus, crocodile, frilled shark, coelacanth fish, purple frog, cedar wood wasp, and horseshoe crab. Their fossils cannot be used to narrowly determine the time they lived.

LESSON 12.2

Evaluate Understanding   L2

Have students use their outlines of this lesson to quiz one another on key concepts.

Reteach   L1

Use Figures 8 and 9 to review the different types of fossils and how they form.

FIGURE 12 Walking Whale This extinct water-dwelling mammal, *Ambulocetus natans*, evolved about 45 million years ago in south Asia. *Ambulocetus*, which means "walking whale," represents one stage in the evolution of modern whales from land animals.

In general, organisms that are well-adapted to their environment survive more often than organisms that are not as well-adapted. As a result, these well-adapted individuals are more likely to pass on their traits to later generations. Over time, natural selection can bring about tremendous changes. For example, the fossil record shows that the ancestors of modern whales were land-dwelling mammals with four legs (**Figure 12**). Natural selection, acting over millions of years, has resulted in the legless, streamlined organisms we know today.

12.2 Assessment

Review Key Concepts

1. List the different types of fossils.

2. Describe the conditions that favor the formation of fossils.

3. In your own words, explain the theory of natural selection.

4. Describe two ways that geologists can use fossils to interpret Earth's history.

Think Critically

5. Compare and Contrast How are compression fossils and impression fossils similar? How are they different?

6. Sequence Describe how a clam might become a fossil.

7. Apply Concepts What is the role of natural selection in evolution?

8. Infer Look at Figure 10. Can any of the fossils in the diagram be used as an index fossil? Explain why or why not.

BIGIDEA EARTH HISTORY

9. Connect Concepts How are the law of superposition and the principle of fossil succession related? How do they help us understand the history of life?

Assessment Answers

1. Petrified fossils, molds and cases, compression fossils, impression fossils, unaltered remains, and trace fossils

2. quick burial, possession of hard parts

3. According to the theory of natural selection, individuals that are better adapted to their environments will survive and pass on their genes more frequently than individuals who are less well-adapted.

4. To correlate rock layers and to reconstruct past environments

5. Both are two-dimensional representations of past life. In a compression fossil, traces of carbon from the organism remain. There is no organic material left in an impression fossil.

6. The shell falls to the bottom and is buried under sediments. Mineral-rich water soaks into the pore spaces. Minerals precipitate and fill in the holes. Over time, the shell dissolves and is replaced with inorganic minerals, forming a fossil.

7. Organisms that are well adapted to the environment survive and reproduce. Over time, this can lead to the evolution of a new species.

8. No, because none is limited to a single rock unit. But the trilobite, skull, and leaf might be of some use because they each occur in only two rock units.

9. The law of superposition states that the oldest rocks are at the bottom of a sequence of rocks. The principle of fossil succession states that layers of rock contain specific fossils that change from layer to layer. Thus, the oldest fossils would be in the oldest layer of rock, which in turn would be at the bottom. Scientists use this information to piece together the recorded history of life.

12.3 Dating with Radioactivity

EARLY GEOLOGISTS like William Smith could only determine the relative ages of rock layers. They could not find exact dates for events in Earth's past. Today, however, we know that Earth is about 4.5 billion years old and that the dinosaurs became extinct about 65 million years ago. To understand the method geologists used to arrive at these dates, you need first to understand radioactivity.

What Is Radioactivity?

Recall that each atom has a nucleus made up of protons and neutrons and that the number of neutrons in the atoms of a given element can vary. Different forms of an element are called *isotopes*.

Radioactive Isotopes In most atoms, the forces that bind protons and neutrons together in the nucleus are strong and balanced. In some isotopes, however, there is an excess of energy within the nucleus. These atoms have unstable nuclei. **Unstable atomic nuclei spontaneously break apart, or decay, releasing energy.** The term for the process by which atoms decay is **radioactivity,** or radioactive decay. **Figure 13** shows the three different types of radioactive decay.

FIGURE 13 Radioactive Decay
In each type of radioactive decay, the number of protons (atomic number) in the nucleus changes, thus producing a different element.

Geologic Time **347**

Key Questions

🔑 **What happens during radioactive decay?**

🔑 **How are isotopes used in radiometric dating?**

🔑 **How can radiometric dating be used to date organic material?**

🔑 **How can radiometric dating be used to infer the age of sedimentary rocks?**

Vocabulary

- radioactivity • half-life
- radiometric dating
- radiocarbon dating

Reading Strategy

Monitor Your Understanding
Preview the key concepts, topics, headings, vocabulary, and figures in this section. Copy the chart below. List two things you expect to learn about each. After reading, state what you learned about each item you listed.

What I expect to learn	What I learned
1. a. ?	b. ?
2. c. ?	d. ?

◼ FOCUS

Lesson Objectives
12.8 **Define** radioactivity and half-life.
12.9 **Explain** radiometric dating.
12.10 **Describe** how carbon-14 is used in radiometric dating.
12.11 **Explain** how radiometric dating of igneous rock layers can help date sedimentary rock layers indirectly.

Build Vocabulary L2
Vocabulary Rating Chart Have students make a four-column chart with the headings "Term," "Can Define or Use It," "Heard or Seen It," and "Don't Know." Have them write *radioactivity, half-life, radiometric dating,* and *radiocarbon dating* in the first column. Students should then rate their knowledge of each term by putting a checkmark in one of the other columns. Ask them to revise their charts after they have read the section.

Reading Strategy L2
Sample answers include:
a. What is radioactivity? **b.** the breakdown of unstable nuclei; **c.** What is half-life? **d.** the time required for one half of the nuclei in a sample to decay to its stable isotope

◼ INSTRUCT

Build Science Skills L2
Use Models Have students draw models of atoms. Student models should show protons (positive charge) and neutrons (neutral charge) in the nucleus. Electrons (negative charge) should orbit outside the nucleus.
Kinesthetic, Logical

Use Visuals L1
Figure 13 Ask: What happens to the number of protons in each case? *(It either increases or decreases.)*
Visual

Use Visuals L1

Figure 14 Have students predict how much of the radioactive parent will remain after six half-lives. *(1/64)* **Ask:** At which point is the parent/daughter ratio 1:1? *(after one half-life)*
Visual

Build Science Skills L2

Apply Concepts Have students review Figure 13 on p. 347. Tell them that the element thorium has an atomic number of 90 and a mass number of 232. **Ask:** If a radioactive isotope of thorium emits six alpha particles and four beta particles during radioactive decay, what are the atomic number and mass number of the stable daughter product? *(Each time beta decay occurs, the atomic number increases by one; mass number does not change. Each alpha decay decreases the atomic number by two and the mass number by four. Thus, for six alpha decays and four betas, the atomic number of the daughter would be 90 − (6 × 2) + 4 = 82. The mass number of the daughter would be 232 − (6 × 4) = 208).*
Logical

FIGURE 14 The Half-Life Decay Curve The radioactive decay curve shows change that is exponential. Half of the radioactive parent isotope remains after one half-life. After a second half-life, one quarter of the parent isotope remains, and so forth. *Interpret Graphs If 1/32 of the parent isotope remains, how many half-lives have passed?*

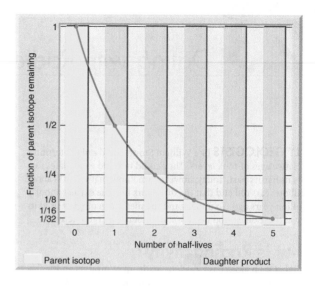

Parent isotope   Daughter product

Radioactive Isotopes Radioactive decay continues, sometimes through many intermediate steps, until a stable, or nonradioactive, isotope is formed. For example, uranium-238 decays over time to form the stable isotope lead-206. An unstable, or radioactive, isotope of an element is called the *parent isotope*. The isotopes that result from the decay of the parent are called the *daughter products*.

Half-Life A half-life is a common way of expressing the rate of radioactive decay. A **half-life** is the amount of time necessary for one half of the nuclei in a sample of radioactive isotope to decay to its stable isotope, as shown in **Figure 14.** If the half-life of the parent isotope is known, and the parent/daughter ratio can be measured, then the age of the sample can be calculated. For example, if the half-life of an unstable isotope is 1 million years, and 1/16 of the parent isotope remains, the sample must be about 4 million years old, since four half-lives have passed.

Radiometric Dating

Radiometric dating is a method of calculating the absolute ages of rocks and minerals that contain certain radioactive isotopes. A rock or mineral's *absolute age* is the approximate number of years before present that it formed. **In radiometric dating, scientists measure the ratio between the radioactive parent isotope and the daughter products in a sample to be dated. The older the sample, the more daughter product it contains.** For igneous rock, radiometric dating establishes when rock minerals crystallized. For metamorphic rock, radiometric dating determines when new minerals formed due to heat, pressure, or fluids. As we will see, radiometric dating is not used to directly date sedimentary rocks.

Differentiated Instruction

ENGLISH LANGUAGE LEARNERS Give ELL students opportunities to interact verbally with non-ELL classmates. Place students in cooperative groups to discuss key concepts or chapter activities. Do not place all ELL students in one group—the goal is to help them improve their English skills in an informal setting. Encourage all students to be supportive during the discussions. For example, if a student easily grasps a difficult concept, he or she can attempt to simplify the concept for others in a relaxed manner.

Table 1 Radioactive Isotopes Frequently Used in Radiometric Dating

Radioactive Parent	Stable Daughter Product	Currently Accepted Half-Life Values
Uranium-238	Lead-206	4.5 billion years
Uranium-235	Lead-207	713 million years
Thorium-232	Lead-208	14.1 billion years
Rubidium-87	Strontium-87	47.0 billion years
Potassium-40	Argon-40	1.3 billion years

How can a radioactive isotope serve as a reliable "clock"? The rates of decay for many isotopes have been precisely measured and do not vary under the physical conditions that exist in Earth's outer layers. Each radioactive isotope has been decaying at a constant rate since the formation of the rocks in which it occurs. The products of decay have also been accumulating at a constant rate. Of the many radioactive isotopes that exist in nature, five have proved particularly useful in providing radiometric ages for ancient rocks. These five radioactive isotopes are listed in **Table 1**.

Limitations of Radiometric Dating An accurate radiometric date can be obtained for a mineral only if there has been no loss of parent or daughter isotope since the mineral's formation. For example, the stable daughter product of potassium is argon gas. To calculate absolute age using potassium and argon, geologists measure the ratio of radioactive potassium-40 atoms to stable argon atoms in a sample. They then use the known half-life of potassium-40 to estimate the sample's age based on the ratio. Given the long half-life of potassium-40, this method can be used to date rocks that are hundreds of millions of years old. However, because it is a gas, argon may leak from minerals and throw off measurements. Cross-checking of samples, using two different radiometric methods, is done whenever possible to ensure accuracy.

Age of Earth Radiometric dating methods have enabled scientists to assign dates to thousands of events in Earth history. Earth's oldest rocks (so far) are metamorphic gneisses in northern Canada. These rocks have been dated at 4.03 billion years. Even older mineral grains have been dated. Tiny crystals of the mineral zircon with radiometric ages as old as 4.3 billion years have been found in younger sedimentary rocks in western Australia. So, Earth is at least that old, but is it even older? To determine the age of Earth, scientists have compared isotope ratios in a variety of meteorites. Assuming that the solar system formed together from the solar nebula, Earth and all meteorites should be the same age, about 4.5 billion years old.

INQUIRY APPLY IT!

Q: *In radioactive decay, is there ever a time when all of the parent material is converted into the daughter product?*

A: Theoretically, no. During a half-life, half of the parent material is converted into the daughter product. Then half of the remaining parent material is converted to the daughter product in another half life, and so on. By converting only half of the parent material with each half-life, there is never a time when all the parent material would be converted. However, after many half-lives, the parent material will be present in such small amounts that it is essentially undetectable.

Facts and Figures

In a sample of uranium-238, unstable nuclei decay and produce a variety of daughter products, including radon—a colorless, odorless, invisible gas. Radon also decays, having a half-life of only about four days. Its decay products are mainly radioactive solids that stick to dust particles that can be inhaled by people. During prolonged exposure to a radon-contaminated environment, some decay will occur while the gas is in a person's lungs, thereby placing the radioactive radon in direct contact with delicate lung tissue. Growing evidence indicates that radon is a significant cause of lung cancer, second only to smoking.

LESSON 12.3

Build Reading Literacy L1

Refer to **p. 246D** in **Chapter 9,** which provides the guidelines for relating cause and effect.

Relate Cause and Effect Remind students that a cause makes something happen; the effect is what happens because of the cause. Have students read the section about dating with carbon-14. **Ask:** Why do all organisms contain a small amount of carbon-14? *(It circulates in the atmosphere and is absorbed by living things.)* Why is the ratio of carbon-14 to carbon-12 constant during an organism's lifetime? *(Carbon-14 is continually replaced.)* At what point does the amount of carbon-14 in an organism begin to decrease? *(when the organism dies and starts to decay)*
Verbal, Logical

FIGURE 15 Radiocarbon Dating
Carbon-14 is used to date organic materials that formed up to about 75,000 years ago. Here, an archaeologist is uncovering the remains of a sea turtle near an ancient stone formation. Radiocarbon dating of the remains will help determine their approximate age.

Dating with Carbon-14

To date organic materials, carbon-14 is used in a method called **radiocarbon dating.** Organic material is a substance that contains carbon and comes from a living thing. Carbon-14 is the radioactive isotope of carbon. Carbon-14 is continuously produced in the upper atmosphere. It quickly becomes incorporated into carbon dioxide, which circulates in the atmosphere and is absorbed by living matter. As a result, all organisms—including you—contain a small amount of carbon-14.

While an organism is alive, the decaying radiocarbon is continually replaced. Thus, the ratio of carbon-14 to carbon-12—the stable isotope of carbon—remains constant. **When an organism dies, the amount of carbon-14 gradually decreases as the carbon-14 decays. By comparing the ratio of carbon-14 to carbon-12 in a sample, radiocarbon dates can be determined.**

Because the half-life of carbon-14 is only 5730 years, it can be used to date events up to about 75,000 years ago. The age of the ancient sea turtle shown in **Figure 15** can be determined using radiocarbon dating. Carbon-14 has become a valuable tool for anthropologists, archaeologists, and historians, as well as for geologists who study recent Earth history.

☑ **Reading Checkpoint** *What is compared when dating samples with carbon-14?*

Radiometric Dating of Sedimentary Rock

Radiometric dating can rarely be used to date sedimentary rocks directly. Sedimentary rocks may contain particles that can be dated. But these particles are not the same age as the rocks in which they occur. The sediment from which the rock formed probably weathered from older rocks. Radiometric dating would not be accurate since the sedimentary rock is made up of so many older rock particles.

Geologists have developed an indirect method of dating sedimentary rocks. **To determine the age of sedimentary rock, geologists must relate the sedimentary rock to datable masses of igneous rock.** Applying Steno's principles, geologists identify two igneous rock masses. One rock mass must be relatively older than the sedimentary rock. The other rock mass must be younger. Radiometric methods can then be used to date the two igneous rock masses. The age of the sedimentary rock must lie between the ages of the igneous rocks. If present, fossils may help refine the estimate.

Facts and Figures

DETERMINING THE AGE OF GRANITE The process of determining the age of a rock can be very hard work. In the case of granite, the rock contains tiny amounts of the crystal zircon, which is an excellent source for determining the rock's age because both uranium and lead stay trapped within the zircon crystal lattice. The hard part is getting the zircon out of the granite. A large block of granite, hundreds of kilograms in mass, is destroyed in order to extract a few microscopic zircon crystals. The granite is crushed, shaken, passed through a magnet, and then successively put in various fluids with densities slightly higher and lower than that of zircon. The final zircon crystals are then dissolved in hydrochloric acid and passed through a machine called a *mass spectrometer,* which counts the individual uranium and lead atoms. These numbers are then used to calculate the age of the granite.

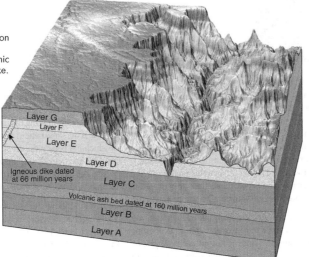

FIGURE 16 Estimating the Age of Sedimentary Rock Layers Sedimentary rock layers can be dated in relation to igneous rocks of known age—in this case, the volcanic ash bed and the igneous dike. *Infer What can you infer about Layers A and B?*

Layer G
Layer F
Layer E
Layer D
Igneous dike dated at 66 million years
Layer C
Volcanic ash bed dated at 160 million years
Layer B
Layer A

Look at **Figure 16.** Using the principle of superposition, you can tell that layers C–G are younger than 160 million years old, since they lie above the dated volcanic ash bed. Using the principle of cross-cutting relationships, you can see that the dike is younger than layers E and F. Therefore layers C–F must be between 160 and 66 million years old.

☑ **Reading Checkpoint** *Why can't radiometric dating be used to determine the absolute age of sedimentary rock?*

12.3 Assessment

Review Key Concepts 🔑

1. What happens to atoms that are radioactive?

2. What is the role of isotopes in radiometric dating?

3. Describe radiocarbon dating.

4. How do geologists use radiometric dating to date sedimentary rock layers indirectly?

Think Critically

5. **Apply Concepts** A geologist wants to use potassium-argon dating to date a granite rock found on the surface. What is a possible source of inaccuracy in dating the rock?

6. **Apply Concepts** Using radiometric dating, a scientist determines that a sample of quartz minerals is 1.2 billion years old. From this, she concludes that the sandstone containing the quartz is also 1.2 billion years old. Explain her mistake.

7. **Interpret Diagrams** In a sample of igneous rock, one-quarter of the isotope thorium-232 remains. How old is the rock? Use Figure 15 and Table 1 to help you.

WRITING IN SCIENCE

8. **Describe** How might radiocarbon dating be used to study an ancient civilization?

Geologic Time **351**

Refer to **p. 186D** in **Chapter 7,** which provides the guidelines for relating text and visuals.

Dating With Tree Rings

Dating With Tree Rings   L2

Background

One of the most basic principles of geology is also used in the study of dendrochronology—the principle of uniformitarianism, which states that the same processes at work today were also active in the past. The doctrine helps dendrochronologists to make inferences about ancient environmental conditions. It also allows them to predict future patterns based on evidence of past conditions. Other doctrines used by dendrochronologists include the principle of limiting factors, which states that life processes, such as growth, are constrained by the most limiting environmental factor of a particular area, such as precipitation. The principle of ecological amplitude states that trees located at the extremes of their species' geographic range will be most vulnerable to changing environmental factors. Other dendro-chronologic principles cover site selection, cross-dating, and sampling techniques.

Teaching Tips

- Obtain several thin cross-sections of tree trunks. Allow students to examine the rings. Have them count the rings and try to establish the age of the tree.

- Tell students that clues to ancient environments can also be determined by examining ice cores. The cores are obtained by drilling through thick layers of ice, which are found in places such as Greenland and Siberia. By analyzing gases and other materials trapped in the layers of ice, scientists can reconstruct past climatic conditions.

Visual

If you look at the top of a tree stump or at the end of a log, you will see that it is made of a series of concentric rings, like those shown in **Figure 17**. Every year in temperate regions, trees add a layer of new wood under the bark. Each of these tree rings becomes larger in diameter outward from the center. During favorable environmental conditions, a wide ring is produced. During unfavorable environmental conditions, a narrow ring is produced. Trees growing at the same time in the same region show similar tree-ring patterns.

Because a single growth ring is usually added each year, you can determine the age of a tree by counting its rings. Cutting down a tree to count the rings is not necessary anymore. Scientists can use small, nondestructive core samples from living trees.

The dating and study of annual rings in trees is called the science of *dendrochronology*. Dendrochronology provides useful information regarding the relative ages for events in the historic and recent prehistoric past. Because tree rings are a storehouse of data, they are a valuable tool in the reconstruction of past environments.

To make the most effective use of tree rings, extended patterns known as ring chronologies are established. They are produced by comparing the patterns of rings among trees in an area. If the same pattern can be identified in two trees, one of which has been given an absolute date based on an independent line of evidence, the second tree can then be dated by aligning its ring pattern to that of the first dated tree. This technique, called cross dating, is illustrated in **Figure 18.**

Cross dating allows the ages of dead tree remains to be dated. Tree-ring chronologies extending back for thousands of years have been established for some regions. To date a timber sample of unknown age, its ring pattern is matched against the reference chronology.

Tree-ring chronologies have important applications in such disciplines as climate, geology, ecology, and archaeology. For example, tree rings are used to reconstruct long-term climate variations within a certain region. Knowledge of such variations is of great value in studying and understanding the recent record of climate change.

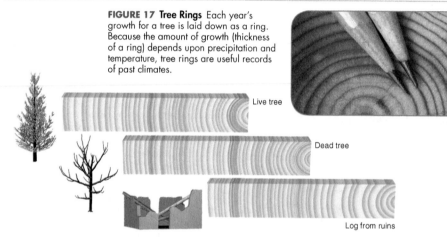

FIGURE 17 Tree Rings Each year's growth for a tree is laid down as a ring. Because the amount of growth (thickness of a ring) depends upon precipitation and temperature, tree rings are useful records of past climates.

Live tree

Dead tree

Log from ruins

FIGURE 18 Cross Dating If a scientist knows the absolute date of a live tree, they can use cross dating to estimate the age of an ancient ruin. First, a tree-ring chronology for the area is established using cores extracted from living trees of known age.

This chronology is extended further back in time by matching overlapping patterns from older, dead trees. Finally, cores taken from beams inside the ruin are dated using the chronology established from the other two sites.

12.4 The Geologic Time Scale

GEOLOGICAL EVENTS by themselves have little meaning until they are put into context. Studying an event in history, whether it be the Civil War or the evolution of mammals, requires a timeline. Among geology's major contributions to human knowledge is the timeline it has developed for Earth history.

What Is the Geologic Time Scale?

Geologists of the eighteenth and nineteenth centuries proposed a sequence of events in Earth's history using relative dating principles. The result is the **geologic time scale,** a timeline of Earth's history. 🔑 **The geologic time scale is a record that includes both geologic events and major developments in the evolution of life.** Today's time scale includes many absolute dates, the result of radiometric dating techniques that became available in the twentieth century. Even with all of our technology, however, the time scale is not considered final or complete. It is constantly revised as new data become available.

FIGURE 19 Around Since the Dinosaurs These cliffs on the coast of England are made of rock that formed about 200 million years ago, which, according to the time scale, was during the time of the dinosaurs.

Key Questions

🔑 *What is the geologic time scale?*

🔑 *How is the geologic time scale constructed?*

Vocabulary

- geologic time scale • eon
- Precambrian time • era
- period • epoch

Reading Strategy

Outline As you read, make an outline of the important ideas in this section. Use the orange headings as the main topics and fill in details from the remainder of the text.

The Geologic Time Scale
I. What Is the Geologic Time Scale?
A. _____? _____
B. _____? _____
II. Structure of the Time Scale
A. _____? _____
B. _____? _____

Geologic Time **353**

1 FOCUS

Lesson Objectives
12.12 Describe the geologic time scale.
12.13 Explain how the geologic time scale is organized.

Build Vocabulary   L2
Paraphrase Tell students to list the vocabulary terms on a sheet of paper, leaving enough space for definitions. As they read, students should write the definitions in their own words.

Reading Strategy   L2
Sample answers include:
I. What is the geologic time scale?
  A. Timeline of Earth's history
    1. Includes geologic events and events in the history of life
    2. Absolute dates added in 20th century
II. Structure of the time scale
  A. Divided into eons, eras, periods, and epochs
    1. First three eons = 88% of Earth's history
    2. More divisions in Phanerozoic because of fossil evidence and better rock record

LESSON 12.4

2 INSTRUCT

Use Visuals L1

Figure 20 Make enlarged copies of the time scale so that all students can read it easily. Ask students to identify the era, period, and epoch in which they live. *(era: Cenozoic; period: Quaternary; epoch: Holocene)* **Ask:** When did the Holocene Epoch begin? *(0.01 million years ago)*
Visual

Integrate Language Arts L2

Recorded history is generally thought to have begun with the Sumerians, who developed cuneiform writing some 5000 years ago. **Ask:** Assuming that Earth is about 4.5 billion years old, what percentage of geologic time is represented by recorded history? *(approximately 0.000001 percent)*
Logical

Eon	Era	Period	Epoch	Millions of years ago
Phanerozoic	Cenozoic	Quaternary	Holocene	0.01
			Pleistocene	2.6
		Neogene	Pliocene	5.3
		(Tertiary)	Miocene	23.0
			Oligocene	33.9
		Paleogene	Eocene	55.8
			Paleocene	65.5
	Mesozoic	Cretaceous		145.5
		Jurassic		199.6
		Triassic		251
	Paleozoic	Permian		299
		Carboniferous / Pennsylvanian		318
		Mississippian		359
		Devonian		416
		Silurian		444
		Ordovician		488
		Cambrian		542
Precambrian		Proterozoic		2500
		Archean		~4000
		Hadean		~4600

FIGURE 20 The Geologic Time Scale This figure is not drawn to scale. The Phanerozoic makes up only about 12 percent of Earth's history. The Phanerozoic eon is broken into more subdivisions than earlier eons because scientists have more data to work with.

Structure of the Time Scale

The geologic time scale is divided into eons, eras, periods, and epochs. **Eons represent the longest intervals of geologic time. Eons are divided into eras. Each era is subdivided into periods. Finally, periods are divided into still smaller units called epochs.** The primary divisions of the time scale are shown in **Figure 20.** In general, divisions between time scale units mark major geologic events, evolutionary changes, or both.

Each division of the time scale has a name. Usually, the name comes from either the area where rocks of the age were first found or from some unique characteristic of the rocks. For example, Jurassic refers to the Jura Mountains of France and Switzerland. The Carboniferous is named for the large coal deposits that formed during that period. *Carboniferous* means "carbon bearing."

Eons Geologists divide Earth's history into four long units called **eons.** About 88 percent of geologic time is made up of the first three of these eons—the Hadean, Archaean, and Proterozoic. During these eons, Earth formed, the atmosphere and oceans developed, and early life evolved. Another term for this long time span is **Precambrian time.**

Precambrian fossils are scarce. One reason for this is that there is very little Precambrian rock at the surface. Over billions of years, most Precambrian rocks have not only been buried by layers and layers of younger rock, but much has also been eroded or metamorphosed, destroying or altering fossils. In addition, for most of Earth's history, life existed only as single-celled organisms, which do not leave easily identifiable fossils. Only very late in the Precambrian did multicelled organisms evolve in the oceans.

About 540 million years ago, the Phanerozoic eon began. The term *Phanerozoic* comes from the Greek words meaning "visible life." The term is appropriate because the rocks of this eon contain abundant fossils. These fossils document the evolution of more complex life forms.

Notice on the time scale the many subdivisions of the Phanerozoic. These subdivisions reflect the large amount of data that geologists have about the rocks and fossils of the Phanerozoic in comparison with data from earlier eons.

Differentiated Instruction

SPECIAL NEEDS For students who have difficulty absorbing large blocks of text, use Figure 20 as a visual aid as you discuss the geologic time divisions. Consider adding benchmarks to the time scale to help students recall the various geologic divisions. For example, you could point out that mass extinctions mark the end of both the Paleozoic and Mesozoic eras. The first fish appear in the fossil record in the Ordovician Period; the first land plants appear in the Silurian Period.

Eras There are three **eras** within the Phanerozoic eon: the Paleozoic, Mesozoic, and Cenozoic eras. *Paleozoic* comes from the Greek words for "ancient life." Most of the major groups of modern organisms, including insects, vertebrates (animals with backbones), and nonflowering plants, evolved during this era. *Mesozoic* means "middle life." During the Mesozoic era, flowering plants evolved and many types of reptiles, including dinosaurs and marine reptiles (**Figure 21**), became abundant. Mammals also evolved during the Mesozoic. The fossil record shows that the Paleozoic and Mesozoic eras both ended with dramatic, worldwide changes in life forms. Many types of organisms became extinct. *Cenozoic* means "recent life." During the Cenozoic era, many different types of mammals and birds evolved, and flowering plants became abundant.

Periods and Epochs Each era is subdivided into **periods.** Different geologic events, environmental conditions, and life forms characterize each period. Traditionally, geologists divided the Cenozoic era into two periods: the Tertiary and Quaternary. Today, most geologists divide the Cenozoic into the Paleogene, Neogene, and Quaternary, as shown in Figure 20.

Periods are divided into still smaller units called **epochs.** You will notice that there are many named epochs within the periods of the Cenozoic era. This again reflects how much data are available about the recent past. The periods of the Mesozoic and Paleozoic eras are also divided in epochs, though they are not usually referred to by specific names. Instead, the terms *early, middle,* and *late* are generally applied to the epochs of these earlier periods.

FIGURE 21 Mesozoic Life Not all life forms in the Mesozoic were big like the dinosaurs. This marine reptile from the Triassic, *Keichousaurus hiu,* was less than a foot long.

12.4 Assessment

Review Key Concepts

1. What is the geologic time scale?

2. What subdivisions make up the geologic time scale?

3. How is the geologic time scale today different from the geologic time scale developed by geologists in the 1800s?

4. Why are there more subdivisions of the time scale for the Phanerozoic eon than for earlier eons?

Think Critically

5. **Interpret Diagrams** To which era does each of the following periods belong: Ordovician, Tertiary, Permian, Triassic?

6. **Calculate** What percentage of geologic time is made up of the Cenozoic era?

WRITING IN SCIENCE

7. **Define** Research one of the periods of the geologic time scale. Write a definition of the period that includes the name of the era to which the period belongs, when the period began and ended, one major event from the period, and an explanation of its name.

Geologic Time **355**

Assessment Answers

1. The geologic time scale divides Earth's history into units that each represent specific amounts of time.
2. eons, eras, periods, and epochs
3. During the 1800s, the geologic time scale was based on relative ages of the rock record. During the 1900s, absolute ages based on radiometric dating were added to the time scale.

4. There is more information in the rock and fossil record about the geologic events of this eon than there is about previous eons. Geologists base subdivisions of the time scale on these events.
5. Paleozoic, Cenozoic, Paleozoic, Mesozoic
6. About 1.4 percent

7. Check that students' definitions contain the requested information about the geologic period.

FOSSIL OCCURRENCE AND THE AGE OF ROCKS L2

Objective
After completing this activity, students will be able to use fossils to assign relative dates to rocks and rock sequences.

> ### Address **Misconceptions** L2

Many people mistakenly think that "cavemen" and dinosaurs coexisted. Remind students that dinosaurs went extinct about 65 million years ago. Have them use the geologic time scale to pinpoint the period that marks the extinction of the dinosaurs. *(Cretaceous)* The species name for humans is *Homo sapiens. Homo sapiens* belong to the group of primates called hominids. Hominids made their first appearance in the fossil record approximately 4.4 million years ago. Have students use the geologic time scale to determine which period marks the appearance of hominids. *(Tertiary)* Students should recognize that tens of millions of years separate the last of the dinosaurs from the earliest human ancestors.
Logical

Skills Interpret Diagrams, Graph, Form a Hypothesis, Infer

Prep Time 5 minutes

Class Time 45 minutes

Teaching Tips
- Encourage students to work in pairs or small groups to complete this investigation.
- To save time, you can plot the data on a graph on the board. Have different volunteers plot the range data for different fossils.
- Have students refer back to Figure 10 on p. 344 for guidance in plotting the range data.

Questioning Strategies
Ask: Which geologic principles are particularly useful for correlating fossils to rock units? *(the law of superposition and the principle of fossil succession)* Which type of fossils do geologists look for when attempting to date rock units? *(index fossils)*

Expected Outcome Students should be able to use the graph to determine the relative age of a rock unit.

Fossil Occurrence and the Age of Rocks

Problem How can the occurrence of fossils and their known age ranges be used to date rocks?

Materials geologic time scale, graph paper, pencil

Skills Interpret Diagrams, Graph, Form a Hypothesis, Infer

Connect to the Big idea Groups of fossil organisms occur in the rock record for specific intervals of time. This time interval is called the fossil's *range.* Knowing the range of the fossils of specific organisms, or groups of organisms, can be used to find the relative age of rock layers. In this laboratory exercise, you will use such information to assign a date to a hypothetical unit of rock.

Procedure
1. A section of rock made up of layers of limestone and shale has been studied and samples have been taken. A large variety of fossils were collected from the rock samples. Use a sheet of graph paper to make a bar graph using the information shown in the Fossil Data Table. Begin by listing the types of fossils on the horizontal axis. Use the figure on the next page to list the units of the geologic time scale on the vertical axis.

2. Transfer the range data of each fossil onto your graph. Draw an X in each box, beginning at the oldest occurrence of the organism up to the youngest occurrence. Shade in the marked boxes. You will end up with bars depicting the geologic ranges of each of the fossils listed.

3. Examine your graph. Are there any time units that contain all of the fossils listed? Write this time period at the bottom of the graph.

Fossil Data Table			
	Type of Fossil	Oldest occurrence	Youngest occurrence
1	Foraminifera	Silurian	Quaternary
2	Bryozoan	Silurian	Permian
3	Gastropod	Devonian	Pennsylvanian
4	Brachiopod	Silurian	Mississippian
5	Bivalve	Silurian	Permian
6	Gastropod	Ordovician	Devonian
7	Trilobite	Silurian	Devonian
8	Ostracod	Devonian	Tertiary
9	Brachiopod	Cambrian	Devonian

Sample Data

	1	2	3	4	5	6	7	8	9
Neogene/Quaternary	x								
Paleogene	x							x	
Cretaceous	x							x	
Jurassic	x							x	
Triassic	x							x	
Permian	x	x			x			x	
Pennsylvanian	x	x	x		x			x	
Mississippian	x	x	x	x	x			x	
Devonian	x	x	x	x	x	x	x	x	x
Silurian	x	x			x	x	x		x
Ordovician						x			x
Cambrian									x

Analyze and Conclude

1. **Interpret Graphs** What is the age of the hypothetical rock layer that these fossils were collected from?

2. **Infer** Based on the age determined, do you think that this group of fossils could be considered index fossils? Why or why not?

3. **Infer** Suppose that the particular trilobite listed in line 7 of the data table is limited to rocks of lower Devonian age and that these trilobite fossils are widespread throughout North America. Can this fossil be considered an index fossil? Why or why not?

4. **Explain** The fossils in this group were collected from limestone and shale rocks. Based on what you have learned about the formation of these rock types, what type of environment did these organisms live in?

5. **Infer** Shale often contains fossils of leaves. If the gastropods listed in line 3 and line 6 were collected from shale containing leaf fossils, could you use radiocarbon dating to assign a numerical date to this rock unit? Explain.

GO FURTHER Use the library or Internet to research these fossils. Find out how some of them are used in the oil industry or the cosmetics industry.

The Geologic Time Scale

Eon	Era	Period	Epoch	Millions of years ago
Phanerozoic	Cenozoic	Quaternary	Holocene	0.01
			Pleistocene	2.6
		Neogene (Tertiary)	Pliocene	5.3
			Miocene	23.0
		Paleogene (Tertiary)	Oligocene	33.9
			Eocene	55.8
			Paleocene	65.5
	Mesozoic	Cretaceous		145.5
		Jurassic		199.6
		Triassic		251
	Paleozoic	Permian		299
		Carboniferous — Pennsylvanian		318
		Carboniferous — Mississippian		359
		Devonian		416
		Silurian		444
		Ordovician		488
		Cambrian		542
Pre-cambrian	Proterozoic			2500
	Archean			~4000
	Hadean			~4600

Geologic Time **357**

Analyze and Conclude

1. The age of the rock unit is Devonian (359 to 416 million years ago).
2. No, because the age is Devonian which covers 31 million years. In terms of geologic time, this is too long to meet the requirements for an index fossil.
3. Yes, because it is widespread, which indicates that it was abundant, and it lived over a short geologic time span.
4. The environment was an ocean.
5. No, radiocarbon methods can only be used on materials that are less than 75,000 years old. The gastropods are much older than that.

GO FURTHER

Sample answer: *Foraminifera* are used to aid oil exploration.
Kinesthetic, Portfolio

21st Century Learning

Self Direction

How old are the rocks where you live?

Encourage students to use the Web or local resources to learn about the geology in your area. **Ask:** How old is the bedrock where you live? Does it consist of a range of ages? Does the rock contain fossils?

Instruct students to use a map of your area to label layers of rock. Students should label each layer with its age and the geologic era in which it was formed. Provide class time for students to present their maps.

Homework Guide

Lesson	Questions
12.1	1, 2, 7, 9–10, 12–15, 28, 29, 32
12.2	3, 6, 16–19, 26, 31, 33
12.3	4, 8, 11, 20–25, 27, 30, 34
12.4	5

12 Study Guide

Big idea ▶ Earth History

12.1 Discovering Earth's History

🔑 Uniformitarianism is the idea that the physical, chemical, and biological laws that operate today also operated in the past.

🔑 The law of superposition, the principle of original horizontality, the principle of cross-cutting relationships, unconformities, and inclusions all help determine the relative ages of rock layers.

🔑 Scientists correlate rock layers at different locations to piece together a more complete interpretation of the rock record.

uniformitarianism (336)
relative dating (337)
law of superposition (337)
principle of original horizontality (338)
principle of cross-cutting relationships (338)
unconformity (339)
correlation (340)

12.2 Fossils: Evidence of Past Life

🔑 The different types of fossils include petrified fossils, molds and casts, compressions, impressions, unaltered remains, and trace fossils.

🔑 Two conditions that favor preservation of an organism as a fossil are rapid burial and the possession of hard parts.

🔑 Fossils enable scientists to correlate rock layers and infer past environments, and they provide evidence for evolution.

🔑 According to natural selection, traits that improve an individual's chance for survival and reproduction will be passed on more frequently to future generations than traits that do not.

extinct (342)
fossil (342)
principle of fossil succession (344)
index fossil (345)
evolution (345)
natural selection (345)
adaptation (345)

12.3 Dating with Radioactivity

🔑 During radioactive decay, unstable atomic nuclei spontaneously break apart, or decay, releasing energy.

🔑 In radiometric dating, scientists measure the ratio between the radioactive parent isotope and the daughter products in a sample to be dated. The older the sample, the more daughter product it contains.

🔑 When an organism dies, the amount of carbon-14 gradually decreases as the carbon-14 decays. By comparing the ratio of carbon-14 to carbon-12 in a sample, radiocarbon dates can be determined.

🔑 To determine the age of sedimentary rock, geologists must relate the sedimentary rock to datable masses of igneous rock.

radioactivity (347)
half-life (348)
radiometric dating (348)
radiocarbon dating (350)

12.4 The Geologic Time Scale

🔑 The geologic time scale is a record that includes both geologic events and major developments in the evolution of life

🔑 Eons represent the longest intervals of geologic time. Eons are divided into eras. Each era is subdivided into periods. Finally, periods are divided into still smaller units called epochs.

geologic time scale (353)
eon (354)
Precambrian time (354)
era (355)
period (355)
epoch (355)

Assessment Answers

Review Content

1. a	**2.** b	**3.** d
4. d	**5.** b	**6.** c
7. b	**8.** b	**9.** a
10. d	**11.** d	

Understand Concepts

12. The rate at which they occur and their relative importance may have changed.
13. These are the only rocks that are laid down horizontally, except for igneous rock extrusive lava flows, ash flows, and falls.
14. The rock that is cut or broken by an intrusion or fault is older than that intrusion or fault.

12 Assessment

Review Content

Choose the letter that best answers the question or completes the statement.

1. What principle states that the physical, chemical, and biological laws that operate today have also operated in the geologic past?
   a. uniformitarianism
   b. theory of evolution
   c. principle of original horizontality
   d. law of superposition

2. What is the name of the process that matches rocks of similar ages in different regions?
   a. indexing
   b. correlation
   c. succession
   d. superposition

3. What name is given to fossils that are both widespread geographically and abundant in number, but are limited to a short span of time in the fossil record?
   a. key   c. relative
   b. succeeding   d. index

4. What is the name of the process during which atomic nuclei decay?
   a. fusion   c. nucleation
   b. correlation   d. radioactivity

5. Which unit of geologic time is the greatest span of time?
   a. era   c. period
   b. eon   d. epoch

6. What are remains or traces of prehistoric life called?
   a. indicators   c. fossils
   b. replicas   d. fissures

7. What name is given to layers of tilted rocks that are overlain by younger, more flat-lying rock layers?
   a. disconformity
   b. angular unconformity
   c. nonconformity
   d. fault

8. What are atoms with the same atomic number but different mass numbers called?
   a. protons   c. ions
   b. isotopes   d. nucleotides

9. Which of Steno's principles states that most layers of sediments are deposited in flat-lying layers?
   a. original horizontality
   b. cross-cutting relationships
   c. fossil succession
   d. superposition

10. What name is given to pieces of rock that are contained within another, younger rock?
    a. intrusions   c. hosts
    b. interbeds   d. inclusions

11. About how old is Earth?
    a. 400,000 years   c. 5.8 million years
    b. 4.0 million years d. 4.5 billion years

Understand Concepts

12. How have the processes that affect Earth's surface changed through time?

13. Why does the law of superposition apply primarily to sedimentary rocks?

14. How are cross-cutting relationships used in relative dating?

15. How do unconformities form?

16. List and briefly describe three different types of fossils.

17. What two conditions increase an organism's chance of becoming a fossil?

18. What did Darwin propose as the mechanism of evolution? Explain.

19. How can certain fossils, such as corals, be used to indicate water temperatures of the past?

20. What is a half-life?

21. Explain how radioactivity and radiometric dating are related.

22. Why can't radiometric dating be used with accuracy on metamorphic rocks?

20. Half-life is the amount of time necessary for one half of the nuclei in a sample of radioactive material to decay to its stable isotope.
21. Radiometric dating makes use of the known decay rates of some radioactive isotopes.
22. Radioactive decay begins as soon as a radioactive mineral is formed. When such a mineral is metamorphosed, it can lose its daughter products. Dating this mineral would result in a younger date than actually is correct.

15. Unconformities form when deposition stops and/or surfaces are eroded, thus leaving a gap in the rock record.
16. Sample answer: Petrified fossils occur when minerals precipitate and fill in spaces within tissue, eventually replacing all of the organic matter. Molds form when an organism is buried and dissolves, preserving only the shape and surface structures. Unaltered remains occur when fossilization preserves all or part of an organism with very little change, such as when an organism is trapped in tree resin that hardens to form amber.

17. the presence of hard parts and rapid burial after death
18. According to Darwin, evolution occurred through the process of natural selection. In natural selection, organisms that are well adapted to their environment survive and pass on their traits to the next generation more frequently than those that are less well-adapted.
19. Some corals live in warm waters today. Using the theory of uniformitarianism, scientists can infer that some fossil corals must have lived in warm waters, too.

ASSESSMENT

Think Critically

23. Relative dating correlates rock layers based on their positions. There is no computation involved; it is all based on observation in the field. Radiometric dating involves calculations and is done in a laboratory.

24. The half-life of carbon-14 is 5730 years.

25. The dates are calculated using the ratio of parent-to-daughter materials. If the system is open and some of the daughter material escapes or some parent material is added, the ratio will not accurately reflect the amount of time that has elapsed.

26. These fossils would have thick, robust shells that could withstand the high energy of the breaking waves.

27. Decay rates do not vary.

Analyze Data

28. Fault A is older because it does not cut through the conglomerate layer, whereas Fault B does.

29. Intrusion B is older because it does not cut through the conglomerate layer, whereas Intrusion A does.

30. Two half-lives have passed; the sample is approximately 2.6 billion years old.

Concepts in Action

31. You can use radiocarbon dating to assign an age to the fossil and decaying plant remains.

32. Sample answer: A modern coastline has sand along the shore, with clams and other shelled organisms living in the sand. If the sequence of rock under study is made of sandstone or limestone with fossils, this may indicate that it once was a shoreline such as the one described above.

33. The adaptations that enabled the organism to survive on the tropical island would not help it survive the cooler, drier conditions. As a result, the organism will probably become extinct unless it evolves new adaptations that enable it to survive the new conditions.

34. We would need to wait 6 half-lives, or 27 billion years.

Think Critically

23. Compare and Contrast Compare the techniques of relative dating to those of radioactive decay dating.

24. Draw Conclusions Why can't carbon-14 be used to date material that is older than 75,000 years?

25. Explain Why is it important to have a closed system when using radioactive decay dating?

26. Predict An analysis of some sedimentary rocks suggests the environment was close to the shoreline where high energy waves hit the shore. Corals and shelled organisms lived here. Describe what their fossils would be like.

27. Apply Concepts Why is radiometric dating the most reliable method of dating events and formations from the geologic past?

Analyze Data

Refer to the diagram to answer Questions 28 and 29.

Conglomerate

Sandstone

Fault A

Intrusion A

Fault B

Intrusion B

Intrusion C

28. Apply Concepts Which fault is older, A or B? Explain how you know.

29. Apply Concepts Which intrusion is older, A or B? Explain how you know.

30. Calculate A sample of potassium-40 has a mass of 12.5 grams. If the sample originally had 50 grams of potassium-40 at the start of radioactive decay, how many half-lives have passed? The half-life of potassium-40 is 1.3 billion years. How old is the sample?

Concepts in Action

31. Apply Concepts Fossilized human remains are sometimes found in bogs in northwestern Europe. These bogs are wet, low-oxygen areas that contain decaying plant material. How would you go about dating such a fossil?

32. Compare and Contrast Apply the concept of uniformitarianism to explain how a particular sequence of rock layers could be interpreted as a former ocean coastline. (*Hint:* compare what you might see at a modern shoreline to what you would see in the rocks).

33. Predict An organism evolves with certain adaptations for survival on a wet, tropical island. Over millions of years, plate movements shift the island into a cooler, drier climate. What might happen to this type of organism over time?

34. Calculate Nuclear power plants produce radioactive waste that must be stored properly until it is no longer harmful to life on Earth. Uranium-238 has a half-life of 4.5 billion years. If, in order to be safe, a uranium sample must decay to 1/64 of its original amount, for how many years must the waste be stored?

Performance-Based Assessment

Communicate Create a poster illustrating the different ways that fossils can form. Be sure to include altered and unaltered remains with examples of both. If possible, include samples of fossils that are found in your area.

Performance-Based Assessment

Student posters should include the different types of fossils discussed in Lesson 12.2, including petrified remains, molds and casts, compression fossils, impression fossils, unaltered remains, and trace fossils. Direct students to appropriate Internet sites or a local library or museum for information about fossils found in your area.

Standardized Test Prep

Use the diagram above to answer Question 1. Choose the letter that best answers the question.

1 When were rock layers A through D uplifted and tilted?
A after deposition of Layer G
B after deposition of Layer F and before deposition of Layer G
C after deposition of Layer D and before deposition of Layer E
D after deposition of Layer A and before deposition of Layer G

2 Whose work became the foundation for the principle of uniformitarianism?
F Charles Darwin
G James Hutton
H William Smith
J Louis Agassiz

3 Using relative dating methods, which of the following are scientists able to do?
A Identify the order in which rock units formed.
B Assign a numerical date to each rock layer studied.
C Determine the age of the fossils within each layer.
D Identify what rock types are present.

Use the diagram below to answer Question 4.

4 How can you tell that intrusion C is older than fault H?
F The top of Intrusion C is eroded.
G Intrusion C is broken by Fault H.
H Fault H ends at the eroded Layer E.
J Both Intrusion C and Fault H end at Layer E.

If You Have Trouble With . . .

Question	1	2	3	4
See Lesson	12.1	12.1	12.1	12.1

Standardized Test Prep
1 C
2 G
3 A
4 G

13 Earth's History Planning Guide

Lesson Objectives		Activities
13.1 Precambrian Time, pp. 364–368 **13.1 Describe** the major geologic developments of Precambrian time. **13.2 Describe** the major evolutionary developments during Precambrian time.		
13.2 The Paleozoic Era, pp. 369–376 **13.3 List** the kinds of environmental changes that have affected the evolution of life over geologic time. **13.4 Describe** the major geologic and evolutionary developments during the Paleozoic era.		**TE** Build Science Skills, p. 375 L2
13.3 The Mesozoic Era, pp. 377–381 **13.5 Describe** the major geologic and evolutionary developments during the Mesozoic era. **13.6 Explain** the cause of the mass extinction at the end of the Mesozoic era.		**TE** Teacher Demo: Forming the Rocky Mountains, p. 379 L2 **TE** Build Science Skills, p. 380 L2
13.4 The Cenozoic Era, pp. 382–385 **13.7 Explain** why mammals became widespread and successful in the Cenozoic era. **13.8 Describe** the major geologic and evolutionary developments during the Cenozoic era.		
Chapter Features and Labs		
Try It What Are Fossils? p. 363		**LM** Determining Geologic Ages L1
Exploration Lab Modeling the Geologic Time Scale, pp. 386–3871		

Ability Levels		Components			
L1	For students who need additional help	SE	Student Edition	LP	Lesson Plans
L2	For all students	TE	Teacher's Edition	AA	Active Art
L3	For students who need to be challenged	LM	Laboratory Manual	PD	Planet Diary
		CT	Chapter Tests	GEODe	Geode CD-ROM
		GRSW	Guided Reading & Study Workbook	eText	
		CTB	Computer Test Bank		

Resources	Lesson Assessment
GRSW Lesson 13.1 **LP** Lesson Planning 13.1 **GEODe** Geologic Time: Geologic Time Scale	**SE** Lesson 13.1 Assessment, p. 368 **eText** Lesson 13.1
GRSW Lesson 13.2 **LP** Lesson Planning 13.2 **AA** Continental Drift **PD** Cretaceous Extinction	**SE** Lesson 13.2 Assessment, p. 376 **eText** Lesson 13.2
GRSW Lesson 13.3 **LP** Lesson Planning 13.3	**SE** Lesson 13.3 Assessment, p. 381 **eText** Lesson 13.3
GRSW Lesson 13.4 **LP** Lesson Planning 13.4	**SE** Lesson 13.4 Assessment, p. 385 **eText** Lesson 13.3

Materials for Activities and Labs

Quantities for each group

STUDENT EDITION

Try It, p. 363
a variety of fossil images or replicas

Exploration Lab, p. 386–387
strip of adding machine paper measuring 5 m or longer, meter-stick or metric measuring tape, pencil

TEACHER'S EDITION

Build Science Skills, p. 375
blackline master of an unlabeled world map for photocopying

Teacher Demo, p. 379
student textbook, towel slightly wider than the textbook

Build Science Skills, p. 380
set of pictures of large reptiles and dinosaurs such as pterosaurs, crocodilians, iguanas, plesiosaurs, raptors, stegosaurs, sauropods, and mosasaurs

Assessment

CHAPTER ASSESSMENT
SE Assessment, pp. 389–390
CT Chapter 13 Test
CTB Chapter 13
eText Chapter 13

21st Century Learning

Interpersonal and Collaborative Skills: What caused the Permian mass extinction? TE p. 391

Common Themes

The rock and fossil records reveal a fascinating history of continental motions and evolution of life. Because there are more rocks and hard-bodied fossils of recent ages, our understanding of recent history is better than that of ancient history.

Space and Time In the Precambrian, the primitive continental crust formed, single-celled and multicelled life evolved, and photosynthetic organisms enriched the atmosphere with oxygen.

The supercontinent Pangaea formed in the Paleozoic era. Almost all major phyla can trace their origins to the famous "Cambrian explosion." By the end of the era, the seas were full of fishes and groups plants and animals had adapted to fully terrestrial lifestyles. The Permian extinction brought the Paleozoic era to a close. It was the single most devastating extinction in Earth history.

The Mesozoic is famous for its reptiles, including the dinosaurs, though mammals made their first appearance in the Mesozoic. Pangaea broke apart during this era and the climate was generally mild. The Mesozoic ended with a mass extinction, most likely triggered by a meteoroid impact.

Ice ages characterize the generally cool Cenozoic era. Mammals diversified and modern humans evolved.

Forces and Motion Earth's resources will last longer if they are carefully managed, a process called conservation. There is a growing awareness of the need for conservation, including efforts to reduce consumption and to reuse and recycle resources where possible.

Matter and Energy A variety of factors including heat flow, volcanism, and atmosphere-ocean feedbacks have allowed the continuous existence of liquid water on Earth's surface, and therefore the continuous existence of life for almost 4 billion years.

Michael Wysession
Washington University

EARTH SCIENCE REFRESHER

Earth as a System The fossil record shows a general trend toward an increasing level of complexity of life-forms. Life has diversified to take advantage of every environmental niche available.

The Evolution of Life

There are two ways to look at the overall picture of the evolution of life. One way is to view the process as including a general increase in complexity. Certainly humans are much more complex systems than the single-celled bacteria and archaea that comprised life during its first few billion years. Surely, the ability to create something like Beethoven's Ninth Symphony has to count for something. However, if life is viewed from a genetic point of view, a very different picture emerges. A tremendous amount of genetic diversity is seen at the single-celled level, but all of multicellular life is genetically similar—variations on a few successful themes.

If life-forms are plotted on a tree that shows the differences between their genetic RNA (ribonucleic acid) makeups, an unusual picture emerges. This tree of life has three main branches: archaea, bacteria, and eukarya. The archaea and bacteria are both simple single-celled organisms called prokaryotes (simple, because they have no cell nuclei). The eukarya are more advanced single-celled organisms, which evolved about a billion

> **Address Misconceptions**
>
> *Students often think that all large reptiles were dinosaurs.* Dinosaurs are one subgroup of reptiles that have certain characteristics in common such as their hip structure and how they walk. For a strategy that helps to overcome this misconception, see **Address Misconceptions on TE p. 380.**

Students often think that early life consisted primarily of plants and animals. Simple single-celled organisms such as bacteria and algae were the first life-forms and came into existence long before plants and animals. For a strategy that helps to overcome this misconception, see **Address Misconceptions on TE p. 386.**

years ago. Where are humans? Humans, along with all other multicellular life forms are on a tiny twig at the far end of the eukarya branch. It seems that life experimented with many different biochemical ways of making single-celled organisms. But when something worked well, it evolved rapidly into the large multicellular plants and animals that we see around us. Genetically speaking, however, these are all similar. We share more than 99 percent of our genes with chimpanzees, more than 90 percent of our genes with mice, and even large numbers of genes with organisms like fruit flies and yeast.

A similar situation was found with fossils from the Cambrian period, when invertebrate life dramatically diversified. Fossils that date from this time, about 540 million years ago, show many bizarre life-forms that have no living equivalents today. With little competition for resources, there were more types of life in existence. However, when a few life-forms did very well, they outcompeted the other life-forms, which became extinct. An analogy would be the many different kinds of flying machines that were proposed and tried about a century ago. Most of today's planes, however, are variations on the most successful model, which is why they look so similar.

One of the species found from the Cambrian period was a flatworm called *Pikaia*, which had a primitive spinal cord structure. All of vertebrate animals—fish, mammals, dinosaurs, snakes, birds, and even humans—could well be simply variations of a single very successful body type that first appeared in a 540-million year old flatworm.

BUILD READING LITERACY
Use Prior Knowledge

Linking New Learning to Familiar Concepts

Strategy Help students construct meaning by linking new information to familiar concepts. Some references indicate that activating prior knowledge is the most important of all reading strategies. Choose a section from Chapter 13, such as pp. 364–368, to use in modeling this strategy.

Example

1. Have students turn to the pre-selected section, read the opening paragraph, and survey the headings and visuals. Ask students to recount experiences they have had with the topic, and what they already know or believe they know about each subheading. Write student responses on the board. If noticeable misconceptions arise during this discussion, begin to address them immediately.

2. Have students generate and write several questions or predictions about the topic, based on their prior knowledge.

3. Ask students to read the section with the purpose of answering their questions or confirming or refuting their predictions. Divide the section into several parts, and have students pause after each part to evaluate or revise predictions.

4. After reading, discuss with students the information they learned. Discuss any new understandings that refute their prior misconceptions.

5. Repeat the process for the chapter's remaining sections.

See TE p. 378 for a script on how to use this strategy with students. For additional strategies, see TE pp. 365, 366, 369, 372, 373, and 383.

ASSESS PRIOR KNOWLEDGE

Use the Chapter Pretest below to assess students' prior knowledge. As needed, review these concepts.

Review Science Concepts

Lesson 13.1 Reviewing that Earth's history is broken into periods and eras based on fossil evidence will help students understand the reasoning behind the geologic time scale. Reviewing the law of superposition will help students understand why Precambrian rocks are rarely exposed at the surface.

Lesson 13.2 Students will need to know that *arid* means "dry" and be able to describe an arid climate so they can understand why certain organisms developed the way they did. Remembering that trees need water, sunlight, and carbon dioxide to survive will help students understand why trees developed when they did and why certain adaptations were beneficial.

Lesson 13.3 Remembering that convection currents in the mantle result in rifts where new oceanic crust is created will help students understand why Pangaea broke apart.

Lesson 13.4 Review with students that in order to reproduce, plants must have a way to get their seeds to another location. Some of the mechanisms of seed dispersal are transport by wind, water, or animals. Reviewing these concepts will help students understand why certain angiosperm adaptations were so significant.

13 Earth's History

Big idea Earth History

Q: How has life on Earth changed through time?

362

Chapter Pretest

1. On what basis is Earth's geologic time scale divided into periods and eras? *(c)*
  a. erosion rates **b.** rock type
  c. fossil evidence **d.** landscape features

2. The law of superposition states that if rock layers have not been overturned, *(a)*
  a. the oldest rock layers are found on the bottom.
  b. the oldest rock layers are found on the top.

  c. the youngest rock layers are found under igneous intrusions.

3. What would you be likely to find in an arid climate? *(b)*
  a. many swamps **b.** vast deserts
  c. large forests

4. What do trees require to perform photosynthesis? *(d)*
  a. water **b.** sunlight
  c. carbon dioxide **d.** all of the above

5. What can cause a continent to break apart? *(a)*
  a. convection currents in the mantle
  b. tsunami
  c. erosion

6. What are some of the ways in which seeds can be carried away from the parent plant? *(by wind, water, and animals)*

Fossil fern

WHAT ARE FOSSILS?

Procedure

1. Your teacher will provide a variety of fossil images or replicas. Observe each one carefully.
2. Share the fossils with your classmates so that you can observe several examples.

Think About It

1. **Observe** What kinds of organisms do the fossils show? What can you infer about the ancient organisms from these fossils?
2. **Infer** How do you think these fossils were formed? What conditions were necessary for their formation?

363

ENGAGE/EXPLORE

WHAT ARE FOSSILS?   L2

Purpose In this activity, students infer the conditions under which an organism lived based on its fossil and imagine the conditions necessary to create a fossil.

Skills Observe, Infer

Prep Time 5 minutes

Materials a variety of fossil images or replicas

Class Time 10 minutes

Teaching Tip Have students make a data table to record their observations and inferences. Columns could include the name of the fossil, when it lived, a sketch of the fossil, and/or the environment where this organism probably lived.

Expected Outcome Students will observe a variety of fossils and make inferences about where the organisms lived and how the fossils were created.

Think About It

1. Answers will depend on the fossils observed. Students should make inferences about the environment where the organism lived.
2. The organism died, was buried in sediment, then the sediment solidified into a rock. A moist environment with fine-grained sediments is necessary to fossil formation.

13.1 Precambrian Time

Lesson Objectives
13.1 **Describe** the major geologic developments of Precambrian time.

13.2 **Describe** the major evolutionary developments during Precambrian time.

Build Vocabulary `L2`
Making Flashcards Have students make flashcards for the vocabulary terms in this lesson and other terms that are new to them, such as *Precambrian*.

Reading Strategy `L2`
1. oxygen
2. shields
3. stromatolites
4. multicellular life

Key Questions

🔑 **What were the major geologic developments during Precambrian time?**

🔑 **What were the major evolutionary developments during Precambrian time?**

Vocabulary
- shield • photosynthesis
- stromatolite • prokaryote
- eukaryote

Reading Strategy
Identify Details As you read the lesson, look for the terms that correctly complete the sentences below.

1. Earth's early atmosphere lacked significant amounts of __?__.
2. Geologists have identified large areas of Precambrian rocks called __?__ on every continent.
3. Ancient cyanobacteria formed the most common Precambrian fossils, known as __?__.
4. The Ediacaran fauna contain the earliest known examples of __?__.

FIGURE 1 Isua Greenstone
These metamorphic rocks found in Greenland are among the oldest known rocks on Earth.

EARTH IS the only place in the universe, as far as we know, that supports life. Life on Earth is everywhere. It is found in boiling hot springs, in the deepest parts of the ocean, and even under the Antarctic ice sheet. But how long is the history of life on Earth? Some scientists interpret traces of carbon in Greenland's ancient Isua greenstone rocks as evidence that life existed as long as 3.8 billion years ago. But other scientists who studied these rocks concluded that the carbon probably was not from living things. More concrete evidence are microscopic fossils, which resemble present-day bacteria, that have been found in 3.5-billion-year-old rock. So, the best estimates put the origin of life at somewhere between 3.8 and 3.5 billion years ago.

Precambrian Earth
Earth's history is about 4.5 billion years long. Eighty-eight percent of this time—from Earth's formation to 542 million years ago—is contained within the Precambrian eon. Geologists know very little about this huge portion of Earth history. Most rocks from this time have been eroded away, subducted, or greatly metamorphosed. Relative dating of Precambrian rocks is difficult because the rocks rarely contain fossils and most Precambrian sedimentary layers have been metamorphosed. Yet key geologic events occurred during Precambrian time. 🔑 **Earth formed about 4.5 billion years ago. During Precambrian time, the atmosphere and oceans formed and plate tectonics began to build up continental landmasses.**

Earth Forms Scientists hypothesize that Earth formed as gravity pulled together dust, rock, and ice in space. As Earth grew, its gravity increased, pulling in more of these materials. The high-velocity impact of rocks from space caused Earth's temperature to steadily increase. In addition, radioactive decay generated enormous amounts of heat—much more heat than it does today. During this period of intense heat, iron, nickel, and other metals began to melt and sink toward Earth's center, forming its iron-rich core. Less-dense materials, such as silicates, floated in a magma ocean. Eventually, these less-dense materials solidified and produced Earth's primitive crust. Between the core and the crust, the solid mantle formed.

The Atmosphere Evolves As dense materials were forming Earth's core and primitive crust, the lightest materials escaped to form a primitive atmosphere. Today, the air you breathe is a stable mixture of nitrogen, oxygen, a small amount of argon, and trace amounts of carbon dioxide and water vapor. Our planet's original atmosphere was very different. It was made up of gases similar to those released in volcanic eruptions—water vapor, carbon dioxide, nitrogen, and several trace gases, but no oxygen.

Some of Earth's earliest life forms dramatically changed the makeup of Earth's atmosphere. About 3.5 billion years ago, bacteria began using carbon dioxide and releasing oxygen. The Precambrian rock record suggests that initially, much of this free oxygen combined with iron and formed iron oxides, or rust. Large deposits of iron-rich Precambrian sedimentary rocks, called *banded iron formations*, provide evidence of this process. As the amount of available iron decreased and the number of oxygen-producing organisms increased, oxygen began to accumulate in the atmosphere. Chemical analysis of Precambrian rocks suggests that a significant amount of oxygen had collected in the atmosphere as early as 2.2 billion years ago.

The Oceans Form Earth's oceans formed as the planet cooled. Water vapor condensed to form clouds, and great rains began. At first the rainwater evaporated in the hot air before reaching the ground or quickly boiled or evaporated when it did reach the ground. This evaporation sped up the cooling of Earth's surface. Torrential rains continued and slowly filled low areas, forming the oceans. About 4 billion years ago, as much as 90 percent of the current volume of seawater was contained in ocean basins. Weathered rock poured into the early ocean, depositing sediments on top of oceanic crust that became the ocean floor and salts that increased the salinity of the water. The early ocean also absorbed massive amounts of carbon dioxide, which left the atmosphere relatively rich in nitrogen.

FIGURE 2 Precambrian Time
Precambrian time represents about 88 percent of Earth's history. Numbers represent the approximate time, in millions of years before present that each division began.
Interpret Visuals *About how long ago did the Proterozoic begin?*

Phanerozoic	Cenozoic 65.1
	Mesozoic 251
	Paleozoic 542
Precambrian	Proterozoic 2500
	Archean ~4000
	Hadean*

Earth forms ~4500

Build Reading Literacy L1

Refer to **p. 446D** in **Chapter 16,** which provides guidelines for sequencing.

Sequence As students read The Atmosphere Evolves, ask them to construct a flowchart showing the steps from the formation of Earth's early atmosphere to today's atmosphere. *(Sample answer: Earth's outer shell melts → Earth's crust cools and solidifies, releasing volcanic gases → water vapor condenses into clouds → torrential rainfall → oceans form → water vapor and carbon dioxide fill the oceans leaving less of those gases in the atmosphere → a nitrogen-rich atmosphere results)*
Visual, Verbal

Answers

Figure 2 *about 2500 million years (2.5 billion years)*

Facts and Figures

EARLY EARTH Early in Earth's history, the planet was hot enough to be mostly, if not entirely, molten. The cause of the high temperatures within Earth's deep interior is mostly due to the intense pressures there (when you squeeze anything, its temperature increases), but some of it is due to the additional heat from impacts and radioactivity and the collapse of the core. Another factor that helped heat the early Earth was the impact of a Mars-sized proto-planet, which also caused the formation of the moon. Interestingly, once the molten mantle started to cool and solidify, it did so from the bottom up. This is because the high pressures at the bottom of the mantle favor a solid state (which takes up less volume). The last part of the mantle to solidify was the asthenosphere, just beneath the lithosphere.

FIGURE 3 Shields Remnants of Precambrian rocks form the continental shields shown here. Shields are largely made up of metamorphosed igneous and sedimentary rocks.

Earth's First Continents Earth's primitive crust was probably made of basalt, similar to the rock formed at today's mid-ocean ridges. Most geologists agree that movements of Earth's early mantle drove some type of platelike motion. According to one model, early continents formed as pieces of crust collided and stuck together. This process, known as *accretion,* shortened and thickened the areas of crust. Over time, accretion formed large crustal blocks called *cratons.* When exposed at the surface, these areas of Precambrian rock are called **shields.** Geologists have found shields on every modern continent, as shown in **Figure 3.**

By the end of the Precambrian eon, an estimated 85 percent of the modern continental crust had formed, but a lot of crust was also destroyed during this time. Crust can be lost by either weathering and erosion, or by subduction. Evidence suggests that during much of the Archean, thin slabs of continental crust were subducted into the mantle. However, by about 3 billion years ago, the early continents had grown thick enough to resist subduction. After that time, weathering and erosion became the primary processes of continental crust destruction. Sediment that resulted from these processes formed early sedimentary rocks.

Continental accretion does not stop once large landmasses form. Continents themselves can collide and attach to form supercontinents. Several supercontinents existed during the Precambrian. The earliest well-documented supercontinent, *Rodinia,* formed about 1.1 billion years ago. Rodinia began to split apart around 750 million years ago. Around this time, between 750 and 600 million years ago, Earth was in the midst of a global ice age. There is evidence of glaciation from this time on every continent.

366 Chapter 13 • Lesson 1

Facts and Figures

PREVIOUS SUPERCONTINENTS The continents have been moving around Earth's surface for at least 4 billion years, and on several occasions they have come together to form supercontinents. The geologic record is incomplete for Earth's early history, but the earliest supercontinent is referred to as *Vaalbara,* and it likely existed 3.1–2.8 billion years ago, and perhaps even earlier.

Later supercontinents include *Kenorland* (2.7–2.5 billion years ago), *Columbia* (1.8–1.5 billion years ago), *Rodinia* (1100–750 million years ago), and *Pannotia* (600–450 million years ago), and correspond to times when multiple mountain ranges (orogenic belts) formed as the result of plate collisions.

Precambrian Life

You would likely not describe the earliest microscopic fossils, called *microfossils,* as anything resembling an organism, though scientists are confident that they are indeed evidence of early bacteria. Fossils from the end of the Precambrian, however, are recognizably animals—odd animals, but certainly animals. Using fossils and other evidence, geologists have reconstructed the amazing evolution of Paleozoic life. **The earliest life probably evolved in the oceans, was single-celled, and did not require oxygen. By the end of the Precambrian, multicellular animals had evolved that required oxygen to live.** These evolutionary events did not happen quickly. There is about three billion years between the ages of the first single-celled fossil and the first fossil of a multicellular animal.

The Earliest Life Scientists do not know exactly when life appeared on Earth or what it looked like. However, they can infer that the earliest life probably evolved in the oceans because water is needed for most life processes. Some scientists think that the first organisms might have resembled the bacteria found near hydrothermal vents in the deep ocean.

Photosynthetic Organisms The first fossil organisms come from 3.5-billion-year-old Precambrian rocks. The fossils are of single-celled organisms that resemble modern-day cyanobacteria. These first organisms must not have required oxygen to survive since Earth's atmosphere contained very little oxygen at the time. Evidence suggests, however, that by 2.2 billion years ago, ancient cyanobacteria were producing large quantities of oxygen by photosynthesis. **Photosynthesis** is the process by which organisms use light energy to convert carbon dioxide and water to oxygen and food in the form of carbohydrates.

Trace fossils called **stromatolites** are the most common Precambrian fossil. Stromatolites, shown in **Figure 4,** are layered mounds of calcium carbonate deposited by ancient cyanobacteria. Today, stromatolites are relatively rare, but they can still be found in warm, shallow water along sheltered coastlines. Because of their incredible similarity to fossil stromatolites, geologists infer that Precambrian stromatolites formed in similar environments.

FIGURE 4 Evidence of Photosynthesis A Fossil stromatolites are very common from the Precambrian. **B** Modern cyanobacteria are similar to those that formed ancient stromatolites.

LESSON 13.1

Use Visuals

Figure 5 This illustration shows an artist's reconstruction of an ancient sea inhabited by Ediacaran organisms. **Ask:** Would you classify Ediacaran animals as prokaryotes or eukaryotes? *(Eukaryotes)* Why? *(All multicelled organisms are eukaryotes.)* Explain that scientists aren't sure whether any animals alive today (such as jellyfish) are descended from Ediacaran animals.

3 ASSESS

Evaluate Understanding

Have students write a five-question quiz for this section. Students should then trade quizzes, answer the questions, and grade each other's answers.

Reteach L1

Have students color-code and illustrate their own version of the geologic time scale. They can then add additional illustrations of life-forms or the positions of landmasses described in this section. Students should then keep this sheet and add to it as they read the rest of the chapter.

Prokaryotes and Eukaryotes Cyanobacteria are prokaryotes. A **prokaryote** is a single-celled organism whose DNA is not contained within a nucleus. Fossil evidence suggests that the first eukaryotes evolved about 2.1 billion years ago. **Eukaryotes** are organisms whose DNA is contained within a nucleus. The first eukaryotes were single-celled and aquatic. Eventually, some eukaryotes began to reproduce sexually. Sexual reproduction dramatically increased the rate of evolutionary change as genes were shuffled and reshuffled as they were passed from parent to offspring over many generations.

Multicellular Life A few hundred million years after sexual reproduction arose, eukaryotic multicellular organisms evolved. Scientists propose that these early multicellular forms experienced a great burst of diversity. In the 1940s, a spectacular variety of Precambrian fossils were discovered in the Ediacara Hills in southern Australia. These organisms, collectively called the *Ediacaran fauna,* are about 600 million years old and have now been found in many parts of the world.

Ediacaran fossils are molds and casts of soft-bodied animals. As you know, fossils of soft-bodied organisms rarely form. To be preserved as fossils, these animals must have been rapidly buried in fine-grained sediment. While a few of the Ediacaran fossils resemble today's marine worms, jellyfish, and corals, many of the organisms are unlike anything alive today. How, or if, Ediacaran animals are related to later organisms is a subject of ongoing debate among scientists.

FIGURE 5 Ediacaran Organisms Scientists have used 600-million-year-old Ediacaran fossils, such as the one seen here, to reconstruct what Earth's first multicellular organisms may have looked like, as shown in the drawing.

13.1 Assessment

Review Key Concepts

1. List the major geologic developments of the early Precambrian eon.

2. Describe the major events in the history of life during the Precambrian eon.

3. Describe the formation and composition of Earth's atmosphere early in the Precambrian.

4. What is a shield?

5. In your own words, write a definition of *photosynthesis.*

Think Critically

6. **Relate Cause and Effect** How did the composition of the atmosphere change during the middle Precambrian? Explain.

7. **Infer** Why are stromatolites considered trace fossils?

8. **Compare and Contrast** How are prokaryotes and eukaryotes similar? How are they different?

9. **Infer** Why are there relatively few fossils of late Precambrian animals?

CONNECTING CONCEPTS

10. **Research** Use library or Internet resources to research one of the major divisions of the Precambrian eon: the Hadean, the Archean, or the Proterozoic. Write a paragraph describing the major events that occurred.

Assessment Answers

1. Earth itself formed about 4.5 billion years ago. Then the atmosphere, oceans, and continents formed.

2. The first single-celled organisms, called prokaryotes, evolved in the oceans. Later, photosynthetic organisms evolved, followed by a more advanced type of single-celled organism called eukaryotes. Late in the Precambrian, the first multicelled organisms evolved.

3. The early atmosphere formed as gases— including water vapor, carbon dioxide, and nitrogen—that were released from inside Earth. The early atmosphere did not contain oxygen.

4. A shield is a large exposed area of Precambrian rock that forms the core of a continent.

5. Process by which plants use carbon dioxide, water, and the energy of sunlight to make food (carbohydrates)

6. As early organisms released oxygen through photosynthesis, oxygen began to build up in the atmosphere.

7. because they are made up of material deposited by cyanobacteria rather than of the fossil remains of the bacteria themselves

8. They are both types of living cells. Unlike prokaryotes, eukaryotes have a nucleus. Eukaryotes are also capable of forming multicelled organisms.

9. Most Precambrian rocks have been eroded away, subducted, or metamorphosed. All of these processes destroy any fossils the rock contains.

10. Students' paragraphs should contain details on major developments during one of the following eons: the Hadean, Archaean, or Proterozoic.

13.2 The Paleozoic Era

THE PALEOZOIC ERA was a time of major developments in the evolution of life, as shown in **Figure 6.** Many of these developments occurred in response to environmental change. The rock record shows that over geologic time, dramatic environmental changes have occurred again and again. 🔑 **Continental movement, mountain building, volcanic activity, climate changes, and rising and falling sea levels have repeatedly affected conditions on Earth throughout geologic time.** Species must get everything they need from their environment, so when the environment changes, they must change with it. The fossil record shows that over generations, species either adapted to shifting environmental conditions, or they die out. The extinction of many groups of organisms in a relatively short time is called a **mass extinction.** The most severe mass extinction of all time marks the end of the Paleozoic era.

Cambrian Period

As during Precambrian time, life in the early Paleozoic was restricted to the seas. But the Cambrian period brought dramatic changes to Earth. In fact, the fossil record shows that there was a tremendous diversity of early Cambrian organisms. 🔑 **Many new groups of organisms evolved in a relatively short time in an event called the *Cambrian explosion.*** Scientists continue to debate just how suddenly this explosion of life occurred, but they do agree that most groups of animals had evolved by the early Cambrian period.

Key Questions

🔑 **What kinds of environmental changes have affected the evolution of life?**

🔑 **What were the major developments in Earth's life forms during the Paleozoic era?**

Vocabulary
- mass extinction
- Gondwana • Laurasia
- amphibian • reptile
- Pangaea

Reading Strategy

Identify Details Make a table to record the geologic events and developments in life forms for each of the Paleozoic periods. As you read, fill in the table with notes.

FIGURE 6 Paleozoic Era During the Paleozoic, life forms evolved that could live on land.
Interpret Visuals *During which period did amphibians evolve?*

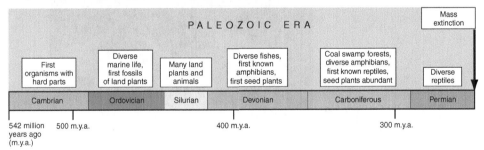

Earth's History **369**

LESSON 13.2

1 FOCUS

Lesson Objectives
13.3 **List** the kinds of environmental changes that have affected the evolution of life over geologic time.
13.4 **Describe** the major evolutionary developments during the Paleozoic era.

Build Vocabulary   L2
Graphic Organizers As they read this lesson, have students develop a concept map or flowchart that includes the vocabulary terms and major concepts for this section.

Reading Strategy   L2
Sample answers: Students' answers should list details of geologic and evolutionary developments for each period of the Paleozoic. Sample answers: Cambrian: warming trend, high sea levels; Cambrian explosion, evolution of hard parts; Ordovician: Gondwana forms, global glaciation; diversification of many organism groups; Silurian: Earth warms, sea levels rise; many groups of fish evolve including jawed fish, plants move onto land; Devonian: Laurasia forms, glaciation; fish diversify even more, amphibians evolve; Carboniferous: warm humid climate, sea levels rose and fell; reptiles evolve, coal swamps common; Permian: Pangaea fully joins, many arid areas; reptiles diversify.

Using Visuals   L2
Figure 6 Ask students to study the timeline of the Paleozoic in Figure 6. **Ask:** What were some major developments of the early Paleozoic? *(Organisms with hard parts evolve, plants and animals move onto land)* What were some major developments of the mid Paleozoic? *(Many fish evolve, amphibians evolve, seed plants evolve)* What were some major developments of the late Paleozoic? *(Coal swamp forests common, reptiles evolve, there is a mass extinction)*
Visual, Verbal

Answers
Figure 6 *Devonian period*

Earth's History **369**

② INSTRUCT

Integrate Biology L2

Trilobites Have students research the different varieties of trilobites. Students should then present their findings to the class, including pictures and a comparison of sizes and structures of the different varieties.
Verbal

Build Reading Literacy L1

Refer to **p. 392D** in **Chapter 14,** which provides guidelines for previewing.

Preview Have students scan the boldfaced material, topic headings, and graphics in this lesson to get an idea of how it is organized and what it is about. This preview of the lesson will help students know where to find the information needed to complete the table for this lesson's reading strategy.
Visual, Verbal

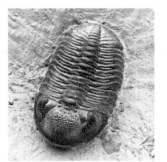

FIGURE 7 Trilobite Cambrian seas were full of trilobites, which were well-adapted to warm, shallow waters.

Cambrian Earth Recall that during the late Precambrian, Earth experienced a great ice age. In contrast, scientists think that the Cambrian climate was generally warm. Warm temperatures melted glaciers and caused sea levels to rise, flooding land with warm, shallow water. This new habitat made ideal conditions for a variety of Cambrian organisms, including the trilobite shown in **Figure 7.**

Cambrian Life The best-known Cambrian fossil collection comes from the 505-million-year-old Burgess shale, a fossil-rich formation in the Canadian Rockies. Most Burgess shale fossils belong to several groups of *invertebrates,* animals that lack a backbone. But the Burgess shale fossils also include early ancestors of *vertebrates,* animals with backbones. **Figure 8** shows how scientists have reconstructed Burgess shale animals and their environment.

Cambrian animals were the first to evolve hard parts, which is one of the reasons they are so well represented in the fossil record. Hard parts likely played a role in the amazing diversification of life during the early Cambrian, as they offer a variety of advantages to organisms that have them. Mollusks such as clams and snails, for example, have hard calcium carbonate shells that provide protection and enable body organs to function in a more controlled environment. Sponges have networks of interwoven silica strands that enable them to grow tall and capture food higher in the water column. Trilobites evolved a tough, flexible external skeleton made of a protein called chitin that allowed them to burrow through soft sediment in search of food, and complex eyes that helped them look for prey and avoid predators. Perhaps because of these adaptations, trilobites became hugely successful in the Cambrian.

☑ **Reading Checkpoint** *What is the Burgess shale?*

FIGURE 8 The Cambrian Sea This artist's reconstruction shows many of the organisms fossilized in the Burgess shale.

370 Chapter 13 • Lesson 2

Differentiated Instruction

SPECIAL NEEDS Graphic organizers are essential to managing the large amount of information presented in this chapter. Help struggling students use the reading strategy for this lesson by having students complete this activity in heterogeneous cooperative groups. Also, remind students to refer back to the geologic time scale on p. 354 in Chapter 12 if they get lost in what they are reading. Tell students to add details to their own version of the scale as they read. (See Reteach in Lesson 13.1.)

FIGURE 9 The Ordovician Sea This reconstruction shows what a community of marine organisms in the Ordovician may have looked like. The large animal with tentacles and a straight shell in the foreground is a cephalopod.

Ordovician Period

Ordovician fossils indicate great invertebrate diversity and the beginnings of life on land. ⟨⟩ **During the Ordovician period, complex communities of invertebrates developed in the oceans and the first land-dwelling plants evolved.**

Ordovician Earth As the Ordovician began, parts of modern-day South America, Africa, Australia, Antarctica, India, and southern Europe were joined together as the landmass **Gondwana.** Plate movements pushed Gondwana south during the Ordovician. Parts of modern-day North America, northern Europe, and Siberia remained near the equator throughout the period.

Ordovician Life Although most major groups of organisms first appeared in the Cambrian, they became diverse in the Ordovician. Paleontologists have discovered many kinds of trilobites, corals, sponges, clams, and shelled organisms called brachiopods. There were also many types of cephalopods, which are a group of mollusks that include octopuses and squid. A large Ordovician cephalopod is shown in the foreground of **Figure 9.**

The Ordovician provides the first fossil evidence for the reef-building invertebrates called bryozoans. Some of the oldest vertebrate fossils also come from the Ordovician in the form of armored jawless fish called ostracoderms. Another major development of the Ordovician was the evolution of land plants. These first plants are known from microfossils and likely resembled small, primitive plants such as liverworts.

Diversity plummeted with a mass extinction at the end of the Ordovician. Geologists think that sea-level changes caused by an ice age may have triggered the extinction event, the second-most-devastating in Earth's history.

Earth's History **371**

Facts and Figures

The thick layers of rock salt and rock gypsum deposited during the early Paleozoic are called evaporite beds because they form as a result of water evaporating and leaving previously dissolved materials behind.

These beds are an important resource for the chemical, rubber, plasterboard, and photographic industries in Ohio, Michigan, and western New York State.

Build Reading Literacy   L1

Refer to **p. 446D** in **Chapter 16,** which provides guidelines for sequencing.

Sequence As students read about the Silurian and Devonian periods, ask them to make a flowchart that shows the major changes that occurred enabling the ancestors of amphibians to live on land. *(Sample answer: fish developed primitive lungs and could stay on land longer → fish spent more and more time on land, so fish with stronger lungs were more likely to survive → fish lungs developed further, making them true air-breathing amphibians → with very little competition on land, amphibians rapidly evolved and diversified.)*
Visual, Verbal

FIGURE 10 Silurian Predator
This eurypterid was a predator that lived in the ocean during the Silurian period.

Silurian Period

Following the mass extinction at the end of the Ordovician, life forms rebounded in the ocean and found new habitats on land. **The Silurian period was a time of reef building and continued evolution of fishes in the seas. By the end of the period, many types of plants and animals had invaded land.**

Silurian Earth The Silurian climate was generally mild. As Earth warmed, glaciers that formed at the end of the Ordovician melted, raising sea levels and flooding low-lying areas. Large barrier reefs formed in the new shallow seas, restricting circulation between shallow marine basins and the open ocean. Water in these basins evaporated, depositing large quantities of rock salt and gypsum.

Silurian Life A great diversity of fearsome jawless fishes evolved during the Silurian, as well as the first freshwater fish and jawed fish. Other ocean organisms of this period include strange-looking arthropods called *eurypterids,* shown in **Figure 10,** and reef-building corals.

On land, small plants similar to mosses spread over moist, lowland areas. During the Silurian, the first vascular plants evolved. The stem of a vascular plant contains thin tubes that carry liquids within the plant. These early plants were leafless spikes about the size of your index finger. There is also fossil evidence that invertebrates, including ancient relatives of modern-day spiders and centipedes, began to adapt to life on land during the Silurian period.

Devonian Period

The Devonian is sometimes called "the age of fishes," but it is also the time during which many types of organisms moved onto land. **During the Devonian period, sharks and other jawed fishes evolved in the seas. On land, plant diversity increased, and the first true trees and forests appeared. The first vertebrates invaded terrestrial habitats toward the end of the period.**

Devonian Earth A world map of Earth during the Devonian is shown in **Figure 11.** Gondwana occupied a large part of the southern hemisphere. To the north, continental landmasses collided to form a new large continent, called **Laurasia,** which included parts of present-day North America, northern Europe, and Siberia. As northern Europe and North America collided, mountains formed. Today, rocks from this mountain-building event make up part of the Appalachian range in the eastern United States.

During the Devonian, Gondwana drifted northward toward Laurasia. The Devonian climate was largely warm and dry. A cooling trend toward the end of the period brought about glaciation and an associated drop in sea level. Scientists hypothesize that these climatic changes may have caused the mass extinction that occurred at the end of the period.

372 Chapter 13 • Lesson 2

Facts and Figures

In the early Paleozoic, a mountain-building event affected eastern North America from the present-day Appalachians to Newfoundland. These mountains have since eroded away, leaving behind deformed strata and a large volume of sedimentary rocks from the weathering of these mountains.

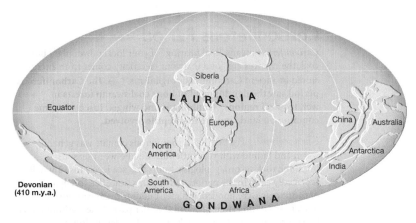

FIGURE 11 Laurasia and Gondwana The supercontinent Gondwana drifted toward the south pole during the Silurian. During the Devonian, it began drifting northward toward the newly formed supercontinent Laurasia.

Devonian Life Major developments in Devonian seas included the appearance of many new types of jawed fishes including sharks. Many Devonian jawed fishes had bony skeletons similar to those of present-day fishes. The sharks, in contrast, had skeletons made of a softer material called cartilage, just like today's sharks. Sponges and new types of corals built reefs in tropical seas.

As land plants continued to evolve and diversify, the first forests grew. Devonian forests were made up of plants, such as club mosses, ferns, and twiglike plants called horsetails, that reproduce using spores. The forests were mostly found near standing water because spore-bearing plants require moist environments to reproduce. True seed plants, whose offspring could sprout away from standing water, appeared in the late Devonian but were rare until the Carboniferous.

Toward the end of the Devonian, vertebrates with four limbs, known as *tetrapods,* evolved from fishes. These early tetrapods were amphibians. An **amphibian** is a four-legged animal, with lungs for breathing, that can live on land but that lays its eggs in water. Early amphibians, such as *Acanthostega* shown in **Figure 12,** probably lived in shallow freshwater habitats. They had primitive lungs as well as gills for breathing. They likely used their limbs to push themselves along in soft mud. Once amphibians made their appearance, they evolved rapidly. This is likely because they lacked competition on land for resources, such as food and space.

The end of the Devonian is marked by a mass extinction that primarily affected marine life. Jawless fish, trilobites, and numerous coral species were particularly devastated.

☑ **Reading Checkpoint** *What is an amphibian?*

FIGURE 12 Land Invader
Amphibians, such as *Acanthostega,* evolved during the Devonian period.

Earth's History **373**

Build Science Skills L2

Interpret Maps Have students look at the map of U.S. coal deposits in Figure 2, page 95. **Ask:** What can you infer about the geologic history of areas where coal is found today? *(During the Carboniferous period, these parts of North America would have had a warm, tropical climate. They would have been covered with large, swampy areas of dense forest.)* Explain to students that the Carboniferous period gets its name from the large coal deposits that began to form during the period. Coal is made up largely of hydrocarbons. The word *carboniferous* means "carbon bearing."
Visual, Logical

Carboniferous Period

Carboniferous means "coal bearing." If your local power plant burns coal, the chances are good that your electricity comes from energy stored in ancient Carboniferous organisms. 🔲 **The Carboniferous period saw the development of huge coal swamp forests in wet, tropical regions. Amphibians and winged insects became common on land, and the first reptiles evolved.**

Carboniferous Earth The Carboniferous climate was generally warm and humid with very little variation between seasons. From the rock record, geologists know that sea levels rose and fell repeatedly early in the period. During this time, flat, low-lying parts of continents were flooded and reef-building organisms formed thick layers of limestone. Toward the later part of the Carboniferous, however, continental crust thickened and sea levels dropped, exposing more land surfaces. By the end of the period, landmasses began to merge and form one giant supercontinent.

Carboniferous Life Among the animals that evolved during the Carboniferous were reptiles. **Reptiles** are a group of generally terrestrial and scaly animals that lay amniotic eggs. *Amniotic eggs* contain water and nutrients for the developing organism and can be laid on land without drying out. The evolution of the amniotic egg enabled reptiles to colonize areas away from water that were unavailable to amphibians.

True seed plants, which could cope with drier climates and live away from standing water, became more common during the Carboniferous. However, the period is better-known for its vast swamp forests of tree ferns, horsetails, and scale trees that grew in wet, tropical regions, as shown in **Figure 13.** These dense forests hosted a tremendous diversity of life, including giant insects and other arthropods. Dragonflies as big as modern birds and centipedes as long as full-grown humans were common.

When the plants and animals in the swamp died, their remains built up in thick layers. Over millions of years, pressure and heat changed these layers of sediment into deposits of coal. American geologists often divide the Carboniferous into the Mississippian and Pennsylvanian periods to distinguish the limestone-rich layers of the Mississippian from the coal-bearing layers of the Pennsylvanian.

☑ **Reading Checkpoint** *How does coal form?*

FIGURE 13 Pennsylvanian Coal Swamp Shown are scale trees (left), seed ferns (lower left), and horsetails (right). Note the large dragonfly.

Facts and Figures

In the Mississippian period, when Laurasia and Gondwana were forming, ancestral North America and Africa collided, producing strong compressional forces that deformed rocks, producing the northern Appalachian Mountains of eastern North America. As Pangaea was forming in the Pennsylvanian period, the African fragment of Gondwana and the southeastern edge of North America collided, forming the southern Appalachian Mountains.

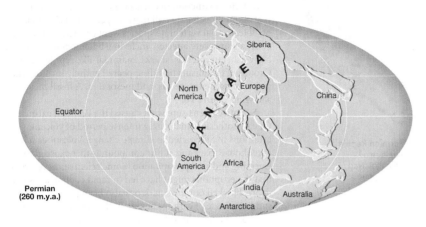

FIGURE 14 Pangaea During the Permian period, plate movements pushed together the major landmasses to form Pangaea.

Build Science Skills

L2

Use Models Tell students that they can model the movement of landmasses that formed the supercontinent Pangaea. Give students photocopies of an outline map of the world. Have them cut out the continents and large landmasses shown on the map of Pangaea in Figure 14 and label them. The outlines of the continents and landmasses can be approximate. Then ask students to position the landmasses on a desktop in the same relative positions as shown in Figure 11 on p. 373. This map shows how Earth's continents were positioned about 150 million years before Pangaea formed. Challenge students to model the formation of Pangaea by sliding the landmasses over the desktop into the positions shown in Figure 14. Ask for volunteers to describe the direction and distance that major landmasses moved as Pangaea formed. **Kinesthetic, Visual**

Permian Period

The Permian period is not as famous for what happened during the time as it is famous for how it ended. 🔑 **The evolution of life during the Permian period continued trends that began during the Carboniferous. But the Permian ended with the greatest mass extinction in geologic history.**

Permian Earth As the Permian period began, Earth's continents were joined in the supercontinent **Pangaea,** seen in **Figure 14.** The formation of Pangaea brought about extreme global environments. Continental glaciers formed where Pangaea extended into the southern polar region and retreated as Pangaea drifted northward. Many of the shallow, continental seas dried up, and deserts formed in the center of Pangaea. Today, huge deposits of red sandstone provide evidence of these deserts. Lush Carboniferous forests of plants dependent on water to reproduce were replaced with communities of more drought-tolerant seed plants.

Permian Life During the Permian period, life forms became more diverse on land and in the oceans. Conifers became abundant. New types of insects, amphibians, and reptiles evolved. One group of early reptiles, the mammal-like reptiles, are ancestors to modern mammals. Fossils show that their legs, skulls, and jawbones were similar to those of mammals. Some mammal-like reptiles, such as *Dimetrodon,* shown in **Figure 15,** had huge "sails" on their backs. These structures, which may have helped regulate body temperature, were formed from elongated spines covered with skin.

FIGURE 15 Mammal-Like? Although it might not look like it, mammal-like reptiles such as *Dimetrodon* are more closely related to mammals than they are to dinosaurs.

Earth's History **375**

Answers

☑ **Reading Checkpoint** *Coal forms as heat and pressure over millions of years changes the buried remains of swamp plants and animals to rock.*

Facts and Figures

Large bodies of water moderate the climate of nearby land areas. Because water heats and cools slower than land does, coastal areas that benefit from sea breezes are warmer in the winter and cooler in the summer. When all the continents merged to form Pangaea, many areas that had been coastal became landlocked in the continent's interior. Interior regions do not benefit from the moderating effects of large bodies of water. So these areas had much hotter summers and much colder winters.

LESSON 13.2

3 ASSESS

Evaluate Understanding L2

Have students review with the class by putting them in cooperative groups to share the tables they made for the Reading Strategy in this section. Encourage students to modify their tables as needed based on discussion with their group.

Reteach L1

Review the essential content of this lesson with students by using the timeline of the Paleozoic period on p. 369. This figure clearly shows the geologic and evolutionary periods. Then use Figure 14 to review how landmasses moved during the late Paleozoic and how these movements would have affected life at that time.

FIGURE 16 Permian Reptile
Mesosaurus was a small freshwater reptile that lived during the Permian period.

The Permian Extinction Nearly 250 million years ago, a mass extinction ended the Permian period. It was the most devastating extinction that has ever occurred. Scientists think that about 96 percent of all marine species and about 70 percent of all terrestrial vertebrate species went extinct. All major groups of organisms were affected, including brachiopods, bryozoans, bony fish, eurypterids, sharks, mammal-like reptiles, and corals. Groups of organisms that disappeared entirely include trilobites, armored fish, eurypterids, and mesosaurs. A fossil mesosaur is shown in **Figure 16**.

Scientists aren't sure what caused the Permian extinction. One hypothesis is that a long intense period of volcanic eruptions in Siberia led to climate change. Volcanoes release greenhouse gases and sulfur compounds that cause global warming and acid precipitation. Some scientists have proposed that the eruptions might have led to rapid cooling as ash and debris blocked out the sun. It has also been proposed that a sudden release of carbon dioxide in the oceans could have caused a massive die-off of marine organisms. Many scientists think that it was a combination of several factors, including climate change and a loss of diverse coastline due to the formation of Pangaea, that caused the extinction. Another hypothesis is that the climate changed in response to an asteroid impact, though not much evidence has been found to support this idea. One thing is for sure, however, something changed at the end of the Permian and most organisms could not adapt. Their extinctions cleared the way for new groups of organisms to flourish in the Mesozoic—among them, the dinosaurs.

13.2 Assessment

Review Key Concepts 🔑

1. What are five examples of environmental changes that affect evolution?

2. List one major evolutionary development for each geologic period of the Paleozoic era.

3. What is a mass extinction?

Think Critically

4. Explain What enabled amphibians to rapidly spread on land?

5. Compare and Contrast Compare and contrast the life that existed at the beginning of the Paleozoic era with the life that existed at the end of the era.

6. Apply Concepts Describe the adaptations that enabled plants and animals to make the transition from water to land.

7. Apply Concepts What is one main way in which reptiles differ from amphibians? How did this difference make reptiles better adapted to some environments of the Permian period?

BIGIDEA EARTH HISTORY

8. Imagine you are uncovering rocks and fossils from a site that was formed during the Paleozoic era. Write a paragraph describing what kinds of fossils you would expect to find as you dig from the surface and move downward.

376 Chapter 13 • Lesson 2

Assessment Answers

1. formation and breakup of continents, mountain building, volcanic activity, changes in climate, changes in sea level
2. Sample answer: Cambrian: evolution of organisms with hard parts; Ordovician: land plants evolve; Silurian: first jawed fishes evolve; Devonian: amphibians evolve; Carboniferous: first reptiles evolve; Permian: mammal-like reptiles evolve
3. An environmental change or geologic event that leads to the extinction of a large number of organisms in a relatively short time

4. Because they had lungs and limbs that could support their weight, amphibians were able to colonize areas that other animals were not. The lack of competition for resources allowed amphibians to be successful.
5. Life at the beginning of the Paleozoic was mostly restricted to water. By the end of the Paleozoic, life had begun to inhabit land at a rapid pace.
6. Life moved onto land as plants developed seeds and other characteristics that allowed them to live without depending on water. Animals developed ways to reproduce away from water.

7. Amphibian eggs must develop in water, but reptiles have amniotic eggs that can be laid on land without drying out. As a result, reptiles could more easily reproduce away from water in the drier conditions caused by the formation of Pangaea.
8. Answers should follow the logical progression of life described in the chapter, but should begin with late Paleozoic life (closer to the surface) and end with early Paleozoic life (deeper).

13.3 The Mesozoic Era

AFTER THE PERMIAN EXTINCTION, the fossil record indicates that millions of years passed before the number and diversity of living things began to increase again. One group that became very abundant and diverse was the ammonites, now extinct mollusks that are related to modern squid and octopus. Ammonites have distinctive, spiral-shaped shells with complex patterns that distinguish species. There were many changes in ocean environments during the Mesozoic era. As a result, many different types of ammonites evolved and became extinct after a few million years. For this reason, they make excellent index fossils. Ammonite index fossils help geologists date sedimentary rock layers from the different periods of the Mesozoic—the Triassic, Jurassic, and Cretaceous. You can see the main events of these periods in the timeline in **Figure 17.**

Triassic Period

The Triassic represents a transitional period from the world as it was in the Paleozoic era to the world of the dinosaurs that characterize the Mesozoic. **Pangaea continued as a single, large landmass through most of the Triassic period. After a slow recovery from the Permian extinction, many kinds of reptiles evolved. Late in the period, the first mammals appeared.**

Key Questions

What were the major geologic and evolutionary developments during the Mesozoic era?

How do scientists explain the mass extinction at the end of the Cretaceous period?

Vocabulary

- mammal • gymnosperm
- angiosperm

Reading Strategy

Summarize Use the orange and blue headings from the lesson to make a bulleted list, leaving spaces under each heading. As you read, fill in the spaces you left with brief summaries of the text.

1 FOCUS

Lesson Objectives
13.5 **Describe** the major geologic and evolutionary developments during the Mesozoic era.
13.6 **Explain** the cause of the mass extinction at the end of the Mesozoic era.

Build Vocabulary [L2]
Using Context Clues Encourage students to keep a list of unfamiliar words they encounter while reading. For each word, they should write a definition based on the context and then verify their definition in a dictionary.

Reading Strategy [L2]
Students' summaries should highlight the major developments of the Mesozoic period.

2 INSTRUCT

Integrate Biology [L2]
Madagascar About 130 million years ago, during the Cretaceous period, Madagascar and India rifted away from Africa, and about 90 million years ago Madagascar separated from India. Since then, Madagascar has been isolated from all other land masses, allowing life to evolve in unique ways. Because of the unusual plant and animal species that have evolved, unlike any others, Madagascar is sometimes called the "eighth continent." Animals like the lemur and fossa are not found anywhere else, and more than 70 percent of all plant species there are unique to the island.

FIGURE 17 Mesozoic Era The Mesozoic is sometimes referred to as the "age of reptiles" because reptiles, including dinosaurs, became so diverse during the era.

MESOZOIC ERA

| Gymnosperms common, mammals evolve, first dinosaurs, first turtles | Dinosaurs diversify, modern fishes evolve, first birds, pterosaurs and aquatic reptiles common | Flowering plants evolve, dinosaurs continue to flourish, mammals diversify | Mass extinction |

| Triassic | Jurassic | Cretaceous |

248 million years ago (m.y.a.)   200 m.y.a.   150 m.y.a.   100 m.y.a.

Earth's History **377**

Build Reading Literacy   L1

Refer to **p. 362D** which provides guidelines for using prior knowledge.

Use Prior Knowledge Students learned about plate tectonics and the causes of plate movements in Chapter 9. **Ask:** What is happening to the Atlantic Ocean today because of plate tectonics? *(It continues to widen because of seafloor spreading.)* What causes seafloor spreading and plate movements? *(convection currents in the mantle)* What Earth activity caused the breakup of Pangaea? *(Tectonic activity/ convection currents drove the breakup of Pangaea.)*
Verbal

Triassic Earth Early in the Triassic, Earth's surface was divided between the supercontinent and a huge ocean, called *Panthalassa* (meaning "all sea"). As in the Permian, the interior regions of Pangaea had a generally warm, dry climate. Coastal regions experienced more seasonal variation, and there is evidence for frequent monsoons. Toward the end of the Triassic, Pangaea began to split apart as Europe and Africa pulled away from North and South America. You could say that the breakup of Pangaea continues today, about 200 million years later.

Triassic Life During the first several million years following the Permian extinction, the fossil record is relatively poor. But, the sudden appearance of many new types of organisms later in the Triassic prompts scientists to conclude that the early Triassic was a time of rapid evolution. The first dinosaurs appear in the Late Triassic, about 230 million years ago. At nearly the same time, the first mammals evolved from a surviving group of mammal-like reptiles. **Mammals** are animals that have hair and nourish their young with milk. Triassic mammals were small and rodentlike.

The fossil record also shows that gymnosperms became common during the Triassic. **Gymnosperms** are a group of plants that bear their seeds on the scales of cones. Unlike plants that reproduce using spores, gymnosperms do not require any amount of standing water for fertilization to occur. Because of this, they were able to colonize the dry interior of Pangaea. Conifers, which first appeared during the Permian period, are gymnosperms. Other gymnosperms included cycads and ginkgoes. Cycads resembled large pineapple plants. Ginkgoes, shown in **Figure 18,** had fan-shaped leaves, much like those of ginkgo trees today.

☑ **Reading Checkpoint** *What is a gymnosperm?*

FIGURE 18 Gymnosperms
Ginkgo trees evolved during the Triassic period. They have survived to the present with relatively little change.

Differentiated Instruction

ENGLISH LANGUAGE LEARNERS In addition to keeping a list of unfamiliar words and defining them based on context, students may also want to write the meaning of the new word in their primary language. Recommend that students list synonyms for their words instead of dictionary definitions. This will allow students to get a general concept of a word's meaning.

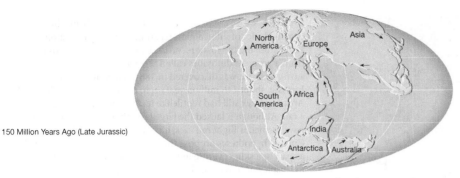

150 Million Years Ago (Late Jurassic)

FIGURE 19 Breaking Up Pangaea By the Late Jurassic period, an ocean began to form between North America and Africa as plate movements split Pangaea. **Interpret Maps** *Which labeled landmass is the farthest from its present north/south location?*

Jurassic Period

Anyone exposed to picture books of dinosaurs would recognize many of the most famous organisms of the Jurassic. **Pangaea continued to split apart during the Jurassic. Dinosaur groups diversified and the first birds evolved.**

Jurassic Earth As rifts formed between parts of Pangaea, seas opened between the continents, as shown in **Figure 19.** At the same time, mountains formed in some areas as oceanic plates subducted beneath continental plates. In North America, tectonic activity extended inland along the entire western part of the continent. The Jurassic climate was generally tropical. Sea levels rose throughout the period, resulting in warm shallow waters covering large parts of North America and Europe.

Jurassic Life Although best-known for its dinosaurs, such as *Brachiosaurus, Stegosaurus,* and *Allosaurus* **(Figure 20),** there was a lot more to Jurassic life. In the oceans, fishes with modern characteristics evolved. Their jaw structures, scales, skeletons, and fins were similar to those of most fishes living today. Aquatic reptiles, such as plesiosaurs and ichthyosaurs, were at their most diverse in the Jurassic. These animals had streamlined bodies similar to those of dolphins, but they kept their reptilian teeth and breathed using lungs. The Jurassic skies were also full of reptiles. Although they first evolved in the Triassic, pterosaurs, became diverse and numerous in the Jurassic.

FIGURE 20 Jurassic Predator Some dinosaurs such as *Allosaurus* were fearsome predators. But there is evidence that many dinosaurs, including some meat-eaters, lived in groups, built nests, and cared for their young.

Earth's History **379**

Facts and Figures

Some geologists think that there is a super-continent cycle that repeats itself about every 500 million years. They think that during this cycle a supercontinent is formed by all of Earth's landmasses coming together, and then the supercontinent is broken apart and the landmasses move away from each other again. Their theory is supported by evidence that a supercontinent called Rodinia broke apart at the end of the Precambrian. Rodinia formed 750 million years ago and broke apart during the late Precambrian and early Proterozoic.

Many students think that all large reptiles were dinosaurs. However, dinosaurs are just one particular group of reptiles that share certain characteristics. Use the Build Science Skills activity below to correct this misconception.

Build Science Skills L2

Classify Before reading this page, have students write down their definitions of a dinosaur. Then, give each student a set of pictures of large reptiles and dinosaurs such as pterosaurs, crocodilians, iguanas, plesiosaurs, raptors, stegosaurs, sauropods, and mosasaurs. Ask students to determine which pictures are of dinosaurs. After students have made their initial classifications, tell them that all dinosaurs were terrestrial (lived on land) and that none could fly. Also tell students that dinosaurs walked with their legs positioned directly under them, like a dog, bird, or human. Other reptiles walked with their legs sprawled out to the side, like a crocodile. Then, have students reclassify their pictures and determine which are dinosaurs.
Visual, Verbal

FIGURE 21 First Bird Although it had many traits in common with dinosaurs, *Archaeopteryx* is considered the first bird because it had feathers capable of powered flight.

FIGURE 22 Cretaceous Plant Eater Ankylosaurs were plant-eating dinosaurs that evolved tough armored plates as protection against predation.

380 Chapter 13 • Lesson 3

Evolution of Birds Recent discoveries, especially in China, have provided a lot of information regarding the early evolution of birds. From studying the fossil record, scientists know that birds evolved from a group of dinosaurs called *theropods*. The first true bird, *Archaeopteryx*, was discovered in 1861 and comes from the Late Jurassic, about 146 million years ago. As you can see in **Figure 21,** *Archaeopteryx* still had reptilelike teeth, claws on its wings, and a tail. Although it lacked the large breastbone that modern birds have to anchor flight muscles, it could probably fly short distances. Current hypotheses propose that feathers, which originally evolved as part of a skin covering in theropod dinosaurs, may have served for display or to regulate body temperature.

☑ **Reading Checkpoint** *What was Archaeopteryx?*

Cretaceous Period

Similar to the Permian, the Cretaceous period may be best-known for how it ended. But before its dramatic end, many familiar groups diversified. **Flowering plants evolved during the Cretaceous alongside new varieties of dinosaurs. Small mammals, insects, and birds all flourished. The period ended with a mass extinction that killed all dinosaurs and many other organisms.**

Cretaceous Earth Earth's major landmasses continued to move apart during the Cretaceous. The climate was generally warm. Early in the period, shallow seas invaded much of western North America. Dense swamps, similar to those of the Paleozoic era, grew in the warm, wet environment. Coal deposits of the western United States and Canada formed from the remains of organisms that grew in the swamps. In the seas near Europe, thick chalk deposits formed from the remains of single-celled ocean organisms.

Cretaceous Life Dinosaurs of the Cretaceous period evolved many different sizes, shapes, and ways of living. The Cretaceous was the time of the fierce *Tyrannosaurus rex*, the horned *Triceratops*, and the gigantic, long-necked plant eater *Apatosaurus*. Other animal groups also appeared and flourished. Snakes evolved early in the Cretaceous. Mammals with more modern characteristics also evolved. The major evolutionary event for plant life was the appearance of angiosperms. **Angiosperms** are plants that produce flowers and seeds with an outer covering. Many modern angiosperms— including trees such as willow, birch, and sassafras—evolved and became common during the Cretaceous.

Facts and Figures

There is a great deal of evidence that a meteorite impact on Mexico's Yucatan Peninsula caused the mass extinction at the end of the Mesozoic. However, there is controversy over this theory partly because tropical plants were barely affected by this extinction event, while plants adapted to a temperate climate were largely destroyed. This does not support the impact theory, which suggests a large ash cloud blocked the sun, causing an extended winter. If this were the case, then tropical plants should have been more affected because they do not have the dormancy adaptations that temperate plants have. Temperate plants should have had the advantage during this extended winter by being able to go dormant and then come back to life after the crisis.

The Cretaceous Extinction

About 65 million years ago, the Cretaceous period ended in a mass extinction that halted the reign of dinosaurs. In all, about 50–60 percent of species, including ammonites, many varieties of land plants, pterosaurs, and large marine reptiles, became extinct. In contrast, smaller reptiles, amphibians, birds, and mammals were relatively unaffected. Unlike the Permian mass extinction, most scientists feel confident that the primary cause of the Cretaceous mass extinction has been identified.

Most scientists think that a large meteorite collided with Earth and caused the mass extinction at the end of the Cretaceous.

The effects of the collision would have been devastating. Tremendous amounts of dust and debris would have been thrown into the atmosphere, blocking out the sun for months or even years. This, in turn, could have caused global cooling and a massive die-off of plant species. Without plants, plant-eating dinosaurs could not survive. Then, the meat-eating dinosaurs also starved and died out.

As shown in **Figure 23,** there is a meteorite impact crater of the correct age near the Yucatán peninsula in Mexico. Scientists have also found a thin, worldwide layer of sediment containing the element iridium. Iridium is a metal that is rare in Earth's crust but that is found in asteroids. Although there may have been other contributing factors, such as volcanic eruptions and disease, most scientists agree that the meteorite impact was the primary cause of the Cretaceous extinction.

FIGURE 23 Impact! Scientists think that the Chicxulub crater was formed by the meteorite that caused the extinction of the dinosaurs.

PLANET DIARY

For links about **The Cretaceous Extinction**, go to PlanetDiary.com/HSES.

13.3 Assessment

Review Key Concepts

1. List one development in evolution for each geologic period of the Mesozoic era.

2. Describe the causes of the mass extinction at the end of the Cretaceous period.

3. What is a mammal?

Think Critically

4. Relate Cause and Effect Would Pangaea's climate during the Triassic have favored amphibians or reptiles? Explain.

5. Contrast How do gymnosperms, such as conifers, differ from spore-bearing plants, such as ferns?

6. Infer What can you infer about the environment of an organism if its fossil is found in limestone? If its fossil is found in coal? Explain.

7. Predict How would you expect fossils to be different above and below the iridium layer deposited at the end of the Cretaceous?

WRITING IN SCIENCE

8. Explain Use library or Internet resources to research a reptile species of the Mesozoic era. Write a paragraph that explains where the fossils of this reptile have been found, the environment in which it lived, and the type of food it ate. Also state whether the reptile still exists or has become extinct.

Earth's History **381**

Build Reading Literacy L1

Refer to **p. 306D** in **Chapter 11,** which provides guidelines for this KWL strategy.

KWL (Know–Want to Know–Learned) Have students make a KWL chart on the extinction of the dinosaurs. Before reading this page, have students list what they already know about the extinction of the dinosaurs and some things they would like to know. After students read the lesson, have them complete the last column with what they learned.
Visual, Verbal

3 ASSESS

Evaluate Understanding L2

Put students in cooperative groups and have them answer the Key Questions at the beginning of this lesson.

Reteach L1

Review content by referring to the summary that each student made for this lesson's Reading Strategy. Help students expand on their summaries as needed to make them complete.

Answers

☑ **Reading Checkpoint** *the first bird*

Assessment Answers

1. Sample answer: Triassic: first mammals evolve; Jurassic: dinosaurs become common in many areas; Cretaceous: flowering plants evolve
2. Scientists think the mass extinction at the end of the Mesozoic was caused by a meteorite impact.
3. An animal that has hair and nourishes its young with milk
4. Pangaea's drier climate would have favored reptiles because their amniotic eggs do not require water to keep them moist.

5. Unlike spore-bearing plants, gymnosperms have seeds and do not require any standing water for fertilization.
6. Limestone generally forms from the shells and skeletons of small ocean organisms. So limestone is found in areas once occupied by ancient seas. Coal forms from the remains of tropical plants that grew in freshwater swamps. So coal deposits reflect a warm land environment in the geologic past.

7. Below the iridium layer, dinosaur fossils could be found. Above the iridium layer, there would be no dinosaurs because they had become extinct.
8. Students' paragraphs should include details on the reptile's geographic range, habitat, and diet. The paragraph should also discuss whether the reptile is extinct or whether related animals survive.

LESSON 13.4

1 FOCUS

Lesson Objectives
13.7 **Explain** why mammals became widespread and successful in the Cenozoic era.

13.8 **Describe** the major geologic and evolutionary developments during the Cenozoic era.

Build Vocabulary [L2]
Lists Have students list the key adaptations in the evolution of angiosperms and mammals. Recommend that students use this lesson, as well as previous lessons in this chapter. *(Sample answer for angiosperms: vascular system, seeds, flowers and covered seeds (fruits))*

Reading Strategy [L2]
What I Expect to Learn (sample answer): Why mammals were so successful in the Cenozoic; What Earth and life were like during the Tertiary; What caused an extinction in the Quaternary. What I Learned (sample answer): Mammals were successful because they had adaptations such as the ability to regulate their body temperature. This enabled them to out-compete reptiles in some areas; Many mountain ranges formed in the Tertiary, grasses and grazers evolved; Scientists think that over-hunting by humans, disease, or climate changes may have caused the large mammal extinction in the Quaternary.

13.4 The Cenozoic Era

Key Questions

🔑 **What adaptations helped mammals succeed in the Cenozoic era?**

🔑 **What were the major geologic and evolutionary developments during the Cenozoic era?**

Vocabulary
• Milankovitch cycle

Reading Strategy
Monitor Your Understanding
Preview the key questions, topic headings, vocabulary, and figures. Make a chart similar to the one below in your notebook. Before you read, fill in the first column. After you read, fill in the second column.

What I Expect to Learn	What I Learned

IF YOU could visit North America shortly after the Cretaceous extinction, you would notice that ecosystems were very different from how they are today. For example, you would not see any grasses or large mammals. Later in the Cenozoic, however, things would begin to look fairly familiar. The term *Cenozoic* means "recent life." Throughout this era, many life forms evolved that were similar to those of the present.

The Rise of Mammals
Many groups of organisms diversified in the Cenozoic, including birds, flowering plants, bony fish, and mammals. During the Mesozoic, mammals were mainly small scavengers and plant-eaters. After the Cretaceous extinction, however, mammals rapidly adapted to fill the environmental roles and habitats once occupied by reptiles. 🔑 **A variety of adaptations enabled mammals to rapidly diversify in the Cenozoic, often out-competing surviving reptiles.** For example, because mammals can maintain a steady internal body temperature, they can survive in cold regions and search for food during any season or time of day. Other adaptations included more efficient hearts and lungs, and the development of insulating body hair. These adaptations allowed mammals to lead more active lives than reptiles.

FIGURE 24 Cenozoic Era Mammals became abundant and diverse during the Cenozoic era.

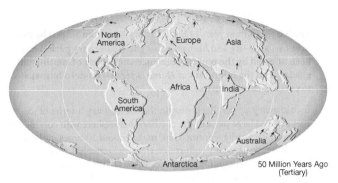

FIGURE 25 Cenozoic Earth Early in the Cenozoic, North America and South America were not connected, India had not collided with Asia, and Australia was still far south of where it is today. **Infer** *How did the distance between Antarctica and Australia change during the Cenozoic?*

Tertiary Period

The Tertiary period extends from 65–1.8 million years ago. 🔑 **During the Tertiary period, mountain building and climate changes accompanied the breakup of Pangaea. Mammals became widespread and diverse worldwide.** On the geologic time scale, the Tertiary is usually divided into the Paleogene and Neogene.

Tertiary Earth Major fragments of Pangaea became separate continents during the Tertiary. As you can see in **Figure 25,** seas separated South America from North America, and Europe from Africa. Plate movements led to major mountain building events in western North America (the Rockies), Europe (the Alps), and Asia (the Himalayas).

There was a general warming trend during the early Tertiary due to a release of greenhouse gases from sea floor sediments. Beginning around 50 million years ago, however, Earth began to cool and many areas had temperate, dry climates. By the late Tertiary, the polar ice caps had formed.

Tertiary Life The Tertiary saw the evolution of many new species, from songbirds to snakes. But the major development of the Tertiary was the evolution of many new types of mammals. Mammals evolved specialized teeth for life in particular environments. For example, meat eaters evolved sharp teeth for cutting and tearing. Rodents developed self-sharpening front teeth for gnawing. Plant eaters developed flat molars with thick enamel for chewing. Some mammals evolved that could take advantage of an abundant new food source—grass. As the climate became cooler and drier, vast grasslands developed. Many types of grazing animals, including the ancestors of cattle and horses, evolved during the Tertiary.

INQUIRY
APPLY IT!

Q: *What are the La Brea tar pits?*

A: The La Brea tar pits, located in downtown Los Angeles, contain fossils of ice-age mammals, including saber-toothed cats and mammoths, that roamed southern California from 8000 to 40,000 years ago. These animals have been preserved in tar that oozed to the surface. So far, scientists have recovered fossils of 59 mammal species and more than 130 bird species.

Earth's History **383**

Integrate Astronomy   [L2]

Earth's Movements Have students read Earth's Orbital Motions in Chapter 21, p. 601. Challenge students to carry out library or Internet research to learn more about variations in Earth's movements. For each type of movement, students should produce a labeled diagram that includes the length of time for the cycle involved. Discuss with the class how these movements can reinforce each other to change the amount of energy that Earth receives from the sun and produce the Milankovitch cycle of ice ages.

Quaternary Period

The last 1.8 million years of Earth history have been shaped by two major factors—ice and humans. ⌐⌐ **The Quaternary period has been affected by the repeated advance and retreat of continental glaciers and the migration of *Homo sapiens*—modern humans—to every corner of Earth.**

Quaternary Earth Beginning in the late Tertiary, a series of ice ages covered large parts of the northern hemisphere with continental glaciers. Glaciers have formed and melted about 30 times in the last 1.8 million years. Many factors determine whether Earth's climate becomes cold enough for an ice age. These factors include ocean currents, the position of the continents, the size of existing ice-covered areas, and the effects of living things on the atmosphere.

In the 1940s, astronomer Milutin Milankovitch proposed that three different cycles, related to Earth's movements, were the main cause of ice ages. These cycles are called **Milankovitch cycles.** For example, there is a 100,000-year cycle related to changes in the shape of Earth's orbit. Earth receives more or less energy from the sun depending on its position within each of the cycles. Milankovitch thought that ice ages occur when solar energy reaching Earth is at a minimum. Scientists today think that Milankovitch cycles provide a partial explanation for recent ice ages, shown in **Figure 26.** But scientists are still looking for a more complete explanation.

Quaternary Life Modern humans, *Homo sapiens,* evolved from ancestors in Africa during the Quaternary between 200,000 and 150,000 years ago. Fossil and DNA evidence suggests that between 65,000 and 50,000 years ago, early humans began to migrate out of Africa to Europe and Asia. Then, as sea levels fell during the last ice age, a land bridge formed that connected Asia and North America near present-day Alaska. Scientists think that this land bridge enabled humans to migrate to the Americas about 14,000 years ago. Today, humans inhabit every continent. Our species has become a powerful factor in changing Earth's environment. This in turn affects the other species with whom we share the planet.

FIGURE 26 Ice Age Cycles Scientists have determined that continental glaciers have advanced and then retreated at roughly 100,000-year intervals over the last 1 million years. Infer *What can you infer about how the amount of solar energy reaching Earth changed between about 30,000 years ago and the present?*

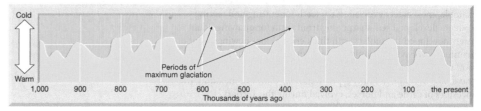

Facts and Figures

EARLY MAMMALS Students may not always remember that mammals began to evolve before the extinction of the dinosaurs. One early mammal, *Morganucodon*, evolved more than 200 million years ago. *Morganucodon* was a small rodent-like mammal that still had some reptilian characteristics. Because the dinosaurs were so succesful in filling so many of the large-animal niches, it wasn't until the dinosaurs were gone, almost 150 million years after the emergence of *Morganucodon*, that mammals became larger, more diverse, and widespread.

One trend in evolution that began in the Tertiary and continued in the Quaternary was the tendency for mammals to become very large. During the ice ages, many large mammals lived on the cold grassland, or steppe, that bordered the ice-covered areas of North America, Europe, and Asia. These mammals included mastodons and mammoths, which were both huge relatives of the elephant. In North America, there were also giant beavers, ground sloths, wolves, bears, saber-toothed cats, and bison. All these mammals became extinct about 10,000 years ago, at the end of the last ice age.

Quaternary Extinction No single hypothesis provides a satisfactory explanation for the extinction of large mammals in the Quaternary. Some scientists have suggested disease or climate changes as possible explanations. Other scientists have suggested that humans hunted the large ice-age mammals to extinction. But skeptics question whether small groups of humans could have caused so many different kinds of animals to become extinct over such a vast area.

☑ **Reading Checkpoint** *What hypotheses have been proposed to explain the extinction of large mammals about 10,000 years ago?*

FIGURE 27 What Happened to Mammoths? Mammoths, related to modern elephants, were among the large mammals that became extinct at the close of the Ice Age.

3 ASSESS

Evaluate Understanding L2

Have students work in small groups to determine the answers to the Lesson Assessment questions.

Reteach L1

Use Figure 24 on p. 382 to reteach the main ideas of this lesson. Have students add information about angiosperms and major continental events during the Cenozoic era to their version of the geologic time scale.

13.4 Assessment

Review Key Concepts 🔒

1. Why did mammals become so successful during the Cenozoic era?

2. List one major evolutionary development for each period of the Cenozoic era.

3. Describe plate movements and mountain building during the Tertiary period.

4. What are Milankovitch cycles?

Think Critically

5. Infer Which would have a better chance of surviving in a cold climate: a mammal or a reptile? Explain.

6. Predict What characteristics would you expect an early mammal that lived in a grassland to have? Explain.

7. Relate Cause and Effect What caused the Alps and Himalayas to form during the Tertiary period?

CONNECTING CONCEPTS

8. Research Scientists think that the Great Rift Valley in East Africa began to form during the late Tertiary period. Use Internet or library resources to research the Great Rift Valley. Write a paragraph describing how it formed and what may happen to it in the future.

Earth's History **385**

Answers

Figure 26 *According to the graph, Earth has grown warmer over the last 30,000 years, so the amount of solar energy Earth receives has probably been increasing due to the Milankovitch cycle.*

☑ **Reading Checkpoint** *Hypotheses include disease, climate changes, and over-hunting by humans.*

Assessment Answers

1. Because they had adaptations that enabled them to out-compete reptiles for resources

2. Sample answer: Tertiary: Grazing animals such as horses evolved; Quaternary: Modern humans evolved.

3. During the Tertiary, plate movements involving North America, Africa and Europe, and India and Asia pushed up the Rocky Mountains, Alps, and Himalayas, respectively.

4. Milankovitch cycles are the periodic cooling and warming of Earth's climate that scientists think cause ice ages. Milankovitch cycles result from changes in Earth's motions that take place over thousands of years.

5. A mammal would have a better chance of surviving because mammals can maintain a steady internal temperature and have hair that provides insulation.

6. Students may mention adaptations such as large, flat teeth for grinding and chewing grasses and hooves for running over open grasslands to escape predators.

7. In the case of the Alps and Himalayas, the collision of continents at convergent plate boundaries caused the mountain building.

8. Sample answer: The Great Rift Valley is forming along a divergent plate boundary. Eventually, if the rift continues to widen, it could become an ocean basin similar to the Red Sea.

MODELING THE GEOLOGIC TIME SCALE L2

Objective

In this activity, students will represent the geologic time scale in a way that allows a clear visual understanding of the time scales involved.

Address Misconceptions

Some students think that early life was primarily plants and animals. However, the first life consisted of simple single-celled organisms called prokarytes, which evolved into two forms: bacteria and archaea. Ancient cyanobacteria began making stromatolites as early as 3.5 billion years ago. This lab will help students see that plants and animals developed rather late in Earth's history.

Skills Measure, Calculate, Interpret Diagrams

Prep Time 5 minutes

Advance Prep You may want to have students do this lab in the hallway, or classroom furniture may need to be rearranged.

Class Time 60 minutes (2 class periods)

Teaching Tip Show students how to use the scale given to plot the first event or two on their timelines. For example, the whole class could start by plotting the end of the Mesozoic and extinction of the dinosaurs 65 mm away from the line they marked as Present, because the scale has 1 mm = 1 million years, and dinosaurs became extinct 65 million years ago. It may also be helpful to review scientific notation with your students prior to doing this activity.

Expected Outcomes Students will construct a roughly 5-m long representation of the geologic time scale and will see that the length of time humans have existed is not even 1 mm on this scale. Students will gain a sense of how long the Precambrian really was and how short the other eras and periods were in comparison.

Modeling the Geologic Time Scale

Problem How can the geologic time scale be represented in a way that allows a clearer visual understanding?

Materials strip of adding machine paper measuring 5 meters or longer, meter stick or metric measuring tape, pencil

Skills Measure, Calculate, Interpret Diagrams

Connect to the Big idea Applying the techniques of geologic dating, the history of Earth has been subdivided into several different units of varying length. The events that make up Earth's history can be arranged within these units to provide a clearer picture of the past. The span of a human life is like the blink of an eye compared to the age of Earth. Because of this, it can be difficult to comprehend the magnitude of geologic time.

Procedure

1. Obtain a piece of adding machine paper slightly longer than 5 meters in length. Draw a line at one end of the paper and label it "Present."

2. Using the following scale, construct a timeline by completing Steps 3 and 4.

   Scale

   1 meter = 1 billion years
   10 centimeters = 100 million years
   1 centimeter = 10 million years
   1 millimeter = 1 million years

3. Using the geologic time scale on page 387 as a reference, divide your timeline into the eons and eras of geologic time. Label each division with its name and indicate its absolute age.

4. Using the information in the chapter, plot and label major evolutionary events on your timeline.

Analyze and Conclude

1. **Calculate** What fraction or percent of geologic time is represented by the Precambrian eon?

2. **Explain** Using your text and class notes as references, explain how scientists decide where to place time scale divisions.

3. **Infer** Suggest one reason why paleontologists have been able to accurately subdivide the Cenozoic periods into epochs.

4. **Analyze Data** How many times longer is the whole of geologic time than the time represented by the 5000 years of recorded history?

5. **Calculate** Scientists think that modern humans evolved about 200,000 years ago. Using this date, calculate the fraction or percent of geologic time that modern humans have been present on Earth.

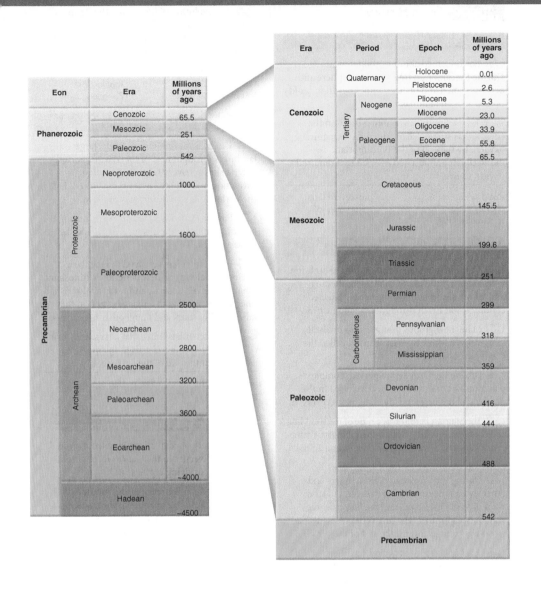

Eon	Era	Millions of years ago
Phanerozoic	Cenozoic	65.5
	Mesozoic	251
	Paleozoic	542
Precambrian	Proterozoic — Neoproterozoic	1000
	Proterozoic — Mesoproterozoic	1600
	Proterozoic — Paleoproterozoic	2500
	Archean — Neoarchean	2800
	Archean — Mesoarchean	3200
	Archean — Paleoarchean	3600
	Archean — Eoarchean	~4000
	Hadean	~4500

Era	Period	Epoch	Millions of years ago
Cenozoic	Quaternary	Holocene	0.01
		Pleistocene	2.6
	Tertiary — Neogene	Pliocene	5.3
		Miocene	23.0
	Tertiary — Paleogene	Oligocene	33.9
		Eocene	55.8
		Paleocene	65.5
Mesozoic	Cretaceous		
			145.5
	Jurassic		
			199.6
	Triassic		
			251
Paleozoic	Permian		
			299
	Carboniferous — Pennsylvanian		318
	Carboniferous — Mississippian		359
	Devonian		416
	Silurian		444
	Ordovician		488
	Cambrian		542
Precambrian			

Analyze and Conclude

1. 3958/4500, or about 88%, is Precambrian

2. They base the divisions on major geologic or evolutionary events documented in the rock and fossil records.

3. The Cenozoic is the most recent era, so the fossils from this time period are the best preserved. This allows scientists to study the fossils in detail and observe even small changes over time.

4. 4,500,000,000/5000 = 900,000 times longer

5. 0.2/4500, or about 0.004%

Visual, Logical

Study Tip

Use Graphic Organizers
Have students make and modify graphic organizers in a format they are comfortable with. Encourage students to produce their own version of the geologic time scale that includes major events for each time period. Students can then use this graphic organizer to prepare for tests.

21st Century Learning

Interpersonal and Collaborative Skills

What caused the Permian mass extinction?

The Permian mass extinction was the most devastating event in the history of life on Earth. About 95 percent of all living species were destroyed. Scientists have several theories about how this occurred. Organize the class into groups of three or four students. Have each group member research the evidence in favor of one of the theories. Groups should be able to describe the time period, what species were common on Earth, and what groups survived the mass extinction. Finally, ask each group to present the evidence for the theories in the form of a mock debate among group members. Have the class vote for the most likely theory, based on the evidence.

Homework Guide

Lesson	Questions
1	1, 2, 11–13, 21–23
2	3–6, 15–17, 20, 24
3	7, 9, 14, 19
4	8, 10, 18, 25–28

13 Study Guide

Big idea ▸ Earth History

13.1 Precambrian Time

🔑 Earth formed about 4.5 billion years ago. During Precambrian time, the atmosphere and oceans formed and plate tectonics began to build up continental landmasses.

🔑 The earliest life probably evolved in the oceans, was single-celled, and did not require oxygen. By the end of the Precambrian, multicellular animals had evolved that required oxygen to live.

shield (366)	prokaryote (368)
photosynthesis (367)	eukaryote (368)
stromatolite (367)	

13.2 The Paleozoic Era

🔑 Continental movement, mountain building, volcanic activity, climate changes, and rising and falling sea levels have repeatedly affected conditions on Earth throughout geologic time.

🔑 Many new groups of organisms evolved in a relatively short time in an event called the *Cambrian explosion*.

🔑 During the Ordovician period, complex communities of invertebrates developed in the oceans and the first land-dwelling plants evolved.

🔑 The Silurian Period was a time of reef-building and continued evolution of fishes in the seas. By the end of the period, many types of plants and animals had invaded land.

🔑 During the Devonian period, sharks and other jawed fishes evolved in the seas. On land, plant diversity increased, and the first true trees and forests appeared. The first vertebrates invaded terrestrial habitats toward the end of the period.

🔑 The Carboniferous period saw the development of huge coal swamp forests in wet, tropical regions. Amphibians and winged insects became common on land, and the first reptiles evolved.

🔑 The evolution of life during the Permian period continued trends that began during the Carboniferous. But the Permian ended with the greatest mass extinction in geologic history.

mass extinction (369)	amphibian (373)
Gondwana (371)	reptile (374)
Laurasia (372)	Pangaea (375)

13.3 The Mesozoic Era

🔑 Pangaea continued as a single, large landmass through most of the Triassic period. After a slow recovery from the Permian extinction, many kinds of reptiles evolved. Late in the period, the first mammals appeared.

🔑 Pangaea continued to split apart during the Jurassic. Dinosaur groups diversified and the first birds evolved.

🔑 Flowering plants evolved during the Cretaceous alongside new varieties of dinosaurs. Small mammals, insects, and birds all flourished. The period ended with a mass extinction that killed all dinosaurs and many other organisms.

🔑 Most scientists think that a large meteorite collided with Earth and caused the mass extinction at the end of the Cretaceous.

mammal (378)	angiosperm (380)
gymnosperm (378)	

13.4 The Cenozoic Era

🔑 A variety of adaptations enabled mammals to rapidly diversify in the Cenozoic, often out-competing surviving reptiles.

🔑 During the Tertiary period, mountain building and climate changes accompanied the breakup of Pangaea. Mammals became widespread and diverse worldwide.

🔑 The Quaternary period has been affected by the repeated advance and retreat of continental glaciers and the migration of *Homo sapiens*—modern humans—to every corner of Earth.

Milankovitch cycle (384)

Assessment Answers

Review Content

1. a	**2.** b	**3.** b
4. a	**5.** c	**6.** b
7. b	**8.** c	**9.** a
10. b		

Understand Concepts

11. Primitive plants dramatically changed the composition of Earth's atmosphere by using carbon dioxide and releasing oxygen through photosynthesis.

12. Shields are exposed areas of Precambrian rock that are found in the interior of every continent.

13 Assessment

Review Content

Choose the letter that best answers the question or completes the statement.

1. Which era spans the least amount of time on the geologic time scale?
   a. Cenozoic
   b. Mesozoic
   c. Paleozoic
   d. Precambrian

2. The most common Precambrian fossils are
   a. fish.
   b. stromatolites.
   c. trilobites.
   d. ferns.

3. Which period is sometimes called the "age of fishes"?
   a. Ordovician
   b. Devonian
   c. Permian
   d. Triassic

4. Modern squids belong to which group of organisms that originated in the Paleozoic?
   a. cephalopods
   b. trilobites
   c. brachiopods
   d. amphibians

5. Jawless fishes that evolved during the Devonian period were
   a. prokaryotes.
   b. amphibians.
   c. vertebrates.
   d. invertebrates.

6. Which adaptation enabled reptiles to out-compete amphibians in dry environments?
   a. gills
   b. amniotic eggs
   c. lungs
   d. webbed feet

7. Reptiles that were adapted to fly included the
   a. plesiosaurs.
   b. pterosaurs.
   c. ichthyosaurs.
   d. tyrannosaurs.

8. Humans first appeared during the
   a. Cretaceous period.
   b. Jurassic period.
   c. Quaternary period.
   d. Tertiary period.

9. Insulating body hair is a characteristic of
   a. mammals.
   b. amphibians.
   c. reptiles.
   d. invertebrates.

10. What evolved during the Cenozoic that enabled the emergence of grazing herbivores?
    a. seed plants
    b. grasses
    c. fruits
    d. carnivorous mammals

Understand Concepts

11. How did plants help change Earth's early atmosphere?

12. What are shields? Where are they found?

13. The photograph below shows evidence of what kind of organism?

14. What significant tectonic activity occurred during the Mesozoic?

15. What present-day continents made up Gondwana?

16. Were trilobites vertebrates or invertebrates?

17. Why were the Ordovician organisms known as ostracoderms important?

18. What development allowed mammals to adapt to different environments successfully?

13. stromatolites
14. Pangaea broke up.
15. South America, Africa, Australia, Antarctica, India, and southern Europe
16. Invertebrates
17. They are the first known vertebrates.
18. Mammals can maintain a steady internal body temperature, which allows them to inhabit colder regions and remain active at different seasons and times of day.

ASSESSMENT

Think Critically

19. Separating out the birds makes it clear that they diversified after the end-Cretaceous extinction.

20. North America was located near the equator. As a result, its climate was suitable for the growth of the lush tropical forests whose remains formed coal deposits.

21. The early rock record has been obscured by Earth processes such as plate tectonics, erosion, and deposition.

22. During Precambrian time, as cyanobacteria began to add oxygen to the atmosphere, much of the oxygen reacted with sedimentary rocks on the surface to form iron oxides. Banded iron formations are deposits of Precambrian sedimentary rock that are rich in these iron oxides.

23. Plants provide the majority of free oxygen in Earth's atmosphere.

24. Some examples could include: Reptiles reproduce by laying amniotic eggs. Amphibians do not have amniotic eggs. Amphibians spend time in water and land environments. Reptiles can inhabit water, land, or air.

25. Scientists think that changes in the amount of energy Earth receives from the sun cause the cooling that leads to ice ages. These changes occur in 100,000 year cycles called Milankovitch cycles after the scientist who developed this hypothesis. Milankovitch cycles result from slight changes in Earth's motions over periods of thousands of years.

26. Many scientists think that after migrating to the Americas about 13,000 years ago, humans hunted large ice-age mammals to extinction.

Concepts in Action

27. (a) Paleozoic, (b) Cenozoic, (c) Precambrian, (d) Mesozoic, (e) Mesozoic, (f) Precambrian, (g) Paleozoic, (h) Paleozoic, (i) Paleozoic, (j) Mesozoic

28. Paragraphs should provide information about how these organisms interact, especially in obtaining food, and how these interactions helped organisms evolve and occupy a variety of niches throughout history. For example, birds that feed on seeds and fruits evolved rapidly during the Cenozoic in close association with the development and spread of flowering plants.

Think Critically

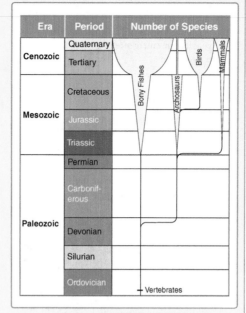

19. Infer Examine the figure above, which shows the relative numbers of species in four groups of vertebrates through time. Archosaurs are a group of reptiles that includes the dinosaurs, pterosaurs, modern crocodiles, and birds. Why do you think that birds are shown separately from the other archosaurs in the diagram, if the point is to show how diversity changed over time?

20. Infer What role did plate tectonics play in determining the conditions that produced North America's coal reserves?

21. Review Why is so little known about the Precambrian time?

22. Relate Cause and Effect What evidence do banded-iron formations provide about oxygen levels in the atmosphere during the early- to mid-Precambrian?

23. Infer What is the major source of free oxygen in Earth's atmosphere?

24. Compare and Contrast Make a list of differences between amphibians and reptiles.

25. Apply Concepts Describe one main hypothesis that explains the cause of ice ages during the Quaternary period.

26. Relate Cause and Effect Why do scientists think large ice-age mammals became extinct about 10,000 years ago?

Concepts in Action

27. Classify Match the following words and phrases to the most appropriate time span. Select among the following: Precambrian, Paleozoic, Mesozoic, and Cenozoic.
  a. Pangaea formed.
  b. Encompasses the least amount of time
  c. Shields
  d. Mammals evolved.
  e. Triassic, Jurassic, and Cretaceous
  f. Formation of most of the world's major iron-ore deposits
  g. "Age of fishes"
  h. Cambrian, Ordovician, and Silurian
  i. Golden age of trilobites
  j. Gymnosperms became abundant.

28. Writing in Science Write a paragraph explaining the relationship between the development and movement of plants, herbivores, and carnivores. You may need to consult a biology text, library, or Internet resources for your answer.

Performance-Based Assessment

Research Research and select several different types of gymnosperm and angiosperm plants that are mentioned in the chapter. Also, research more primitive plants that existed before gymnosperms. Write a paragraph describing each plant, including information on its physical structure, reproduction, and characteristics that might cause it to be more successful in some eras than in others.

Performance-Based Assessment

Research should focus on such gymnosperms as cycads, conifers, and ginkgoes. Angiosperms should include monocots such as irises, lilies, and grasses and dicots such as legumes, mustards, and fruit trees. Students might also research specific plants of the coal swamps of the Pennsylvania period such as scale trees, seed ferns, and scouring rushes.

Standardized Test Prep

Choose the letter that best answers the question or completes the statement.

1 Early in Earth's history, which gas was largely removed from the atmosphere and became more concentrated in seawater?
   A oxygen
   B carbon dioxide
   C argon
   D hydrogen

2 Which of the following major groups of organisms evolved most recently?
   F fishes
   G amphibians
   H mollusks
   J cephalopods

The following diagram shows major evolutionary innovations in the history of animals. Use the diagram to answer Questions 3 and 4.

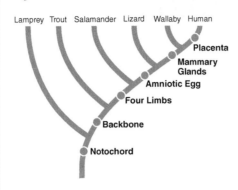

3 According to the diagram, which characteristic is shared by humans, wallabies, and trout?
   A backbone
   B four limbs
   C amniotic egg
   D mammary glands

4 Which of the following animals has four limbs and a backbone, but does not have an amniotic egg?
   F lamprey
   G trout
   H salamander
   J lizard

If You Have Trouble With . . .				
Question	1	2	3	4
See Lesson	13.1	13.2	13.2	13.2

14 The Ocean Floor Planning Guide

Lesson Objectives		Activities
14.1 The Vast World Ocean, pp. 394–400		TE Teacher Demo: One Ocean, p. 394 L2
14.1 **Recognize** that most of Earth's surface is covered by water.		SE Map It: Distribution of Land and Water, p. 395
14.2 **List** Earth's four main ocean basins and identify their locations.		
14.3 **Describe** the topography of the ocean floor and **compare** it to land.		
14.4 **Identify** and **describe** three major technologies used to study the ocean floor.		
14.2 Ocean Floor Features, pp. 401–405		TE Teacher Demo: Sediment Buildup, p. 404 L2
14.5 **List** the three main regions of the ocean floor.		
14.6 **Differentiate** between the continental margins of the Atlantic and Pacific Oceans.		
14.7 **Explain** the formation of new ocean floor at deep-ocean trenches, abyssal plains, and mid-ocean ridges.		
14.3 Seafloor Sediments, pp. 407–409		TE Build Science Skills, p. 408 L2
14.8 **List** the three types of ocean floor sediments.		TE Teacher Demo: Biogenous Deposits, p. 409 L2
14.9 **Describe** the formation of terrigenous, biogenous, and hydrogenous sediments.		
14.4 Resources from the Seafloor, pp. 410–413		SE Quick Lab: Evaporative Salts, p. 412 L2
14.10 **Identify** ocean resources used for energy production.		
14.11 **Explain** how gas hydrates are formed.		
14.12 **List** other types of ocean resources.		
Chapter Features and Labs		
Try It How Does Particle Size Affect Settling Rates, p. 393		LM Modeling the Ocean Floor L1
Earth & Its Systems Explaining Coral Atolls–Darwin's Hypothesis, p. 406: ES.2.b, ES.7.a, ES.7.b		
Exploration Lab Modeling Seafloor Depth Transects, pp. 414–415: ES.1.a, ES.1.b, ES.1.c, ES.1.d		

Ability Levels		Components			
L1	For students who need additional help	SE	Student Edition	LP	Lesson Plans
L2	For all students	TE	Teacher's Edition	AA	Active Art
L3	For students who need to be challenged	LM	Laboratory Manual	PD	Planet Diary
		CT	Chapter Tests	GEODe	Geode CD-ROM
		GRSW	Guided Reading & Study Workbook	eText	
		CTB	Computer Test Bank		

Resources	Lesson Assessment
GRSW Lesson 14.1 **LP** Lesson Planning 14.1 **PD** Mapping the Ocean Floor	**SE** Lesson 14.1 Assessment, p. 400 **eText** Lesson 4.1
GRSW Lesson 14.2 **GEODe** Ocean: Floor of the Ocean **LP** Lesson Planning 14.2	**SE** Lesson 14.2 Assessment, p. 405 **eText** Lesson 4.2
GRSW Lesson 14.3 **LP** Lesson Planning 14.3	**SE** Lesson 14.3 Assessment, p. 409 **eText** Lesson 4.3
GRSW Lesson 14.4 **LP** Lesson Planning 14.4	**SE** Lesson 14.4 Assessment, p. 413 **eText** Lesson 4.4

Materials for Activities and Labs

Quantities for each group

STUDENT EDITION

Try It, p. 393
2 large transparent containers, water, clay, sand, 2 sheets of white paper, hand lens, stopwatch

Quick Lab, p. 412
400 mL beaker, table salt, tablespoon, balance, glass stirrer

Exploration Lab, pp. 414–415
shoe box, modeling clay, aluminum foil, pencil, scalpel, graph paper, ruler

TEACHER'S EDITION

Teacher Demo, p. 394
world globe

Teacher Demo, p. 404
small glass aquarium tank, rocks, pebbles, coarse gravel, coarse and fine aquarium sand, bone meal or other fine material that settles out but does not dissolve quickly in water

Teacher Demo, p. 408
prepared microscope slides of diatoms, foraminifera, and radiolaria; or photographic slides of photomicrographs of these organisms and a slide projector

Assessment

CHAPTER ASSESSMENT
SE Assessment, pp. 417–418
CT Chapter 14 Test
CTB Chapter 14
eText Chapter 14

21st Century Learning

Accountability and Adaptability: How has life on the ocean floor changed our views about life?, TE p. 416

Michael Wysession
Washington University

Common Themes

Seventy-one percent of Earth's surface is covered by ocean water. There are four main ocean basins: the Pacific, Atlantic, Indian, and Arctic. The bathymetry of the ocean seafloor is very varied, a result of many different geological processes.

Space and Time The margins of continents (including the continental shelf, slope, and rise) are often under sea water. The ocean floor is deepest at trenches, where oceanic lithosphere sinks back into the mantle. The seafloor bathymetry also varies with the presence of seamounts, fracture zones, and mid-ocean ridges. Ocean sediments (formed chemically, biologically, or carried in from the continents) cover most of the ocean floor. These sediments are shallowest at mid-ocean ridges, and often thickest along continental margins.

Forces and Motion The ocean seafloor forms at mid-ocean ridges, which rest higher than the surrounding basin seafloor because the new rock is hot and buoyant. Hot water circulating through the mid-ocean ridge system removes metals and minerals from the crust out of hydrothermal vents.

Matter and Energy A variety of technologies are used to investigate the ocean. Sonar is used to map seafloor bathymetry. Microwaves transmitted from satellites are used to map the ocean surface and seafloor features. Underwater submersibles directly investigate the seafloor.

Earth as a System The ocean is the source of many important natural resources such as oil, natural gas, gas hydrates (as of yet untapped), sand, gravel, salts, and metals.

EARTH SCIENCE REFRESHER

Guyots, Parabolas, and Sea Level

When new ocean lithosphere forms at mid-ocean ridges, the rock is very hot, so it is less dense than surrounding rock. As a result, the ridges rise higher than the average seafloor depth. As the ocean plate cools, it becomes denser and therefore sinks. The result is that the ocean floor continues to sink after it forms at a ridge (until it reaches equilibrium, after about 80 million years). This is why guyots, flat-topped seamounts, are so common. Oceanic islands are continuously sinking along with the entire seafloor.

Interestingly, the bathymetry of the cooling, sinking seafloor has a particular shape. It turns out that the cooling of the ocean plate occurs most rapidly right after it forms, and then gradually cools more slowly. The result is that the distance away from the ridge is proportional to the square of the temperature of the ocean plate, and therefore the depth to the seafloor. Any curve with an equation such as y 5 x2 is a parabola, so the bathymetry of the seafloor makes the shape of a parabola as it moves away from the ridge.

> Address **Misconceptions**
>
> *Many students may think that features such as seamounts and mid-ocean ridges formed exclusively in the past, and fail to recognize the ongoing processes that continue to shape the ocean floor. Explain that tectonic activity continues to cause changes in ocean topography. For a strategy that helps to overcome this misconception, see* **Address Misconceptions** *of* **TE p. 404.**

One very important result of the sinking of cooling ocean lithosphere concerns global sea levels. During the Cretaceous Period, sea levels were about 300 m higher than the present time, flooding major portions of the continents. However, if all of Earth's glacial ice were melted today, sea level would only rise about 80 m. How, then, is it possible to flood the continents? It turns out that during the Cretaceous Period there were many ridge systems, and plate velocities were relatively fast. This meant that there was a lot of warm ocean lithosphere, so the average level of the seafloor was much higher than today. If you lift up the seafloor, the water gets pushed up onto the continents. This has happened several times in Earth's history, with the result that many parts of the continents that are now far from the ocean are covered with horizontal layers of sedimentary rock like shale, sandstone, and limestone, all of which formed under water.

The Ocean Seafloor Mineral Factory

The theory of plate tectonics explains many things about Earth's geology, but one of the most relevant has to do with the global distribution of resources of metals and ores. It turns out that high concentrations of metals and ores are often found at subduction zones or ancient subduction zones. Why is this? The answer, interestingly, begins at mid-ocean ridges. The high volumes of water circulating through the mid-ocean ridge act like a chemical factory, removing metals and ores from the ocean crust. Cold water is pulled into the crust, and as it heats up, it begins to dissolve out incompatible elements like metals. This can be seen at mid-ocean ridge thermal vents, which are so rich in metals that the water is black. When the hot water rises up into the ocean, however, the metals precipitate out onto the seafloor. Then, these metals are carried toward an ocean trench along the ocean floor, like a slow conveyor belt. Upon reaching the trench of the subduction zone, some of the metals are scraped off into accretionary wedges. Others are subducted, but rise back up as part of the magma that forms subduction zone volcanoes. In either case, the process of plate tectonics removes metals and ores from ocean crust and concentrates it at subduction zones.

BUILD READING LITERACY
Preview

Understanding Text Structure
Skim Ahead to Understand Text Organization
Strategy Get an advance idea of how the text is organized and activate prior knowledge. This prereading strategy involves skimming the titles, headings, visuals, and boldfaced text. Like checking a roadmap before beginning a trip, previewing helps the reader to recall familiar material and to prepare to learn new material. Before students begin to read, select a portion of Chapter 14 for them to preview, such as pp. 394–400.

Example
1. Ask students to look at the chapter title, section titles, and heads. Tell them to notice whether the terms and concepts mentioned are familiar or unfamiliar.
2. Have students look at the Reading Strategy for the specific section to be previewed.
3. Ask students to compare the key questions and the boldfaced statements in the section.
4. Have students look at the visuals in the section and (where possible) relate each to a specific heading.
5. You may wish to have students prepare a study guide using the headings, key questions, and vocabulary as categories in a chart showing the section organization. Have students read the selected pages in depth, filling in the chart with details as they read.

See TE p. 402 for a script on how to use this strategy with students. For additional strategies, see TE pp. 399 and 408.

CHAPTER 14

ASSESS PRIOR KNOWLEDGE

Use the Chapter Pretest below to assess students' prior knowledge. As needed, review these concepts.

Review Science Concepts

Lesson 14.1 Reviewing the size and geography of the ocean basins will help students recognize the importance of Earth's oceans as a component of Earth Science. Learning about methods used to map the ocean floor leads to an understanding of the multidisciplinary nature of oceanography.

Lesson 14.2 Knowledge of the features of the ocean floor and how they are formed allows students to compare the geology of the ocean floor with the geology of land features.

Lesson 14.3 Understanding how ocean sediments form gives students an opportunity to explore how geology, biology, and chemistry contribute to the study of oceanography.

Lesson 14.4 Knowledge of how energy and mineral resources form on and under the ocean floor helps ensure that students understand the economic importance of ocean resources and the technological challenges involved in recovering those resources.

Review Math Skills

Calculate: Line Graphs Students need to calculate rates of speed and graph data.

Direct students to the **Math Skills** in the **Skill Handbook** at the end of the student text.

14 The Ocean Floor

Big idea

Water Planet

Q: What is at the bottom of the ocean?

392

Chapter Pretest

1. Approximately how much of Earth's surface is covered by ocean? *(c)*
 a. 60% **b.** 66%
 c. 71% **d.** 78%

2. Which of the following is not a feature found on the ocean floor? *(b)*
 a. abyssal plain
 b. coral atoll
 c. submarine canyon
 d. guyot

3. Sediments that cover the ocean floor come from which of the following? *(d)*
 a. life forms
 b. land
 c. water
 d. all of the above

4. Name the Earth's four main ocean basins. *(Pacific, Atlantic, Indian, Arctic)*

5. Name three kinds of technologies used to study the ocean floor. *(sonar, satellite, submersibles)*

6. Name at least five natural resources that are mined from the ocean floor. *(oil, natural gas, gas hydrates, sand and gravel, evaporative salts, manganese nodules)*

Below is a familiar scene in sunlit seawater, but what lies beyond in the darkness of deep waters?

INQUIRY

TRY IT!

HOW DOES PARTICLE SIZE AFFECT SETTLING RATES?

Procedure

1. Fill two large transparent containers with water. Place two samples of sediment, one clay and one sand, on separate sheets of white paper. Examine the sediments with a hand lens. Determine which sediment sample has larger-sized particles. Record your observations.

2. Carefully measure 1 tbsp of the clay sample. Hold the spoon directly above the first container and pour the clay into the water. Using a stopwatch, time how long it takes for the entire clay sample to reach the bottom of the container and settle. Record the time.

3. Repeat Step 2 using the second container and the sand sample. Be sure to hold the spoon the same distance from the container as you did in the clay sample.

Think About It

1. **Draw Conclusions** Which sample had smaller particles? Which sample took longer to settle in the water? Explain the general relationship between sediment size and settling rates.

2. **Predict** Both of these sediments enter ocean water from rivers. Predict which type of sediment would be found closest to the coast. Which will be found farther away? Explain.

393

ENGAGE/EXPLORE

INQUIRY
TRY IT!

HOW DOES PARTICLE SIZE AFFECT SETTLING RATES? **L2**

Purpose In this activity, students will begin to
- recognize that sediment particle size affects settling rate.
- understand that settling rates affect how far sediments can be carried by river water that enters the ocean.

Skills Measure, Infer

Prep Time 15 minutes

Materials 2 large transparent containers, water, clay, sand, 2 sheets of white paper, hand lens, stopwatch

Class Time 15–20 minutes

Teaching Tip It may take a long time for the clay sample to settle out of the water. You may wish to ask students to compare the settling rates of gravel and sand instead.

Expected Outcome Clay sample has smaller particles and takes longer to settle. Sand has larger particles and takes less time to settle.

Think About It

1. The clay sample has smaller particles and takes longer to settle. The smaller and finer the sediment, the longer it will take to settle.
2. Sand, which is larger, will settle first and will be found closer to the coast. Clay takes longer to settle, will be carried farther by ocean currents, and will reach areas farther from the coast.

1 FOCUS

Lesson Objectives

14.1 **Recognize** that most of Earth's surface is covered by water.

14.2 **List** Earth's four main ocean basins and **identify** their locations.

14.3 **Describe** the topography of the ocean floor and **compare** it to land.

14.4 **Identify** and **describe** three major technologies used to study the ocean floor.

Build Vocabulary L2

Word Parts Before students read this lesson, ask them to write the meanings of the prefix *bathy-* and the suffix *-metry*. Then have them write what they think the word *bathymetry* means. After students read the lesson, have them discuss whether their prediction was correct.

Reading Strategy L2

a. measurement of ocean depths and charting the shape of the ocean floor
b. small underwater craft used for deep-sea research

2 INSTRUCT

(Teacher **Demo**)

One Ocean L2

Purpose Students see how Earth's ocean basins are connected.

Materials world globe

Procedure Have students point out the regions on the globe where oceans connect.

Expected Outcome Students will see that the Atlantic, Pacific, and Indian Oceans connect in the region surrounding Antarctica. The Atlantic and Pacific Oceans connect with the Arctic Ocean.
Visual, Logical

Key Questions

🔑 How much of Earth's surface is covered by ocean?

🔑 How can the world ocean be divided?

🔑 How does the topography of the ocean floor compare to that on land?

🔑 What types of technology are used to study the ocean floor?

Vocabulary

- bathymetry
- submersible

Reading Strategy

Build Vocabulary Draw a table similar to the one below that includes all the vocabulary terms listed for the section. As you read the section, define each term in your own words.

Vocabulary Term	Definition
bathymetry	a. _____ ?
submersible	b. _____ ?

HOW DEEP is the deepest part of the ocean? How much of Earth is covered by ocean? What does the ocean floor look like? Humans have long been interested in finding answers to these questions. However, it was not until relatively recently that these questions could be answered. Suppose, for example, that all of the water were drained from the ocean. What would we see? Plains? Mountains? Canyons? Plateaus? You may be surprised to find that the ocean conceals all of these features, and more.

Geography of the Oceans

Look at **Figure 1.** You can see why the "blue planet" or the "water planet" are appropriate nicknames for Earth. 🔑 **Nearly 71 percent of Earth's surface is covered by the world ocean.**

Northern Hemisphere

North Pole

FIGURE 1 The World Ocean These views of Earth show how a single interconnected world ocean covers much of Earth.

South Pole

Southern Hemisphere

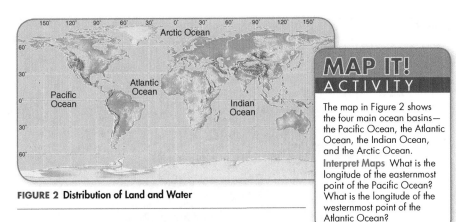

FIGURE 2 Distribution of Land and Water

MAP IT!
ACTIVITY

The map in Figure 2 shows the four main ocean basins— the Pacific Ocean, the Atlantic Ocean, the Indian Ocean, and the Arctic Ocean.

Interpret Maps What is the longitude of the easternmost point of the Pacific Ocean? What is the longitude of the westernmost point of the Atlantic Ocean?

Although the ocean makes up a much greater percentage of Earth's surface than the continents, it has only been since the late 1800s that the ocean became an important focus of study. New technologies have allowed scientists to collect large amounts of data about the ocean. As technology has advanced, the field of oceanography has grown. *Oceanography* is a science that draws on the methods and knowledge of geology, chemistry, physics, and biology to study all aspects of the world ocean.

The area of Earth's surface is about 510 million square kilometers. Approximately 360 million square kilometers consists of oceans and smaller seas such as the Mediterranean Sea and the Caribbean Sea. Continents and islands comprise the remaining 150 million square kilometers. 🔑 **The world ocean can be divided into four main ocean basins—the Pacific Ocean, the Atlantic Ocean, the Indian Ocean, and the Arctic Ocean.** The locations of these ocean basins are shown in **Figure 2.**

The Pacific Ocean is the largest and deepest ocean basin. In fact, it is the largest single geographic feature on Earth. It covers more than half of the ocean surface area on Earth and has an average depth of 3940 meters.

The Atlantic Ocean is about half the size of the Pacific Ocean, and is not quite as deep. It is a relatively narrow ocean compared to the Pacific. The Atlantic and Pacific Oceans are bounded to the east and west by continents.

The Indian Ocean is slightly smaller than the Atlantic Ocean, but it has about the same average depth. Unlike the Pacific and Atlantic oceans, the Indian Ocean is located largely in the Southern Hemisphere.

The Arctic Ocean is about 7 percent of the size of the Pacific Ocean. It is only a little more than one-quarter as deep as the rest of the oceans.

☑ **Reading Checkpoint** *What are the four main ocean basins?*

Integrate Math L2

Geometry and Projections Explain to students that the map pictured on this page is a Mercator projection. Because Earth is a sphere, two-dimensional representations of Earth invariably have some distortion. On projections such as this, the degree of distortion increases with distance from the equator. **Ask:** Where on this projection is distortion greatest? *(the northern and southern extremes, or the poles)* What landmasses do you think are the most distorted? *(Greenland and Antarctica)* Explain in geometric terms why these landmasses are so distorted. *(Because Earth is a sphere, lines of longitude come closer together as distance from the equator increases. These lines meet at the poles. To represent a spherical body as a two-dimensional grid, the lines run parallel rather than meeting at the poles, and the features between them become stretched.)* **Visual, Logical**

Answers

MAP IT! easternmost point of Pacific: approximately 70°W; westernmost point of Atlantic: approximately 100°W

☑ **Reading Checkpoint** *Pacific Ocean, Atlantic Ocean, Indian Ocean, Arctic Ocean*

Differentiated Instruction

VISUALLY IMPAIRED Provide students with a relief world map or globe. Allow students to experience the interconnected nature of the world's oceans by helping them trace the outlines of the oceans with their fingers. Students can also compare the sizes of Earth's four main ocean basins. This learning tool can be used by both visually impaired students and tactile learners. (A relief map of the ocean floor can be used in a similar way to allow students to experience deep ocean trenches, ridges, seamounts, and guyots.)

Use Visuals `L1`

Figure 3 Have students examine the map showing the topographic features of the ocean floor. **Ask:** In which ocean basin are most of the oceanic trenches located? *(Pacific)* Which ocean basins contain mid-ocean ridges? *(Atlantic, Indian* and *Pacific)* What is the major undersea geological feature in the Atlantic Ocean? *(Mid-Atlantic Ridge)*

Build Science Skills `L2`

Pose Questions Have students write one or more questions they have about the characteristics of the ocean floor. Ask them to formulate each question so that it could be used as the basis for scientific research. *(Sample questions: Do ocean floor features have an effect on currents? What methods can be used to determine if life exists on all areas of the ocean floor?)* After students have written their questions, ask them to describe how they might go about answering their questions. *(Sample answers: Examine how current flow changes as water passes by ocean floor features. Design an experiment or field study to test different devices used to detect organisms living at great depths.)* If necessary, assist students in phrasing their questions so that they can serve as the basis for a scientific inquiry.
Verbal, Logical

FIGURE 3 A Map of the Ocean Floor The ocean floor contains mountain ranges, trenches, and flat regions called abyssal plains. **Interpret Diagrams** *List all of the features you can identify in the figure.*

Mapping the Ocean Floor

If all the water were drained from the ocean basins, chains of volcanoes, tall mountain ranges, trenches, and large plateaus would be revealed. **The topography—shape and landforms—of the ocean floor is as diverse as that of continents.** The topographic features of the ocean floor are shown in **Figure 3.**

Considering that it is not possible to drain the ocean, how do scientists know what the ocean floor looks like? An understanding of ocean-floor features came with the development of techniques to

396 Chapter 14 • Lesson 1

Facts and Figures

On average, the depth of the oceans is more than four times the elevation of the continents. The average elevation of the continents is about 840 m above sea level. The average depth of the oceans is 3729 m. If Earth's solid mass were perfectly smooth and spherical, ocean water would cover it all to a depth of more than 2000 m.

Greenland

Arctic
Mid-Ocean Ridge

Asia

Gibbs
Fracture
Zone

Puerto-Rico
Trench

Atlantic
Ocean

Red Sea
Rift

Demerara
Abyssal Plain

Mid-Atlantic Ridge

Africa

Mid-Indian Ridge

South
America

St. Paul
Fracture
Zone

Indian
Ocean

Peru-Chile
trench

Southeast Indian Ridge

Southwest Indian Ridge

South Sandwich
Trench

Weddell Abyssal Plain

Key: ⇌ transform fault

to measure the depth of the oceans. **Bathymetry** (*bathos* = depth, *metry* = measurement) is the measurement of ocean depths and the charting of the topography of the ocean floor.

The first understanding of the ocean floor's topography did not unfold until the historic three-and-a-half-year voyage of the HMS *Challenger*. From December 1872 to May 1876, the *Challenger* expedition made the first study of the global ocean ever attempted by one group. The ship's crew and researchers traveled through every ocean except for the Arctic for a total of 127,500 kilometers.

Integrate Social Studies   L2

Challenger Expedition Explain to students that the journey of the *HMS Challenger* is considered by many to be the birth of oceanography. Before the *Challenger* Expedition, enough information about Earth's oceans had been collected to make scientists and sailors alike realize that an extensive ocean survey would be of great benefit. The success of the expedition inspired the launching of many subsequent ocean research surveys. Point out to students that the expedition took place during a time when most ships used wind and sail for propulsion, and submarine cables carried most transoceanic communications. **Ask:** In what ways would data on ocean currents, prevailing winds, and weather patterns collected by *Challenger* scientists have been useful to others? *(added to knowledge about the oceans; provided help to sailors and ship captains trying to chart the best course for a journey)* In what ways would depth measurements and other data about the nature of the ocean bottom have been helpful to others? *(assist companies in making decisions about where and how to lay submarine cables)*
Verbal

Answers

Figure 3 *mid-ocean ridges, trenches, abyssal plains, seamounts*

Facts and Figures

The Challenger Expedition took data from 362 locations scattered throughout the Atlantic, Pacific, and Indian Oceans. Scientists traveling with the expedition took charge of different research aspects. Matthew Maury (1806–1873), an American naval officer, was in charge of charts and instruments. Edward Forbes (1815–1854) was a British biologist who had already done extensive research in shallower waters

around Britain and in the Aegean Sea. Forbes led the expedition's collection and analysis of biological specimens. Before the expedition, Forbes had predicted that life would not be found below about 2000 m in the deep sea. Challenger Expedition findings proved that life existed at least as deep as 6000 m; it is now known that life exists even at the bottom of the deepest ocean trenches.

Build Math Skills L1

Line Graphs Have students graph sonar results for a hypothetical transect of the ocean bottom. Provide students with the following time intervals for four sonar data points, each taken 10 km apart. Sample data: 3.2 s, 5.5 s, 7.2 s, 6.4 s. First, have students calculate the depth for each data point (time/2 × 1500 m/s). *(3.2 s: 2400 m; 5.5 s: 4125 m; 7.2 s: 5400 m; 6.4 s: 4800 m)* Second, invite students to graph their results, placing distance (km) between data points on the *x*-axis and depth (m) on the *y*-axis. Have students connect their data points to create a line on the graph. Ask students what the line represents. *(a rough profile of part of the ocean floor)*
Logical, Visual

Build Science Skills L2

Infer Remind students of the difference between sound waves and microwaves. Sound waves are produced by vibrating matter. Microwaves are a form of electromagnetic energy. **Ask:** Which type of wave has more energy? *(microwaves)* Why can't sound waves be used to gather ocean height data from satellites? *(Sound waves must have a medium to travel through. Satellites orbit high in Earth's atmosphere, where there are too few molecules to transmit sound.)*
Logical, Verbal

FIGURE 4 Sonar Methods
A By using sonar, oceanographers can determine the depth of the ocean floor in a particular area.

B Modern multibeam sonar obtains a profile of a narrow swath of ocean floor every few seconds.

Throughout the voyage, the scientists sampled various ocean properties. They measured water depth by lowering weighted ropes that were kilometers long. Modern-day researchers no longer have to wait for long ropes to be dropped overboard to reveal ocean depths. 🔖 **Today's technology—particularly sonar, satellites, and submersibles—allows scientists to study the ocean floor in a more efficient and precise manner than ever before.**

Sonar In the 1920s, a technological breakthrough occurred with the invention of sonar, a technique that uses sound to detect objects or to aid navigation. Sonar is an acronym for **so**und **na**vigation and **r**anging. Some types of sonar are also referred to as echo sounding. Sonar can be used to measure ocean depths by transmitting sound waves toward the ocean bottom, as shown in **Figure 4A.** With simple sonar, a sensitive receiver detects the echo reflected from the bottom. Then a clock precisely measures the time interval to fractions of a second. Depth can be calculated from the speed of sound waves in water—about 1500 meters per second—and the time required for the energy pulse to reach the ocean floor and return. The depths determined from continuous monitoring of these echoes are plotted. In this way a profile of the ocean floor is obtained.

In the last few decades, researchers have designed even more sophisticated sonar that can be used to map the ocean floor. In contrast to simple sonar, multibeam sonar uses more than one sound source and listening device. As shown in **Figure 4B,** this technique obtains a profile of a narrow strip of ocean floor rather than obtaining the depth of a single point every few seconds.

These profiles are recorded every few seconds as the research vessel advances. When a ship uses multibeam sonar to map a section of ocean floor, it travels through the area in a regularly spaced back-and-forth pattern. Not surprisingly, this method is known as "mowing the lawn."

Satellites Measuring the shape of the ocean surface from space is another technological breakthrough that has led to a better understanding of the ocean floor. After compensating for waves, tides, currents, and atmospheric effects, scientists discovered that the ocean surface is not perfectly flat. Gravity attracts water toward regions where massive ocean floor features occur. Therefore, mountains and ridges produce elevated areas on the ocean surface. Features such as canyons and trenches cause slight depressions.

The differences in ocean-surface height caused by ocean floor features are not visible to the human eye. However, satellites are able to measure these small differences by bouncing microwaves off the ocean surface. **Figure 5** shows how the outgoing radar pulses are reflected back to a satellite. The height of the ocean surface can be calculated by knowing the satellite's exact position. Devices on satellites can measure variations in ocean surface height as small as 3 to 6 centimeters. This type of data has added greatly to the knowledge of ocean-floor topography. Cross-checked with traditional sonar depth measurements, the data are used to produce detailed ocean-floor maps, such as the one shown in Figure 3.

☑ **Reading Checkpoint** *How do satellites help us learn about the shape of the ocean floor?*

FIGURE 5 **Satellite Method** Satellites can be used to measure ocean surface height. The data collected by satellites can be used to predict the location of large features on the ocean floor. This method of data collection is much faster than using sonar.

The Ocean Floor **399**

PLANET DIARY

For links about **Mapping the Ocean Floor**, visit PlanetDiary.com/HSES.

Build Reading Literacy

L1

Refer to **p. 216D** in **Chapter 8,** which provides guidelines for this compare and contrast strategy.

Compare and Contrast After students have read the sections on bathymetric methods, have them create a table that compares simple sonar, multibeam sonar, and satellite bathymetry technologies in terms of data collection method used and the type of data obtained. Ask students to summarize advantages or disadvantages of each technology with respect to the others.

	Simple sonar	Multibeam sonar	Satellite
Method	Sound waves	Sound waves	Microwaves
Type of data	Ocean floor depth	Ocean floor depth	Ocean surface height, correlated to ocean depth
Advantages	Simple to use	More detailed	Most detailed of all
Disadvantages	Time-consuming	Time-consuming	Must be cross-checked with sonar measurements

Verbal, Visual

Answers

☑ **Reading Checkpoint** *Satellites bounce microwaves off the ocean surface. Outgoing radar pulses are reflected back to the satellite and can be used to detect differences in sea surface height that can be correlated to ocean floor features.*

LESSON 14.1

Build Science Skills `L2`

Communicate Results Have students work in small groups to research information about submersibles and the scientists who use them. Have each group investigate a different submersible. Possibilities include William Beebe's sphere, *Trieste, Alvin,* and *Jason.* Have the groups orally present their findings to the class.

3 ASSESS

Evaluate Understanding `L2`

To assess students' knowledge of lesson content, have them write a short paragraph comparing the ocean floor to Earth's landmasses. Have them write another paragraph describing how sonar, satellites, and submersibles can be used to gather data about the deep ocean.

Reteach `L1`

Have students make a timeline that describes how bathymetric techniques have changed over the years since the *Challenger* expedition. Invite students to explain their timelines and each of the methods shown on their timelines to the class.

FIGURE 6 Submersible The *DeepWorker* can reach depths of 600 meters and carries one passenger. Many of its functions are controlled by a computer at the surface so that the passenger can concentrate on exploration.

Submersibles A **submersible** is a small underwater craft used for deep-sea research. Submersibles are used to collect data about areas of the ocean that were previously unreachable by humans. Submersibles are equipped with a number of instruments ranging from thermometers to cameras to pressure gauges. The operators of submersibles can record video and take photographs of creatures that live in the deep ocean. They can also collect water samples and sediment samples for analysis.

The first submersible was used in 1934 by William Beebe. He descended to a depth of 923 meters off of Bermuda in a steel sphere that was tethered to a ship. Since that time, submersibles have become much more sophisticated. In 1960, Jacques Piccard descended in the untethered submersible *Trieste* to 10,912 meters below the ocean surface into the Mariana Trench. *Alvin* is a sumbersible owned by the United States Navy that can descend about 4500 meters and carry a crew of three.

Today, many submersibles are unmanned and operated remotely by computers. These remotely operated vehicles (ROVs) can remain underwater for long periods. They collect data, record video, use sonar, and collect sample organisms with remotely operated arms. Autonomous underwater vehicles (AUVs) collect data about the seafloor, search for landmines, or search for potential mining sites without receiving commands from the surface.

14.1 Assessment

Review Key Concepts 🔑

1. Compare the area of Earth's surface covered by ocean with the area covered by land.

2. Name the four ocean basins. Which of the four ocean basins is the largest? Which is located almost entirely in the Southern Hemisphere?

3. How does the topography of the ocean floor compare to that on land? Name three topographic features found on the ocean floor.

4. What types of technology are used to study the ocean floor?

5. Describe how sonar is used to determine ocean floor depth.

Think Critically

6. **Compare and Contrast** Compare and contrast the use of satellites and submersibles to collect data about the topography of the ocean floor.

7. **Infer** Why are deep-sea exploration and data collection difficult?

MATH PRACTICE

8. **Calculate** Assuming the average speed of sound waves in water is 1500 meters per second, determine the water depth in meters if a sonar signal requires 4.5 seconds to hit the bottom and return to the recorder.

Assessment Answers

1. Nearly 71 percent of Earth's surface is covered by oceans, 29 percent is covered by land.
2. Pacific Ocean, Atlantic Ocean, Indian Ocean, Arctic Ocean; Pacific Ocean; Indian Ocean
3. The topography of the ocean floor is as diverse as that of continents. Three topographic features: mid-ocean ridges, trenches, abyssal plains.
4. sonar, satellites, submersibles

5. Sonar works by transmitting sound waves to the ocean bottom. A receiver intercepts the echo reflected from the ocean bottom and a clock measures the time it takes for the sound wave to travel to the ocean bottom and back.
6. Both are used to find out more about the seafloor's topography. Satellites use remote sensing to bounce microwaves off the sea surface to determine differences in height. Submersibles can be manned or unmanned,

travel to deep areas, and record data with video and other instruments.
7. The deep ocean is a harsh environment for humans—cold, dark, and under high pressure. It is difficult to supply submersibles with power for continuous use.
8. 4.5 s/2 × 1500 m/s = 3375 m

14.2 Ocean Floor Features

OCEANOGRAPHERS studying the topography of the ocean floor have divided the floor into three major regions. 🔑 **The ocean floor regions are the continental margins, the ocean basin floor, and the mid-ocean ridge.** The map in **Figure 7** outlines these regions for the North Atlantic Ocean. The profile at the bottom of the illustration shows the varied topography.

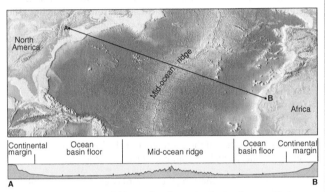

FIGURE 7 Topography of the North Atlantic Ocean Basin Beneath the map is a profile of the area between points A and B. The profile has been exaggerated 40 times to make the topographic features more distinct.

Continental Margins

The zone of transition between a continent and the adjacent ocean basin floor is known as the **continental margin.** 🔑 **In the Atlantic Ocean, thick layers of undisturbed sediment cover the continental margin. This region has very little volcanic or earthquake activity.** This is because the continental margins in the Atlantic Ocean are not associated with plate boundaries. The continental margins in the Pacific Ocean are associated with plate boundaries. 🔑 **In the Pacific Ocean, oceanic crust is plunging beneath continental crust. This force results in a narrow continental margin that experiences both volcanic activity and earthquakes.** Figure 8 on the next page shows the features of a continental margin found along the Atlantic coast.

Key Questions

🔑 **What are the three main regions of the ocean floor?**

🔑 **How do continental margins in the Atlantic Ocean differ from those in the Pacific Ocean?**

🔑 **How are deep-ocean trenches formed?**

🔑 **How are abyssal plains formed?**

🔑 **What is formed at mid-ocean ridges?**

Vocabulary
- continental margin
- continental shelf
- continental slope
- submarine canyon
- turbidity current
- continental rise
- ocean basin floor
- abyssal plain
- seamount
- mid-ocean ridge
- seafloor spreading

Reading Strategy

Outline Before you read, make an outline of this section. Use the orange headings as the main topics and the blue headings as subtopics. As you read, add supporting details.

I. Continental Margins
A. Continental Shelf
B. Continental Slope
C. _____ ?
II. _____ ?
A. _____ ?

The Ocean Floor **401**

1 FOCUS

Lesson Objectives
14.5 **List** the three main regions of the ocean floor.
14.6 **Differentiate** between the continental margins of the Atlantic and Pacific Oceans.
14.7 **Explain** the formation of deep-ocean trenches and abyssal plains and how new ocean floor is formed at mid-ocean ridges.

Build Vocabulary L2
Concept Map Have students make a concept map using the term *ocean floor features* as the starting point. All the vocabulary terms in this lesson should be used.

Reading Strategy L2
  C. Continental Rise
II. Ocean Basin Floor
  A. Deep-Ocean Trenches
  B. Abyssal Plains
  C. Seamounts and Guyots
III. Mid-Ocean Ridges
  A. Seafloor Spreading
  B. Hydrothermal Vents

2 INSTRUCT

Use Visuals L1
Figure 7 Point out to students that the profile shown below the map is a side view of the ocean floor along the line between points A and B on the map. **Ask:** Why do the topographic features have to be exaggerated to make them more distinct? *(The scale of the map is so large that the elevation differences between ocean floor, continental margin, and mid-ocean ridge would not be visible. If the map were 40 times larger, the exaggeration wouldn't be necessary, but the map would be too large to print.)* Look back at the map of the ocean floor shown in Figure 3. How would a profile of the Pacific Ocean basin differ from this profile of the Atlantic Ocean? *(The profile of the Pacific Ocean basin would not show a central mid-ocean ridge. Instead, depending on how the transect line is drawn, it would show trenches, chains of volcanic islands, or coral atolls.)*
Visual, Logical

LESSON 14.2

Build Reading Literacy L1

Refer to **p. 392D** in this chapter, which provides the guidelines for this previewing strategy.

Preview Have students skim headings, titles of visuals, and boldfaced text for Lesson 14.2 Ocean Floor Features. Invite them to think in broad terms about what they will read. **Ask:** What do the orange heads have in common? *(They are all parts of the ocean floor.)* What do the blue section heads have in common? *(Most are terms for smaller features of the ocean, usually associated with one of the three parts of the ocean.)*
Visual, Logical

Integrate Biology L2

Sunlight and Ocean Life Explain that the ocean bottom along the continental margins supports a greater variety of living organisms than other regions of the ocean floor. Tell students that sunlight penetrates ocean water to an average depth of about 300 meters. **Ask:** What kinds of organisms form the basis of almost every food chain? *(organisms capable of photosynthesis)* Why does the continental shelf support a greater amount and variety of life than deeper parts of the ocean floor? *(Sunlight can penetrate to the bottom of at least some parts of the continental shelf; algae and other photosynthetic organisms can live on the bottom and serve as the basis for ocean food chains along the continental shelf. Deeper regions of the ocean floor do not receive sunlight and so do not support photosynthetic organisms that would form the basis of food chains.)*
Logical, Verbal

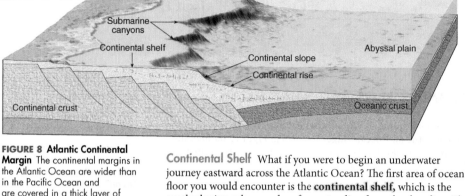

FIGURE 8 Atlantic Continental Margin The continental margins in the Atlantic Ocean are wider than in the Pacific Ocean and are covered in a thick layer of sediment.
Compare and Contrast *What are two ways in which an illustration of the continental margin in the Pacific Ocean would differ from this illustration of the continental margin in the Atlantic Ocean?*

Continental Shelf What if you were to begin an underwater journey eastward across the Atlantic Ocean? The first area of ocean floor you would encounter is the **continental shelf,** which is the gently sloping submerged surface extending from the shoreline. The shelf is almost nonexistent along some coastlines. However, the shelf may extend seaward as far as 1500 kilometers along other coastlines. On average, the continental shelf is about 80 kilometers wide and 130 meters deep at its seaward edge. The average steepness of the shelf is equal to a drop of only about 2 meters per kilometer. The slope is so slight that it cannot be detected by the human eye.

Continental shelves have economic and political significance. **Continental shelves contain important mineral deposits, large reservoirs of oil and natural gas, and huge sand and gravel deposits.** The waters of the continental shelf also contain important fishing grounds, which are significant sources of food.

Continental Slope Marking the seaward edge of the continental shelf is the **continental slope.** This slope is steeper than the shelf, and it marks the boundary between continental crust and oceanic crust. The continental slope can be seen in Figure 8. Although the steepness of the continental slope varies greatly from place to place, it averages about 5 degrees. In some places the slope may exceed 25 degrees. The continental slope is a relatively narrow feature, averaging only about 20 kilometers in width.

Deep, steep-sided valleys known as **submarine canyons** are cut into the continental slope. These canyons may extend to the ocean basin floor. Some of these canyons appear to be extensions of river valleys, but many of them do not line up in this manner.

Figure 9 shows how submarine canyons may form. Most information suggests that submarine canyons have been eroded, at least in part, by turbidity currents. **Turbidity currents** are occasional movements of dense, sediment-rich water down the continental slope. The currents form when sand and mud on the continental shelf and slope are disturbed—perhaps by an earthquake—and become suspended in the water.

Differentiated Instruction

ENGLISH LANGUAGE LEARNERS Tell students that the words *abyss* and *floor* are used as synonyms with reference to the deep ocean bottom. Explain that the word *abyss* means a "bottomless depth" and historically has been used to describe the unknown. Before people developed technologies for deep sea exploration, the bottom of the ocean was considered by many to be the abyss referred to in many myths—a bottomless pit that humans could not know or understand. The word *floor* means "the ground surface." Its use as a descriptor of the ocean bottom is more recent, and does not imply a sense of the unknown.

Submarine canyons

Turbidity current

Turbidity current

FIGURE 9 Submarine Canyons Some submarine canyons appear to be extensions of river valleys. Others were formed and continue to be eroded by turbidity currents.

Because muddy water is denser than normal seawater, it flows down the slope and erodes and accumulates more sediment. Erosion from these muddy torrents is thought to be the major force in the formation of most submarine canyons. Narrow continental margins, such as the one along the California coast, are marked with many submarine canyons.

Turbidity currents are known to be an important mechanism of sediment transport in the ocean. Turbidity currents erode submarine canyons and deposit sediments on the deep-ocean floor.

Continental Rise In regions where trenches do not exist, the steep continental slope merges into a more gradual incline known as the **continental rise.** The continental rise consists of a thick layer of sediment that moved downslope from the continental shelf to the deep-ocean floor. Here the steepness of the slope drops to about 6 meters per kilometer. Whereas the width of the continental slope averages about 20 kilometers, the continental rise may be hundreds of kilometers wide.

☑ **Reading Checkpoint** *Compare and contrast the continental slope and continental rise.*

Ocean Basin Floor

Between the continental margin and mid-ocean ridge lies the **ocean basin floor.** The size of this region—almost 30 percent of Earth's surface—is comparable to the percentage of land above sea level. This region includes very flat regions known as abyssal plains, deep-ocean trenches, and tall volcanic peaks called seamounts and guyots.

INQUIRY APPLY IT!

Q: *Have humans ever explored the deepest ocean trenches? Does anything live there?*

A: Humans have indeed visited the deepest part of the oceans—where there is crushing high pressure, complete darkness, and near-freezing water temperatures. In January 1960, U.S. Navy Lt. Don Walsh and explorer Jacques Piccard descended to the bottom of the Challenger Deep region of the Mariana Trench in the deep-diving submersible *Trieste*. It took more than five hours to reach the bottom at 10,912 meters—a record depth of human descent that has not been broken. They did see some organisms that are adapted to life in the deep such as a small flatfish, a shrimp, and some jellyfish.

Sediment Buildup **L2**

Purpose Demonstrate to students how layers of sediment build up over time on the ocean floor, covering irregular rock to form a flat abyssal plain.

Materials small glass aquarium tank, rocks, pebbles, coarse gravel, coarse and fine aquarium sand, bone meal or other fine material that settles out but does not dissolve quickly in water

Procedure Use rocks, pebbles, and gravel to make a model of an irregular ocean floor in the bottom of the aquarium tank. Fill tank 2/3 full of water. As students watch, sprinkle the top of the water with coarse sand and let it settle to the bottom. After it has settled, add a layer of fine sand and let it settle. Repeat alternating layers of sand and other materials.

Expected Outcome As the layers build up, the bottom of the tank will slowly be covered with a smooth layer that models the appearance of an abyssal plain.
Visual, Kinesthetic

  L2

Many students think that Earth's features, including the ocean floor, are unchanging or formed only in the past. To help students realize that tectonic activity and plate motions continue to alter Earth's surface, have them investigate rates of seafloor spreading. Explain to students that new crust is created at spreading centers. You may choose to limit the scope of their research to the Mid-Atlantic Ridge. *(According to the United States Geological Survey, the Mid-Atlantic Ridge is spreading at a rate of about 2.5 cm per year.)*
Logical

Geologist's Sketch

FIGURE 10 Abyssal Plain Cross Section Rock structures beneath the ocean floor can be mapped with seismic reflection profiles. The procedure is similar to sonar, but sounds are produced by explosions. This seismic reflection profile and matching sketch is of a portion of the Madeira abyssal plain in the eastern Atlantic. They reveal how the irregular oceanic crust is buried by sediment.

Abyssal Plains **Abyssal plains** are deep, extremely flat features. In fact, these regions are possibly the most level places on Earth. Abyssal plains have thick accumulations of fine sediment that have buried an otherwise rugged ocean floor, as shown in **Figure 10**. 🔎 **The sediments that make up abyssal plains are carried there by turbidity currents or deposited as a result of suspended sediments settling.** Abyssal plains are found in all oceans of the world. However, the Atlantic Ocean has the most extensive abyssal plains because it has few trenches to catch sediment carried down the continental slope.

Deep-Ocean Trenches Deep-ocean trenches are long, narrow creases in the ocean floor that form the deepest parts of the ocean. Most trenches are located along the margins of the Pacific Ocean, and many exceed 10,000 meters in depth. A portion of the Mariana Trench—the Challenger Deep—has been measured at 11,022 meters below sea level and is the deepest known place on Earth.

🔎 **Trenches form at sites of plate convergence where one moving plate descends beneath another and plunges back into the mantle.** Earthquakes and volcanic activity are associated with these regions. The volcanic activity along the margins of the Pacific Ocean is the reason why the region is often called the *Ring of Fire*.

Seamounts and Guyots The volcanic peaks that dot the ocean floor, but are not tall enough to break through the ocean surface, are called **seamounts.** These steep-sided cone-shaped peaks are found on the floors of all the oceans. However, the greatest number have been identified in the Pacific. Some seamounts form at volcanic hot spots. An example is the Hawaiian-Emperor Seamount chain, shown in Figure 3. This chain stretches from the Hawaiian Islands to the Aleutian trench.

Once seamounts reach the surface, they form islands. Over time, running water and wave action erode these volcanic islands to near sea level. Over millions of years, the islands gradually sink and may disappear below the water surface. This process occurs as the moving plate slowly carries the islands away from the elevated oceanic ridge or hot spot where they originated. Once the inactive volcano is again submerged, the structure is called a *guyot*.

☑ **Reading Checkpoint** *What are abyssal plains?*

Mid-Ocean Ridges

The **mid-ocean ridge** is an interconnected system of mostly underwater mountains that have developed on newly formed ocean crust. This system is the longest topographic feature on Earth's surface. It exceeds 70,000 kilometers in length. The mid-ocean ridge winds around the globe similar to the way a seam winds over the surface of a baseball.

The term *ridge* may be misleading because the mid-ocean ridge is not narrow. It has widths from 1000 to 4000 kilometers and may occupy as much as one half of the total area of the ocean floor. Another look at Figure 3 shows that the mid-ocean ridge is broken into segments. These are offset by large transform faults where plates slide past each other horizontally, resulting in shallow earthquakes.

Iceland is actually a section of the mid-Atlantic ridge that is above sea level. **Figure 11** shows a diver swimming in an Icelandic lake between the North American and Eurasian Plates.

Seafloor Spreading A high amount of volcanic activity takes place along the crest of the mid-ocean ridge. This activity is associated with seafloor spreading. **Seafloor spreading** occurs at divergent plate boundaries where two lithospheric plates are moving apart. ⬦ **New ocean floor is formed at mid-ocean ridges as magma rises between the diverging plates and cools.**

Hydrothermal Vents Hydrothermal vents form along mid-ocean ridges. These are zones where mineral-rich water, heated by the newly formed oceanic crust, escapes through cracks in oceanic crust. As the super-heated, mineral-rich water comes in contact with cold water, minerals containing metals such as sulfur, iron, copper, and zinc precipitate and form chimney-like structures.

FIGURE 11 Mid-Atlantic Ridge
This diver is swimming in fresh water, but he is swimming along the Mid-Atlantic Ridge in Iceland between the North American Plate and the Eurasian Plate. Iceland experiences relatively frequent volcanic activity due to its location at a site of seafloor spreading.

14.2 Assessment

Review Key Concepts ⬦

1. What are the three main regions of the ocean floor?

2. How do continental margins in the Atlantic Ocean differ from those in the Pacific Ocean?

3. What are abyssal plains? How are abyssal plains formed?

4. What are trenches? How are deep-ocean trenches formed?

5. What is formed at mid-ocean ridges?

Think Critically

6. **Compare and Contrast** Compare and contrast seamounts and guyots.

7. **Apply Concepts** Explain how turbidity currents are related to submarine canyons.

BIGIDEA WATER PLANET

8. **Describe** Imagine you are about to take an underwater journey in a submersible across the Atlantic Ocean. Write a paragraph describing the ocean floor features you will see on your journey.

The Ocean Floor **405**

3 ASSESS

Evaluate Understanding L2

Have students draw and label a profile of the ocean floor that includes examples of the following: continental margin, continental slope, continental rise, ocean floor, mid-ocean ridge, abyssal plain, submarine trench, seamount, and guyot.

Reteach L1

Have students work in pairs to produce a set of flashcards for each of the lesson's vocabulary terms. Students can use the cards to quiz each other.

Answers

☑ **Reading Checkpoint** *deep, extremely flat regions of the ocean floor*

Assessment Answers

1. continental margin, ocean basin floor, mid-ocean ridge
2. Continental margins in the Atlantic Ocean consist of thick layers of undisturbed sediment and there is little volcanic or earthquake activity. In Pacific Ocean margins, oceanic crust is being pushed beneath continental crust, leaving narrow margins with volcanic and earthquake activity.
3. Trenches are long, narrow creases in the seafloor. They are formed at convergence sites where one plate descends beneath another and plunges back into the mantle.

4. Abyssal plains are deep, extremely flat features of the ocean floor. They are formed as sediments from coastal regions are transport-ed far out to sea and settle to the ocean floor, and as materials from the water column above settle to the bottom.
5. new ocean floor
6. A seamount is an underwater volcano that has not reached the surface of the water yet. A guyot is a volcanic island that has been eroded and sunk back under the water's surface.

7. Turbidity currents consist of dense, mud-choked water that flows down the continental slope. As the currents flow, they erode and accumulate more sediment, creating submarine canyons.
8. Student responses may vary but should include the continental shelf and continental rise, the ocean basin floor with abyssal plains and possibly seamounts, trenches, or a mid-ocean ridge.

The Ocean Floor **405**

Explaining Coral Atolls—
Darwin's Hypothesis **L2**

Have students use an atlas to identify the locations of coral atolls worldwide. **Ask:** At what latitudes are the majority of Earth's coral reefs found? *(tropical latitudes)* What does Darwin's hypothesis of atoll formation imply about the relationship between the rate of growth of coral reefs and the rate at which a volcano sinks? *(In regions where atolls form, corals are able to build reefs at the same rate that the volcano beneath them subsides.)* According to the theory of plate tectonics, what would cause a volcano to sink below the ocean surface? *(Over time, hot ocean seafloor moves away from mid-ocean ridges, cooling and sinking as it becomes more dense. Volcanic islands thus gradually sink below the ocean surface.)*
Visual, Verbal

Explaining Coral Atolls—Darwin's Hypothesis

Coral atolls are ring-shaped structures that often extend several thousand meters below sea level. Corals are soft-bodied, colonial animals that are about the size of an ant. Corals get some nutrients and oxygen from photosynthetic algae that live within their bodies. Most corals protect themselves by precipitating a hard external skeleton made of calcium carbonate. Their skeletons fuse into large structures called coral reefs, which grow over many centuries.

The Habitat of Corals

Corals, like most animals, require specific environmental conditions to survive. Although some types of coral, called deep-sea coral, can grow and produce reefs deep below the ocean surface, the corals that produce atolls cannot. These corals require clear sunlit water—for the photosynthetic algae—and water temperatures of 18°C to 30°C. As a result, reef growth is limited beyond a depth of 45 meters.

Darwin's Observations

So how can these corals build thick atolls that extend thousands of meters deep? The naturalist Charles Darwin was one of the first to formulate a hypothesis on the origin of atolls. From 1831 to 1836, he sailed aboard the British ship HMS *Beagle* during its famous voyage around the world. In various places Darwin noticed a series of stages of coral-atoll development. Development begins with a fringing reef that forms along the sides of a volcanic island, as shown in **Figure 12.** As the volcanic island slowly sinks, the fringing reef becomes a barrier reef. An atoll forms when the volcano sinks completely underwater but the coral reef remains near the surface.

Darwin's Hypothesis

Figure 12 is a drawing that summarizes Darwin's hypothesis about atoll formation. As a volcanic island slowly sinks, the corals continue to build the reef upward. When the base of the reef gets too deep, the coral animals abandon their old calcium carbonate skeletons and move upward where they produce new ones. This explains how living coral reefs, which are restricted to shallow water, have built structures that now exist in much deeper water.

The theory of plate tectonics supports Darwin's hypothesis of atoll formation. Plate tectonics explains how the elevation of a volcanic island changes over long periods of time and how the island eventually disappears. As the hot seafloor moves away from the mid-ocean ridge, it becomes denser and sinks, which lowers the elevation of volcanic islands that are rooted in the seafloor. Darwin's hypothesis is also supported by evidence from drilling that shows volcanic rock is beneath the oldest and deepest coral reef structures.

FIGURE 12 Formation of a Coral Atoll A A fringing coral reef forms around a volcanic island. **B** As the volcanic island sinks, the fringing reef slowly becomes a barrier reef. **C** Eventually, the volcano is completely underwater and a coral atoll remains.

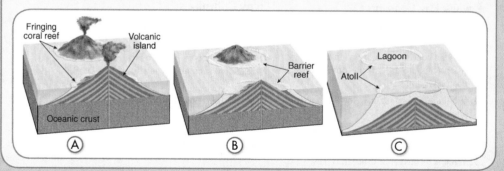

14.3 Seafloor Sediments

EXCEPT FOR steep areas of the continental slope and the crest of the mid-ocean ridge, most of the ocean floor is covered with sediment. Some of this sediment has been deposited by turbidity currents. The rest has slowly settled onto the seafloor. The thickness of ocean-floor sediments varies. Some trenches act as traps for sediment originating on the continental margin. The accumulation may approach 10 kilometers in thickness. In general, however, accumulations of sediment are about 500 to 1000 meters.

Generally, coarser sediments, such as sand, cover the continental shelf and slope while finer sediments, such as clay, cover the deep-ocean floor. Various types of sediment accumulate on nearly all areas of the ocean floor in the same way dust accumulates in all parts of your home. Even the deep-ocean floor, far from land, receives small amounts of windblown material and microscopic parts of organisms.

Types of Seafloor Sediments

Ocean-floor sediments are usually mixtures of the various sediment types. Ocean-floor sediments can be classified according to their origin into three broad categories: terrigenous sediments, biogenous sediments, and hydrogenous sediments. Over millions of years, marine sediments such as sand or the shells and skeletons of ocean organisms can form sedimentary rock. For example, chalk is a form of limestone made up mostly of the tiny shells of one-celled ocean organisms.

Terrigenous Sediment **Terrigenous sediment** is sediment that originates on land. **Terrigenous sediments consist primarily of mineral grains that were eroded from continental rocks and transported to the ocean.** Larger particles such as gravel and sand usually settle rapidly near shore. Finer particles such as clay can take years to settle to the ocean floor and may be carried thousands of kilometers by ocean currents. Clay accumulates very slowly on the deep-ocean floor. To form a 1-centimeter abyssal clay layer, for example, could take 50,000 years. In contrast, on the continental margins near the mouths of large rivers, terrigenous sediment accumulates rapidly and forms thick deposits. In the Gulf of Mexico, for instance, the sediment is many kilometers thick.

The Ocean Floor **407**

Key Questions

🗝 **What are the three types of ocean-floor sediments?**

🗝 **What does terrigenous sediment consist of?**

🗝 **What is the composition of biogenous sediment?**

🗝 **How is hydrogenous sediment formed?**

Vocabulary

- terrigenous sediment
- biogenous sediment
- calcareous ooze
- siliceous ooze
- hydrogenous sediment
- manganese nodule

Reading Strategy

Summarize Make a table like the one below that includes all the headings for the section. Write a brief summary of the text for each heading.

Seafloor Sediments
I. Types of Seafloor Sediments
• Terrigenous sediments originated on land.
• Biogenous sediments are biological in origin.
• _____?

1 FOCUS

Lesson Objectives

14.8 **List** the three types of ocean floor sediments.

14.9 **Describe** the formation of terrigenous, biogenous, and hydrogenous sediments.

Build Vocabulary

Word Parts Have students break the words *terrigenous, biogenous,* and *hydrogenous* into parts, using a dictionary to find the meaning of each part. (*terri-* is from *terra* which means "earth" or "ground"; *bio-* means "life"; *hydro-* means "water"; *-genous* means "producing", "yielding", "origin.")

Reading Strategy

Seafloor Sediments
I. Types of Seafloor Sediments • Terrigenous sediments originated on land. They come from minerals of continental rocks. These sediments are composed of sand and gravel. • Biogenous sediments are biological in origin. They come from shells and skeletons of marine animals and algae. These sediments are composed of calcareous ooze, siliceous ooze, and phosphate-rich material. • Hydrogenous sediments originated in ocean water. They are crystallized through chemical reactions. These sediments are composed of manganese nodules, calcium carbonates, and evaporites.

2 INSTRUCT

Build Science Skills

Predict After students have read the introduction, **ask:** Why do sediment deposits near the continental margins tend to be thicker than those on the floor of the open ocean, far from land? *(Water from rivers and runoff from coastal land transports land sediments to margins. This sediment source does not exist in the open ocean.)*
Logical, Verbal

LESSON 14.3

Biogenous Deposits L2

Purpose Students observe similarities and differences among the types of organisms that form biogenous sediment deposits.

Materials prepared microscope slides of diatoms, foraminifera, and radiolaria; or photographic slides of photomicrographs of these organisms and a slide projector

Procedure Have students examine prepared slides under the microscope or view projected photographic slides. Inform students that these organisms are single-celled members of the phylum protista. Diatoms are algae (plant-like protists) that make their own food through photosynthesis. Foraminifera and radiolaria are animal-like protists that feed on other microscopic organisms. Have students observe similarities and differences among the organisms shown.

Expected Outcome Students will observe that these organisms all have hard structures that vary in shape from species to species and can be preserved after the organisms' soft tissues decay.
Visual

Build Science Skills L2

Student Activity: Classify Have students collect information about products that contain diatomaceous earth. Suggest that students look for these products in local grocery, hardware, auto supply, pool supply, and garden supply stores. By reading the labels, students can collect data about the uses for each product. Challenge students to identify the general applications diatomaceous earth is used for *(filters, abrasives, absorbents)* and classify each product they investigated according to its general application. *(Sample answers: filters: pool cleaning equipment; abrasives: toothpaste, garden insect control; absorbents: materials for cleaning chemical spills)*
Logical, Interpersonal

Build Reading Literacy L1

Refer to **p. 362D** in **Chapter 13**, which provides the guidelines for this Use Prior Knowledge strategy.

Use Prior Knowledge Before students read this lesson, have them make a list of the kinds of materials they think make up the sediment deposits on the ocean floor. After they have read the lesson, have students revise their lists.
Logical, Intrapersonal

FIGURE 13 Biogenous Sediments
The microscopic shells of radiolarians and foraminifers are examples of biogenous sediments. This photomicrograph has been enlarged hundreds of times.

INQUIRY APPLY IT!

Q: *Do we use diatoms in any products?*

A: Diatoms are used in filters for refining sugar and cleaning water in swimming pools. They also are mild abrasives in household cleaning products, polishing products, and facial scrubs; and absorbents for chemical spills.

Biogenous Sediment **Biogenous sediment** is sediment that is biological in origin. **Biogenous sediments consist of shells and skeletons of marine animals and algae.** This debris is produced mostly by microscopic organisms living in surface waters. Once these organisms die, their hard shells sink, accumulating on the seafloor.

The most common biogenous sediment is calcareous ooze. **Calcareous ooze** is produced from the calcium carbonate shells of organisms and has the consistency of thick mud. When calcium carbonate shells slowly sink into deeper parts of the ocean, they begin to dissolve. In ocean water deeper than about 4500 meters, these shells completely dissolve before they reach the bottom. As a result, calcareous ooze does not accumulate in the deeper areas of ocean basins.

Other biogenous sediments include siliceous ooze and phosphate-rich material. **Siliceous ooze** is composed primarily of the shells of single-cell organisms, such as diatoms and radiolarians, that contain silica. The shells of these organisms are shown in **Figure 13.** Phosphate-rich biogenous sediments come from the bones, teeth, and scales of fish and other marine organisms. **Figure 14** shows the distribution of different types of sediment.

☑ **Reading Checkpoint** *Name two types of biogenous sediments.*

Hydrogenous Sediment **Hydrogenous sediment consists of minerals that crystallize directly from ocean water through various chemical reactions.** These sediments make up only a small portion of the overall sediment in the ocean. They do, however, have many different compositions and are distributed in many different environments. Some of the most common types of hydrogenous sediment are listed below.

- **Manganese nodules** are hard lumps of manganese, iron, and other metals. These metals precipitate around an object such as a grain of sand. The nodules can be up to 20 centimeters in diameter and are often scattered across large areas of the deep ocean floor.
- Calcium carbonates form by precipitation directly from ocean water in warm climates. If this material is buried and hardens, a type of limestone forms. Most limestone, however, is composed of biogenous sediment.
- Evaporites form where evaporation rates are high and there is restricted open-ocean circulation. As water evaporates from such areas, the remaining water becomes saturated with dissolved minerals that precipitate. Collectively termed "salts," some evaporite minerals do taste salty, such as halite, or common table salt. Other salts do not taste salty, such as the calcium sulfate minerals anhydrite ($CaSO_4$) and gypsum.

Differentiated Instruction

ENGLISH LANGUAGE LEARNERS Help students understand chemical terms in this lesson by explaining their derivations. Tell students that *sulfides* are substances that contain the element sulfur. *Carbonates* contain the element carbon. The term *evaporites* is derived from the word *evaporation.*

Terrigenous | Coarse nearshore deposits | Fine clay (mud) | Biogenous | Calcareous ooze | Siliceous ooze

Seafloor Sediment and Climate Data Most seafloor sediments contain the remains of organisms that once lived near the sea surface. When these organisms die, their shells slowly settle to ocean floor as sediment. These sediments can provide data about changes in worldwide climate over time, because the numbers and types of organisms that live near the ocean surface change in predictable ways when the climate changes.

For researchers to examine the sediments, ships with drills extract deep cores of sediments. Then researchers examine the layers of sediment and draw conclusions about how the climate has changed over time based on the type of and amount of remains they discover in the samples.

FIGURE 14 Distribution of Seafloor Sediments Coarse-grained terrigenous deposits dominate continental margin areas. Fine-grained clay, or mud, is more common in the deepest areas of the ocean basins.
Infer *Why are fine-grained sediments more common in the deepest areas of the ocean basins?*

14.3 Assessment

Review Key Concepts 🔑

1. What are the three types of seafloor sediments?

2. What does terrigenous sediment consist of?

3. What is the composition of biogenous sediment?

4. How is hydrogenous sediment formed?

5. Why are seafloor sediments useful in studying past climates?

Think Critically

6. Compare and Contrast Compare and contrast calcareous ooze and siliceous ooze.

7. Predict Would you expect to find more evaporites in an area of warm water that receives large amounts of sunlight such as the Red Sea or in an area of cold water that receives less sunlight such as the Greenland Sea?

CONNECTING CONCEPTS

8. Apply Concepts An oceanographer is studying sediment samples from the Bahama Banks. The sediments have a high amount of calcium carbonate. They are labeled biogenous but are later found to contain no shells from organisms that typically make up calcareous ooze. What other explanation is there for the origin of these sediments?

Use Visuals L1

Figure 14 Have students examine the map showing the distribution of marine sediments in the world's oceans. **Ask:** What kinds of terrigenous sediments are shown on the map? *(coarse nearshore deposits and fine abyssal clay)* How do the locations of two types of terrigenous deposits differ? *(Fine-grained clays are found farther from landmasses; coarser deposits are closer to landmasses.)* According to the map, which type of biogenous sediment appears to be more common? *(biogenous calcareous ooze)* Which type of sediment is found along the west coast of North America? The east coast of North America? *(biogenous siliceous ooze; terrigenous coarse nearshore deposits)*
Visual, Logical

3 ASSESS

Evaluate Understanding L2

Present students with a blank table that lists the three major categories of seafloor sediments down the left column. The center column should be titled Origin. The right column should be labeled Composition. Have students fill in the Origin and Composition columns.

Reteach L1

Have each student write ten questions that cover the content of this lesson. Invite students to use their questions to quiz each other.

Answers

Figure 14 *They are smaller and carried farther by ocean curents than coarser sediments that settle closer to shore.*

☑ **Reading Checkpoint** *calcareous ooze, siliceous ooze*

Assessment Answers

1. terrigenous, biogenous, hydrogenous
2. mineral grains weathered from continental rocks
3. shells and skeletons of marine animals and algae
4. minerals crystallize directly from the water through chemical reactions
5. Seafloor sediments containing the remains of organisms are deposited in layers. By studying the types of organisms in different layers, scientists can form hypotheses about Earth's climate during different time periods.
6. Calcareous ooze and siliceous ooze both have the consistency of thick mud and are examples of biogenous sediments. Calcareous ooze is formed from the calcium carbonate hard parts of organisms. Siliceous ooze is formed from the siliceous shells of organisms.

Calcareous ooze is not found below depths of 4500 m.
7. area of warm water with lots of sunlight because these conditions are more favorable for evaporation
8. They are hydrogenous, formed from calcium carbonate precipitating directly from seawater.

14.4 Resources from the Seafloor

1 FOCUS

Lesson Objectives

14.10 **Identify** ocean resources used for energy production.

14.11 **Explain** how gas hydrates are formed.

14.12 **List** other types of ocean resources.

Build Vocabulary [L2]

Paraphrase Have students explain, in their own words, the meaning of the new vocabulary term in this lesson, plus the terms *evaporative salts* and *halite*. Have students write their definitions and share them.

Reading Strategy [L2]

a. rock fragments and shells of marine organisms
b. landfill, recreational beaches, concrete
c. diamonds, tin, platinum, titanium

2 INSTRUCT

Address Misconceptions [L2]

Students may have the misconception that sand contains only the element silicon. However, the term *sand* refers to particle size (smaller than gravel but larger than silt) rather than to mineral content. Ask students to explain how they think sand is formed. Guide them to understand that sand particles are made up of minerals that come primarily from weathered and eroded rocks, which have varying compositions. Sand particles can also come from pulverized shells of marine organisms.
Logical

Key Questions

🔑 **Which ocean resources are used for energy production?**

🔑 **How are gas hydrates formed?**

🔑 **What other resources are derived from the ocean?**

Vocabulary

• gas hydrate

Reading Strategy

Identify Details Copy the concept map below. As you read, complete it to identify details about resources from the ocean.

THE OCEAN FLOOR is rich in mineral and energy resources.
Recovering them, however, often involves technological challenges and high costs. As technology improves we are able to access some of these resources more efficiently. However, the ocean's resources are finite and need to be managed carefully.

Energy Resources

Most of the value of nonliving resources in the ocean comes from their use as energy products. 🔑 **Oil and natural gas are the main energy products currently being obtained from the ocean floor.** Other resources may be used as a source of energy in the future.

Oil and Natural Gas The ancient remains of organisms are the source of today's deposits of offshore oil and natural gas. These organisms were buried within sediments before they could decompose. After millions of years of exposure to heat from Earth's interior and pressure from overlying rock, the remains were transformed into oil and natural gas. The percentage of world oil produced from offshore regions has increased from trace amounts in the 1930s to more than 30 percent today. Part of this increase is due to advances in the technology of offshore drilling platforms.

Major offshore reserves exist in the Persian Gulf, in the Gulf of Mexico, off the coast of southern California, and in the North Sea. Additional reserves may be located off the north coast of Alaska and in the Canadian Arctic, Asian seas, Africa, and Brazil. One environmental concern about offshore exploration is the possibility of oil spills caused by accidents during drilling, such as the spill that resulted from the *Deepwater Horizon* explosion in April 2010. The oil polluted the waters of the Gulf of Mexico and caused massive environmental damage to the coasts of Alabama and Mississippi.

FIGURE 15 Accessing Resources Offshore drilling rigs tap the oil and natural gas reserves of the continental shelf. These platforms are near Santa Barbara, California. Infer *What changes to the marine environment may occur as a result of drilling for oil?*

FIGURE 16 Gas Hydrates
A A sample from the ocean floor has layers of white, icelike gas hydrate mixed with mud.

B Gas hydrates evaporate when exposed to surface conditions, releasing natural gas that can be burned.

Gas Hydrates Compact chemical structures made of water and natural gas are called **gas hydrates**. The most common type of natural gas is methane, which produces methane hydrate. Gas hydrates occur beneath permafrost areas on land and under the ocean floor at depths below 525 meters.

🔑 **Most oceanic gas hydrates are formed when bacteria break down organic matter trapped in ocean-floor sediments.** The bacteria produce methane gas along with small amounts of ethane and propane. These gases combine with water in deep-ocean sediments and are trapped.

Vessels that have drilled into gas hydrates have brought up samples of mud mixed with chunks of gas hydrates similar to the one shown in **Figure 16A.** These chunks evaporate quickly when they are exposed to the relatively warm, low-pressure conditions at the ocean surface. Gas hydrates resemble chunks of ice but ignite when lit by a flame, as shown in **Figure 16B.** The hydrates burn because methane and other flammable gases are released as gas hydrates evaporate.

An estimated 20 quadrillion cubic meters of methane are locked up in sediments containing gas hydrates. This amount is double the amount of Earth's known coal, oil, and natural gas reserves combined. One drawback to using gas hydrates as an energy source is that they rapidly break down at surface temperatures and pressures. In the future, however, these ocean-floor reserves of energy may help fill our energy needs.

☑️ **Reading Checkpoint** *What happens when gas hydrates are brought to the surface?*

LESSON 14.4

Students may not think that ordinary tap water contains minerals that would precipitate out during evaporation. Guide students to understand that, because water is the universal solvent, there is virtually always something dissolved in it. Heat tap water in a pan with a black Teflon© coating. When the water boils off, a white residue of mineral salts remains. Explain that there are a number of physical and chemical processes that can be used to remove non-water molecules and ions from a sample of water. Have students look up information about the effectiveness of various water purification methods, such as distillation, active carbon filtration, and ozone treatment systems.
Logical, Verbal

EVAPORATIVE SALTS `L2`

Objective
Students observe that any salt dissolved in water is left behind when the water evaporates.

Skills Observe, Measure, Compare and Contrast, Draw Conclusions, Predict

Prep Time 10 minutes

Class Time 10–15 minutes to set up; 5 minutes to make final measurements

Expected Outcome Students find that all of the salt they put into the water is left behind when the water evaporates.

Analyze and Conclude
1. The masses should be equal.
2. It is left behind (precipitates out).
3. Certain areas with proper conditions could be used to evaporate water and collect solid salt.
Kinesthetic, Logical

For Enrichment `L3`

Have students evaporate water taken from a variety of sources (tap water, rainwater, bottled water) to determine if an evaporite is left behind. Students could test any evaporite they obtain for the presence of minerals.

FIGURE 17 Evaporative Salts
Common table salt, or halite, is harvested from the salt left behind when ocean water evaporates. About 30 percent of the world's salt is produced from seawater that has evaporated.

Other Resources

Other major resources from the ocean floor include **evaporative salts, sand and gravel, and manganese nodules.** These materials are used in construction, food processing, and manufacturing technological devices.

Evaporative Salts When seawater evaporates, salts increase in concentration until they are no longer dissolved. When the concentration becomes high enough, the salts precipitate out of solution and form salt deposits. These deposits can then be harvested, as shown in **Figure 17.** The most economically important salt is halite (NaCl)—common table salt. Halite is widely used for seasoning, curing, and preserving foods. It is also used in agriculture, in the clothing industry for dyeing fabric, and to de-ice roads.

Sand and Gravel The offshore sand-and-gravel industry is second in economic value only to the offshore oil industry. Sand and gravel, which include rock fragments that are washed out to sea and shells of marine organisms, are mined by offshore barges using suction devices. The difference between sand and gravel is particle size—gravel particles are larger than sand particles. Sand and gravel are used for many purposes including landfill, to fill in beaches, and to make concrete.

Some materials of high economic value are associated with offshore sand and gravel deposits. Diamonds, for example, are recovered from gravels offshore of South Africa and Australia. Sediments rich in tin have been mined from some offshore areas of Southeast Asia. Some Florida beach sands are rich in titanium.

INQUIRY QUICK LAB

EVAPORATIVE SALTS

Materials
- 400 mL beaker • 100 mL water • table salt
- tablespoon • balance • glass stirrer

Procedure
1. Place the empty beaker on the balance and add between 3 and 5 tablespoons of the salt. Measure the combined mass of the beaker and the salt. Record the measurement and remove the beaker from the balance.
2. Add 100 mL of water to the beaker and stir until the salt is dissolved.
3. Place the beaker in a warm, sunny area and allow the water to evaporate.

4. When all of the water has evaporated, place the beaker and its remaining contents on the balance and record the measurement.

Analyze and Conclude
1. **Compare** How did the mass of the beaker and salt before the water was added compare to the mass of the beaker and salt after the water evaporated?
2. **Draw Conclusions** What happened to the salt when the water evaporated?
3. **Predict** How could the oceans be used as a source of salt?

Facts and Figures

In Earth's geologic history, there have been incidents in which an entire body of salt water evaporated away. The evidence for this includes extensive deposits of evaporite minerals, including one in the Mediterranean Sea. Evidence suggests that, about 6 million years ago, the Mediterranean Sea was cut off from the Atlantic Ocean at the Strait of Gibraltar. The Mediterranean Sea almost completely evaporated within a few thousand years, leaving a thick deposit of evaporites on the hot, dry basin floor. A half million years later, water re-entered the Mediterranean Sea, filling it with seawater again.

Manganese Nodules As described earlier, manganese nodules are hard lumps of manganese and other metals that precipitate around a smaller object. **Figure 18** shows manganese nodules on the deep-ocean floor. They contain high concentrations of manganese and iron, and smaller concentrations of copper, nickel, and cobalt, all of which have a variety of industrial uses. Cobalt, for example, is important because it is required to produce strong alloys with other metals. These alloys are used in high-speed cutting tools, powerful permanent magnets, and jet engine parts. With current technology, mining the deep-ocean floor for manganese nodules is possible, but the cost is so high that it would not be profitable.

Manganese nodules are widely distributed along the ocean floor, but not all regions have the same potential for mining. Good locations for mining must have a large amount of nodules that contain an optimal mix of copper, nickel, and cobalt. Sites like this are limited. In addition, it is difficult to establish mining rights far from land. Also, there are environmental concerns about disturbing large portions of the deep-ocean floor.

FIGURE 18 Manganese Nodules These manganese nodules lie thousands of meters beneath the ocean surface on the Pacific Ocean floor south of Tahiti. **Apply Concepts** *How do manganese nodules form?*

14.4 Assessment

Review Key Concepts

1. What are the main energy resources from the ocean?

2. How are gas hydrates formed?

3. What drawbacks are associated with harvesting ocean resources for energy use?

4. What other resources besides energy resources are derived from the ocean?

5. What are the uses of evaporative salts?

6. What are manganese nodules? Why is it difficult to recover them from the ocean?

Think Critically

7. Make Generalizations How does technology influence the availability of resources from the ocean?

8. Infer Near-shore mining of sand and gravel can result in large amounts of sediments being suspended in water. How might this affect marine organisms living in the area?

CONNECTING CONCEPTS

9. Explain Why are most sand and gravel deposits found on the continental shelf? What type of sediment is sand and gravel?

The Ocean Floor **413**

MODELING SEAFLOOR DEPTH TRANSECTS L2

Objectives

In this activity, students will

- create a model of a portion of the seafloor.
- simulate depth measurements made by depth sounding.
- infer from depth measurements the region of the ocean floor their model represents.

Skills Measure, Graph, Infer, Draw Conclusions

Prep Time 15 minutes to assemble materials

Class Time 30 minutes for Part A; 30 minutes for Part B

Teaching Tips

- Instruct students to limit their model to a continental margin, an ocean basin floor, or a mid-ocean ridge.
- Supervise students' model-making and make suggestions about ensuring their models will be decipherable by others during Part B.
- Make sure the size of the rulers used in this activity will enable students to make measurements precise enough to allow them to reach a conclusion.
- Encourage students to take measurements along two or more transect lines.

Modeling Seafloor Depth Transects

Problem How can the topography of an ocean basin be determined?

Materials shoe box, modeling clay, aluminum foil, pencil, scalpel, graph paper, ruler

Skills Measure, Graph, Infer, Draw Conclusions

Connect to the Big idea Oceanographers use a number of methods to determine the depth and topography of the ocean floor. Technology, such as sonar, satellites, and submersibles, have allowed scientists to produce detailed maps of the ocean floor in each ocean basin. In this lab, you will model a seafloor depth transect to determine the topography of an ocean basin created by your classmates.

Procedure

Part A: Making a Model of the Seafloor

1. Look at Figure 3, Figure 8, and the figure below to determine which area of the ocean floor you will model.

Be sure to identify the specific features that would be found in the area. For example, a model of the continental margin would include the continental shelf, continental slope, continental rise, and some submarine canyons. A model of the ocean basin floor would include abyssal plains, deep-sea trenches, seamounts, and guyots. Do not discuss your plan with students outside your group.

2. Once you have determined which area you will model, use the clay to make a contoured model of the seafloor inside the shoe box.

3. Obtain a piece of aluminum foil that is large enough to cover the top of the shoe box and fold over the sides of the box about an inch all the way around.

4. Spread the foil flat on your lab table. Place the ruler lengthwise on the foil, parallel to the edge of the foil. The line formed by the edge of the ruler will be your transect line.

5. Use a pencil to make tick marks on the foil piece every centimeter along the entire length of the foil.

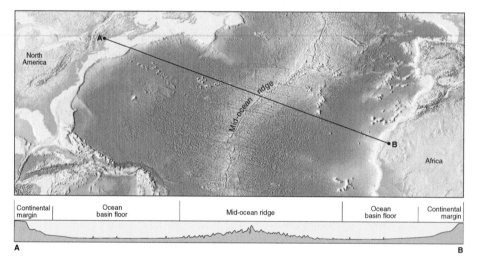

6. Hold the foil in place over the top of the box. Remove the top of the box and set the foil piece down in place of the top. Secure the foil in place on top of the box by turning down the foil over the sides of the box. Be sure the foil is taut.

7. Exchange boxes with another group from your class. Do not remove foil from the box that you receive.

Part B: Completing a Depth Transect

8. Label your graph paper. The *x*-axis will be "Distance along Transect Line" in centimeters, and the *y*-axis will be "Depth" in centimeters. Make tick marks along the *x*-axis once every centimeter. Make tick marks along the *y*-axis every half of a centimeter. **NOTE:** You may also use a computer to produce your graph.

9. Use the scalpel to carefully make a slit in the foil along the first centimeter mark. **CAUTION:** *The scalpel is extremely sharp. Handle it carefully.* After cutting the foil, gently place the ruler through the slit until it makes contact with the clay in the box. Be sure to hold the ruler straight and take the depth measurement. Record your data on the graph.

10. Repeat Step 9 for each point along the foil. When you are done, you should have a depth profile for the entire length of the box along your transect line.

11. Remove the foil from the box and examine the topography of the model.

Analyze and Conclude

1. Infer Based on your contour profile, what part of the ocean floor was being modeled? Check your

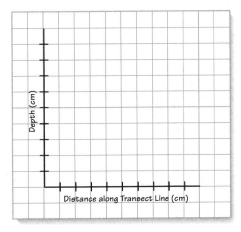

answer with the group that created the model. Were you correct? Why or why not?

2. Compare How does the profile on your graph compare with the contour of the model? Are there any major features in the model that did not appear on your graph? Why or why not?

3. Analyze Data What could you have done to make your profile match the topography more accurately?

4. Explain Before sonar was used to measure ocean depth, a less sophisticated method was used. A long line of rope with a lead weight on the end was tossed over the side of a ship and lowered until the weight hit the bottom. How is this method similar to what you did in the lab? How can the rope method lead to inaccuracies when trying to build an ocean-floor profile?

Study Tip

Get Into the Habit of Actively Studying Each Day Encourage students to schedule a specific time each day to study. Suggest that they allot part of that time to outline information from their text or class notes, in addition to completing assignments.

Accountability and Adaptability

How has life on the ocean floor changed our views about life?
The environments found on ocean floors were not well explored until recently. The organisms scientists have found in these extreme environments have changed our ideas about life on Earth and the possibility of life on other planets. Ask students to research the organisms living in seafloor sediments or deep-sea hydrothermal vents. Encourage them to learn how the discovery of some of these organisms has changed scientists' ideas about life on Earth or extraterrestrial life. Finally, ask students to present what they discover to the class or post their findings in a class blog or wiki, if available. Students should be prepared to follow up with answers to classmates' comments or questions.

Homework Guide

Lesson	Questions
1	1–3, 11–14, 24, 25, 29
2	4–6, 15–18, 26, 27, 30, 33
3	7, 8, 20, 21, 28, 31
4	9, 10, 22, 23

Big idea Water Planet

14.1 The Vast World Ocean

🔑 Nearly 71 percent of Earth's surface is covered by the world ocean.

🔑 The world ocean can be divided into four main ocean basins—the Pacific Ocean, the Atlantic Ocean, the Indian Ocean, and the Arctic Ocean.

🔑 The topography—shape and landforms—of the ocean floor is as diverse as that of continents.

🔑 Today, technology—particularly sonar, satellites, and submersibles—allows scientists to study the ocean floor in a more efficient and precise manner than ever before.

bathymetry (397)
submersible (400)

14.2 Ocean Floor Features

🔑 The ocean floor regions are the continental margins, the ocean basin floor, and the mid-ocean ridge.

🔑 In the Atlantic Ocean, thick layers of undisturbed sediment cover the continental margin. This region has very little volcanic or earthquake activity.

🔑 In the Pacific Ocean, oceanic crust is plunging beneath continental crust. This force results in a narrow continental margin that experiences both volcanic activity and earthquakes.

🔑 Continental shelves contain important mineral deposits, large reservoirs of oil and natural gas, and huge sand and gravel deposits.

🔑 The sediments that make up abyssal plains are carried there by turbidity currents or are deposited as a result of suspended sediments settling.

🔑 Trenches form at sites of plate convergence where one moving plate descends beneath another and plunges back into the mantle.

🔑 New ocean floor is formed at mid-ocean ridges as magma rises between the diverging plates and cools.

continental margin (401)
continental shelf (402)
continental slope (402)
submarine canyon (402)
turbidity current (402)
continental rise (403)
ocean basin floor (403)
abyssal plain (404)
seamount (404)
mid-ocean ridge (405)
seafloor spreading (405)

14.3 Seafloor Sediments

🔑 Ocean-floor sediments can be classified according to their origin into three broad categories: terrigenous sediments, biogenous sediments, and hydrogenous sediments.

🔑 Terrigenous sediments consist primarily of mineral grains that were eroded from continental rocks and transported to the ocean.

🔑 Biogenous sediments consist of shells and skeletons of marine animals and algae.

🔑 Hydrogenous sediment consists of minerals that crystallize directly from ocean water through various chemical reactions.

terrigenous sediment (407)
biogenous sediment (408)
calcareous ooze (408)
siliceous ooze (408)
hydrogenous sediment (408)
manganese nodule (408)

14.4 Resources from the Seafloor

🔑 Oil and natural gas are the main energy products currently being obtained from the ocean floor.

🔑 Most oceanic gas hydrates are formed when bacteria break down organic matter trapped in ocean-floor sediments.

🔑 Other major resources from the ocean floor include evaporative salts, sand and gravel, and manganese nodules.

gas hydrate (411)

Assessment Answers

Review Content

1. d	**2.** c	**3.** b	**4.** a
5. b	**6.** b	**7.** b	**8.** a
9. c	**10.** b		

Understand Concepts

11. Earth is called the "blue planet" because nearly 71 percent of Earth's surface is covered by ocean.

12. Bathymetry is the measurement of ocean depths and charting the shape or topography of the ocean floor; sonar, satellites, submersibles

13. Multibeam sonar uses more than one sound source and listening device. This allows scientists to obtain a profile of a narrow strip of floor and from that build a swath of detailed coverage.

14 Assessment

Review Content

Choose the letter that best answers the question or completes the statement.

1. Approximately what percentage of Earth's surface is covered by oceans?
   a. 40
   b. 50
   c. 60
   d. 70

2. Which ocean basin is the largest?
   a. the Atlantic
   b. the Indian
   c. the Pacific
   d. the Arctic

3. The use of sound waves to determine the depth of the ocean is called
   a. submarine sounding.
   b. sonar.
   c. satellite altimetry.
   d. submersible sounding.

4. The gently sloping submerged surface that extends from the shoreline toward the ocean basin floor is the continental
   a. shelf.
   b. slope.
   c. rise.
   d. margin.

5. Submarine canyons are thought to have been formed by
   a. tsunamis.
   b. turbidy currents.
   c. sunken ships.
   d. subduction.

6. Important mineral deposits, including large reservoirs of oil and natural gas, are associated with
   a. the ocean basin floor.
   b. the continental shelf.
   c. abyssal plains.
   d. the continental rise.

7. Calcareous ooze is an example of
   a. terrigenous sediment.
   b. biogenous sediment.
   c. hydrogenous sediment.
   d. a combination of hydrogenous and terrigenous sediment.

8. Sediments that consist of mineral grains that were eroded from continental rocks are called
   a. terrigenous.
   b. biogenous.
   c. hydrogenous.
   d. hydrates.

9. What could gas hydrates be used for?
   a. as landfill
   b. to make concrete
   c. as a source of energy
   d. as a source of cobalt and copper

10. Economically valuable materials such as diamonds, tin, and platinum are associated with which ocean floor resource?
    a. oil and natural gas
    b. sand and gravel
    c. evaporative salts
    d. manganese nodules

Understand Concepts

11. Why is Earth called the "blue planet"?

12. What is bathymetry? What techniques do scientists use to discover more about the bathymetry of ocean basins?

13. Why is multibeam sonar more efficient than simple sonar at collecting data from the ocean floor?

14. Compare and contrast the size and topography of the Atlantic Ocean basin to that of the Pacific Ocean basin.

15. What is a continental shelf? What economic significance do continental shelves have?

16. Compare and contrast deep-ocean trenches and mid-oceanic ridges.

17. In which ocean basin are most trenches found? Why?

18. What is the difference between terrigenous sediments and biogenous sediments?

19. Explain the process by which hydrogenous sediments are formed.

20. Why is it uncommon to find calcareous ooze in deep-ocean basins?

21. From which area of the ocean basin are the resources of oil and natural gas harvested?

22. What current disadvantages exist to using gas hydrates as a form of energy?

23. What are the uses for sand and gravel harvested from the continental shelf?

17. The Pacific Ocean; plates in the Pacific Ocean are converging

18. Terrigenous sediments are formed from weathered continental rocks. Biogenous sediments are formed from the remains of marine animals and algae.

19. Hydrogenous sediments are formed when minerals crystallize directly from seawater through various chemical reactions.

20. As the calcium carbonate shells of organisms sink into deeper parts of the ocean they dissolve. In seawater deeper than 4500 m, the shells dissolve completely before they reach the bottom.

21. the continental shelf

22. Gas hydrates evaporate quickly when brought to the surface.

23. Sand and gravel are used to make concrete, for landfill, and to fill recreational beaches.

14. The Pacific Ocean basin is about twice the size of the Atlantic Ocean basin. Both have a variety of topographic features including mid-ocean ridges, abyssal plains, and seamounts. Trenches are more prevalent in the Pacific Ocean than the Atlantic Ocean. The continental margins of the Pacific Ocean are narrow and have more volcanic and earthquake activity than Atlantic Ocean margins. Plates in the Pacific Ocean are converging.

15. The continental shelf is the gently sloping submerged surface extending from shoreline to the continental slope. Continental shelves contain mineral deposits, large reservoirs of oil and natural gas, as well as huge sand and gravel deposits.

16. Deep-ocean trenches are formed at convergence sites where one plate is being pushed beneath another, descending into Earth's mantle. Mid-ocean ridges are areas of divergence where new ocean floor is formed.

ASSESSMENT

Think Critically

24. A large portion of the Southern Hemisphere is covered by ocean water. In the Northern Hemisphere, there are more continents that separate ocean basins.

25. Gravity attracts water toward regions in the ocean where massive seafloor features occur. This creates elevations or depressions in sea surface height that can be measured using satellites.

26. Passive continental margins are not areas of convergence. There is little volcanic and earthquake activity on passive plate margins. Active plate margins are areas of convergence where one plate is descending beneath another. They are associated with volcanic and earthquake activity.

27. Mid-ocean ridges are far from coastal areas so there is less sediment reaching these areas. Also mid-ocean ridges are the site of new seafloor formation where sediments have not had a chance to settle.

28. Student responses will vary but should show an understanding that manganese nodules have to be collected from great depths in the ocean where it is dark. The nodules are spread apart and would need to be located with accuracy. Accept all answers with reasonable supporting arguments.

Math Skills

29. 1500 m/s · 10 s = 15,000 m
15,000 m/1500 m/s = 10 s
30. 2.5 cm/yr × 7 yr = 17.5 cm
31. 4 km = 4000 m
4000 m ÷ 360 m/day = 11.11 days

Concepts in Action

32. Student graphs should reflect the data given in the table with the x-axis being the station number and the y-axis being depth.
33. seamount or guyot

Performance-Based Assessment

Students' research and presentations on an ocean resource will vary but should accurately reflect proper and thorough research of the topic.

24. Interpret Visuals Reexamine Figure 1. Why do you think that the Northern Hemisphere is called the "land hemisphere" and the Southern Hemisphere is called the "water hemisphere"?

25. Communicate A friend says that because of gravity we can learn about the topography of the ocean floor. Explain why this is true.

26. Infer The continental margin of the Atlantic Ocean is often referred to as a "passive" continental margin whereas Pacific Ocean continental margins are referred to as "active." Infer what the characteristics of passive and active continental margins would be.

27. Infer There is usually very little sediment accumulation found at mid-ocean ridges. Why do you think this is true?

28. Apply Concepts Imagine you have been asked to invent a device that would be used to retrieve manganese nodules. What characteristics would the device have in order to successfully achieve this goal?

Math Skills

29. Calculate Assuming the average speed of sound waves in water is 1500 meters per second, determine, in seconds, how long it would take a sonar signal to hit the bottom and return to the recorder if the water depth is 7500 meters.

30. Calculate The rate of seafloor spreading in the Atlantic Ocean has been estimated to be about 2.5 centimeters per year. By how many centimeters will the Atlantic Ocean basin increase over a period of 7 years?

31. Calculate If the settling rate of very fine sand in the open ocean is 360 meters per day, how many days will it take for the sediment to reach the ocean floor at a depth of 4 kilometers?

Concepts in Action

Use the table below to answer Questions 32 and 33.

The table shows the kind of data that a simple sonar echo sounder would provide. The sonar is taken along a transect line in the Pacific Ocean. The stations are approximately 500 meters apart from each other.

Sonar Data			
Station Number	Depth (in meters)	Station Number	Depth (in meters)
1	5500	7	3110
2	5550	8	3285
3	4540	9	3490
4	4000	10	4000
5	3675	11	4675
6	3355	12	5000

32. Make Graphs Plot these points on a sheet of graph paper.

33. Interpret Graphs The data recorded in the table was taken over a portion of the ocean basin floor in the Pacific Ocean. What ocean basin feature could be between stations 2 and 12?

Performance-Based Assessment

Research Choose a resource that is harvested from the ocean. Research information about how the resource is formed, where in the ocean it is harvested, what methods and equipment are used in the harvesting of the resource, what it is used for, and if there are any negative impacts on the marine environment as a result of harvesting the resource. Present the results of your research to your class in the form of an oral presentation.

Standardized Test Prep

Choose the letter that best answers the question.

1 Which of the following is *not* true of deep ocean trenches?
A They are long and narrow depressions in the ocean floor.
B They are sites where plates plunge back into the mantle.
C They are geologically very stable.
D They may act as sediment traps.

2 Movements of sediment-rich water down the continental slope are known as—
F streaming currents
G longshore currents
H turbidity currents
J avalanches

Use the diagram below to answer Questions 3 and 4.

3 Which letter represents the continental margin?
A A
B B
C C
D D

4 Which letter represents the continental rise?
F A
G B
H C
J D

5 Which of the following is the *best* description of abyssal plains?
A extremely flat regions of ocean floor
B long, narrow creases in the ocean floor
C areas where two lithospheric plates are moving apart
D gently sloping submerged surfaces along a shoreline

6 How do offshore oil deposits form?
F The ancient remains of microscopic organisms are exposed to heat and pressure for millions of years.
G Heat energy and minerals are released through the mid-ocean ridges that circle Earth's oceans.
H Minerals, such as halite, contained in ocean water precipitate and sink to the ocean floor.
J Bacteria rapidly break down minerals contained in ocean-floor sediments.

If You Have Trouble With . . .

Question	1	2	3	4	5	6
See Lesson	14.2	14.2	14.2	14.2	14.2	14.4

The Ocean Floor **419**

15 Ocean Water and Ocean Life Planning Guide

BIGIDEA: WATER PLANET

Lesson Objectives		Activities
15.1 The Composition of Seawater, pp. 422–427		TE Teacher Demo: Synthetic Seawater, p. 423 **L1**
15.1 **Identify** the units used to express the salinity of ocean water.		TE Teacher Demo: Solar Incidence Angles, p. 424 **L2**
15.2 **List** the sources of salt in ocean water.		
15.3 **Recognize** the factors that affect the density of ocean water.		
15.4 **Compare and contrast** the three main zones of the open ocean.		
15.2 The Diversity of Ocean Life, pp. 428–432		
15.5 **Recognize** how marine organisms can be classified.		
15.6 **Differentiate** between plankton and nekton.		
15.7 **Describe** the area of the ocean in which most benthic organisms live.		
15.8 **List** the factors used to divide the ocean into marine zones.		
15.3 Oceanic Productivity, pp. 433–437		TE Teacher Demo: Build an Energy Pyramid, p. 436 **L2**
15.9 **List** the factors that influence a region's photosynthetic productivity.		
15.10 **Describe** the transfer of energy from one trophic level to another.		
15.11 **Describe** the value of food webs.		
Chapter Features and Labs		
Try It How Does Salinity Affect the Density of Water? p. 421		
How Earth Works Ocean Life, pp. 338–339		
Exploration Lab How Does Temperature Affect Water Density? pp. 440–441		

Ability Levels	Components		
L1 For students who need additional help	SE Student Edition	LP Lesson Plans	
L2 For all students	TE Teacher's Edition	AA Active Art	
L3 For students who need to be challenged	LM Laboratory Manual	PD Planet Diary	
	CT Chapter Tests	GEODe Geode CD-ROM	
	GRSW Guided Reading & Study Workbook	eText	
	CTB Computer Test Bank		

Resources	Lesson Assessment
GRSW Lesson 15.1 **LP** Lesson Planning 15.1	**SE** Lesson 15.1 Assessment, p. 427 **eText** Lesson 15.1
GRSW Lesson 15.2 **LP** Lesson Planning 15.2	**SE** Lesson 15.2 Assessment, p. 432 **eText** Lesson 15.2
GRSW Lesson 15.3 **LP** Lesson Planning 15.3 **PD** Photosynthesis in the Oceans **AA** Ocean Food Web	**SE** Lesson 15.3 Assessment, p. 437 **eText** Lesson 15.3

Materials for Activities and Labs

Quantities for each group

STUDENT EDITION

Try It, p. 421
2 500-mL graduated cylinders, fresh water, salt water, small rubber ball or stopper small enough to fit inside the graduated cylinders

Exploration Lab, pp. 440–441
2 100-mL graduated cylinders, 2 test tubes, 2 beakers, food coloring or dye, stirrer, ice, tap water, graph paper, colored pencils

TEACHER'S EDITION

Teacher Demo, p. 423
samples of some or all of the chemical salts found in seawater: sodium chloride ($NaCl$), magnesium chloride ($MgCl$), sodium sulfate (Na_2SO_4), calcium chloride ($CaCl_2$), potassium chloride (KCl), sodium bicarbonate ($NaHCO_3$), potassium bromide (KBr), hydrogen borate (H_3BO_3), strontium chloride ($SrCl_2$), sodium fluoride (NaF), scale, 10 small beakers, 1 large beaker, stirring rod

Teacher Demo, p. 424
flashlight or slide/filmstrip projector

Teacher Demo, p. 436
classroom chalkboard, optional drawings or cutouts of ocean producers and consumers shown in Figure 18

Assessment

CHAPTER ASSESSMENT
SE Assessment, pp. 443–444
CT Chapter 15 Test
CTB Chapter 15
eText Chapter 15

21st Century **Learning**

Economic Literacy: How can overfishing affect the economy? p. 442

Common Themes

The oceans are rich and diverse with life, with a photosynthetic productivity that is of the same order as life on land. Life has existed in the oceans for roughly 4 billion years, and has adapted to many different ocean environments.

Space and Time The ocean is effectively layered due to vertical differences in temperature, salinity, and the amount of sunlight received. Marine organisms are classified by where they live in the ocean and how they move: plankton float near the surface, nekton swim (at a variety of depths), and benthos live at the seafloor. The first life on Earth may have evolved at undersea mid-ocean ridges.

Forces and Motion The factors that affect ocean life include the availability of sunlight, distance from shore, and water depth. Different zones of ocean life (photic, aphotic, intertidal, neritic, oceanic, pelagic, and benthic) are determined based on these factors.

Matter and Energy Salts comprise about 3.5 percent of the composition of seawater, with most of this being sodium chloride (NaCl). Variations in salinity, which are relatively small, occur largely because of geographic changes in evaporation rates and the influx of fresh water.

The temperature of deep seawater is about 2°C everywhere, but surface temperatures vary, largely according to latitude.

Earth as a System Primary productivity of life occurs primarily through photosynthesis, and varies according to latitude. Chemical energy passes through a food chain from one trophic level to the next.

Michael Wysession
Washington University

EARTH SCIENCE REFRESHER

Seawater and Life

The ocean contained large numbers of organic molecules early on in its history. These organic molecules occur naturally—they are even found within meteorites. It is not until these molecules developed into cell membranes that enclosed self-replicating "genetic" molecules that we consider life to have began. However, even in the simple one-celled organisms (usually divided into two classes—archaea and bacteria), the fluid inside the cell membrane remained remarkably close to the composition of seawater, and it has been this way since.

Evolutionary Survival Techniques

Life in the oceans is much more diverse than it was several billion years ago. Part of the reason for this is the wide variety of adaptations that have developed in organisms over time. For example, it is thought that mitochondria and the chloroplasts in plant

> **Address Misconceptions**
>
> *Students may think that the salt in ocean water is composed simply of sodium chloride, common table salt.* Show students samples of several of the following chemical salts found in ocean water, to give them an idea of the variety of salts in the ocean: sodium chloride (NaCl), magnesium chloride ($MgCl_2$), sodium sulfate (Na_2SO_4), calcium chloride ($CaCl_2$), potassium chloride (KCl), sodium bicarbonate ($NaHCO_3$), potassium bromide (KBr), hydrogen borate (H_3BO_3), strontium chloride ($SrCl_2$), sodium fluoride (NaF). For a strategy that helps to overcome this misconception, see **Address Misconceptions** on TE p. 423.

Students may think that higher trophic levels actually contain more energy than lower trophic levels because they may reason that energy accumulates as you move up a food chain. Emphasize that the solar energy absorbed by producers is the only energy available to all the succeeding levels of the food chain. For a strategy that helps to overcome the misconception, see **Address Misconceptions** on **TE p. 436.**

cells were once separate one-celled organisms that existed in a symbiotic relationship with their host cells. At some point in the evolution of life, these "pre-mitochondria" invaded other one-celled organisms, and the arrangement was of benefit to both. The mitochondria provided energy to the host cell, and the host provided a safe, comfortable place for the mitochondria.

A wide variety of symbiotic relationships exists among ocean life-forms. For instance, the tentacles of the sea anemone contain poisons that are used to capture fish for food. However, the clownfish is immune to the toxin. The clownfish cleans the anemone's tentacles, and the anemone protects the clownfish from predators. In this symbiotic relationship, both survive better with each other than without.

One of the most important factors affecting the evolution of ocean species is the interaction of predators and prey. In fact, the sudden burst in ocean life diversity at the start of the Cambrian period is likely a result of this. During this time adaptations, such as hard shells, greater speed, and camouflage, developed that helped prey escape and hide from predators. Through the process of natural selection, adaptations in predators also developed such as sharper teeth and keen eyesight. Over time, most ocean life-forms have gone extinct, replaced by organisms that did a better job of surviving and reproducing in whatever niche they occupied. However, a few life-forms, such as the shark and nautilus, have changed very little over hundreds of millions of years.

BUILD READING LITERACY
Predict

Previewing to Predict Content

Strategy Help students activate their prior knowledge about a topic and become actively engaged in reading. The process of making and confirming predictions also helps students correct their own misconceptions. Before the students begin, have them focus on one topic in Chapter 15, such as the introductory paragraph on p. 422.

Example

1. Introduce students to the topic by having them read the heading and subheadings.

2. Ask students what they think they will learn about the topic.

3. Have a student read aloud the first Key Question on the side of the page.

4. Have another student read aloud the Preview instructions in the Reading Strategy.

5. Based on what they've read so far, ask students to predict the content of the section. Write their predictions on the board.

6. Have a student read aloud the boldfaced key statement on p. 422. Then, have other students read aloud the boldfaced statement on p. 426.

7. Discuss with students the predictions on the board. Allow them to revise the predictions if they wish.

8. Have students read through the section independently. Afterward, ask which of their predictions were confirmed. Point out that there's nothing wrong with making an incorrect prediction. Predicting can help readers learn more about a topic.

See TE p. 425 for a script on how to use this strategy with students. For additional strategies, see TE pp. 428 and 435.

CHAPTER 15

ASSESS PRIOR KNOWLEDGE

Use the Chapter Pretest below to assess students' prior knowledge. As needed, review these concepts.

Review Science Concepts

Lesson 15.1 A knowledge of the effects of salinity and density on ocean water leads to an understanding of the major characteristics of the world ocean and how those characteristics vary from one part of the globe to another.

Lesson 15.2 A knowledge of the classification of ocean life and the marine zones in which they live helps students recognize the diversity and importance of ocean dwelling organisms.

Lesson 15.3 A knowledge of how energy moves from one trophic level to another in ocean environments is essential for an understanding of how ocean organisms survive.

15 Ocean Water and Ocean Life

Big idea

Water Planet

Q: What factors affect life in the ocean?

420

Chapter Pretest

1. What units are typically used to describe the salinity of ocean water? *(c)*
- **a.** percent
- **b.** parts per billion
- **c.** parts per thousand
- **d.** parts per million

2. At which temperature would the density of seawater be the greatest? *(d)*
- **a.** 35°C
- **b.** 25°C
- **c.** 15°C
- **d.** 5°C

3. The top layer of ocean water through which sunlight penetrates is the _____. *(b)*
- **a.** aphotic zone
- **b.** photic zone
- **c.** benthos
- **d.** oceanic zone

4. What is the difference between plankton and nekton? *(Plankton are moved by ocean currents; nekton can swim independent of ocean currents.)*

5. True or False: All producer organisms living in the ocean perform photosynthesis. *(False)*

INQUIRY
TRY IT!

HOW DOES SALINITY AFFECT THE DENSITY OF WATER?

Procedure

1. Pour 400 mL of fresh water into a 500-mL graduated cylinder. Pour 400 mL of salt water into a second 500-mL graduated cylinder. Precise measurement is important.

2. Gently place a small rubber ball or stopper in the fresh water. Record the new water level. Remove the object from the water and dry it off thoroughly.

3. Repeat Step 2 using the salt water and record your observations.

Think About It

1. Calculate What volume of fresh water was displaced by the object? What volume of salt water was displaced by the floating object?

2. Draw Conclusions As the density of water increases, the volume of liquid displaced by an object decreases. Which water is more dense—fresh water or salt water?

3. Draw Conclusions How does salinity affect the density of water?

421

A humpback whale breaches off the coast of Vancouver Island in Canada.

ENGAGE/EXPLORE

INQUIRY
TRY IT!

HOW DOES SALINITY AFFECT THE DENSITY OF WATER?

Purpose In this activity, students begin to recognize the relationship between the salinity and density of water and understand that higher salinity correlates with higher density.

Skills Measure, Infer

Prep Time 10 minutes

Materials 2 500-mL graduated cylinders, fresh water, salt water, small rubber ball or stopper small enough to fit inside the graduated cylinders

Class Time 15 minutes

Teaching Tip The floating object could be a "superball" (small, very bouncy ball), a rubber stopper, the screw cap from a glass vial, or anything from the laboratory that will fit in the mouth of the graduated cylinder but has enough mass and density to displace a measurable amount of water and stay afloat. A cork is too light and a marble too heavy.

Expected Outcome The floating object will displace more fresh water, indicating that fresh water has a lower density.

Think About It

1. Student answers will vary depending on the floating object used in the experiment, but the volume of salt water displaced should be less than the volume of fresh water displaced.

2. salt water

3. The addition of salt increases the density of water.

1 FOCUS

Lesson Objectives

15.1 **Identify** the units used to express the salinity of ocean water.

15.2 **List** the sources of salt in ocean water.

15.3 **Recognize** the factors that affect the density of ocean water.

15.4 **Compare and contrast** the three main zones of the open ocean.

Build Vocabulary `L2`

Word Parts Before students read this lesson, ask them to write the meanings of the prefix *thermo-* ("heat") and the suffix *-cline* ("slope"). Then have students write a definition for what they think the word *thermocline* means. After students read the lesson, have them examine their definition and discuss whether it needs to be changed.

Reading Strategy `L2`

a. evaporation, runoff, ice formation, melting of ice

Sample additional questions and answers for **b.** to **g.**: What are the sources of sea salts? *(weathered rocks, volcanic eruptions)* What factors affect seawater temperature? *(sunlight, depth)* What factors affect seawater density? *(salinity, temperature)*

2 INSTRUCT

Use Visuals `L1`

Figure 1 Have students examine the graph. **Ask:** Which of these two types of measures—mass or volume—is used to determine the percentages of salts and water in a sample of seawater? *(mass)* What unit of measure is used? *(grams)* Why do you suppose salinity is usually expressed as "parts per thousand" instead of "percent" or "parts per hundred"? *(easier to use in calculations, because fewer decimal places are required)*
Visual

15.1 The Composition of Seawater

Key Questions

 What units are used to express the salinity of ocean water?

 What are the sources of salt in ocean water?

 What factors affect the density of ocean water?

 What are the three main zones of the open ocean?

Vocabulary

• salinity • thermocline
• density • pycnocline

Reading Strategy

Preview Copy the table shown below. Before you read, preview the figures in this section and add three more questions to the table. As you read, write answers to your questions.

Questions About Seawater	Answers
What processes affect seawater salinity?	a. ___?___
b. ___?___	c. ___?___
d. ___?___	e. ___?___
f. ___?___	g. ___?___

WHAT IS THE difference between pure water and seawater? One of the most obvious differences is that seawater contains dissolved substances that give it a salty taste. Seawater consists of about 3.5 percent dissolved mineral substances that are collectively termed "salts." Although the percentage of dissolved components may seem small, the actual quantity is huge because the ocean is so vast.

These dissolved substances include sodium chloride, other salts, metals, and even dissolved gases. In fact, every known naturally occurring element is found dissolved in at least trace amounts in seawater. The salt content of seawater makes it unsuitable for drinking by land organisms or for irrigating most crops. Seawater is also corrosive to many materials. However, the ocean is full of life adapted to this environment.

Salinity

Salinity (*salinus* = salt) refers to the total amount of solid material dissolved in water. It is the ratio of the mass of dissolved substances to the mass of the water sample. Many common quantities are expressed in percent (%), which is parts per hundred. **Because the proportion of dissolved substances in seawater is such a small number, oceanographers typically express salinity in parts per thousand (‰).** The average salinity of seawater is 3.5% or 35‰. **Figure 1** shows the principal elements that contribute to the ocean's salinity. Most of the salt in seawater is sodium chloride, common table salt.

Sources of Sea Salts What are the primary sources of dissolved substances in the ocean? **Chemical weathering of rocks on the continents is one source of elements found in seawater.** These dissolved materials reach the ocean through runoff from rivers and streams at an estimated rate of more than 2.3 billion metric tons per year. **The second major source of elements found in seawater is from Earth's interior.** Through volcanic eruptions, large quantities of water vapor and other gases have been emitted into the atmosphere during much of geologic time. Scientists think that this is the principal source of water in the oceans. About 4 billion years ago, as Earth's temperature cooled, the water vapor condensed and torrential rains filled the ocean basins with water.

Certain elements—particularly chlorine, bromine, sulfur, and boron—were emitted from volcanoes along with the water. These elements occur in the ocean in much greater quantities than could be explained by weathering of rocks alone.

Evidence suggests that the composition of seawater has been relatively stable for millions of years. Material is removed at about the same rate that it is added. Organisms remove material as they build hard structures, such as shells. Materials also precipitate out of the water in sediment.

Processes Affecting Salinity Because the ocean is well mixed, the concentrations of the major components in seawater are fairly constant throughout the ocean. Surface salinity variation in the open ocean normally ranges from 33‰ to 38‰. Salinity varies depending on the amount of water in the solution.

Figure 2 shows some of the different processes that affect the amount of water in seawater, thereby affecting salinity. Some processes add large amounts of fresh water to seawater, decreasing salinity. These processes include precipitation, runoff from land, and icebergs and sea ice melting. In areas of great precipitation, such as in the mid-latitudes and near the equator, salinity is below average.

Other processes increase salinity by removing large amounts of water from seawater. These processes include evaporation and the formation of sea ice. High salinities, for example, are found where evaporation rates are high, as is the case in the dry regions roughly between 25 and 35 degrees north or south latitude.

Surface salinity in polar regions varies seasonally due to the formation and melting of sea ice. When seawater freezes in winter, salts do not become part of the ice. Therefore, the salinity of the remaining seawater increases. In summer when sea ice melts, the addition of mostly freshwater decreases the seawater's salinity.

FIGURE 1 Salts in Seawater
This circle graph shows that 1000 grams of seawater with a salinity of 35‰ consists of 965 grams of water and 35 grams of salts and other solids dissolved in the water.

Other components 14.4%

Na$^+$ 30.6%

Cl$^-$ 55.0%

Dissolved components

Water 965 grams

Salts 35 g

Seawater Salinity = 35‰

FIGURE 2 Natural Processes Affect the Salinity of Seawater
Apply Concepts *Which processes decrease the salinity of seawater? Which processes increase it?*

Icebergs

Sea ice

Runoff

Evaporation

Ocean Water and Ocean Life **423**

Differentiated Instruction

Ocean Water and Ocean Life **423**

Build Science Skills L2

Infer Ask students to refer to the line graph in Figure 3 and a world map or globe to answer the following questions. **Ask:** At which latitude is sea surface salinity the lowest? *(60°N)* Where on the globe is this region located? *(near the Arctic circle)* During what season(s) of the year were salinity data for latitude 60°N probably taken? *(spring or summer)* How do you know? *(Ice probably was melting, which decreases salinity.)* In what ways can temperature affect salinity? *(Above-freezing temperatures allow polar ice to melt, adding fresh water to the ocean surface and decreasing salinity. Ice formation in below-freezing temperatures removes fresh water, increasing salinity.)*
Visual, Logical

(Teacher **Demo**)

SOLAR INCIDENCE ANGLES L2

Purpose Students observe the difference in the angle of incidence of the sun's rays at the equator and the poles.

Materials flashlight or slide/filmstrip projector

Procedure Darken the room. Aim the light perpendicular to the ceiling, and have students measure or estimate the area illuminated. Explain to students that this is similar to the angle at which the sun's light reaches equatorial regions of Earth. Next, slant the light so that it covers a much larger area. Encourage students to estimate or measure the illuminated area. Explain to students that this is more like the angle at which the sun's light reaches the polar regions of Earth. Point out to students that the energy emitted from the light source is unchanged, but a smaller amount of light energy is reaching each unit of the illuminated area.

Expected Outcome Students observe that light energy from the sun is more concentrated in equatorial regions, which explains why temperatures are warmer at the equator than at the poles.
Visual, Logical

FIGURE 3 Effect of Latitude on Temperature and Salinity This graph shows the variations in ocean surface temperature (top curve) and surface salinity (lower curve) at different latitudes.
Interpret Graphs *At which latitudes is sea surface temperature highest? Why?*

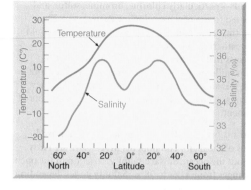

Ocean Temperature Variation

The temperature of the ocean contributes to global climate and is important to marine organisms. Latitude and water depth are two factors that influence the temperature of water masses.

Temperature Variation With Latitude **The ocean's surface water temperature is affected by the amount of solar radiation received, which is primarily due to latitude.** The graph in **Figure 3** shows this relationship. Due to the angle at which the sun's rays strike Earth, the intensity of solar radiation in high latitudes is much less than the intensity of solar radiation received in latitudes closer to the equator. Therefore, lower sea surface temperatures are found in high-latitude regions. Higher sea surface temperatures are found in low-latitude regions.

Temperature Variation With Depth If you lowered a thermometer from the surface of the ocean into deeper water, what temperature pattern do you think you would find? Surface waters are warmed by the sun. They generally have higher temperatures than deeper waters. However, the observed temperature pattern depends on the latitude.

FIGURE 4 Temperature and Depth These graphs show the variations in ocean water temperature with depth for low-latitude and high-latitude regions.
Apply Concepts *Why is the thermocline absent in the high latitudes?*

Figure 4 shows two graphs of temperature versus depth: one for low-latitude regions and one for high-latitude regions. The low-latitude graph shows high temperature at the surface. However, the temperature decreases rapidly with depth because of the inability of the sun's rays to penetrate very far into the ocean. At a depth of about 1000 meters, the temperature remains just a few degrees above freezing; it is relatively constant from this level down to the ocean floor. The **thermocline** (*thermo* = heat, *cline* = slope) is the layer of ocean water between about 300 meters and 1000 meters, where there is a rapid change of temperature with depth. The thermocline is a very important structure in the ocean because it creates a vertical barrier to many types of marine life.

Facts and Figures

The salinity of seawater is about four times greater than the salinity of body fluids. If seawater enters the digestive system, it causes internal membranes to lose water through osmosis, which transports water molecules from areas of higher concentrations to areas of lower concentrations. Drinking seawater would cause water from one's body fluids to move into the digestive tract and eventually be expelled from the body, causing dehydration. This can be a problem if seawater is consumed in large amounts, but an occasional swallow when swimming or snorkeling is nothing to worry about.

The high-latitude graph in Figure 4 shows a very different pattern from the low-latitude graph. Surface water temperatures in high latitudes are much cooler than in low latitudes. Deeper in the ocean, the temperature of the water is similar to that at the surface, so the line remains vertical with no thermocline. A water column with no thermocline is called *isothermal* (*iso* = same, *thermo* = heat).

☑ **Reading Checkpoint** *What is the thermocline?*

Ocean Density Variation

Density is defined as mass per unit volume. It can be thought of as a measure of how heavy something is for its size. For example, an object that has low density seems lightweight for its size, such as a dry sponge. An object that has high density, such as cement, seems heavy for its size. Density is an important property of ocean water because it determines the water's vertical position in the ocean. Density differences cause large masses of ocean water to sink below other masses or to float.

Factors Affecting Seawater Density 🔊 **Seawater density is influenced by two main factors: salinity and temperature.** An increase in salinity adds dissolved substances and results in an increase in seawater density. Although now a lake, the Dead Sea was once connected to the Mediterranean Sea. The salinity of the Dead Sea is ten times the average salinity of seawater. As a result, it has high buoyancy that allows swimmers, such as the one in **Figure 5,** to float easily.

An increase in temperature results in a decrease in seawater density. Generally, temperature has a greater influence over surface seawater density because the temperature of surface seawater tends to vary more than its salinity. Cold, polar regions with seawater that has high salinity contain the most dense seawater in the world.

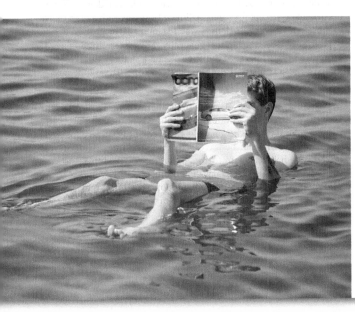

FIGURE 5 Floating in the Dead Sea

Ocean Water and Ocean Life **425**

Facts and Figures

Seawater has unique thermal properties that make it resistant to changes in temperature. Many marine species cannot withstand rapid temperature changes. Researchers have concluded that the ocean's stability as a habitat has been instrumental in the development of life on Earth. Scientists who study the effects of global warming indicate that atmospheric warming would eventually be transferred to the ocean,

potentially affecting marine organisms. A research project conducted by scientists at the Scripps Institute of Oceanography in the 1990s used sound waves transmitted across an ocean basin to measure ocean temperature. The speed of sound in seawater increases as the water temperature increases, so in the future, if the oceans are getting warmer, the sound would take less time to travel the same distance.

Use Visuals   L1

Figure 4 Have students examine the two graphs. **Ask:** What is the temperature range within the thermocline at low latitudes? *(approximately 24°C to 4°C)* What is the lowest water temperature shown on the graph? *(approximately 2°C)* What is the range of depths at which water of this temperature is found at low latitudes? *(from approximately 1500 m to below 3000 m)* At high latitudes? *(from the surface to below 3000 m)*
Visual, Verbal

Build Reading Literacy   L1

Refer to **p. 420D** in this chapter, which provides the guidelines for predicting.

Predict Have students preview the remainder of this lesson by looking over the headings, figures, figure captions, and boldfaced terms. Ask students to write their predictions of how seawater density is affected by salinity and by temperature. After students have read the lesson, have them evaluate their predictions and make changes, if necessary.
Verbal, Logical

Integrate Physics   L2

Weight and Density Remind students that the weight of a given volume of material increases as its density increases. **Ask:** What physical force causes water of a higher density to sink below water of a lower density? *(gravity)*
Logical

Answers

Figure 3 *Sea surface temperature is highest at the equator and low latitudes because these areas receive the highest intensity of solar radiation.*

Figure 4 *The thermocline is absent in the high latitudes because the temperature of surface water is closer to the temperature of deeper water.*

☑ **Reading Checkpoint** *The thermocline is the layer of ocean water between about 300 m and 1000 m, where there is a rapid change of temperature with depth.*

Ocean Water and Ocean Life **425**

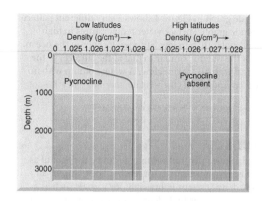

FIGURE 6 Density and Depth The graphs show variations in ocean water density with depth for low-latitude and high-latitude regions. *Interpret Graphs What is the difference between the low-latitude graph and the high-latitude graph? Why does this difference occur?*

Density Variation With Depth By sampling ocean waters, oceanographers have learned that temperature and salinity—and the water's resulting density—vary with depth. **Figure 6** shows two graphs of density versus depth. One graph shows the density for low-latitude regions and the other for high-latitude regions. The **pycnocline** (*pycno* = density, *cline* = slope) is the layer of ocean water between about 300 meters and 1000 meters where there is a rapid change of density. A pycnocline presents a significant barrier to mixing between low-density water above and high-density water below. A pycnocline is not present in high latitudes where the water column is about the same density throughout.

☑ **Reading Checkpoint** *How does an increase in temperature affect the density of seawater?*

Ocean Layering

The ocean, similar to Earth's interior, is layered according to density. Low-density water exists near the surface, and higher-density water occurs below. Except for some shallow inland seas with a high rate of evaporation, the highest-density water is found at the greatest ocean depths. 🔲 **Oceanographers generally recognize a three-layered structure in most parts of the open ocean: a shallow surface mixed zone, a transition zone, and a deep zone.** These zones are shown in **Figure 7.**

Surface Mixed Zone Because solar energy comes in contact with the ocean surface, water temperature is highest at the surface. The *surface mixed zone* is the area of the surface formed by the mixing of water by waves, currents, and tides. The surface mixed zone has nearly uniform temperatures. The depth and temperature of this layer vary, depending on latitude and season. The zone usually extends to about 300 meters, but it may extend to a depth of 450 meters. The surface mixed zone accounts for only about 2 percent of ocean water.

Surface mixed zone (2%)

Transition zone (18%)

Deep zone (80%)

Ocean floor

60°N   40°   20°   0°   20°   40°   60°S

FIGURE 7 Ocean Zones
Oceanographers recognize three main zones of the ocean based on water density, which varies with temperature and salinity. Note that the three layers do not form at high latitudes.

Transition Zone Below the sun-warmed surface mixed zone, the temperature drops abruptly with depth as was seen in Figure 4. Here, a distinct layer called the transition zone sits between the warm surface layer above and the deep zone of cold water below. The transition zone includes a thermocline and an associated pycnocline. This zone accounts for about 18 percent of ocean water.

Deep Zone Below the transition zone is the deep zone. Sunlight does not reach this zone, and water temperatures are just a few degrees above freezing. As a result, water density remains constant and high. The deep zone includes about 80 percent of ocean water.

In high latitudes, open ocean water does not form the three-layered structure shown in Figure 7. The three layers do not develop because there is no rapid change in temperature or density with depth. Therefore, good vertical mixing between surface and deep waters can occur in high-latitude regions. Here, cold, high-density water forms at the surface, sinks, and initiates deep-ocean currents that travel toward the equator.

15.1 Assessment

Review Key Concepts

1. What is salinity?

2. What units are used to express the salinity of ocean water?

3. What are the sources of salt in ocean water?

4. Explain the relationship between latitude and sea surface temperature.

5. What factors affect the density of ocean water?

6. What are the three main zones of the open ocean?

Think Critically

7. **Infer** Why does the salinity of seawater remain relatively constant over time?

8. **Summarize** Explain the general pattern of temperature variation with depth in low-latitude ocean water.

WRITING IN SCIENCE

9. **Describe** Write a paragraph that describes the different characteristics of the three zones of the open ocean. Include an explanation of why polar regions do not exhibit the same pattern of water layers.

Ocean Water and Ocean Life **427**

Use Visuals L1

Figure 4 After students have read the description of the transition zone, have them look back at Figure 4. **Ask:** What is the depth range of the transition zone as shown in this graph? *(region of most abrupt temperature change, from about 300–1000 m)*
Visual

3 ASSESS

Evaluate Understanding L2

To assess students' understanding of lesson content, present them with an unlabeled diagram showing an ocean profile similar to the one shown in Figure 7. Have students label the three ocean zones, or layers, and use arrows to indicate the direction in which water temperature increases at lower latitudes, and the direction in which density increases at lower latitudes.

Reteach L1

Have students work in pairs to make a set of flash cards for all the vocabulary terms in this lesson. Have students use the flash cards to quiz each other on the definitions.

Answers

Figure 6 *Pycnocline is not present in high latitude waters. This occurs because density does not vary with depth at high latitudes.*

☑ **Reading Checkpoint** *As temperature increases, density decreases.*

Assessment Answers

1. Salinity is the total amount of solid material dissolved in water.
2. parts per thousand
3. chemical weathering of rocks on continents; Earth's interior
4. Sea surface temperature is higher at the equator and low latitudes. Sea surface temperature decreases as latitude increases.
5. temperature and salinity
6. surface mixed zone, transition zone, deep zone

7. Dissolved components are being removed as rapidly as they are being added.
8. Temperature decreases with increasing depth; a thermocline is present between 300 m and 1000 m.
9. The surface mixed zone has the warmest temperatures and the most light. Water is well mixed by waves, currents, and tides. The water temperature is nearly uniform. The transition zone includes the thermocline and pycnocline in which both temperature and density change rapidly with depth. Sunlight does not reach the deep zone where water is near freezing in temperature. This pattern does not exist at polar latitudes where seawater is isothermal and of uniform density, which allows for good vertical mixing in the water column.

1 FOCUS

Lesson Objectives

15.5 **Recognize** how marine organisms can be classified.

15.6 **Differentiate** between plankton and nekton.

15.7 **Describe** the area of the ocean in which most benthic organisms live.

15.8 **List** the factors used to divide the ocean into marine zones.

Build Vocabulary

Concept Map Have students make a concept map using the term *marine life zones* as the starting point that connects to the following three terms: *availability of sunlight, distance from shore,* and *depth.* Students should use the following terms to complete their concept map: *pelagic zone, photic zone, oceanic zone, benthic zone, abyssal zone, intertidal zone,* and *neritic zone.*

Reading Strategy **L2**

a. plankton capable of photosynthesis
b. diatoms
c. animal plankton
d. larval fish
e. organisms capable of moving independently of ocean currents
f. fish
g. organisms living on or near the ocean bottom
h. marine worms

2 INSTRUCT

Build Reading Literacy **L2**

Refer to **p. 362D** in **Chapter 13,** which provides the guidelines for using prior knowledge.

Use Prior Knowledge Have students write the names of several ocean organisms they know about or have heard about. Next to each name, have students write a description of the organism, where it lives, and how it obtains food. After students have read the lesson, have them review their lists and make corrections, if necessary.
Logical

Key Questions

 How can marine organisms be classified?

What is the difference between plankton and nekton?

In which area of the ocean can most benthos organisms be found living?

What factors are used to divide the ocean into marine life zones?

Vocabulary

- photosynthesis
- plankton • phytoplankton
- zooplankton • nekton
- benthos • photic zone
- intertidal zone
- neritic zone
- oceanic zone
- pelagic zone
- benthic zone
- abyssal zone

Reading Strategy

Build Vocabulary Copy the table below. As you read, add definitions and examples to complete the table.

Definitions		Examples
Plankton: organisms that drift with ocean currents		bacteria
Phytoplankton:	a. ___?___	b. ___?___
Zooplankton:	c. ___?___	d. ___?___
Nekton:	e. ___?___	f. ___?___
Benthos:	g. ___?___	h. ___?___

A WIDE VARIETY of organisms inhabit the marine environment. These organisms range in size from microscopic bacteria and algae to the largest organisms alive today—blue whales, which can be as long as three buses lined up end to end. Marine biologists have identified more than 250,000 marine species. This number is constantly increasing as new organisms are discovered. There are advantages and disadvantages to living in a marine environment. One advantage is that there is plenty of water. One disadvantage is that moving through water can be difficult. The success of marine organisms depends on their ability to avoid predators, find food, and cope with the challenges of their environment.

Classification of Marine Organisms

 Marine organisms can be classified according to where they live and how they move. They can be classified as either plankton (floaters), nekton (swimmers), or benthos (bottom dwellers). Most marine organisms live in the sunlit surface of the ocean, where photosynthesis is possible. Organisms that perform **photosynthesis** use water, carbon dioxide, and energy from sunlight to produce carbohydrates for food. These organisms directly or indirectly provide food for the vast majority of marine organisms. Because oxygen is a waste product of photosynthesis, photosynthesizing organisms also are an important source of atmospheric oxygen.

Plankton **All organisms that drift with ocean currents, including algae, tiny animals, and bacteria, are known as plankton** (*planktos* = wandering). Many plankton can also swim, but either move very weakly or move only vertically.

FIGURE 8 Plankton Plankton are organisms that drift with ocean currents.

A This photograph shows a variety of phytoplankton from the Atlantic Ocean. **B** The zooplankton shown here include copepods and the larval stages of other common marine organisms.

Among plankton, the organisms that perform photosynthesis are called **phytoplankton.** Most phytoplankton, such as diatoms, are microscopic. Animal plankton are called **zooplankton.** Zooplankton include the larval stages of many marine organisms such as fish, sea stars, lobsters, and crabs. **Figure 8** shows members of each group.

Nekton 🔲 **All animals capable of moving independently of the ocean currents, by swimming or other means of propulsion, are called nekton** (*nektos* = swimming). Nekton can determine their position within the ocean and in many cases complete long migrations. Nekton include most adult fish and squid, marine mammals, and marine reptiles. **Figure 9** shows examples of nekton.

Fish may appear to exist everywhere in the oceans, but they are more abundant near continents and islands and in colder waters. Some fish, such as salmon, swim upstream in freshwater rivers to spawn. Many eels do just the reverse, growing to maturity in fresh water and then swimming out of the streams to breed in the depths of the ocean.

Benthos 🔲 **Organisms that live on or in the ocean bottom are called benthos** (*benthos* = bottom). **Figure 10** shows some examples of benthos. The shallow coastal ocean floor contains a wide variety of physical conditions and nutrient levels. Most benthos can be found living in this area. Shallow coastal areas are the only locations where large brown algae, often called seaweeds, are found attached to the bottom. These are the only areas of the seafloor that receive enough sunlight for the algae to survive.

Throughout most of the deeper parts of the seafloor, where photosynthesis cannot occur, animals live in perpetual darkness. They must feed on each other or on whatever nutrients fall from the productive surface waters. The deep-sea bottom is an environment of coldness, stillness, and darkness. Under these conditions, life progresses slowly. Organisms that live in the deep sea usually are widely distributed because physical conditions vary little on the deep-ocean floor.

FIGURE 9 Nekton Nekton include all animals capable of moving independently of ocean currents. **A** This squid can use propulsion to move through the water. **B** This school of grunts swims through the water with ease.
Infer *Why do you think some organisms are classified as plankton during some stages of their lives and nekton during other stages?*

FIGURE 10 Benthos Benthos are organisms living on or in the ocean bottom. Benthic organisms include sea stars **(A)** and crabs **(B).**

Facts and Figures

Of the more than 300 shark species, about 80 percent are unable to harm people or rarely encounter people. The largest shark—also the largest fish in the world—is the whale shark (*Rhincodon typus*). It reaches lengths of up to 15 m but eats only plankton and is therefore not considered dangerous. The great white shark (*Carcharodon carcharias*) is a predator that feeds preferentially on pinnipeds (seals and sea lions) and has attacked humans swimming or surfing in pinniped habitat areas. A great white can grow to 7 m long and weigh up to 2250 kg. Sharks are classified as nekton.

LESSON 15.2

Integrate Biology · L2

Explain to students that the giant tubeworms living in hydrothermal vent communities do not have digestive systems. Even so, they can grow up to 3 m long. When scientists first discovered these organisms, they were baffled as to how they could grow so large with no obvious means of obtaining energy. Eventually, scientists learned that the worms get all the nutrition they need from bacteria living inside their body cavities. Encourage students to look up more information about hydrothermal vents and the biological communities they support.
Verbal, Logical

Use Community Resources · L2

Aquarium Field Trip Take students on a field trip to a local public aquarium or museum with ocean life exhibits. Alternatively, students could visit a pet store that specializes in saltwater aquariums. Have students write a short paper describing one or more organisms they observe during their visit. Encourage students to classify each of their organisms as belonging to plankton, nekton, or benthos; to identify the ocean zone in which the organism lives; and to explain how the organism obtains food.
Kinesthetic, Logical

FIGURE 11 Hydrothermal Vents
A When super-heated water meets cold seawater, "black smoke" forms as minerals precipitate from the water. **B** Tube worms up to 3 meters in length are among the organisms that live on hydrothermal vents.

Hydrothermal Vents Among the most unusual seafloor discoveries of the last several decades have been the hydrothermal vents along the mid-ocean ridge. Here seawater seeps into the ocean floor through cracks in the crust.

The water becomes super-heated and saturated with minerals. Eventually the heated water escapes back into the ocean. When the hot water comes in contact with the surrounding cold water, the minerals precipitate out, giving the water the appearance of black smoke. These geysers of hot water are referred to as black smokers, such as the one shown in **Figure 11**.

At some vents water temperatures of 100°C or higher support communities of benthic organisms found nowhere else in the world. In fact, hundreds of new species have been discovered surrounding these deep-sea habitats since scientists found vents along the Galápagos Rift in 1977. Chemicals from the vents are an energy source for bacteria. These bacteria produce sugars and other foods that enable them and many other organisms to live in this very extreme environment.

Marine Life Zones

The distribution of marine organisms is affected by the chemistry, physics, and geology of the ocean. Marine organisms are influenced by a variety of physical factors. 🔑 **Three factors are used to divide the ocean into distinct marine life zones: the availability of sunlight, the distance from shore, and the water depth.** The different zones in which marine life can be found are shown in **Figure 12**.

Availability of Sunlight The part of the ocean into which sunlight penetrates is called the **photic zone** (*photos* = light). The clarity of seawater is affected by many factors, such as the amount of plankton, suspended sediment, and decaying organic particles in the water. In addition, the amount of sunlight varies with atmospheric conditions, time of day, season, and latitude.

The *euphotic zone* is the portion of the photic zone near the surface where light is strong enough for photosynthesis to occur. In the open ocean, this zone can reach a depth of 100 meters, but the zone will be much shallower close to shore where water clarity is typically reduced. In the euphotic zone, phytoplankton use sunlight to produce food that directly or indirectly feeds most ocean life.

Although photosynthesis cannot occur much deeper than 100 meters, there is enough light in the lower photic zone for marine animals to avoid predators, find food, recognize other members of their species, and locate mates. Below this zone is the *aphotic zone,* where there is no sunlight.

☑ **Reading Checkpoint** *What is the difference between the photic zone and the aphotic zone?*

Differentiated Instruction

BEHAVIORALLY DISORDERED Have students work together to make a two-dimensional model of ocean life zones on the classroom bulletin board. Students can use Figure 12 as a starting point. Challenge students to draw or paint and label continental shelf, continental slope, ocean basin, photic zone, aphotic zone, and benthic zone on a large piece of poster board or butcher paper. Have students add labeled organisms to appropriate areas of their model. Students can make their own drawings of organisms, cut out photographs from old magazines, or photocopy illustrations from books.

Distance from Shore Marine life zones can also be subdivided based on distance from shore. The area where the land and ocean meet and overlap is the **intertidal zone.** This narrow strip of land between high and low tides is alternately covered and uncovered by seawater with each tidal change. It appears to be a harsh place to live with crashing waves, periodic drying out, and rapid changes in temperature, salinity, and oxygen concentrations. However, the species that live here are well adapted to the constant environmental changes.

Seaward from the low-tide line is the **neritic zone.** This zone covers the gently sloping continental shelf. The neritic zone can be very narrow or may extend hundreds of kilometers from shore. It is often shallow enough for sunlight to reach all the way to the ocean floor, putting it entirely within the photic zone.

Although the neritic zone covers only about 5 percent of the world ocean, it is rich in biomass and number of species. Many organisms find the conditions here ideal because photosynthesis occurs readily, runoff from the land supplies nutrients, and the bottom provides shelter and habitat. This zone is so rich with life that it supports 90 percent of the world's commercial fisheries.

Beyond the continental shelf is the **oceanic zone.** The open ocean reaches great depths. As a result, surface waters typically have lower nutrient concentrations because nutrients tend to sink from the photic zone to the deep-ocean floor. This low nutrient concentration usually results in smaller populations than are found in the more productive neritic zone.

FIGURE 12 Marine Life Zones
The ocean is divided into marine life zones, based on availability of light, distance from shore, and water depth.
Interpret Visuals *Why are phytoplankton and larger algae found only in the photic zone?*

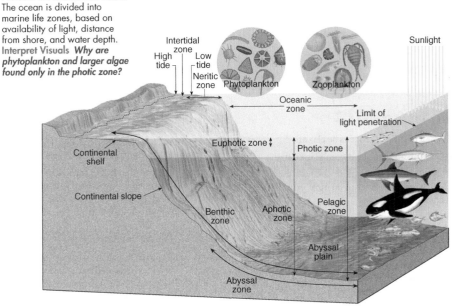

Build Science Skills L2

Classify After students have finished reading about marine life zones, have them make a table with two columns. Have students label the left column Photic Zone and the right column Aphotic Zone. Ask students to place each of the following marine life zones in the correct column: intertidal, neritic, oceanic, benthic, abyssal. If necessary, offer students the hint that some marine life zones may exist in both photic and aphotic zones. *Photic: intertidal, neritic, oceanic (partly), pelagic (partly) benthic (partly); Aphotic: benthic (partly), oceanic (partly), pelagic (partly), abyssal*
Logical

Use Visuals L1

Figure 12 Have students examine the drawing of the ocean basin. **Ask:** What marine life zones are found on or above the continental shelf? *(intertidal, neritic, photic)* Where does photosynthesis take place? *(euphotic zone)*
Visual, Logical

Build Science Skills L2

Infer. After students have examined Figure 12, **ask:** Should all intertidal and neritic organisms be classified as benthos? Why? *(No. Not all of the organisms in these zones live on the ocean bottom. Some of these organisms, including many fish species, jellyfish, and plankton, live above bottom in the water column.)*
Logical, Verbal

Answers

Figure 12 *Both types of organisms need sunlight for photosynthesis.*

☑ **Reading Checkpoint** *Sunlight penetrates the photic zone; no sunlight reaches the aphotic zone.*

Differentiated Instruction

GIFTED Invite interested students to make classroom exhibits describing an ecosystem from one of the marine life zones. For example, students could put together a labeled photo collage of intertidal benthos organisms or a poster depicting a pelagic food web.

LESSON 15.2

❸ ASSESS

Evaluate Understanding `L2`

To assess students' understanding of lesson content, present a profile of the ocean floor and have them label the locations of the following marine life zones: intertidal, neritic, oceanic, benthic, abyssal, photic, aphotic, and euphotic.

Reteach `L1`

Help students review the marine life zones by asking them to identify similarities and differences in pairs of terms, such as *intertidal* zone and *neritic* zone *(both in photic zone, continental shelf region, include benthos, nekton, and plankton; intertidal is between tides, neritic is below tides)*; *phytoplankton* and *zooplankton* *(float with ocean currents, found in oceanic and intertidal zones, phytoplankton photosynthesize, zooplankton do not)*; *benthic* zone and *abyssal* zone *(both involve ocean bottom, abyssal is deep ocean bottom only)*

INQUIRY
APPLY IT!

Q: *How do deep-sea organisms find their way around without sunlight?*

A: More than half of deep-sea organisms—including fishes, jellies, crustaceans, and deep-sea squid—are bioluminescent, which means they can produce light. These organisms produce light through a chemical reaction in specially designed structures or cells called *photophores*. Some of these cells contain luminescent bacteria that live symbiotically within the organism. In a world of darkness, the ability to produce light can be used to attract prey, define territory, communicate with others, or avoid predators.

Water Depth A third method of classifying marine habitats is based on water depth. These three zones—the pelagic, benthic, and abyssal—are shown on the previous page in Figure 12. Open ocean of any depth is called the **pelagic zone**. Animals in this zone swim or float freely. The photic part of the pelagic zone is home to plankton and nekton, such as tuna, sea turtles, and dolphins. Giant squid and other species that are adapted to life in deep water inhabit the aphotic zone.

The **benthic zone** includes any sea-bottom surface regardless of its distance from shore. It is mostly inhabited by benthos such as giant kelp, sponges, crabs, sea anemones, sea stars, and marine worms that attach to, crawl upon, or burrow into the seafloor.

The **abyssal zone** is a subdivision of the benthic zone. The abyssal zone includes the deep-ocean floor, such as abyssal plains. This zone is characterized by extremely high water pressure, consistently low temperature, no sunlight, and sparse life. Food sources at abyssal depths typically come from the surface, such as decaying particles that steadily "rain" down. These particles provide food for filter feeders, brittle stars, and burrowing worms. Other food arrives as large fragments or entire bodies of dead organisms that sink from the surface. These pieces supply meals for fish that are actively seeking food, such as the grenadier, tripodfish, and hagfish.

15.2 Assessment

Review Key Concepts ⟳

1. How can marine organisms be classified?

2. What is the difference between plankton and nekton?

3. In which area of the ocean do most benthic organisms live?

4. What factors are used to divide the ocean into marine life zones?

5. Why is the neritic zone rich in living things?

6. What are two reasons that scientists were surprised to find so many different forms of life on hydrothermal vents?

Think Critically

7. Infer Why do many fish in the abyssal zone locate food through chemical sensing?

8. Infer Organisms that live in the intertidal zone must deal with harsh and changing conditions. What types of adaptations would benefit organisms living in this zone?

BIGIDEA WATER PLANET

9. Make a table to organize the information about marine life zones presented in this section. Include the basis by which the zone is classified, any subdivisions of the zone, and the characteristics of each zone.

Assessment Answers

1. by where they live and how they move
2. Nekton are able to move independently of ocean currents. Plankton are not.
3. on the shallow coastal ocean floor
4. availability of sunlight, distance from shore, water depth
5. Conditions are ideal for photosynthesis because there is light and nutrients from runoff; the bottom provides shelter and habitat.

6. high temperatures on the vent and high pressure
7. The abyssal zone is vast and there is no light. With no light, fish cannot use eyesight to find food.
8. Students' answers will vary but should show that they understand the factors an organism living in the intertidal zone has to deal with. Answers may include having a shell that can be sealed to prevent drying out, having a

way to attach firmly to rocks, having a shell to protect against wave action, being able to live in an area with a wide temperature and salinity range.
9. Student tables should reflect the material presented in this section.

15.3 Oceanic Productivity

LIKE OTHER ECOSYSTEMS on Earth, organisms in the marine environment are interconnected through the web of food production and consumption. Marine producers include phytoplankton, larger algae such as seaweeds, and bacteria. Consumers include crabs, clams, sea stars, fish, dolphins, and whales. Why are some regions of the ocean teeming with life, while other areas seem barren? The answer is related to the amount of primary productivity in various parts of the ocean.

Primary Productivity

Primary productivity is the production of organic compounds from inorganic substances through photosynthesis or chemosynthesis. Recall that photosynthesis is the use of light energy to convert water and carbon dioxide into energy-rich glucose molecules. **Chemosynthesis** is the process by which certain microorganisms produce organic molecules from inorganic nutrients using chemical energy. For example, bacteria in hydrothermal vent communities use hydrogen sulfide as an energy source. These bacteria are producers that support the hydrothermal vent communities.

🔑 **Two factors influence a region's photosynthetic productivity: the availability of nutrients and the amount of solar radiation, or sunlight.** Primary producers need nutrients such as nitrogen, phosphorus, and iron. Lack of nutrients can be a limiting factor in productivity. Thus, the most abundant marine life exists where there are ample nutrients and sunlight. Oceanic productivity varies dramatically because of the uneven distribution of nutrients throughout the photic zone and the availability of solar energy due to seasonal changes.

FIGURE 13 Great Barrier Reef The abundance of life found in coral reef communities is supported by high levels of primary productivity.

Ocean Water and Ocean Life **433**

Key Questions

🔑 *What factors influence a region's photosynthetic productivity?*

🔑 *Describe the transfer efficiency between trophic levels.*

🔑 *How do food webs show the relationships among organisms in an ecosystem?*

Vocabulary

• primary productivity
• chemosynthesis
• trophic level
• food chain • food web

Reading Strategy

Identify Main Ideas Copy the table below. As you read, write the main idea of each topic.

Topic	Main Idea
Productivity in polar oceans	a. ___?___
Productivity in tropical oceans	b. ___?___
Productivity in temperate oceans	c. ___?___

LESSON 15.3

1 FOCUS

Lesson Objectives
15.9 **List** the factors that influence a region's photosynthetic productivity.
15.10 **Describe** the transfer of energy from one trophic level to another.
15.11 **Describe** the value of food webs.

Build Vocabulary L2
Paraphrase Help students understand the terms *primary productivity* and *trophic level* by explaining their meanings using words students are already familiar with. *Primary productivity* can be described as the amount of light (or chemical) energy that is turned into food by producer organisms. The term *trophic* refers to nutrition, and *trophic level* refers to the amount of food energy available to organisms at each step in a food chain.

Reading Strategy L2
a. Phytoplankton peaks in May, and zooplankton peaks in July and August; limited by availability of solar energy.
b. limited by lack of nutrients because of permanent thermocline that prevents mixing of warm surface water with colder, deeper, nutrient-rich water
c. lowest in winter and summer, higher in fall, highest in spring; limited by solar energy in winter and fall, by nutrients in summer and spring

2 INSTRUCT

Build Science Skills L2
Compare and Contrast Have students describe the similarities and differences of photosynthesis and chemosynthesis. *(Similarities: Both produce organic compounds from inorganic substances. Differences: Photosynthesis uses light and is performed by most producer organisms; chemosynthesis uses inorganic molecules from the environment and is performed by bacteria in hydrothermal vent communities.)* **Logical, Verbal**

LESSON 15.3

Use Visuals L1

Figure 14 Explain to students that this graph shows the relative numbers of phytoplankton and zooplankton biomass over time. Inform students that biomass data represents the total mass of the organisms sampled. **Ask:** Biomass data on what phytoplankton organism is given in this graph? *(diatoms)* During what season does the phytoplankton biomass reach its peak? *(spring)* During what season does the zooplankton biomass reach its peak? *(summer)*
Visual

Build Science Skills L2

Infer After students examine Figure 14, **ask:** Why is there a lag time between the peak biomass of phytoplankton and the peak biomass of zooplankton? *(Zooplankton feed on phytoplankton. Zooplankton that obtain plenty of food will reproduce, producing more zooplankton. As long as there are plenty of phytoplankton, the zooplankton will continue to increase in numbers.)*
Visual, Logical

FIGURE 14 Productivity in a Polar Ocean One example of productivity in polar oceans is illustrated by the Barents Sea.
Interpret Graphs **Describe the relationship between the zooplankton and phytoplankton populations.**

FIGURE 15 Water Layers in the Tropics The permanent thermocline in tropical oceans prevents the mixing of surface and deep water masses. Productivity is limited by the amount of nutrients in surface waters.

434 Chapter 15 • Lesson 3

Productivity in Polar Oceans Polar regions such as the Arctic Ocean's Barents Sea, off the northern coast of Europe, experience continuous darkness for about three months of winter and continuous sunlight for about three months during summer. Productivity of phytoplankton, mostly single-celled algae called diatoms, peaks there during May. This trend is shown in the graph in **Figure 14.** During May the sun rises high enough in the sky so that sunlight penetrates deep into the water. The increase in available light results in an increase in the diatom population. Zooplankton now have a greater food source than before and their population also increases. As Figure 14 shows, the zooplankton biomass peaks in July and continues at a relatively high level until winter darkness begins in October.

Recall that density and temperature change very little with depth in polar regions and mixing occurs between surface waters and deeper, nutrient-rich waters. In the summer, however, melting ice produces a thin, low-salinity surface layer that does not readily mix with the deeper waters. This lack of mixing between water masses is crucial to summer productivity, because it helps prevent phytoplankton from being carried into deeper, darker waters. Instead, they are concentrated in the sunlit surface waters where they reproduce continuously.

Because of the supply of nutrients rising from deeper waters, high-latitude surface waters typically have high nutrient concentrations. **The availability of solar energy, however, is what limits photosynthetic productivity in polar areas.**

Productivity in Tropical Oceans You may be surprised to learn that productivity is low in tropical regions of the open ocean. Because the sun is more directly overhead, light penetrates much deeper into tropical oceans than in temperate and polar waters. Solar energy also is available year-round. However, productivity is low because a permanent thermocline prevents mixing between surface waters and nutrient-rich deeper waters. **Figure 15** shows how water masses are separated in the tropics. The thermocline is a barrier that cuts off the supply of nutrients from deeper waters below. **Productivity in tropical regions is limited by the lack of nutrients.** These areas have so few organisms that they are considered biological deserts.

Differentiated Instruction

ENGLISH LANGUAGE LEARNERS Help students understand the biological terms in this lesson by having them explore word parts and word roots. Explain that the term *productivity* is related to the word "produce."

Have students look up the definitions of *product, producer,* and *produce.* Explain to students that the suffix *-synthesis* is a word that implies the meaning "to put together." *Trophic* means "of or relating to nutrition."

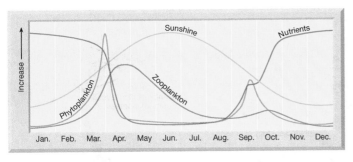

FIGURE 16 **Productivity in Northern Hemisphere, Temperate Oceans** The graph shows the relationship among phytoplankton, zooplankton, amount of sunshine, and nutrient levels for surface waters.
Interpret Graphs *What happens to phytoplankton in the spring and in the fall?*

Productivity in Temperate Oceans Productivity is limited by available sunlight in polar regions and by nutrient supply in the tropics. **In temperate regions, which are found at mid-latitudes, seasonal changes influence levels of sunlight and nutrient supply which, in turn, influence productivity.** These relationships are shown in **Figure 16.**

▶ *Winter* Productivity in temperate oceans is very low during winter, even though nutrient concentration is highest at this time. The reason is that solar energy is limited because days are short, and the sun angle is low. As a result, the depth at which photosynthesis can occur is so shallow that phytoplankton populations are low.

▶ *Spring* The sun rises higher in the sky during spring, allowing photosynthesis to occur at greater depths. A spring bloom of phytoplankton occurs because solar energy and nutrients are available. Eventually, a seasonal thermocline develops and traps algae in the euphotic zone. The algae consume nutrients in the euphotic zone and the supply is quickly depleted. Productivity decreases sharply. Even though the hours of daylight, and thus available sunlight, are increasing, productivity during the spring bloom is limited by the lack of nutrients.

▶ *Summer* The sun rises even higher in the summer, so surface waters in temperate parts of the ocean continue to warm. A strong seasonal thermocline develops that prevents the mixing of surface and deeper waters. Nutrients depleted from surface waters cannot be replaced by those from deeper waters. Throughout summer, the phytoplankton population remains relatively low.

▶ *Fall* Solar radiation decreases in the fall as the sun moves lower in the sky. Surface water temperatures drop and the summer thermocline diminishes. Nutrients return to the surface layer as increased wind strength mixes surface waters with deeper waters. These conditions produce a fall bloom of phytoplankton, which is much less dramatic than the spring bloom. The fall bloom is very short-lived because sunlight becomes the limiting factor as winter approaches.

PLANET DIARY

For an activity on **Photosynthesis in the Oceans,** visit PlanetDiary.com/HSES

Ocean Water and Ocean Life **435**

Facts and Figures

Earth's average surface temperature has been increasing over the past 130 years, likely as a result of human activities that increase carbon dioxide (CO_2) in the atmosphere. Stimulating a rise in ocean productivity has been suggested as a way of removing CO_2 from the atmosphere, because phytoplankton take in CO_2 during photosynthesis. Increasing the number of photosynthetic aquatic organisms would increase the amount of CO_2 removed from the atmosphere.

Iron has been identified as the nutrient that limits productivity in some ocean regions. Tests conducted in the Pacific Ocean showed that adding finely ground iron increases productivity up to 30 times. Some scientists fear that fertilizing the ocean with iron could upset the ocean's natural chemical balance and alter the global marine ecosystem. Others claim that stimulating productivity is a promising solution for helping to reduce atmospheric CO_2.

LESSON 15.3

Address Misconceptions   L2

Students may think that higher trophic levels actually contain more energy than lower trophic levels because they may reason that energy accumulates as you move up a food chain. Emphasize that the energy gained by producers through photosynthesis and chemosynthesis is the only energy available to all the succeeding levels of the food chain. Ask students to think about what happens to the energy captured by the producers of a food chain and then stored in food molecules. *(The producers use some of this energy to carry out life processes, such as making more food. Much of this energy is released to the environment as heat energy. The remaining energy is transferred to organisms at the next trophic level when the organisms consume the producers.)* Challenge students to describe how this process could result in an increase in net energy as you move up the levels of a food chain. *(It cannot. Energy is used to make new cells and conduct other life processes, but no energy is added.)*

Teacher Demo

BUILD AN ENERGY PYRAMID   L2

Purpose Students will observe how total available energy decreases at successive levels of a food chain or food web.

Procedure Draw a large pyramid shape on the board. Draw four horizontal lines across the pyramid to make five trophic levels. In each level, write the number of units of energy available as given in Figure 17. Write names of the organisms that make up each trophic level. Ask for students' input as you make an energy pyramid for the organisms as shown in the food web in Figure 18. Instead of numbers, each level of this pyramid should contain the names of organisms belonging to that level.

Expected Outcome Students should see that the shape of the pyramid is a visual representation of the decrease in available energy at higher levels of a food chain or food web.
Visual, Logical

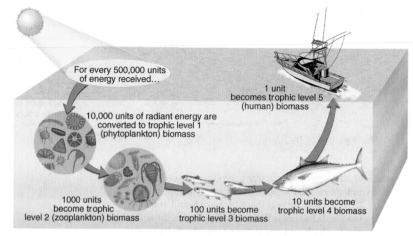

FIGURE 17 Energy Flow in an Ecosystem For every 500,000 units of radiant energy input available to the producers, only one unit of mass is added to the fifth trophic level. **Calculate** *What is the average transfer efficiency for phytoplankton? What is it for all of the other trophic levels?*

Oceanic Feeding Relationships

Phytoplankton, plants, and bacteria are the main oceanic producers. As producers make food available to the animals of the ocean, energy passes from one feeding population to the next. Only a small percentage of the energy taken in at any level is passed to the next one because energy is lost as heat at each level. As a result, the producers' biomass in the ocean is many times greater than the mass of top consumers, such as sharks.

Trophic Levels Chemical energy stored in the mass of the ocean's producers is transferred to the animal community mostly through feeding. Zooplankton are herbivores (*herba* = grass, *vora* = eat) that consume phytoplankton. Larger herbivores feed on brown algae and marine plants that grow attached to the ocean bottom near shore. The herbivores are eaten by carnivores (*carni* = meat, *vora* = eat). Smaller carnivores are eaten by larger carnivores, and so on. Each of these feeding stages is called a **trophic level.**

Transfer Efficiency **The transfer of energy between trophic levels is very inefficient.** The transfer efficiencies of different primary producer species vary, but the average is only about 2 percent. This means that 2 percent of the light energy absorbed by primary producers is stored as chemical energy in food and made available to herbivores. **Figure 17** shows the passage of energy between trophic levels through an entire ecosystem—from the solar energy used by phytoplankton to a top-level carnivore, humans.

Facts and Figures

Generally, individual members of a feeding population are larger, but not too much larger, than the organisms they eat. There are conspicuous exceptions, however, such as the blue whale. Up to 30 m long, the blue whale is possibly the largest animal that has ever existed on Earth. Yet it feeds mostly on krill—shrimp-like crustaceans—that have a maximum length of only 6 cm.

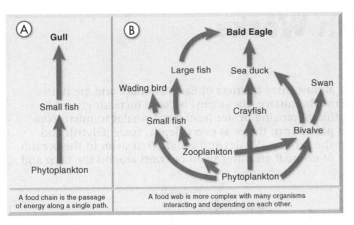

FIGURE 18 A Food Chain and Food Web of the Chesapeake Bay
A A food chain is the passage of energy along a single path. **B** A food web is a complex series of feeding relationships with many organisms interacting and depending on each other.

A food chain is the passage of energy along a single path.

A food web is more complex with many organisms interacting and depending on each other.

Food Chains and Food Webs A **food chain** is a sequence of organisms through which energy is transferred, starting with the primary producer. A herbivore eats the producer, then a carnivore eats the herbivore. The chain culminates with the "top carnivore," which is not usually preyed upon by any other organism.

Figure 18A shows a simple food chain. Feeding relationships are rarely as simple as this food chain suggests. More often, top carnivores in a food chain feed on a number of different animals, each of which feeds on a variety of organisms. These feeding relationships form a **food web. Figure 18B** shows a food web found in the Chesapeake Bay.

🔑 **Food webs are used to evaluate relationships in ecosystems because they show how the success or failure of one population could affect other populations.** For example, what could happen to small fish if a disease struck crayfish? With fewer crayfish to eat phytoplankton, small fish and zooplankton would have more food. If the zooplankton population also grew in size, the small fish could have a great increase in food supply.

15.3 Assessment

Review Key Concepts 🔑

1. What factors influence a region's photosynthetic productivity?

2. Describe the transfer efficiency between trophic levels.

3. Identify one food chain in the food web shown in Figure 18B.

4. What limits primary productivity in tropical oceans? Why?

Think Critically

5. Compare and Contrast Compare and contrast photosynthesis and chemosynthesis. Give examples of organisms that perform each process.

6. Draw Conclusions Explain why producers are the first trophic level in a food chain or food web.

MATH PRACTICE

7. Calculate If 700,000 energy units are received by phytoplankton in the ocean surface, approximately how many energy units will reach a consumer that is in the fourth trophic level of a food chain?

Ocean Water and Ocean Life   **437**

Objectives

In this feature, students will
- describe the conditions in each of the ocean's vertical zones.
- identify the special features and phenomena that allow organisms to survive in the different vertical zones.
- explain how atolls are formed.

Build Vocabulary [L2]

Define Terms Write *bioluminescence, eyespots, hydrothermal vents,* and *atoll* on the board. Have students review the material on this page and the next to define each term. Then discuss how each feature or phenomenon supports ocean life.

2 INSTRUCT

Bellringer [L2]

Ask students to name as many organisms as they can that live in the ocean. Make a list of all of these organisms on the board.
Logical

Use Visuals [L1]

Have students examine the chart of vertical zones on this page. **Ask:** How many of those organisms did you name in the Bellringer activity? Then have them list the animals they do not recognize. Discuss with the class the possible reasons certain animals are less familiar than others. *(Sample answer: Animals that live deeper in the ocean are not seen in aquariums or zoos.)*
Visual

How Earth Works

Ocean Life

The world's oceans cover almost three quarters of Earth's surface and are home to a vast array of life. Below the surface, the oceans become increasingly cold and dark. Even so, living things, ranging in size from giant whales to microscopic floating organisms called **plankton,** thrive at every depth. Some jellyfish and turtles float or swim near the surface. Whales and squid often swim in the ocean's middepths. A whole host of unusual creatures swim or crawl around the deep and dark ocean depths.

Elongate Fangjaw

Photophores

Life in the ocean zones

Portuguese man-of-war

Flying fish

Shelf

Oarweed

Shark

Brain coral

Mackerel

Turtle

Sponges

Slope

Octopus

Sperm whale

Hatchet fish

Sea pens

Rat-tail

Sea spider

Gulper eel

Rise

Anglerfish

Sea cucumbers

Abyss

Deep-sea anemone

Sponges

Tripod fish

Brittle star

Photic zone
Seasonal changes in water temperature

200 m (660 ft)
Twilight zone
Water temperature drops

1000 m (3300 ft)
Aphotic zone
Water very cold and pitch black

4000 m (13,120 ft)
Abyss
Dark and cold

6000 m (19,700 ft)

Deep-sea trench
Life exists below this depth.

▲ BIOLUMINESCENCE
Some fish, such as this elongate fangjaw (above), have special organs called photophores that give off a glow. In this process, called **bioluminescence,** fish use the light to recognize members of their own species or as lures for attracting prey.

A school of chromis swims among coral off the coast of the Maldives in the Indian Ocean.

▲ VERTICAL ZONES
Oceanographers divide the oceans into zones based on depth. Each zone is home to living things that are adapted to survive at that depth. For example, deep-water animals cope with darkness, very cold temperatures, and pressures that would crush a human. Some creatures can survive in more than one zone. In addition, some organisms live exclusively on or near the seafloor, while others float or swim in the water column.

438 Chapter 15

Facts and Figures

To study the deepest regions of the sea, scientists at Woods Hole Oceanographic Institute in Woods Hole, Massachusetts, use a deep submergence vehicle, or deep-sea sub, called *Alvin. Alvin* is approximately 7 m long and 3.6 m high. It can carry three scientists to a depth of 4000 m—the top of the abyss. The submersible's video equipment records life in deep ocean regions, and its manipulators, or long arms, collect specimens. In recent years, *Alvin* has helped scientists explore hydrothermal vents.

Growth of a coral atoll

1. Coral starts to grow around a volcanic island.

2. As the volcano becomes dormant, it gets cooler and denser, causing the island to gradually sink. Sand collects on the growing coral reef and forms land.

3. The island disappears. Vegetation grows on the atoll that remains.

Australian sea lions are marine mammals that breathe air, feed at sea, and breed on land.

▲ **CORAL REEFS**
A coral is a tubular soft bodied animal with tentacles. Most corals attach to a surface and build reefs in the warm, shallow, brightly lit waters of the continental shelf. Other reefs are ring-shaped **atolls** around a lagoon of shallow water. Atolls grow over millions of years.

▲ **PHOTIC ZONE**
Sunlight supports the growth of algae, sea grasses, and other plants on which some sea creatures feed. Marine mammals, squid, fish, and other animals have to be strong swimmers to move in the surface currents. Sea grasses and coral reefs provide food, shelter, and breeding sites for a variety of creatures.

HYDROTHERMAL VENTS ▶
On the deep ocean floor, hot, mineral-rich water gushes from cracks, called **hydrothermal vents.** Bacteria feed on chemicals in this water, forming the basis of a food chain that does not rely on sunlight and plants. Giant tube worms, clams, and blind white crabs are some organisms that live around these vents.

Worms and crabs near a hydrothermal vent.

BRIGHT COLORS
Many fish that live in the photic zone have bright colors that attract mates and confuse predators. Complex coloration makes it hard to detect the outline of a fish. Some fish have eyespots, or false eyes. As a predator attacks the false head, the fish darts off in the opposite direction. ▼

Forcepsfish

False eyes

Assessment

1. **Key Terms** Define (a) plankton, (b) bioluminescence, (c) atoll, (d) hydrothermal vent.

2. **Ecosystems** Why does most photosynthesis occur near the ocean surface but not near the deep ocean floor?

3. **Physical Processes** How can the emergence of a volcano lead to the growth of coral and the formation of an atoll?

4. **Ecosystems** How are some fish in the photic zone specially adapted to attract mates or to escape predators?

5. **Think Critically** **Analyzing Processes** Suppose that changes in the environment cause a decline in the population of photosynthesizing marine organisms and corals. How might that environmental change also cause damage to populations of fish, marine mammals, and other sea creatures?

439

3 ASSESS

Evaluate Understanding L2

Have students choose one of the organisms in the vertical zone chart they find particularly interesting. Ask them to do research in the library or on the Internet to find out about the organism's features and adaptations. Have them summarize why the organism lives in its particular part of the ocean.

Reteach L1

Have students identify the world's major coral reefs and find out what steps have been taken to protect them. Have each student write a pamphlet that describes rules and regulations that visitors to reefs must obey. Post the pamphlets on a bulletin board. Discuss what students learned.

Assessment Answers

1. **(a)** microscopic floating organisms; **(b)** glow given off by special fish organs called photophores; **(c)** ring-shaped coral reef around a lagoon of shallow water; **(d)** crack on deep ocean floor through which hot, mineral-rich water gushes

2. Photosynthesis requires sunlight, and sunlight does not penetrate to the deep ocean floor.

3. Coral grows around a volcanic island and as the island sinks, sand collects on the coral reef and forms land. Then vegetation grows on the atoll that remains.

4. Some fish use bioluminescence to attract prey, and many fish have eyespots or bright colors that confuse predators.

5. Such a change in the environment would disrupt the food chain and would cause fish, mammals, and other sea creatures to starve.

HOW DOES TEMPERATURE AFFECT WATER DENSITY? **L2**

Objectives
After completing this activity, students will be able to
- create a model of how temperature affects water density.
- plot density data on a line graph.
- infer how environmental conditions in different ocean regions affect, and are affected by, temperature-related differences in water density.

Skills Observe, Graph, Infer, Draw Conclusions

Prep Time 15 minutes to assemble materials

Advance Prep Photocopy the graph on page 441 for each student.

Class Time 20 minutes for Part A; 20 minutes for Part B

Teaching Tip Instruct students to pour the colored water into the graduated cylinders slowly, to limit the effect of mechanical mixing on their experiment.

Expected Outcome Students will infer from their measurements that cold water is denser than warmer water, and that colder water tends to sink beneath warmer water.

How Does Temperature Affect Water Density?

Problem How can you determine the effects of temperature on water density?

Materials 100-mL graduated cylinders (2), test tubes (2), beakers (2), food coloring or dye, stirrer, ice, tap water, graph paper, colored pencils

Skills Observe, Graph, Infer, Draw Conclusions

Connect to the `Big idea` Ocean water temperature varies from equator to poles and with depth. Both temperature and salinity affect the density of seawater. However, seawater density is more sensitive to temperature changes than it is to salinity. Surface water cools in the polar regions, sinks, and moves toward the tropics.

Procedure
Part A

1. In a beaker, mix cold tap water with several ice cubes. Stir until the water and ice are well mixed.
2. Fill a graduated cylinder with 100 mL of the cold water from the beaker. The graduated cylinder should not contain any pieces of ice.
3. Put 2 to 3 drops of dye in a test tube and fill it 1/2 full with hot tap water.
4. Pour the contents of the test tube slowly into the graduated cylinder and record your observations.
5. Add a test tube full of cold tap water to the second beaker. Mix in 2 to 3 drops of dye and a handful of ice. Stir the solution thoroughly.
6. Fill the second test tube 1/2 full of the solution from Step 5. Do not allow any ice into the test tube.
7. Fill the second graduated cylinder with 100 mL of hot tap water.
8. Pour the test tube of cold liquid slowly into the cylinder of hot water. Record your observations.
9. Clean the glassware and return it along with the other materials to your teacher.

Part B

1. Copy the graph on the next page onto a separate sheet of graph paper.
2. Using the data in Table 1, plot a line on your graph for temperature. Using a different colored pencil, plot a line for density on the same graph.

Analyze and Conclude

1. **Observe** What differences did you observe in the behavior of the two water samples in Part A? Which water sample was the most dense in each experiment?
2. **Infer** How does temperature affect the density of water?
3. **Draw Conclusions** If two water samples of equal mass had equal salinities, which sample would be more dense: water sample A, which has a temperature of 25°C, or water sample B, which has a temperature of 14°C?

SURFACE TEMPERATURE AND DENSITY

Table 1 Idealized Ocean Surface Water Temperatures and Densities at Various Latitudes

Latitude	Surface Temperature (C)	Surface Density (g/cm³)
60N	5	1.0258
40N	13	1.0259
20N	24	1.0237
0	27	1.0238
20S	24	1.0241
40S	15	1.0261
60S	2	1.0272

4. Interpret Graphs Describe the density and temperature characteristics of water in equatorial regions. Compare these characteristics to water found in polar regions.

5. Infer What is the reason that higher average surface densities are found in the Southern Hemisphere?

6. Communicate Write a lab report describing your procedures in this experiment and how you reached your conclusions.

Analyze and Conclude

1. The hot water remained on the surface of the cooler water. The cold water sank beneath the warmer water in the cylinder. The cold water has the highest density in both experiments.
2. As temperature decreases, water density increases.
3. Water Sample B
4. The water in equatorial regions is warm and the density is low. The water in polar regions is cold and the density is high.
5. The temperature of surface waters is cooler.
6. Check students' answers for clear explanations and reasoning.

GO FURTHER

Have students repeat this lab and include temperature measurements in their data collection. Students can determine how much of a temperature difference is required to produce density differences that result in layering.
Kinesthetic, Interpersonal

Study Tip

Organize New Information
Have students make vocabulary flashcards by writing a vocabulary term on one side of a card and the definition on the other. Along with the definitions, students can include examples or simple diagrams. Have students quiz each other using the cards.

Think Visually

a. pelagic zone
b. benthic zone
c. intertidal zone
d. oceanic zone

21st Century Learning

Economic Literacy

How can overfishing affect the economy?
The oceans provide fish and other seafood for large populations of people. However, as human populations have grown, so has the demand for seafood. This demand, along with improved fishing techniques, has caused a decline in the populations of many species of fish. Have students use the Web to research a declining population of a commercially important marine fish, such as Atlantic salmon, swordfish, or cod. They should learn the economic importance of this fish and the possible effects on the fishing industry and its customers if this fish population continues to decline. Tell them to research a solution to the problem. Then have them use a computer presentation tool to make a report and present it to the class.

Homework Guide

Lesson	Questions
1	1–4, 11–15, 24, 25, 30, 31
2	5–8, 16–19, 32
3	9–10, 20–23, 26–29

Big idea ▸ Water Planet

15.1 The Composition of Seawater

Because the proportion of dissolved substances in seawater is such a small number, oceanographers typically express salinity in parts per thousand (‰).

Chemical weathering of rocks on the continents is one source of elements found in seawater.

The second major source of elements found in seawater is from Earth's interior.

The ocean's surface water temperature is affected by the amount of solar radiation received, which is primarily due to latitude.

Seawater density is influenced by two main factors: salinity and temperature.

Oceanographers generally recognize a three-layered structure in most parts of the open ocean: a shallow surface mixed zone, a transition zone, and a deep zone.

salinity (422)   density (425)
thermocline (424)   pycnocline (426)

15.2 The Diversity of Ocean Life

Marine organisms can be classified according to where they live and how they move.

Plankton are organisms that drift with ocean currents, including algae, animals, and bacteria.

All animals capable of moving independently of the ocean currents, by swimming or other means of propulsion, are called nekton.

Organisms that live on or in the ocean bottom are called benthos.

Three factors are used to divide the ocean into distinct marine life zones: the availability of sunlight, the distance from shore, and the water depth.

photosynthesis (428)   intertidal zone (431)
plankton (428)   neritic zone (431)
phytoplankton (429)   oceanic zone (431)
zooplankton (429)   pelagic zone (432)
nekton (429)   benthic zone (432)
benthos (429)   abyssal zone (432)
photic zone (430)

442 Chapter 15 • Study Guide

15.3 Oceanic Productivity

Two factors influence a region's photosynthetic productivity: the availability of nutrients and the amount of solar radiation, or sunlight.

The availability of solar energy limits photosynthetic productivity in polar areas.

Productivity in tropical regions is limited by the lack of nutrients.

In temperate regions, which are found at mid-latitudes, seasonal changes influence levels of sunlight and nutrient supply which, in turn, influence productivity.

The transfer of energy between trophic levels is very inefficient.

Food webs are used to evaluate relationships in ecosystems because they show how the success or failure of one population could affect other populations.

primary productivity (433)
chemosynthesis (433)
trophic level (436)
food chain (437)
food web (437)

Think Visually

Use the information in the chapter to complete the web diagram on marine life zones.

Assessment Answers

Review Content

1. c	**2.** c	**3.** c
4. d	**5.** b	**6.** d
7. b	**8.** c	**9.** b
10. d		

Understand Concepts

11. because the proportion of dissolved substances in seawater is such a small number
12. water vapor that originated in Earth's interior; as Earth cooled, the water vapor condensed and torrential rains filled ocean basins. Certain elements exist in ocean water in much greater abundance than can be explained by weathering from rocks alone.

15 Assessment

Review Content

Choose the letter that best answers the question or completes the statement.

1. The most abundant salt in seawater is
   a. calcium chloride. c. sodium chloride.
   b. magnesium chloride. d. sodium fluoride.

2. Which process does NOT lead to a decrease in the salinity of seawater?
   a. runoff from land c. evaporation
   b. precipitation d. sea ice melting

3. Which term refers to the layer of water in which there is a rapid change of temperature with depth in the ocean?
   a. pycnocline c. thermocline
   b. abyssal zone d. isothermal line

4. Which is NOT a zone in the three-layered structure of the ocean according to density?
   a. surface mixed zone c. transition zone
   b. deep zone d. intertidal zone

5. Organisms that drift with ocean currents are
   a. nekton. c. neritic.
   b. plankton. d. pelagic.

6. Which term describes the upper part of the ocean into which sunlight penetrates?
   a. neritic zone c. oceanic zone
   b. intertidal zone d. photic zone

7. Phytoplankton are usually found in the
   a. benthic zone. c. abyssal zone.
   b. photic zone. d. aphotic zone.

8. The use of light energy by organisms to convert water and carbon dioxide into organic molecules is
   a. chemosynthesis. c. photosynthesis.
   b. decomposition. d. consumption.

9. During which season does primary productivity reach its peak in polar oceans?
   a. spring c. fall
   b. summer d. winter

10. In temperate oceans, primary productivity is limited by
    a. nutrients and oxygen concentration.
    b. nutrients and water temperature.
    c. sunlight and oxygen concentration.
    d. sunlight and nutrients.

Understand Concepts

11. Why is salinity expressed in parts per thousand instead of percent?

12. What is the principal source of water in oceans? Why did scientists reach this conclusion?

13. Explain how the salinity of water in polar regions varies seasonally.

14. What is the range of salinity for surface waters in the open ocean?

15. Is there a thermocline present in high-latitude ocean waters? Why or why not?

16. Compare and contrast phytoplankton and zooplankton.

17. What factors may affect the depth of the photic zone in any given area of the ocean?

18. What is the oceanic zone? What limits the amount of production in the oceanic zone?

19. What is the difference between the pelagic zone and the benthic zone?

20. How does the permanent thermocline in tropical oceans affect primary productivity in those areas?

Copy the diagram onto a separate sheet of paper and use it to answer Questions 21 and 22.

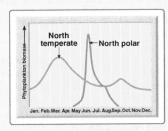

21. Draw a line on the graph that correctly represents the productivity of tropical oceans year-round.

22. Draw a line on the graph that represents the changes in zooplankton population in north temperate oceans throughout the course of a year.

23. What is the difference between a food chain and a food web?

20. limits mixing of nutrient-rich deeper waters with nutrient-poor surface waters; so productivity is limited by low-nutrient availability.

21. The graph should include an increase in productivity beginning in February with a bloom in mid-March to April. Productivity steadily decreases from there with a slight increase and small bloom again in September–October, after which productivity decreases again.

22. The zooplankton population should reflect the increases and decreases in productivity with a month's lag time.

23. A food chain is a simple model that shows how energy is transferred from one species to another. A food web is a more complex model that shows interrelationships among several species.

---

13. Seasonal variation exists because of the melting and formation of sea ice. In summer, when ice melts, salinity decreases. In winter, when ice forms, salinity increases.

14. from 33 percent to 38 percent

15. No, because surface waters in high latitudes are cooler and similar in temperature to deeper waters, so there is no rapid change in temperature with depth.

16. Both drift with ocean currents. Phytoplankton are producers that perform photosynthesis in surface waters. Zooplankton are consumers.

17. amount of plankton, suspended sediment, and decaying organic particles present in the water; the amount of sunlight available

18. ocean area beyond the continental shelf; low nutrient concentrations

19. pelagic: open ocean of any depth; benthic: any ocean bottom regardless of distance from shore

ASSESSMENT

Think Critically

24. higher; amount of evaporation that is taking place exceeds the amount of freshwater input from precipitation and runoff. Evaporation leaves salt behind, leading to increased salinity levels.

25. B, A, C; B will be closest to the surface; C will be closest to the bottom

26. Because there is no thermocline or pycnocline in polar waters, there is good vertical mixing between surface water and deeper nutrient-rich water. This allows nutrients to reach surface waters, where photosynthesis takes place, which allows for increased productivity.

27. The phytoplankton population increases in productivity and undergoes a bloom during the spring, when solar energy and nutrients are available. After this productivity drops off due to lack of available nutrients. The zooplankton population follows the curve of the phytoplankton biomass with about a month's lag time.

28. Productivity begins to increase again in August leading to a small bloom of phytoplankton in September, after which productivity declines again. The zooplankton population stays relatively low with a small increase in biomass in October following the phytoplankton bloom. The fall bloom is much smaller than the spring bloom.

29. The fall bloom would occur in March and April and the spring bloom would occur during September.

Concepts in Action

30. a thermocline

31. Temperature variation with depth is present in temperate and tropical oceans. This occurs because solar radiation heats surface waters so that they have higher temperatures than the deeper layers beneath them. As temperature increases, the density of water decreases. The layer of warm surface water sits on top of the colder, higher density water with little mixing.

32. The zooplankton are feeding on phytoplankton at night, when numbers are highest after a full day of photosynthesis. Zooplankton also avoid predation by spending daylight hours at depth.

Think Critically

24. Relate Cause and Effect In the Red Sea, evaporation values are higher than the values of precipitation and river runoff, particularly in summer months. Do you think that the salinity of the water here is higher or lower than average ocean water salinity? Why?

25. Draw Conclusions Water Mass A is 2°C with a salinity of 34.50‰. Water Mass B is 2°C with a salinity of 34.00‰. Water Mass C is 2°C with a salinity of 34.78‰. Order the water masses from lowest density to highest density. Which water mass will be nearest the surface? Which will be closest to the bottom?

26. Relate Cause and Effect Explain how the phytoplankton productivity in polar waters is related to the fact that density and temperature change very little with depth in polar waters.

Use the figure below to answer Questions 27–29.

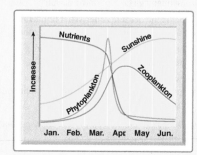

27. Apply Concepts The graph shows the productivity in temperate oceans in the Northern Hemisphere for the first half of the year. Describe what is happening to the phytoplankton and zooplankton populations in the graph. Explain what factors are affecting productivity.

28. Infer Describe what the graph would look like if it were extended through December. How is it different than the January through June portion?

29. Draw Conclusions How would this graph be different if it were for a temperate ocean in the Southern Hemisphere?

Performance-Based Assessment

Student answers will vary but their designs should indicate that they have considered the size of phytoplankton and the motion of ocean currents.

Concepts in Action

Use the table below to answer Questions 30 and 31.

Depth (m)	Temperature (C)
0	23
200	22.5
400	20
600	14
800	8
1000	5
1200	4.5
1400	4.5
1600	4

30. Interpret Data An oceanographer recorded the temperature data in the table above for an area of ocean water. Graph the data on a sheet of graph paper. What feature exists between 400 and 1200 meters?

31. Apply Concepts For which area of the world ocean would this temperature variation with depth be present? What processes cause this to occur?

32. Form a Hypothesis It has been observed that some species of zooplankton migrate vertically in ocean water. They spend the daylight hours at deeper depths of about 200 meters and at night move to the surface. Formulate a hypothesis that might explain this behavior.

Performance-Based Assessment

Design Equipment Imagine you have been asked to collect marine plankton samples from surface waters near the coast. Recall that many plankton are microscopic or nearly so and that by definition, plankton drift with currents. Design a piece of equipment that will allow you to collect the plankton so that they can be brought to the lab and examined under a microscope. Include the materials you will use to construct the equipment, a drawing of it, and an explanation of how it should be used in the field.

Standardized Test Prep

Choose the letter that best answers the question.

1 The total amount of solid material dissolved in water is known as—
   A sediment load
   B salinity
   C total dissolved solids
   D density

2 Thermoclines in oceans are best developed at—
   F lower latitudes
   G higher latitudes
   H both high and low latitudes
   J regions close to continents

3 Which term describes a rapid change in density with depth?
   A thermocline
   B halocline
   C isocline
   D pycnocline

4 Animals capable of moving independently of ocean currents, by swimming or other means of propulsion, are called—
   F benthos
   G plankton
   H nekton
   J pelagic

5 During which season is productivity the greatest in temperate waters?
   A spring   **C** fall
   B summer   **D** winter

6 Which of the following changes would occur to the food web below if the population of copepods was killed by a bacterial disease?
   F The sand eel population would decline because the copepods are their only food source.
   G The mollusk larvae population would decrease because the arrow worms would depend more heavily on that food source.
   H Neither F nor G.
   J Both F and G.

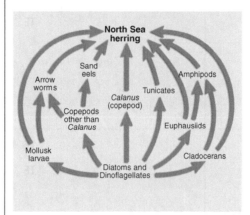

If You Have Trouble With . . .

Question	1	2	3	4	5	6
See Lesson	15.1	15.1	15.1	15.2	15.3	15.3

16 The Dynamic Ocean Planning Guide

BIGIDEA: WATER PLANET

Lesson Objectives		Activities
16.1 Ocean Circulation, pp. 448–454 16.1 **Explain** how surface currents develop. 16.2 **Describe** how ocean currents affect climate. 16.3 **State** the importance of upwelling. 16.4 **Describe** the formation of density currents.		SE Map It: Ocean Surface Currents, p. 449 L2 TE Teacher Demo: Creating Density Currents, p. 451 L2
16.2 Waves and Tides, pp. 455–460 16.5 **Describe** how ocean waves get their energy. 16.6 **State** three factors that determine the characteristics of a wave. 16.7 **Describe** how energy moves through a wave. 16.8 **Explain** the forces that produce tides.		TE Teacher Demo: Wave Motion, p. 455 L2
16.3 Shoreline Processes and Features, pp. 461–467 16.9 **List** the agents responsible for the movement of sediments along the shoreline. 16.10 **Explain** how refraction affects wave action along the shore. 16.11 **Describe** the processes that form shoreline features. 16.12 **List** the structures that can be built to protect a shoreline.		TE Build Science Skills, p. 465 L2 TE Build Science Skills, p. 466 L2
Chapter Features and Labs		
Try It How Do Ocean Waves Form? p. 447		LM Shoreline Features L1
Earth & Its Systems Shoes and Toys as Drift Meters, p. 454		
Exploration Lab Graphing Tidal Cycles, pp. 468–469		

Ability Levels

L1	For students who need additional help
L2	For all students
L3	For students who need to be challenged

Components

SE	Student Edition	LP	Lesson Plans
TE	Teacher's Edition	AA	Active Art
LM	Laboratory Manual	PD	Planet Diary
CT	Chapter Tests	GEODe	Geode CD-ROM
GRSW	Guided Reading & Study Workbook	eText	
CTB	Computer Test Bank		

Resources	Lesson Assessment
GRSW Lesson 16.1 **LP** Lesson Planning 16.1	**SE** Lesson 16.1 Assessment, p. 453 **eText** Lesson 16.1
GRSW Lesson 16.2 **LP** Lesson Planning 16.2	**SE** Lesson 16.2 Assessment, p. 460 **eText** Lesson 16.2
GRSW Lesson 16.3 **GEODe** Oceans: Coastal Processes **LP** Lesson Planning 16.3	**SE** Lesson 16.3 Assessment, p. 467 **eText** Lesson 16.3

Materials for Activities and Labs

Quantities for each group

STUDENT EDITION

Try It, p. 447
rectangular clear plastic container, water, fan with high and low settings, ruler

Exploration Lab, pp. 468–469
graph paper, pencil

TEACHER'S EDITION

Teacher Demo, p. 451
2 deep and clear containers, ice water, salt, tap water, food coloring, 2 smaller and clear containers

Teacher Demo, p. 455
coiled spring toy

Build Science Skills, p. 465
materials for building models of erosional and depositional features

Assessment

CHAPTER ASSESSMENT

SE	Assessment, pp. 471–472
CT	Chapter 16 Test
CTB	Chapter 16
eText	Chapter 16

21st Century Learning

Creativity and Intellectual Curiosity: How Can Tides Be Used To Generate Electricity? TE p. 470

Common Themes

Michael Wysession
Washington University

Ocean water is constantly in motion. The breakwaters, sea walls, and other types of structures built to protect property are evidence of the effects the ocean can have on shorelines.

Space and Time The gravitational attraction of the moon and sun causes tides. The patterns of tides and tidal currents vary according to location, and change with the relative positions of the moon, the sun, and Earth.

Forces and Motion Surface currents follow the general pattern of wind belts, and often form gyres as a result of the Coriolis effect. Upwelling, induced by wind, involves the rising of cold, nutrient-rich water. Deep-ocean currents are driven by density differences due to variations in temperature and salinity.

Matter and Energy Ocean waves are a transfer of energy, originating from the wind, across the ocean surface. The height, wavelength, and period of the waves are influenced by wind speed and duration. Waves erode shorelines through wave impact and abrasion. Near-shore waves also transport sediment and are responsible for deposition of sedimentary features like spits and barrier islands. Shoreline erosion and deposition tend to straighten out coastlines that may be irregular due to changes in sea level.

Earth as a System Ocean currents, controlled by the outlines of the continents, move water through a global set of interconnected cycles.

EARTH SCIENCE REFRESHER

Geologic Battle Over Coastlines

Geologic processes operating within shore environments tend to make jagged coastlines straight. Any promontories of rock that stick out away from the shore erode more quickly than the rest of the shoreline due to the process of wave refraction, which bends waves toward the promontories. Any bays and inlets tend to fill in quickly because water moves slowly, allowing sediment to settle. Why, then, aren't all coastlines perfectly straight? The reason is that sea levels are constantly changing, revealing new jagged coastlines.

Sometimes sea level changes because of tectonics. For example, in regions where ocean plate subduction is occurring, such as off the coast of Oregon and Washington, the edge of the continent rises and falls over relatively short time periods. As the ocean plate slowly subducts, it pulls down the overriding continental edge. Then when a large earthquake occurs, the continental plate detaches from the ocean plate and snaps back up suddenly. Over a cycle of hundreds of years, the coastline may be pulled down and snapped back up many meters or tens of meters.

With the recent rise in global sea level due to the melting of glacial ice, many coastlines around the world have been submerged. The new coastlines are jagged because they show the contours of flooded former river valleys, such as the Pamlico and Albemarle Sounds in Figure 23, or glacial valleys, such as the fjords in Norway. If sea level stays constant for awhile, these coastlines will again begin to straighten, but as soon as the sea level changes again, new coastlines will be exposed.

Salt added to water does not change the density of the water. Actually, salty water is much denser than water without salt, and the more salt that is added, the denser the water becomes. For a strategy that helps to overcome this misconception, see **Address Misconceptions** and the **Teacher Demo** on **TE p. 451.**

Why the Mediterranean Sea Doesn't Overflow

If you ever go to Gibraltar, you will notice a strange thing: water from the Atlantic Ocean is constantly pouring eastward into the Mediterranean Sea. There is always an eastward current. This is strange because many rivers like the Nile and Danube eventually flow into the Mediterranean. Why doesn't the Mediterranean Sea overflow? What happens to the water?

Two factors explain why the Mediterranean does not overflow. First, the sunny, dry climate of the area causes a high rate of evaporation. The high evaporation rate causes the surface water to have high salinity. The dense, salty surface water eventually sinks and flows westward into the Atlantic. Although it appears that water is flowing only eastward, it actually is flowing in both directions.

BUILD READING LITERACY

Sequence

Ordering Events

Strategy Help students understand and visualize the steps in a process, or the order in which events occur. Sequences frequently involve cause-effect relationships. Readers can construct graphic organizers to help them visualize and comprehend a sequence. For most sequences, flowcharts are the graphic of choice. However, cycle diagrams are more appropriate for cycles. Before students begin, locate a description or figure in the text of a several-step process or a chain of causes and effects.

Example

1. Have students read the passage or study the figure, thinking about what takes place first, second, third, and so on. Point out that the text will not always use order words such as *first, next, then,* and *finally.*

2. Ask students to list the steps or events in order.

3. If the passage or figure describes a chain of steps or events, draw a flowchart on the board, having students write each part of the process in a separate box.

4. If the passage describes a cycle, use a cycle diagram to show the sequence.

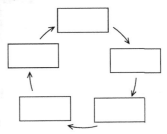

5. Have students locate additional examples of sequential relationships in the text or visuals of the chapter.

See TE p. 453 for a script on how to use this strategy with students. For additional strategies, see TE pp. 452, 456, 458, 464, and 465.

CHAPTER 16

16 The Dynamic Ocean

Big idea — **Water Planet**

Q: How does ocean movement affect land?

446

Chapter Pretest

1. How does heating water affect its density? *(b)*
   a. It increases.   **b.** It decreases.
   c. It remains the same.

2. What does cold water tend to do when it comes in contact with warm water? *(a)*
   a. sink   **b.** rise
   c. stay in place

3. As you are standing in the ocean, what do passing waves usually do? *(c)*
   a. carry you in to shore

   b. carry you out to sea
   c. move you up and down

4. If you enter the ocean directly in front of your beach blanket and swim for about an hour, where will you most likely be when you come out of the water? *(b)*
   a. directly in front of your beach blanket
   b. further up the beach in the direction the waves are moving
   c. further down the beach, opposite to the direction the waves are moving

5. At point A on the beach the waves come in rapidly, and hit with great force. At point B on the same beach, the waves come in slowly with very little force. At which location(s) would you expect to see the most erosion? *(a)*
   a. point A
   b. point B
   c. Points A and B would have the same amount of erosion.

INQUIRY
TRY IT!

HOW DO OCEAN WAVES FORM?

Procedure

1. Fill a rectangular, clear, plastic container with water to within about 3 cm of the top of the container.

2. Place a fan next to the container, aiming the flow of air toward the water. **CAUTION:** *Make sure the cord and the fan do not come in contact with the water in the container.*

3. Turn the fan on low power for 2 to 3 minutes. Observe what effect blowing air has on the water in the container. Using a ruler, measure the size of the waves produced. Record your observations and data.

4. Turn the fan off and allow the water in the container to settle. Repeat Step 3 with the fan on high power.

Think About It

1. **Infer** Where does the energy to produce most ocean waves come from?

2. **Draw Conclusions** What is the relationship between the speed of the wind and the size of a wave?

These sea arches are evidence that the force of moving water has a large impact on landforms over time.

447

ENGAGE/EXPLORE

HOW DO OCEAN WAVES FORM? L2

Purpose In this activity, students will discover how wind causes waves and observe that stronger winds result in taller waves.

Skills Observe

Prep Time 10 minutes

Materials rectangular clear plastic container, water, fan with high and low settings, ruler

Advance Prep You may want to set up the containers and fans ahead of time. You may also want to test how much water can be put in the container, and how far away the fan needs to be so as not to splash water out of the container.

Class Time 10 minutes

Safety Make sure that students do not let the cord or fan touch the water.

Teaching Tip Waves can be produced simply by blowing on the water, and the waves can be shown to the class by putting the clear container on an overhead projector.

Expected Outcome Students will discover that wind causes waves, and stronger wind results in taller waves.

Think About It
1. wind
2. As wind speed increases, wave height increases.

LESSON 16.1

1 FOCUS

Lesson Objectives

16.1 **Explain** how surface currents develop.

16.2 **Describe** how ocean currents affect climate.

16.3 **State** the importance of upwelling.

16.4 **Describe** the formation of density currents.

Build Vocabulary [L2]

Paraphrase Have students define the words in this lesson using their own words. For example, students may define *gyre* as "flow of water in a large circle."

Reading Strategy [L2]

Possible responses are as follows:

a. caused by wind

b. circular movement of water

c. Currents transfer heat from hotter regions to cooler regions and modify climate.

d. cold water exposed at the surface

e. vertical currents caused by density differences; denser water sinks

f. Cold surface water sinks at the poles because it is dense.

g. causes increased salinity and increased density

h. Ocean water moves around Earth because of density differences.

16.1 Ocean Circulation

Key Questions

⌘ **How do surface currents develop?**

⌘ **How do ocean currents affect climate?**

⌘ **Why is upwelling important?**

⌘ **How are density currents formed?**

Vocabulary

- ocean current
- surface current
- gyre • Coriolis effect
- upwelling • density current

Reading Strategy

Identify Main Ideas
Copy the table below into your notebook. Leave space to expand the table. As you read, write the main idea of each topic.

Topic	Main Idea
Surface currents	a. _____ ?
Gyres	b. _____ ?
Ocean currents and climate	c. _____ ?
Upwelling	d. _____ ?

OCEAN WATER IS constantly in motion, powered by many different forces. Winds, for example, produce waves such as the ones shown in **Figure 1.** Masses of ocean water move horizontally from one area to another. Masses of ocean water also move vertically as denser masses sink below masses that are less dense.

Surface Circulation

Ocean currents are masses of ocean water that flow from one place to another. The amount of water can be large or small. Ocean currents can be at the surface or deep below the surface. The formation of currents can be simple or complex. In all cases, however, the currents involve water masses in motion. Anyone who navigates the ocean needs to be aware of currents. By understanding the direction and strength of ocean currents, sailors soon realize that their voyage time can be reduced if they travel with a current.

Surface Currents **Surface currents** are movements of water that flow horizontally in the upper part of the ocean's surface. ⌘ **Surface currents develop from friction between the ocean and the wind that blows across its surface.** Some of these currents do not last long, and they affect only small areas.

FIGURE 1 Wind's Effects Wind not only produces waves, it also provides the force that drives the ocean's surface circulation.

FIGURE 2 **Ocean Surface Currents** This map shows average surface ocean currents from February to March.

② INSTRUCT

Use Visuals   L1

Figure 2 This map shows ocean surface currents all over the world. **Ask:** What happens to ocean currents when they hit a land mass? *(They are deflected parallel to the shore.)* Why do gyres in the northern Atlantic and northern Pacific oceans mostly rotate clockwise? *(The Coriolis effect causes currents to be deflected to the right in the Northern Hemisphere.)* Why do gyres in the southern Atlantic and southern Pacific oceans mostly rotate counterclockwise? *(The Coriolis effect causes currents to be deflected to the left in the Southern Hemisphere.)*
Visual

Such water movements are responses to local or seasonal influences. Other surface currents, such as those shown in **Figure 2,** are more permanent and extend over large portions of the oceans. These major horizontal movements of surface waters are closely related to the general circulation pattern of the atmosphere.

Gyres Huge circular-moving current systems dominate the surfaces of the oceans. These large whirls of water within an ocean basin are called **gyres** (gyros = a circle). There are five main ocean gyres: the North Pacific Gyre, the South Pacific Gyre, the North Atlantic Gyre, the South Atlantic Gyre, and the Indian Ocean Gyre.

Although wind is the force that generates surface currents, other factors also influence the movement of ocean waters. The most significant of these is the Coriolis effect. The **Coriolis effect** is the deflection of currents away from their original course as a result of Earth's rotation. 🗝 **Because of Earth's rotation, currents are deflected to the right in the Northern Hemisphere and the left in the Southern Hemisphere.** As a consequence, gyres flow in opposite directions in the two hemispheres.

For example, trace the path of water in the North Atlantic Gyre in Figure 2. As water moves north from Florida in the Gulf Stream and North Atlantic Current, it is deflected to the right, or eastward. Water moving south in the Canary Current is deflected westward into the North Equatorial Current. This gyre moves in a clockwise direction. Now look at the South Atlantic Gyre. Because the Coriolis effect deflects its current to the left, this gyre flows counterclockwise.

☑ **Reading Checkpoint** What is a gyre?

The Dynamic Ocean **449**

MAP IT!
ACTIVITY

Figure 2 shows that the ocean's circulation is organized into five huge currents called gyres.

Interpret Maps Which currents make up the Indian Ocean Gyre?

Draw Conclusions Find the West Wind Drift on the map. Explain why the West Wind Drift is the only current that completely encircles Earth.

Answers

MAP IT!

The Indian Ocean Gyre consists of South Equatorial Current, Agulhas Current, West Wind Drift, and West Australian Current.

The West Wind Drift can encircle Earth because there are no land masses/continents obstructing its path.

☑ **Reading Checkpoint** A gyre is a circular-moving current system within an ocean basin.

Differentiated Instruction

ENGLISH LANGUAGE LEARNERS Teach students that *gyre* comes from the word *gyros,* which means "circle." List several other words containing this root, and have students look up their definitions. Have students explain what all the words have in common. For example: *gyre, gyroscope, gyrate, gyration,* and *gyroscopic* all have to do with moving in a circle. Also introduce students to the Greek food, the gyro, which is meat that rotates on a spit and is served in a pita. Show students a picture of a gyro.

Build Science Skills L3

Student Activity: Apply Concepts The flow of wind and ocean currents transports heat from Earth's equator to the poles, modulating climate and reducing temperature extremes across the planet's surface. Earth's continents strongly affect the path of wind and water flow, so the size and location of land masses also regulate Earth's climate. Ask students to find maps showing Earth's arrangement of land masses during the Permian and the arrangement of land masses today. Alternatively, you may present maps to the class. The U.S. Geologic Society has several examples on their Web site. Direct students' attention to the differences in the two maps.

Point out to students that during the day, cool breezes typically flow from the ocean along coastlines. **Ask:** What can you infer about the land temperatures during the Permian, compared to the land temperatures in the present day? *(Because Earth's continents were joined into a megacontinent during the Permian, there was a lot less coastline. Most of Earth's land was cut off from cooling ocean breezes, so the land was probably much hotter on average than it is today.)*

Large ocean currents transport heat from the equator to the poles. But, continents can get in the way of these currents, forcing ocean water to flow around them. **Ask:** How do you predict that ocean currents were different in the Permian, compared to today? *(During the Permian, the megacontinent restricted the flow of the ocean on nearly one half of the planet. But, the opposite hemisphere was one giant ocean, so ocean currents probably transported heat very efficiently from the equator to the poles. The result would be less of a temperature difference between the equator and the poles. The polar oceans were likely warmer than they are today.)* For ice caps to form at Earth's poles, very cold temperatures must persist for a long period of time. **Ask:** Based on your conclusions about ocean currents during the Permian, did ice caps exist at Earth's poles then? *(Because heat was transported very efficiently from the equator to the poles during the Permian, it's unlikely that the oceans were cold enough for ice caps to form.)*
Visual, Logical

FIGURE 3 Gulf Stream This false-color satellite image of sea-surface temperatures shows the course of the Gulf Stream. The warm waters of the Gulf Stream are shown in red and orange along the east coast of Florida and the Carolinas. The surrounding colder waters are shown in green, blue, and purple. Compare this image to the map of the Gulf Stream in Figure 2.

Ocean Currents and Climate Ocean currents have an important effect on climates. Ocean water in areas closer to the equator absorbs more energy from the sun than does water farther from the equator. **When currents from low-latitude regions move into higher latitudes, they transfer heat from warmer to cooler areas on Earth.** The Gulf Stream, a warm water current shown in **Figure 3,** is an excellent example of this phenomenon. The Gulf Stream brings warm water from the equator northward to the North Atlantic Current. This current allows Great Britain and much of northwestern Europe to be warmer during the winter than areas of similar latitudes such as Alaska and Newfoundland. The prevailing westerly winds carry this warming effect far inland. For example, Berlin, Germany (52 degrees north latitude), has an average January temperature similar to that experienced in New York City, which lies 12 degrees to the south.

The effects of these warm ocean currents are felt in the middle latitudes mostly in the winter. In contrast, the influence of cold currents is most felt in the tropics or during summer months in the middle latitudes. Cold currents begin in cold high-latitude regions. **As cold water currents travel toward the equator, they help moderate the warm temperatures of adjacent land areas.** Such is the case for the Benguela Current along western Africa, the Peru Current along the west coast of South America, and the California Current. These currents are shown in Figure 2.

Ocean currents play a major role in maintaining Earth's heat balance. They do this by transferring heat from the tropics, where there is an excess of heat, to the polar regions, where there is less heat. Ocean water movement accounts for about a quarter of this heat transport. Winds transport the remaining three-quarters.

Upwelling In addition to producing horizontal surface currents, winds can also cause vertical water movements. A common wind-induced vertical movement is called **upwelling,** which is the rising of cold water to replace warmer surface water that has been displaced by wind. Upwelling is most characteristic along the west coasts of continents, most notably along California, western South America, and West Africa. When upwelling occurs along coasts, it may be referred to as coastal upwelling.

Upwelling occurs in these areas when winds blow toward the equator and parallel to the coast. Coastal winds combined with the Coriolis effect cause surface water to move away from shore. As the warm surface layer moves away from the coast, it is replaced by colder water that upwells from below the surface. This slow upward movement of water from depths of 50 to 300 meters brings up water that is cooler than the original surface water and results in lower surface water temperatures near the shore.

Facts and Figures

During upwelling, cold water is exposed at the surface when the warm surface layer of water is removed by strong winds. Upwelling of nutrient rich cold water is critical to fishing industries all over the world, but it is especially important off the coast of Peru. Unfortunately, El Niño events often disrupt upwelling by reducing surface wind speeds, which causes terrible consequences for fishes.

⚟ **Upwelling brings dissolved nutrients, such as nitrates and phosphates, to the ocean surface.** These nutrient-enriched waters from below promote the growth of microscopic plankton, which in turn support extensive populations of fish and other marine organisms. **Figure 4** is a satellite image that shows high levels of productivity due to coastal upwelling off the southwest coast of Africa.

☑ **Reading Checkpoint** *What is upwelling?*

Deep-Ocean Circulation

In contrast to the largely horizontal movements of surface currents, deep-ocean circulation has a significant vertical component. It accounts for the thorough mixing of deep-water masses. Vertical currents of ocean water that result from density differences among water masses are called **density currents.** Denser water sinks and slowly spreads out beneath the surface. ⚟ **An increase in seawater density can be caused by a decrease in temperature or an increase in salinity.** Processes that increase the salinity of surface water include evaporation and the formation of sea ice. Processes that decrease the salinity of water include precipitation, runoff from land, icebergs melting, and sea ice melting. Density changes due to salinity variations are important in very high latitudes, where water temperature remains low and relatively constant.

Evaporation Density currents can result from increased salinity of ocean water due to evaporation. For example, climate conditions in the Mediterranean Sea include a dry northwest wind and sunny days. Due to these factors water evaporates from the Mediterranean Sea faster than it is replaced by precipitation. When seawater evaporates, salt is left behind, and the salinity of the remaining water increases. The surface waters of the Mediterranean Sea have a salinity of about 38‰ (parts per thousand). In the winter months, this water flows out of the Mediterranean Sea into the Atlantic Ocean. At 38‰, this water sinks because it is more dense than the Atlantic Ocean surface water at 35‰. This Mediterranean water mass can be tracked as far south as Antarctica.

FIGURE 4 Effects of Upwelling This image from the SeaStar satellite shows chlorophyll concentration along the southwest coast of Africa. High chlorophyll concentrations, in red, indicate high amounts of photosynthesis, which is linked to upwelling nutrients.

FIGURE 5 A Scene in the Mediterranean A sunny day, such as the one shown here in Loutro on the south coast of Crete, contributes to the salinity of the Mediterranean Sea.

The Dynamic Ocean **451**

Facts and Figures

Before large ocean currents like the Gulf Stream were understood, people wondered why a boat trip west across the Atlantic Ocean took nearly two weeks longer than the trip back east. Ben Franklin's cousin, Timothy Folger, advised Franklin that this was because the captains of many ships were not aware of the Gulf Stream Current that flowed west to east across the Atlantic. Franklin then shared this information with the mariners by making a map showing the Gulf Stream. This map allowed sailors attempting to go from east to west to avoid being slowed down by this powerful current.

Build Reading Literacy L1

Refer to page **246D** in **Chapter 9,** which provides guidelines for relating cause and effect.

Relate Cause and Effect Once students have read this lesson, **Ask:** What are the possible causes for an increase in density? *(temperature decrease and salinity increase)* How does temperature affect density? *(Higher temperatures result in lower density, while colder temperatures result in higher density.)* How does salinity affect density? *(Higher salinity results in higher density.)* How does evaporation affect density? *(Evaporation leads to higher salinity and thus higher density.)*
Verbal, Logical

Use Visuals L1

Figure 7 Be sure students understand the orientation of this cross section by comparing it geographically to the map in Figure 2. The cross section would be represented by a north-south line through the Atlantic Ocean. **Ask:** Why don't the arrows on the two figures match? *(Figure 2 shows surface currents; Figure 7 shows density currents.)* Describe the probable temperature and salinity characteristics and general movements of the Antarctic Bottom Water. *(cold and highly saline; forms in the Antarctic, sinks, and flows northward along the ocean floor as far as 20°N latitude)* Describe the probable temperature and salinity characteristics and general movements of the water from the Mediterranean. *(warm and highly saline; flows westward into the Atlantic, cools, and sinks slightly as most of it heads toward the equator)*

FIGURE 6 Sea Ice in the Arctic Ocean When seawater freezes, sea salts do not become part of the ice, leading to an increase in the salinity of the surrounding water.
Draw Conclusions How does this process lead to the formation of a density current?

PLANET DIARY

For links about
Deep-Ocean Currents,
visit PlanetDiary.com/HSES.

FIGURE 7 Deep-Ocean Circulation This cross section of the Atlantic Ocean shows the deep-water circulation of water masses formed by density currents.

Sea Ice Most water involved in density currents begins in high latitudes at the surface. In these regions, surface water becomes cold, sea ice forms, and the water's salinity increases. Eventually, the surface water mass becomes denser than the masses beneath it and it sinks. Once this water sinks, it is removed from the physical processes that increased its density in the first place. Its temperature and salinity remain largely unchanged during the time it is in the deep ocean. Because of this, oceanographers can track the movements of density currents in the deep ocean. By knowing the temperature, salinity, and density of a water mass, scientists are able to map the slow circulation of the water mass through the ocean.

Figure 7 shows some of the different water masses created by density currents in the Atlantic Ocean. Near Antarctica, surface conditions produce the highest density water in the world. This cold, salty water slowly sinks to the sea floor, then moves throughout the ocean basins in slow currents. After sinking from the surface of the ocean, deep waters will not reappear at the surface for an average of 500 to 2000 years.

Key
AIW: Antarctic Intermediate Water **MW:** Mediterranean Water **NADW:** North Atlantic Deep Water **ABW:** Antarctic Bottom Water

452 Chapter 16 • Lesson 1

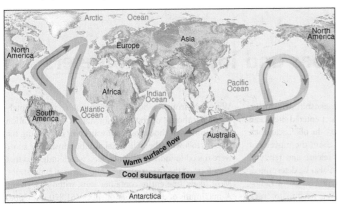

FIGURE 8 A Continuous Current This "conveyor belt" model of ocean circulation shows a warm surface current with an underlying cool current.

A Conveyor Belt A simplified model of ocean circulation is similar to a conveyor belt that travels throughout the world. **Figure 8** shows this conveyor belt model in which warm water in the ocean's upper layers flows toward the poles. When the water reaches the poles, its temperature drops and salinity increases, making it more dense. Because the water is dense, it sinks and moves toward the equator. It returns to the equator as cold, deep water that eventually upwells along a coast, or another ocean feature such as a seamount, and completes the circuit. As this "conveyor belt" current moves around the globe, it influences global climate by converting warm water to cold water and releasing heat to the atmosphere.

16.1 Assessment

Review Key Concepts

1. How do surface currents develop?

2. What is the Coriolis effect? How does it influence the direction of surface currents flowing in the ocean?

3. How do ocean currents affect climate?

4. Why is upwelling important?

5. How are density currents formed?

Think Critically

6. **Apply Concepts** The average surface water temperature off of the coast of Ecuador is 21°C. The average surface water temperature off of the coast of Brazil at the same latitude is about 27°C. Explain why there is such a difference in water temperature between these areas at the same latitude.

7. **Infer** During an El Niño event, the upwelling of cold, nutrient-rich water stops in areas off the coast of Peru. How might this affect the food web in this area?

WRITING IN SCIENCE

8. **Explain** During the 1700s, mail ships sailed back and forth between England and America. It was noted that it took the ships two weeks longer to go from England to America than to travel the same route from America to England. It was determined that the Gulf Stream was delaying the ships. Write a paragraph explaining why this is true. Use Figure 2 to explain how sailors could avoid the Gulf Stream when sailing to America.

The Dynamic Ocean **453**

Build Reading Literacy   L1

Refer to **p. 446D,** which provides guidelines for sequencing.

Sequence As students read the section A Conveyor Belt, ask them to draw a flowchart showing the movement of water starting with the phrase "warm water flows toward poles" and ending with the phrase "the cycle repeats." (For example: warm water flows toward poles → temperature drops and salinity increases → density increases → dense water moves toward equator → cold, deep water upwells → upwelled water warms → the cycle repeats)
Visual, Verbal

3 ASSESS

Evaluate Understanding   L2

Ask students to use Figure 2 to predict the movement of an abandoned boat left adrift in the Atlantic Ocean off the coast of Florida (the Bermuda Triangle).

Reteach   L1

Have students write a short story describing the voyage of a droplet of water through the ocean. The droplet should start and end near the north pole.

Answers

Figure 6 As salinity increases, the density of water increases. As surface water becomes denser than underlying water, it sinks, forming a density current.

Assessment Answers

1. from friction between the ocean and the wind that blows across its surface
2. The deflection of currents away from their original course as a result of Earth's rotation is the Coriolis effect. It causes currents in the Northern Hemisphere to turn to the right and currents in the Southern Hemisphere to turn to the left.
3. Warm water currents that come from equatorial regions transfer heat to cooler areas of Earth. Cold water currents from the poles moderate temperatures of adjacent land areas.

4. Upwelling brings dissolved nutrients to the ocean surface, providing the necessary nutrients for phytoplankton to undergo photosynthesis.
5. They are formed when the density of water changes due to a change in salinity or temperature.
6. The cold-water current off of the coast of Ecuador comes from high latitudes. The warm-water current off of the coast of Brazil comes from the equator.
7. Without the nutrients, productivity significantly declines, leaving many organisms

with too little food or no food source. Organisms will either starve or must seek out another food source.
8. Sample answer: When ships traveled from England to America they had to move against the direction of the Gulf Stream, thus delaying their arrival. Ships could cross the Gulf Stream at its northern end and travel near the coast between the current and land to avoid having to move against the current.

Shoes and Toys as Drift Meters

Teaching Tips

- Have students read this feature in groups and then share their feelings about what they read. Students may wonder about the environmental impact of ships spilling their cargo, or how scientists were able to find out when and where cargo was lost and then found.
- Discuss what this feature reveals about the stories of people setting adrift a message in a bottle. *(The message could travel great distances as the bottle drifts on ocean currents. Quite possibly the bottle will be washed onshore in a distant land.)*

Interpersonal, Verbal

EARTH & ITS SYSTEMS

Shoes and Toys as Drift Meters

Any floating object can serve as a makeshift drift meter, as long as it is known where the object entered the ocean and where it was retrieved. The path of the object can then be inferred, providing information about the movement of surface currents. If the times of release and retrieval are known, the speed of currents can also be determined. Oceanographers have long used drift bottles—a radio-transmitting device set adrift in the ocean—to track the movement of currents and, more recently, to refine computer models of ocean circulation.

Many objects have accidentally become drift meters when ships have lost some (or all) of their cargo at sea. In this way, athletic shoes helped oceanographers advance the understanding of surface circulation in the North Pacific Ocean. In May 1990, the container vessel *Hansa Carrier* was traveling from South Korea to Seattle, Washington, when it encountered a severe North Pacific storm. During the storm the ship lost 21 deck containers overboard, including five that held athletic shoes. The shoes that were released from their containers floated and were carried east by the North Pacific Current. Within six months, thousands of the shoes began to wash up along the beaches of Alaska, Canada, Washington, and Oregon—over 2400 kilometers from the site of the spill. The inferred course of the shoes is shown in **Figure 9.** A few shoes were found on beaches in northern California, and over two years later shoes from the spill were even recovered from the north end of the main island of Hawaii.

With help from the beachcombing public and remotely based lighthouse operators, information on the location and number of shoes collected was compiled during the months following the spill. Serial numbers inside the shoes were traced to individual containers, which indicated that only four of the five containers had released their shoes. Most likely, one entire container sank without opening. A maximum of 30,910 pairs of shoes (61,820 individual shoes) were released. Before the shoe spill, the largest number of drift bottles purposefully released at one time by oceanographers was about 30,000. Although only 2.6 percent of the shoes were recovered, this compares favorably with the 2.4 percent recovery rate of drift bottles released by oceanographers conducting research.

In January 1992, another cargo ship lost 12 containers overboard during a storm to the north of where the shoes had previously spilled. One of these containers held 29,000 packages of small, floatable, colorful plastic bathtub toys in the shapes of blue turtles, yellow ducks, red beavers, and green frogs. Even though the toys were housed in plastic packaging glued to a cardboard backing, studies showed that after 24 hours in seawater, the glue deteriorated, thereby releasing over 100,000 individual floating toys.

The floating bathtub toys began to come ashore in southeast Alaska 10 months later, which verified computer models of North Pacific circulation. The models indicate that many of the bathtub toys will continue to be carried by the Alaska Current and will eventually disperse throughout the North Pacific Ocean.

Since 1992, oceanographers have continued to study ocean currents by tracking other floating items spilled from cargo ships, including 34,000 hockey gloves, 5 million plastic building blocks, and an unidentified number of small plastic doll parts.

FIGURE 9 The map shows the path of drifting shoes and recovery locations from a spill in 1990.

16.2 Waves and Tides

MOST OCEAN currents are not visible to the human eye, but waves and tides are the easiest ocean movements to observe. The movement of ocean water can be a powerful thing. Waves created by storms release energy when they crash along the shoreline. Wind-generated waves provide much of the energy that shapes and changes shorelines over time.

Waves

Waves can transfer energy from a storm far out at sea over distances of several thousand kilometers. That's why even on calm days waves travel across the ocean surface. The power of waves is most noticeable along the shore, the area where land and sea meet and waves are constantly rolling in and breaking. Sometimes the waves are low and gentle. Other times waves, such as the ones shown in **Figure 10,** are powerful as they pound the shore.

If you make waves by tossing a pebble into a pond, splashing in a pool, or blowing across the surface of a glass of water, you are transferring energy to the water. The waves you see are just the visible evidence of the energy passing through the water. When observing ocean waves, remember that you are watching energy travel through a medium, in this case, water.

FIGURE 10 The Force of Breaking Waves These waves are slamming into a seawall that was built at Sea Bright, New Jersey, to protect the nearby electrical lines and houses from the force of the waves.

The Dynamic Ocean **455**

Key Questions

🔑 From where do ocean waves obtain their energy?

🔑 What three factors affect the characteristics of a wave?

🔑 How does energy move through a wave?

🔑 What causes tides?

Vocabulary

- wave height • wavelength
- wave period • fetch
- tide • tidal range
- spring tide • neap tide

Reading Strategy

Build Vocabulary Copy the table below. As you read the section, define in your own words each vocabulary word listed in the table.

Vocabulary Term	Definition
Wave height	a. ?
Wavelength	b. ?
Wave period	c. ?
Fetch	d. ?

1 FOCUS

Lesson Objectives

16.5 **Describe** how ocean waves get their energy.

16.6 **State** three factors that determine the characteristics of a wave.

16.7 **Describe** how energy moves through a wave.

16.8 **Explain** the forces that produce tides.

Build Vocabulary [L2]

Concept Map As they read this lesson, have students make a concept map that includes all the vocabulary terms for this section.

Reading Strategy [L2]

Sample Answers:
a. height of wave
b. length of wave
c. time between waves
d. distance wind blows across open water

(Teacher **Demo**)

WAVE MOTION [L2]

Purpose Students will see that wave energy travels without causing individual particles of the medium to move very much.

Materials coiled spring toy

Procedure Have a student hold one end of a coiled spring toy without moving it. Stretch the spring out, gather a few rings together, and then release them all at once while still holding the end of the spring in your hand.

Expected Outcomes Students will notice that the energy of the wave will move from one end of the toy to the other, even though individual rings move only a small amount back and forth.
Visual, Kinesthetic

LESSON 16.2

❷ INSTRUCT

Build Reading Literacy `L1`

Refer to **p. 278D** in **Chapter 10,** which provides guidelines for identifying main ideas and details.

Identify Main Idea/Details Have students use the section called Wave Characteristics to determine the characteristics of a wave *(height, length, and period)*, and the factors that determine a wave's characteristics *(wind speed, length of time wind has blown, and fetch)*.
Verbal

Build Science Skills `L2`

Use Models Have students draw a simple wave diagram showing the general shape of a wave. Have them label wave height, wavelength, crest, and trough.
Visual

Build Reading Literacy `L1`

Refer to **p. 92D** in **Chapter 4,** which provides guidelines for using context clues.

Use Context Clues Have students read the section called Wave Motion and study Figure 11 to determine the meaning of *waveform (shape of the wave).*
Visual, Verbal

Q: *Do waves always travel in the same directions as currents?*

A: Not in all cases. Most surface waves travel in the same direction as the wind blows, but waves radiate outward in all directions from the disturbance that creates them. In addition, as waves move away from the sea area where they were generated, they enter areas where other currents exist. As a result, the direction of wave movement is often unrelated to that of currents. In fact, waves can even travel in a direction completely opposite to that of a current. A rip current, for example, moves away from the shoreline, opposite to the direction of incoming waves.

Wave Characteristics **Most ocean waves obtain their energy and motion from the wind.** When a breeze is less than 3 kilometers per hour, only small waves appear. At greater wind speeds, more stable waves gradually form and advance with the wind.

Characteristics of ocean waves are illustrated in **Figure 11.** The tops of the waves are the crests, which are separated by troughs. Halfway between the crests and troughs is the still water level, which is the level that the water would occupy if there were no waves. The vertical distance between trough and crest is called **wave height.** The horizontal distance between two successive crests or two successive troughs is the **wavelength.** The time it takes one full wave—one wavelength—to pass a fixed position is the **wave period.**

 The height, length, and period that are eventually achieved by a wave depend on three factors: (1) wind speed; (2) length of time the wind has blown; and (3) fetch. **Fetch** is the distance that the wind has traveled across open water. As the quantity of energy transferred from the wind to the water increases, both the height and steepness of the waves also increase. Eventually, a critical point is reached at which waves grow so tall that they topple over, forming ocean breakers called whitecaps.

Wave Motion Waves can travel great distances across ocean basins. In one study, researchers tracked waves generated near Antarctica as they traveled through the Pacific Ocean basin. After traveling for a week and more than 10,000 kilometers, the waves finally expended their energy along the shoreline of the Aleutian Islands of Alaska.

Water itself does not travel the entire distance of a wave. As a wave travels, the water particles pass the energy along by moving in a circle. This movement, shown in Figure 11, is called *circular orbital motion.* **Circular orbital motion allows energy to move forward through the water while the water particles that transmit the wave move around in a circle.**

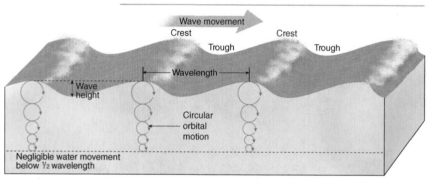

FIGURE 11 Anatomy of a Wave The diagram shows the parts of a non-breaking wave and the movement of particles under the surface.

Differentiated Instruction

SPECIAL NEEDS Students often have difficulty understanding how a wave can appear to move from one place to another while the actual water particles simply move in a circle. Help students understand this with a physical example. Have students in your class do "the wave" that is done at sporting events. **Ask:** Did the wave travel across the room? *(yes)* Did any students have to travel across the room to produce this result? *(no)* How did each student move to pass the wave along? *(up and down, in place)*
Kinesthetic, Visual

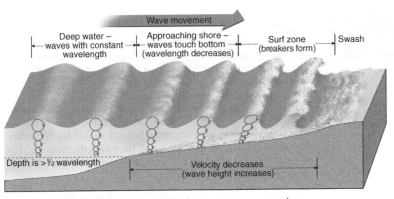

Wave movement

Deep water – waves with constant wavelength | Approaching shore – waves touch bottom (wavelength decreases) | Surf zone (breakers form) | Swash

Depth is > ½ wavelength

Velocity decreases (wave height increases)

FIGURE 12 Breaking Waves Changes occur as a wave moves onto shore. As the waves touch bottom, wave speed decreases. The decrease in wave speed results in a decrease in wavelength and an increase in wave height.

Observations of a floating object, such as a toy boat, reveal that it moves not only up and down but also slightly forward and backward with each successive wave. This movement results in a circle that returns the object to essentially the same place in the water.

The energy transferred by the wind to the water is transmitted not only along the surface of the sea but also downward. However, beneath the surface, the circular motion rapidly diminishes until—at a depth equal to one-half the wavelength measured from still water level—the movement of water particles becomes very slight. In Figure 11, the dramatic decrease of wave energy with depth is shown by the rapidly decreasing diameters of water-particle orbits.

Breaking Waves As long as a wave is in deep water, it is unaffected by water depth. However, when a wave approaches the shore, the water becomes shallower and influences wave behavior. The wave begins to "feel bottom" at a water depth equal to half of its wavelength. Such depths interfere with water movement at the base of the wave and slow its advance. Figure 12 shows the changes that occur as a wave moves onto shore.

As a wave advances toward the shore, the slightly faster waves farther out to sea catch up and decrease its wavelength. As the speed and length of the wave decrease, the wave grows higher. Finally, a critical point is reached when the wave is too steep to support itself, and the wave front collapses, or breaks, causing water to advance up the shore.

The turbulent water created by breaking waves is called surf. On the landward margin of the surf zone, the sheet of water from collapsing breakers, called *swash*, moves up the slope of the beach. When the energy of the swash has been expended, the water flows back down the beach toward the surf zone as backwash.

☑ Reading Checkpoint At what depth do the characteristics of a wave begin to change as it approaches the shore?

The Dynamic Ocean 457

Facts and Figures

Strong backwash may result in a rip current. Rip currents are strong but narrow currents that move rapidly out to sea. If severe rip currents are present, beaches may be closed or swimming may be forbidden. Rip currents can be dangerous to swimmers, carrying them quickly out to very deep water.

Anyone caught in a rip current should immediately swim parallel to shore (perpendicular to the rip current) to get out of the narrow rip current. Attempts to swim directly back to shore while still in the rip current will not work and may lead to drowning.

Build Reading Literacy L1

Refer to **p. 306D** in **Chapter 11,** which provides guidelines for the KWL strategy (Know-Want to Know-Learned).

KWL Have students make a KWL chart on tides. Before reading this section, have students list what they already know about tides and some things they would like to know. After reading this section, have students complete the last column with what they learned. Check students' charts to make sure they understood the section. Remediate as needed.

Visual, Verbal

Q: *Where is the world's largest tidal range?*

A: The world's largest tidal range is found in the northern end of Nova Scotia's 258-kilometer-long Bay of Fundy. During maximum spring tide conditions, the tidal range at the mouth of the bay is only about 2 meters. However, the tidal range progressively increases from the mouth of the bay inward because the natural geometry of the bay concentrates tidal energy. In the eastern end of the bay, the maximum spring tidal range is about 17 meters. This extreme tidal range leaves boats high and dry during low tide.

Tides

Tides are regular changes in the elevation of the ocean surface. Their rhythmic rise and fall along coastlines has been noted throughout history. But the cause of tides was not well understood until Sir Isaac Newton applied the law of universal gravitation to them. Newton showed that there is a mutually attractive force—gravity—between any two bodies, such as between Earth and the moon. The strength of gravity between two objects decreases as the distance between the objects increases. At any given time, different areas of Earth's surface are different distances from the moon. The pull of the moon's gravity is greater at parts of Earth's surface that are closer to the moon and less at parts that are farther from the moon.

The Cause of Tides Ocean tides result from differences in the gravitational attraction exerted upon different parts of Earth's surface by the moon and, to a lesser extent, by the sun. The primary body that influences the tides is the moon, which makes one complete revolution around Earth every 29 and a half days. The sun, however, also influences the tides. It is far larger than the moon, but because it is much farther away, its effect is considerably less. In fact, the sun's tide-generating effect is only about 46 percent that of the moon's.

Think about the gravitational forces between the moon and Earth. This gravitational pull is strongest on the side of Earth closest to the moon and weakest on the far side of Earth from the moon. This difference causes Earth to be stretched slightly. The shape of the solid Earth is not affected much by this pull. However, the world ocean is much more mobile than the solid portions of Earth and a *tidal bulge* is produced as water is pulled toward the moon, as shown in **Figure 13.** A second tidal bulge is produced on the other side of Earth due to inertia—the tendency of an object, in this case water, to move in a straight line.

Because the position of the moon in relation to Earth changes only moderately in a single day, the tidal bulges remain in place while Earth rotates "through" them. For this reason, if you stand on a seashore for 24 hours, Earth will rotate you through alternating areas of higher and lower water. As you are carried into each tidal bulge, the tide rises. As you are carried into the troughs between the tidal bulges, the tide falls. Most coastal locations experience two high tides and two low tides each day.

FIGURE 13 Tidal Bulges on Earth Caused by the Moon
Interpret Visuals *When Earth is in this position, is North America experiencing low tide or high tide?*

Facts and Figures

The moon's gravitational pull does not just affect the oceans. It also causes a *solid body tide* of the Earth, stretching the solid Earth slightly and causing the land to pull back from the ocean water on the side of Earth far from the moon. Earth's solid tides are about 1/2 m in amplitude. On the side of Earth closer to the moon, the ocean is pulled toward the moon more than the solid Earth is pulled because the mass of the water is so much less than the mass of Earth. The moon's gravitational pull causes tidal bulges on opposite sides of Earth.

FIGURE 14 Earth-Moon-Sun Positions and the Tides
A When Earth, moon, and sun are aligned, spring tides are experienced. **B** When Earth, moon, and sun are at right angles to each other, neap tides are experienced.

Describe *How does the sun influence the formation of spring and neap tides?*

Tidal Cycle Although the sun is farther away from Earth than the moon, the gravitational attraction between the sun and Earth does play a role in producing tides. The sun's influence produces smaller tidal bulges. These tidal bulges are the result of the same forces involved in the bulges created by the moon. The influence of the sun on tides is most noticeable near the times of new and full moons. During these times, the sun and moon are aligned, and their forces are combined, as shown in **Figure 14A.** The combined gravity of these two tide-producing bodies causes larger tidal bulges (higher high tides) and larger tidal troughs (lower low tides). The result is a larger than normal **tidal range,** which is the difference in height between successive high and low tides.

Spring tides are tides that have the greatest tidal range due to the alignment of Earth, the moon, and the sun. They are experienced during new and full moons. Conversely, at about the time of the first and third quarters of the moon, the gravitational forces of the moon and sun act on Earth at a right angle, as shown in **Figure 14B.** The sun and moon partially offset the influence of the other. As a result, the daily tidal range is less. These tides are called **neap tides.** Each month there are two spring tides and two neap tides, each about one week apart.

☑ **Reading Checkpoint** *What is the tidal range?*

FIGURE 15 High Tide and Low Tide in a Village in Nova Scotia

The Dynamic Ocean **459**

LESSON 16.2

Use Tables and Graphs Have students study Figure 16. **Ask:** How many hours apart are the high tides in a mixed tidal pattern? *(12)* In a diurnal tidal pattern? *(24)* In a semidiurnal pattern? *(12)*
Visual

3 ASSESS

Evaluate Understanding **L2**

Review vocabulary with the class by putting students in groups to share their vocabulary concept maps. Encourage students to modify their concept maps as needed based on the discussion with their group.

Reteach **L1**

Have students make colored and labeled sketches of a wave and sketches of spring and neap tides that show the positions of Earth, sun, moon, and tidal bulges.

(A) **DIURNAL TIDAL PATTERN**

(B) **SEMIDIURNAL TIDAL PATTERN**

(C) **MIXED TIDAL PATTERN**

FIGURE 16 Tidal Patterns
The high points in these graphs represent high tides and the low points represent low tides.

Tidal Patterns You now know the basic causes and types of tides. However, many factors—including the shape of the coastline, the configuration of ocean basins, and water depth—greatly influence the tides. Consequently, tides at various locations respond differently to the tide-producing forces. This being the case, the nature of the tide at any coastal location can be determined most accurately by actual observation. The predictions in tidal tables and tidal data on nautical charts are based on such observations.

🔑 **Three main tidal patterns exist worldwide: diurnal tides, semidiurnal tides, and mixed tides.** A *diurnal* tidal pattern is characterized by a single high tide and a single low tide each tidal day, as shown in the graph in **Figure 16A.** Tides of this type occur along the northern shore of the Gulf of Mexico.

A *semidiurnal* tidal pattern exhibits two high tides and two low tides each tidal day. The two highs are about the same height, and the two lows are about the same height. **Figure 16B** shows a semidiurnal tide pattern. This type of tidal pattern is common along the Atlantic Coast of the United States.

A *mixed* tidal pattern, shown in **Figure 16C,** is similar to a semidiurnal pattern except that it is characterized by a large inequality in high water heights, low water heights, or both. There are usually two high and two low tides each day. However, the high tides are of different heights, and the low tides are of different heights. Such tides are found along the Pacific Coast of the United States and in many other parts of the world.

16.2 Assessment

Review Key Concepts 🔑

1. From where do ocean waves obtain their energy?

2. What three factors determine the height, length, and period of a wave?

3. How does energy move by means of a wave?

4. What changes occur in a wave as it approaches shore?

5. Which celestial bodies influence Earth tides?

6. What force produces tides?

7. What are the three types of tidal patterns?

Think Critically

8. **Infer** Two waves have the same fetch and were created by winds of equal speed. Why might one wave be higher than the other?

9. **Relate Cause and Effect** Explain how gravity leads to tides in Earth's oceans.

10. **Compare and Contrast** Compare and contrast spring tides and neap tides.

MATH PRACTICE

11. **Calculate** Wavelength, wave period, and wave speed can be related to each other in the equation:

$$\frac{\text{wavelength}}{\text{wave period}} = \text{wave speed}$$

If wavelength = 187 meters, and wave speed = 16.8 meters per second, what is the period of this wave?

Assessment Answers

1. wind
2. wind speed, the length of time the wind has blown, fetch
3. Circular orbital motion allows energy to move forward through a wave, while the individual water particles that transmit the wave move around in a circle.
4. As a wave approaches the shore, its speed and wavelength decrease. This causes the wave height to increase. The wave becomes too steep to support itself, and it breaks, causing water to advance up the shore.

5. the sun and the moon
6. gravity
7. diurnal, semidiurnal, mixed
8. The wind blew for a longer time to create the larger wave.
9. On the side of Earth closest to the moon, the force of gravity on the oceans is larger than the force on the solid Earth. This creates a tidal bulge. Inertia affects the water on the other side of Earth due to Earth's rotation, creating a similar tidal bulge.
10. Both are tides produced as a result of the Earth–moon–sun system and the position

of each body relative to the other. When the Earth, moon, and sun are aligned, spring tides, which have the largest tidal range, are produced. When the Earth, moon, and sun are at right angles to each other, neap tides, which have the smallest tidal range, are produced.
11. 187 m ÷ 16.8 m/s = 11.13 s
The period is 11.13 seconds.

16.3 Shoreline Processes and Features

BEACHES AND SHORELINES are constantly undergoing changes as the force of waves and currents act on them. During calm weather, wave action is minimal. During storms, however, waves are capable of causing much erosion—the movement of material from one place to another. The pressure exerted by Atlantic waves in wintertime, for example, averages 10,000 kilograms per square meter. The force during storms is even greater. These forces contribute to the fascinating assortment of shoreline features found along the world's coastal regions.

Forces Acting on the Shoreline

When people think of beaches, they think of sandy areas where people lie in the sun and stroll along the water's edge. Technically, a **beach** is the accumulation of sediment found along the shore of a lake or ocean. Beaches are composed of whatever sediment is locally available. They may be made of mineral particles from the erosion of beach cliffs or nearby coastal mountains. Some beaches have a significant biological component. For example, most beaches in southern Florida are composed of shell fragments and the remains of coastal marine organisms. Beaches can be thought of as material in transit along the shoreline. The action of waves and abrasion greatly changes the shape of beaches and shorelines over time.

Wave Impact Waves that crash along the beach are constantly moving sediment. **Waves along the shoreline are constantly eroding, transporting, and depositing sediment. Many types of shoreline features can result from this activity.** During calm weather, wave action is minimal. During storms, however, waves are capable of causing much erosion. The impact of large, high-energy waves against the shore can be awesome in its violence. Each breaking wave may hurl thousands of tons of water against the land, sometimes causing the ground to tremble.

It is no wonder that cracks and crevices are quickly opened in cliffs, coastal structures, and anything else that is subjected to these enormous impacts. Water is forced into every opening, causing air in the cracks to become highly compressed by the thrust of crashing waves. When the wave subsides, the air expands rapidly. This expanding air dislodges rock fragments and enlarges and extends preexisting fractures.

Key Questions

 How are sediments along the shoreline moved?

 How does refraction affect wave action along the shore?

 What do longshore currents do?

 By which processes do shoreline features form?

 What structures can be built to protect a shoreline?

 What is beach nourishment?

Vocabulary

- beach • wave refraction
- longshore current
- barrier island

Reading Strategy

Summarize Read the section on wave refraction. Then copy and complete the concept map below to organize what you know about refraction.

LESSON 16.3

1 FOCUS

Lesson Objectives
16.9 **List** the agents responsible for the movement of sediments along the shoreline.
16.10 **Explain** how refraction affects wave action along the shore.
16.11 **Describe** the processes that form shoreline features.
16.12 **List** the structures that can be built to protect a shoreline.

Build Vocabulary L2
Using Context Clues Encourage students to keep a list of unfamiliar words they encounter while reading. For each word they should write a definition based on the context, and then have them verify their definition with a dictionary.

Reading Strategy L2
a. bending of waves
b. erosion
c. deposition

LESSON 16.3

2 INSTRUCT

Use Visuals L1

Figure 17 Have students observe the shape and texture of the feature shown in this figure. **Ask:** What could have caused this? *(waves crashing into the cliff)* Why is it so smooth? *(The sand carried by crashing waves acts like sandpaper on the cliff.)* What will most likely happen to the trees on top of this cliff? *(They will eventually fall into the ocean.)*
Visual

Build Science Skills L2

Predict Have students look at Figure 18 and the reading passage to learn that erosion is concentrated on the headlands and that deposition is concentrated in the bays. Based on this observation, have students predict how the coastline in Figure 18 will eventually look. *(Eventually, the headlands will erode back and the bays will fill forward until the two meet, forming a smooth coastline without headlands or bays.)*
Visual, Logical

Use Community Resources L2

If possible, bring students to a nearby beach to observe wave motion and the shoreline features formed by waves.
Visual, Kinesthetic

Use Visuals L1

Figure 18 Direct students' attention to Figure 18. **Ask:** Where is most erosion occurring in this diagram? *(headland in the middle)* What evidence suggests the headland once extended further into the sea? *(Rocky remnants are off-shore from the headland)*

FIGURE 17 Erosion Abrasion has undercut this sandstone cliff at Gabriola Island, British Columbia, Canada.

Abrasion In addition to the erosion caused by wave impact and pressure, erosion caused by abrasion is also important. In fact, abrasion is probably more intense in the surf zone than in any other environment. Abrasion is the sawing and grinding action of rock fragments in the water. Smooth, rounded stones and pebbles along the shore are evidence of the continual grinding action of rock against rock in the surf zone. Such fragments are also used as "tools" by waves as they cut horizontally into the land, as shown in the sandstone in **Figure 17.**

Wave Refraction The bending of waves, called **wave refraction,** plays an important part in shoreline processes. Wave refraction affects the distribution of energy along the shore. It strongly influences where and to what degree erosion, sediment transport, and deposition will take place.

Most waves move toward the shore at a slight angle, rather than straight on. However, when they reach the shallow water of a smoothly sloping bottom, the wave crests are refracted, or bent, and tend to line up nearly parallel to the shore. Such bending occurs because the part of the wave nearest the shore touches bottom and slows first, whereas the part of the wave that is still in deep water continues forward at its full speed. The change in speed causes wave crests to become nearly parallel to the shore.

Because of refraction, wave energy is concentrated against the sides and ends of headlands that project into the water, whereas wave action is weakened in bays. A *bay* is an indentation in a shoreline. This type of wave action along irregular coastlines is illustrated in **Figure 18.** Waves reach the shallow water in front of the headland sooner than they do in the bays. Therefore, wave energy is concentrated in this area, leading to erosion. By contrast, refraction in the bays causes waves to spread out and expend less energy. This refraction leads to deposition and the formation of sandy beaches.

FIGURE 18 Wave Refraction Waves are refracted as they come into shore. Wave energy is concentrated at the headlands and dispersed in the bays. **Infer** *What processes occur as a result of wave refraction on this shoreline?*

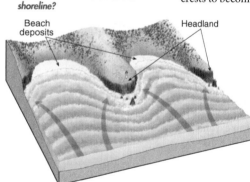

Beach deposits

Headland

Differentiated Instruction

ENGLISH LANGUAGE LEARNERS Show English Language Learners pictures of beaches that show some natural features, such as dunes and tidal pools. Teach students that beaches are a type of shore. Have students infer the meaning of *beach towel, beach umbrella, beached whale, beach buggy,* and *beachcomber.* Allow students to use a dictionary. Check students' answers, and clarify their answers as needed.

Path of sand particles

Beach drift

Longshore current

Longshore Transport Although waves are refracted, most still reach the shore at a slight angle. As a result, the uprush of water, or swash, from each breaking wave is at a slight angle to the shoreline. However, the backwash is straight down the slope of the beach. The effect is a zigzag pattern along the beach face. This movement, called *beach drift*, can transport sand and pebbles hundreds or even thousands of meters daily. These angled waves also produce currents within the surf zone. The currents flow parallel to the shore and move large amounts of sediment along the shore. **Figure 19** shows this type of current, which is called a **longshore current.**

The water in the surf zone is turbulent, which means there is a lot of movement. **Turbulence allows longshore currents to easily move the fine suspended sand and to roll larger sand and gravel particles along the bottom.** Longshore currents can change direction when the direction that waves approach the beach changes with the seasons. Generally, longshore currents flow southward along both the Atlantic and Pacific shores of the United States.

☑ **Reading Checkpoint** *What causes longshore currents?*

Erosional Features

Shoreline features vary depending on the type of rocks exposed along the shore, the intensity of waves, coastal currents, and whether the coast is stable, sinking, or rising. **Shoreline features that originate primarily from erosion are called erosional features. Sediment that is transported along the shore and deposited in areas where energy is low produce depositional features.**

Erosional features are common along the rugged and irregular New England coast and along the steep shorelines of the West Coast of the United States. Wave erosion is steadily wearing away the California coast. Where the coast is made up of sedimentary rock, average erosion is 15 to 30 centimeters per year. But where the coast consists of soil and sand, erosion can be as high as 2 to 3 meters per year. Coastal erosion is a hazard to structures built on cliffs and bluffs along the shore.

The Dynamic Ocean **463**

LESSON 16.3

Build Science Skills · L2

Compare and Contrast Students should make flashcards of each feature described in this chapter. The sketch and feature's name should be on one side of the card, and how the feature forms and if it is erosional or depositional should be on the other side. The sketches can be done on full-size paper or on index cards. Features include the following: wave-cut cliff, wave-cut platform, sea arch, sea stack, spit, baymouth bar, tombolo, and barrier islands. Sketches of the following would also be useful, along with a description of why they are used: groin, breakwater, and seawall. Ask students to compare and contrast various features.
Visual, Kinesthetic

Build Reading Literacy · L1

Refer to **p. 556D** in **Chapter 20,** which provides guidelines for active comprehension.

Active Comprehension Ask students to write down some things they would like to know about shoreline features. Have some students share their responses with the class, and record these responses on the board where they can be referred to at the end of the section.
Verbal

FIGURE 20 Sea Arch In time, the sea arch will collapse and form a sea stack similar to the sea stack on the left side of the photograph.

FIGURE 21 Baymouth Bar
This high-altitude image shows a baymouth bar along the coast of Martha's Vineyard, Massachusetts.

baymouth bar

The cliffs along California's coast form as tectonic processes slowly uplift coastal land. At the same time, the energy of ocean waves undercuts the cliffs. Over time, this process produces features such as wave-cut cliffs, wave-cut platforms, sea arches, and sea stacks.

Wave-Cut Cliffs and Platforms

Wave-cut cliffs result from the cutting action of the surf against the base of coastal land. As erosion progresses, rocks that overhang the notch at the base of the cliff crumble into the surf, and the cliff retreats. A relatively flat, benchlike surface, called a wave-cut platform, is left behind by the receding cliff. The platform broadens as the wave attack continues. Some debris produced by the breaking waves remains along the water's edge as sediment on the beach. The rest of the sediment is transported farther seaward.

Sea Arches and Sea Stacks

Headlands that extend into the sea are vigorously attacked by waves because of refraction. The surf erodes the rock selectively and wears away the softer or more highly fractured rock at the fastest rate. At first, sea caves may form. When two caves on opposite sides of a headland unite, a sea arch such as the one in **Figure 20** results. Eventually, the sea arch may fall in, leaving an isolated remnant, or sea stack, on the wave-cut platform.

☑ **Reading Checkpoint** *How does a sea arch form?*

Depositional Features

Sediment eroded from beaches is transported along the shore and deposited in areas where wave energy is low. Such processes produce many depositional features.

Spits, Bars, and Tombolos

Where longshore currents and other surf zone currents are active, several features may develop. A *spit* is an elongated ridge of sand that projects from the land into the mouth of an adjacent bay. Often the end in the water hooks landward in response to the dominant direction of the longshore current. The term *baymouth bar* is applied to a sandbar that completely crosses a bay, sealing it off from the open ocean. Find the baymouth bar in **Figure 21.** Such a feature tends to form across bays in which currents are weak and spits extend across. A *tombolo* is a ridge of sand that connects an island to the mainland or to another island. A tombolo forms in much the same way as a spit. **Figure 22** shows how tomobolos and other features form as a shoreline changes over time.

Facts and Figures

Wave deposition can produce dramatic land features. The long, curving arm of Cape Cod, Massachusetts is a prime example. Cape Cod was originally a moraine—a pile of till deposited at the leading edge of a glacier that covered the Northeast during the most recent ice age. At that time, about 20,000 years ago, the sea level was low, and the moraine was deposited on dry land. Since that time, the sea level has risen and the moraine has become subjected to wave erosion. Sediment from the loose pile of till has been carried northward along the shore, continually extending the arm of land in that direction.

VISUAL SUMMARY

EVOLUTION OF SHORELINE FEATURES

FIGURE 22 Over time erosion and deposition transform an irregular coastline into one that is smooth and straight.

Bay Headland Headland

Sea stack

①

Spit Tombolo Sea arch

②

Spit

Wave-cut cliff Sea stack

③

Spit Wave-cut cliff Beach deposits

Baymouth bar Longshore current

Wave-cut platform

④

The Dynamic Ocean **465**

Build Reading Literacy   L1

Refer to **p. 216D** in **Chapter 8,** which provides the guidelines for comparing and contrasting.

Compare and Contrast Advise students to make a compare and contrast table about erosional and depositional features. Similarities may include the following: caused by waves and constantly changing. Differences may include the following: erosional features are caused by fast moving waves while depositional features are caused by slower moving waves, and erosional features tend to shrink over time while depositional features tend to grow over time.
Verbal, Visual

Build Science Skills

Use Models Have students construct three-dimensional models of the erosional and depositional features described in this lesson. Students may make individual models of each feature or one large model of an erosional coastline and another of a depositional coastline.
Visual, Kinesthetic

Answers

☑ **Reading Checkpoint** *Sea arches form when two caves (eroded by surf) on opposite sides of a headland unite.*

Use Visuals

Figure 23 Tell students that the thin, nearly continuous stretch of land just offshore in this figure is a chain of barrier islands. After they have finished reading the lesson, arrange students in cooperative groups. **Ask:** How might barrier islands benefit coastal areas on the other side of the sound? *(Barrier islands absorb much of the energy from incoming waves, protecting the sound from rough seas and the coasts further inland from intense erosion. Barrier islands are like natural breakwaters.)* What do you think would happen on a barrier island during a storm? *(The island might flood or suffer severe erosion.)* What risks are people taking when they live on barrier islands? *(Storms may damage or even destroy their property.)*
Interpersonal

Build Science Skills

Make Judgments Suggest that students prepare for a mock town meeting. Assign one group of students to speak out against beach nourishment and another group to speak in favor of this intervention.
Group, Interpersonal

FIGURE 23 Barrier Islands
The islands along the coast of North Carolina are examples of barrier islands.

FIGURE 24 Breakwater These breakwaters, built along a Chesapeake Bay shoreline, should help protect the shoreline from erosion by absorbing force from strong waves.

Barrier Islands The Atlantic and Gulf Coastal Plains are relatively flat and slope gently seaward. The shore zone in these areas is characterized by barrier islands. **Barrier islands** are narrow sandbars parallel to, but separated from, the coast at distances from 3 to 30 kilometers offshore. From Cape Cod, Massachusetts, to Padre Island, Texas, nearly 300 barrier islands rim the coast. The barrier islands along the coast of North Carolina are shown in **Figure 23**.

Barrier islands may have formed in several ways. Some began as spits that were later cut off from the mainland by wave erosion or by the general rise in sea level following the last glacial period. Others were created when turbulent waters in the line of breakers heaped up sand that had been scoured from the bottom. Finally, some barrier islands may be former sand-dune ridges that began along the shore during the last glacial period, when sea level was lower. As the ice sheets melted, sea level rose and flooded the area behind the beach-dune complex.

☑ **Reading Checkpoint** *What is a barrier island?*

Stabilizing the Shore

Shorelines are among Earth's most dynamic places. They change rapidly in response to natural forces. Storms are capable of eroding beaches and cliffs at rates that far exceed the long-term average erosion. Such bursts of accelerated erosion not only affect the natural evolution of a coast but can also have a profound impact on people who live in the coastal zone. Erosion along the coast causes significant property damage. Huge sums of money are spent annually to repair damage and to prevent or control erosion.

Protective Structures 🔊 Groins, breakwaters, and seawalls are some structures built to protect a coast from erosion or to prevent the movement of sand along a beach. *Groins* are sometimes constructed to maintain or widen beaches that are losing sand. A groin is a barrier built at a right angle to the beach to trap sand that is moving parallel to the shore.

Protective structures, such as the *breakwaters* shown in **Figure 24**, can also be built parallel to the shoreline. Their purpose is to protect boats or eroding shorelines from the force of large breaking waves by creating a quiet water zone near the shore. A *seawall* is another protective structure built parallel to the shore. A seawall is designed to shield the coast and defend property from breaking waves. Waves expend much of their energy as they move across an open beach. Seawalls reduce this process by reflecting the force of unspent waves seaward.

Facts and Figures

At 21 stories high, the Cape Hatteras lighthouse in North Carolina is the tallest lighthouse in the United States, and is one of our nation's most prominent landmarks. The lighthouse was built in 1870 on a barrier island, 457 m from the shoreline, to warn sailors of dangerous waters. Waves gradually eroded at the barrier island, bringing the ocean as close as 37 m from the lighthouse. In 1970 the U.S. Navy started building groins and adding sand to the beach to protect the lighthouse from further erosion, but their attempts failed. Ultimately, in 1999, the National Park Service decided to move the entire lighthouse 884 m further inland for protection.

Protective structures often only offer temporary solutions to shoreline problems. The structures themselves interfere with the natural processes of erosion and deposition. Then more structures may need to be built in order to counteract the new problems that arise. Many scientists feel that using protective structures to divert the ocean's energy causes more harm than good.

Beach Nourishment 🔑 **Beach nourishment is the artificial addition of large quantities of sand to the beach system.** It is an attempt to stabilize shoreline sands without building protective structures. Examine the before and after photographs shown in **Figure 25.** By building the beaches seaward, both beach quality and storm protection are improved. However, the same processes that removed the sand in the first place will eventually wash away the replacement sand as well.

Beach nourishment can be very expensive because huge volumes of sand must be transported to the beach from offshore areas, nearby rivers, or other source areas for sand. Beach nourishment can also have detrimental effects on local marine life. For example, beach nourishment at Waikiki Beach, Hawaii, involved replacing the natural coarse beach sand with softer, muddier sand. Destruction of the softer sand by breaking waves increased the water's turbidity, or "cloudiness," and killed offshore coral reefs.

FIGURE 25 Miami Beach A Before beach nourishment **B** After beach nourishment **Explain** *What are the advantages and disadvantages of beach nourishment?*

3 ASSESS

Evaluate Understanding L2

Have students use their flashcards to quiz each other on their ability to recognize erosional and depositional structures. As a class, revisit the questions students had at the beginning of the chapter to see if students can now answer these questions.

Reteach L1

Use the sketches and descriptions of each term that students recorded as they read, or use their three-dimensional models to review the lesson's main concepts.

16.3 Assessment

Review Key Concepts 🔑

1. How are sediments along the shoreline moved?

2. What effect does wave impact have on shorelines?

3. How does refraction affect wave action along the shore?

4. What do longshore currents do?

5. By which processes do shoreline features form?

6. Name three examples of shoreline features formed by erosion.

7. How do barrier islands form?

8. What structures can be built to protect a shoreline?

9. What is beach nourishment?

Think Critically

10. Explain How can beach nourishment be helpful? How can it be harmful?

11. Compare and Contrast Compare and contrast a tombolo and a barrier island.

12. Relate Cause and Effect A breakwater is built to reduce wave action in near-shore areas. How might the reduced wave action along the shore behind the breakwater affect sediment deposition? What problems might this cause?

BIGIDEA WATER PLANET

13. Summarize Examine Figure 22. In your own words summarize how waves and currents changed this shoreline over time.

The Dynamic Ocean **467**

Answers

Figure 25 *Protective structures do not have to be built to stabilize shorelines. It can be expensive and the natural processes that eroded the original sand will eventually erode the replacement sand. It can have negative effects on marine life. It can only be used successfully in a few areas.*

☑ **Reading Checkpoint** *A barrier island is a narrow sandbar parallel to, but separate from, the coast at distances from 3 to 30 km offshore.*

Assessment Answers

1. erosion and deposition
2. Wave impact leads to shoreline erosion.
3. Wave energy is concentrated against the headlands, and it is weakened in bays.
4. They move fine suspended sand and roll larger sand and gravel along the bottom and along the shore.
5. erosion and sediment transportation and deposition
6. Any three: wave-cut cliff, wave-cut platform, sea arches, sea stacks

7. Some may have originated as spits that were severed from the mainland, others formed when turbulent waters in the line of breakers heaped up sand scoured from the bottom, some may be former sand-dune ridges that are no longer attached to the mainland due to ice melting.
8. groins, breakwaters, seawalls
9. adding large quantities of sand to the beach system to stabilize the shoreline
10. improved beach quality and storm protection; but expensive and can harm local marine life

11. both formed by deposition; a tombolo connects an island to the mainland or to another island; a barrier island is separate from the coast
12. The reduced wave action behind the breakwater allows sand to accumulate. The protected area will eventually fill with sand, while the downstream beach erodes.
13. Waves and currents led to erosion and deposition. Initially the coastline was irregular, but over time it became smoother and straighter as features such as headlands and sea stacks eroded.

GRAPHING TIDAL CYCLES **L2**

Objective
After completing this activity, students will be able to use tidal data to determine the tidal pattern an area experiences.

Skills Graph, Interpret Data, Infer, Draw Conclusions

Prep Time 15 minutes

Advanced Prep You may want to plot the data yourself before students begin so you can more easily help them set up their axes and so that you can tell quickly if students are graphing correctly.

Class Time 1 block or 2 periods

Teaching Tip Show students how to divide each day into 6-hour intervals on the *x*-axis in order to plot correctly. Then plot the first few points with the class on the board or on an overhead projector. Figure 16 on page 460 will help students answer Question 1.

Expected Outcome Students will draw a graph showing the regular rise and fall of tides to determine the tidal pattern for an area.

INQUIRY ?
EXPLORATION LAB

Graphing Tidal Cycles

Problem How can you determine the tidal pattern an area experiences?

Materials graph paper, pencil

Skills Graph, Interpret Data, Infer, Draw Conclusions

Connect to the **Big idea** Tides are the cyclical rise and fall of sea level caused by the gravitational attraction between Earth and the moon and, to a lesser extent, between Earth and the sun. Gravitational pull creates a bulge in the ocean on the side of Earth nearest the moon. A similar bulge forms on the other side of Earth due to inertia. Tides develop as the rotating Earth moves through these bulges, causing periods of high and low water. In this lab, you will graph tidal data to determine whether an area has diurnal, semidiurnal, or mixed tides.

Procedure

1. Label the graph paper as below to make a graph of the tidal cycle. The *x*-axis should be in days, and the *y*-axis should be in feet. As shown below, place the *x*-axis at the top of the graph, rather than at the bottom.

2. Use the data in **Table 1** to make a graph of the tidal cycle.

Sample Tidal Curve

High tide in Nova Scotia's Bay of Fundy

Low tide in the same area

Analyze and Conclude

1. **Apply Concepts** What tidal pattern does this area experience? Explain how you determined this.

2. **Calculate** What is the greatest tidal range for the data you graphed? What is the least tidal range? What types of tides correspond to each of these tidal ranges?

3. **Draw Conclusions** Based on your graph, identify the days when each moon phase could have occurred: new moon, first quarter moon, full moon, last quarter moon. How do you know this?

4. **Apply Concepts** On January 5th (Day 5 on the table) at 9:00 A.M., Jarred anchored his boat in about 4 feet of water at the beach. When he returned at 3:30 that afternoon, the boat was in the sand. What had happened? How long did Jarred have to wait to leave the area in his boat?

Table 1 Tidal Data for Long Beach, New York, January 2003

Day	Time	Height	Time	Height	Time	Height	Time	Height
			All times are listed in Local Standard Time (LST). All heights are in feet.					
1	05:45 A.M.	5.5	12:16 P.M.	−0.7	06:12 P.M.	4.4	———	—
2	12:18 A.M.	−0.5	06:35 A.M.	5.6	01:07 P.M.	−0.8	07:03 P.M.	4.4
3	01:10 A.M.	−0.5	07:23 A.M.	5.5	01:56 P.M.	−0.8	07:53 P.M.	4.4
4	01:59 A.M.	−0.4	08:11 A.M.	5.4	02:42 P.M.	−0.7	08:42 P.M.	4.3
5	02:45 A.M.	−0.2	08:59 A.M.	5.1	03:25 P.M.	−0.5	09:32 P.M.	4.2
6	03:30 A.M.	0.0	09:47 A.M.	4.8	04:07 P.M.	−0.3	10:23 P.M.	4.0
7	04:14 A.M.	0.3	10:35 A.M.	4.6	04:49 P.M.	−0.1	11:12 P.M.	3.9
8	05:01 A.M.	0.6	11:22 A.M.	4.3	05:32 P.M.	0.2	11:59 P.M.	3.9
9	05:54 A.M.	0.8	12:09 P.M.	4.0	06:18 P.M.	0.4	———	—
10	12:45 A.M.	3.9	06:56 A.M.	0.9	12:57 P.M.	3.7	07:10 P.M.	0.5
11	01:31 A.M.	3.9	07:59 A.M.	0.9	01:47 P.M.	3.5	08:02 P.M.	0.5
12	02:19 A.M.	4.0	08:57 A.M.	0.8	02:41 P.M.	3.4	08:53 P.M.	0.5
13	03:10 A.M.	4.1	09:50 A.M.	0.6	03:39 P.M.	3.5	09:41 P.M.	0.4
14	04:02 A.M.	4.3	10:38 A.M.	0.3	04:34 P.M.	3.6	10:28 P.M.	0.2
15	04:51 A.M.	4.6	11:26 A.M.	0.1	05:23 P.M.	3.7	11:15 P.M.	0.1
16	05:36 A.M.	4.8	12:12 P.M.	−0.1	06:08 P.M.	3.9	———	—
17	12:02 A.M.	−0.1	06:17 A.M.	5.0	12:57 P.M.	−0.3	06:51 P.M.	4.1
18	12:49 A.M.	−0.2	06:58 A.M.	5.1	01:40 P.M.	−0.5	07:32 P.M.	4.2
19	01:35 A.M.	−0.4	07:38 A.M.	5.2	02:22 P.M.	−0.6	08:15 P.M.	4.3
20	02:20 A.M.	−0.4	08:21 A.M.	5.2	03:30 P.M.	−0.7	09:01 P.M.	4.4
21	03:05 A.M.	−0.4	09:07 A.M.	5.1	03:44 P.M.	−0.7	09:51 P.M.	4.5
22	03:52 A.M.	−0.3	09:58 A.M.	4.9	04:27 P.M.	−0.6	10:44 P.M.	4.6
23	04:43 A.M.	−0.1	10:52 A.M.	4.7	05:13 P.M.	−0.4	11:37 P.M.	4.7
24	05:43 A.M.	0.1	11:48 A.M.	4.4	06:08 P.M.	−0.2	———	—
25	12:32 A.M.	4.7	06:53 A.M.	0.2	12:47 P.M.	4.2	07:11 P.M.	−0.1
26	01:30 A.M.	4.8	08:06 A.M.	0.2	01:50 P.M.	3.9	08:17 P.M.	0.0
27	02:31 A.M.	4.8	09:12 A.M.	0.1	02:57 P.M.	3.8	09:19 P.M.	0.0
28	03:35 A.M.	4.8	10:13 A.M.	−0.1	04:05 P.M.	3.9	10:17 P.M.	−0.1
29	04:37 A.M.	5.0	11:09 A.M.	−0.3	05:07 P.M.	4.0	11:13 P.M.	−0.2
30	05:33 A.M.	5.1	12:01 P.M.	−0.5	06:01 P.M.	4.2	———	—
31	12:06 A.M.	−0.3	06:22 A.M.	5.2	12:51 P.M.	−0.6	06:50 P.M.	4.3

Source: Center for Operational Oceanographic Products and Services, National Oceanographic and Atmospheric Association, National Ocean Service.

Analyze and Conclude

1. Semidiurnal; this can be determined by studying the graph produced from the data. The area has two high tides and two low tides in approximately a 24-hour period, with the high tides being similar height and the low tides being similar height.

2. 6.4 feet; 2.6 feet; spring tides and neap tides respectively

3. A new moon or a full moon could have occurred on Day 2. A new moon or a full moon could have occurred on Day 20. These days correspond with the highest tidal range, or spring tides. A first or third quarter moon could have occurred on Day 11. A first or third quarter moon could have occurred on Day 26. These days correspond with the lowest tidal range, or neap tides.

4. The tide went out while Jarred was gone. At 3:25 P.M. low tide occurred. He would have to wait until the tide came in again, so there would be enough water for him to move his boat. The longest he would have had to wait is about six hours, until high tide occurred at 9:32 P.M.

Visual, Logical

STUDY GUIDE

Study Tip

Make Flashcards

Teach students to make flashcards of the vocabulary, sketches, and processes they need to know for each chapter. Students can use the flashcards to quiz themselves or others. Advise students to keep their flashcards even after the chapter test is over, so the same cards can be used to study for their final exams or standardized tests.

21st Century Learning

Creativity and Intellectual Curiosity

How can tides be used to generate electricity?

In the search for energy alternatives to fossil fuels, many people are looking for ways to harness the ocean's energy. Encourage interested students to investigate systems for generating electricity using tides and waves. Ask them to prepare an electronic presentation that details at least two systems that seem promising. Presentations should describe how each system works, using illustrations if available. Presentations should also include a discussion of any possible disadvantages of each system. For example, is the system safe for wildlife, or does it interfere with other uses of the coastline?

During their research, students are likely to find a wide variety of sources. Ask each student to provide a list of sources and to discuss the reliability of each source. Ask them to discuss the reliability of each information source. For example, students should note whether information was provided by a company that would profit from the system and how this might affect reliability.

Homework Guide

Lesson	Questions
1	1–5, 11–15, 23, 28, 29
2	6, 16–19, 24, 26, 27, 30
3	7–10, 20–22, 25

16 Study Guide

Big idea Water Planet

16.1 Ocean Circulation

🔑 Surface currents develop from friction between the ocean and the wind that blows across its surface.

🔑 Because of Earth's rotation, currents are deflected to the right in the Northern Hemisphere and to the left in the Southern Hemisphere.

🔑 When currents from low-latitude regions move into higher latitudes, they transfer heat from warmer to cooler areas on Earth.

🔑 As cold water currents travel toward the equator, they help moderate the warm temperatures of adjacent land areas.

🔑 Upwelling brings dissolved nutrients, such as nitrates and phosphates, to the ocean surface.

🔑 An increase in seawater density can be caused by a decrease in temperature or an increase in salinity.

ocean current (448)
surface current (448)
gyre (449)
Coriolis effect (449)
upwelling (450)
density current (451)

16.2 Waves and Tides

🔑 Most ocean waves obtain their energy and motion from the wind.

🔑 The height, length, and period that are eventually achieved by a wave depend on three factors: (1) wind speed; (2) length of time the wind has blown; and (3) fetch.

🔑 Circular orbital motion allows energy to move forward through the water while the individual water particles that transmit the wave move around in a circle.

🔑 Ocean tides result from differences in the gravitational attraction exerted upon different parts of Earth's surface by the moon and, to a lesser extent, by the sun.

🔑 Three main tidal patterns exist worldwide: diurnal tides, semidiurnal tides, and mixed tides.

wave height (456)
wavelength (456)
wave period (456)
fetch (456)
tide (458)
tidal range (459)
spring tide (459)
neap tide (459)

16.3 Shoreline Processes and Features

🔑 Waves along the shoreline are constantly eroding, transporting, and depositing sediment. Many types of shoreline features can result from this activity.

🔑 Because of refraction, wave energy is concentrated against the sides and ends of headlands that project into the water, whereas wave action is weakened in bays.

🔑 Turbulence allows longshore currents to easily move the fine suspended sand and to roll larger sand and gravel particles along the bottom.

🔑 Shoreline features that originate primarily from the work of erosion are called erosional features. Sediment that is transported along the shore and deposited in areas where energy is low produce depositional features.

🔑 Groins, breakwaters, and seawalls are some structures built to protect a coast from erosion or to prevent the movement of sand along a beach.

🔑 Beach nourishment is the artificial addition of large quantities of sand to the beach system.

beach (461)
wave refraction (462)
longshore current (463)
barrier island (466)

470 Chapter 16 • Study Guide

Assessment Answers

Review Content

1. b	**2.** a	**3.** d
4. c	**5.** d	**6.** b
7. a	**8.** c	**9.** d
10. b		

Understand Concepts

11. Coriolis effect deflects currents from their original course due to the rotation of Earth. In the Northern Hemisphere, currents are deflected to the right. In the Southern Hemisphere, currents are deflected to the left.
12. Cold ocean currents travel from the poles toward the equator and moderate warm temperatures on adjacent landforms.

16 Assessment

Review Content

Choose the letter that best answers the questions or completes the statement.

1. An ocean current moving from the equator toward a pole is
   a. cold.
   b. warm.
   c. cold in the Northern Hemisphere and warm in the Southern Hemisphere.
   d. warm in the Northern Hemisphere and cold in the Northern Hemisphere.

2. Because of the Coriolis effect, surface currents in the Southern Hemisphere are deflected
   a. to the left.   c. north.
   b. to the right.   d. south.

3. Which term describes the rising of cold water from deeper layers to replace warmer surface water?
   a. density current   c. surface current
   b. downwelling   d. upwelling

4. The energy and motion of most waves is derived from
   a. currents.   c. wind.
   b. tides.   d. gravity.

5. The five huge circular-moving systems of ocean surface currents are called
   a. density currents. c. drifts.
   b. fetches.   d. gyres.

6. Daily changes in the elevation of the ocean surface are called
   a. surface currents. c. waves.
   b. tides.   d. density currents.

7. Which of the following results from wave refraction?
   a. Wave energy is concentrated on headlands projecting into the water.
   b. Wave energy is concentrated in the recessed areas between headlands.
   c. Wave energy is largely dissipated before waves reach the shore.
   d. Headlands are enlarged because sediment is deposited on their seaward side.

8. The movement of water within the surf zone that parallels the shore is called
   a. tidal current.   c. longshore current.
   b. density current.   d. surface current.

9. Which describes a ridge of sand that connects an island to the mainland or another island?
   a. baymouth bar   c. sea stack
   b. sea arch   d. tombolo

10. Which is created through the process of erosion?
    a. baymouth bar   c. spit
    b. sea arch   d. tombolo

Understand Concepts

11. Describe the influence that the Coriolis effect has on the movement of ocean waters.

12. Describe the effect that cold ocean currents have on the climates of adjacent land areas.

13. What role do ocean currents play in maintaining Earth's heat balance?

14. Describe coastal upwelling and the effect it has on fish populations.

15. Where and how is the densest water in all the oceans formed?

Use the figure below to answer Questions 16–18.

16. Identify which wave characteristics are represented by A and C.

17. Explain what B represents. What happens to a floating object as a wave passes through the water?

18. What factors can lead to an increase in the height of this wave?

The Dynamic Ocean **471**

17. B represents the circular orbital motion a water particle undergoes as a wave passes through the water. A floating object moves up and backward as the crest approaches, then down and forward after the crest passes. As the trough approaches, the object continues to move, down and backward, then rises and moves backward again as the next crest advances.

18. an increase in wind speed, length of time the wind has blown, and/or the fetch

19. A diurnal tidal pattern is characterized by a single high tide and a single low tide each tidal day. Tides of this type occur along the northern shore of the Gulf of Mexico. A semidiurnal tidal pattern exhibits two high tides and two low tides each tidal day, with the two highs about the same height and the two lows about the same height. This type of tidal pattern is common along the Atlantic Coast of the United States.

20. Refraction in bays causes waves to diverge and expend less energy, leading to deposition of sediments and the formation of sandy beaches.

21. Wave-cut cliffs result from the cutting action of the surf against the base of coastal land. As erosion progresses, rocks overhanging the notch at the base of the cliff crumble into the surf and the cliff retreats. A relatively flat, benchlike surface, called a wave-cut platform, is left behind by the receding cliff.

22. Any two: groin, breakwater, seawall

13. They transfer heat from the tropics, where there is an excess of heat, to the polar regions, where there is a heat deficit. Ocean water movements account for about one quarter of this heat transport.

14. Coastal upwelling is vertical circulation that brings cool, nutrient-rich water from depth to the surface to replace warm surface waters moved by wind. The nutrient-rich water supports high productivity and a large population of phytoplankton and subsequently fish and other marine consumers.

15. The densest water is formed near Antarctica. As sea ice forms, the already cold surface water becomes more dense and sinks to the bottom.

16. A is the wavelength; C is the wave height.

ASSESSMENT

Think Critically

23. Student responses will vary but should indicate an understanding of the processes that lead to upwelling. Winds and moving water under the influence of the Coriolis effect cause surface water to move away from shore. As the surface layer moves away from the coast, it is replaced by water that "upwells" from below the surface.

24. spring tide; new moon

25. Rivers contain sediments weathered from continental rocks, some of which is deposited on beaches and shorelines when the rivers reach the sea. If a river is dammed, sediment input is reduced and the beach can be narrowed by erosion when existing sediment is carried away and not replaced.

26. Tides are a result of the gravitational attraction between Earth and the moon and Earth and the sun. On the side of Earth closest to the moon, gravity pulls water toward the moon producing a tidal bulge. On the side of Earth farthest from the moon, inertia causes an equally large tidal bulge to form on the side of Earth directly opposite the moon. The sun's gravity only accounts for about half the influence on Earth's tides, even though it is far more massive than the moon, because the distance between Earth and the moon is far less than the distance between Earth and the sun.

Math Skills

27. $\dfrac{1}{7} = \dfrac{\text{wave height } (x)}{50 \text{ m}}$

$7x = 50 \text{ m}$

$7x = \dfrac{50 \text{ m}}{7}$

$x = 7.14 \text{ m}$

Concepts in Action

28. Antarctica Bottom Water (ABW) is very cold and salty, and it is the densest water of the three. North Atlantic Deep Water (NADW) is also cold and salty, and it is formed through the same process as ABW. It is not as dense as ABW. Mediterranean Water (MW) is warmer, but very salty, as it is formed when high rates of evaporation occur in the Mediterranean Sea. This is why it is more dense than the surface water.

---

19. Compare and contrast a diurnal tidal pattern with a semidiurnal tidal pattern.

20. How does wave refraction result in sediment deposition in some shoreline areas?

21. How are a wave-cut cliff and wave-cut platforms related?

22. What are two types of protective structures used to stop erosion on beaches?

Think Critically

23. Use Models Create a diagram that models the steps involved in the process of upwelling.

24. Apply Concepts What type of tide is experienced when Earth, the moon, and the sun are in the positions shown in the figure below? What is the phase of the moon in the diagram?

25. Predict Predict the effect that the damming of rivers would have on beaches.

26. Relate Cause and Effect Discuss the origin of tides. Explain why the sun's influence on Earth's tides is only about half that of the moon's, even though the sun is much more massive than the moon.

Math Skills

27. Calculate As waves enter shallow water and decrease in speed, wave height increases and eventually a wave will break. The point at which a wave will break can be calculated using the formula for wave steepness: steepness = wave height/wavelength. When the steepness of a wave reaches 1/7, the wave will break. If the wavelength of a wave is 50 m, at what height will the wave break?

Concepts in Action

28. Apply Concepts Re-examine Figure 7. Describe the probable temperature and salinity characteristics for each water mass: Antarctic Bottom Water, North Atlantic Deep Water, and Mediterranean Water.

29. Infer How do you think an increase in Earth's surface temperature would affect the "conveyor belt" model of currents in the ocean?

30. Interpret Graphs The graph below shows a tidal curve for Seattle, Washington. What type of tidal pattern does Seattle experience?

Performance-Based Assessment

Synthesize Investigate the problems associated with shoreline development. Choose a coastal area that is experiencing problems with shoreline erosion. What actions have been taken to try to resolve the problems? Have the actions been effective? Why or why not? What are the advantages and disadvantages to different methods of preventing shoreline erosion? Offer a solution for the area you investigated.

---

29. If Earth's surface temperature warmed, the conveyor belt may stop. The conveyor belt is driven by the formation of deep cold water in the North Atlantic and Antarctica. If temperatures warm, the temperature of ocean surface water would increase, making water less dense. Also, sea ice would melt, decreasing the salinity of ocean water in these areas, and sea ice may not form, both of which would lead to water being less dense. If the surface water in the poles does not sink, the conveyor belt does not run.

30. mixed

Performance-Based Assessment

Student responses will vary but should indicate an understanding of the scope of the problem they investigated.

Standardized Test Prep

Tips for Success

Anticipate the Answer When answering a multiple-choice question, a useful strategy is to cover up the given answers and supply your own answer. Then compare your answer with those listed and select the one that most closely matches your answer.

Practice anticipating the answer in this question.

When waves reach shallow water, they are often bent and may become almost parallel to shore. This process is referred to as—

A oscillation
B refraction
C reflection
D abrasion

(Answer: B)

Choose the letter that best answers the question.

1 Which of the following statements correctly explains a wave in the open ocean?
A Water particles move in a circular path.
B Waves continue to move without change, regardless of depth.
C The waveform moves forward, and the water particles also advance.
D A floating object does not move at all as a wave passes through the water.

2 A barrier built at a right angle to the beach to trap sand that is moving parallel to the shore is known as a—
F seawall   H groin
G headland   J sea stack

3 In the open sea, the movement of water particles in a wave becomes negligible at a depth equal to—
A one-fourth the wavelength
B one-third the wavelength
C one-half the wavelength
D three-fourths the wavelength

4 What happens as a wave approaches the shore?
F wavelength decreases and wave height increases
G wavelength increases and wave height increases
H wave speed decreases and wave height decreases
J wave period decreases and wave height decreases

Use the figure below to answer Question 5.

5 What current in the North Atlantic Gyre is represented by B? Is this current a warm water current or a cold water current?
A Gulf Stream Current; warm
B Gulf Stream Current; cold
C North Equatorial Current; warm
D North Equatorial Current; cold

If You Have Trouble With . . .

Question	1	2	3	4	5
See Lesson	16.2	16.3	16.2	16.2	16.1

The Dynamic Ocean **473**

17 Earth's Atmosphere Planning Guide

Lesson Objectives		Activities
17.1 Atmosphere Characteristics, pp. 476–482 17.1 **Compare and contrast** weather and climate. 17.2 **Explain** why seasonal changes occur.		TE Build Science Skills, p. 479 L2 TE Teacher Demo: Angles and Seasons, p. 481 L2
17.2 Heating the Atmosphere, pp. 483–487 17.3 **Explain** how heat and temperature are related. 17.4 **List** the three major mechanisms of heat transfer. 17.5 **Describe** how the atmosphere is affected by heat transfer mechanisms.		TE Teacher Demo: Heat Conduction, p. 484 L2 TE Build Science Skills, p. 484 L2 TE Build Science Skills, p. 486 L2
17.3 Temperature Controls, pp. 488–493 17.6 **Explain** what a temperature control is. 17.7 **Compare and contrast** the heating of land and water. 17.8 **Explain** why some clouds reflect a portion of sunlight back to space.		TE Teacher Demo: Heating of Land and Water, p. 490 L2 SE Map It: World Isothermal Map, p. 493 L2

Chapter Features and Labs

Try It Modeling the Angle of the Sun, p. 475		LM Determining How Temperature Changes with Altitude L1
How Earth Works Earth's Atmosphere, pp. 494–495		LM Investigating Factors That Control Temperature L2
Exploration Lab Heating Land and Water, pp. 496–497		

Ability Levels		Components			
L1	For students who need additional help	**SE**	Student Edition	**LP**	Lesson Plans
L2	For all students	**TE**	Teacher's Edition	**AA**	Active Art
L3	For students who need to be challenged	**LM**	Laboratory Manual	**PD**	Planet Diary
		CT	Chapter Tests	**GEODe**	Geode CD-ROM
		GRSW	Guided Reading & Study Workbook	**eText**	
		CTB	Computer Test Bank		

Resources	Lesson Assessment
GRSW Lesson 17.1 **LP** Lesson Planning 17.1 **PD** Atmosphere **AA** Seasons	**SE** Lesson 17.1 Assessment, p. 482 **eText** Lesson 17.1

GRSW Lesson 17.2
LP Lesson Planning 17.2
GEODe The Atmosphere:
  Heating the
  Atmosphere
	SE Lesson 17.2
	  Assessment, p. 487
	eText Lesson 17.2

GRSW Lesson 17.3 **LP** Lesson Planning 17.3	**SE** Lesson 17.3 Assessment, p. 493 **eText** Lesson 17.3

Materials for Activities and Labs

Quantities for each group

STUDENT EDITION

Try It, p. 475
dark construction paper, flashlight, pencil

Exploration Lab, pp. 496–497
2 250-mL beakers, dry sand, tap water, ring stand, light source, 2 flat wooden sticks, 2 thermometers, graph paper, 3 colored pencils

TEACHER'S EDITION

Build Science Skills, p. 479
6 identical heavy books, 6 sheets of scrap paper

Teacher Demo, p. 481
narrow-beam flashlight, globe on stand

Teacher Demo, p. 484
red candle, wood, metal, and plastic rods of the same length (at least 15 cm), 500-mL beaker, water, hot plate

Build Science Skills, p. 484
crumpled-up piece of scrap paper

Build Science Skills, p. 486
flashlight or other strong light source

Teacher Demo, p. 490
2 500-mL beakers, water, sand or dry soil, 2 thermometers, sunny window or lamp with 100-W bulb

Assessment

CHAPTER ASSESSMENT
SE Assessment, pp. 499–500
CT Chapter 17 Test
CTB Chapter 17
eText Chapter 17

21st Century **Learning**

Global Awareness: How Does Latitude Affect Climate?
TE p. 498

Common Themes

Weather is the state of the atmosphere at a particular place for a short period of time. Climate is a generalization of the weather conditions at a particular place over a long period of time. The major components of weather and climate are air temperature, humidity, cloudiness, precipitation, air pressure, and wind.

Space and Time The atmosphere is 99 percent nitrogen (N_2) and oxygen (O_2). Though existing only in trace amounts, gases like carbon dioxide (CO_2), water vapor (H_2O), and ozone (O_3) play important roles for weather and climate. Air pressure decreases dramatically with height above ground, though the temperature profile is more complicated. The atmosphere is described as having four layers: troposphere, stratosphere, mesosphere, and thermosphere.

Forces and Motion The atmosphere is heated by solar radiation, which can be scattered, reflected, or absorbed by air molecules and the ground. The greenhouse effect is a result of the atmosphere's absorption of long-wavelength radiation radiated by Earth's ground after it has been heated by the sun.

Matter and Energy Heat is transferred by three mechanisms: conduction, convection, and radiation. All three of these processes operate in the atmosphere. The atmosphere's temperature is affected by differential heating of land and water, altitude, geographic position, cloud cover, and the patterns of ocean currents.

Earth as a System Humans exert a tremendous influence on the atmosphere through changes in ground cover and the emission of different gases.

Michael Wysession
Washington University

EARTH SCIENCE REFRESHER

Water in the Atmosphere

If all of the water in the atmosphere was removed, it would make a liquid layer only 2 mm thick. This is remarkable, given that all of the water of the hydrologic cycle must pass through the atmosphere. The solution to this paradox is that water has a very short residence time in the atmosphere, usually less than a day. As soon as it gets evaporated, it precipitates out. So even though there is not a lot of water in the atmosphere at any given moment, a vast amount of water is continually moving through the atmosphere. About 1100 km³ of water is evaporated every day—about 400,000 km³ every year. This is equal to a cube of water about 75 km on a side.

When this water precipitates out of the atmosphere, it converts its gravitational potential energy into work. The result is that water is the primary mechanism for shaping the surface of the continents. The amount of work done by water returning to the oceans is equal to about 90 Mississippi Rivers flowing

> ### Address **Misconceptions**
>
> *Students often think that when liquid water turns into water vapor, it breaks apart into hydrogen and oxygen. Students also sometimes have trouble distinguishing between water vapor and liquid water in the atmosphere. Actually, water vapor is a gas made up of individual water molecules that are too small to see. Different amounts of water vapor in the air make the air feel dry or humid. Liquid water in the atmosphere is usually in the form of tiny droplets. For a strategy that helps to overcome this misconception, see* **Address Misconceptions** on TE p. 477.

over a 1-km cliff. No wonder mountains get eroded away so quickly (geologically speaking). All of this water must flow through the atmosphere, which contains only 0.001 percent of Earth's surface water at any given moment.

Radiation

The atmosphere responds in many different ways to the different sources of radiation that affect it. Most important, of course, is the radiation from the sun. But also important is the radiation from objects on Earth's surface (rock, plants, water, ice), as well as gases in the atmosphere itself. It is sometimes hard for students to understand that all objects are constantly absorbing and re-radiating electromagnetic radiation, because we can't see most of it. The sun's radiation is peaked in the visible range, which is why the eyes of animals have evolved to see "visible" light. But if you use infrared goggles, you can see the radiation that we emit, even at nighttime. Colder objects emit longer wavelength radiation—the U.S. Navy can track icebergs in the North Atlantic Ocean by using microwave signals.

Trade-Off Between Altitude and Latitude

The drop-off of atmospheric pressure with altitude is dramatic. Even though some air exists many hundreds of kilometers above Earth's surface, half of the air is found below an altitude of 5.6 km. Any student who has ever climbed very tall mountains will understand this. The air becomes so thin that breathing becomes difficult. Also, the risk of sunburn becomes very great—there is much less air to filter out the sun's radiation. Sleeping at high altitudes can also be difficult, as it is not uncommon to wake up repeatedly, gasping for air. Understandably, this atmospheric change also has a tremendous effect on ecosystems. You can be in a region that has a temperate forest climate, but if you climb up a local mountain, you might find plants and animals that are common to tundra climates.

BUILD READING LITERACY
Monitor Your Understanding

Self-Questioning and Self-Adjusting While Reading

Strategy Help students read and understand difficult technical material. Present the three steps in the example below, reviewing the fix-up strategies in Step 2. Before students begin, assign a section in Chapter 17, such as Lesson 17.1, pp. 476–482, for them to read.

Example

1. Self-Question Have students read the paragraphs under each heading, stopping often to ask, "Do I understand this?" "Is this clear?" and "Does this answer my questions about _____?"

2. Identify Trouble Spots and Apply Fix-up Strategies

- **Reread/Adjust Reading Pace** When students do not understand a paragraph, have them reread each sentence slowly.

- **Clarify** When students encounter a difficult paragraph, suggest they state what they do understand, talk through confusing points or steps in a process, or relate new information to concepts and examples that are already familiar to them.

- **Read Ahead/Use Visuals and Captions** Show students how to use visuals and captions to help clarify a process or a concept. Suggest that they can also read ahead to see whether a process or concept is discussed further as part of another concept.

- **Use Outside Resources** Point out, too, that students should seek assistance from friends, teachers, or other resources. Hearing additional examples or more than one person's explanation often aids comprehension.

3. Self-Check After students read, have them check their understanding by summarizing or retelling the main idea of a paragraph or section.

See TE p. 485 for a script on how to use this strategy with students. For additional strategies, see TE pp. 480 and 491.

ASSESS PRIOR KNOWLEDGE

Use the Chapter Pretest below to assess students' prior knowledge. As needed, review these concepts.

Review Science Concepts

Lesson 17.1 Review what a gas is and the concept of a mixture to help students understand Earth's atmosphere and how the mixture of these gases are essential to our existence. Reviewing the concept of pressure will ensure that students understand how air pressure changes with altitude.

Lesson 17.2 Reviewing the nature of electromagnetic radiation and how it travels will help students understand the energy that comes from the sun and how that energy produces our weather.

Lesson 17.3 Review the concept of specific heat capacity.

Review Math Skills

Calculate with Significant Figures
Remind students that when multiplying, the measurement with the smallest number of significant figures determines the number of significant figures in the answer. Direct students to the Math Skills section in the Skills Handbook at the end of the student text.

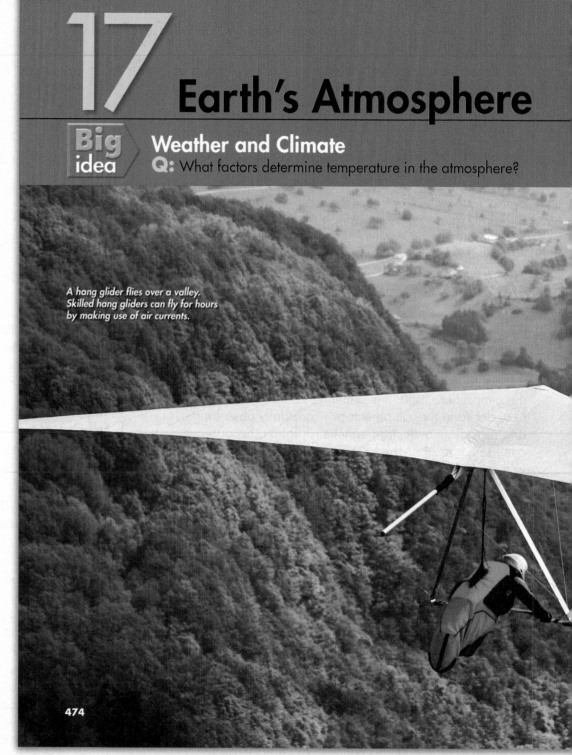

17 Earth's Atmosphere

Big idea

Weather and Climate

Q: What factors determine temperature in the atmosphere?

A hang glider flies over a valley. Skilled hang gliders can fly for hours by making use of air currents.

474

Chapter Pretest

1. What are the main components of the atmosphere? *(b)*
  a. oxygen and carbon dioxide
  b. oxygen and nitrogen
  c. nitrogen and carbon dioxide
  d. oxygen and water vapor

2. True or False: The seasons are caused by changes in Earth's distance from the sun. *(False)*

3. True or False: Heat is energy transferred between objects (matter) that are at different temperatures. *(True)*

4. What are three mechanisms of heat transfer? *(c)*
  a. conduction, emission, and radiation
  b. conduction, convection, and reflection
  c. conduction, convection, and radiation
  d. scattering, convection, and radiation

5. Does land or water heat more rapidly? *(Land heats more rapidly.)*

6. If you move from sea level to a location in the mountains, how will the temperature change? *(It will get colder.)*

MODELING THE ANGLE OF THE SUN

Procedure

1. Place a sheet of dark construction paper on a desk or tabletop. Hold a flashlight approximately 10 cm above the paper. The flashlight should be held at a 90° angle and pointed toward the paper.
2. Darken the room and turn on the flashlight. Have a partner trace the perimeter of the light on the paper.
3. Repeat step 2, but this time, tilt the flashlight so that it is at a 45° angle to the paper. The end of the flashlight should be 10 cm above the paper. Have a partner trace the perimeter of the light on the paper.

Think About It

1. **Observe** Describe the sizes and shapes of the light on the paper for steps 2 and 3.
2. **Model** Suppose the flashlight represents the sun and the paper represents Earth's surface. Which angle gives more energy, per unit area, on the surface of Earth?

475

ENGAGE/EXPLORE

INQUIRY
TRY IT!

MODELING THE ANGLE OF THE SUN `L2`

Purpose In this activity, students compare a model of two angles of the sun in relation to Earth's surface. They conclude which angle concentrates the most energy from the sun.

Skills Observe, Model

Prep Time 5 minutes

Materials sheet of dark construction paper, flashlight, pencil

Class Time 10 minutes

Expected Outcome Students will conclude that when the sun is directly overhead, its energy is more concentrated than when the sun moves to one side.

Think About It

1. When the flashlight is held at a 90° angle to the paper, the bright spot is smaller and circular in shape; when the light is held at a 45° angle, the spot is larger, its brightness is less intense, and the shape is stretched out, or more oblong.

2. More energy per unit area would be concentrated on Earth's surface with the sun directly overhead, than when the sun is located to one side.

LESSON 17.1

❶ FOCUS

Lesson Objectives
17.1 **Compare** and contrast weather and climate.

17.2 **Explain** why seasonal changes occur.

Build Vocabulary [L2]
Word Part Analysis Ask students what the word *sphere* means. Tell them it's a three-dimensional object in which all points are equidistant from a fixed point, like a ball or globe. Tell them that *atmos-* comes from the Greek word meaning "vapor." The word *atmosphere* thus refers to the spherical layer of gases, or "vapors," around Earth. Have students try to figure out what the words on the vocabulary list that end in *sphere* mean, based on their prefixes. If they cannot figure a word out, have them look it up. (*tropo-* means "change"; *strato-* means "layer"; *meso-* means "middle"; *thermo-* means "heat")

Reading Strategy [L2]
Venn Diagram
a. Northern Hemisphere: June 21 or 22; Southern Hemisphere: December 21 or 22. For the summer solstice in the Northern Hemisphere, the sun's rays are directly over the Tropic of Cancer; for the summer solstice in the Southern Hemisphere, the sun's rays are directly over the Tropic of Capricorn.
b. Both summer and winter solstices represent extremes in the solar energy received by Earth. Both result from Earth's 23 1/2 degree axis tilt toward the North Star.
c. Northern Hemisphere: December 21 or 22; Southern Hemisphere: June 21 or 22. For the winter solstice in the Northern Hemisphere, the sun's rays are directly over the Tropic of Capricorn; for the winter solstice in the Southern Hemisphere, the sun's rays are directly over the Tropic of Cancer.

17.1 Atmosphere Characteristics

Key Questions
⬭ **How does weather differ from climate?**

⬭ **Why do seasonal changes occur?**

Vocabulary
- ozone
- troposphere
- stratosphere
- mesosphere
- thermosphere
- summer solstice
- winter solstice
- autumnal equinox
- spring equinox

Reading Strategy
Compare and Contrast Copy the Venn diagram below. As you read, complete the diagram by comparing and contrasting summer and winter solstices.

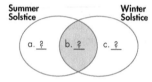

EARTH'S ATMOSPHERE is unique. No other planet in our solar system has an atmosphere with the exact mixture of gases or the moisture conditions and heat needed to sustain life as we know it. The gases that make up Earth's atmosphere and the controls to which they are subject are vital to our existence. In this chapter, you will begin to examine the ocean of air in which we live.

The state of the atmosphere at a given time and place is known as *weather*. The combination of Earth's motions and energy from the sun produces a variety of weather. As shown in **Figure 1,** weather influences our everyday activities. ⬭ **Weather refers to the state of the atmosphere at any given time and place. Weather is constantly changing. Climate, however, is based on observations of weather that have been collected over many years. Climate helps describe all the weather conditions of a place or region.** Climate often is defined as "average weather," but this is not a complete description. Climate also includes variations and extremes in weather. For example, farmers need to know the average rainfall during a growing season. But they also need to know the frequency of extremely wet and extremely dry years. The most important measurable properties of weather and climate are air temperature, humidity, type and amount of precipitation, air pressure, and the speed and direction of the wind.

☑ **Reading Checkpoint** How does weather differ from climate?

FIGURE 1 Weather
Washington, D.C., experienced record-breaking snowfalls in back-to-back storms during the winter of 2011.

Composition of the Atmosphere

The composition of the atmosphere has changed dramatically over Earth's nearly 4.6 billion year history. The atmosphere is thought to have started as gases that were emitted during volcanic eruptions. Evidence indicates that oxygen did not start to accumulate in the atmosphere until about 2.5 billion years ago. The atmosphere continues to exchange material with the oceans and life on Earth's surface.

Major Components Sometimes the term *air* is used as if it were a specific gas, which it is not. Air is a mixture of different gases and particles, each with its own physical properties. The composition of air varies from time to time and from place to place. However, if the water vapor, dust, and other variable components were removed from the atmosphere, its makeup would be very stable worldwide up to an altitude of about 80 kilometers.

Look at **Figure 2.** Two gases—nitrogen and oxygen—make up 99 percent of the volume of clean, dry air. Although these gases are the most common components of air, they don't affect the weather much. The remaining 1 percent of dry air is mostly the inert gas argon (0.93 percent) plus tiny quantities of a number of other gases. Carbon dioxide is present in only small amounts (approximately 0.039 percent), but it is an important component of air. Carbon dioxide is an active absorber of energy given off by Earth. Therefore, it plays a significant role in heating the atmosphere.

Variable Components Important materials that vary in the air from time to time and place to place include water vapor, dust particles, and ozone. These components also can have significant effects on weather and climate.

The amount of water vapor varies from almost none to about 4 percent by volume. Why is such a small quantity so significant? Water vapor is the source of all clouds and precipitation. Like carbon dioxide, water vapor absorbs heat given off by Earth. It also absorbs some solar energy.

Movements of the atmosphere allow a large quantity of solid and liquid particles to be suspended within it. Although visible dust sometimes clouds the sky, these relatively large particles are too heavy to stay in the air for very long. Still, many particles are microscopic and remain suspended for longer periods of time. These particles include sea salts from breaking waves, fine soil blown into the air, smoke and soot from fires, pollen and microorganisms lifted by the wind, dust from meteorites, and ash and dust from volcanic eruptions.

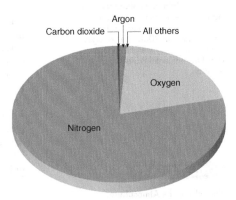

FIGURE 2 Volume of Clean, Dry Air
Nitrogen and oxygen dominate the volume of gases composing dry air.

Earth's Atmosphere **477**

LESSON 17.1

FIGURE 3 Primary Pollutants in the Atmosphere This circle graph shows major primary pollutants for the United States in 2008. Percentages are calculated by weight. Source: U.S. Environmental Protection Agency.

PLANET DIARY

For links on the **Atmosphere**, visit PlanetDiary.com/HSES.

Another important variable component of the atmosphere is ozone. **Ozone** is a form of oxygen that combines three oxygen atoms into each molecule (O_3). Ozone is not the same as the oxygen we breathe, which has two atoms per molecule (O_2). There is very little ozone in the atmosphere, and it is not distributed evenly. It is concentrated in a layer located between 10 and 50 kilometers above Earth's surface. Ozone can also be found near ground level. However, ground-level ozone is an air pollutant.

At 10 to 50 kilometers above Earth's surface, oxygen molecules (O_2) are split into single atoms of oxygen (O) when they absorb ultraviolet (UV) radiation emitted by the sun. Ozone is then produced when a single atom of oxygen (O) and a molecule of oxygen (O_2) collide. Ozone is concentrated in this altitude range because the UV radiation from the sun is sufficient to produce single atoms of oxygen. In addition, there are enough gas molecules to bring about the required collisions.

The ozone layer is crucial to life on Earth. Ozone absorbs potentially harmful UV radiation from the sun. 🔑 **If ozone did not filter most UV radiation and all of the sun's UV rays reached the surface of Earth, our planet would be uninhabitable for many living organisms.**

Human Influence Air pollutants are airborne particles and gases that occur in concentrations large enough to endanger the health of organisms. Primary pollutants, shown in **Figure 3,** are emitted directly from identifiable sources. Emissions from transportation vehicles account for nearly half the primary pollutants by weight.

Secondary pollutants are not emitted directly into air. They form in the atmosphere when reactions take place among primary pollutants and other substances. For example, after the primary pollutant sulfur dioxide enters the atmosphere, it combines with oxygen to produce sulfur trioxide. Then the sulfur trioxide combines with water to create sulfuric acid, an irritating and corrosive substance. Rain that contains high amounts of sulfuric acid is called acid rain. Acid rain can be harmful to forests and aquatic life in lakes and streams.

Reactions triggered by strong sunlight are called *photochemical reactions.* For instance, when nitrogen oxides absorb solar radiation, a chain of complex reactions begins. If certain volatile organic compounds are present, secondary products form that are reactive, irritating, and toxic. This noxious mixture of gases and particles is called *photochemical smog.* Ground-level ozone is also a component of photochemical smog.

☑ **Reading Checkpoint** *What are secondary pollutants?*

Facts and Figures

Significant improvements in air quality have occurred since the U.S. Environmental Protection Agency initiated air-pollution control programs. Between 1970 and 2000, national total emissions of primary pollutants declined by about one third. This occurred during a period when the U.S. population increased by about one third, and vehicle miles traveled rose nearly 130 percent. Despite continued improvements in air quality, standards have not yet been met in large numbers of places. According to the World Health Organization (WHO), exposure to air pollution causes nearly 2 million premature deaths worldwide each year.

FIGURE 4 Atmospheric Pressure vs. Altitude
This graph shows how atmospheric pressure varies with altitude.
Compare *How do changes in air pressure at low altitudes compare with air pressure changes at high altitudes?*

Height and Structure of the Atmosphere

Where does the atmosphere end and outer space begin? There is no sharp boundary. 🔑 **The atmosphere thins as you travel away from Earth until there are too few gas molecules to detect.**

Pressure Changes To understand the vertical extent of the atmosphere, examine **Figure 4,** which shows changes in atmospheric pressure with height. Atmospheric pressure is caused by the weight of the air above. At sea level, the average pressure is slightly more than 1000 millibars, or slightly more than 1 kilogram per square centimeter. One half of the atmosphere by mass lies below an altitude of 5.6 kilometers. Above 100 kilometers, only 0.00003 percent of all the gases making up the atmosphere exist.

Temperature Changes The pictures of snow-capped mountains rising above snow-free valleys shown in **Figure 5** might remind you that Earth's atmosphere becomes colder as you climb higher. But not all layers of the atmosphere show this temperature pattern.

FIGURE 5 Atmospheric Temperature Changes
In Jasper National Park in Alberta, Canada, snowy mountaintops contrast with warmer, snow-free lowlands below.

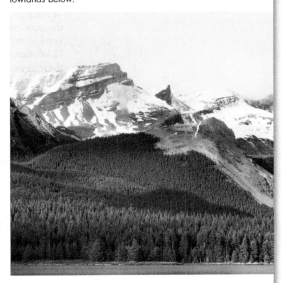

Build Reading Literacy L1

Refer to **p. 186D** in **Chapter 7,** which provides the guidelines for relating text and visuals.

Relate Text and Visuals Have students read the text on p. 480 that describes the features of the layers of the atmosphere. Have students use Figure 6 to describe how temperature changes as you go up through the atmosphere. *(It decreases with altitude in the troposphere; it remains constant in the lower part of the stratosphere and then gradually increases until 50 km above Earth; it decreases with height in the mesosphere; and it increases again in the thermosphere.)*
Visual

Use Visuals L1

Figure 6 Use this diagram to discuss layers of the atmosphere. **Ask:** What is the lowest level of the atmosphere, and what happens there? *(troposphere; essentially all important weather phenomenon occur)* What is the second-lowest level of the atmosphere, and what important gas is found there? *(stratosphere; ozone)* What are the third and upper levels of the atmosphere? *(mesosphere; thermosphere)*
Visual, Logical

FIGURE 6 Thermal Structure of the Atmosphere The change in air temperature within a layer of the atmosphere is different for each of the four layers of the atmosphere. **Interpret** *How do air temperatures change with height in the mesosphere?*

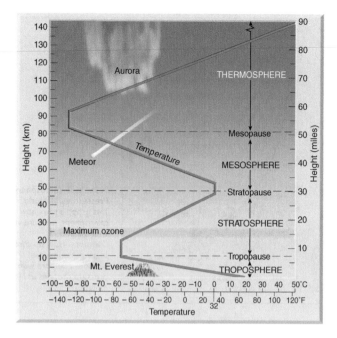

⬤ **The atmosphere can be divided vertically into four layers based on temperature. Figure 6** illustrates these layers. The bottom layer, where temperature decreases with an increase in altitude, is the **troposphere.** It is in this layer that essentially all important weather phenomena occur. The thickness of the troposphere is not the same everywhere. It varies with latitude and the season. On average, the temperature drop continues to a height of about 12 kilometers, where the outer boundary of the troposphere, called the *tropopause,* is located.

Beyond the tropopause is the **stratosphere.** In the stratosphere, the temperature remains constant to a height of about 20 kilometers. It then begins a gradual increase in temperature that continues until the *stratopause,* at a height of nearly 50 kilometers above Earth's surface. Temperatures increase in the stratosphere because the atmosphere's ozone is concentrated here. Recall that ozone absorbs ultraviolet radiation from the sun. As a result, the stratosphere is heated.

In the third layer, the **mesosphere,** temperatures again decrease with height until the *mesopause.* The mesopause is more than 80 kilometers above the surface and the temperatures approach −90°C. The fourth layer extends outward from the mesopause and has no well-defined upper limit. It is the **thermosphere,** a layer that contains only a tiny fraction of the atmosphere's mass. Temperatures increase in the thermosphere because oxygen and nitrogen absorb short-wave, high-energy solar radiation.

Facts and Figures

The rate of temperature decrease in the troposphere is called the environmental lapse rate. Its average value is 6.5°C/km. This figure is known as the normal lapse rate. The environmental lapse rate can be highly variable. To determine the actual environmental lapse rate, as well as to gather information about vertical changes in pressure, wind, and humidity, meteorologists use radiosondes. A radiosonde is an instrument that transmits data by radio as it is carried up by a weather balloon through the atmosphere.

Earth-Sun Relationships

Nearly all of the energy that drives Earth's variable weather and climate comes from the sun. Earth absorbs only a tiny percentage of the energy given off by the sun—less than one two-billionth. This may seem insignificant, but the amount is several hundred thousand times the electrical-generating capacity of the United States.

Solar energy is not distributed evenly over Earth's surface. The amount of energy received varies with latitude, time of day, and season. These variations in solar heating are caused by the motions of Earth relative to the sun and by variations in Earth's land and ocean surface. It is the unequal heating of Earth that creates winds and drives the ocean's currents. These movements transport heat from the tropics toward the poles, thus driving the phenomena we call weather.

Earth's Motions Earth has two principal motions—rotation and revolution. *Rotation* is the spinning of Earth about its axis. The axis is an imaginary line running through the north and south poles. Our planet rotates once every 24 hours, producing the daily cycle of daylight and darkness. *Revolution* is the movement of Earth in its orbit around the sun. Earth travels at nearly 113,000 kilometers per hour in an elliptical orbit about the sun.

Earth's Orientation and Seasons We know that it is colder in the winter than in the summer. But why? Length of day and a gradual change in the angle of the noon sun above the horizon affect the amount of energy Earth receives. **Seasonal changes occur because Earth's position relative to the sun continually changes as it travels along its orbit.** Earth's axis is not perpendicular to the plane of its orbit around the sun. Instead it is tilted 23.5 degrees from the perpendicular, as shown in **Figure 7**. Because the axis remains pointed toward the North Star as Earth moves around the sun, the position of Earth's axis relative to the sun's rays is constantly changing. If the axis were not tilted, we would not have seasonal changes.

Sun's Apparent Path The changing orientation of Earth relative to the sun causes the sun's apparent path to vary with latitude and season. The angle of the noon sun can vary by up to 47 degrees (−23.5 degrees to +23.5 degrees) for many locations during the year. A mid-latitude city like New York, located about 40 degrees north latitude, has a maximum noon sun angle of 73.5 degrees when the sun's vertical rays reach their farthest northward location in June. Six months later, New York has a minimum noon sun angle of 26.5 degrees.

☑ **Reading Checkpoint** *In which direction does Earth's axis point?*

FIGURE 7 **Tilt of Earth's Axis** Earth's axis always points toward the North Star as it revolves around the sun. Rays striking Earth at a low angle (toward the poles) must travel through more of the atmosphere than rays striking at a high angle (around the equator).

Angles and Seasons [L2]

Purpose Students observe how differences in the angle of the sun's rays affect heating of Earth's surface.

Materials narrow-beam flashlight, globe on stand

Procedure Dim the room lights. Position the globe similarly to how Earth is shown in Figure 7. First, shine the light around 23 degrees S so it makes a tight circle. Explain that this represents summer in the Southern Hemisphere. Then move the flashlight and beam up to about 23 degrees N (keeping the flashlight horizontal). Ask students to describe how the area covered by the light changed, and what season this represents in the Northern Hemisphere.

Expected Outcome The light spreads out to cover a greater area, which represents winter in the Northern Hemisphere. Make sure students understand that the light from the flashlight represents a fixed amount of energy. When it spreads out, it may look as if more energy is hitting the surface of the globe. Actually, the same amount of energy is being spread out over a larger area.
Visual, Logical

Answers

Figure 6 *Air temperatures decrease with height in the mesosphere.*

☑ **Reading Checkpoint** *Earth's axis points toward the North Star.*

LESSON 17.1

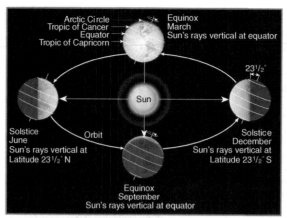

FIGURE 8 Solstices and Equinoxes
The solstices and equinoxes mark the beginning of the four seasons: summer, fall, winter, and spring. The sun's rays are vertical at 23.5 degrees north latitude on June 20 or 21. This accounts for the warm temperatures of the summer season in the Northern Hemisphere.

Solstices and Equinoxes On or around June 20 or 21 each year, Earth's axis is such that the Northern Hemisphere is "leaning" 23.5 degrees toward the sun, as shown on the left side of **Figure 8.** This date is known as the **summer solstice,** or the first "official" day of summer. Six months later, in December, when Earth has moved to the opposite side of its orbit, the Northern Hemisphere leans 23.5 degrees away from the sun. December 21 or 22 is the **winter solstice,** the first day of winter. On days between these extremes, Earth's axis is leaning at amounts less than 23.5 degrees to the rays of the sun.

The equinoxes occur midway between the solstices. September 22 or 23 is the date of the **autumnal equinox** and the start of autumn in the Northern Hemisphere. The **spring equinox** occurs on or around March 19 or 20, and it marks the start of spring for the Northern Hemisphere. On these dates, the vertical rays of the sun strike the equator (0 degrees latitude) because Earth is in a position in its orbit such that the axis is tilted neither toward nor away from the sun.

Length of Daylight The length of daylight compared to darkness also is determined by Earth's position in orbit. All latitudes receive 12 hours of daylight during the vernal (spring) and autumnal equinoxes (equal night). The length of daylight on the summer solstice in the Northern Hemisphere is greater than the length of darkness. The farther you are north of the equator on the summer solstice, the longer the period of daylight. When you reach the Arctic Circle, at 66.5 degrees north latitude, daylight lasts 24 hours.

17.1 Assessment

Review Key Concepts 🔑

1. Compare and contrast weather and climate.

2. Why do seasonal changes occur?

3. How much of Earth's atmosphere is located below about 5.6 kilometers?

4. How do ozone molecules form in the stratosphere?

5. In which layers of the atmosphere does temperature increase with increasing height?

Think Critically

6. **Apply Concepts** Explain what would happen to air temperatures in the troposphere if carbon dioxide were removed from air.

CONNECTING CONCEPTS

7. **Explain** Using Figure 8, explain why the summer and winter solstices and the spring and autumnal equinoxes occur at opposite times in the Northern and Southern hemispheres.

Assessment Answers

1. Climate is a description of aggregate weather conditions for an area, and weather is the state of the atmosphere at a given moment in time.
2. Seasonal changes occur because Earth's axis is tilted. Earth's orientation to the sun continually changes as it travels along its orbit.
3. About 50 percent of Earth's atmosphere is below about 5.6 km.

4. Ozone forms when a single atom of oxygen (O) collides with a diatomic molecule of oxygen (O_2).
5. Temperature increases with height in the stratosphere and thermosphere.
6. Because carbon dioxide absorbs heat from Earth efficiently, air temperatures would decrease if it were removed from the troposphere.

7. The combination of Earth's tilt and its revolution around the sun cause the solstices and equinoxes to be opposite in the Northern Hemisphere and Southern Hemisphere. In the Northern Hemisphere, the maximum energy from the sun is received on the summer solstice, June 21 or 22; in the Southern Hemisphere, the maximum energy is received on the winter solstice, December 21 or 22.

17.2 Heating the Atmosphere

THE CONCEPTS of heat and temperature often are confused. The phrase "in the heat of the day" is one common expression in which the word "heat" is misused to describe the concept of temperature. **Heat is the energy transferred from one object to another because of a difference in their temperatures.** All matter is composed of atoms or molecules that possess *kinetic energy*, or the energy of motion. **Temperature** is a measure of the average kinetic energy of the individual atoms or molecules in a substance. When energy is transferred to the gas atoms and molecules in air, those particles move faster and air temperature rises. When air transfers energy to a cooler object, its particles move more slowly, and air temperature drops.

Energy Transfer as Heat

Three mechanisms of energy transfer as heat are conduction, convection, and radiation. All three processes, illustrated in **Figure 9,** happen simultaneously in the atmosphere. These mechanisms operate to transfer energy between Earth's surface (both land and water) and the atmosphere.

Conduction Anyone who has touched a metal spoon that was left in a hot pan has experienced the result of heat conducted through the spoon. **Conduction** is the transfer of heat through matter by molecular activity. The energy of molecules is transferred by collisions from one molecule to another. Heat flows from the higher temperature matter to the lower temperature matter.

FIGURE 9 Energy Transfer as Heat A pot of water on the campfire illustrates the three mechanisms of heat transfer.

Convection
Conduction
Radiation

Earth's Atmosphere **483**

Key Questions

How are heat and temperature related?

What are the three major mechanisms of heat transfer?

How is the atmosphere affected by each of the heat transfer mechanisms?

Vocabulary

- heat • temperature
- conduction • convection
- radiation • reflection
- scattering
- greenhouse effect

Reading Strategy

Use Prior Knowledge Before you read, copy the table below and write your definition for each vocabulary term. After you read, write the scientific definition of each term and compare it with your original definition.

Term	Your Definition	Scientific Definition
Heat	a. ?	b. ?
Temperature	c. ?	d. ?

HEAT CONDUCTION L2

Purpose Students observe differences in the ability of different substances to conduct heat.

Materials red candle, wood, metal, and plastic rods of the same length (at least 15 cm), 500-mL beaker, water, hot plate

Procedure Before doing the demo, use the candle to drip spots of wax at about 1-cm intervals onto all of the rods. Then, place the rods in about 1 cm of water in the beaker. Put the beaker on the hot plate and turn it on. Ask students to predict what they think will happen. Have them observe what actually happens. Then ask them to explain their observations.

Expected Outcome The wax dots will melt in order from the bottom up. The dots on the metal rod will melt the fastest (since metal conducts heat the best), followed by the plastic and then the wood.
Visual, Logical

Build Science Skills L2

Student Activity: Use Models Have students work in pairs to develop ways to model the three methods of heat transfer. Give each pair a crumpled-up piece of scrap paper and tell them it represents heat. Each student represents a molecule. Tell students to use physical movements to model each method of transfer. For example, to demonstrate conduction, students can pass the ball directly to the partner; for convection, students can carry the ball to the partner; and for radiation, students can throw the ball to the partner.
Kinesthetic, Logical

The ability of substances to conduct heat varies greatly. Metals are good conductors, as those of us who have touched hot metal have quickly learned. Air, however, is a very poor conductor of heat. Because air is a poor conductor, conduction is important only between Earth's surface and the air directly in contact with the surface. For the atmosphere as a whole, conduction is the least important mechanism of heat transfer.

Convection Much of the heat transfer that occurs in the atmosphere is carried on by convection. **Convection** is the transfer of heat by mass movement or circulation within a substance. It takes place in fluids, such as the ocean and air, where the atoms and molecules are free to move about. Convection also takes place in solids, such as Earth's mantle, that behave like fluids over long periods.

The pan of water in Figure 9 shows circulation by convection. Radiation from the fire warms the bottom of the pan, which conducts heat to the water near the bottom of the container. As the water is heated, it expands and becomes less dense than the water above. The warmer, less dense water rises above the cooler water. At the same time, cooler, denser water near the top of the pan sinks to the bottom, where it becomes heated. As long as the water is heated unequally, it will continue to circulate. In much the same way, most of the heat acquired by radiation and conduction in the lowest layer of the atmosphere is transferred by convective flow.

☑ **Reading Checkpoint** *What is convection?*

Electromagnetic Waves The sun is the ultimate source of energy that causes our weather. Visible light, radiant heat energy, and ultraviolet rays from the sun are some of the forms of energy in the electromagnetic (EM) spectrum, shown in **Figure 10.** All of the radiation in this spectrum consists of electromagnetic waves. Electromagnetic waves consist of changing electric and magnetic fields. The source of all electromagnetic waves is vibrating charges. Although different types of EM waves have different energies, they all travel through the vacuum of space at 300,000 kilometers per second. They travel only slightly slower through our atmosphere.

**FIGURE 10
Electromagnetic Spectrum**
Electromagnetic energy is classified according to wavelength in the electromagnetic spectrum.

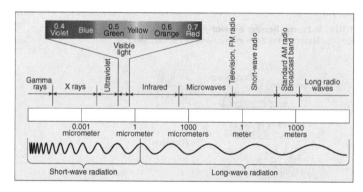

Differentiated Instruction

GIFTED Have students develop a computer graphics presentation that compares the different mechanisms of heat transfer. The presentations should include both diagrams and photographs.

FIGURE 11 Visible Light Visible light consists of an array of colors commonly called the colors of the rainbow.

Imagine what happens when you toss a pebble into a pond. Ripples are made and move away from the location where the pebble hit the water's surface. Much like these ripples, electromagnetic waves move out from their source and come in various sizes. Electromagnetic waves are classified by their wavelength, or the distance from one crest to the next. Radio waves have the longest wavelengths, ranging to tens of kilometers. Gamma waves are the shortest, and are less than a billionth of a centimeter long.

Visible light is the only portion of the electromagnetic spectrum you can see. White light is really a mixture of colors, as shown in the rainbow in **Figure 11.** Each color corresponds to a specific wavelength. By using a prism, white light can be divided into the colors of the rainbow, from violet with the shortest wavelength—0.4 micrometer—to red with the longest wavelength—0.7 micrometer (1 micrometer is 0.0001 centimeter).

Radiation The third mechanism of heat transfer is radiation, as shown in Figure 9. **Radiation** travels out in all directions from its source. Unlike conduction and convection, which need material to travel through, the transfer of heat energy by radiation can occur through the vacuum of space. Solar energy reaches Earth by radiation.

To understand how the atmosphere is heated, it is useful to think about four laws governing radiation.

1. **All objects, at any temperature, emit radiant energy.** Not only hot objects like the sun but also Earth—including its polar ice caps—continually emit radiant energy.
2. **Hotter objects radiate more total energy per unit area than colder objects do.**
3. **The hottest radiating bodies produce the shortest wavelengths of maximum radiation.** For example, the sun, with a surface temperature of nearly 6000°C, radiates maximum energy at 0.5 micrometers, which is in the visible range. The maximum radiation for Earth occurs at a wavelength of 10 micrometers, well within the infrared range.
4. **Objects that are good absorbers of radiation are good emitters as well.** Gases are selective absorbers and radiators. The atmosphere does not absorb certain wavelengths of radiation, but it is a good absorber of other wavelengths.

Earth's Atmosphere **485**

Use Visuals L1

Figure 12 Use the diagram to discuss what happens to solar radiation. **Ask:** What percentage of radiation is reflected from clouds? *(20 percent)* What percentage of radiation is lost to space by reflection and scattering? *(30 percent)* What types of radiation are absorbed by land and sea? *(direct and diffused radiation)*
Visual

Build Science Skills L2

Student Activity: Apply Concepts Dim the room lights and shine a beam of light through the air from a large flashlight or other strong light source. Have students look at the beam and describe what they see. *(tiny particles)* Ask students what phenomenon allows them to see these particles. *(scattering)*
Logical

FIGURE 12 Solar Radiation
This diagram shows what happens, on average, to incoming solar radiation by percentage.

FIGURE 13
Reflection vs. Scattering
A Reflected light bounces back with the same intensity.

B Scattering produces more light rays with a weaker intensity.

What Happens to Solar Radiation?

When radiation strikes an object, there usually are three different results.

1. **Some energy is absorbed by the object.** When radiant energy is absorbed, it is converted to heat and causes a temperature increase.
2. **Substances such as water and air are transparent to certain wavelengths of radiation.** These substances transmit the radiant energy. Radiation that is transmitted does not contribute energy to the object.
3. **Some radiation may bounce off the object without being absorbed or transmitted.** **Figure 12** shows what happens to incoming solar radiation, averaged for the entire globe.

Reflection and Scattering **Reflection** occurs when an electromagnetic wave bounces off an object. The reflected radiation has the same intensity as the incident radiation. In contrast, **scattering** produces a larger number of weaker rays that travel in different directions, as shown in **Figure 13.** Scattering disperses waves both forward and backward. However, more energy is dispersed in the forward direction. About 30 percent of the solar energy reaching the outer atmosphere is reflected back to space. This 30 percent includes the amount of energy sent skyward by scattering. This energy is lost and does not heat Earth's atmosphere.

Small dust particles and gas molecules in the atmosphere scatter some incoming radiation in all directions. This explains how light reaches into the area beneath a shade tree, and how a room is lit in the absence of direct sunlight. Scattering also accounts for the brightness and even the blue color of the daytime sky. About half of the solar radiation that is absorbed at Earth's surface arrives as scattered radiation.

Facts and Figures

The fraction of the total radiation that is reflected by a surface is called its albedo. The albedo for Earth as a whole (the planetary albedo) is 30 percent. The albedo varies considerably from place to place and time to time in the same location. Albedo can vary with amount of cloud cover and particles in the air, as well as the nature of the surface and the angle of the sun's rays. A lower sun angle means that the rays pass through more of the atmosphere, and more solar radiation is lost. Albedo can be as low as 5 percent for a forest and as high as 90 percent for fresh snow. Students will read about cloud cover and albedo on page 492.

Absorption About 50 percent of the solar energy that strikes the top of the atmosphere reaches Earth's surface and is absorbed, as shown in Figure 12. Most of this energy is then reradiated skyward.

The atmosphere efficiently absorbs the longer wavelengths emitted by Earth. Water vapor and carbon dioxide are the major absorbing gases. When a gas molecule absorbs these waves, this energy is transformed into molecular motion that can be detected as a rise in temperature. Gases in the atmosphere eventually radiate some of this energy away. Some energy travels skyward, where it may be reabsorbed by other gas molecules. The rest travels earthward and is again absorbed. In this way, Earth's surface is continually supplied with heat from the atmosphere as well as from the sun.

Without these absorbing gases in our atmosphere, Earth would not be a suitable habitat for most types of living things on Earth today. This phenomenon has been termed the **greenhouse effect** because it was once thought that greenhouses were heated in a similar manner. (A more important factor in keeping a greenhouse warm is that the greenhouse itself prevents the mixing of air inside with cooler air outside.)

There is an overall balance of energy transfer into and out of Earth's atmosphere. Over time, incoming solar radiation is absorbed, reflected, or reradiated. As a result, the atmosphere's average temperature tends to remain constant from year to year. But the atmosphere's average temperature can and does change. It changes if there are factors that disturb its energy balance.

Photosynthesis Some incoming solar radiation is not absorbed or reradiated. Instead, plants and some other living things use the energy from this radiation in photosynthesis. Thus solar energy is the main energy source for virtually all life on Earth.

17.2 Assessment

Review Key Concepts

1. How are heat and temperature related?

2. List and describe the three major mechanisms of heat transfer in the atmosphere.

3. How is the atmosphere affected by
a. convection?
b. conduction?
c. radiation?

4. Describe what happens to solar radiation when it strikes an object.

5. Contrast reflection and scattering.

Think Critically

6. Apply Concepts Dark objects tend to absorb more radiation than light-colored objects. Explain whether dark objects or light objects on Earth's surface would be better radiators of heat.

WRITING IN SCIENCE

7. Describe Write a paragraph that describes the four laws governing radiation. Use examples wherever possible.

BIGIDEA WEATHER AND CLIMATE

8. Relate Cause and Effect Explain how radiation from the sun affects Earth's climate.

Earth's Atmosphere **487**

Assessment Answers

1. Both arise from thermal vibrations in atoms and molecules. Heat is energy transferred between objects at different temperatures. Temperature is the average kinetic energy of particles in the substance.

2. Conduction: heat transfer through matter by particle activity. Convection: heat transfer by mass movement within a substance. Radiation: energy transfer by electromagnetic waves.

3. a. Much of the heat transfer in the atmosphere is carried by convection. Most of the heat acquired by radiation and conduction in the lowest layer of the atmosphere is transferred by convective flow. **b.** Conduction is most important between Earth's surface and the air directly in contact with the surface. **c.** Solar energy reaches Earth by radiation. The radiation can be absorbed, transmitted, or reflected. The radiant energy that is absorbed is converted to heat and causes an increase in temperature.

4. It can be absorbed, transmitted, reflected, or scattered.

5. Reflection: radiation bouncing off an object at the same angle and intensity as the incident radiation. Scattering: radiation bouncing off in all directions with intensities that are weaker than the incident radiation.

6. Because good absorbers also tend to be good radiators of heat, dark-colored objects are expected to be better radiators than light-colored objects.

7. Student paragraphs should clearly state the fundamental principles of radiation, and they should include examples to reinforce the principles.

8. Some of the sun's radiation is absorbed by land and sea or by water vapor and carbon dioxide in the atmosphere. This absorbed radiation affects Earth's climate by supplying heat to Earth's surface.

Earth's Atmosphere **487**

1 FOCUS

Lesson Objectives
17.6 **Explain** what a temperature control is.
17.7 **Compare and contrast** the heating of land and water.
17.8 **Explain** why some clouds reflect a portion of sunlight back to space.

Build Vocabulary L2
LINCS Have students use the LINCS strategy to learn and review the terms *albedo, windward, leeward,* and *isotherm.* In LINCS exercises, students **L**ist what they know about each term, **I**magine a picture that describes the word, **N**ote a "sound-alike" word, **C**onnect the terms to the sound-alike word by making up a short story, and then perform a brief **S**elf-test.

Reading Strategy L2
a. slight temperature variation
b. more extreme temperature variation

2 INSTRUCT

Build Science Skills L2
Interpret Photographs Have students look at Figure 14 carefully. **Ask:** What is inside this shelter? *(an electrical thermometer called a thermistor)* Why does the thermistor need to be protected by a shelter? *(Direct sunlight would spoil the temperature readings, and it needs to be protected from breaking.)* Why does the shelter need to have vents for air flow? *(The air inside the shelter cannot get hotter than the outside air.)*
Logical, Visual

17.3 Temperature Controls

Key Questions
🔑 **What is a temperature control?**

🔑 **How do the heating of land and water differ?**

🔑 **Why do some clouds reflect a portion of sunlight back to space?**

Vocabulary
• albedo • isotherm

Reading Strategy
Preview Copy the table below. Before you read, use Figure 15 to describe the temperature variations for Vancouver and Winnipeg.

Temperature Variations		
Vancouver	a.	?
Winnipeg	b.	?

TEMPERATURE IS ONE of the basic elements of weather and climate. When someone asks what it is like outside, air temperature is often the first element we mention. At a weather station, the temperature is read on a regular basis from instruments mounted in an instrument shelter similar to the one in **Figure 14.** The shelter protects the instruments from direct sunlight and allows a free flow of air.

Why Temperatures Vary
A temperature control is any factor that causes temperature to vary from place to place and from time to time. Earlier in this chapter you examined the most important cause for temperature variations—differences in the receipt of solar radiation. Because variations in the angle of the sun's rays and length of daylight depend on latitude, they are responsible for warmer temperatures in the tropics and colder temperatures toward the poles. Seasonal temperature changes happen as the sun's vertical rays move toward and away from a particular latitude during the year. 🔑 **Factors other than latitude that exert a strong influence on temperature include differences in the heating of land and water, altitude, geographic position, cloud cover, and ocean currents.**

☑ **Reading Checkpoint** *List three factors that influence temperature.*

FIGURE 14
Measuring Temperature
This instrument shelter contains an electrical thermometer called a thermistor.

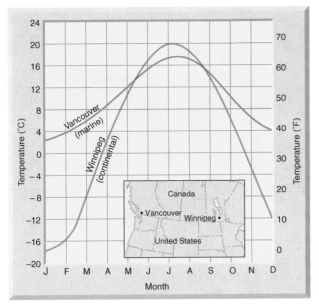

FIGURE 15 **Mean Monthly Temperatures for Vancouver and Winnipeg** Winnipeg illustrates the greater extremes associated with an interior location. **Calculate** *How much lower is Winnipeg's January mean temperature than Vancouver's? Calculate the temperature to the nearest degree.*

Land and Water The heating of Earth's surface controls the temperature of the air above it. To understand variations in air temperature, we consider the characteristics of the surface. Different land surfaces absorb varying amounts of incoming solar energy. The largest contrast, however, is between land and water. ▭ **Land heats more rapidly and to higher temperatures than water. Land also cools more rapidly and to lower temperatures than water.** Temperature variations, therefore, are considerably greater over land than over water.

Monthly temperature data for two cities, shown in **Figure 15,** show the influence of a large body of water. Vancouver, British Columbia, is located along the Pacific coast and receives winds off the Pacific Ocean. Winnipeg, Manitoba, is far from the influence of water. Both cities are at about the same latitude, so they experience similar lengths of daylight and angles of the sun's rays. Winnipeg, however, has much greater temperature extremes than Vancouver does. Vancouver's moderate year-round climate is due to its location by the Pacific Ocean.

Temperature variations in the Northern and Southern hemispheres are compared in **Table 1.** Water accounts for 61 percent of the Northern Hemisphere, and land accounts for the remaining 39 percent. In the Southern Hemisphere, 81 percent of the surface is water and only 19 percent of the surface is land. Because the Southern Hemisphere has a greater percentage of surface water, it shows smaller annual temperature variations than the Northern Hemisphere.

Table 1 Variation in Annual Mean Temperature Range with Latitude

Latitude	Northern Hemisphere (°C)	Southern Hemisphere (°C)
0	0	0
15	3	4
30	13	7
45	23	6
60	30	11
75	32	26
90	40	31

Earth's Atmosphere **489**

HEATING OF LAND AND WATER `L2`

Purpose Students observe how land and water heat up at different rates.

Materials 2 500-mL beakers, water, sand or dry soil, 2 thermometers, sunny window or lamp with 100-W bulb

Procedure Before the demo, half-fill one beaker with water and the other with sand or dry soil. Put a thermometer into each (well below the surface of the soil), and set them aside until they both reach room temperature. Show students the beakers and that both are at the same temperature. Place them in a sunny spot or under a hot lamp. As students what they think will happen. Check the thermometers regularly until you see a noticeable difference. Ask students to explain the results.

Expected Outcome The temperature of the soil will increase much more quickly than the temperature of the water.

Visual, Logical

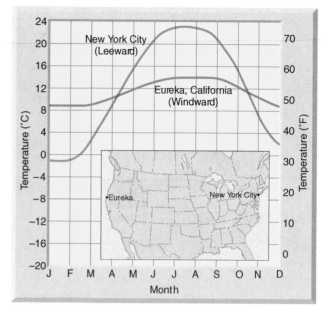

FIGURE 16 Mean Monthly Temperatures for Eureka and New York City Eureka is strongly influenced by prevailing ocean winds, and New York City is not.

Geographic Position The geographic setting can greatly influence local temperatures. A coastal location where prevailing winds blow from the ocean onto the shore is called a windward coast. A windward coast experiences considerably different temperatures than does a coastal location where the prevailing winds blow from the land toward the ocean (a leeward coast). A windward coast will experience the full moderating influence of the ocean—cool summers and mild winters, compared to an inland station at the same latitude. In contrast, a leeward coast will have a more continental temperature pattern because winds do not carry the ocean's influence onshore. Eureka, California, and New York City illustrate this effect, as shown in **Figure 16.** The annual temperature range in New York City is 19°C greater than Eureka's range.

Seattle and Spokane, both in the state of Washington, illustrate another aspect of geographic position—mountains that act as barriers. Although Spokane is only about 360 kilometers east of Seattle, the towering Cascade Range separates the cities. As a result, Seattle's temperatures show a marine influence, but Spokane's are more typically continental, as shown in **Figure 17.** Spokane is 7°C cooler than Seattle in January and 4°C warmer than Seattle in July. The annual range in Spokane is 11°C greater than in Seattle. The Cascade Range cuts Spokane off from the moderating influence of the Pacific Ocean.

Altitude Two cities in Ecuador, Quito and Guayaquil, demonstrate the influence of altitude on mean temperature. Both cities are near the equator and relatively close to one another, as shown in **Figure 18.**

490 Chapter 17 • Lesson 3

Facts and Figures

There are many reasons the temperature of land and water rises at different rates. First, water has a much higher specific heat than land, so it heats up more slowly. Second, land surfaces are opaque, so energy is absorbed only at the surface. Water absorbs energy to a depth of several meters. Third, when surface water is heated, it often mixes with water below it, distributing the heat through a larger mass of water. Fourth, evaporation, which is a cooling process, is greater from water surfaces than from land.

FIGURE 17 **Mean Monthly Temperatures for Seattle and Spokane** The Cascade Mountains cut off Spokane from the moderating influence of the Pacific Ocean. **Interpret Graphs** *How does this affect Spokane's annual temperature range?*

The annual mean temperature at Guayaquil is 25°C, compared to Quito's mean of 13°C. If you note these cities' elevations, you can understand the temperature difference. Guayaquil is only 12 meters above sea level, whereas Quito is high in the Andes Mountains at 2800 meters.

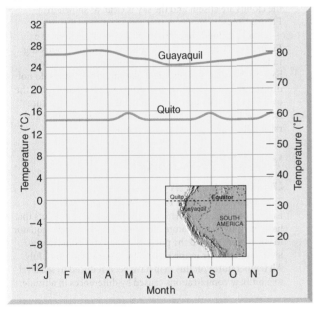

FIGURE 18 **Mean Monthly Temperatures for Quito and Guayaquil** Quito's altitude is much higher than Guayaquil's, causing Quito to experience cooler temperatures than Guayaquil.

Build Reading Literacy

Refer to **p. 246D** in **Chapter 9,** which provides the guidelines for relating cause and effect.

Relate Cause and Effect Have students read the passage Geographic Position on p. 490. Explain that the temperature of water changes less throughout the year than the temperature of land. The more constant temperature of water causes the air passing over water to also have less temperature change throughout the year. If the air blows from water onto land, then the effect will be to moderate the climate of the land. **Ask:** What cause and effect relationship explains climates where the wind blows from land to ocean? *(The temperature of the air over land changes much more throughout the year than the temperature of air over water. The effect is that areas affected by air blowing off land have climates with a wider range of temperatures.)*
Logical

Build Science Skills L2

Infer Tell students that San Francisco is on the Pacific coast. Denver is at a similar latitude, but it is high in the Rocky Mountains and far inland. Ask students to infer what differences in climate they would expect to see between these two cities and to explain why. *(San Francisco will have a much more moderate climate than Denver because San Francisco is on a windward coast, and Denver is inland. Denver experiences colder winters due to its high elevation. But it also experiences warmer summers because it does not receive the cooling winds from the oceans that San Francisco receives.)*
Logical

Answers

Figure 17 *Spokane's annual temperature range is greater because it is cut off from the influence of the Pacific Ocean.*

FIGURE 19 Cloud Cover

A During daylight hours, clouds reflect solar radiation back to space.

B At night, clouds absorb radiation from the land and reradiate some of it back to Earth, increasing nighttime temperatures.

Use Visuals L1

Figure 19 Use the diagrams to help students understand the effect cloud cover has on temperature. **Ask:** What is happening to the solar radiation in Figure A? *(The clouds are reflecting the solar energy back into space.)* How do the clouds during the day affect the temperature? *(Because they reflect the solar radiation, less radiation reaches the surface of Earth, so the temperatures are lower.)* What is happening in Figure B? *(The clouds are absorbing radiation from land and reradiating some of it back to land.)* How do the clouds affect the temperature? *(The clouds increase the temperature because they are reradiating the radiation from the land, increasing the temperature.)* Why do clouds during the day and night affect temperature differently? *(They block the radiation in different ways. During the day, they block the sun's radiation, and during the night they block the radiation from land.)*
Visual, Logical

Use Community Resources L2

Invite a climatologist from a local college to visit the classroom and discuss factors that affect climate and worldwide temperature patterns. Ask students to prepare questions for the climatologist in advance. Remind them to use *Who, What, Where, When, Why,* and *How* questions.
Interpersonal

Cloud Cover and Albedo **Albedo** is the fraction of total radiation that is reflected by any surface. **Many clouds have a high albedo, and therefore reflect a significant portion of the sunlight that strikes them back to space.** The extent of cloud cover is a factor that influences temperatures in the lower atmosphere. Since clouds reduce the amount of incoming solar radiation, the maximum temperatures on a cloud-covered day will be lower than on a day when the clouds are absent and the sky is clear, as shown in **Figure 19A.**

At night, clouds have the opposite effect, as shown in **Figure 19B.** Clouds act as a blanket by absorbing outgoing radiation emitted by Earth and reradiating a portion of it back to the surface. Thus, nighttime air temperatures do not drop as low on a cloudy night compared to a clear night. The overall effect of cloud cover reduces the daily temperature range by lowering the daytime maximum temperature and raising the nighttime minimum temperature.

World Distribution of Temperature

Take a moment to study **Figure 20,** which is a world isothermal map. **Isotherms** are lines that connect points that have the same temperature. From hot colors near the equator to cool colors toward the poles, this map shows mean sea-level temperatures in the seasonally extreme month of July. All temperatures on this map have been reduced to sea level to eliminate complications caused by differences in altitude.

Facts and Figures

The highest temperature ever recorded at Earth's surface is nearly 59°C. It was recorded on September 13, 1922, at Azizia, Libya, in North Africa's Sahara Desert. Not surprisingly, the lowest temperature was measured in Antarctica. It was –89°C. This temperature was recorded at the Russian Vostok Station on August 24, 1960. The greatest annual range of temperatures is in Siberia (eastern Russia). Temperatures in Verkhoyansk, Siberia have gone from –68°C to 37°C, a span of 105°C.

FIGURE 20 World Isothermal Map

On this map, you can study global temperature patterns and the effects of the controlling factors of temperature, especially latitude, distribution of land and water, and ocean currents. The isotherms generally trend east and west and show a decrease in temperatures from the tropics toward the poles. This map emphasizes the importance of latitude as a control on incoming solar radiation, which in turn heats Earth's surface and the atmosphere above it.

MAP IT!
ACTIVITY

The map in Figure 20 shows the distribution of world mean sea-level temperatures averaged for the month of July.

Interpret Maps Estimate the latitude range for temperatures between 20 and 25 degrees Celsius in the Northern Hemisphere. Approximate to the nearest 5 degrees latitude for each extreme.

Predict Do you expect the color of the temperature band to change near the equator for the month of January? Explain your prediction.

17.3 Assessment

Review Key Concepts

1. What is a temperature control?
2. How do the heating of land and water differ?
3. Why do many clouds reflect a significant amount of sunlight back to space?
4. Why do some coastal cities experience a moderation of temperature from water, while others do not?
5. List four specific controls of atmospheric temperature.

Think Critically

6. **Infer** Look back at the graph in Figure 18. Why do the temperatures of these two cities stay within a limited range throughout the year?

MATH PRACTICE

7. **Calculate** Using the data in Table 1, determine the latitude that shows the greatest variation in annual mean temperature between the Northern and Southern Hemispheres.

Earth's Atmosphere **493**

3 ASSESS

Evaluate Understanding L2

Ask students to describe and explain three factors that have a strong influence on temperature.

Reteach L1

Use Figure 19 to review how clouds affect surface temperatures during the day and night.

Answers

MAP IT! The latitude range for temperatures between 0 and 25 degrees Celsius in the Northern Hemisphere is approximately 10°N latitude to 55°N latitude.

The color of the temperature band does not change. Regions near the equator receive about the same amount of solar radiation all year long.

Assessment Answers

1. A temperature control is any factor that causes temperature to vary from place to place and from time to time.
2. Land heats and cools more rapidly and to greater temperature extremes than water does.
3. Clouds reflect a significant amount of sunlight back to space because of their high albedos.

4. Some coastal cities are influenced more strongly from prevailing ocean winds than others are.
5. Accept any of the following: latitude, altitude, geographic position, continental versus marine positions, ocean currents.

6. because they are both located near the equator and receive about the same amount of solar radiation all year long
7. 60°

How Earth Works

How Earth Works

Earth's Atmosphere

The outermost part of Earth is the atmosphere, a multilayered mixture of gases (such as nitrogen, oxygen, and water vapor) and tiny solid particles. The atmosphere extends at least 1000 km (600 miles) above the solid surface of Earth, but about half of its mass is in the lowest 3.5 miles (5.6 km). The atmosphere's gases support life on Earth. They also protect Earth from the sun's harmful rays.

The layer of the atmosphere closest to land is the **troposphere,** which contains the air that we breathe. Here, temperature and humidity change rapidly, and the air is turbulent, creating weather patterns.

1 FOCUS

Objectives
In this feature, students will be able to
- name the layers of Earth's atmosphere and the gases it contains.
- describe how the atmosphere supports human and plant life on Earth.
- explain how the atmosphere was formed and how the hole in the ozone layer formed.

Build Vocabulary   L2
Understand Terms Have students explain how the stratosphere differs from the troposphere. Then have them use the terms to write sentences.

2 INSTRUCT

Bellringer   L1

Ask students what images come to mind when they think of Earth's atmosphere.
Ask: Do you usually think about the atmosphere as just containing the bottom layer where weather occurs? *(Answers will vary.)* Do you know what that layer is called? *(troposphere)* Do you know how many other layers there are? *(three other layers)*
Logical

Build Science Skills   L2

Use a Chart Discuss the role of oxygen and carbon dioxide in Earth's atmosphere. Then have volunteers draw a cause-and-effect chart on the board to show the cycle of how gases are created and used by humans and plants.
Visual

▲ OXYGEN FROM PHOTOSYNTHESIS
Oxygen is a relative newcomer in Earth's atmosphere. It has come from plants and phytoplankton that, during **photosynthesis,** use carbon dioxide to make their food, while giving out oxygen. The earliest photosynthesizing organisms, which probably looked like these phytoplankton, evolved about 3.5 billion years ago.

THE ATMOSPHERE FROM SPACE ▶
Viewed from space, Earth looks totally unlike other planets of our solar system. It is partly shrouded in white clouds, which swirl in patterns, sometimes releasing precipitation. **Clouds** are masses of tiny particles of water and dust floating in the atmosphere. A very low cloud is called fog.

OXYGEN CYCLE ▶
A vast store of oxygen exists in oceans, rocks, and the atmosphere. Oxygen released by phytoplankton and plant photosynthesis balances oxygen used by people and animals.

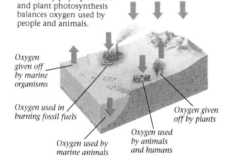

A large amount of oxygen is stored in the atmosphere

Oxygen given off by marine organisms

Oxygen used in burning fossil fuels

Oxygen used by marine animals

Oxygen used by animals and humans

Oxygen given off by plants

FERTILE LAND ▶
The atmosphere helps life to flourish on Earth. It offers protection from harmful radiation and provides nourishment for both plants and animals. Winds in the troposphere moderate daily and seasonal temperatures by distributing heat around the world.

494 Chapter 17

Facts and Figures

Although the entire troposphere contains oxygen, the amount of oxygen varies at different altitudes. The summit of Mount Everest is the highest point on Earth, measuring about 8.8 km high. At that level, oxygen levels are extremely low, which makes climbing Everest very dangerous. If climbers do not get enough oxygen, they become dizzy and disoriented. Today, climbing teams carry tanks of oxygen with them in their efforts to reach the summit.

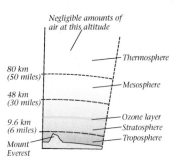

▲ LAYERS OF ATMOSPHERE
Earth's atmosphere has several layers. The heights of these layers vary with season and latitude. Weather is confined to the troposphere, and almost all clouds are within this level. In the stratosphere lies the ozone layer that protects life on Earth from harmful UV radiation.

▲ COMPOSITION OF ATMOSPHERE
Earth's atmosphere is largely composed of nitrogen and oxygen. Water vapor, argon, and carbon dioxide, as well as many other gases, are also present, though at much lower concentrations. Note that the amount of water vapor in Earth's atmosphere varies significantly with location. Above deserts, there is almost no water vapor present, while above tropical regions, the atmosphere can be nearly 4 percent water vapor. An average value of 2 percent is shown here.

▲ OZONE HOLE
The **ozone layer** is a region of ozone gas in the stratosphere that absorbs the sun's harmful ultraviolet rays. The ozone layer is vital for the survival of life on Earth. The thickness of the ozone layer varies naturally, affected by processes such as volcanic eruptions. In the 1980s, a hole in the ozone layer over Antarctica was discovered. Scientists hypothesized that the hole was caused by gases called chlorofluorocarbons (CFCs). CFCs were used at that time as propellants in spray cans, such as hair spray. These gases break down ozone in the stratosphere. As a result, the ozone layer got thinner each winter, and the hole got wider. At times, the ozone hole has grown large enough to threaten parts of South America. Today, the ozone hole has shrunk in response to an international agreement banning the use of chlorofluorocarbons in 1989.

◄ VOLCANIC GASES
About 4 billion years ago, Earth's atmosphere was very different than it is today. The early atmosphere was made up of mostly nitrogen and carbon dioxide, with small amounts of sulfur, carbon monoxide, and methane. These gases were spewed out by volcanoes.

Assessment

1. **Key Terms** Define **(a)** troposphere, **(b)** photosynthesis, **(c)** cloud, **(d)** ozone layer.

2. **Physical Processes** How was Earth's atmosphere formed?

3. **Natural Resources** How does carbon dioxide support life?

4. **Geographic Tools** Within which layer of the atmosphere is the ozone layer found? What is the function of the ozone layer?

5. **Critical Thinking** **Analyze Processes** Study the diagram showing the oxygen cycle. **(a)** How would extensive deforestation affect the oxygen cycle? **(b)** Which processes of the cycle release oxygen (which may be converted to ozone in the upper atmosphere later)?

495

Assessment Answers

1. (a) layer of the atmosphere closest to land; **(b)** the process during which plants use carbon dioxide to make their food, while giving out oxygen; **(c)** a mass of tiny particles of water and dust floating in the atmosphere; **(d)** a band of ozone gas that absorbs the sun's harmful ultraviolet rays

2. It was formed mainly from gases spewed from volcanoes. Some gases, such as oxygen, formed later.

3. Plants and phytoplankton use carbon dioxide to complete the process of photosynthesis.

4. Earth's ozone layer is found in the stratosphere. The ozone layer prevents harmful UV rays from reaching Earth.

5. (a) It would reduce the number of oxygen-producing plants. **(b)** Photosynthesis by land plants and marine organisms releases oxygen.

HEATING LAND AND WATER `L2`

Objectives
In this activity, students will
- conduct an experiment investigating the differential heating of dry sand, water, and damp sand.
- measure temperature changes in these materials with time as they are exposed to radiation from a light source.
- interpret time/temperature data obtained from irradiating the materials with a light source.

Skills Model, Observe, Measure, Analyze Data

Prep Time 10 minutes

Alternative Materials pencils and tape (for suspending thermometers), beakers could be 200-mL

Advance Prep Copy and distribute the data table and graph sheet so students don't have to copy each themselves. Set up each beaker and mount thermometers to save class time for students' observations and discussion of Analyze and Conclude questions.

Class Time 40 minutes

Teaching Tip Copying and handing out the sample graph in this lab will ensure that students will not write in their textbooks.

Expected Outcome Students will observe that dry sand, which represents land, heats up faster than water does. Damp sand does not heat up as quickly as dry sand. Dry sand achieves a higher temperature when irradiated than damp sand and water do.

INQUIRY ?
EXPLORATION LAB

Heating Land and Water

Problem How do the heating of land and water compare?

Materials 2 250-mL beakers, dry sand, tap water, ring stand, light source, 2 flat wooden sticks, 2 thermometers, graph paper, 3 colored pencils

Skills Model, Observe, Measure, Analyze Data

Connect to the `Big idea` In this lab you will model the difference in the heating of land and water when they are subjected to a source of radiation. You first will assemble simple tools. Then you will observe and record temperature data. Finally, you will explain the results of the experiment and how they relate to the moderating influence of water on air temperatures near Earth's surface.

Procedure
Part A: Preparing for the Experiment
1. On a separate sheet of paper or on a computer spreadsheet, copy the data table shown.
2. Pour 200 mL of dry sand into one of the beakers. Pour 200 mL of water into the other beaker.

Land and Water Heating Data Table											
	Starting Temperature	1 min	2 min	3 min	4 min	5 min	6 min	7 min	8 min	9 min	10 min
Water											
Dry sand											
Damp sand											

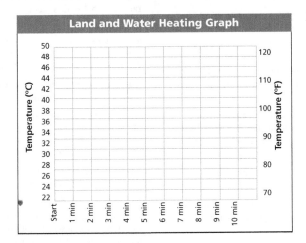

Land and Water Heating Graph

Analyze and Conclude
1. Student graphs should have three different-colored lines on them: one representing water, another representing dry sand, and the last line representing damp sand. The graphs should indicate that dry sand heats up faster and hotter than water and damp sand. Check student graphs for appropriate labels or a key.
2. Dry sand heats up and gets hotter faster than water does.
3. Dry sand heats up faster and gets hotter faster than damp sand does.
4. Lafayette, Indiana, would show the greater annual temperature range because of its continental location.
5. Answers will vary.
Visual, Logical

3. Hang a light source from a ring stand so that it is about 5 inches above the beaker of sand and the beaker of water. The light should be situated so that it is at the same height above both beakers, as shown in the photo.

4. Using the wooden sticks, suspend a thermometer in each beaker. The thermometer bulbs should be just barely below the surfaces of the sand and the water.

5. Record the starting temperatures for both the dry sand and the water in the data table.

Part B: Heating the Beakers

Caution *Do not touch the light source or the beakers without using thermal mitts.*

6. Turn on the light. Observe and record the temperatures in the data table at one-minute intervals for 10 minutes.

7. Turn off the light for several minutes. Dampen the sand with water and record the starting temperature for damp sand. Repeat step 6 for the damp sand.

Analyze and Conclude

1. **Use Tables and Graphs** Use a computer to graph the data you collected on a graph like the one above. Plot the temperatures for the water, dry sand, and damp sand. Use a different color line to connect the points for each material. Include labels for the lines or a key to the graph.

2. **Compare and Contrast** How does the changing temperature differ for dry sand and water when they are exposed to equal amounts of radiation?

3. **Compare and Contrast** How does the changing temperature differ for dry sand and damp sand when they are exposed to equal amounts of radiation?

4. **Apply** Locate Eureka, California, and Lafayette, Indiana, on a map. Infer which city would show the greatest annual temperature range. Explain your answer.

5. **Communicate** Write a lab report explaining your procedures and conclusions for this lab.

Study Tip

Organize New Information

Tell students that learning detail-oriented information is easier when using strategies such as making outlines of a section, making charts of details, making graphic organizers, and making flashcards. Tell students that by using these techniques and reviewing them daily, they can avoid "cramming" for a test.

Think Visually

a. altitude changes
b. troposphere (or mesosphere)
c. mesosphere (or troposphere)

21st Century Learning

Global Awareness

How does latitude affect climate?
Several factors determine the climate in any area. Temperatures are affected by latitude, water bodies, altitude, geography, and prevailing winds. Ask pairs of students to work together to find graphs of the mean monthly temperatures for your town and for a town on another continent that is at the same latitude as your town. Then, ask students to prepare a report in which they write an explanation for any differences or similarities between the temperature graphs. Student reports should include both graphs and maps of the two locations. Encourage students to post their reports to a class blog or wiki, if available.

Homework Guide

Lesson	Questions
1	1–4, 8–10, 12, 15, 18, 19, 23, 24, 29
2	5, 6, 13, 16, 20, 30
3	7, 11, 14, 17, 21, 22, 25–28

---

17 Study Guide

Big idea Weather and Climate

17.1 Atmosphere Characteristics

Weather refers to the state of the atmosphere at any given time or place. Weather is constantly changing. Climate is the sum of all statistical weather information that helps describe a place or region.

Water vapor is the source of all clouds and precipitation. Like carbon dioxide, it absorbs heat given off by Earth as well as some solar energy.

If ozone did not filter most UV radiation, Earth would be uninhabitable for many living organisms.

The atmosphere thins as you travel away from Earth, until there are too few gas molecules to detect.

The atmosphere can be divided vertically into four layers based on temperature.

Seasonal changes occur because Earth's position relative to the sun continually changes as it travels along its orbit.

ozone (478)	summer solstice (482)
troposphere (480)	winter solstice (482)
stratosphere (480)	autumnal equinox (482)
mesosphere (480)	spring equinox (482)
thermosphere (480)	

17.2 Heating the Atmosphere

Heat is the transfer of energy between two objects resulting from differences in their temperatures. Temperature is a measure of the average kinetic energy of individual particles.

Three mechanisms of heat transfer are conduction, convection, and radiation. Unlike conduction and convection, radiant energy can travel through the vacuum of space.

All objects, at any temperature, emit radiant energy. Hotter objects radiate more total energy per unit area than colder objects do. The hottest radiating bodies produce the shortest wavelengths of maximum radiation. Objects that are good absorbers of radiation are good emitters as well.

498 Chapter 17 • Study Guide

Objects can absorb, transmit, scatter, or reflect radiation that strikes them.

heat (483)	radiation (485)
temperature (483)	reflection (486)
conduction (483)	scattering (486)
convection (484)	greenhouse effect (487)

17.3 Temperature Controls

Factors other than latitude that exert a strong influence on temperature include heating of land and water, altitude, geographic position, cloud cover, and ocean currents.

Land heats more rapidly and to higher temperatures than water. Land also cools more rapidly and to lower temperatures than water.

Many clouds have a high albedo, and therefore reflect a significant portion of the sunlight that strikes them back to space.

albedo (492)	isotherm (492)

Think Visually

Concept Map Copy the concept map below onto a sheet of paper. Use information from the chapter to complete the concept map.

Assessment Answers

Review Content

1. a	2. d	3. c
4. b	5. c	6. d
7. c	8. c	9. c
10. d		

Understand Concepts

11. Dry land heats and cools faster and to greater temperature extremes than water does.
12. In the stratosphere, UV radiation is absorbed by diatomic oxygen (O_2) molecules, causing some to split and produce monatomic (O) oxygen. In the presence of a catalyst, O and O_2 collide to form ozone (O_3).

17 Assessment

Choose the letter that best answers the question or completes the statement.

1. What is a description of atmospheric conditions over a long period of time?
   a. climate
   b. meteorology
   c. precipitation
   d. weather

2. The bottom layer of the atmosphere in which we live is called the
   a. mesosphere.
   b. stratosphere.
   c. thermosphere.
   d. troposphere.

3. Which form of radiation has the longest wavelength?
   a. blue light
   b. infrared
   c. radio waves
   d. ultraviolet

4. This layer of atmosphere contains ozone that filters UV radiation.
   a. mesosphere
   b. stratosphere
   c. thermosphere
   d. troposphere

5. The average kinetic energy of all the atoms and molecules that make up a substance is referred to as
   a. radiation.
   b. greenhouse effect.
   c. temperature.
   d. heat.

6. The two principle absorbers of radiation emitted by Earth's surface are carbon dioxide and
   a. nitrogen.
   b. oxygen.
   c. ozone.
   d. water vapor.

7. On a map showing temperature distributions, what are the lines connecting points of equal temperature?
   a. isobars
   b. isotemps
   c. isotherms
   d. equigrads

8. Which gas is most abundant in clean, dry air?
   a. argon
   b. carbon dioxide
   c. nitrogen
   d. oxygen

9. Select the best description of air.
   a. It is a compound.
   b. It is an element.
   c. It is a mixture.
   d. It is mainly oxygen and carbon dioxide.

10. Earth's atmosphere is thought to have become enriched in which gas about 2.5 billion years ago?
    a. argon
    b. carbon dioxide
    c. nitrogen
    d. oxygen

Understand Concepts

11. Why are temperature variations greater over dry land than they are over water?

12. Describe how the ozone in the stratosphere forms.

13. Describe the three types of heat transfer in the atmosphere.

14. In what ways can geographic position be considered a temperature control?

15. Describe the two principle motions of Earth.

16. Explain why Earth's troposphere is mainly heated from the ground up.

17. Describe the effects of cloud cover on air temperature.

18. Why do temperatures increase in the stratosphere?

19. What causes the position of the noon sun to vary by as much as 47 degrees over a year's time?

Use the figure below to answer Question 20.

20. The illustration below shows two ways that radiation bounces off objects. Identify the process shown in each diagram. What clues in the illustration helped you identify these processes?

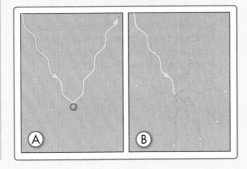

16. Radiation emitted by Earth is absorbed by atmospheric gases, resulting in the troposphere being heated from the ground up.

17. During daylight, clouds reflect solar radiation back to space. At night, clouds slow the loss of heat. The net effect of these processes is that the daily temperature range is reduced.

18. Ozone is concentrated in this layer. Ozone molecules absorb UV radiation from the sun and heat up.

19. The variation is caused by a combination of Earth's 23 1/2 degree axis tilt and its annual revolution around the sun.

20. Diagram A is reflection and diagram B is scattering. Diagram A: The incoming ray and the reflected ray encounter and bounce off the object at the same angle, and the thicknesses of both rays are the same, indicating the same intensity for both. Diagram B: The thicknesses of the rays bouncing off are less than the incident ray and the rays are bouncing off in different directions.

---

13. Air in direct contact with Earth's surface is heated by energy transfer as molecules collide with each other (conduction). Lower layers of atmosphere are warmed, become less dense and are forced upward, where they cool and sink (convection). Earth's surface receives radiation from the sun. Earth's surface, in turn, re-radiates longer-wavelength radiation that is absorbed by atmospheric gases (radiation).

14. When a location is near a source of water, cut off from prevailing winds over water or in a continental interior location, it is a geographic position that also is a temperature control.

15. Rotation: Earth spins about its axis; one rotation occurs every 24 hours. Revolution: Earth completes one elliptical orbit about the sun each year.

ASSESSMENT

Think Critically

21. Snow, clouds, white sand, and light-colored soil have high albedos compared to other surfaces.

22. September 22–23 (autumnal equinox): From September to December, Earth is tilted so that the Southern Hemisphere receives more sunlight.

23. The altitude of the noon sun and length of day would remain the same at each latitude throughout the year and no seasonal variations would occur.

Math Skills

24. The temperature would decrease by 13°C (6.5°C/km × 2 km = 13°C). The air temperature would be 23°C − 13°C = 10°C.

Concepts in Action

25. Yakutsk is located at a high latitude and in the center of a large landmass, far from any marine influence.

26. Less ocean area would lead to much larger temperature extremes on Earth. Many organisms that exist on Earth today might not be able to survive such extremes.

27. Water vapor is the source of all clouds and precipitation. Both water vapor and carbon dioxide are efficient absorbers of heat in the troposphere. Without these gases most life forms on Earth could not exist.

28. The higher the temperature of a radiating body, the shorter the wavelengths of the radiation that it emits.

29. In regions where isotherms are closely spaced, the temperature changes more rapidly over a given distance on Earth's surface.

30. Student paragraphs should include environments that have good reflecting surfaces, such as clouds, snow, light-colored soil, and water.

21. **Analyze Data** Using the data in the table, determine which types of surfaces have the highest average albedos.

Albedo of Various Surfaces	
Surface	**Percent Reflected**
Clouds, stratus	
<150 meters thick	25–63
150–300 meters thick	45–75
300–600 meters thick	59–84
Average of all types and thicknesses	50–55
Concrete	17–27
Crops, green	5–25
Forest, green	5–10
Meadows, green	5–25
Plowed field, moist	14–17
Road, blacktop	5–10
Sand, white	30–60
Snow, fresh-fallen	80–90
Snow, old	45–70
Soil, dark	5–15
Soil, light (or desert)	25–30
Water	8*

*Typical albedo value for a water surface. The albedo of a water surface varies greatly depending upon the angle of the sun.

22. **Apply Concepts** Determine the date after which the length of daylight gets progressively longer going south from the equator. Use Figure 8 to explain your answer.

23. **Infer** Give an example of how the Earth system might be affected if Earth's axis were perpendicular to the plane of its orbit instead of being tilted 23.5 degrees.

24. **Calculate** Assume that the average rate of temperature decrease in the troposphere is 6.5°C/km. Using this rate, determine the air temperature at a height of 2 kilometers if the temperature at sea level were 23°C.

25. **Infer** Yakutsk is located in Siberia at about 60 degrees north latitude. This Russian city has one of the highest average annual temperature ranges in the world: 62.2°C. Explain the reasons for the very high annual temperature range.

26. **Predict** Speculate on the changes in global temperatures that might occur if Earth had substantially more land area and less ocean area than it does at present. How might such changes influence the biosphere?

27. **Apply Concepts** Why are carbon dioxide and water vapor such important components in Earth's atmosphere? What would happen to life forms on Earth if these gases were no longer present in the atmosphere?

28. **Explain** State the relationship between the temperature of a radiating body and the wavelengths of radiation that it emits.

29. **Interpret Visuals** Refer to Figure 20. What can you determine about temperatures in regions where isotherms are closely spaced, compared with regions where isotherms are farther apart?

30. **Writing in Science** Write a paragraph that describes two environmental settings where you would expect the albedo of surfaces to be high. Your scenarios can describe any reasonable area on Earth's surface. Be sure to include as much detail as possible in your paragraph.

Design an Experiment Design and conduct an experiment that models how variations in color of an object can affect the amount of radiation it absorbs. As a first step, write a clear hypothesis statement. Then plan the materials you will need to design the experiment. Have your teacher approve your plan before you begin.

Performance-Based Assessment

Experimental designs will vary. Students should be careful to control all dependent variables other than the one they are testing (color of object).

Standardized Test Prep

Choose the letter that best answers the question.

1 Which of these gases plays a more important role in weather processes than the others?
A argon
B carbon dioxide
C nitrogen
D oxygen

2 Practically all clouds and storms occur in this layer of the atmosphere.
F mesosphere
G stratosphere
H thermosphere
J troposphere

3 The primary wavelengths of radiation emitted by Earth's surface are—
A longer than those emitted by the sun
B shorter than those emitted by the sun
C about the same as those emitted by the sun
D about the same as UV radiation

4 Which of the following is true about equinoxes?
F They occur in June and December.
G The sun's vertical rays are striking either the Tropic of Cancer or the Tropic of Capricorn.
H Lengths of daylight and darkness are equal everywhere.
J The length of daylight in the Arctic and Antarctic Circles is 24 hours.

Use the graph below to answer Question 5.

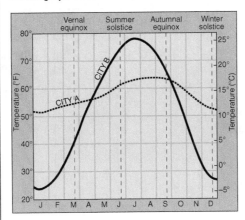

5 Determine the difference in December mean temperatures for cities A and B.
A −2°C
B 10°C
C 12°C
D 14°C

If You Have Trouble With . . .					
Question	1	2	3	4	5
See Lesson	17.1	17.1	17.2	17.1	17.3

18 Moisture, Clouds, and Precipitation Planning Guide

Lesson Objectives		Activities
18.1 Water in the Atmosphere, pp. 504–509		TE Teacher Demo: Water From Plants, p. 507 [L2]
18.1 **Identify** the gas that is most important for understanding atmospheric processes.		TE Build Science Skills, p. 508 [L2]
18.2 **Describe** what happens during a change of state.		
18.3 **Compare and contrast** the abilities of cold air and warm air to hold water vapor.		
18.4 **Define** relative humidity.		
18.5 **Describe** the factors that affect the relative humidity of air.		
18.2 Cloud Formation, pp. 510–516		TE Teacher Demo: Compression and Expansion, p. 511 [L2]
18.6 **Describe** what happens to air when it is compressed or allowed to expand.		TE Build Science Skills, p. 514 [L2]
18.7 **List** four mechanisms that cause air to rise.		TE Teacher Demo: Making a Cloud, p. 515 [L2]
18.8 **Compare and contrast** movements of stable and unstable air.		
18.9 **Describe** the conditions in air that favor condensation of water.		
18.3 Cloud Types and Precipitation, pp. 517–522		TE Build Science Skills, p. 519 [L2]
18.10 **Describe** how clouds are classified.		TE Teacher Demo: Making Hail, p. 522 [L2]
18.11 **Compare and contrast** clouds and fogs.		
18.12 **Explain** what must happen for precipitation to form.		
18.13 **Identify** what controls the type of precipitation that reaches Earth's surface.		
Chapter Features and Labs		
Try It What Causes Condensation? p. 503		LM Recipe for a Cloud [L2]
Earth & Its Resources Atmospheric Stability and Air Pollution, p. 523		
Exploration Lab Measuring Humidity, pp. 524–525		

	Ability Levels		Components				
	L1 For students who need additional help	SE	Student Edition	LP	Lesson Plans		
	L2 For all students	TE	Teacher's Edition	AA	Active Art		
	L3 For students who need to be challenged	LM	Laboratory Manual	PD	Planet Diary		
		CT	Chapter Tests	GEODe	Geode CD-ROM		
		GRSW	Guided Reading & Study Workbook	eText			
		CTB	Computer Test Bank				

Resources	Lesson Assessment
GRSW Lesson 18.1 LP Lesson Planning 18.1	SE Lesson 18.1 Assessment, p. 509 eText Lesson 18.1
GRSW Lesson 18.2 LP Lesson Planning 18.2 PD Orographic Lifting and Rainfall GEODe The Atmosphere: Moisture and Cloud Formation	SE Lesson 18.2 Assessment, p. 516 eText Lesson 18.2
GRSW Lesson 18.3 LP Lesson Planning 18.3	SE Lesson 18.3 Assessment, p. 522 eText Lesson 18.3

Materials for Activities and Labs

Quantities for each group

STUDENT EDITION

Try It, p. 503
250-mL beaker, tap water, ice, thermometer

Exploration Lab, pp. 524–525
calculator, water at room temperature, psychrometer (alternative materials for psychrometer: 2 thermometers, cotton gauze, paper fan, string)

TEACHER'S EDITION

Teacher Demo, p. 507
small potted house plant, clear plastic bag

Build Science Skills, p. 508
long human hair, tape, ring stand or other support, small washer or button, toothpick, index card, small cardboard box

Teacher Demo, p. 511
bicycle tire, bicycle pump, can of compressed air duster

Build Science Skills, p. 514
helium balloon, hot water, cold water, thermometer, meter stick, stopwatch or clock with second hand, other materials of the students' choosing

Teacher Demo, p. 515
valve stem from a car or bicycle, 2-hole rubber stopper, glass tubing, rubber tubing, hose clamp, warm water, Erlenmeyer flask, match, bicycle pump, sheet of black paper, flashlight

Build Science Skills, p. 519
log book

Teacher Demo, p. 522
salt, water, 600-mL beaker, stirring rod, large test tube, crushed ice

Assessment

CHAPTER ASSESSMENT
SE   Assessment, pp. 527–528
CT   Chapter 18 Test
CTB   Chapter 18
eText   Chapter 18

21st Century Learning

Critical Thinking and Systems Thinking: How Can You Measure Dew Point? TE p. 526

Common Themes

Water plays a dominant role in atmospheric processes, even though it is a tiny component of it. This is partly due to water's unique ability to exist in three states—solid, liquid, and vapor—at Earth's surface. Clouds form from the condensation of water vapor.

Space and Time In the troposphere, there are three main types of clouds: cirrus, cumulus, and stratus. However, the forms that these clouds take also depend upon whether they are at high, middle, or low altitudes within the troposphere. Clouds at Earth's surface are known as fog.

Forces and Motion Water vapor condenses when it gets cold, and temperature gets higher with altitude, so clouds form when moist air is lifted. Air gets lifted by several different mechanisms including orographic lifting (over mountains), frontal wedging, convergence, and localized convective lifting (due to regional warming). Stable air masses, such as those that occur with temperature inversions, resist lifting, so clouds don't form.

Matter and Energy There are two ways to describe humidity, or the amount of water vapor in the atmosphere. One description is the relative humidity, which is the amount of water vapor in air compared to the maximum amount of water vapor that could occur in the air at the current temperature and pressure. The other is the dew point, which is the temperature at which the water vapor of a given parcel of air would begin to condense.

Earth as a System Precipitation, in the form of rain, snow, sleet, glaze, and hail, occurs when cloud droplets become too large to stay suspended in air. Precipitation forms the basis of the erosion of continental surfaces.

Michael Wysession
Washington University

EARTH SCIENCE REFRESHER

Temperature Inversions and Smog in Los Angeles

When people think of urban smog, Los Angeles often comes to mind. However, it turns out that the smog in Los Angeles is variable depending upon the time of year. Smog tends to be much worse in summer than in winter. The reason for this has to do with the effect of temperature inversions on convection.

During the winter time, the average temperature in Los Angeles is about 12°C. Bordering Los Angeles on the east are the San Gabriel Mountains, and on the other side of these mountains there is a plateau that includes the Mojave Desert. While we usually think of deserts as being hot places, this is not true in the winter if they are at high elevation and far from water.

While the low elevation and proximity of the Pacific Ocean keep Los Angeles warm in winter, this is not the case for the desert plateau, where temperatures drop to about 7°C in the winter. The result is that it is hard for smog to stay over Los Angeles for extended periods of time. The warm Los Angeles air rises, and is replaced by cold air from the desert that comes down over the mountains. Convection is allowed to occur, and the smog gets swept away.

Address Misconceptions

Students may have many misconceptions about what clouds are made of and how they form. They may think that clouds are made of smoke or water vapor. They may think that clouds form when bodies of water boil. For a strategy that helps to overcome these misconceptions, see **Address Misconceptions** on **TE p. 517.**

Students may think that condensation occurs when air turns into a liquid. In fact, condensation consists of water droplets, and water vapor is only a small part of air. The remaining components of air remain as gases. For a strategy that helps to overcome these misconceptions, see **Address Misconceptions** *on* **TE p. 506.**

This is not what usually happens during the summer, however. During summer months, the average temperature in Los Angeles is about 24°C, but the temperature up in the desert is even warmer—about 29°C. Instead of being 5° colder, it is now 5°warmer. That means that the warm, smog-filled air in Los Angeles has nowhere to go, because the air over the mountains is even warmer. If air comes over the mountains from the desert, it is even warmer than the city air, so it rests on top of it. This is called a temperature inversion. Cold, heavy air rests below warm, more buoyant air, so there is no convection.

Ironically, temperature inversions in many parts of the world are often associated with clear, cloud-free skies at night, when the ground cools efficiently, but radiates energy that heats the atmosphere. This is not the case for Los Angeles, where summertime smog can get trapped against the mountains for extended periods of time.

BUILD READING LITERACY
Visualize

Forming Mental Pictures

Strategy Help students understand and recall complex text by forming mental pictures as they read. In some cases, visual elements of the text can aid students in visualizing; in other cases students must rely solely on text descriptions. Choose several paragraphs from Chapter 18, such as the four on pp. 512–513. If possible, include at least one paragraph that has an accompanying figure and at least one other paragraph that refers to concepts or events that are not illustrated in visual elements, such as diagrams, charts, graphs, or photographs.

Example

1. Have students keep their books closed. Tell them to listen while you read and visualize, or form mental pictures of, each object or action you read about.

2. Then, read a paragraph or so aloud, pausing frequently to demonstrate, by thinking aloud, how to visualize each thing described. When reading complex or technical text, pausing after reading each phrase will often be appropriate.

3. Tell students to continue visualizing. Slowly and clearly, read on. Then, select a logical stopping point and discuss with students the images they visualized.

4. If there is an accompanying figure, have students open to it and see how it compares with their visualizing. Point out that visuals in the text help readers picture what they are reading.

5. Have students work with partners to practice by taking turns reading and visualizing aloud. Tell them to expand on visuals that appear in the text and to describe their own mental images of ideas or events that are not shown in visuals.

See TE p. 507 for a script on how to use this strategy with students. For additional strategies, see TE pp. 512 and 518.

ASSESS PRIOR KNOWLEDGE

Use the Chapter Pretest below to assess students' prior knowledge. As needed, review these concepts.

Review Science Concepts

Lesson 18.1 Review the different states of matter and transitions among them.

Lesson 18.2 Review how air behaves when it is compressed and when it expands.

Lesson 18.3 Review the basic types of clouds and precipitation.

Review Math Skills

Data Tables Review with students how data tables are organized and how units of measurement are shown. Direct students to the Math Skills in the Skills Handbook at the end of the student text.

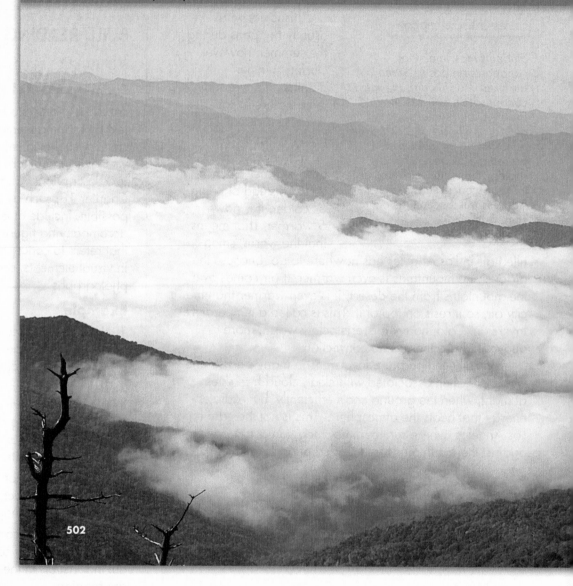

18 Moisture, Clouds, and Precipitation

Big idea **Weather and Climate**

Q: What processes are involved in cloud formation and precipitation?

502

Chapter Pretest

1. What are the three states of matter? *(b)*
 a. gas, liquid, and vapor
 b. gas, liquid, and solid
 c. vapor, liquid, and solid
 d. gas, vapor, and solid

2. True or False: Heat is released when water evaporates. *(False)*

3. What is the change from a gas to a liquid state called? *(condensation)*

4. What will happen if air is heated by the ground below it? *(The air will rise.)*

5. On what basis are clouds classified? *(c)*
 a. form and thickness
 b. color and height
 c. form and height
 d. form and precipitation

6. True or False: Small particles of ice that fall as precipitation are called sleet. *(True)*

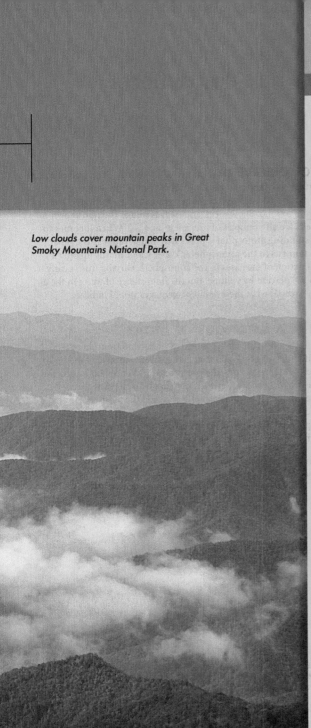

Low clouds cover mountain peaks in Great Smoky Mountains National Park.

WHAT CAUSES CONDENSATION?

Procedure

1. Fill a 250-mL beaker about one-third full of tap water. Gradually add ice to the beaker. Gently stir the water-ice mixture with a thermometer.

2. Be sure to keep the thermometer in the water–ice mixture. Record the temperature at the moment water begins to form on the outside surface of the beaker.

Think About It

1. **Observe** At what temperature did water first appear on the outside of the beaker?

2. **Infer** Where did the water that formed on the beaker's outer surface come from?

3. **Apply Concepts** Describe a process in nature that results from condensation with a change in temperature.

503

ENGAGE/EXPLORE

WHAT CAUSES CONDENSATION?

Purpose In this activity, students think about the cause of condensation.

Skills Observe, Infer

Prep Time 5 minutes

Materials 250-mL beaker, tap water, ice, thermometer

Class Time 10 minutes

Safety Remind students to handle glass thermometers carefully.

Expected Outcome Condensation forms on the outside of the beaker.

Think About It

1. Temperatures should agree with dew-point temperature of air where the experiment is carried out. Students could check online meteorological resources for local dew-point temperatures for the day of the experiment. They also could measure the dew point if a psychrometer is available or can be constructed. Determinative tables for dew-point temperature also would be needed. See the Laboratory Manual for a dew-point table.

2. The water came from water vapor in the air.

3. Processes include dew, fog, or cloud formation.

1 FOCUS

Lesson Objectives

18.1 **Identify** the gas that is most important for understanding atmospheric processes.

18.2 **Describe** what happens during a change of state.

18.3 **Compare and contrast** the abilities of cold air and warm air to hold water vapor.

18.4 **Define** relative humidity.

18.5 **Describe** the factors that affect the relative humidity of air.

Build Vocabulary L2

Word Forms Point out that the words *evaporation, vapor,* and *vaporization* are related. Water vapor is a gas. The words *evaporation* and *vaporization* both contain the word *vapor,* and both essentially mean the same thing: the process by which a liquid changes into a gas, or vapor.

Reading Strategy L2

Sample answers:
a. Water is important for cloud formation.
b. how clouds form
c. Clouds form when air rises, expands, and cools to the dew point.
d. Water is important for precipitation.
e. how precipitation forms
f. Precipitation forms by Bergeron or collision-coalescence processes.

18.1 Water in the Atmosphere

Key Questions

 Which gas is most important for understanding atmospheric processes?

 What happens during a change of state?

 How do warm and cold air compare in their ability to hold water vapor?

 What is relative humidity?

 What can change the relative humidity of air?

Vocabulary

- precipitation • latent heat
- evaporation • condensation
- sublimation • deposition
- humidity • saturated
- relative humidity • dew point
- hygrometer

Reading Strategy

Monitor Your Understanding
Before you read, copy the table. List what you know about water in the atmosphere and what you would like to learn. After you read, list what you have learned.

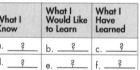

What I Know	What I Would Like to Learn	What I Have Learned
a. ___?___	b. ___?___	c. ___?___
d. ___?___	e. ___?___	f. ___?___

AS YOU OBSERVE day-to-day weather changes, you can see the powerful role of water in the air. Water vapor is the source of all condensation and **precipitation,** which is any form of water that falls from a cloud. Snow, sleet, and hail, as well as the rain shown in **Figure 1,** are all examples of precipitation. When it comes to understanding atmospheric processes, water vapor is the most important gas in the atmosphere. Water vapor makes up only a small fraction of the gases in the atmosphere, varying from nearly 0 to about 4 percent by volume. But the importance of water in the air greatly exceeds what these small percentages would indicate.

Water's Changes of State

Water is the only substance that exists in Earth's atmosphere as a solid, liquid, and gas. Water can change from one state of matter to another—at temperatures and pressures experienced on Earth. This unique property allows Earth's water supply to circulate through the oceans, the atmosphere, solid Earth, and the biosphere in the water cycle. All water in the cycle eventually passes through the atmosphere as water vapor, even though the atmosphere only holds enough to make a global layer of water about 2 mm deep.

☑ **Reading Checkpoint** *What is the range in volume percent of water in the atmosphere?*

FIGURE 1
Precipitation
This downpour shows how precipitation can affect daily activities.

SOLID   LIQUID   GAS

Sublimation
Heat absorbed (2834 joules)

Melting
Heat absorbed (334 joules)

Evaporation
Heat absorbed (2500 joules)

Freezing
Heat released (334 joules)

Condensation
Heat released (2500 joules)

at 0°C

Deposition
Heat released (2834 joules)

— Releases latent heat
— Absorbs latent heat

FIGURE 2 Changes of State
The heat energy, in joules, is indicated for 1 gram of water.

Solid to Liquid 🔑 **The process of changing state requires that energy is transferred in the form of heat.** When heat is transferred to a glass of ice water, the temperature of the ice water remains a constant 0°C until all the ice has melted. If adding heat does not raise the temperature, then where does this energy go? In this case, the added heat breaks apart the crystal structure of the ice cubes. The bonds between water molecules in the ice crystals are broken forming the noncrystalline substance liquid water. You know this process as *melting*.

The heat used to melt ice does not produce a temperature change, so it is referred to as **latent heat.** *Latent* means "hidden," like the latent fingerprints hidden at a crime scene. This energy, measured in joules or calories, becomes stored in the liquid water and is not released as heat until the liquid returns to the solid state.

Latent heat plays a crucial role in many atmospheric processes. For example, the release of latent heat aids in forming the towering clouds often seen on warm summer days. It is the major source of energy for thunderstorms, tornadoes, and hurricanes.

Liquid to Gas The process of changing a liquid to a gas is called **evaporation.** You see in **Figure 2** that it takes approximately 2500 joules to convert 1 gram of liquid water at 0°C to water vapor. The energy absorbed by the water molecules during evaporation gives them the motion needed to escape the surface of the liquid and become a gas. This energy is referred to as *latent heat of vaporization.*

During the process of evaporation, the higher-temperature, faster-moving molecules escape the surface. As a result, the average molecular motion (temperature) of the remaining molecules is reduced. This is why evaporation is considered a cooling process. You might have experienced this effect when stepping dripping wet from a swimming pool or bathtub. It takes considerable energy to evaporate water. In this situation, the energy comes from your skin—hence you feel cool.

Moisture, Clouds, and Precipitation **505**

2 INSTRUCT

Integrate Biology   L2

The Water Cycle Tell students that the water cycle is essential to life on land. Water evaporates from the oceans and from the leaves of plants. Some of the water vapor condenses and falls as precipitation over land. As the precipitation runs over the land back to the oceans, it is drunk by animals and absorbed by plants through their roots. **Ask:** What would happen if water evaporated and condensed at temperatures not found on Earth's surface? *(The water cycle would not exist.)* What effect would this have on life on Earth? *(Life would not be able to survive on land.)* **Logical**

Use Visuals   L1

Figure 2 Review the meaning of joules with students. Use this diagram to explain how water changes from one state to another. **Ask:** Which processes absorb heat? *(melting, evaporation, and sublimation)* Which processes release heat? *(freezing, condensation, and deposition)* Give an everyday example of one of the processes shown. *(Sample answers include ice cubes freezing in a freezer and water boiling in a pot on the stove.)* **Visual, Logical**

Integrate Biology   L2

Perspiration Tell students that the body cools itself by producing perspiration, or sweat. Sweat is mostly water. **Ask:** How does perspiration cool the body? *(As water evaporates, it absorbs heat from the skin.)* Why do you think perspiration cools the body more effectively when the air is dry? *(The water evaporates more easily when there is less water vapor already in the air.)* **Logical**

Differentiated Instruction

ENGLISH LANGUAGE LEARNERS Use a Cloze strategy for students with very limited English proficiency. Have students fill in the blanks in the following sentences while reading Water's Changes of State. **The three states of matter are _____, liquid, and _____. Changing state requires that _____ be absorbed or _____. The heat used to melt** ice is _____ heat. The process of changing from liquid to gas is _____. The change from water vapor to liquid is _____. The conversion of a solid directly to a gas is _____. *(gas, solid, energy, released, latent, evaporation, condensation, sublimation)*

Answers

☑ **Reading Checkpoint** *Atmosphere is nearly 0 to about 4 percent water by volume.*

LESSON 18.1

Address Misconceptions L2

Students may think that condensation occurs when air turns into a liquid. Emphasize that condensation consists of water droplets, and that water vapor is only a small part of air. The remaining components of air remain as gases. Have students draw diagrams of molecules to represent the main gases in air and draw an arrow from a water molecule to a drawing of a water droplet.
Logical, Visual

Address Misconceptions L2

Students may be somewhat misled by the phrase "amount of water vapor air can hold" in the text. Explain that while this is a convenient phrase, air does not actually "hold" water the way a sponge does. Water vapor evaporates and condenses in response to changes in temperature independently of the gases in air. In fact, it would do so even if those other gases were not present.
Logical

The opposite process where water vapor changes to the liquid state is called **condensation.** In the atmosphere, condensation generates clouds and fog. For condensation to occur, molecules of water vapor must release their stored heat energy, called *latent heat of condensation*, equal to what was absorbed during evaporation. This released energy plays an important role in producing violent weather and can transfer great quantities of heat from tropical oceans toward the poles.

Solid to Gas Water also can be transformed from a solid to a vapor state. **Sublimation** is the conversion of a solid directly to a gas, without passing through the liquid state. You may have observed this change in watching the sublimation of dry ice, or frozen carbon dioxide. Dry ice sometimes is used to generate "smoke" in theatrical productions. **Deposition** is the reverse process, the conversion of a vapor directly to a solid. This change happens when water vapor is deposited as frost on cold objects such as grass or windows.

Humidity

The general term for the amount of water vapor in air is **humidity.** Meteorologists use several methods to express the water-vapor content of the air. These include relative humidity and dew-point temperature.

Saturation Imagine a closed jar half full of water and half full of dry air. As the water begins to evaporate from the water surface, a small increase in pressure can be detected in the air above. This increase is the result of the motion of the water-vapor molecules that were added to the air through evaporation. As more and more molecules escape from the water surface, the pressure in the air above increases steadily. This forces more and more water molecules to return to the liquid. Eventually, the number of water-vapor molecules returning to the surface will balance the number leaving. At that point, the air is said to be **saturated.** The amount of water vapor required for saturation depends on temperature as shown in **Table 1.** When saturated, warm air contains more water vapor than saturated cold air.

Relative Humidity The most familiar and most misunderstood term used to describe the moisture content of air is relative humidity. **Relative humidity is a ratio of the air's actual water-vapor content compared with the amount of water vapor air can hold at that temperature and pressure.** Relative humidity indicates how near the air is to saturation, rather than the actual quantity of water vapor in the air.

Table 1 Water Vapor Needed for Saturation		
Temperature		Water Vapor Content at Saturation (grams per kilograms of air)
°C	°F	
−40	−40	0.1
−30	−22	0.3
−20	−4	0.75
−10	14	2
0	32	3.5
5	41	5
10	50	7
15	59	10
20	68	14
25	77	20
30	86	26.5
35	95	35
40	104	47

Facts and Figures

Freezer burn is a term used to describe the dried-out appearance of food that has been left in a frost-free freezer for long periods of time. Frost-free freezers circulate fairly dry air. This causes ice on the freezer walls to sublimate and be removed by the circulating air. This process, however, also removes moisture from frozen foods that are not in airtight containers. Over a few months, these foods dry out rather than actually burning.

FIGURE 3 Relative Humidity Relative humidity varies with temperature. When the temperature in the flask decreased from 20°C to 10°C, the relative humidity increased to 100 percent. When the temperature was decreased further, some of the water vapor condensed to liquid water.

Relative humidity can be changed in two ways. First, it can be changed by adding or removing water vapor. In nature, moisture is added to air mainly by evaporation from the oceans and smaller bodies of water.

Second, because the amount of moisture needed for saturation depends on temperature, relative humidity varies with temperature. Notice in **Figure 3** that when the flask is cooled from 20°C to 10°C, the relative humidity increases from 50 to 100 percent. However, once the air is saturated, further cooling does not change the relative humidity. Further cooling causes condensation, which keeps the air at its saturation level for the temperature. When air far above Earth's surface is cooled below its saturation level, some of the water vapor condenses to form clouds. Because clouds are made of liquid droplets, this moisture is no longer part of the water-vapor content of the air. **To summarize, when the water-vapor content of air remains constant, lowering air temperature causes an increase in relative humidity, and raising air temperature causes a decrease in relative humidity.**

Build Reading Literacy L1

Refer to **p. 502D,** which provides the guidelines for visualizing.

Visualize Tell students that forming a mental image of concepts they are learning helps them remember new concepts. After students have read about saturation and relative humidity, have them visualize the individual water molecules moving from the surface of the water into the air and back into the water. Then encourage students to draw diagrams that demonstrate these processes.
Visual

(Teacher **Demo**)

WATER FROM PLANTS L2

Purpose Students will observe transpiration from plants and condensation of water.

Materials small potted house plant, clear plastic bag

Procedure Cover the plant with the plastic bag, and leave it in a sunny spot for about 15 minutes. Then have students observe the inside of the bag. Ask students what they see on the inside of the bag. *(droplets of water)* Then ask where the water came from. *(It came from the plant's leaves.)* Explain that the release of water by plants is called transpiration. Ask what process formed the droplets on the inside of the bag. *(condensation)*

Expected Outcome Droplets of water will form on the inside of the bag.
Visual, Logical

FIGURE 4 Dew The water droplets on this spider web formed when the air temperature dropped below the dew point.

Dew Point Another important measure of humidity is the dew-point temperature. The dew-point temperature or simply the **dew point** is the temperature to which a parcel of air would need to be cooled to reach saturation. If the same air was cooled further, the air's excess water vapor would condense, typically as dew, fog, or clouds. During evening hours, objects near the ground often cool below the dew-point temperature and become coated with water. This is known as dew, shown on the spider web in **Figure 4.**

For every 10°C increase in temperature, the amount of water vapor needed for saturation doubles. Therefore, relatively cold saturated air at 0°C contains about half the water vapor of saturated air at a temperature of 10°C, and roughly one-fourth that of hot saturated air with a temperature of 20°C as shown in Table 1. Because the dew point is the temperature at which saturation occurs, high dew-point temperatures indicate moist air, and low dew-point temperatures indicate dry air.

Measuring Humidity Relative humidity is commonly measured by using a **hygrometer.** One type of hygrometer, called a psychrometer, consists of two identical thermometers mounted side by side. One thermometer, the dry-bulb thermometer, gives the present air temperature. The other, called the wet-bulb thermometer, has a thin cloth wick tied around the end.

To use the psychrometer, the cloth wick is saturated with water and air is continuously passed over the wick. In a sling psychrometer like the one shown in **Figure 5,** air is passed over the wick by swinging the instrument. Water evaporates from the wick, and the heat absorbed by the evaporating water makes the temperature of the wet bulb drop. The loss of heat that was required to evaporate water from the wet bulb lowers the thermometer reading. This temperature is referred to as the wet-bulb temperature.

508 Chapter 18 • Lesson 1

Facts and Figures

You may have noticed that dew often forms on grass. The reason for this is that grass releases water vapor in a process called transpiration. On calm nights, this causes the relative humidity of the air near the grass to be much higher than the relative humidity of the air even a few inches above the surface. As a result, dew forms on grass before it does on most other objects.

The amount of cooling that takes place is directly proportional to the dryness of the air. The drier the air, the more moisture evaporates, and the lower is the temperature of the wet bulb. The larger the difference is between temperatures observed on the thermometers, the lower the relative humidity. If the air is saturated, no evaporation will occur, and the two thermometers will have identical readings. To determine the precise relative humidity and to calculate the dew point, standard tables are used.

A psychrometer would not be all that useful in a weather balloon used to monitor conditions in the upper atmosphere. A different type of hygrometer is used in instrument packages that transmit data back to a station on the ground. The electric hygrometer contains an electrical conductor coated with a chemical that absorbs moisture. The passage of current varies with the amount of moisture absorbed.

FIGURE 5
Sling Psychrometer
This psychrometer is used to measure both relative humidity and dew point.
Interpret Photographs
Identify the wet bulb and the dry bulb in this photograph.

INQUIRY
APPLY IT!

Q: *Why is the air in buildings so dry in the winter?*

A: If the water-vapor content of air stays constant, an increase in temperature lowers the relative humidity, and a drop in temperature raises the relative humidity. During winter months, outside air is comparatively cold. When this air is drawn into a building, it is heated to room temperature. This causes the relative humidity to drop, often to uncomfortably low levels of 10 percent or lower. Living with dry air can mean static electrical shocks, dry skin, sinus headaches, or even nosebleeds.

18.1 Assessment

Review Key Concepts

1. What is the most important gas for understanding atmospheric processes?

2. What happens to heat during a change of state?

3. How does the temperature of air influence its ability to hold water?

4. What does relative humidity describe about air?

5. List two ways that relative humidity can be changed.

6. What does a low dew point indicate about the moisture content of air?

Think Critically

7. **Interpret Visuals** Study Figure 2. For 1 gram of water, how do the energy requirements for melting and evaporation compare?

MATH PRACTICE

8. **Calculate** The air over Fort Myers, Florida, has a dew point of 25°C. Fort Myers has twice the water vapor content of the air over St. Louis, Missouri, and four times the water vapor content as air over Tucson, Arizona. Determine the dew points for St. Louis and Tucson.

Moisture, Clouds, and Precipitation **509**

Use Community Resources

Invite a meteorologist to the class to discuss relative humidity and other weather factors. Ask students to prepare questions in advance to ask the visitor.
Interpersonal

3 ASSESS

Evaluate Understanding L2

Ask students to describe at least three changes of state and explain whether heat is absorbed or released during each change. For each change of state, students should name the process and describe the type of change. For example, for sublimation, students would indicate that the phase change is from solid to gas and that heat is absorbed.

Reteach L1

Use Figure 3 to review the concept of relative humidity. Make sure to emphasize the difference between humidity and relative humidity. **Ask:** How does lowering air temperature affect relative humidity? *(It increases relative humidity.)* How does raising air temperature affect relative humidity? *(It decreases relative humidity.)*

Answers

Figure 5 *The wet-bulb thermometer is on the left. The dry-bulb thermometer is on the right.*

Assessment Answers

1. Water vapor is the most important.
2. Heat is absorbed or released, depending on the change of state.
3. When saturated, warm air contains more water vapor than cold air.
4. Relative humidity describes how near the air is to being saturated.

5. Relative humidity can be changed by adding or removing water vapor or by changing temperature.
6. The air is dry.
7. More energy is required for evaporation to occur than for melting to occur. About 7.5 times more energy is required for evaporation.

8. St. Louis dew point: 15°C; Tucson dew point: 5°C

18.2 Cloud Formation

Lesson Objectives

18.6 **Describe** what happens to air when it is compressed or allowed to expand.

18.7 **List** four mechanisms that cause air to rise.

18.8 **Compare and contrast** movements of stable and unstable air.

18.9 **Describe** the conditions in air that favor condensation of water.

Build Vocabulary L2

LINCS Have students use the LINCS strategy to learn and review the terms *adiabatic, orographic,* and *inversion.* In LINCS exercises, students **L**ist what they know about each term, **I**magine a picture that describes the word, **N**ote a "sound-alike" word, **C**onnect the terms to the sound-alike word by making up a short story, and then perform a brief **S**elf-test.

Reading Strategy L2

a. Adiabatic temperature changes are those that occur without the addition or subtraction of heat.

b. Stability measurements are made using meteorological instruments that measure the temperature profile of the atmosphere.

c. Degrees of stability relate to the tendency of air to resist vertical movement (stable) ranging to air that tends to rise (unstable).

Key Questions

 What happens to air when it is compressed or allowed to expand?

 List four mechanisms that can cause air to rise.

 Contrast movements of stable and unstable air.

 What conditions in air favor condensation of water?

Vocabulary

- dry adiabatic rate
- wet adiabatic rate
- orographic lifting
- front • temperature inversion
- condensation nuclei

Reading Strategy

Identify Main Ideas Copy the table. As you read, write the main idea for each topic.

Topic	Main Idea
Adiabatic temperature changes	a. ___?___
Stability measurements	b. ___?___
Degrees of stability	c. ___?___

RECALL THAT CONDENSATION occurs when water vapor changes to a liquid. Condensation may form dew, fog, or clouds. Although these three forms are different, all require saturated air to develop. Saturation occurs either when enough water vapor is added to air or, more commonly, when air is cooled to its dew point.

Near Earth's surface, heat is quickly exchanged between the ground and the air above. During evening hours, the surface radiates heat away, causing the surface and adjacent air to cool rapidly. This radiational cooling causes the formation of dew and some types of fog. In contrast, clouds, such as those shown in **Figure 6,** often form during the warmest part of the day. Clearly, some other process must cool air enough to generate clouds.

Air Compression and Expansion

If you have pumped up a bicycle tire, you might have noticed that the pump barrel became warm. The increase in temperature you felt resulted from the work you did on the air to compress it. When air is compressed, the motion of gas molecules increases and the air temperature rises. The opposite happens when air is allowed to escape from a bicycle tire. The air expands and cools. The expanding air pushes on the surrounding air and cools by an amount equal to the energy expended while pushing on the surrounding air.

FIGURE 6 Clouds Clouds form when air is cooled to its dew point.

Adiabatic Temperature Changes Temperature changes that happen even though heat isn't added or subtracted are called *adiabatic temperature changes*. They result when air is compressed or allowed to expand. **When air is allowed to expand, it cools, and when it is compressed, it warms.**

Expansion and Cooling As you travel from Earth's surface upward through the atmosphere, the atmospheric pressure decreases. This happens because there are fewer and fewer gas molecules. Any time a volume of air moves upward, it passes through regions of successively lower pressure. As a result, the ascending air expands and cools. Unsaturated air cools at the constant rate of 10°C for every 1000 meters of ascent. In contrast, descending air encounters higher pressures, compresses, and is heated 10°C for every 1000 meters it moves downward. This rate of cooling or heating applies only to unsaturated air and is called the **dry adiabatic rate.**

If a parcel of air rises high enough, it will eventually cool to its dew point. Here the process of condensation begins. From this point on as the air rises, latent heat of condensation stored in the water vapor will be released. Although the air will continue to cool after condensation begins, the released latent heat works against the adiabatic cooling process. This slower rate of cooling caused by the addition of latent heat is called the **wet adiabatic rate.** Because the amount of latent heat released depends on the quantity of moisture present in the air, the wet adiabatic rate varies from 5–9°C per 1000 meters.

Figure 7 shows the role of adiabatic cooling in the formation of clouds. Note that from the surface up to the condensation level the air cools at the dry adiabatic rate. The wet adiabatic rate begins at the condensation level.

☑ **Reading Checkpoint** *What happens to heat stored in water vapor when it is cooled to its dew point?*

FIGURE 7 Cloud Formation by Adiabatic Cooling Rising air cools at the dry adiabatic rate of 10°C per 1000 meters, until the air reaches the dew point and condensation (cloud formation) begins. As air continues to rise, the latent heat released by condensation reduces the rate of cooling.
Interpret Visuals *Use this diagram to determine the approximate air temperature at 3500 m.*

---

② INSTRUCT

(Teacher **Demo**)

COMPRESSION AND EXPANSION

Purpose Students observe how compression and expansion of air cause temperature changes.

Materials bicycle tire, bicycle pump, can of compressed air duster

Procedure Ask students what they think will happen to the bicycle pump when you use it to add air to the tire. Pump up the tire a bit, then let the student feel the barrel of the pump. Ask them why the pump got warm. *(Energy was used to compress the air.)* Now ask students what they think will happen to the can of compressed air duster when you release some air from it. Release some air, then let students feel the can. Ask them why the can became cold. *(Energy was absorbed by the expanding air.)*

Expected Outcomes The bicycle pump will get warm, and the can will get cold.
Kinesthetic, Logical

Build Science Skills

Relate Cause and Effect Go through each step in what happens as a parcel of air rises through the atmosphere. **Ask:** Why does air cool as it rises? *(It expands, a process that absorbs heat.)* Why does air cool more slowly after it reaches its dew point? *(Above the dew point, condensation begins. Condensation releases heat, which somewhat counteracts the cooling effect of expansion.)* Why does the wet adiabatic rate vary? *(The amount of heat released varies with the amount of moisture. The more moisture, the more heat is released and the slower the cooling is.)*
Logical

Differentiated Instruction

ENGLISH LANGUAGE LEARNERS Students who are learning English can benefit from real-life examples that relate to science content. Encourage students to think of observations they have made about rising objects or processes that cause objects to rise. For example, they likely have seen a helium balloon rising. They may also have seen wedges such as those used as doorstops. Encourage students to share their observations with the class.

Answers

Figure 7 *The temperature is −0.5°C.*

☑ **Reading Checkpoint** *Latent heat is released.*

VISUAL SUMMARY

PROCESSES THAT LIFT AIR

FIGURE 8 There are four different mechanisms that can cause air to rise—orographic lifting, frontal wedging, convergence, and localized convective lifting.
Relate Cause and Effect *Why does the warm air mass move upward over the cold air mass?*

FIGURE 8
A Orographic Lifting Mountains are a barrier to air flow and force air to ascend.

B Frontal Wedging Warm, less dense air rises above cooler, denser air.

Processes That Lift Air

In general, air resists vertical movement. Air located near the surface tends to stay near the surface. Air far above the surface tends to remain far above the surface. Some exceptions to this happen when conditions in the atmosphere make air buoyant enough to rise without the aid of outside forces. In other situations, clouds form because there is some mechanical process that forces air to rise. **Four mechanisms that can cause air to rise are orographic lifting, frontal wedging, convergence, and localized convective lifting.**

Orographic Lifting When elevated terrains, such as mountains, act as barriers to air flow and force air to ascend, this is called **orographic lifting.** Look at **Figure 8A.** As air goes up a mountain slope, adiabatic cooling often generates clouds and precipitation. Many of the rainiest places on Earth are located on these windward mountain slopes.

By the time air reaches the leeward side of a mountain, which is away from the wind, much of the air's moisture has been lost. If the air descends, it warms adiabatically. This makes condensation and precipitation even less likely. A *rain shadow desert* can occur on the leeward side of the mountain. For example, the Great Basin Desert of the western United States lies only a few hundred kilometers from the Pacific Ocean, cut off from the ocean's moisture by the Sierra Nevada Mountains.

Frontal Wedging If orographic lifting were the only mechanism that lifted air, the relatively flat central portion of North America would be an expansive desert instead of the nation's breadbasket. Fortunately, this is not the case.

In central North America, masses of warm air and cold air collide, producing a **front.** Here the cooler, denser air acts as a barrier over which the warmer, less dense air rises. This process, called *frontal wedging,* is shown in **Figure 8B.** Weather-producing fronts are associated with specific storm systems called middle-latitude cyclones. You will study these in the Weather Patterns and Severe Storms chapter.

Facts and Figures

The phrase *parcel of air* is often used in meteorology to help understand and simplify discussion of principles. It refers to an imaginary volume of air isolated from other air by, for example, a thin elastic cover. (Picture a hot-air balloon.) A parcel is typically considered to be a few hundred cubic meters in volume.

It is assumed to act independently of the surrounding air. It is also assumed that no heat is transferred into or out of the parcel. Although parcels are imaginary, over short time periods, a parcel is a good model for the actual behavior of a volume of air moving vertically through the atmosphere.

Convergence Recall that the collision of contrasting air masses forces air to rise. In a more general sense, whenever air in the lower atmosphere flows together, lifting results. This is called *convergence*. When air flows in from more than one direction, it must go somewhere. Because it cannot go down, it goes up, as shown in **Figure 8C**. This leads to adiabatic cooling and possibly cloud formation.

The Florida peninsula provides an example of how convergence can cause cloud development and precipitation. On warm days, the airflow is from the ocean to the land along both coasts of Florida. This leads to a pileup of air along the coasts and general convergence over the peninsula. This pattern of air movement and the uplift that results is helped along by intense solar heating of the land. The result is that the peninsula of Florida experiences the greatest number of mid-afternoon thunderstorms in the United States.

Localized Convective Lifting On warm summer days, unequal heating of Earth's surface may cause pockets of air to be warmed more than the surrounding air. For example, air above a paved parking lot will be warmed more than the air above an adjacent wooded park. Consequently, the parcel of air above the parking lot, which is warmer and less dense than the surrounding air, will move upward, as shown in **Figure 8D**. These rising parcels of warmer air are called *thermals*. The process that produces rising thermals is *localized convective lifting*. Birds such as hawks and eagles use these thermals to carry them to great heights where they can gaze down on unsuspecting prey. People have learned to use these warm parcels effectively for hang gliding. When warm parcels of air rise above the condensation level, clouds form. These clouds may produce mid-afternoon rain showers.

☑ **Reading Checkpoint** *What are thermals?*

C Convergence Air is forced to rise when two air masses collide.

D Localized Convective Lifting Unequal heating of Earth's surface causes parcels of air to rise.

Moisture, Clouds, and Precipitation **513**

Use Visuals

Figure 8: C and D Use this diagram to explain convergence and convective lifting. **Ask:** What happens when two similar air masses converge and collide? *(Air is forced up at the center, possibly causing cloud formation.)* How does local convective lifting occur? *(A pocket of air may be warmed more than surrounding air, causing it to rise.)* What happens when such a parcel rises above the condensation level? *(Water vapor condenses, forming clouds.)*
Visual, Logical

Integrate Biology

Birds and Thermals Tell students that using thermals is important to many birds of prey, such as hawks and vultures. **Ask:** How do birds of prey use thermals? *(Birds use thermals to be carried up to great heights, where they can look for prey.)* What would happen if the birds could not use thermals? What problem would this cause? *(Birds would have to flap their wings to gain altitude. Doing so would waste a lot of energy.)*
Logical

Answers

Figure 8 *Warm air is less dense, and therefore more buoyant, than the cold air mass is.*

☑ **Reading Checkpoint** *Thermals are rising parcels of air that are warmer than surrounding air.*

Stability

If a volume of air was forced to rise, its temperature would drop because of expansion. If this volume of air was cooler than the surrounding environment, it would be denser, and if allowed to do so, it would sink to its original position. Air of this type, called *stable air*, resists vertical movement.

Density Differences If this imaginary volume of rising air was warmer and therefore less dense than the surrounding air, it would continue to rise until it reached an altitude where its temperature equaled that of its surroundings. This is exactly how a hot-air balloon works. The balloon rises as long as it is warmer and less dense than the surrounding air, as shown in **Figure 9**. This type of air is classified as *unstable air.* **Stable air tends to remain in its original position, while unstable air tends to rise.**

Stability Measurements Air stability is determined by measuring the temperature of the atmosphere at various heights. The rate of change of air temperature with height is called the *environmental lapse rate*. This rate is determined from observations made by aircraft and by radiosondes. A *radiosonde* is an instrument designed to collect weather data high in the atmosphere. Radiosondes are often carried into the air by balloons.

Degrees of Stability Air is stable when the temperature decreases gradually with increasing altitude. The most stable conditions happen when air temperature actually increases with height, called a **temperature inversion.** Temperature inversions frequently happen on clear nights as a result of radiation cooling off Earth's surface.

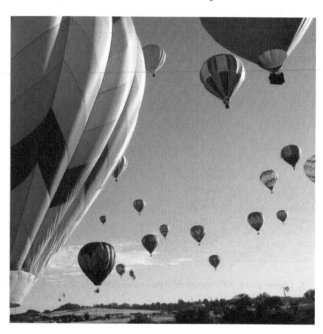

FIGURE 9 Unstable Air Hot-air balloons will rise as long as the air inside them is warmer than the air in the atmosphere surrounding them.

514 Chapter 18 • Lesson 2

Facts and Figures

A hot-air balloon has three main parts: the basket, the envelope, and the burner. The basket holds the balloonist, passengers, propane tanks, navigation equipment, and other needed supplies. The basket is often made out of wicker because it is fairly lightweight but also strong and flexible enough to absorb some of the energy of landings. The envelope, which is essentially a large nylon bag, holds the hot air. The burner is somewhat like a giant Bunsen burner. It burns propane that is stored as a liquid in large tanks. When the balloonist fires the burner, it heats the air inside the balloon and increases its buoyancy, lifting the balloon. To lower the balloon, the balloonist pulls a cord that opens a parachute valve at the top of the balloon and lets some of the hot air out.

The inversion is created because the ground and the air immediately above the ground will cool more rapidly than air higher above the ground. Under these conditions, there is very little vertical air movement. In contrast, air is considered unstable when the air close to the surface of Earth is significantly warmer than the air higher above the surface, indicating a large environmental lapse rate. Under these conditions, the air actually turns over, as the warm air below rises and is displaced by the colder air higher above the ground.

Stability and Daily Weather Recall that stable air resists vertical movement and that unstable air rises freely. But how do these facts apply to the daily weather?

Because stable air resists upward movement, you might conclude that clouds won't form when stable conditions are present in the atmosphere. Although this seems reasonable, remember that there are processes that force air above Earth's surface. These include orographic lifting, frontal wedging, and convergence. When stable air is forced above Earth's surface, the clouds that form are widespread and have little vertical thickness when compared to their horizontal dimension. Precipitation, if any, is light to moderate.

In contrast, clouds associated with the lifting of unstable air are towering and often generate thunderstorms and occasionally even a tornado. For this reason, on a dreary, overcast day with light drizzle, stable air has been forced above Earth's surface. During a day when cauliflower-shaped clouds appear to be growing as if bubbles of hot air are surging upward, the air moving up is unstable. **Figure 10** shows cauliflower-shaped clouds caused by the rising of unstable air.

☑ **Reading Checkpoint** *What types of weather can result when stable air rises?*

FIGURE 10 Clouds from Unstable Air These clouds provide evidence of unstable conditions in the atmosphere.

Moisture, Clouds, and Precipitation **515**

Build Science Skills [L2]

Compare and Contrast Compare the behavior of stable and unstable air parcels. **Ask:** What factors cause stable air to rise? *(orographic lifting, frontal wedging, and convergence)* Why are clouds formed from stable air widespread and thin? *(Because the air is stable, it all stays at roughly the same altitude.)* What factors cause unstable air to rise? *(localized convective lifting)* Why are clouds formed from unstable air often towering? *(Strong convection lifts and spreads the clouds out vertically.)* **Logical**

Teacher **Demo**

MAKING A CLOUD [L2]

Purpose Students observe how a cloud forms.

Materials valve stem from a car or bicycle, 2-hole rubber stopper, glass tubing, rubber tubing, hose clamp, warm water, Erlenmeyer flask, match, bicycle pump, sheet of black paper, flashlight

Procedure In advance, insert a valve stem from a car or bicycle into one hole of a 2-hole rubber stopper. Insert a piece of glass tubing into the other hole and attach a piece of rubber tubing to the glass tubing, Clamp off the rubber tubing. Pour a small amount of warm water into an Erlenmeyer flask. In front of students, light a match and hold it inside the flask for a few seconds. Insert the stopper into the flask and use a bicycle pump to increase the pressure of the flask. Stand up a sheet of black paper behind the flask and shine a flashlight through it. Now open the clamp. Ask students what they observed. *(A cloud forms.)* Ask why it formed. *(When the clamp was opened, there was a sudden drop in pressure in the flask because the air expanded. As a result, the air cooled adiabatically, and water vapor condensed and formed a cloud of droplets.)* Ask what the role of the smoke was. *(It provided condensation nuclei on which the droplets could form.)*

Expected Outcome A small cloud will form inside the flask.
Visual, Logical

Answers

☑ **Reading Checkpoint** *Clear weather may occur or light-to-moderate precipitation.*

Moisture, Clouds, and Precipitation **515**

3 ASSESS

Evaluate Understanding **L2**

Ask students in turn to explain one process that lifts air. Encourage them to draw diagrams on the board to help explain the process.

Reteach **L1**

Use Figure 7 to review adiabatic cooling and its role in cloud formation. Explain why the moist adiabatic rate is slower than the dry adiabatic rate.

Condensation

Recall that condensation happens when water vapor in the air changes to a liquid. This may be in the form of dew, fog, or clouds. **For any of these forms of condensation to occur, the air must be saturated.** Saturation occurs most commonly when air is cooled to its dew point, or less often when water vapor is added to the air.

Types of Surfaces Generally, there must be a surface for water vapor to condense on. When dew forms, objects at or near the ground, such as grass and car windows, serve this purpose. But when condensation occurs in the air above the ground, tiny bits of particulate matter, called **condensation nuclei,** serve as surfaces for water-vapor condensation. These nuclei are important because if they are absent, a relative humidity much above 100 percent is needed to produce clouds.

Particles in the Lower Atmosphere Condensation nuclei such as microscopic dust, smoke, and salt particles from the ocean are abundant in the lower atmosphere. Because of these plentiful particles, relative humidity rarely exceeds 100 percent. Some particles, such as ocean salt, are especially good nuclei because they absorb water. When condensation takes place, the initial growth rate of cloud droplets is rapid. It diminishes quickly because the excess water vapor is quickly absorbed by the numerous competing particles. This results in the formation of a cloud consisting of millions upon millions of tiny water droplets. These droplets are all so fine that they remain suspended in air. In the next lesson, you will examine types of clouds and the precipitation that forms from them.

18.2 Assessment

Review Key Concepts

1. Describe what happens to air temperature when work is done on the air to compress it.

2. What does *stability* mean in terms of air movement?

3. List four mechanisms that cause air to rise.

4. Describe conditions that cause condensation of liquid water in air.

5. What is a temperature inversion?

6. Which types of condensation nuclei are especially good for condensation to form?

Think Criticallly

7. **Form a Hypothesis** Study a world map. Hypothesize about other regions on Earth, other than the Florida peninsula, where convergence might cause cloud development and precipitation.

CONNECTING CONCEPTS

8. **Explain** Review the atmospheric temperature changes that occur due to altitude. Then write a paragraph explaining how these differ from adiabatic temperature changes in parcels of air.

BIGIDEA WEATHER AND CLIMATE

9. **Relate Cause and Effect** Describe how the process of frontal wedging is involved in cloud formation.

516 Chapter 18 • Lesson 2

Assessment Answers

1. Air temperature rises when work is done on the air to compress it.
2. Stable air tends to remain in its original position, while unstable air tends to rise.
3. The mechanisms are frontal wedging, orographic lifting, convergence, and localized convective lifting.
4. Condensation of liquid water in air occurs when the air is saturated.

5. A temperature inversion is a stable-air situation in which air temperature increases with height.
6. Good condensation nuclei are those that absorb water, such as ocean salt.
7. Sample answer: Yucatan Peninsula; peninsulas in Northern Australia; New Zealand; Indonesia; tropical islands in general

8. The general cooling trend with height in the troposphere is called the environmental lapse rate. This is different from parcels of air that rise, expand, and cool adiabatically.
9. In the process of frontal wedging, masses of warm air and cold air collide. The presence of the cold air causes the warmer, less dense air to rise resulting in cloud formation.

18.3 Cloud Types and Precipitation

CLOUDS ARE AMONG the most striking and noticeable effects of the atmosphere and its weather. Clouds are a result of condensation best described as visible mixtures of tiny droplets of liquid water or tiny crystals of ice. Clouds are of interest to meteorologists because clouds show what is going on in the atmosphere. If you try to recognize different types of clouds, you might find it hard to do. But, if you learn the basic classification scheme for clouds, recognizing cloud types will be easy.

Types of Clouds

Cloud Forms Clouds are classified on the basis of their form and height. The three basic forms are: cirrus, cumulus, and stratus. All other clouds reflect one of these three basic forms or are combinations or modifications of them.

▶ **Cirrus Clouds** Cirrus (*cirrus* = a curl of hair) clouds are white, thin, and found high in the atmosphere. They can occur as patches or as delicate veil-like sheets or extended wispy fibers that often have a feathery appearance. An example of cirrus clouds is shown in **Figure 11.**

▶ **Cumulus Clouds** Cumulus (*cumulus* = a pile) clouds consist of rounded individual cloud masses. The clouds in Figure 10 in the previous lesson are cumulus clouds. Normally, they have a flat base and the appearance of rising domes or towers. These clouds are frequently described as having a structure resembling a cotton ball.

FIGURE 11 Cirrus Clouds
These thin, white clouds that are high in the atmosphere are cirrus clouds.

Key Questions

- How are clouds classified?
- How are clouds and fogs similar and different?
- What must happen in order for precipitation to form?
- What controls the type of precipitation that reaches Earth's surface?

Vocabulary

- cirrus • cumulus • stratus
- Bergeron process
- supercooled water
- supersaturated air
- collision-coalescence process

Reading Strategy

Build Vocabulary Copy the table. As you read, add definitions.

Vocabulary Term	Definition
Cirrus	a. ___?___
Cumulus	b. ___?___
Stratus	c. ___?___
Coalescence	d. ___?___

1 FOCUS

Lesson Objectives

18.10 **Describe** how clouds are classified.

18.11 **Compare and contrast** clouds and fogs.

18.12 **Explain** what must happen for precipitation to form.

18.13 **Identify** what controls the type of precipitation that reaches Earth's surface.

Build Vocabulary L2

Concept Map Have students make concept maps of the types of clouds. Have them start with Clouds at the top and put the three families of clouds classified by height on the next level. Below that, they should put the types of clouds within each family, and on the last row, some details about each one.

Reading Strategy L2

a. clouds that are high, white, and thin
b. clouds that consist of rounded individual cloud masses
c. clouds that occur as sheets or layers that cover much or all of the sky
d. the process in which larger drops fall through clouds, collide, and join together with smaller, slower droplets

2 INSTRUCT

Address **Misconceptions** L2

Students may have many misconceptions about what clouds are made of and how they form. They may think that clouds are made of smoke or water vapor. They may think that clouds form when bodies of water boil. Have students make flowcharts with diagrams to show that clouds are made of tiny water droplets, and form when air containing water vapor is cooled.
Logical, Visual

Build Reading Literacy L1

Refer to **p. 278D** in **Chapter 10,** which provides the guidelines for identifying main ideas and details.

Identify Main Idea/Details Have students read Types of Clouds on pp. 517–520. Ask them to identify the main idea of each subheading. Point out that the main idea is usually in the first or second sentence of a subheading. Encourage students to use this exercise in the notes they use to study.
Verbal

Use Visuals L1

Figure 12 Use this diagram to explain the different types of clouds and their names.
Ask: To what does "stratus" refer? *(clouds that cover much of the sky)* What can you tell about cirrocumulus clouds from their name? *(They are high-level clouds made up of individual rounded cloud masses.)* Are you likely to see all of these kinds of clouds in the sky at the same time? Explain your answer. *(No, because many of the clouds form under different atmospheric conditions.)*
Visual, Verbal

► *Stratus Clouds* **Stratus** (*stratum* = a layer) clouds are best described as sheets or layers that cover much or all of the sky. While there may be minor breaks, there are no distinct individual cloud units.

Levels of Cloud Heights There are three levels of cloud heights: high, middle, and low, as shown in **Figure 12.** High clouds normally have bases above 6000 meters. Middle clouds generally occupy heights from 2000 to 6000 meters. Low clouds form below 2000 meters. The altitudes listed for each height category are not hard and fast. There is some seasonal and latitudinal variation. For example, at high latitudes or during cold winter months in the mid-latitudes, high clouds often are found at lower altitudes.

► *High Clouds* Three cloud types make up the family of high clouds: cirrus, cirrostratus, and cirrocumulus. As shown in **Figure 12,** cirrocumulus clouds consist of fluffy masses, while cirrostratus clouds are flat layers. All high clouds are thin and white and are often made up of ice crystals. This is because of the low temperatures and small quantities of water vapor present at high altitudes. These clouds are not considered precipitation makers. However, when cirrus clouds are followed by cirrocumulus or cirrostratus clouds and increased sky coverage, they may warn of approaching stormy weather.

► *Middle Clouds* Clouds found in the middle range, from about 2000 to 6000 meters, have the prefix *alto-* as part of their name.

FIGURE 12 Cloud Classification
Clouds are classified according to form and height.
Interpret Visuals Which cloud types are the chief precipitation makers?

Differentiated Instruction

BEHAVIORALLY DISORDERED Have students work in groups to make a set of flashcards. Each card should contain information about a different type of cloud. One side of the card should have the name of the cloud (for example, *altostratus*) and three categories of color-keyed questions: Form of cloud, Height of cloud, Typical weather. Color key the answers on the other side of the card. *(flat layers, middle height, infrequent light snow or drizzle)* Students can use the cards to support one another in small study groups.

Altocumulus clouds are composed of rounded masses that differ from cirrocumulus clouds in that altocumulus clouds are larger and denser, as shown in **Figure 12.**

Altostratus clouds create a uniform white to grayish sheet covering the sky with the sun or moon visible as a bright spot. Infrequent light snow or drizzle may accompany these clouds.

▶ *Low Clouds* There are three members in the family of low clouds: stratus, stratocumulus, and nimbostratus. As illustrated in **Figure 12,** stratus clouds are a uniform, foglike layer of clouds that frequently covers much of the sky. Occasionally, these clouds may produce light precipitation. When stratus clouds develop a scalloped bottom that appears as long parallel rolls or broken rounded patches, they are called stratocumulus clouds.

Nimbostratus clouds derive their name from the Latin word *nimbus,* which means "rainy cloud," and *stratus,* which means "to cover with a layer." As the name suggests, nimbostratus clouds are one of the main precipitation makers. Nimbostratus clouds form during stable conditions. You might not expect clouds to develop in stable air. But cloud growth of this type is common when air is forced upward, as occurs along a mountain range, a front, or where converging winds cause air to rise. Such a forced upward movement of stable air can result in a cloud layer that is largely horizontal compared to its depth.

☑ **Reading Checkpoint** What does the Latin word *stratus* mean?

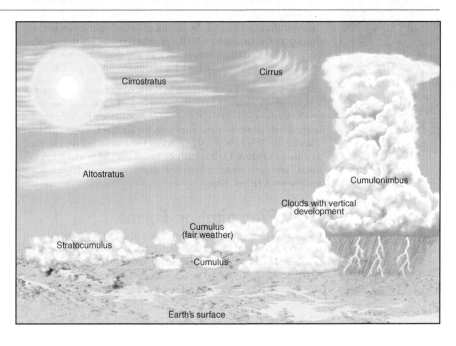

Moisture, Clouds, and Precipitation **519**

Build Science Skills L2

Classify Show students photographs of a variety of clouds. Have students classify the clouds according to Figure 12.
Visual

Build Science Skills L2

Student Activity: Observe Ask students if they have ever wondered how some people can look out the window and predict the weather. Explain that learning to observe and identify clouds will help develop the ability to predict weather. Have students keep a log of cloud and weather observations for at least one month. For each page of their logs, have students record the date and time of observation; a description and drawing of the cloud cover, including the general altitude (high, middle, low), percent of sky coverage, and the thickness or relative height of clouds; a general description of any weather phenomena, such as wind or precipitation; and the temperature (either specific readings or general terms). After a period of time, students should analyze their observations and look for patterns between clouds and weather.
Visual, Logical

Answers

Figure 12 *The chief precipitation makers are nimbostratus and cumulonimbus clouds.*

☑ **Reading Checkpoint** Stratus *means "to cover with a layer."*

Compare and Contrast Make sure that students understand the similarities and differences between fog and other types of clouds. **Ask:** What is a fog? *(It is a cloud with its base at or very near the ground.)* How are fog and other clouds similar? *(They are the same physically.)* How are fog and other clouds different? *(Clouds result from air rising and cooling adiabatically. Fogs form as a result of radiation cooling, movement of air over a cold surface, or evaporation of water vapor.)*
Logical

Clouds of Vertical Development Some clouds do not fit into any of the three height categories mentioned. Such clouds have their bases in the low height range but often extend upward into the middle or high altitudes. They all are related to one another and are associated with unstable air. Although cumulus clouds are often connected with fair weather, they may grow dramatically under the proper circumstances. Once upward movement is triggered, acceleration is powerful, and clouds with great vertical range form. The end result often is a cumulonimbus cloud that may produce rain showers or a thunderstorm.

Fog

Physically, there is no difference between a fog and a cloud. Their appearance and structure are the same. The difference is the method and place of formation. Clouds result when air rises and cools adiabatically. Most fogs are the result of radiational cooling or the movement of air over a cold surface. Fogs also can form when enough water vapor is added to the air to bring about saturation. **Fog is defined as a cloud with its base at or very near the ground.** When fog is dense, visibility may be only a few dozen meters or less, making travel not only difficult but often dangerous.

Fogs Caused by Cooling A blanket of fog is produced in some West Coast locations when warm, moist air from the Pacific Ocean moves over the cold California Current and then is carried onshore by prevailing winds. Fogs also can form on cool, clear, calm nights when Earth's surface cools rapidly by radiation. As the night progresses, a thin layer of air in contact with the ground is cooled below its dew point. As the air cools, it becomes denser and drains into low areas such as river valleys, where thick fog accumulations may occur.

Fogs Caused by Evaporation When cool air moves over warm water, enough moisture may evaporate from the water surface to produce saturation. As the rising water vapor meets the cold air, it immediately condenses and rises with the air that is being warmed from below. This type of fog over water has a steaming appearance, as shown in **Figure 13.** It is fairly common over lakes and rivers in the fall and early winter, when the water may still be relatively warm and the air is rather crisp.

FIGURE 13 Fog When water vapor rising from the warm lake water meets cold air, the water vapor condenses to form fog.

How Precipitation Forms

Cloud droplets are very tiny, averaging less than 20 micrometers in diameter. Because of their small size, the rate at which cloud droplets fall is incredibly slow. Most cloud droplets would evaporate before falling a few meters into unsaturated air below. **For precipitation to form, cloud droplets must grow in volume by roughly one million times.**

Cold Cloud Precipitation

The process that generates much of the precipitation in the middle latitudes occurs in cold clouds and is called the **Bergeron process.** The Bergeron process, shown in **Figure 14,** relies on two physical processes: supercooling and supersaturation. Cloud droplets do not freeze at 0°C as expected. In fact, pure water suspended in air does not freeze until it reaches a temperature of nearly −40°C. Water in the liquid state below 0°C is said to be **supercooled water.** Supercooled water will readily freeze if it touches a solid object. Freezing nuclei are materials that have a crystal form that closely matches that of ice. Freezing nuclei can cause supercooled water to freeze.

When air is saturated (100 percent relative humidity) with respect to water, it is **supersaturated air** (greater than 100 percent humidity) with respect to ice. Ice crystals cannot coexist with water droplets in the air because the air "appears" supersaturated to the ice crystals. Any excess water vapor becomes ice that lowers the relative humidity near the surrounding droplets. Water droplets then evaporate to provide a continual source of water vapor for the growth of ice crystals.

Because the level of supersaturation with respect to ice can be quite high, the growth of ice crystals is rapid enough to produce crystals that are large enough to fall. As they fall, the ice crystals contact cloud drops causing them to freeze. A chain reaction can occur and large crystals, called *snowflakes,* form. When the surface temperature is above 4°C, snowflakes usually melt before they reach the ground.

Warm Cloud Precipitation

Much rainfall can be associated with clouds located well below the freezing level, especially in the tropics. In warm clouds, the mechanism that forms raindrops is the **collision-coalescence process.** Some water-absorbing particles, such as salt, can remove water vapor from the air at relative humidities less than 100 percent, forming drops that are quite large. As these large droplets move through the cloud, they collide and coalesce (join together) with smaller, slower droplets.

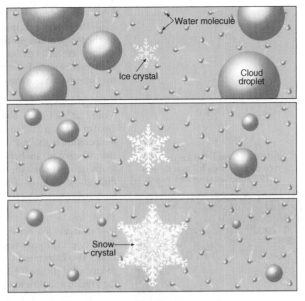

FIGURE 14 The Bergeron Process
Ice crystals grow at the expense of cloud droplets until they are large enough to fall. The size of these particles has been greatly exaggerated.

Facts and Figures

The highest average annual rainfall on Earth was recorded at a station on Mount Waialeule, Hawaii. The station is on a windward mountain slope and gets an average of 1234 cm of rain a year. The record for most rainfall in a 12-month period occurred at Cherrapunji, India, where 2647 cm fell. Over one third of this rainfall—930 cm—fell in the month of July alone. This is 10 times more rain than Chicago receives in an average year.

LESSON 18.3

MAKING HAIL `L2`

Purpose Students will observe the process by which hailstones form.

Materials salt, water, 600-mL beaker, stirring rod, large test tube, crushed ice

Procedure Put 15 g of salt and 50 mL of water into a 600-mL beaker. Stir the water until most of the salt dissolves. Clean a large test tube thoroughly and put 15 mL of cold water in it. Place the test tube in the beaker. Add crushed ice to the beaker until it is almost full. Tell students to watch the next step closely. Take the test tube out of the beaker and drop a small chip of ice into it. Ask students what they observed. *(A layer of ice formed on the ice chip.)* Tell students that hailstones form by a similar process.

Expected Outcome A layer of ice will quickly form around the ice chip.
Visual

3 ASSESS

Evaluate Understanding `L2`

Ask students to draw flowcharts showing the major steps in the Bergeron process of precipitation formation. Their charts should show at least three steps and be consistent with the text and Figure 14.

Reteach `L1`

Use Figure 12 to review different types of clouds. Ask students to explain the name of a cloud and describe the type of weather associated with it.

Forms of Precipitation

The type of precipitation that reaches Earth's surface depends on the temperature profile in the lowest few kilometers of the atmosphere. A *temperature profile* is the way the air temperature changes with altitude. Even on a hot summer day, a heavy downpour may have begun as a snowstorm high in the clouds overhead.

Rain and Snow In meteorology, the term *rain* means drops of water that fall from a cloud and have a diameter of at least 0.5 mm. Smaller drops are called *drizzle*. Recall that when the surface temperature is above 4°C, snowflakes usually melt and continue their descent as rain before they reach the ground. At very low temperatures (when the moisture content of air is low) light, fluffy snow made up of individual six-sided ice crystals forms. At temperatures warmer than −5°C, ice crystals join into larger clumps.

Sleet, Glaze, and Hail *Sleet* is the fall of small particles of clear-to-translucent ice. For sleet to form, a layer of air with temperatures above freezing must overlie a subfreezing layer near the ground. *Glaze,* also known as freezing rain, results when raindrops become supercooled (below 0°C) as they fall through subfreezing air near the ground and turn to ice when they impact objects.

Hail is produced in cumulonimbus clouds. Hailstones begin as small ice pellets that grow by collecting supercooled water droplets as they fall through a cloud. If the ice pellets encounter a strong updraft, they may be carried upward and begin the downward journey once more. Each trip through the supercooled portion of the cloud may be represented by another layer of ice. One hailstone, shown in **Figure 15,** actually grew to weigh 766 grams.

FIGURE 15 Hail This largest recorded hailstone fell over Kansas in 1970 and weighed 766 grams.

18.3 Assessment

Review Key Concepts

1. How are clouds classified?
2. Compare and contrast clouds and fogs.
3. What must happen in order for precipitation to form?
4. Describe how the temperature profile of air near Earth's surface controls the type of precipitation that falls to the ground.

Think Critically

5. **Predict** What type of precipitation would fall to Earth's surface if a thick layer of air near the ground was −8°C?

6. **Classify** Identify the following cloud types as producers of heavy, light, or generally no precipitation.
   a. cirrocumulus
   b. cumulonimbus
   c. stratus
   d. nimbostratus

BIGIDEA WEATHER AND CLIMATE
7. **Compare and Contrast** Write a paragraph comparing the Bergeron and collision-coalescence processes. Relate each to the type(s) of precipitation that can result.

Assessment Answers

1. Clouds are classified according to form and height.
2. Clouds and fogs are physically the same. Fogs are clouds with their bases at or very near the ground.
3. Cloud droplets must increase in volume by about one million times.
4. Ice crystals formed at higher layers in the atmosphere become liquid and fall as rain if temperatures are warm enough near the ground. The thickness of layers at certain temperatures must also be thick enough to impart a change in the type of precipitation.
5. Light, fluffy snow would fall.
6. **a.** generally no precipitation
   b. heavy precipitation
   c. light or no precipitation
   d. light-to-heavy precipitation

7. Both processes are mechanisms that produce precipitation. The Bergeron process occurs in cold clouds and can result in any form of precipitation. The collision-coalescence process occurs in warm clouds and generally produces rain. Paragraphs should include a clear topic statement and several minor sentences that provide detail.

Atmospheric Stability and Air Pollution

Local air quality is closely linked to the atmosphere's ability to scatter pollutants. If the air into which pollution is released is not dispersed, the air will become more toxic. Two of the most important atmospheric conditions affecting the distribution of pollutants are wind speed and atmospheric stability.

High wind speeds mix polluted air into a larger volume of surrounding air, causing the pollution to be more diluted. When winds are slower, there is less turbulence and mixing, so the concentration of pollutants is higher.

Atmospheric stability is a measure of air's ability to flow vertically. When the atmosphere is unstable, air can flow vertically, dispersing pollutants away from their source on Earth's surface. During a temperature inversion, the atmosphere is very stable and it does not move much vertically. Warm air overlying cooler air acts as a lid and prevents upward air flow, which traps pollutants below, as shown in **Figure 16.**

While all temperature inversions form close to Earth's surface, some form closer than others. A surface inversion develops close to the ground on clear and relatively calm nights because the ground is a better radiator of heat than the air above it. Radiation from the ground to the clear night sky causes more rapid cooling at the surface than higher in the atmosphere. The result is that the air close to the ground is cooled more than the air above, yielding a temperature profile similar to the one shown in **Figure 17.** After sunrise, the ground is heated and the inversion disappears.

Although surface inversions usually are shallow, they may be thick in regions where the land surface is uneven. Because cold air is denser than warm air, the chilled air near the surface gradually drains from slopes into adjacent lowlands and valleys. As might be expected, these thicker surface inversions will not spread out as quickly after sunrise.

FIGURE 16
Air Pollution in Downtown Los Angeles Temperature inversions act as lids to trap pollutants below.

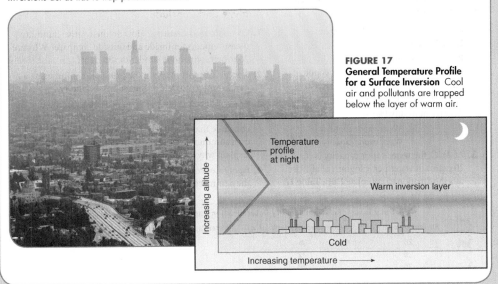

FIGURE 17
General Temperature Profile for a Surface Inversion Cool air and pollutants are trapped below the layer of warm air.

Moisture, Clouds, and Precipitation **523**

Atmospheric Stability and Air Pollution   L2

Background

- The strength of the wind and the stability of the air are critical because they determine how rapidly pollutants are diluted by mixing with the surrounding air after leaving the source.

- The distance between Earth's surface and the height to which vertical air movements extend is termed the *mixing depth.* Generally, the greater the mixing depth, the better the air quality. When the mixing depth is several kilometers, pollutants are mixed through a large volume of cleaner air and dilute rapidly. When the mixing depth is shallow, pollutants are confined to a much smaller volume of air and concentrations can reach unhealthy levels.

- Because heating of Earth's surface by the sun enhances convectional movements, mixing depths are usually greater during the afternoon hours. For the same reason, mixing depths during the summer months are typically greater than during the winter months.

- Many extensive and long-lived air-pollution episodes are linked to temperature inversions that develop in association with the sinking air that characterizes slow-moving centers of high pressure. As the air sinks to lower altitudes, it is compressed and so its temperature rises. Because turbulence is almost always present near the ground, this lowermost portion of the atmosphere is generally prevented from participating in the general subsidence. Thus, an inversion develops aloft between the lower turbulent zone and the subsiding warmed layers above.

Teaching Tip

Ask students to research various methods that meteorologists use to define atmospheric stability. Have them explain each method and cite the pros and cons of each use.

MEASURING HUMIDITY L2

Objectives
In this activity, students will
- calculate relative humidity from air moisture content data.
- determine the relative humidity inside and outside using a psychrometer.

Skills Observe, Measure, Analyze Data, Calculate

Prep Time 10 minutes

Alternative Materials (if a psychrometer is not available) 2 thermometers, cotton gauze, paper fan, string

Class Time 30 minutes

Teaching Tip To save time, construct the wet-bulb thermometer before the lab.

It may be helpful to refer students to the Relative Humidity Chart in Appendix F on p. 747 of the Student Edition.

Expected Outcomes Students will practice calculating relative humidity from the moisture content of air. They also will experience using a psychrometer and determinative tables to determine the relative humidity in the classroom and outside. Relative humidity will vary widely with location; students can compare outside measurements with local meteorological data if they are available.

Sample Data
Procedure 3.
Data Table 1 Relative Humidity Determination Based on Water Vapor Content

Air Temperature (°C)	Water Vapor Content (g/kg)	Water Vapor Capacity (g/kg)	Relative Humidity (%)
25	5	20	25
25	12	[20]	[60]
25	18	[20]	[90]

Procedure 4. 51 percent

Measuring Humidity

Problem How can relative humidity be determined?

Materials calculator, water at room temperature, psychrometer
Alternative materials for psychrometer: 2 thermometers, cotton gauze, paper fan, string

Skills Observe, Measure, Analyze Data, Calculate

Connect to the Big idea Relative humidity is a measurement used to describe water vapor in the air. In general, it expresses how close the air is to saturation. In this lab, you will use a psychrometer and a data table to determine the relative humidity of air.

Procedure

Part A: Calculating Relative Humidity From Water Vapor Content

1. On a sheet of paper, make a copy of **Data Table 1.**

2. Relative humidity is the ratio of the air's water vapor content to its water vapor capacity at a given temperature. Relative humidity is expressed as a percent.

   Relative humidity (%) =
   $$\frac{\text{Water vapor content}}{\text{Water vapor capacity}} \times 100$$

3. At 25°C, the water vapor capacity is 20 grams of water per kilogram of air. Use this information to complete **Data Table 1.**

Part B: Determining Relative Humidity Using a Psychrometer

4. A psychrometer consists of two thermometers. The wet-bulb thermometer has a cloth wick that is wet with water and spun for about 1 minute. Relative humidity is determined from the difference in temperature reading between the dry-bulb temperature and the wet-bulb temperature, by using **Data Table 2.** For example, suppose a dry-bulb temperature is measured as 20°C, and a wet-bulb temperature is 14°C. Read the relative humidity from **Data Table 2.**

5. If a psychrometer is not available, construct a wet-bulb thermometer by tying a piece of cotton gauze around the end of a thermometer. Wet it with room-temperature water, and fan it until the temperature stops changing.

6. Make wet-bulb and dry-bulb temperature measurements for air in your classroom and air outside the school building. On a separate sheet of paper, make a copy of **Data Table 3.** Record your measurements. Use your measurements and **Data Table 2** to determine the relative humidity inside and outside.

Analyze and Conclude

1. **Compare and Contrast** How do the relative humidity measurements for inside and outside compare? Why are your determinations similar or different?

2. **Apply Concepts** Explain the principle behind using a psychrometer to determine relative humidity.

3. **Apply Concepts** Suppose you hear on the radio that the relative humidity is 90 percent on a winter day. Can you conclude that this air contains more moisture than air on a summer day with a 40 percent relative humidity? Explain why or why not.

4. **Apply Concepts** Why is a cool basement often damp in the summer?

Data Table 1 Relative Humidity Determination Based on Water Vapor Content			
Air Temperature (C)	Water Vapor Content (g/kg)	Water Vapor Capacity (g/kg)	Relative Humidity (%)
25	5	20	25
25	12		
25	18		

Data Table 2 Relative Humidity (percent)

Dry-bulb Temperature (°C)	Depression of Wet-bulb Temperature (Dry-bulb Temperature − Wet-bulb Temperature = Depression of the Wet Bulb)																					
	1	2	3	4	5	6	7	8	9	10	11	12	13	14	15	16	17	18	19	20	21	22
−20	28																					
−18	40																					
−16	48	0																				
−14	55	11																				
−12	61	23																				
−10	66	33	0																			
−8	71	41	13																			
−6	73	48	20	0																		
−4	77	54	43	11																		
−2	79	58	37	20	1																	
0	81	63	45	28	11																	
2	83	67	51	36	20	6																
4	85	70	56	42	27	14																
6	86	72	59	46	35	22	10	0														
8	87	74	62	51	39	28	17	6														
10	88	76	65	54	43	33	24	13	4													
12	88	78	67	57	48	38	28	19	10	2												
14	89	79	69	60	50	41	33	25	16	8	1											
16	90	80	71	62	54	45	37	29	21	14	7	1										
18	91	81	72	64	56	48	40	33	26	19	12	6	0									
20	91	82	74	66	58	51	44	36	30	23	17	11	5	0								
22	92	83	75	68	60	53	46	40	33	27	21	15	10	4	0							
24	92	84	76	69	62	55	49	42	36	30	25	20	14	9	4	0						
26	92	85	77	70	64	57	51	45	39	34	28	23	18	13	9	5						
28	93	86	78	71	65	59	53	47	42	36	31	26	21	17	12	8	2					
30	93	86	79	72	66	61	55	49	44	39	34	29	25	20	16	12	8	4				
32	93	86	80	73	68	62	56	51	46	41	36	32	27	22	19	14	11	8	4			
34	93	86	81	74	69	63	58	52	48	43	38	34	30	26	22	18	14	11	8	5		
36	94	87	81	75	69	64	59	54	50	44	40	36	32	28	24	21	17	13	10	7	4	
38	94	87	82	76	70	66	60	55	51	46	42	38	34	30	26	23	20	16	13	10	7	5
40	94	89	82	76	71	67	61	57	52	48	44	40	36	33	29	25	22	19	16	13	10	7

Relative Humidity Values

Data Table 3 Relative Humidity Determinations Using Dry- and Wet-Bulb Thermometers

	Inside	Outside
Dry-bulb temperature (°C)		
Wet-bulb temperature (°C)		
Difference between dry-bulb and wet-bulb temperatures (°C)		
Relative humidity (%)		

Analyze and Conclude

1. Outdoor relative humidity determinations can be compared to meteorological reports for the day. Indoor relative humidity will vary widely depending on whether classrooms are air-conditioned, what season it is, or other variables.

2. Relative humidity determinations with the psychrometer depend on the evaporation rate of the wick on the wet bulb. The drier the air, the larger the wet-bulb temperature will be depressed, and the lower the relative humidity.

3. No; relative humidity depends on the capacity of air to hold water, which varies with temperature. The actual water content of winter air with 90 percent relative humidity can be less than summer air with 40 percent relative humidity.

4. The relative humidity will increase as air is cooled in the basement.

Kinesthetic, Logical

Change Subjects and Take Breaks
Tell students that when they feel that they are losing their ability to focus, they should change the task they are working on, the subject they are studying, or even the room they are in. Suggest that students organize all their subjects into manageable blocks. When students have finished one block, they should switch to another block in another part of the subject or to a different subject. Encourage students to take five-minute breaks every 30–40 minutes to refresh themselves.

Think Visually

a. form
b. cumulus (or stratus)
c. stratus (or cumulus)
d. high (or low)
e. low (or high)

21st Century Learning

Critical Thinking and Systems Thinking

How can you measure dew point?
As discussed in Lesson 18.1, dew point is one indication of the humidity of air. Have students research a simple method for measuring the dew point. Encourage them to develop a plan for measuring the dew point. They must assemble the necessary materials, and measure the dew point on several days. Encourage students to take notes about the weather conditions as they make their measurements. Ask pairs of students to work together to discern and describe any patterns they notice in the data. Finally, students should tabulate and post their results and information in a data sheet alongside the official weather values for those days in your location.

Homework Guide

Lesson	Questions
1	1–3, 5, 9, 13, 16, 18, 25–27, 30
2	4, 11, 12, 15, 17, 19–23, 28, 29
3	6–8, 10, 14, 24

---

18 Study Guide

Big idea Weather and Climate

18.1 Water in the Atmosphere

🔑 Water vapor is the most important gas in the atmosphere for understanding atmospheric processes.

🔑 The process of changing state requires that energy is transferred in the form of heat.

🔑 When saturated, warm air contains more water vapor than saturated cold air.

🔑 Relative humidity is a ratio of the air's actual water-vapor content compared with the amount of water vapor needed for saturation at that temperature and pressure.

🔑 When the water-vapor content of air remains constant, lowering air temperature causes an increase in relative humidity, and raising air temperature causes a decrease in relative humidity.

precipitation (504)	humidity (506)
latent heat (505)	saturated (506)
evaporation (505)	relative humidity (506)
condensation (506)	dew point (508)
sublimation (506)	hygrometer (508)
deposition (506)	

18.2 Cloud Formation

🔑 When air is allowed to expand, it cools, and when it is compressed, it warms.

🔑 Four mechanisms that can cause air to rise are orographic lifting, frontal wedging, convergence, and localized convective lifting.

🔑 Stable air tends to remain in its original position, while unstable air tends to rise.

🔑 For condensation of water to occur, the air must be saturated.

dry adiabatic rate (511)	front (512)
wet adiabatic rate (511)	temperature inversion (514)
orographic lifting (512)	condensation nuclei (516)

18.3 Cloud Types and Precipitation

🔑 Clouds are classified on the basis of their form and height.

🔑 Fog is a cloud with its base at or very near the ground.

🔑 In order for precipitation to form, cloud droplets must grow in volume by roughly one million times.

🔑 The type of precipitation that reaches Earth's surface depends on the temperature profile in the lowest few kilometers of the atmosphere.

cirrus (517)
cumulus (517)
stratus (518)
Bergeron process (521)
supercooled water (521)
supersaturated air (521)
collision-coalescence process (521)

Think Visually

Copy the concept map below onto a sheet of paper. Use information from the chapter to complete the concept map.

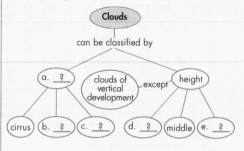

Assessment Answers

Review Content

1. c	**2.** a	**3.** c
4. a	**5.** b	**6.** b
7. a	**8.** c	**9.** d
10. a		

Understand Concepts

11. Towering clouds form that often produce heavy thunderstorms or other severe weather.
12. When air in the lower atmosphere flows together, lifting occurs, often causing clouds and precipitation.
13. The cold glass cools the air in contact with it below the air's dew point, and water vapor condenses on the glass.
14. Condensation is the process of changing water vapor to the liquid state. Precipitation is any form of water that falls from a cloud.

18 Assessment

Choose the letter that best answers the question or completes the statement.

1. What is the general term for water vapor in air?
   a. capacity
   b. condensation
   c. humidity
   d. saturation

2. During which process does water vapor change to the liquid state?
   a. condensation
   b. deposition
   c. melting
   d. sublimation

3. The ratio of air's actual water-vapor content to the amount of water needed for saturation is the
   a. adiabatic rate.
   b. dew point.
   c. relative humidity.
   d. water capacity.

4. What are visible mixtures of tiny water droplets or ice crystals suspended in air?
   a. clouds
   b. dew
   c. hail
   d. sleet

5. Air that has a 100 percent relative humidity is said to be
   a. dry.
   b. saturated.
   c. stable.
   d. unstable.

6. Compared to clouds, fogs are
   a. a different composition.
   b. at lower altitudes.
   c. colder.
   d. thicker.

7. Which of the following clouds are high, white, and thin?
   a. cirrus
   b. cumulus
   c. nimbostratus
   d. stratus

8. Which of the following words means "rainy cloud"?
   a. cirrus
   b. cumulus
   c. nimbus
   d. stratus

9. Which of the following substances changes from one state of matter to another at temperatures and pressures experienced at Earth's surface?
   a. carbon dioxide
   b. nitrogen
   c. oxygen
   d. water

10. Which of the following forms when supercooled raindrops freeze on contact with solid objects near Earth's surface?
    a. freezing rain
    b. hail
    c. sleet
    d. snow

Understand Concepts

11. What happens when unstable air is forced to rise?

12. Describe the conditions that might cause convergence.

13. As you drink an ice-cold beverage on a hot day, the outside of the glass becomes wet. Explain why this happens.

14. What is the difference between condensation and precipitation?

15. Why does air cool when it rises through the atmosphere? What is this type of cooling known as?

16. Write a general statement relating air temperature and the amount of water vapor needed to saturate the air.

17. Describe the difference between clouds and water vapor.

18. List two changes of state for water that cause latent heat to be released.

Use the figure below to answer Questions 19 and 20.

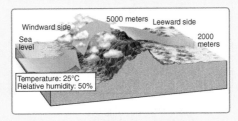

19. Which air-lifting mechanism is shown?

20. Use the dry adiabatic rate of 10°C per kilometer to determine the air temperature on the windward side of the mountains at an altitude of 500 meters.

---

15. Air expands as it rises, which causes it to cool. This type of cooling is known as adiabatic cooling.
16. The warmer the air temperature, the more water vapor is needed to saturate the air.
17. Clouds are composed of liquid water droplets or ice particles. Water vapor is water in the gaseous state.
18. Two changes of state are water vapor changing to liquid water (condensation) and liquid water changing to ice (freezing).
19. The mechanism is orographic lifting.
20. The temperature is 20°C.

ASSESSMENT

Think Critically

21. Thermals are warm air parcels that are less dense than surrounding air. Their buoyancy gives birds lift as they glide above them.

22. Some types of pavement, such as blacktop, in urban areas have low reflecting capabilities, and therefore low albedos. When these areas absorb sunlight, they obtain heat that is then transferred to the atmosphere above the pavement, causing hot pockets of air to form and rise by localized convective uplift.

23. In general, when unstable air rises it produces towering clouds and heavy precipitation. In contrast, a stable air mass resists movement vertically (does not turn over), which may stagnate weather patterns.

24. Low lying areas such as river valleys should be avoided because thick fog accumulations may form in them.

Math Skills

25. a. 47 g/kg
b. 3.5 g/kg
c. 2 g/kg

26. It decreases by 3.5 g/kg. This is a 50% decrease.

27. 7 g/kg ÷ 10 g/kg × 100 = 70%

Concepts in Action

28. Moist air from the Pacific Ocean is forced up the windward slope by orographic lifting, causing cloud formation and heavy precipitation.

29. Heat is absorbed when ice changes to water (melting), when water changes to water vapor (evaporation), and when ice turns directly to water vapor without passing through the liquid state (sublimation). Heat is liberated during condensation, freezing, and deposition.

30. Student paragraphs should reflect the following concepts: An increase in elevation often brings more precipitation, especially on windward slopes. A decrease in the area covered by forests and other types of vegetation would reduce precipitation because less moisture would be added to the atmosphere by transpiration from plants. Winds blowing more frequently from an adjacent body of water would increase the amount of precipitation as more moisture is brought to the area.

Think Critically

21. **Apply Concepts** What is the physical property of thermals that helps birds of prey? Describe how this physical property helps these birds.

22. **Apply Concepts** Explain how urban areas contribute to localized convective lifting.

23. **Identify Cause and Effect** Describe how atmospheric stability affects daily weather. Include specific examples.

24. **Apply Concepts** In general, when traveling in foggy conditions, what types of topography should you be most cautious of?

Math Skills

Use the table below to answer Questions 25–27.

Water Vapor Needed for Saturation		
Temperature		Mass of water vapor per kg of air (g/kg)
°C	°F	
−40	(−40)	0.1
−30	(−22)	0.3
−20	(−4)	0.75
−10	(14)	2
0	(32)	3.5
5	(41)	5
10	(50)	7
15	(59)	10
20	(68)	14
25	(77)	20
30	(86)	26.5
35	(95)	35
40	(104)	47

25. **Analyze Data** According to the table, how much water vapor is required to saturate a kilogram of air at each of the following temperatures?
a. 40°C
b. 0°C
c. −10°C

26. **Calculate** How does the amount of water vapor required to saturate 1 kilogram of air change when it is cooled from 10°C to 0°C?

27. **Calculate** Use the table to determine the relative humidity of air at 15°C when its water vapor content is 7 g/kg.

Concepts in Action

28. **Infer** Mount Waialeale, Hawaii, is located on a windward mountain slope. A weather station there records the highest average annual rainfall at 1234 cm. Explain what processes could contribute to this extreme rainfall.

29. **Interpret Visuals** After studying Figure 2, summarize the processes by which water changes from one state of matter to another. For each case, point out whether heat energy is absorbed or released.

30. **Writing in Science** The amount of precipitation that falls at any particular place and time is controlled by the quantity of moisture in the air and many other factors, which may include (1) an increase in the elevation of the land, (2) a decrease in the area covered by forests and other types of vegetation, and (3) an increase in the percentage of time that the winds blow from an adjacent body of water. Write a paragraph explaining how each of these factors might change the precipitation at a particular location.

Performance-Based Assessment

Design an Experiment Design and conduct an experiment that explores daily variations in temperature and relative humidity. As a first step, write a clear hypothesis statement. Then plan and design the experiment. Include sample data tables in your plan. Have your teacher approve your plan before you begin.

Performance-Based Assessment

Student hypotheses should state that relative humidity decreases as daytime temperatures increase. Students should plan times to make relative humidity measurements that are spaced throughout the day. Equipment needed is the same as that used in the Exploration Lab.

Standardized Test Prep

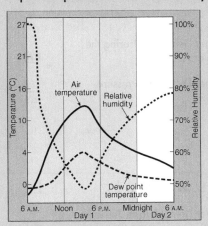
Choose the letter that best answers the question.

1 The dew point is the temperature at which—
  A cumulus clouds change to cirrus clouds
  B hailstones are formed
  C liquid water changes to vapor
  D air becomes saturated with water vapor

2 Which process is most important for cloud formation?
  F cooling by compression of air
  G cooling by contact with a cold surface
  H cooling by expansion of air
  J cooling by radiation from Earth's surface

3 The process by which water vapor changes directly to a solid is—
  A condensation
  B deposition
  C evaporation
  D sublimation

Use the graph below to answer Question 4.

Graph 2 Temperature and Relative Humidity

4 According to this graph, when is relative humidity at its maximum?
  F midnight
  G 6 A.M.
  H noon
  J 6 P.M.

If You Have Trouble With . . .

Question	1	2	3	4
See Lesson	18.1	18.2	18.1	18.2

Standardized Test Prep
1 D
2 H
3 B
4 G

19 Air Pressure and Wind Planning Guide

BIGIDEA: WEATHER AND CLIMATE

Lesson Objectives		Activities
19.1 Understanding Air Pressure, pp. 532–536 19.1 **Describe** how air pressure is exerted on objects. 19.2 **Explain** how changes in air pressure affect the mercury column of a barometer. 19.3 **Identify** the ultimate energy source for wind. 19.4 **Describe** how the Coriolis effect influences freely moving objects.		**TE** Teacher Demo: Measuring the Mass of Air, p. 532 [L2] **TE** Teacher Demo: Air Pressure, p. 533 [L2]
19.2 Pressure Centers and Winds, pp. 537–542 19.5 **Explain** how winds blow around pressure centers in the Northern and Southern Hemispheres. 19.6 **Describe** the air pressure patterns within cyclones and anticyclones. 19.7 **Describe** how friction controls the net flow of air around a cyclone and an anticyclone. 19.8 **Explain** how the unequal heating of Earth's surface affects the atmosphere.		**TE** Build Science Skills, p. 537 [L2] **TE** Teacher Demo: Warm Air Rises, p. 538 [L2]
19.3 Regional Wind Systems, pp. 543–548 19.9 **Identify** the causes of local winds. 19.10 **Describe** the general movement of weather in the United States. 19.11 **Compare and contrast** weather patterns characteristic of El Niño and La Niña events.		**TE** Teacher Demo: Differential Heating, p. 544 [L2] **SE** **Map It:** Global Precipitation, p. 548 [L2]
Chapter Features and Labs		
Try It How Do Gradients Influence Speed? p. 531		**LM** Analyzing Pressure Systems [L2]
Earth & Its Systems Tracking El Niño from Space, p. 549		
Exploration Lab Observing Wind Patterns, pp. 550–551		

Ability Levels

L1 For students who need additional help
L2 For all students
L3 For students who need to be challenged

Components

SE	Student Edition	LP	Lesson Plans
TE	Teacher's Edition	AA	Active Art
LM	Laboratory Manual	PD	Planet Diary
CT	Chapter Tests	GEODe	Geode CD-ROM
GRSW	Guided Reading & Study Workbook	eText	
CTB	Computer Test Bank		

Resources	Lesson Assessment
GRSW Lesson 19.1 **LP** Lesson Planning 19.1 **AA** Air Pressure **GEODe** The Atmosphere: Air Pressure and Wind	**SE** Lesson 19.1 Assessment, p. 536 **eText** Lesson 19.1
GRSW Lesson 19.2 **LP** Lesson Planning 19.2 **PD** Weather Forecasting	**SE** Lesson 19.2 Assessment, p. 542 **eText** Lesson 19.2
GRSW Lesson 19.3 **LP** Lesson Planning 19.3	**SE** Lesson 19.3 Assessment, p. 548 **eText** Lesson 19.3

Materials for Activities and Labs

Quantities for each group

STUDENT EDITION

Try It, p. 531
textbooks, wood blocks, or other items to raise one end of ramp; wood plank to use as ramp; tennis ball; stopwatch

Exploration Lab, pp. 550–551
1 copy each of Figure 1 and Figure 2 from the Earth Science Laboratory Manual, paper, pencil

TEACHER'S EDITION

Teacher Demo, p. 532
balloon, balance scale

Teacher Demo, p. 533
drinking glass, water, cardboard, sink or basin

Build Science Skills, p. 537
globe, pointer

Teacher Demo, p. 538
2 meter sticks, 2 large paper grocery bags, string, tape, lamp with incandescent bulb

Teacher Demo, p. 544
2 containers, soil, water, 2 thermometers

Assessment

CHAPTER ASSESSMENT
SE Assessment, pp. 553–554
CT Chapter 19 Test
CTB Chapter 19
eText Chapter 19

21st Century Learning

Problem Identification, Formulation, and Solution: What Effects has El Niño Had on Your Weather? TE p. 552

Common Themes

Weather is a complicated and hard-to-predict result of interactions between atmospheric pressure, ocean temperatures, and land conditions.

Space and Time The atmosphere applies air pressure, which is exerted in all directions, and can be measured with a barometer. Wind is the result of air flowing from areas of high pressure to areas of low pressure.

Forces and Motion Wind patterns are controlled by atmospheric pressure differences, the Coriolis effect, and friction. Steep pressure gradients cause strong winds. The Coriolis effect is a result of Earth's rotation. In the Northern Hemisphere, winds blow inward and counterclockwise around an area of low pressure, forming a cyclone; winds blow outward and clockwise around an area of high pressure, forming an anticyclone. Bad weather is often associated with cyclones.

Matter and Energy Global wind patterns result from the atmospheric heat transfer system, which moves warm air toward the poles and cool air toward the equator, as well as from the Coriolis effect and the locations of continents. Local winds often result from daily changes in temperature that result from topographic variations (like between mountains and valleys) or changes in surface composition (like between land and ocean).

Earth as a System Changes in ocean currents, like with the El Niño and La Niña conditions, can have significant effects on weather patterns.

Michael Wysession
Washington University

EARTH SCIENCE REFRESHER

The Coriolis Effect

The Coriolis effect often seems very mysterious to students. Contrary to popular myth, the Coriolis effect is too small to make your sink drain in a clockwise direction (try it—about half the time it will drain clockwise; the other half, counter-clockwise). However, the Coriolis effect is noticeable in some everyday applications. As you will see on TE p. 535 (Facts and Figures), the Coriolis effect can have a measurable change in the path of a hard-hit baseball.

One of the most famous results of the Coriolis effect occurred in 1915 in a sea battle between the British and German navies near the Falkland Islands, off the coast of South America. To the surprise of the gunners of the British ships, their usually accurate shots were landing almost 100 m to the left of their targets (the German ships). While the British engineers certainly knew about the Coriolis effect, they had calibrated their guns for the Northern Hemisphere, where the Coriolis effect made their shots veer to the right. Here in the Southern Hemisphere, the Coriolis effect made the shots veer to the left. As a result of their mistaken calibration, they actually doubled the Coriolis effect's change in their cannon targets.

Address Misconceptions

Students may have the misconception that no outside factor except heat is required to cause masses of warm air to rotate as they rise upward in the atmosphere. Point out that the cyclonic motion in low-pressure cells is primarily a result of the Coriolis effect. For a strategy that helps to overcome this misconception, see **Address Misconceptions** on **TE p. 538.**

The Coriolis effect is also important in another, less observable, way. It is the Coriolis effect on the flow of liquid iron in Earth's outer core that is responsible for Earth's magnetic field. The outer core's liquid iron is vigorously convecting as it cools off, losing its heat to the surrounding mantle. As this liquid flows, the Coriolis effect causes it to move in a spiraling motion, just like flowing air in the atmosphere. Because the core's liquid iron is electrically charged, the spiraling motion creates a magnetic field, which we can measure at the surface. We not only use the magnetic field for navigation (as do some migratory birds, which have been found to have magnetite mineral grains in their brains!), but the magnetic field protects Earth from the ionized particles of the solar wind, which would otherwise be harmful for life.

The Worst Wind Ever

Doppler radar has clocked wind speeds in some tornadoes at over 500 km per hour. However, the world's record for the greatest wind speed recorded on land is 372 km/h, recorded during a storm at the top of Mt. Washington in New Hampshire. This record wind, the strongest ever recorded on an anemometer, occurred on April 12, 1934. Mt. Washington is the tallest mountain in New England, and because of its height and location, is often subject to some incredibly bad storms, which is why it has had weather observatories on its summit dating back to 1870. The mountain's summit now has a state-of-the-art weather station and museum. In 1934, however, the meteorologists' ability to survive and maintain the station's operation during the record storm was as remarkable as the wind speeds themselves.

BUILD READING LITERACY
Make Inferences
Reading Between the Lines

Strategy Help students fill in information not found in the text by drawing on prior knowledge and using context clues. To use this strategy, students must identify their prior knowledge, recognize clues in the text, and make connections between their prior knowledge and text clues to make an inference. The passage Non-Rotating Earth Model on p. 540 in Lesson 19.2 provides a sample.

Example

1. Read aloud or have students read aloud a portion of the chosen text. Point out an example of the author's referring to something without explaining it completely. Tell students that texts often do not explain every detail because they assume that the reader has a certain amount of background knowledge.

2. Model this strategy by thinking aloud. First, mention facts you already know that are directly related to the subject, either from your own experience or from what you have read about it previously in the text.

3. Next, read text clues aloud and point out what those clues tell about the concept.

4. Then, explain what you understand about the text by combining your prior knowledge and text clues.

5. Have students read the next paragraph or two silently, applying the strategies to make an inference. Discuss their inferences.

6. Repeat this process, having students work with partners to find other opportunities to make inferences in the chapter.

See TE pp. 534 and 539 for a script on how to use this strategy with students. For additional strategies, see TE p. 546.

CHAPTER 19

ASSESS PRIOR KNOWLEDGE

Use the Chapter Pretest below to assess students' prior knowledge. As needed, review these concepts.

Review Science Concepts

Lesson 19.1 Reviewing the definition of air pressure and learning how friction, the Coriolis effect, and air pressure differences affect winds will help students begin to understand the mechanisms that drive Earth's weather.

Lesson 19.2 Knowledge of cyclonic and anticyclonic pressure centers and Earth's global winds gives students further understanding of how air pressure patterns affect weather.

Lesson 19.3 Learning how locally generated pressure gradients produce small-scale winds further enhances student understanding of weather. Learning how El Niño and La Niña events affect air movement, locally as well as globally, helps students recognize the complexity of Earth's weather patterns.

Review Math Skills

Analyze Data, Measure, Calculate
Students need to analyze data shown on a weather map and calculate how often winds blow from different directions in the mapped area.

Direct students to the Math Skills in the Skills Handbook at the end of the student text.

19 Air Pressure and Wind

Big idea | **Weather and Climate**
Q: What determines local and global wind patterns?

530

Chapter Pretest

1. What source of energy fuels the wind? *(sunlight)*

2. Which of the following statements about air pressure is NOT true? *(d)*
  a. Air pressure is exerted in all directions.
  b. Air pressure equals weight of air.
  c. Air pressure is measured using the element mercury.
  d. Air pressure is not associated with weather.

3. What instrument is used to measure air pressure? *(a)*
  a. barometer   **b.** anemometer
  c. hygrometer   **d.** thermometer

4. Which of the following is influenced by the Coriolis effect? *(b)*
  a. wind speed
  b. wind direction
  c. air pressure
  d. pressure gradients

5. Which of the following statements about wind is true? *(d)*
  a. Wind always blows in the same direction.
  b. Wind always blows at the same speed.
  c. Wind is not affected by air pressure.
  d. Wind direction in one place can change over the course of a day.

Wind farms such as this one in Southern California harness energy from wind to generate electricity.

INQUIRY ?
TRY IT!

HOW DO GRADIENTS INFLUENCE SPEED?

Procedure

1. Build a steep ramp using textbooks, wooden blocks, or other items in your classroom. Roll a tennis ball down the ramp.
2. Now build another ramp. This ramp should have a slope, or gradient, that is much less steep. Keep the length of the ramp the same as in step 1.
3. Roll the tennis ball down the second ramp. Compare the speeds of the ball for both ramps.

Think About It

1. **Observe** Which ramp setup caused the ball to roll the fastest?
2. **Apply Concepts** Like the ramps you built, air pressure also forms gradients. Wind is air that flows down the "slopes" of air pressure gradients. What air pressure conditions do you think would favor faster wind speeds?

531

ENGAGE/EXPLORE

INQUIRY
TRY IT!

HOW DO GRADIENTS INFLUENCE SPEED?   L2

Purpose In this activity, students begin to recognize that the steepness of a gradient affects the speed of matter falling, or flowing, down that gradient. They also begin to understand that an increase in the steepness of an air pressure gradient will increase wind speed.

Skills Observe, Apply Concepts

Prep Time 15 minutes

Materials textbooks; wood blocks, or other items to raise one end of ramp; wood plank to use as a ramp; tennis ball; stopwatch

Class Time 15–20 minutes

Expected Outcome The speed of the tennis ball increases with the steepness of the ramp.

Think About It

1. Students will note faster speeds for steeper ramps made from the same materials.
2. Students will infer that large changes in air pressure, or "steeper" air pressure gradients, would cause faster wind speeds.

1 FOCUS

Lesson Objectives

19.1 **Describe** how air pressure is exerted on objects.

19.2 **Explain** how changes in air pressure affect the mercury column of a barometer.

19.3 **Identify** the ultimate energy source for wind.

19.4 **Describe** how the Coriolis effect influences freely moving objects.

Build Vocabulary   L2

Visualize Explain to students that the Coriolis effect is named after French mathematician Gaspard Gustave de Coriolis, who described the effect of Earth's rotation on the direction of winds and ocean currents in 1835. Tell students that they may remember the term more easily if they produce a mental picture. Have them imagine looking down at Earth from a high-altitude aircraft traveling in a straight line heading south from the north pole and watching the globe rotate beneath them as they move from one pole to the other.

Reading Strategy   L2

a. Air pressure is measured with barometers, using the principle that fluids will deform if the weight of air is exerted on them. **b.** the pressure gradient, Coriolis effect, and friction

2 INSTRUCT

(Teacher **Demo**)

MEASURING THE MASS OF AIR   L2

Purpose Students prove air has mass by comparing the mass of a balloon when empty and when filled with air.

Materials balloon, balance

Procedure Blow up a balloon and determine its mass using a balance. Remove the balloon, release the air, and replace the balloon on the balance. Find the mass again.

Expected Outcome Students will see that the empty balloon is lighter than the air-filled balloon.

Visual, Logical

19.1 Understanding Air Pressure

Key Questions

🔑 **Describe** how air pressure is exerted on objects.

🔑 **What happens to the mercury column of a barometer when air pressure changes?**

🔑 **What is the ultimate energy source for wind?**

🔑 **How does the Coriolis effect influence free-moving objects?**

Vocabulary

- air pressure • barometer
- isobars • pressure gradient
- Coriolis effect • jet stream

Reading Strategy

Identify Main Ideas Copy the table below. As you read, write the main ideas for each topic.

Topic	Main Ideas
Air Pressure Defined	Air pressure is the weight of air above. It is exerted in all directions.
Measuring Air Pressure	a. _____?
Factors Affecting Wind	b. _____?

OF THE VARIOUS elements of weather and climate, changes in air pressure are the least noticeable. When you listen to a weather report, you probably focus on precipitation, temperature, and humidity. Most people don't wonder about air pressure. Although you might not perceive hour-to-hour and day-to-day variations in air pressure, they are very important in producing changes in our weather. For example, variations in air pressure from place to place can generate winds such as those shown in **Figure 1.** The winds, in turn, bring change in temperature and humidity. Air pressure is one of the basic weather elements and is an important factor in weather forecasting. Air pressure is closely tied to the other elements of weather in a cause-and-effect relationship.

Air Pressure

Air pressure is simply the pressure exerted by the weight of air above. Average air pressure at sea level is about 1 kilogram per square centimeter. This pressure is roughly the same pressure that is produced by a column of water 10 meters in height. You can calculate that the air pressure exerted on the top of a 50-centimeter-by-100-centimeter school desk exceeds 5000 kilograms, which is about the mass of a 50-passenger school bus. Why doesn't the desk collapse under the weight of the air above it? 🔑 **Air pressure is exerted in all directions—down, up, and sideways. The air pressure pushing down on an object balances the air pressure pushing up on the object.**

☑ **Reading Checkpoint** What is average air pressure at sea level?

FIGURE 1 Winds These palm trees in Corpus Christi, Texas, are being pounded by hurricane-force winds.

Imagine a tall aquarium that has the same dimensions as the desktop in the previous example. When this aquarium is filled to a height of 10 meters, the water pressure at the bottom equals 1 atmosphere, or 1 kilogram per square centimeter. Now imagine what will happen if this aquarium is placed on top of a student desk so that all the force is directed downward. The desk collapses because the pressure downward is greater than the pressure exerted in the other directions. When the desk is placed inside the aquarium and allowed to sink to the bottom, however, the desk does not collapse in the water because the water pressure is exerted in all directions, not just downward. The desk, like your body, can withstand the pressure of 1 atmosphere.

Measuring Air Pressure

When meteorologists measure atmospheric pressure, they use a unit called the millibar (mb). Standard sea-level pressure is 1013.2 millibars. You might have heard the phrase "inches of mercury," which is used by the media to describe atmospheric pressure. In 1643, Torricelli, a student of the famous Italian scientist Galileo, invented the mercury barometer. A **barometer** is a device used for measuring air pressure (*bar* = pressure, *metron* = measuring instrument).

Torricelli correctly described the atmosphere as a vast ocean of air that exerts pressure on us and all objects around us. To measure this force, he filled a glass tube, closed at one end, with mercury. He then put the tube upside down into a dish of mercury, as shown in **Figure 2A**. The mercury flowed out of the tube until the weight of the column was balanced by the pressure that the atmosphere exerted on the surface of the mercury in the dish. In other words, the weight of the mercury in the column (tube) equaled the weight of the same size column of air that extended from the ground to the top of the atmosphere.

When air pressure increases, the mercury in the barometric tube rises. When air pressure decreases, so does the height of the mercury column. With some improvements, the mercury barometer is still the standard instrument used today for measuring air pressure.

The need for a smaller and more portable instrument for measuring air pressure led to the development of the *aneroid barometer*. The aneroid barometer uses a metal chamber with some air removed. This partially emptied chamber is extremely sensitive to variations in air pressure. It changes shape and compresses as the air pressure increases, and it expands as the pressure decreases. One advantage of the aneroid barometer is that it can be easily connected to a recording device, as shown in **Figure 2B**. The device, called a barograph, provides a continuous record of pressure changes over time.

FIGURE 2
Two Types of Barometers
A Mercury Barometer Standard atmospheric pressure at sea level is 29.92 inches of mercury.
B Aneroid Barometer The recording mechanism provides a continuous record of pressure changes over time.
Apply Concepts *How would a continuous record help weather forecasters?*

Air Pressure and Wind **533**

Differentiated Instruction

ENGLISH LANGUAGE LEARNERS Explain to students that *gradient* comes from the word *grade*. Have students discuss the various definitions of the word *grade* and write a sentence using each meaning. *(to arrange in a scale or series, as in to assign a grade; to level off to a smooth surface, as in grading a building site prior to construction; the degree of slope in a road or other surface)*

LESSON 19.1

Use Visuals L1

Figure 3 Have students examine the isobar lines on the weather map. **Ask:** What symbol signifies calm air? Where is this symbol located on this map? *(two concentric circles; in California and Arizona)* How do the wind symbols signify wind speed? *(The number and length of feathers on the symbol increase with wind speed; flag shapes are used in place of multiple feathers at speeds of 55 mph and greater.)* Explain that the circle at the base of each wind flag indicates the location where the wind measurement was taken.
Visual, Logical

Build Reading Literacy L1

Refer to **p. 530D,** which provides the guidelines for making inferences.

Make Inferences Review the kinetic theory of matter, which states that the particles of a gas are always in motion. **Ask:** How does the kinetic theory of matter explain why atmospheric gases move from areas of higher pressure to areas of lower pressure? *(The higher the pressure, the more dense the gas, which means the particles of the gas are closer together and collide with one another more often. Collisions add to the motion of the particles, gradually moving them out into areas of lower pressure and density, where collisions become less frequent.)*
Verbal, Logical

FIGURE 3 Isobars Isobars, with numbers indicating air pressure in millibars, connect places having equal air pressure. The lines connected to the circles indicate the speed and direction of wind. Wind blows toward the circles. **Interpret Visuals** *Use the data on this map to explain which pressure cell, high or low, has the fastest wind speeds.*

Factors Affecting Wind

As important as vertical motion is, far more air moves horizontally, the phenomenon we call wind. What causes wind?

 Wind is the result of horizontal differences in air pressure. Air flows from areas of higher pressure to areas of lower pressure. You may have experienced this flow of air when opening a vacuum-packed can of nuts or tennis balls. The noise you hear is caused by air rushing from the higher pressure outside the can to the lower pressure inside. Wind is nature's way of balancing such inequalities in air pressure.

 The unequal heating of Earth's surface generates pressure differences. Solar radiation is the ultimate energy source for most wind.

If Earth did not rotate, and if there were no friction between moving air and Earth's surface, air would flow in a straight line from areas of higher pressure to areas of lower pressure. But both factors do exist, so the flow of air is not that simple.

 Three factors combine to control wind: pressure differences, the Coriolis effect, and friction.

Pressure Differences Wind is created by differences in pressure—the greater these differences are, the greater the wind speed is. Over Earth's surface, variations in air pressure are determined from barometric readings taken at hundreds of weather stations. These pressure data are shown on a weather map, such as the one in **Figure 3,** using isobars. **Isobars** are lines on a map that connect places of equal air pressure. The spacing of isobars indicates the amount of pressure change occurring over a given distance. These pressure changes are expressed as the **pressure gradient.**

Symbol for Wind Speed	Miles per hour
⊚	Calm
—	1–2
⌐	3–8
⌐	9–14
⌐	15–20
⌐	21–25
⌐	26–31
⌐	32–37
⌐	38–43
⌐	44–49
⌐	50–54
⌐	55–60
⌐	61–66
⌐	67–71
⌐	72–77
⌐	78–83
⌐	84–89
⌐	119–123

534 Chapter 19 • Lesson 1

Facts and Figures

The only force acting on a stationary parcel of air is the pressure-gradient force. Once the air begins to accelerate, the Coriolis effect deflects it—to the right in the Northern Hemisphere, to the left in the Southern Hemisphere. Greater wind speeds result in a stronger Coriolis effect, therefore a stronger deflection, until the pressure-gradient force is equal and opposite to the force of the Coriolis effect. At this point the wind direction is parallel to the isobars and the flow is called a geostrophic wind. Geostrophic winds occur only where isobars are straight and evenly spaced, and where there are no frictional forces. They are rare in nature, though airflow in the upper troposphere can sometimes closely approach geostrophic winds.

A steep pressure gradient, similar to a ball rolling down a steep hill, causes greater acceleration of a parcel of air. A less steep pressure gradient causes a slower acceleration. **Closely spaced isobars indicate a steep pressure gradient and high winds. Widely spaced isobars indicate a weak pressure gradient and light winds.** The pressure gradient is the driving force of wind. The pressure gradient has both magnitude and direction. Its magnitude is reflected in the spacing of isobars. The direction of force is always from areas of higher pressure to areas of lower pressure and at right angles to the isobars. Friction affects wind speed and direction. The Coriolis effect affects wind direction only.

Coriolis Effect The weather map in **Figure 3** shows typical air movements associated with high- and low-pressure systems. Air moves out of the regions of higher pressure and into the regions of lower pressure. However, the wind does not cross the isobars at right angles as you would expect based solely on the pressure gradient. This change in movement results from Earth's rotation and has been named the **Coriolis effect.**

The Coriolis effect describes how Earth's rotation affects moving objects. All free-moving objects or fluids, including the wind, are deflected to the right of their path of motion in the Northern Hemisphere. In the Southern Hemisphere, they are deflected to the left. The reason for this deflection is illustrated in **Figure 4.** Imagine the path of a rocket launched from the North Pole toward a target located on the equator. The true path of this rocket is straight, and the path would appear to be straight to someone out in space looking down at Earth. However, to someone standing on Earth, it would look as if the rocket swerved off its path and landed 15 degrees to the west of its target.

This slight change in direction happens because Earth would have rotated 15 degrees to the east under the rocket during a one-hour flight. The counterclockwise rotation of the Northern Hemisphere causes path deflection to the right. In the Southern Hemisphere, the clockwise rotation produces a similar deflection, but to the left of the path of motion.

The apparent shift in wind direction is attributed to the Coriolis effect. This deflection: 1) is always directed at right angles to the direction of airflow; 2) affects only wind direction and not wind speed; 3) is affected by wind speed—the stronger the wind, the greater the deflection; and 4) is strongest at the poles and weakens toward the equator, becoming nonexistent at the equator.

FIGURE 4 The Coriolis Effect
Because Earth rotates 15° each hour, the rocket's path is curved and veers to the right from the North Pole to the equator.
Calculate *How many degrees does Earth rotate in one day?*

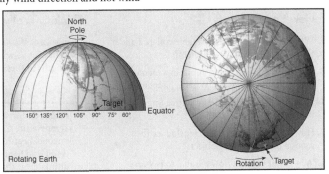

North Pole

150° 135° 120° 105° 90° 75° 60°   Target   Equator

Rotating Earth

Rotation   Target

Integrate Physics   **L2**

Gas Laws Review with students the laws that describe the behavior of enclosed gases. Charles's law states that the volume of a given amount of gas is directly proportional to its temperature, assuming constant pressure. Boyle's law states that the volume of a fixed amount of gas is inversely proportional to the pressure, assuming constant temperature. The combined gas law describes the interrelationships of temperature, pressure, and volume of a fixed amount of gas. **Ask:** In what way do the gas laws, which are stated in terms of enclosed gases, apply to gases in the atmosphere? *(Gases in the atmosphere are not in a closed system. However, the relationship between temperature and pressure, as described by the gas laws, still applies. As temperature decreases, pressure decreases. A decrease in pressure results from an increase in volume which, in turn, decreases the density of the gases. Density differences help explain the movement of air masses. The direction of motion of a mass of atmospheric gas at one temperature and pressure is influenced by other, nearby masses of different temperatures and pressures. For example, a mass of high-pressure, dense air will tend to move into an area of lower-pressure, less dense air— either up into the less dense regions of the atmosphere or into a neighboring area of low pressure.)*
Verbal, Logical

Answers

Figure 3 *For this particular map, isobar lines are most closely spaced in the low-pressure cell, which indicates fastest wind speeds in this cell.*

Figure 4 *360°*

Facts and Figures

Over very short distances, the Coriolis effect is too small to be noticed. Nevertheless, in the middle latitudes the Coriolis effect is great enough to potentially affect the outcome of a baseball game. A ball hit a horizontal distance of 100 m in 4 s down the right field line will be deflected 1.5 cm to the right by the Coriolis effect. This could be just enough to turn a potential home run into a foul ball.

LESSON 19.1

Build Science Skills L2

Compare and Contrast Help students distinguish the effects of friction from the effects of the Coriolis force on wind direction. Point out that in the upper atmosphere, only the Coriolis effect and pressure gradients determine wind direction. At altitudes up to about 1 kilometer, wind speed and direction are affected by those two factors plus friction. **Ask:** How does friction interact with the Coriolis effect? *(The Coriolis effect increases with wind speed. Friction decreases wind speed, which in turn decreases the directional influence of the Coriolis effect at lower altitudes.)*
Verbal, Logical

3 ASSESS

Evaluate Understanding L2

Have students write a paragraph describing how air pressure gradients produce wind and how the Coriolis effect and friction influence wind speed and/or direction. *(Dense air in areas of higher pressure move toward less dense air in areas of lower pressure. This flow of air is the wind. The Coriolis effect deflects wind motion relative to the ground because of Earth's rotation, but does not affect wind speed. Friction between air and the ground reduces wind speed at low altitudes.)*

Reteach L1

Have students work in pairs or small groups to explain to each other how air pressure gradients form and how they produce wind. Students should also explain how the Coriolis effect influences wind direction and how friction influences wind speed and direction. Listen to student explanations and offer corrections as needed.

VISUAL SUMMARY

EFFECT OF FRICTION

FIGURE 5 A Upper-level wind flow is balanced by the Coriolis effect and pressure gradient forces. **B** Friction causes surface winds to cross isobars and move toward lower-pressure areas.

Friction The effect of friction on wind is important only within one kilometer of Earth's surface. Friction acts to slow air movement, which changes wind direction. To illustrate friction's effect on wind direction, first think about a situation in which friction does not play a role in wind direction.

When air is above the friction layer, the pressure gradient causes air to move across the isobars. As soon as air starts to move, the Coriolis effect acts at right angles to this motion. The faster the wind speed is, the greater the deflection. The pressure gradient and Coriolis effect balance in high-altitude air, and wind generally flows parallel to isobars, as shown in **Figure 5A.** The most prominent features of airflow high above the friction layer are the jet streams. **Jet streams** are fast-moving rivers of air near the tropopause, which can be as high as 16 kilometers over the equator and 6 kilometers over the geographic poles. Jet streams travel between 120 and 240 kilometers per hour in a west-to-east direction. One jet stream is situated over the polar front, which is the zone separating cool polar air from warm subtropical air. Jet streams were first encountered by high-flying bombers during World War II.

For air close to Earth's surface, the roughness of the terrain determines the angle of airflow across the isobars. Over the smooth ocean surface, friction is low, and the angle of airflow is small. Over rugged terrain, where the friction is higher, winds move more slowly and cross the isobars at greater angles. As shown in **Figure 5B,** friction causes wind to flow across the isobars at angles as great as 45 degrees. Slower wind speeds caused by friction decrease the Coriolis effect.

19.1 Assessment

Review Key Concepts 🔑

1. Why don't objects such as a table collapse under the weight of the air above them?

2. Suppose the height of a column in a mercury barometer is decreasing. What is happening?

3. What is the ultimate energy source for most wind?

4. How does the Coriolis effect influence the motion of free-moving objects?

5. Why do jet streams flow parallel to isobars?

Think Critically

6. **Interpret Visuals** Study Figures 5A and 5B. Why are the wind arrows drawn to different lengths in these figures?

CONNECTING CONCEPTS

7. **Apply Concepts** Review Lesson 17.3 Temperature Controls. Describe examples of unequal heating of Earth's atmosphere that could lead to air pressure differences that would ultimately influence wind.

Assessment Answers

1. because air pressure is exerted in all directions
2. Air pressure is decreasing.
3. the sun
4. The Coriolis effect deflects free-moving objects to the right (in the Northern Hemisphere) or to the left (in the Southern Hemisphere).

5. Because jet streams are generally above the friction layer, the effect of friction is negligible. Jet stream wind direction is balanced by the pressure gradient and the Coriolis effect. The net effect of the balance is for winds to flow parallel to isobars.
6. Different lengths represent different magnitudes; the longer the arrow, the faster the wind speed.

7. Unequal heating of Earth's surface by solar radiation results from differences in angles of incident radiation and differential heating of land and water. Unequal heating produces air pressure differences that in turn drive global circulation of air.

19.2 Pressure Centers and Winds

PRESSURE CENTERS are among the most common features on any weather map. By knowing just a few basic facts about centers of high and low pressure, you can increase your understanding of present and forthcoming weather. You can make some weather generalizations based on pressure centers. For example, centers of low pressure are frequently associated with cloudy conditions and precipitation. By contrast, clear skies and fair weather may be expected when an area is under the influence of high pressure, as shown in **Figure 6.**

Highs and Lows

Lows, or **cyclones** (*kyklon* = moving in a circle) are centers of low pressure. Highs, or **anticyclones,** are centers of high pressure. In cyclones, the pressure decreases from the outer isobars toward the center. In anticyclones, just the opposite is the case—the values of the isobars increase from the outside toward the center.

FIGURE 6 High Pressure Weather These people in New York's Central Park are enjoying weather associated with a high-pressure center.

Air Pressure and Wind **537**

Key Questions

⚷ *Describe how winds blow around pressure centers in the Northern and Southern Hemispheres.*

⚷ *What are the air pressure patterns within cyclones and anticyclones?*

⚷ *How does friction control net flow of air around a cyclone and an anticylone?*

⚷ *How does the atmosphere attempt to balance the unequal heating of Earth's surface?*

Vocabulary

- cyclone ● anticyclone
- trade winds ● westerlies
- polar easterlies
- polar front ● monsoon

Reading Strategy

Compare and Contrast
Copy the table below. As you read about pressure centers and winds, fill in the table indicating to which hemisphere the concept applies. Use N for Northern Hemisphere, S for Southern Hemisphere, and B for both.

Cyclones rotate counterclockwise.	a. ___?___
Net flow of air is inward around a cyclone.	b. ___?___
Anticyclones rotate counterclockwise.	c. ___?___

LESSON 19.2

1 FOCUS

Lesson Objectives

19.5 **Explain** how winds blow around pressure centers in the Northern and Southern Hemispheres.

19.6 **Describe** the air pressure patterns within cyclones and anticyclones.

19.7 **Describe** how friction controls the net flow of air around a cyclone and an anticyclone.

19.8 **Explain** how the unequal heating of Earth's surface affects the atmosphere.

Build Vocabulary · L2

Concept Map Have students make a concept map using the term *global winds* as the starting point. All the vocabulary terms in this lesson except *cyclone* and *anticyclone* should be used. Have students include the definitions of the vocabulary terms in their concept maps.

Reading Strategy · L2

a. N
b. B
c. S

2 INSTRUCT

Build Science Skills · L2

Student Activity: Use Models Have students use a globe to review and demonstrate the Coriolis effect. One student can rotate the globe while the other uses a pointer to show a flow of air moving straight down from a pole to the equator. Students can also use the model to compare the direction in which airflow is deflected in the Northern and Southern Hemispheres. **Ask:** Seen from Earth's orbit, what is the relationship between Earth's surface and the line along which the air is flowing? *(Earth rotates beneath the line of airflow.)* Seen from Earth's surface, what appears to be happening? *(Earth's rotation makes it appear that the airflow is deflected to one side—to the right in the Northern Hemisphere, to the left in the Southern Hemisphere.)* **Visual, Verbal**

WARM AIR RISES **L2**

Purpose Students see that air rises upward as it is warmed by a heat source.

Materials 2 meter sticks, 2 large paper grocery bags, string, tape, lamp with incandescent bulb

Procedure Tape string to the bottom of each bag. Tie the two strings to a meter stick, as far apart as possible. The bags should be hanging upside down. Use more string to hang this meter stick at its balance point from another meter stick that rests between two student desks. Place the lamp beneath one of the bags and switch it on.

Expected Outcomes The lamp heats the air inside the bag, causing it to rise above the other bag and showing that warm air rises.

Visual, Logical

Students may have the misconception that no outside factor except heat is required to cause masses of warm air to rotate as they rise upward in the atmosphere. Point out that the cyclonic motion in low-pressure cells is primarily a result of the Coriolis effect. As a follow-up, **ask:** What is the primary cause of the anticyclonic motion of high-pressure cells? *(Coriolis effect)*

Verbal, Logical

FIGURE 7 Cyclonic and Anticyclonic Winds This map shows cyclonic and anticyclonic winds in the Northern Hemisphere. The purple arrows show that winds blow into and counterclockwise around a low. Around a high, winds blow outward and clockwise. Pressure is measured in millibars.

Cyclonic and Anticyclonic Winds You learned that the two most significant factors that affect wind are the pressure gradient and the Coriolis effect. Winds move from higher pressure to lower pressure and are deflected to the right or left by Earth's rotation. **When the pressure gradient and the Coriolis effect are applied to pressure centers in the Northern Hemisphere, winds blow counterclockwise around a low. Around a high, winds blow clockwise.** Notice the wind directions in **Figure 7**.

In the Southern Hemisphere, the Coriolis effect deflects the winds to the left. Therefore, winds around a low move clockwise. Winds around a high move counterclockwise. **In both hemispheres, differences in air pressure cause a net flow of air inward around a cyclone and a net flow of air outward around an anticyclone.**

Weather and Air Pressure Rising air is associated with cloud formation and precipitation, whereas sinking air produces clear skies. Imagine a surface low-pressure system where the air is spiraling inward. Here the net inward movement of air causes the area occupied by the air mass to shrink—a process called *horizontal convergence.* Whenever air converges (or comes together) horizontally, it must increase in height to allow for the decreased area it now occupies. This increase in height produces a taller and heavier air column. A surface low can exist only as long as the column of air above it exerts less pressure than does the air in surrounding regions. This seems to be a paradox—a low-pressure center causes a net accumulation of air, which increases its pressure.

☑ **Reading Checkpoint** *What type of weather is associated with rising air?*

Differentiated Instruction

VISUALLY IMPAIRED Help visually impaired students compare cyclones and anticyclones by using their hands to model the motions of these phenomena. Explain that, in the Northern Hemisphere, cyclonic winds blow inward and counterclockwise around a low-pressure center. Have students use one hand to represent Earth's surface. This hand remains stationary. They can use the other hand to make the counterclockwise, inward motion of a cyclonic wind. Then have students use the same hand to make the clockwise, outward motion of an anticyclonic wind in the Northern Hemisphere.

AIRFLOW PATTERNS, SURFACE AND ALOFT

FIGURE 8 Air spreads out, or diverges, above surface cyclones, and comes together, or converges, above surface anticyclones. The red arrows represent warmer air, and the blue arrows represent cooler air.
Apply Concepts *Why is fair weather associated with a high?*

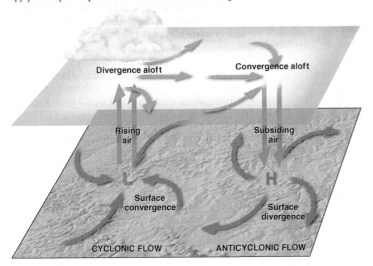

Divergence aloft   Convergence aloft

Rising air   Subsiding air

Surface convergence   Surface divergence

L   H

CYCLONIC FLOW   ANTICYCLONIC FLOW

In order for a surface low to exist for very long, converging air at the surface must be balanced by outflows aloft. For example, surface convergence could be maintained if divergence, or the spreading out of air, occurred above the low at a rate equal to the inflow below. **Figure 8** shows the relationship between surface convergence (inflow) and divergence (outflow) needed to maintain a low-pressure center. Surface convergence around a cyclone causes a net upward movement. Because rising air often results in cloud formation and precipitation, a low-pressure center is generally related to unstable conditions and stormy weather.

Like cyclones, anticyclones also must be maintained from above. Outflow near the surface is accompanied by convergence in the air above and a general sinking of the air column, as shown in Figure 8.

Weather Forecasting Now you can see why weather reports emphasize the locations and possible paths of cyclones and anticyclones. The villain in these reports is always the low-pressure center, which can produce bad weather in any season. Lows move in roughly a west-to-east direction across the contiguous United States, and they require a few days, and sometimes more than a week, for the journey. Their paths can be somewhat unpredictable, making accurate estimation of their movement difficult. Because surface conditions are linked to the conditions of the air above, it is important to understand total atmospheric circulation.

Air Pressure and Wind **539**

Build Reading Literacy **L1**
Refer to **p. 530D**, which provides the guidelines for making inferences.

Make Inferences After students have finished reading this section, **ask:** What does sunlight have to do with the occurrence of rainy weather? *(Sunlight warms the atmosphere. Differential warming produces pressure gradients, which result in the formation of high- and low-pressure centers. Winds blow toward low-pressure centers, bringing moist air in which clouds can form.)*
Verbal, Logical

Use Visuals   **L1**

Figure 8 After students have examined the illustration, **ask:** Where does air enter a cyclonic flow? *(at Earth's surface)* Where does air leave a cyclonic flow? *(aloft)* Where does air enter an anticyclonic flow? *(aloft)* Where does air leave an anticyclonic flow? *(at Earth's surface)*
Visual, Verbal

PLANET DIARY

For an activity on **Weather Forecasting**, visit PlanetDiary.com/HSES.

Answers

Figure 8 *Convergence aloft causes a column of air to sink, producing a zone of high pressure and fair weather. Sinking air is compressed and warmed as it nears Earth's surface, which discourages cloud formation.*

☑ **Reading Checkpoint** *cloud formation and precipitation*

Facts and Figures

Accurate forecasts require that meteorologists not only predict the movement of low-pressure centers, but also determine if the airflow aloft will intensify an embryo storm or act to suppress its development. Surface cyclones would quickly eradicate themselves—not unlike the incoming rush of air that occurs when a vacuum-packed can is opened—without divergence in the air above. As a result, meteorologists must base their forecasts on data from upper and lower atmospheric conditions. Because of the close relationship between conditions at the surface and aloft, understanding of total atmospheric circulation, particularly in the mid-latitudes, is very important.

Global Winds

The underlying cause of wind is the unequal heating of Earth's surface. In tropical regions, more solar radiation is received than is radiated back to space. In regions near the poles the opposite is true—less solar energy is received than is lost. **The atmosphere balances these differences by acting as a giant heat-transfer system. This system moves warm air toward high latitudes and cool air toward the equator.** On a smaller scale, but for the same reason, ocean currents also contribute to this global heat transfer. Global circulation is very complex, but you can begin to understand it by first thinking about circulation that would occur on a non-rotating Earth.

> ☑ **Reading Checkpoint** *How does the atmosphere balance the unequal heating of Earth's surface?*

Nonrotating Earth Model On a hypothetical nonrotating planet with a smooth surface of either all land or all water, two large, thermally produced, convection cells would form, as shown in **Figure 9.** In a *convection cell*, air circulates because warmer, less dense air rises above cooler, denser air. The heated air at the equator would rise until it reached the tropopause—the boundary between the troposphere and the stratosphere. The tropopause, acting similar to a lid, would deflect this air toward the poles. Eventually, the upper-level airflow would reach the poles, sink, spread out in all directions at the surface, and move back toward the equator. Once at the equator, it would be reheated and begin its journey over again. This hypothetical circulation system has upper-level air flowing toward the pole and surface air flowing toward the equator.

Rotating Earth Model If the effect of rotation were added to the global circulation model, the two-cell convection system would break down into smaller cells. **Figure 10** illustrates the three pairs of cells that carry on the task of redistributing heat on Earth—Hadley cells, Ferrel cells, and polar cells. The polar cells and tropical Hadley cells retain the characteristics of the thermally generated convection described earlier. The nature of circulation at the middle latitudes, however, is more complex.

FIGURE 9 Circulation on a Nonrotating Earth
A simple convection system is produced by unequal heating of the atmosphere. Here, and in other illustrations, the red arrows represent warmer air and the blue arrows represent cooler air.
Relate Cause and Effect *Why would air sink after reaching the poles?*

Facts and Figures

George Hadley, an English meteorologist of the eighteenth century, first proposed the simple convection system pictured in Figure 9. Because Earth rotates, however, meteorologists had to develop a more complex global circulation model. This model is pictured in Figure 10 and has three cells on each side of the equator. The Hadley cells, also called tropical cells, are shown north and south of the equator. The next cell is the mid-latitude cell. It is also called a Ferrel cell after William Ferrel, a nineteenth century American meteorologist who helped explain atmospheric circulation at mid-latitudes. The third type of cell is the polar cell.

Near the equator, rising air produces a pressure zone known as the equatorial low—a region characterized by abundant precipitation. As shown in Figure 10, the upper-level flow from the equatorial low reaches 20 to 30 degrees, north or south latitude, and then sinks back toward the surface. This sinking of air and its associated heating due to compression produce hot, arid conditions. The center of this zone of sinking dry air is the subtropical high, which encircles the globe near 30 degrees north and south latitude. The great deserts of Australia, Arabia, and the Sahara in North Africa exist because of the stable dry conditions associated with the subtropical highs.

At the surface, airflow moves outward from the center of the subtropical high. Some of the air travels toward the equator and is deflected by the Coriolis effect, producing the trade winds. **Trade winds** are two belts of winds that blow almost constantly from easterly directions. The trade winds are located between the subtropical highs and the equator. The remainder of the air travels toward the poles and is deflected, generating the prevailing **westerlies** of the middle latitudes. The westerlies make up the dominant west-to-east motion of the atmosphere that characterizes the regions on the poleward side of the subtropical highs. As the westerlies move toward the poles, they encounter the cool polar easterlies in the region of the subpolar low. The **polar easterlies** are winds that blow from the polar high toward the subpolar low. These winds are not constant winds like the trade winds. In the polar region, cold polar air sinks and spreads toward the equator. The interaction of these warm and cool air masses produces the stormy belt in the middle latitudes known as the **polar front.**

This simplified global circulation is dominated by four pressure zones. The subtropical and polar highs are areas of dry subsiding (sinking) air that flows outward at the surface, producing the prevailing winds. The low-pressure zones of the equatorial and subpolar regions are associated with inward and upward airflow accompanied by clouds and precipitation.

☑ **Reading Checkpoint** *What is the polar front?*

FIGURE 10 Circulation on a Rotating Earth This model of global air circulation proposes three pairs of cells.
Interpret Visuals *Describe the patterns of air circulation at the equatorial and subpolar lows.*

Use Visuals L1

Figure 10 After students have read Rotating Earth Model and examined the illustration, **ask:** What happens to warm equatorial air that has risen into the upper atmosphere? *(It moves toward the poles until it reaches latitudes of 20 or 30 degrees, then sinks downward.)* What kind of weather is characteristic of regions around 20 to 30 degrees latitude? *(dry, hot)* What factor is primarily responsible for the trade winds? *(Coriolis effect)* What factors produce the polar front? *(meeting of the warmer westerlies with the colder polar easterlies)* What kind of weather is characteristic of the polar front? *(stormy)*
Visual, Logical

Address **Misconceptions** L2

Students may think that heat is "lost" from air as it sinks toward Earth's surface in a high-pressure center. Explain to students that the term *adiabatic* refers to the cooling or warming of air caused when air is allowed to expand or is compressed, not because heat is added to or subtracted from the system. In other words, no heat enters or leaves the system. Compression of air as it sinks creates adiabatic heating. Expansion of air as it rises creates adiabatic cooling. The air continues to cool as it rises until it reaches its dew point. Then condensation takes place and clouds begin to form.
Ask: How does adiabatic cooling help explain why precipitation is associated with low-pressure centers but not high-pressure centers? *(Rising air in a low-pressure center becomes cool enough for condensation. Sinking air in a high-pressure system is heated adiabatically, preventing condensation.)*
Verbal

Answers

Figure 9 *Air becomes more dense as it cools, causing it to sink.*

Figure 10 *Both are zones where two cells, or air masses, converge at Earth's surface and air rises, forming zones of low pressure.*

☑ **Reading Checkpoint** *The atmosphere transfers heat by moving warm air toward high latitudes and cool air toward the equator.*

☑ **Reading Checkpoint** *the stormy belt where subpolar westerlies and polar easterlies meet*

Air Pressure and Wind **541**

LESSON 19.2

Build Science Skills `L2`

Apply Concepts Use a world map to help students visualize the movement of monsoons in south Asia. Have them picture a high-pressure system above the land that pushes air out to sea. Then have them picture how heat from the land during summer causes air to rise, producing a low-pressure system that pulls in moist air from the ocean.
Visual, Logical

3 ASSESS

Evaluate Understanding `L2`

Have students write a paragraph comparing and contrasting cyclonic and anticyclonic winds. Have students write a second paragraph explaining how each of the following global winds is formed: trade winds, westerlies, and polar easterlies.

Reteach `L2`

Draw a globe on the board or use a laminated world map. On the map, draw in each type of global wind while explaining its formation to students. Use Figure 10 as a reference.

FIGURE 11 Average Surface Pressure and Global Circulation, July In July, low-pressure cells develop over the continents in the Northern Hemisphere.

Influence of Continents
Where landmasses break up the ocean surface, large seasonal temperature differences disrupt the global pattern of pressure zones in the atmosphere. Large landmasses, particularly in the Northern Hemisphere, become cold in the winter when a seasonal high-pressure system develops. From this high-pressure system, surface airflow is directed off the land. In the summer, landmasses are heated and develop low-pressure cells, which permit air to flow onto the land as shown in **Figure 11**. These seasonal changes in wind direction are known as the **monsoons.** During warm months, areas such as India experience a flow of warm, water-laden air from the Indian Ocean, which produces the rainy summer monsoon. The winter monsoon is dominated by dry continental air. A similar situation exists to a lesser extent during summer over North America. Rising, unstable air along the western side of the Bermuda High brings rain to the East Coast. At the same time, thunderstorms occur in the Southwest as moist air streams into the region from the Gulf of Mexico and the Gulf of California.

19.2 Assessment

Review Key Concepts 🔑

1. Describe how winds blow around pressure centers in the Northern Hemisphere.

2. Compare the air pressure for a cyclone with that for an anticyclone.

3. How do differences in air pressure control the net flow of air around a cyclone and an anticyclone?

4. Describe how the atmosphere balances the unequal heating of Earth's surface.

5. What is the only truly continuous pressure belt? Why is it continuous?

6. In general, what type of weather can you expect if a low-pressure system is moving into your area?

Think Critically

7. Identify Cause and Effect What must happen in the air above for divergence at the surface to be maintained? What type of pressure center accompanies surface divergence?

MATH PRACTICE

8. Interpret Maps Examine Figure 7. What is the approximate range of barometric pressure indicated by the isobars on the map? What is the pressure interval between adjacent isobars?

542 Chapter 19 • Lesson 2

Assessment Answers

1. In the Northern Hemisphere, winds blow counterclockwise and inward around a low, and clockwise and outward around a high.
2. In cyclones, air pressure decreases toward the center of the cell. In anticyclones, air pressure increases toward the center of the cell.
3. The effect of differences in air pressure is to cause a net flow of air inward around a cyclone and a net flow outward about an anticyclone.

4. The atmosphere acts like a huge heat-transfer system, transporting warm air from the equator toward the poles and cold air from the poles toward the equator.
5. The subpolar low in the Southern Hemisphere; no landmasses break up the pressure system.
6. cloud formation and precipitation
7. Convergence must occur aloft in order for a surface divergence to be maintained.

A surface divergence is associated with a high-pressure center.
8. 992 (−) to 1020 (+) millibars. In other words, the map includes pressures a bit less than 992 millibars and a bit more than 1020 millibars. Isobar interval equals 4 millibars.

19.3 Regional Wind Systems

CIRCULATION IN THE middle latitudes is complex and does not fit the convection system described for the tropics. Between about 30 and 60 degrees latitude, the general west-to-east flow, known as the *westerlies*, is interrupted by migrating cyclones and anticyclones. In the Northern Hemisphere, these pressure cells move from west to east around the globe.

Local Winds

Small-scale winds produced by a locally generated pressure gradient are known as *local winds*. **The local winds are caused either by topographic effects or by variations in surface composition—land and water—in the immediate area.**

Land and Sea Breezes In coastal areas during the warm summer months, the land surface is heated more intensely during the daylight hours than an adjacent body of water is heated. As a result, the air above the land surface heats, expands, and rises, creating an area of lower pressure. As shown in **Figure 12,** a *sea breeze* then develops because cooler air over the water at higher pressure moves toward the warmer land and low pressure air. The breeze starts developing shortly before noon and generally reaches its greatest intensity during the mid- to late afternoon. These relatively cool winds can be a moderating influence on afternoon temperatures in coastal areas.

FIGURE 12 **Sea Breeze** During daylight hours, the air above land heats and rises, creating a local zone of lower air pressure. Cooler, denser air over the water moves onto the land, generating a sea breeze. Pressure is measured in millibars (mb).

Key Questions

What causes local winds?

Describe the general movement of weather in the United States.

What happens when unusually strong, warm ocean currents flow along the coasts of Ecuador and Peru?

How is a La Niña event triggered?

Vocabulary

- prevailing wind
- anemometer • El Niño
- La Niña

Reading Strategy

Preview Copy the table below. Before you read, use Figure 18 to locate examples of the driest and wettest regions on Earth. After you read, identify the dominant wind system for each location.

Precipitation	Location	Dominant Wind System
Extremely low	a. ___?___	b. ___?___
Extremely high	c. ___?___	d. ___?___

Air Pressure and Wind **543**

LESSON 19.3

Use Visuals `L1`

Figure 13 After students have examined the illustration, **ask:** Does a land breeze move toward the land or away from the land? *(away from the land)* Why do land breezes usually take place at night? *(After sunset, both land and water begin to cool, but land cools more rapidly.)*
Visual, Logical

Build Science Skills `L2`

Compare and Contrast Have students create a table that contrasts sea, land, valley, and mountain breezes.

	Direction	Day/Night	Cause
sea	toward land	day	sun heats land faster than water; air above land rises, causing low pressure zone
land	toward sea	night	land cools faster than water; air above land sinks, causing high pressure zone relative to air above water
valley	upslope	day	air along slopes heats faster than air above valley, glides up slope because it is less dense
mountain	downslope	night	air along slopes cools faster than air above valley, sinks down slope into valley

Verbal, Logical

(Teacher **Demo**)

DIFFERENTIAL HEATING `L2`

Purpose Students observe that soil heats faster than water.

Materials 2 containers, soil, water, 2 thermometers

Procedure Fill the two containers 2/3 full, one with water and the other with soil. Place a thermometer in each container and place both in a hot, sunny location. Record the initial temperature and the temperature of each container every five minutes for 25 minutes. Graph and compare the results.

Expected Outcome Soil heats faster than water.
Visual, Kinesthetic

FIGURE 13 Land Breeze At night, the land cools more rapidly than the sea, generating an offshore flow called a land breeze.

Infer *How would the isobar lines be oriented if there were no air pressure change across the land–water boundary?*

At night, the reverse may take place. The land cools more rapidly than the sea, and a *land breeze* develops, as shown in **Figure 13.** The cooler air at higher pressures over the land moves to the sea, where the air is warmer and at lower pressures.

Small-scale sea breezes also can develop along the shores of large lakes. People who live in a city near the Great Lakes, such as Chicago, recognize this lake effect, especially in the summer. They are reminded daily by weather reports of the cooler temperatures near the lake as compared to warmer outlying areas.

Valley and Mountain Breezes A daily wind similar to land and sea breezes occurs in many mountainous regions. During daylight hours, the air along the slopes of the mountains is heated more intensely than the air at the same elevation over the valley floor. Because this warmer air on the mountain slopes is less dense, it glides up along the slope and generates a *valley breeze*, as shown in **Figure 14A.** The occurrence of these daytime upslope breezes can often be identified by the cumulus clouds that develop on adjacent mountain peaks.

After sunset, the pattern may reverse. The rapid cooling of the air along the mountain slopes produces a layer of cooler air next to the ground. Because cool air is denser than warm air, it moves downslope into the valley. Such a movement of air, illustrated in **Figure 14B,** is called a *mountain breeze.* In the Grand Canyon at night, the sound of cold air rushing down the sides of the canyon can be louder than the sound of the Colorado River below.

The same type of cool air drainage can occur in places that have very modest slopes. The result is that the coldest pockets of air are usually found in the lowest spots. Like many other winds, mountain and valley breezes have seasonal preferences. Although valley breezes are most common during the warm season when solar heating is most intense, mountain breezes tend to be more dominant in the cold season.

☑ **Reading Checkpoint** *What type of local wind can form in the Grand Canyon at night?*

FIGURE 14 Mountain and Valley Breezes

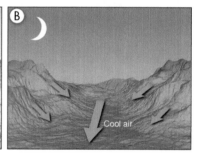

A Valley Breeze Heating during the day generates warm air that rises from the valley floor.

B Mountain Breeze After sunset, cooling of the air near mountain slopes can result in cool air moving into the valley.

544 Chapter 19 • Lesson 3

Differentiated Instruction

ENGLISH LANGUAGE LEARNERS Explain that the terms *prevailing* and *predominant* are synonyms. They are adjectives that mean "having superior strength, influence, or authority." Have students look up the definitions of verb forms of these words and use each in a sentence. Then ask students to look up definitions for the related verb *dominate* and the related adjective *dominant.* You may also choose to ask students to compare and contrast the meanings of all six words, as well as the suffix *pre-*.

How Wind Is Measured

Two basic wind measurements—direction and speed—are particularly important to the weather observer. Winds are always labeled by the direction from which they blow. A north wind blows from the north toward the south. An east wind blows from the east toward the west. The instrument most commonly used to determine wind direction is the wind vane, shown in **Figure 15.** Wind vanes are commonly located on buildings, and they always point into the wind. The wind direction is often shown on a dial connected to the wind vane. The dial indicates wind direction, either by points of the compass—N, NE, E, SE, etc.—or by a scale of 0° to 360°. On the degree scale, 0° or 360° is north, 90° is east, 180° is south, and 270° is west.

☑ **Reading Checkpoint** *Toward which direction does a SE wind blow?*

Wind Direction When the wind consistently blows more often from one direction than from any other, it is called a **prevailing wind.** Recall the prevailing westerlies that dominate circulation in the middle latitudes. 🔑 **In the United States, the westerlies consistently move weather from west to east across the continent.** Within this general eastward flow are cells of high and low pressure with the characteristic clockwise and counterclockwise flows. As a result, the winds associated with the westerlies, as measured at the surface, often vary considerably from day to day and from place to place. In contrast, the direction of airflow associated with the trade winds is much more consistent.

Wind Speed The instrument commonly used to measure wind speed is an **anemometer** (*anemo* = wind, *metron* = measuring instrument). One type of anemometer, a cup anemometer, is shown in Figure 15. The wind speed is read from a dial much like the speedometer of an automobile. Places where winds are steady and speeds are relatively high are potential sites for tapping wind energy.

A *wind sock* is a simple device that can be used to determine both wind direction and wind speed. A wind sock is a cone-shaped bag that is open at both ends and is free to change position with shifts in wind direction. The degree to which the sock is inflated is an indication of wind speed. Wind socks are commonly used at small airports and landing strips.

FIGURE 15 Wind Vane and Cup Anemometer
Interpret Visuals *How does the position of a wind vane tell you which direction the wind is blowing?*

LESSON 19.3

Build Reading Literacy `L1`

Refer to **p. 246D** in **Chapter 9,** which provides the guidelines for relating cause and effect.

Relate Cause and Effect As they read through the text on El Niño and La Niña, have students make a flowchart showing the cause-effect chain that results in an El Niño event. *(Sample answer: high pressure over western Pacific → warm water pileup in eastern Pacific that prevents cold water upwelling and promotes formation of low air pressure zone → inland areas receive abnormal amounts of rain → trade winds weaken or may reverse direction → subtropical and mid-latitude jet streams are displaced → abnormal rainfall in Florida/ southern United States and mild winter temperatures west of the Rocky Mountains)*
Verbal, Logical

FIGURE 16 Normal Conditions Trade winds and strong equatorial ocean currents flow toward the west.

El Niño and La Niña

Look at **Figure 16.** The cold ocean Peruvian current flows toward the equator along the coasts of Ecuador and Peru. This flow encourages upwelling of cold nutrient-filled waters that support the growth of plankton—a food source for millions of fish, particularly anchovies. Near the end of the year, however, a warm ocean current that flows southward along the coasts of Ecuador and Peru replaces the cold Peruvian current. During the nineteenth century, the local residents named this warm current El Niño ("the child"). Normally, these warm countercurrents last for a few weeks and then give way to the cold Peruvian flow again.

El Niño 🔑 **At irregular intervals of three to seven years, these warm countercurrents become unusually strong and replace normally cold offshore waters with warm equatorial waters.** Scientists use the term **El Niño** for these episodes of ocean warming that affect the eastern tropical Pacific.

The onset of El Niño is marked by abnormal weather patterns that drastically affect the economies of Ecuador and Peru. As shown in **Figure 17,** these unusually strong countercurrents accumulate large quantities of warm water that block the upwelling of colder, nutrient-filled water. As a result, the anchovies starve, devastating the local fishing industry. At the same time, some inland areas that are normally arid receive an abnormal amount of rain. Here, pastures and cotton fields have yields far above the average. These climatic fluctuations have been known for years, but they were originally considered local phenomena. It now is understood that El Niño is part of the global circulation and that it affects the weather at great distances from Peru and Ecuador.

546 Chapter 19 • Lesson 3

Facts and Figures

The seesaw pattern of atmospheric pressure changes between the eastern and western Pacific is called the Southern Oscillation. During average years, high pressure over the eastern Pacific causes surface winds and warm equatorial waters to flow westward. The result is a pileup of warm water in the western Pacific, which promotes the lowering of air pressure. An El Niño event begins as surface pressure increases in the western Pacific and decreases in the eastern Pacific. This air pressure reversal weakens or may even reverse the trade winds, and results in an eastward movement of the warm waters that had accumulated in the western Pacific.

FIGURE 17 El Niño
Warm countercurrents cause the reversal of pressure patterns in the western and eastern Pacific.

When an El Niño began in the summer of 1997, forecasters predicted that the pool of warm water over the Pacific would displace the paths of both the subtropical and midlatitude jet streams, as shown in Figure 17. The jet streams steer weather systems across North America. As predicted, the subtropical jet stream brought rain to the Gulf Coast. Tampa, Florida, received more than three times its normal winter precipitation. The mid-latitude jet stream pumped warm air far north into the continent. As a result, winter temperatures west of the Rocky Mountains were significantly above normal.

☑ **Reading Checkpoint** *What is an El Niño, and what effect does it have on weather?*

La Niña The opposite of El Niño is an atmospheric phenomenon known as **La Niña.** Once thought to be the normal conditions that occur between two El Niño events, meteorologists now consider La Niña an important atmospheric phenomenon in its own right. ☞ **Researchers have come to recognize that when surface temperatures in the eastern Pacific are colder than average, a La Niña event is triggered that has a distinctive set of weather patterns.** A typical La Niña winter blows colder than normal air over the Pacific Northwest and the northern Great Plains. At the same time, it warms much of the rest of the United States. The Northwest also experiences greater precipitation during this time. During the La Niña winter of 1998–99, a world-record snowfall for one season occurred in Washington State. La Niña can also increase hurricane activity. A recent study concluded that the cost of hurricane damage in the United States is 20 times greater in La Niña years as compared to El Niño years.

The effects of both El Niño and La Niña on world climate are widespread and vary greatly. These phenomena remind us that the air and ocean conditions of the tropical Pacific influence weather almost everywhere.

Air Pressure and Wind **547**

Integrate Physics L2

Thermal Energy Transfer Remind students that heat is the transfer of energy between two objects of different temperatures. Heat can be transferred directly, when the objects are in contact. It also can be transferred indirectly, by radiation and convection. Radiation is the transfer of energy via electromagnetic waves. Convection is the transfer of energy by fluid motion. In a fluid, convection works when colder, denser fluid sinks below warmer, less dense fluid. **Ask:** Which of these three types of heat transfer is involved in El Niño formation and the weather patterns that result? *(All three; direct transfer takes place between ocean water and air. Radiation transfers heat from sun to land and atmosphere. Convection is the airflow that occurs between high- and low-pressure regions.)*
Verbal, Logical

Answers

☑ **Reading Checkpoint** *An episode—occurring every three to seven years—of ocean warming that affects the eastern tropical Pacific; warm countercurrents become unusually strong and replace normally cold offshore waters with warm equatorial waters.*

Facts and Figures

When winds blow along the surface of the ocean, the water is not pushed along directly in front of the wind. Instead, it is deflected by about 45 degrees as a result of the Coriolis effect. When surface waters are deflected, colder, deeper water rises to take its place.

This cold water is richer in nutrients than warmer surface water and promotes highly productive coastal fisheries. In years when coastal upwelling does not occur, coastal fish populations may be reduced or absent.

LESSON 19.3

3 ASSESS

Evaluate Understanding `L2`

To assess students' knowledge of lesson content, have them write a short description of each of the four types of local winds. Then have students write two or three sentences describing the events that give rise to an El Niño event.

Reteach `L1`

Have students draw and label their own diagrams illustrating sea, land, valley, and mountain breezes. Allow students to use Figures 12, 13, and 14 as references, if needed.

Answers

MAP IT! Northern Africa receives less than 400 mm in average annual precipitation.

Precipitation in northern Africa is influenced by subtropical high pressure cells.

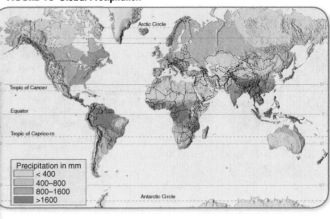

FIGURE 18 Global Precipitation

Precipitation in mm
- < 400
- 400–800
- 800–1600
- >1600

MAP IT! ACTIVITY

The map in Figure 18 shows average annual precipitation in millimeters. **Interpret Maps** Determine the range of precipitation that dominates Northern Africa.

Relate Cause and Effect Which weather pattern influences precipitation in this area?

Global Distribution of Precipitation

Figure 18 shows that the tropical region dominated by the equatorial low is the rainiest region on Earth. It includes the rain forests of the Amazon basin in South America and the Congo basin in Africa. In these areas, the warm, humid trade winds converge to yield abundant rainfall throughout the year. In contrast, areas dominated by the subtropical high-pressure cells are regions of extensive deserts. Variables other than pressure and wind complicate the pattern. For example, the interiors of large land masses commonly experience decreased precipitation. However, you can explain a lot about global precipitation if you apply your knowledge of global winds and pressure systems.

19.3 Assessment

Review Key Concepts 🔑

1. What are local winds, and how are they caused?

2. Describe the general movement of weather in the United States.

3. What happens when strong, warm countercurrents flow along the coasts of Ecuador and Peru?

4. How is a La Niña event recognized?

5. What two factors mainly influence global precipitation?

Think Critically

6. **Interpret Visuals** Study Figure 17. How could air pressure changes resulting from El Niño influence weather patterns in this region?

BIGIDEA WEATHER AND CLIMATE

7. **Compare and Contrast** Write a paragraph comparing the features and effects of El Niño and La Niña. Include specific weather patterns associated with each phenomenon.

Assessment Answers

1. Local winds are small-scale winds caused by local variations in air pressure, which are caused by topography and unequal heating of land and water, or unequal heating of air above slopes and valleys.
2. from west to east
3. An El Niño event blocks normal upwelling of cold, nutrient-laden waters off the shores of these countries, and causes heavy precipitation inland. El Niño can have far-reaching effects on weather patterns of regions that are great distances from Ecuador and Peru.
4. La Niña is triggered when surface temperatures in the eastern Pacific are colder than average.
5. rising or falling air and the distribution of land and water influence air moisture content and precipitation
6. Warm water near Ecuador and Peru would heat air and cause it to rise, producing lower pressure and precipitation. Regions north of Australia that normally receive more warm water would experience higher pressure, possibly leading to drought.
7. Student paragraphs should contrast the ocean water temperature conditions that trigger each phenomenon and describe how these in turn influence air pressure. Specific examples of weather associated with El Niño and La Niña also should be included in the paragraph.

Tracking El Niño from Space

The images in **Figure 19** show the progression of the 1997–98 El Niño. This El Niño episode was particularly strong. The images were derived from data collected by the satellite TOPEX/Poseidon.* This satellite bounces radar signals off the ocean surface to precisely measure the distance between the satellite and the sea surface. When combined with high-precision data from the Global Positioning System (GPS) of satellites, maps of sea-surface topography such as these can be produced. These maps show the relative positions and elevations of the sea surface. The presence of hills indicates warmer-than-average water, and the areas of low topography, or valleys, indicate cooler-than-normal water, because liquid water expands as it warms and contracts as it cools. Using water topography, scientists can determine the speed and direction of surface ocean currents.

The colors in these images show sea-level height relative to the average. When you focus on the images, remember that hills are warm colors and valleys are cool colors. The white and red areas indicate places of higher-than-normal sea-surface heights. In the white areas, the sea surface is between 14 and 32 centimeters above normal. In the red areas, sea level is elevated by about 10 centimeters. Green areas indicate average conditions, whereas blue shows zones that are at least 18 centimeters below average sea level.

The images show the progression of the large warm-water mass from west to east across the equatorial Pacific Ocean. At its peak in November 1997, the surface area covered by the warm water mass was about one and one half times the size of the 48 contiguous United States. The amount of warm water added to the eastern Pacific with a temperature between 21°C and 30°C was about 30 times the combined volume of the water in all of the United States Great Lakes.

Source: NASA's Goddard Space Flight Center

FIGURE 19
Progression of the 1997–98 El Niño

April 25, 1997

July 25, 1997

November 10, 1997

March 14, 1998

Tracking El Niño from Space `L2`

Background The image for April 25, 1997, shows the Pacific Ocean on the eve of the 1997–1998 El Niño event. By examining the images for July 25 and November 10, you can see the dramatic buildup of warm water (white and red areas) in the eastern Pacific and the enlarging region of cooler water (purple) in the western Pacific. By the time of the March 14, 1998, image, the area of warm water in the eastern Pacific was much smaller.

Teaching Tip
- The directional terms *eastern Pacific* and *western Pacific* may give some students trouble, since the eastern Pacific Ocean borders the western coast of the United States. **Ask:** What continents are bordered by the eastern Pacific Ocean? *(North America and South America)*
- As students examine each of the four images in Figure 19, **ask:** What colors indicate warmer than average water temperatures? *(white and red)* What colors indicate cooler than average water temperatures? *(purple)* Where is the warm water mass located on July 25 and November 10? *(eastern Pacific)* What does the map indicate about the warm water mass on March 14? *(It is dissipating.)*

OBSERVING WIND PATTERNS L2

Objective

After completing this activity, students will be able to:

- interpret diagrams of surface barometric pressure and high- and low-pressure cells.
- summarize basic characteristics of air movement in high- and low-pressure cells.
- compare and contrast air movement in pressure cells in the Northern and Southern Hemispheres.

Skills Observe, Analyze Data, Calculate

Prep Time 15 minutes

Advance Prep Use the diagrams provided in the Earth Science Laboratory Manual or copy the diagrams in the manual for students.

Class Time 30 minutes

Teaching Tip Using copies of these diagrams from the lab manual will ensure that students will not write in their textbooks.

Expected Outcome Students will become familiar with air pressure data plotted on maps. They will learn to interpret how air moves in a given region as indicated by isobar lines.

INQUIRY

EXPLORATION LAB

Observing Wind Patterns

Problem How can surface barometric pressure maps be interpreted?

Materials 1 copy each of **Figure 1** and **Figure 2**, paper, pencil

Skills Observe, Analyze Data, Calculate

Connect to the `Big idea` Atmospheric pressure and wind are two elements of weather that are closely related. Most people don't usually pay attention closely to the pressure given in a weather report. However, pressure differences in the atmosphere drive the winds that often bring changes in temperature and moisture.

Procedure

1. Look at Figure 1. This map shows surface global wind patterns and average global barometric pressure in millibars for January.

2. Examine the individual pressure cells in Figure 1. Then complete the diagrams in your copy of Figure 2. Label the isobars with appropriate pressures, and use arrows to indicate the surface air movement in each pressure cell.

3. Copy the data table on the next page. Indicate the movements of air in high- and low-pressure cells by completing the table.

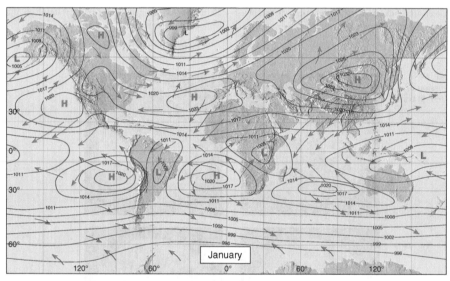

FIGURE 1 Surface Global Wind Patterns and Average Global Barometric Pressure

Analyze and Conclude

1. **Compare and Contrast** Summarize the differences and similarities in surface air movement between a Northern Hemisphere cyclone and a Southern Hemisphere cyclone.

2. **Interpret Visuals** Use your textbook as a reference to locate and write the name of each global wind belt at the appropriate location on your copy of the map in Figure 1. Also indicate the region of the polar front.

3. **Apply Concepts** Label areas on your copy of Figure 1 where you would expect high wind speeds to occur.

4. **Apply Concpets** Label an area on your copy of Figure 1 where circulation is most like the idealized global wind model for a rotating Earth. Explain why this region on Earth is so much like the model.

FIGURE 2 Isobars

Northern Hemisphere

High

Low

Southern Hemisphere

High

Low

Air Movement in Pressure Cells Data Table				
Air Movement	Northern Hemisphere High	Northern Hemisphere Low	Southern Hemisphere High	Southern Hemisphere Low
into/out of				
rises/sinks				
rotates CW/CCW*				

*CW = clockwise; CCW = counterclockwise

Answers to Procedure Questions

2.
Northern Hemisphere

High (Anticyclone)

Low (Cyclone)

Southern Hemisphere

High (Anticyclone)

Low (Cyclone)

3. Table 1 Air Movement in Pressure Cells

Air Movement	N. Hem. High	N. Hem. Low	S. Hem. High	S. Hem. Low
into/out of	out of	into	out of	into
rises/sinks	sinks	rises	sinks	rises
rotates CW/CCW*	CW	CCW	CCW	CW

*CW = clockwise; CCW = counterclockwise

Analyze and Conclude

1. In a Northern Hemisphere cyclone, air rotates counterclockwise, whereas air rotates clockwise in an anticyclone. These rotation directions result from the Coriolis effect and so they are reversed for cyclones and anticyclones in the Southern Hemisphere. In either hemisphere, the net flow of air is inward for a cyclone and outward for an anticyclone. This net effect inward and outward is due to friction. Also, air sinks in an anticyclone and rises in a cyclone in both hemispheres.

2. Student locations of wind belts, pressure zones, and fronts should be like those in Figure 10 on p. 541 of the textbook. Use latitudes for these zones as indicated in Figure 10.

3. Areas of high wind speed correlate to closely spaced isobars on the map.

4. Students should locate the subpolar low in the Southern Hemisphere, at approximately 60 degrees south latitude. There are no landmasses in the region of this subpolar low to create seasonal temperature differences. Therefore, the air circulation pattern is not disrupted.

Visual, Logical

Prioritize

Tell students to make a list of all the study tasks they need to accomplish. Tell them to schedule study time realistically and stick to their deadlines.

Think Visually

a. wind speed
b. stronger winds
c. polar areas

21st Century Learning

Problem Identification, Formulation, and Solution

What effects has El Niño had on your weather?

El Niño affects winter weather in North America and occurs roughly every 2 to 7 years. The winters of 1972–73, 1982–83, and 1997–98 had extreme El Niños. Have students use the Internet to find out how El Niño may have affected the winter weather where you live. Suggest they first look up the average monthly winter temperatures and precipitation during two of the El Niño years listed above. Then have them look up the same data for four non-El Niño years. Ask them to make a table to show the differences. Have them identify any patterns in the data and predict how weather will be affected by the next El Niño. Then have students post their results and analysis on a class blog or present them to the class.

Homework Guide

Lesson	Questions
1	1, 2, 8, 9, 11–13, 22, 28
2	3–5, 7, 10, 14, 15, 18–21, 23
3	6, 16, 17, 24–27, 29

19 Study Guide

Big idea ▸ Weather and Climate

19.1 Understanding Air Pressure

🔑 Air pressure is exerted in all directions—down, up, and sideways. The air pressure pushing down on an object balances the air pressure pushing up on the object.

🔑 When air pressure increases, the mercury in a barometric tube rises. When air pressure decreases, so does the height of the mercury column.

🔑 Wind is the result of horizontal differences in air pressure. Air flows from areas of higher pressure to areas of lower pressure.

🔑 The unequal heating of Earth's surface generates pressure differences. Solar radiation is the ultimate energy source for most wind.

🔑 Three factors control wind: pressure differences, the Coriolis effect, and friction.

🔑 Closely spaced isobars indicate a steep pressure gradient and high winds. Widely spaced isobars indicate a weak pressure gradient and light winds.

🔑 The Coriolis effect describes how Earth's rotation affects moving objects. All free-moving objects or fluids, including the wind, are deflected to the right of their path of motion in the Northern Hemisphere. In the Southern Hemisphere, they are deflected to the left.

air pressure (532)   Coriolis effect (535)
barometer (533)   jet stream (536)
isobars (534)
pressure gradient (534)

19.2 Pressure Centers and Winds

🔑 In cyclones, the pressure decreases from the outer isobars toward the center. In anticyclones, just the opposite is the case—the values of the isobars increase from the outside toward the center.

🔑 When the pressure gradient and the Coriolis effect are applied to pressure centers in the Northern Hemisphere, winds blow counterclockwise around a low. Around a high, they blow outward and clockwise.

552 Chapter 19 • Study Guide

🔑 In both hemispheres, differences in air pressure cause a net flow of air inward around a cyclone and a net flow of air outward around an anticyclone.

🔑 The atmosphere balances differences in solar radiation in the tropics and the poles by acting as a giant heat-transfer system. This system moves warm air toward high latitudes and cool air toward the equator.

cyclone (537)   polar easterlies (541)
anticyclone (537)   polar front (541)
trade winds (541)   monsoon (542)
westerlies (541)

19.3 Regional Wind Systems

🔑 The local winds are caused either by topographic effects or by variations in surface composition—land and water—in the immediate area.

🔑 In the contiguous United States, the westerlies consistently move weather from west to east across the continent.

🔑 At irregular intervals of three to seven years, warm equatorial currents along the coasts of Ecuador and Peru become unusually strong and replace normally cold offshore waters with warm waters. This occurrence is referred to as an El Niño event.

🔑 When surface temperatures in the eastern Pacific are colder than average, a La Niña event is triggered that has a distinctive set of weather patterns.

prevailing wind (545)   El Niño (546)
anemometer (545)   La Niña (547)

Think Visually

Copy the concept map below onto a sheet of paper. Use information from the chapter to complete the concept map.

Assessment Answers

Review Content

1. c	**2.** a	**3.** c
4. d	**5.** a	**6.** a
7. a	**8.** c	**9.** c
10. c		

Understand Concepts

11. An aneroid barometer consists of evacuated metal chambers that compress as air pressure increases and expand when air pressure decreases.

12. Closely spaced isobars indicate a strong wind; widely spaced isobars indicate a light wind.

19 Assessment

Review Content

Choose the letter that best answers the question or completes the statement.

1. The mercurial barometer was invented by
   a. Galileo.   c. Torricelli.
   b. Newton.   d. Watt.

2. The force exerted by the air above is called
   a. air pressure.   c. divergence.
   b. convergence.   d. the Coriolis effect.

3. What are centers of low pressure called?
   a. air masses   c. cyclones
   b. anticyclones   d. jet streams

4. Variations in air pressure from place to place are the principal cause of
   a. clouds.   c. hail.
   b. lows.   d. wind.

5. In the winter, large landmasses often develop a seasonal
   a. high-pressure system.
   b. low-pressure system.
   c. typhoon.
   d. trade wind.

6. A sea breeze is most intense
   a. during mid- to late afternoon.
   b. in the late morning.
   c. late in the evening.
   d. at sunrise.

7. What is the pressure zone that is associated with rising air near the equator?
   a. equatorial low   c. subtropical low
   b. equatorial high   d. subtropical high

8. What are high-altitude, high-velocity winds?
   a. cyclonic currents c. jet streams
   b. isobars   d. pressure gradients

9. Where is deflection of wind due to the Coriolis effect the strongest?
   a. near the equator c. near the poles
   b. in the midlatitudes d. near the westerlies

10. In what stormy region do the westerlies and polar easterlies converge?
    a. equatorial low   c. polar front
    b. subpolar high   d. subtropical front

Understand Concepts

11. Describe how an aneroid barometer works.

12. Write a general statement relating the spacing of isobars to wind speed.

13. Describe the weather that usually accompanies a
    a. drop in barometric pressure.
    b. rise in barometric pressure.

14. How does the Coriolis effect modify air movement in the Southern Hemisphere?

15. The trade winds originate from which pressure zone?

16. List and briefly describe three examples of local winds.

17. On a wind vane with a degree scale, which type of wind is indicated by 90 degrees?

Use the figure below to answer Questions 18–20.

18. In diagram A, what type of surface air flow is shown?

19. What type of surface pressure system is illustrated in diagram B?

20. Select the diagram in which air at the surface first begins to pile up.

13. A drop in barometric pressure is associated with converging winds and ascending air; therefore it is often associated with clouds and precipitation. In contrast, a rise in air pressure is associated with fair weather.

14. The deflective force of Earth's rotation (Coriolis effect) causes air to be deflected to the left of its path of motion in the Southern Hemisphere.

15. Trades winds originate from the subtropical highs.

16. Sample answer: Three examples of local winds are sea breezes, land breezes, and mountain breezes. Sea and land breezes result from pressure changes associated with differential heating of land and water. Mountain breezes result when air near mountain slopes cools at night by rapid radiation cooling and descends down mountain slopes.

17. an east wind

18. surface divergence

19. low (cyclone)

20. diagram B

ASSESSMENT

Think Critically

21. The winds west of a cyclone in the Northern Hemisphere would be northwest or west-northwest; winds west of an anticyclone would be south to southeast.

22. Because wind turbines would be used in regions with high sustained winds, you would look for a place marked by closely spaced isobars.

23. Regions dominated by low-pressure systems are expected to be cloudy with abundant precipitation, which would support abundant vegetation. Clear skies and desert conditions with sparse vegetation are expected for regions with sustained high-pressure centers.

Math Skills

24. NW/SW/W, or westerlies
25. about 6 percent
26. about 37 percent

Concepts in Action

27. Students' answers obviously will depend on their locations, but reasonable answers should indicate colder and wetter conditions in the Pacific Northwest, and warming trends for most of the rest of the United States. In addition, Southeastern and Gulf Coast states could see increasing hurricane activity.

28. Standard sea level pressure in centimeters equals 76 cm of mercury. The height of standard sea level pressure if a water barometer is used would need to be 13 times higher than 76 cm, or 988 cm.

29. In general, low-pressure regions form over warm water, and high-pressure regions form over cold water.

21. **Predict** If you are in the Northern Hemisphere and are directly west of the center of a cyclone, what most likely will be the wind direction? What will the wind direction be if you are west of an anticyclone in the Northern Hemisphere?

22. **Apply Concepts** If you were looking for a location to place a wind turbine to generate electricity, how would you use the spacing of isobars in making your decision?

23. **Hypothesize** What differences in the biosphere would you predict for areas dominated by low-pressure systems compared to those dominated by high-pressure systems?

The red lines on the map below indicate wind direction. The length of each line indicates the percent of the total winds that come from this direction. Use the illustration to answer Questions 24–26.

24. **Analyze Data** According to the map, which winds dominate this region?

25. **Measure** About what percent of the time do winds blow from the east?

26. **Calculate** Determine the approximate percent of time that winds blow from either the west or the northwest in this area.

27. **Predict** How might a La Niña event impact the weather in your area?

28. **Apply Concepts** Mercury is 13 times heavier than water. If you built a barometer using water rather than mercury, how tall would it have to be to record standard sea-level pressure? Express your answer in centimeters. (*Hint:* How many centimeters of mercury represent standard sea-level pressure?)

29. **Interpret Visuals** After studying Figure 16, explain the relationship between water temperature and the type of air pressure system that develops.

Observe For two weeks, keep a daily air pressure, wind, and precipitation log in your science notebook. Be sure to note any changes, and note if any of the changes occur over the course of a single day. At the end of two weeks, organize your information into a data table. Prepare a short summary that includes any patterns you determine among these variables. Report the results orally to your class.

Performance-Based Assessment

Student reports should include observations in an organized table or spreadsheet format. They should express relationships observed among air pressure, wind, and precipitation.

Standardized Test Prep

Choose the letter that best answers the question.

1 The Sahara desert in North Africa and the Australian desert, as well as others, are associated with which pressure zone?
A equatorial low
B polar high
C subpolar low
D subtropical high

2 What does a steep air pressure gradient cause?
F high winds
H variable winds
G light winds
J north winds

3 Low-pressure systems are usually associated with—
A descending air
B diverging surface winds
C clear weather
D precipitation

4 A sea breeze usually originates during the—
F evening and flows toward the land
G day and flows toward the land
H evening and flows toward the water
J day and flows toward the water

Use the illustration below to answer Questions 5 and 6.

5 Using this scale, determine the standard sea level pressure in millibars and inches of mercury. Express your answers to the nearest millibar and to the nearest hundredth of an inch.
A 1013 mb; 29.92 inches
B 29.92 mb; 1013 inches
C 1016 mb; 30.01 inches
D 30.01 mb; 1016 inches

6 What is the corresponding pressure, in millibars, for a pressure measurement of 30.30 inches of mercury?
F 1016 mb
G 1017 mb
H 1024 mb
J 1026 mb

If You Have Trouble With . . .						
Question	1	2	3	4	5	6
See Lesson	19.2	19.1	19.2	19.3	19.1	19.1

Air Pressure and Wind **555**

20 Weather Patterns and Severe Storms Planning Guide

BIGIDEA: WEATHER AND CLIMATE

Lesson Objectives		Activities
20.1 Air Masses, pp. 558–563 20.1 **Define** air mass. 20.2 **Explain** how air masses are classified. 20.3 **Explain** the characteristic features of each air mass class. 20.4 **Explain** the influence of continental polar and maritime tropical air masses on the majority of North America.		TE Teacher Demo: Air Masses in a Bottle, p. 559 L2 SE **Map It:** Lake-Effect Snowstorms, p. 561 L2
20.2 Fronts, pp. 564–570 20.5 **Describe** the formation of a front. 20.6 **Differentiate** among the formation of a warm front, cold front, stationary front, and occluded front. 20.7 **Describe** the weather patterns associated with each type of front.		TE Build Science Skills, p. 566 L2 TE Teacher Demo: Getting to the Point of Fronts, p. 568 L2
20.3 Severe Storms, pp. 571–577 20.8 **Explain** the formation of a thunderstorm. 20.9 **Describe** the conditions needed for a tornado to form. 20.10 **Identify** the conditions that must exist for a hurricane to form.		TE Teacher Demo: Homemade Tornado, p. 573 L2
Chapter Features and Labs		
Try It How Can You Model the Movement of Air in a Tornado? p. 557		LM Analyzing Severe Weather Data L2
How Earth Works Winds and Storms, pp. 578–579		LM Interpreting Weather Diagrams L2
Exploration Lab Middle Latitude Cyclones, pp. 580–581		LM Creating a Weather Station L2

Ability Levels		Components			
L1 For students who need additional help		**SE**	Student Edition	**LP**	Lesson Plans
L2 For all students		**TE**	Teacher's Edition	**AA**	Active Art
L3 For students who need to be challenged		**LM**	Laboratory Manual	**PD**	Planet Diary
		CT	Chapter Tests	**GEODe**	Geode CD-ROM
		GRSW	Guided Reading & Study Workbook	**eText**	
		CTB	Computer Test Bank		

Resources	Lesson Assessment
GRSW Lesson 20.1 **LP** Lesson Planning 20.1 **GEODe** The Atmosphere: Basic Weather Patterns	**SE** Lesson 20.1 Assessment, p. 563 **eText** Lesson 20.1
GRSW Lesson 20.2 **LP** Lesson Planning 20.2	**SE** Lesson 20.2 Assessment, p. 570 **eText** Lesson 20.2
GRSW Lesson 20.3 **LP** Lesson Planning 20.3 **PD** Links on Hurricanes, Cyclones, and Typhoons	**SE** Lesson 20.3 Assessment, p. 577 **eText** Lesson 20.3

Materials for Activities and Labs

Quantities for each group

STUDENT EDITION

Try It, p. 557
2 1-L transparent plastic soda bottles from which the labels have been removed, flat rubber washer with a 3/8" hole in the center, duct tape, scissors, tap water, 30-mL liquid dishwashing soap, paper towels to wipe up spills, 1/4 teaspoon glitter or plastic confetti

Exploration Lab, pp. 580–581
tracing paper, sharp pencil, paper clips or removable tape, metric ruler, colored pencils

TEACHER'S EDITION

Teacher Demo, p. 559
2 wide-mouthed jars of the same size, matches, small pan, hot water, ice cubes, flashlight

Build Science Skills, p. 566
red and blue clay

Teacher Demo, p. 568
pencil

Teacher Demo, p. 573
piece of sturdy cardboard; glue; 2 transparency sheets; small hand-held, battery-operated fan; small plastic bowl; clear plastic plant dish, approximately 7" in diameter with a hole cut in the middle; water; dry ice

Assessment

CHAPTER ASSESSMENT
SE Assessment, pp. 583–584
CT Chapter 20 Test
CTB Chapter 20
eText Chapter 20

21st Century Learning

Problem Identification, Formulation, and Solution: What are the hazards of severe weather?, TE p. 582

Common Themes

Weather is a result of the movement of different air masses. Storms result from interactions between these air masses.

Space and Time Air masses are classified by temperature (tropical or polar) and place of origin (continental or maritime).

Fronts are boundaries between two air masses, and are often the location of storms and precipitation. Warm fronts involve warm air moving into cooler air. Cold fronts involve cold air moving into warmer air. Occluded fronts occur when a cold front overtakes a warm front, lifting warm air away from surface.

Forces and Motion Most weather in the United States is produced by middle-latitude cyclones, traveling west to east. A cyclone at the ground involves convergence of air toward a low pressure zone, and is accompanied by divergence of air high in the jet stream.

Matter and Energy About 100,000 thunderstorms associated with cumulonimbus clouds occur in the United States each year. Thunderstorms form when warm humid air rises and moisture precipitates out. They can be the sites of tornadoes, areas of rotating wind and intense low pressure, which can extend down from a cumulonimbus cloud during a thunderstorm.

Earth as a System Hurricanes are large tropical cyclones involving an interaction of ocean, atmosphere, and land systems that begin over the ocean, but can move onto land. Hurricanes can be very destructive, involving tremendous winds and flooding.

Michael Wysession
Washington University

EARTH SCIENCE REFRESHER

Lightning and Thunder

Lightning and thunder are some of the most dramatic aspects of thunderstorms. They occur when electrical current is transferred between locations within the clouds, or between the clouds and the ground. Differences in electrical charge at the top and bottom of cumulonimbus clouds build up during the repeated vertical motions of rain and ice within the clouds. The transfer of current is visible, and this is the lightning. If the current reaches the ground, a return stroke of current occurs, and this is usually brighter then the down stroke.

There is a tremendous amount of energy in a lightning stroke—about 1–10 billion joules, enough to supply the electricity for a home for more than a month. Along the path of the lightning, the air gets heated to temperatures on the order of 25,000°C—hotter than the surface of the sun! This sudden increase in temperature causes the air to rapidly expand as a shock wave, which then converts into a booming sound wave we hear as thunder. We see the lightning almost instantaneously because of the great speed of light, with the sound of the thunder arriving later. Because the speed of sound in air is about 335 m/s (depending upon the temperature of the air), if you divide the number of seconds between the lightning and thunder by 3, you will get the distance of the lightning in kilometers.

Address **Misconceptions**

Students may think that the terms warm front *and* cold front *are actually referring to masses of warm air and cold air.* This is not true. A warm front brings an air mass with warmer air into an area, and a cold front brings cooler air into an area. For a strategy that helps to overcome this misconception, see **Address Misconceptions** on TE p. 566.

The United States National Lightning Detection Network identifies about 22 million cloud-to-ground flashes every year. In the United States, about 100 people are killed and 500 injured by lightning each year. It is estimated that you therefore have a 1 in 600,000 chance of being killed or injured by lightning each year. Most lightning occurs in the direct region of a storm, but some strikes are more than 100 km long, and have been known to hit the ground far from a storm, in areas of blue sky.

Lightning plays an important geological role because it can often cause forest fires. These fires reduce ground cover, and therefore increase the susceptibility of the land to erosion and mass wasting. Vegetation has evolved , which can adapt to forest fires that occur from lightning strikes. In fact, there are some plants that have seeds that are only released following a fire. These are the first plants to regenerate, followed by successions of other kinds of vegetation. Ironically, putting out the small fires that repeatedly occur from lightning strikes can cause a buildup of undergrowth, which can result in a catastrophic fire when it does burn.

BUILD READING LITERACY
Active Comprehension
Engaging Interest in a Topic
Strategy Stimulate students' interest in a topic prior to reading. As with the KWL strategy, students generate questions based on their curiosity. Interest is thus translated into a purpose for reading. Looking for answers to the questions during reading helps keep students engaged in what they are reading. Before students begin reading, choose an opening paragraph from one of the sections in Chapter 20, for example, the first paragraph on p. 558.

Example
1. Have a student read the opening paragraph.
2. Ask the group, "What more would you like to know about storms and weather?" Make a list of student responses.
3. Tell students to read the remainder of the section, keeping the questions in mind as they read.
4. After reading, you may discuss the extent to which each question was answered by the text. Ask students also to comment on any new information they learned that was surprising.
5. Have students work in small groups, applying the active comprehension strategy to the reading of each section of the chapter.

See TE p. 567 for a script on how to use this strategy with students. For additional strategies, see TE pp. 561 and 576.

ASSESS PRIOR KNOWLEDGE

Use the Chapter Pretest below to assess students' prior knowledge. As needed, review these concepts.

Review Science Concepts

Lesson 20.1 An understanding of how water is a part of the atmosphere and the conditions that dictate how much water vapor can exist in the atmosphere will help students understand how polar and tropical air masses are different.

Lesson 20.2 Reviewing air pressure and the movement of air from areas of high pressure to areas of low pressure will help explain the movement of air masses along fronts.

Lesson 20.3 Reviewing the different types of clouds and their formation is essential for an understanding of the formation of severe storms in the atmosphere.

20 Weather Patterns and Severe Storms

Big idea Weather and Climate

Q: How are air masses and severe weather related?

556

Chapter Pretest

1. True or False: More water vapor can exist in warm air than in cold air. *(True)*

2. When water vapor in air condenses, what must occur in order for clouds to form? *(c)*
   a. The air is heated.
   b. Snow falls.
   c. The air is cooled.
   d. The air is superheated.

3. Explain briefly how wind forms. *(Wind is the result of the horizontal movement of air from an area of high pressure to an area of low pressure.)*

4. What are low, sheetlike clouds called? *(c)*
   a. cirrus clouds
   b. cumulus clouds
   c. stratus clouds
   d. cirrocumulus clouds

5. Where would the air contain the most moisture—over Kenya or over Antarctica? Why? *(over Kenya because the air is warmer there)*

On June 20, 2011, a tornado spins violently in Nebraska.

INQUIRY
TRY IT!

HOW CAN YOU MODEL A TORNADO?

Procedure

1. Pour water into a 1-L plastic bottle until it is about two-thirds full. Wipe off any water from the outside and the opening.
2. Without getting any of either substance on the outside of the bottle, add about 30 mL of liquid dishwashing soap and a spoonful of glitter to the water.
3. Center a washer on the mouth of the bottle.
4. Invert another 1-L bottle and place its mouth over the washer.
5. Without moving the washer, wrap duct tape around the mouths of the bottles to seal them.
6. Quickly invert the bottles so that the bottle holding the water is on top. Then, while holding the top bottle, carefully swirl the bottles in a counterclockwise direction.
7. Observe your mini-tornado.

Think About It

1. **Observe** How did the water move in the bottle?
2. **Use Models** What might the glitter represent?
3. **Form a Hypothesis** What forces probably acted on the water?

557

ENGAGE/EXPLORE

INQUIRY
TRY IT!

HOW CAN YOU MODEL A TORNADO?

Purpose In this activity, students will use water to model the movement of air in a tornado.

Skills Observe, Use Models, Form Hypotheses

Prep Time 10 minutes to gather materials

Materials (per pair of students) 2 1-L transparent plastic soda bottles from which the labels have been removed, flat rubber washer with a 3/8" hole in the center, duct tape, scissors, tap water, 30-mL liquid dishwashing soap, paper towels to wipe up spills, 1/4 teaspoon glitter or plastic confetti

Advance Prep Have each student bring from home one 1-L transparent plastic soda bottle from which the label has been removed.

Class Time 15–20 minutes

Safety Students should wipe up any spills immediately to avoid slips and falls.

Teaching Tip Remind students to keep the outsides of the bottles—including the necks—dry.

Expected Outcome Students will observe the formation of a vortex that forms as centripetal force on the water causes the water to spin.

Think About It
1. The swirling water (vortex) moved in a counterclockwise direction within the top bottle and down into the bottom bottle.
2. The glitter represents debris carried by the swirling winds of a tornado.
3. Students may recognize that momentum or centripetal forces caused the water to swirl. Gravity caused the water to move into the lower bottle.

1 FOCUS

Lesson Objectives
20.1 **Define** air mass.
20.2 **Explain** how air masses are classified.
20.3 **Explain** the characteristic features of each air mass class.
20.4 **Explain** the influence of continental polar and maritime tropical air masses on the majority of North America.

Build Vocabulary L2
Paraphrase Ask students to write the vocabulary words on a sheet of paper. Instruct students to write a definition, in their own words, for each term as they encounter the term while going through the chapter. After writing their own definition, they should also write a complete sentence using the term.

Reading Strategy L2
a. an immense body of air in the troposphere characterized by similar temperatures and amounts of moisture at any given altitude
b. area over which an air mass gets its characteristic properties of temperature and moisture
c. cold air mass that forms at high latitudes toward Earth's poles
d. warm air mass that forms at low latitudes
e. dry air mass that forms over land
f. humid air mass that forms over water

20.1 Air Masses

Key Questions
🔑 **What is an air mass?**

🔑 **What happens as an air mass moves over an area?**

🔑 **How are air masses classified?**

🔑 **Which air masses influence much of the weather in North America?**

🔑 **Why do continental tropical air masses have little effect on weather in North America?**

Vocabulary
• air mass

Reading Strategy
Build Vocabulary Copy the table. As you read this section, write a definition for each of the terms in the table. Refer to the table as you read the rest of the chapter.

Term	Definition
Air mass	a. ___?___
Source region	b. ___?___
Polar air mass	c. ___?___
Tropical air mass	d. ___?___
Continental air mass	e. ___?___
Maritime air mass	f. ___?___

SEVERE STORMS are among nature's most destructive forces. Every spring and summer, newspapers and television report the damage caused by short, violent windstorms called tornadoes. The force of tornado winds can be almost unbelievably strong, causing damage such as that shown in **Figure 1.** Then, during the late summer and early fall, hurricanes form over Earth's tropical oceans. As hurricanes move toward land, the strong winds and heavy rains produced by these storms often cause tremendous destruction along their paths. Thunderstorms are the type of severe storm that is probably most familiar to you. Thunderstorms produce heavy rains, thunder, and lightning.

Violent weather is scary and dramatic, but normal, day-to-day weather—the weather you hear about every day on TV—is interesting, too. The factors that determine everyday weather also affect storms. You can't understand the causes of storms until you learn about the atmospheric conditions that most often affect the daily weather.

FIGURE 1 Tornado Damage The force of the wind during a tornado was strong enough to drive a piece of metal into this utility pole.

Air Masses and Weather

For the many people who live in the middle latitudes, which include much of the United States, summer heat waves and winter cold spells are familiar experiences. During summer heat waves, several days of high temperatures and high humidity often end when a series of storms pass through the area. This stormy weather is followed by a few days of relatively cool weather. By contrast, winter cold spells are often characterized by periods of frigid temperatures under clear skies. These bitter cold periods are usually followed by cloudy, snowy, relatively warm days that seem mild when compared to those just a day earlier. In both of these situations, periods of fairly constant weather conditions are followed by a short period of changes in the weather. What do you think causes these changes?

PLANET DIARY

For links about **Tornadoes**, go to PlanetDiary.com/HSES.

Air Masses The weather patterns just described result from air masses on the move. ⟨⟩ **An air mass is an extremely large body of air that is located in the troposphere and is characterized by similar temperatures and amounts of moisture at any given altitude.** An air mass can be 1600 kilometers or more across and several kilometers thick. Because of its size, it may take several days for an air mass to move over an area. Because the air mass takes a long time to move, the area experiences fairly constant weather. A situation in which the weather is fairly constant is called *air-mass weather*. Some day-to-day changes in the weather within the air mass may occur, but the events will be very unlike those in a nearby air mass.

Movement of Air Masses When an air mass moves out of the region over which it formed, it carries its temperature and moisture conditions with it. **Figure 2** shows the path of an air mass as it moves from northern Canada to Mexico. A cold, dry air mass from northern Canada is shown moving southward. The initial temperature of the air mass is −46°C. The air mass warms 13 degrees by the time it reaches Winnipeg. The air mass continues to warm as it moves southward through the Great Plains and into Mexico. Throughout its southward journey, as the air mass becomes warmer, it also brings some of the coldest weather of the winter to the places in its path. ⟨⟩ **As an air mass moves, its characteristics change and so does the weather in the area over which it moves.**

☑ **Reading Checkpoint** What is an air mass? What happens as it moves over an area?

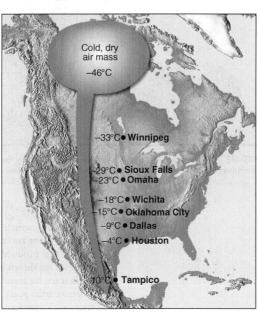

FIGURE 2 Air Mass on the Move
As a frigid Canadian air mass moves southward, it brings colder weather to the area over which it moves. **Calculate** *How much warmer was the air mass when it reached Tampico, Mexico, than when it formed?*

Map labels:
Cold, dry air mass −46°C
−33°C Winnipeg
−29°C Sioux Falls
−23°C Omaha
−18°C Wichita
−15°C Oklahoma City
−9°C Dallas
−4°C Houston
10°C Tampico

---

2 INSTRUCT

(Teacher **Demo**)

AIR MASSES IN A BOTTLE L2

Purpose Students will observe what occurs when hot and cold air masses collide.

Materials 2 wide-mouthed jars of the same size, matches, small pan, hot water, ice cubes, flashlight

Procedure Before planning and implementing this demonstration, check your district's and state's policy on open flames in the classroom. If the following procedure conforms to regulations, you can proceed with the demo. Begin by placing the hot water in the pan. Place one of the jars in the pan. Using the matches, fill both jars with smoke. Place the second jar on top of the one in the pan. Place the ice cubes on top of the second jar. Darken the classroom and use the flashlight to observe the movement of the smoke within the jars.

Expected Outcomes The hot air will rise in the first jar; the cold air will sink in the second jar
Kinesthetic, Visual

Answers

Figure 2 *56°C warmer*

☑ **Reading Checkpoint** *An air mass is an immense body of air in the troposphere characterized by similar temperatures and amounts of moisture at any given altitude. As it moves, the characteristics of an air mass change and the weather in the area over which the air mass moves also changes.*

Differentiated Instruction

ENGLISH LANGUAGE LEARNERS Direct students to Figure 3 on p. 560. Before they read, have them use the figure to make a list of the four types of air masses impacting North America. Students should add definitions for the terms to the glossary as they read the section.

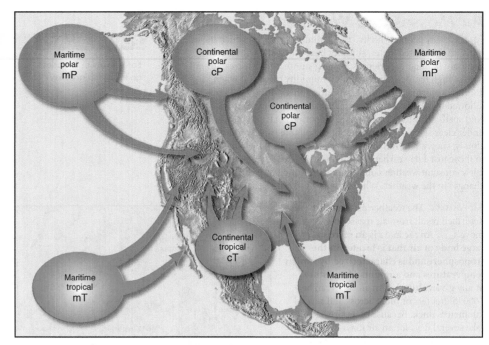

FIGURE 3 Types of Air Masses Air masses are classified by the region over which they form.
Interpret Maps *What kinds of air masses influence the weather patterns along the west coast of the United States?*

Classifying Air Masses

The area over which an air mass gets its characteristic properties of temperature and moisture is called its *source region*. The source regions that produce air masses that influence the weather in North America are shown in **Figure 3.** Air masses are named according to their source region. Polar (P) air masses form at high latitudes toward Earth's poles. Air masses that form at low latitudes are tropical (T) air masses. The terms *polar* and *tropical* describe the temperature characteristics of an air mass. Polar air masses are cold, while tropical air masses are warm.

 In addition to their overall temperature, air masses are classified according to the surface over which they form. Continental (c) air masses form over land. Maritime (m) air masses form over water. The terms *continental* and *maritime* describe the moisture characteristics of the air mass. Continental air masses are likely to be dry. Maritime air masses are humid.

Using this classification scheme, there are four basic types of air masses. A *continental polar (cP) air mass* is dry and cool. A *continental tropical (cT) air mass* is dry and warm or hot. *Maritime polar (mP)* and *maritime tropical (mT)* air masses both form over water. But a maritime polar air mass is much colder than a maritime tropical air mass.

560 Chapter 20 • Lesson 1

Facts and Figures

Maritime polar air originates over cold ocean currents or high-latitude ocean waters. This air does not have as much moisture content as mT air, yet it can produce widespread rain or snow. This air mass is notorious for producing fog, drizzle, cloudy weather, and long-lasting light-to-moderate rain. Maritime polar air changes as it moves over elevated terrain. On the windward side of mountain ranges, mP air can produce an abundance of rain and snow. Once on the lee side of mountains, the mP air mass modifies into a continental air mass. These air masses produce cold fronts, but the air is not as cold as polar fronts. They are often referred to as "Pacific fronts" or "back-door cold fronts." Maritime polar air occurs frequently in the Pacific Northwest and to a lesser degree in New England.

Map

FIGURE 4 **Lake-Effect Snowstorms** Some areas that border the Great Lakes are prone to huge snowstorms.

Key
Snowbelts

Thunder Bay
ONTARIO
MN
Marquette
WI
MI
NY
Rochester
Buffalo
IO
Chardon
IL
PA
IN
OH
0 100 200 300 km

MAP IT!
ACTIVITY

Marquette, Michigan, is southeast of Thunder Bay, Ontario, as the map in **Figure 4** shows.

Identify What type of air mass influences the weather of these two cities in the winter?

Infer Which of these cities receives more snow in an average winter? Why?

Build Reading Literacy   L1

Refer to **p. 334D** in **Chapter 12,** which provides the guidelines for outlining.

Outline Have students read the lesson. Then, have students use the headings as major divisions in an outline. Allow students to refer to their outlines when answering the questions in the Lesson 20.1 Assessment.
Visual

Weather in North America

🔑 **Much of the weather in North America, especially weather east of the Rocky Mountains, is influenced by continental polar (cP) and maritime tropical (mT) air masses.** Figure 3 shows where these air masses originate.

Continental Polar Air Masses Continental polar air masses are uniformly cold and dry in winter and cool and dry in summer. In summer, cP air masses may bring a few days of relatively cooler weather. In winter, this continental polar air brings the clear skies and cold temperatures characteristic of a cold wave.

Continental polar air masses are not, as a rule, associated with heavy precipitation. However, those that cross the Great Lakes during late autumn and winter sometimes bring snowstorms to the land areas that the wind reaches after crossing over water. These localized snowstorms, which are known as *lake-effect snows,* make the New York cities of Buffalo and Rochester, shown in **Figure 4,** among the snowiest cities in the United States. The areas that receive heavy snow are known as *snowbelts.*

What causes lake-effect snow? During late autumn and early winter, the difference in temperature between the lakes and adjacent land areas can be large. The temperature contrast can be especially great when a very cold cP air mass pushes southward across the lakes. When this occurs, the air picks up large quantities of heat and moisture from the relatively warm lake surface. By the time it reaches the opposite shore, the air mass is humid and unstable. Heavy snow, such as that shown in **Figure 5,** is possible.

☑ **Reading Checkpoint** *What causes large amounts of snow to fall on the southern and eastern shores of the Great Lakes?*

FIGURE 5 **Digging Out** A lake-effect snowstorm dropped 175 cm (69 in.) of snow on Chardon, Ohio.

Answers

Figure 3 *maritime polar (mP) and maritime tropical (mT) air masses*

MAP IT! *Continental polar air masses influence the weather in this region.*

Because it is on the downwind side of Lake Superior, Marquette receives more snow than Thunder Bay does.

☑ **Reading Checkpoint** *Continental polar air masses, crossing the Great Lakes, cause heavy lake-effect snows.*

Facts and Figures

On November 20–23, 2000, Buffalo, NY, and the surrounding area were hit with a 60-hour lake-effect snowstorm. During the period, the storm dumped up to 79 cm of snow and was the most widespread and significant November lake-effect storm since 1996, when a longer lasting storm dropped about a meter of snow.

The November 2000 storm had frequent lightning as snow showers grew heavy.

Snow fell at the rate of 5–10 cm per hour for several hours. The timing of the most intense snowfall could not have been worse. It hit just before the evening commute. Thousands were reported to have spent the night in their cars or to have taken shelter in stores and hotels. Many schoolchildren and school buses became trapped. It was the most disruptive storm in the Buffalo area since the blizzard of 1977.

Build Science Skills　L2

Use Tables and Graphs Have students make a table to compare and contrast the four basic types of air masses.
Intrapersonal, Verbal

Build Reading Literacy　L1

Refer to **p. 124D** in **Chapter 5**, which provides the guidelines for summarizing.

Summarize Have students summarize what they have learned in this lesson by listing the characteristics of each type of air mass. Ask them to make a two-column chart with the column headings "Air mass type" and "Characteristics." (You may alternatively draw a chart on the board to make this an interactive class activity.) Make sure students describe four air masses: cP, cT, mP, and mT.
Portfolio, Group

Use Community Resources　L2

Invite students to find out what types of air masses commonly affect their region. Encourage them to consult periodicals at their local library. If their sources do not explicitly mention a specific type of air mass, have them record temperature and precipitation data. Then lead a discussion about what air masses are likely to cause such conditions.
Verbal, Group

Answers

Figure 7 *The cP air mass acquires moisture as it slowly moves over the ocean to become an mP air mass.*

☑ **Reading Checkpoint** *When the maritime polar air mass advances against the western mountains, uplift produces heavy rain or snow on the windward slopes of the mountains.*

FIGURE 6 Rain Storm over Florida Bay in the Florida Keys

Maritime Tropical Air Masses Maritime tropical air masses also play a dominant role in the weather of North America. These air masses are warm and loaded with moisture. In addition, they are usually unstable. Maritime tropical air is the source of much, if not most, of the precipitation received in the eastern two thirds of the United States. The heavy precipitation shown in **Figure 6** is the result of maritime tropical air masses moving through the area. In summer, when a mT air mass invades the central and eastern United States, it brings the high temperatures and oppressive humidity typically associated with its source region.

Maritime Polar Air Masses During the winter, maritime polar air masses that affect weather in North America come from the North Pacific. Such air masses often begin as cP air masses in Siberia (northern Asia). The cold, dry continental polar air changes into relatively mild, humid, unstable maritime polar air during its long journey across the North Pacific (**Figure 7**). As this maritime polar air arrives at the western shore of North America, it is often accompanied by low clouds and showers. When this maritime polar air advances inland against the western mountains, uplift of the air produces heavy rain or snow on the windward slopes of the mountains (the sides that the wind passes over first).

Maritime polar air masses also originate in the North Atlantic off the coast of eastern Canada. These air masses influence the weather of the northeastern United States. In winter, when New England is on the northern or northwestern side of a passing low-pressure center, the counterclockwise winds draw in maritime polar air. The result is a storm characterized by snow and cold temperatures, known locally as a nor'easter.

☑ **Reading Checkpoint** *What happens when maritime polar air crosses western mountains?*

FIGURE 7 Source of Maritime Polar Air Masses During winter, maritime polar (mP) air masses in the northern Pacific Ocean usually begin as continental polar (cP) air masses in Siberia.
Infer *What happens to the mP air masses as they cross the Pacific?*

FIGURE 8 Indian Summer A cT air mass produces a few days of warm weather amid the cool days of fall.

Continental Tropical Air Masses Continental tropical air masses begin in the southwestern United States and Mexico during the summer. **Only occasionally do cT air masses move outside their source regions.** However, when a cT air mass does move from its source region in the summer, it can cause extreme heat and drought in the Great Plains. Movement of such air masses in the fall results in mild weather, often called Indian summer, in the Great Lakes region.

PLANET DIARY

For links about **Tropical Storms**, go to PlanetDiary.com/HSES.

Evaluate Understanding　L2

Have each student write a paragraph explaining the term *air-mass weather*. *(Answers should include the fact that weather is a result of moving air masses. Because air masses are so huge, it usually takes several days for them to move over an area. This causes fairly constant weather, known as air mass weather.)*

Reteach　L1

Use Figure 3 to review the classification of air masses.

20.1 Assessment

Review Key Concepts

1. What is an air mass?

2. What happens as an air mass moves over an area?

3. How are air masses classified?

4. Which types of air masses have the greatest effect on weather in North America?

5. Why do continental tropical air masses have little effect on weather in North America?

Think Critically

6. **Compare and Contrast** Compare and contrast the four types of air masses.

7. **Explain** Explain which type of air mass could offer relief from a scorching summer to the Midwestern United States. Justify your choice.

8. **Apply Concepts** How can continental polar air be responsible for lake-effect snowstorms in the Great Lakes region?

9. **Identify** Look again at Figure 3. What kinds of air masses influence the weather patterns over Florida?

10. **Infer** What kind of weather could be expected in southern Canada if an mT air mass was to invade the region in mid-July?

WRITING IN SCIENCE

11. **Explain** Pick one of the air masses shown in Figure 3 that affects the weather in your area. Write a paragraph that explains the weather typically associated with the air mass in both the summer and the winter.

Weather Patterns and Severe Storms **563**

Assessment Answers

1. an immense body of air in the troposphere characterized by similar temperatures and amounts of moisture at any given altitude
2. The air mass changes the weather in the area over which it moves.
3. by temperature and the surface over which they form
4. continental polar and maritime tropical air masses
5. Such air masses rarely move from their source regions.

6. They are similar in that each influences weather in North America. They differ in that continental air masses form over land and thus are dry. Maritime air masses form over water and thus are wet. Polar air masses are cold, while tropical air masses are warm.
7. A continental polar (cP) air mass is cool and dry and is usually associated with high pressure and clear skies. Such an air mass would offer relief from hot summer weather.

8. Although cP air masses are cold and dry, they acquire moisture and some heat as they cross the relatively warm lakes. The addition of moisture and the increase in temperature make the air masses unstable, causing snow to fall downwind of the lakes.
9. maritime tropical and continental polar
10. Oppressively hot and humid weather typical of the source region of the air mass would occur in southern Canada.
11. Answers will depend on students' choices of air masses. Sample answer: Continental polar air masses bring clear skies and cold temperatures in winter and relatively cool, dry days in summer.

20.2 Fronts

LESSON 20.2

1 FOCUS

Lesson Objectives
20.5 **Describe** the formation of a front.
20.6 **Differentiate** among the formation of a warm front, cold front, stationary front, and occluded front.
20.7 **Describe** the weather patterns associated with each type of front.

Build Vocabulary L2
Web Diagram Have students construct a web diagram of the vocabulary words in this lesson. The main concept (fronts) should be at the top of the diagram. Ask students to provide one descriptive statement for each of the other vocabulary words.

Reading Strategy L2
I. A. warm air moves into an area formerly covered by cooler air
B. light-to-moderate precipitation over wide area for extended time
II. A. cold air moves into region occupied by warmer air
B. heavy downpours and winds followed by drop in temperature
III. Stationary front
A. flow of air parallel along front
B. gentle-to-moderate precipitation
IV. Occluded front
A. a cold front overtakes a warm front
B. light precipitation

2 INSTRUCT

Use Visuals L1
Figure 9 Direct students' attention to the photograph. **Ask:** What type of precipitation is falling? *(a light rain)* What do you know about the general weather conditions in this area based on the photograph? *(The temperature is above freezing.)*
Visual

Key Questions
🔑 *What happens when two air masses meet?*

🔑 *How is a warm front produced?*

🔑 *What is a cold front?*

🔑 *What is a stationary front?*

🔑 *What are the stages in the formation of an occluded front?*

🔑 *What is a middle-latitude cyclone?*

🔑 *What fuels a middle-latitude cyclone?*

Vocabulary
• front • warm front
• cold front • stationary front
• occluded front

Reading Strategy
Outline As you read, make an outline like the one below. Include information about how each of the weather fronts discussed in this section forms and the weather associated with each.

Fronts
I. Warm front
A. _____ ?
B. _____ ?
II. Cold front
A. _____ ?
B. _____ ?

AIR MASSES have different temperatures and amounts of moisture, depending on their source. What happens when air masses come together?

Formation of Fronts
🔑 **When two air masses with different properties meet, they form a front.** A **front** is a boundary between two contrasting air masses. Fronts are often associated with some form of precipitation. Most weather fronts are between 15 and 200 kilometers wide. Above Earth's surface, the surface of the front slopes at a low angle, so that warmer, less dense air overlies cooler, denser air.

Occasionally, the air masses on both sides of a front move in the same direction and at the same speed. When this happens, the front acts simply as a barrier that travels with the air masses. In most cases, however, the distribution of pressure across a front causes one air mass to move faster than the other. When this happens, one air mass advances into another, and some mixing of air occurs.

FIGURE 9 Precipitation from a Storm in South Africa Storms often form along fronts.

FIGURE 10 **Formation of a Warm Front** A warm front forms when warm air moves into an area formerly occupied by cooler air. The affected area has warmer temperatures and light to moderate precipitation.

Types of Fronts

Fronts are often classified according to the temperature of the advancing front. There are four types of fronts: warm fronts, cold fronts, stationary fronts, and occluded fronts.

Warm Fronts A **warm front** is a front along which a warm air mass rises over a retreating mass of cool air. ▭ **A warm front forms when warm air moves into an area formerly covered by cooler air.** On a weather map, the surface position of a warm front is shown by a red line with red semicircles. The semicircles point toward the cooler air mass.

The slope of the warm front is very gradual, as shown in **Figure 10.** As warm air rises, it cools to produce clouds and frequently precipitation. The sequence of clouds shown in Figure 10 typically comes before a warm front. The first sign of the approaching warm front is the appearance of cirrus clouds. As the front comes closer, cirrus clouds change into cirrostratus clouds, which blend into denser sheets of altostratus clouds. About 300 kilometers ahead of the front, thicker stratus and nimbostratus clouds appear, and rain or snow begins.

Because of their slow rate of movement and very low slope, warm fronts usually produce light to moderate precipitation over a large area for an extended period. A gradual increase in temperature occurs with the passage of a warm front. The increase is most apparent when a large temperature difference exists between adjacent air masses. In the Northern Hemisphere, a wind shift from the east to the southwest is associated with a warm front.

☑ **Reading Checkpoint** What causes a warm front to form?

Use Visuals L1

Figure 10 Have students examine the diagram of a warm front in the figure. **Ask:** As a warm front approaches, what type of weather can you expect? *(rainy weather)* Describe how the sky conditions change as a warm front approaches. *(It becomes increasingly cloudy.)* **Visual**

Build Science Skills L2

Apply Concepts Students will be more likely to process and remember information about fronts if they can connect this information to their daily experiences. First, gather and display current weather maps. (Many national newspapers have maps that show notable air masses and fronts. Online resources, such as accuweather.com, also have current national and regional weather maps.) Next, ask students to describe local weather conditions. Then discuss how their observations relate to the data presented in the maps. **Verbal, Visual**

Answers

☑ **Reading Checkpoint** *When warm air moves into an area formerly covered by cooler air, a warm front forms.*

Differentiated Instruction

ENGLISH LANGUAGE LEARNERS Students who are learning English can benefit from real-life examples that relate to science content. Encourage students to think of observations they have made about the weather. For example, ask students if they notice that after a severe, rather fast-moving thunderstorm, it tends to be cooler for the next few days. Explain that this is because a cold front moved into the area, bringing thunderstorms and cooler weather.

Build Science Skills L2

Student Activity: Use Models
Provide students with red and blue clay.
The red clay will represent a warm air mass,
and the blue clay will represent a colder air
mass. Ask students to use the clay to model
one of the four fronts discussed in the text.
They should then present their model to the
class, explaining the motion of each air
mass.
Kinesthetic, Interpersonal

Address Misconceptions L2

Students may think that the terms *warm
front* and *cold front* are actually referring
to masses of warm air and cold air. It is
important that they realize that warm and
cold are comparative terms. For example,
a warm front may pass through Iowa in the
middle of February. This warm air mass may
have a temperature of –26°C when the air
mass already in place has a temperature of
–32°C. Death Valley in the middle of July
may have a cold front move through that
brings temperatures of 46°C, while the air
in place may have a temperature of 49°C.
Emphasize to students that a warm front
brings warmer air to an area and a cold
front brings cooler air.
Verbal

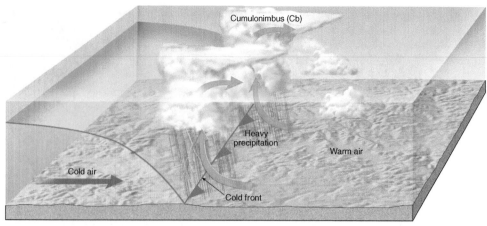

FIGURE 11 Formation of a Cold Front A cold front forms when cold air moves into an area occupied by warmer air. The affected area experiences thunderstorms if the warm air is unstable.

Cold Fronts You can see the process in which a cold front forms in **Figure 11.** **A cold front forms when cold, dense air moves into a region occupied by warmer air.** As this cold front moves, it becomes steeper. On average, cold fronts are about twice as steep as warm fronts and advance more rapidly than warm fronts do. These two differences—rate of movement and steepness of slope—account for the more violent weather associated with a cold front. On a weather map, the surface position of a cold front is shown by a blue line edged with blue triangles pointing toward the warmer air mass.

The forceful lifting of air along a cold front can lead to heavy rain and gusty winds. As a cold front approaches, cumulonimbus clouds often can be seen in the distance. Once the cold front has passed, temperatures drop and wind shifts. The weather behind a cold front is dominated by a cold air mass. So, weather clears soon after a cold front passes. When a cold front moves over a warm area, low cumulus or stratocumulus clouds may form behind the front.

☑ **Reading Checkpoint** *How are cold fronts different from warm fronts?*

Stationary Fronts Occasionally, the flow of air on either side of a front is neither toward the cold air mass nor toward the warm air mass, but almost parallel to the line of the front. **When the surface position of the front does not move, a stationary front has formed.** In a **stationary front,** two air masses come together but neither displaces the other. Gentle to moderate precipitation can occur. On a weather map, stationary fronts are shown by blue triangles on one side of the front and red semicircles on the other.

Occluded Fronts An occluded front is diagrammed in **Figure 12.** 🔊 **When a cold front overtakes a warm front, an occluded front forms.** On a weather map, an occluded front is shown by a purple line with triangles and semicircles. An occluded front develops as the advancing cold air wedges the warm front upward. The weather associated with an occluded front is generally complex. Most precipitation is associated with warm air being forced upward. When conditions are suitable, however, the newly formed front is capable of making light precipitation of its own.

The descriptions of weather associated with fronts are general descriptions. The weather along any individual front may or may not conform to the idealized descriptions you've read about. Fronts, like all aspects of nature, do not always behave as we would expect.

Middle-Latitude Cyclones

In the Northern Hemisphere, a *cyclone* is a system with winds spinning counterclockwise with an area of low pressure at the center. The main weather producers in this country are middle-latitude cyclones. On weather maps, these low-pressure areas are shown by the letter L.

🔊 **A middle-latitude cyclone is a large center of low pressure that generally travels from west to east and causes stormy weather.** The air in a middle-latitude cyclone moves in a counterclockwise direction and toward the center of the low. Most middle-latitude cyclones have a cold front, and frequently a warm front, extending from the central area. Forceful lifting of air causes the formation of clouds that drop abundant precipitation.

How do cyclones form? The stages of cyclone formation are diagrammed in **Figure 13.** The first stage is the development of a stationary front. The front forms as two air masses with different temperatures move in opposite directions. Over time, the front takes on a wave shape. The wave is usually hundreds of kilometers long.

As the wave develops, warm air moves towards Earth's poles. There it invades the area formerly occupied by colder air. Meanwhile, cold air moves toward the equator. This change in airflow near the surface is accompanied by a change in pressure. The result is a counterclockwise airflow in the Northern Hemisphere.

FIGURE 12 When a cold front overtakes a warm front, an occluded front forms, producing a complex weather pattern.

① A cold front moves toward a warm front, forcing warm air aloft.

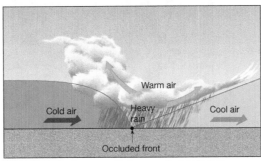

② A cold front merges with the warm front to form an occluded front that drops heavy rains.

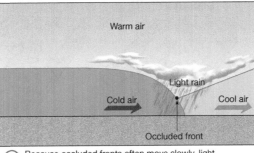

③ Because occluded fronts often move slowly, light precipitation can fall for several days.

Weather Patterns and Severe Storms **567**

Build Reading Literacy 🔲 L1

Refer to **p. 556D** in this chapter, which provides the guidelines for active comprehension.

Active Comprehension Instruct students to read the first two paragraphs of Middle-Latitude Cyclones on p. 567. **Ask:** What more would you like to know about middle-latitude cyclones or Where does the weather in your area come from? You will need to make connections for students between the weather and their lives. For example, students may notice from weather reports on television or on the Internet that stormy weather seems to move from the west to the east. Write down several students' responses on the board. Have students continue reading the lesson and examine Figure 14 on p. 569. While reading, have students consider the questions they had about the material. Have students discuss the lesson content, making sure that each question raised at the beginning is answered or that students know where to look for the answer. **Verbal**

Answers

☑ **Reading Checkpoint** *Cold fronts are much steeper than warm fronts and advance more rapidly than warm fronts do, causing more violent weather to form.*

Facts and Figures

ONE-EYED STORMS Have students consider the word *Cyclops.* These giants of Greek mythology had a single eye in the middle of their foreheads. This word comes from the Greek word *Kyklōps,* which means "round-eyed." The word *cyclone* has a similar meaning. It comes from the Greek word *kykloein,* which means "to circle around." Students can think of cyclones as one-eyed monsters.

LESSON 20.2

(Teacher **Demo**)

GETTING TO THE POINT OF FRONTS [L2]

Purpose Students will observe the motion of mid-latitude cyclones.

Materials pencil

Procedure This activity may be performed as a demonstration, or each student can participate individually. Place a pencil between your hands. Explain that your hands represent two different air masses and the gap between them is the front. Slowly move your right hand forward and your left hand backward. This models the movement of the wind in a stationary front. Direct students' attention to the movement of the pencil.

Expected Outcome The pencil should move in a counterclockwise direction. This models the movement of a mid-latitude cyclone.
Kinesthetic, Visual

Integrate Language Arts [L2]

Cyclones Ask students to study Figure 13. The development of a middle-latitude cyclone is complex. Engage students in a discussion about the complexity of this diagram. So much information is conveyed here that often students may feel that they have not gathered all the information they need from it. Challenge them to write a descriptive narrative, explaining the formation of a middle-latitude cyclone in their own words. Students should share their narratives with small groups to make sure that all the steps have been covered.
Verbal, Interpersonal

MIDDLE-LATITUDE CYCLONE MODEL
FIGURE 13 Cyclones have a fairly predictable life cycle.

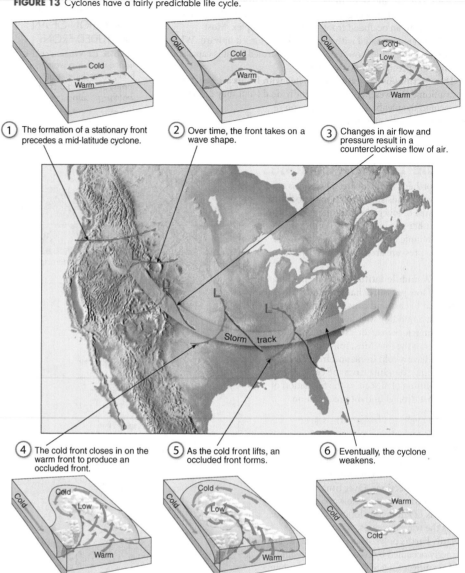

1. The formation of a stationary front precedes a mid-latitude cyclone.
2. Over time, the front takes on a wave shape.
3. Changes in air flow and pressure result in a counterclockwise flow of air.
4. The cold front closes in on the warm front to produce an occluded front.
5. As the cold front lifts, an occluded front forms.
6. Eventually, the cyclone weakens.

FIGURE 14 Cyclone
This is a satellite view of a mature cyclone over the eastern United States.

Occlusion Recall that a cold front advances faster than a warm front. When this occurs in the development of a middle-latitude cyclone, the cold front closes in and eventually lifts the warm front, as Figure 13 shows. This process, known as *occlusion,* forms an occluded front. As occlusion begins, the storm often gets stronger. Pressure at the storm's center falls, and wind speeds increase. In the winter, heavy snowfalls and blizzardlike conditions are possible during this phase.

As more of the warm air is forced to rise, there are smaller differences in air pressure. In a day or two, the entire warm area is displaced. Only cold air surrounds the cyclone at low levels. The horizontal temperature difference that existed between the two air masses is gone. At this point, the cyclone has exhausted its source of energy. Friction slows the airflow near the surface, and the once highly organized counterclockwise flow fades away.

The Role of Airflow Aloft

In an *anticyclone* in the Northern Hemisphere, winds move in a clockwise direction. Airflow aloft plays an important role in maintaining both cyclonic and anticyclonic circulation. In fact, cyclones and anticyclones are actually generated by upper-level flow.

Cyclones often exist for a week or longer. For this to happen, surface convergence must be offset by outflow somewhere higher in the atmosphere. As long as the spreading out of air high up is equal to or greater than the surface inflow, the low-pressure system can be sustained. **More often than not, air high up in the atmosphere fuels a middle-latitude cyclone.**

☑ **Reading Checkpoint** *How do middle-latitude cyclones form and develop?*

Weather Patterns and Severe Storms **569**

Use Visuals L1

Figure 14 Instruct students to study the details of the cyclone in the figure. **Ask:** In what direction is the air spinning in this cyclone? *(counterclockwise)* **Visual**

Build Reading Literacy L1

Refer to **p. 186D** in **Chapter 7,** which provides the guidelines for relating text and visuals.

Relate Text and Visuals The text describes Figure 14 as a "mature cyclone." Ask students to describe what has happened to form this mature cyclone. *(A cold front has overtaken and lifted up a warm front to form an occluded front.)* Now ask students to compare Figures 13 and 14. **Ask:** Which phase of Figure 13 is most representative of Figure 14? *(Both 4 and 5 are acceptable answers, although the occluded front in Figure 14 seems to be well-developed, making 5 the better answer.)* **Ask:** What weather conditions would this phase of a cyclone produce? *(high wind speeds and heavy precipitation)* **Verbal, Visual**

Answers

☑ **Reading Checkpoint** *The first stage is the development of a front. Over time, the front takes on a wave shape. Changes in air flow and pressure result in a counterclockwise flow of air. The cold front eventually closes in on the warm front to produce an occluded front. As the cold front lifts the warm front, an occluded front forms. Eventually, the cyclone weakens.*

LESSON 20.2

3 ASSESS

Evaluate Understanding   [L2]

Have each student write a paragraph explaining the relationship between fronts and precipitation. *(Answers will vary, but students should mention that precipitation is often associated with fronts.)*

Reteach   [L1]

Review the fact that the main weather producers in the United States are middle-latitude cyclones. Use Figure 14 as a visual aid to discuss how middle-latitude cyclones work.

Answers

Figure 15 *Both result from changes in surface pressure. Both systems depend on the flow of air high in the atmosphere to maintain their circulation. Cyclones are fueled by upward air movement and reduced surface pressure. Anticyclones form as the result of the downward movement of air and increased surface pressure.*

Assessment Answers

1. They form a front, which is a boundary that separates two air masses.
2. Warmer air moves into an area formerly covered by cooler air.
3. A cold front forms when colder, denser air moves into a region occupied by warmer air.
4. Occasionally, the flow of air on either side of a front is neither toward the cold air mass nor toward the warm air mass, but almost parallel to the line of the front. The surface position of the front does not move, and a stationary front forms.
5. A cold front moves toward a warm front, forcing warmer air aloft. The cold front merges with the warm front to form an occluded front that drops heavy rains. The heavy rains are followed by periods of light precipitation.

570 Chapter 20

FIGURE 15 **Air Flow in Cyclones and Anticyclones** Movements of air high in the atmosphere fuel the cyclones and anticyclones near Earth's surface. **Compare and Contrast** *Compare and contrast the movement of air in cyclones and anticyclones.*

Because cyclones bring stormy weather, they have received far more attention than anticyclones. However, a close relationship exists between these two pressure systems. As shown in **Figure 15**, the surface air that feeds a cyclone generally originates as air flowing out of an anticyclone. As a result, cyclones and anticyclones typically are found next to each other. Like a cyclone, an anticyclone depends on the flow of air high in the atmosphere to maintain its circulation. In an anticyclone, air spreading out at the surface is balanced by air coming together from high up.

20.2 Assessment

Review Key Concepts

1. What happens when two air masses with different properties meet?
2. How does a warm front form?
3. What is a cold front?
4. What is a stationary front?
5. What are the stages in the formation of an occluded front?
6. What is a middle-latitude cyclone?
7. What causes a middle-latitude cyclone to sustain itself?

Think Critically

8. **Compare and Contrast** Compare and contrast warm fronts and cold fronts.
9. **Interpret Visuals** Use Figure 15 and what you know about Earth's atmosphere to describe the air movement and pressure conditions associated with both cyclones and anticyclones.

WRITING IN SCIENCE

10. **Explain** Write a paragraph to explain this statement: The formation of an occluded front marks the beginning of the end of a middle-latitude cyclone.

570 Chapter 20 • Lesson 2

6. a large center of low pressure that generally travels from west to east in the contiguous United States and causes stormy weather
7. airflow aloft
8. Both fronts form when two air masses meet. Warm fronts form when warmer air moves into a region formerly occupied by cold air. Cold fronts form when colder air moves into a region occupied by warmer air. Warm fronts move more slowly and have more gradual slopes.

9. Cyclones are fueled by upward air movement and reduced surface pressure. Anticyclones form as the result of the downward movement of air and increased surface pressure. In the northern hemisphere cyclones rotate counterclockwise and air flows in toward the center and anticyclones rotate clockwise and air flows out from the center.
10. An occluded front forms as fast-moving cold air catches up to a warm front. The warmer air then is forced aloft and eventually dissipates. When this warmer air is gone, there is little condensation and therefore little precipitation.

20.3 Severe Storms

SEVERE WEATHER has a fascination that everyday weather does not provide. For example, a thunderstorm with its jagged lightning and booming thunder can be an awesome sight. However, the damage and destruction caused by severe weather can be frightening. A single severe storm can cause billions of dollars in property damage as well as many deaths. This section discusses three types of severe storms and their causes.

Thunderstorms

Have you ever seen a small whirlwind carry dust or leaves upward on a hot day? Have you observed a bird glide effortlessly skyward on an invisible updraft of hot air? If so, you have observed the effects of the vertical movements of relatively warm, unstable air. Thunderstorms develop because of a similar thermal kind of instability. **A thunderstorm is a storm that generates lightning and thunder. Thunderstorms frequently produce gusty winds, heavy rain, and hail.** A thunderstorm may be produced by a single cumulonimbus cloud and influence only a small area. Or it may be associated with clusters of cumulonimbus clouds that stretch for kilometers along a cold front.

FIGURE 16 Jagged Fork in the Sky Lightning is a spectacular and potentially dangerous feature of a thunderstorm.

Key Questions

- What is a thunderstorm?
- What causes a thunderstorm to form?
- What is a tornado?
- How does a tornado form?
- What is a hurricane?
- How does a hurricane form?

Vocabulary

- thunderstorm • tornado
- hurricane • eye wall
- eye • storm surge

Reading Strategy

Identify Cause and Effect Copy the table and complete it as you read this section.

Severe Storms	Causes	Effects
Thunderstorms	a. ?	b. ?
Tornadoes	c. ?	d. ?
Hurricanes	e. ?	f. ?

1 FOCUS

Lesson Objectives

20.8 **Explain** the formation of a thunderstorm.

20.9 **Describe** the conditions needed for a tornado to form.

20.10 **Identify** the conditions that must exist for a hurricane to form.

Build Vocabulary   L2

Venn Diagram Have students make a Venn diagram of hurricanes and tornadoes.

Reading Strategy   L2

a. warm, humid air rising in an unstable environment

b. gusty winds, heavy rain, thunder and lightning

c. associated with thunderstorms and the development of a mesocyclone

d. violent windstorm, isolated path

e. ocean water temperatures warm enough to provide heat and moisture to air

f. widespread damage as winds can reach 300 km/h

2 INSTRUCT

Use Visuals   L1

Figure 16 Ask students to look at the photograph in Figure 16. **Ask:** What type of clouds is probably in the area in this photograph? *(cumulonimbus clouds)* **Visual**

LESSON 20.3

① Cumulus stage ② Mature stage ③ Dissipating stage — 0°C — Heavy rain — Light rain

Location of Thunderstorms At any given time, there are an estimated 2000 thunderstorms in progress on Earth. As you might expect, the greatest number occurs in the tropics where warmth, plentiful moisture, and instability are common atmospheric conditions. About 45,000 thunderstorms take place each day. More than 16 million occur annually around the world. The United States experiences about 100,000 thunderstorms each year, most frequently in Florida and the eastern Gulf Coast region. Most parts of the country have from 30 to 100 storms each year. The western coast of the United States has little thunderstorm activity because warm, moist, unstable maritime tropical air seldom penetrates this region.

Development of Thunderstorms **Thunderstorms form when warm, humid air rises in an unstable environment.** The development of a thunderstorm generally involves three stages. During the *cumulus stage,* shown in **Figure 17,** strong updrafts, or upward movements of air, supply moist air. Each new surge of warm air rises higher than the last and causes the cloud to grow vertically. A tall cumulus cloud that usually produces rain is called a *cumulonimbus cloud.*

Usually within an hour of the first updraft, the *mature stage* begins, as shown in Figure 17. At this point in the development of the thunderstorm, the number and size of the cloud's water droplets and ice crystals are too great for the updrafts to support. So, heavy precipitation falls from the cloud. The mature stage is the most active stage of a thunderstorm. Strong winds, lightning, heavy precipitation, and sometimes hail are produced during this stage.

Eventually, downdrafts, or downward movements of air, dominate throughout the cloud, as shown in Figure 17. This final stage is called the *dissipating stage.* During this stage, the cooling effect of the falling precipitation and the flowing in of colder air from high above cause the storm to die down.

The life span of a single cumulonimbus unit within a thunderstorm is only about an hour or two. As the storm moves, however, fresh supplies of warm, humid air generate new cumulonimbus units to replace those that are scattering.

☑ **Reading Checkpoint** *Describe the stages in the development of a thunderstorm.*

Tornadoes

A **tornado** is a violent windstorm that takes the form of a rotating column of air called a *vortex*. 🔑 **A tornado's vortex extends downward from a cumulonimbus cloud all the way to the ground.** Some tornadoes consist of a single vortex. But within many stronger tornadoes, smaller vortexes rotate within the main funnel. These smaller vortexes have diameters of only about 10 meters and rotate very rapidly. .

Location and Development of Tornadoes In the United States, about 770 tornadoes are reported each year. Tornadoes can occur anywhere in the United States, but they occur most frequently in Florida and the south-central part of the country. These severe storms can occur at any time during the year. However, the frequency of tornadoes is greatest from April through June. In December and January, tornadoes are far less frequent than in the spring and early summer.

🔑 **Most tornadoes form in association with severe thunderstorms.** An important process in the formation of many tornadoes is the development of a mesocyclone. A *mesocyclone* is a vertical cylinder of rotating air that develops in the updraft of a thunderstorm. The formation of this large vortex begins as strong winds high up in the atmosphere cause winds lower in the atmosphere to roll, as shown in **Figure 18**. In Figure 18, you can see that strong thunderstorm updrafts cause this rolling air to tilt. Once the air is completely vertical, the mesocyclone is well established. The formation of a mesocyclone does not necessarily mean that a tornado will follow.

INQUIRY APPLY IT!

Q: *What is the most destructive tornado on record?*

A: The Tri-State Tornado, which occurred on March 18, 1925, started in southeastern Missouri and remained on the ground over a distance of 352 kilometers, until it reached Indiana. Casualties included 695 people dead and 2027 injured. Property losses were also great, with several small towns almost totally destroyed.

VISUAL SUMMARY

FORMATION OF A MESOCYCLONE

FIGURE 18 A mesocyclone can occur before the formation of a tornado.
1 First, stronger winds aloft cause lower winds to roll.
2 Updrafts tilt the rolling air so that it becomes nearly vertical.
3 When the rotating air is completely vertical, the mesocyclone is established.

Spinning along horizontal axis — Stronger winds — Weaker winds ①

Thunderstorm forming — Updraft ②

Clouds overshoot top of thunderstorm — Mesocyclone (3 to 10 km diameter) — Tornado — Air inflow ③

HOMEMADE TORNADO L2

Purpose Students will observe a visual model of a tornado.

Materials piece of sturdy cardboard; glue; 2 transparency sheets; small hand-held, battery-operated fan; small plastic bowl; clear plastic plant dish, approximately 7" in diameter with a hole cut in the middle; water; dry ice

Procedure Glue the plastic bowl to the center of the cardboard. Glue half of one of the transparency sheets to one side of the bowl. Glue the rest of the sheet in a half circle around the bowl without touching the bowl. Glue the second sheet to the opposite side of the cup in the same manner. The two sheets must overlap but not touch. Pour about half a cup of water in the cup. Using gloves, add a few small pieces of dry ice to the water. Place the plant dish upside down on top of the transparencies. Turn on the fan and place it in the hole, facing up to draw air up.

Expected Outcome Students should see the "smoke" from the dry ice form in a tornado pattern as it flows past the transparency sheets with the air being drawn up.
Kinesthetic, Visual

Answers

Figure 17 *The clouds vary in height, the smallest being the cloud that initiates the storm.*

☑ **Reading Checkpoint** *During the cumulus stage, strong updrafts supply moist air that causes the cloud to grow vertically. Usually within about an hour of the initial updraft, heavy precipitation is released from the cloud. Gusty winds, lightning, and sometimes hail also are experienced during this stage. Eventually, downdrafts dominate throughout the cloud and the storm dies down.*

Facts and Figures

The largest recorded tornado was in Hallam, Nebraska on May 22, 2005. This tornado was nearly 4 km wide. This is probably close to the maximum size for tornadoes, but it is possible that larger, unrecorded tornadoes have occurred. At its most intense, the Hallam tornado reached a rating of F4. This rating scale is described in Table 1 on p. 574.

LESSON 20.3

Storm Warnings Accurate storm predictions and warnings can help to minimize the loss of property and of life. The National Weather Service has developed a system to inform the public of the likelihood of a storm event in their area. They use the terms *watch* and *warning* to relay the imminent danger. A hurricane watch means that hurricanes are possible in the area within 36 hours. A hurricane warning means that hurricanes are expected in the area within 24 hours. A tornado watch means that conditions are favorable for a tornado in the area. A tornado warning means that a tornado has been sighted or has been seen on radar. Challenge students to devise a plan of action that should be taken during a hurricane watch and warning or a tornado watch and warning. Ask them to present their findings to the class in the form of a poster or an emergency bulletin.
Interpersonal

FIGURE 19 Joplin, May 22, 2011
A tornado that began outside Joplin, Missouri, caused terrible destruction. This photograph shows lightning (the blue light) within the tornado's vortex.

Tornado Intensity Air pressure within some tornadoes has been estimated to be as much as 10 percent lower than air pressure immediately outside the storm. The low pressure within a tornado causes air near the ground to rush into a tornado from all directions. As the air streams inward, it spirals upward around the core. Eventually, the air merges with the airflow of the cumulonimbus cloud that formed the storm. Because of the tremendous amount of pressure change associated with a strong tornado, maximum winds can sometimes approach 480 kilometers per hour. One scale used to estimate tornado intensity is the Fujita tornado intensity scale, shown in **Table 1.** Because tornado winds are difficult to measure directly, a rating on this scale is usually determined by assessing the worst damage produced by a storm. The 2011 tornado in Joplin, Missouri, shown in **Figure 19,** was a level F5 storm.

Tornado Warning The Storm Prediction Center (SPC), which is part of the National Atmospheric and Oceanic Administration, is located in Norman, Oklahoma. The SPC monitors different kinds of severe weather. The SPC's mission is to provide timely and accurate forecasts and watches for severe thunderstorms and tornadoes. Tornado watches alert people to the possibility of tornadoes in a specified area for a particular time period. A tornado warning is issued when a tornado has actually been sighted in an area or is indicated by weather radar.

Table 1 Fujita Tornado Intensity Scale		
Intensity	Wind Speed Estimates (km/h)	Typical Damage
F0	< 116	Light damage. Some damage to chimneys; branches broken off trees; shallow-rooted trees pushed over; sign boards damaged.
F1	116–180	Moderate damage. Peels surface off roofs; mobile homes pushed off foundations or overturned; moving cars blown off roads.
F2	181–253	Considerable damage. Roofs torn off frame houses; mobile homes demolished; large trees snapped or uprooted; light-object missiles generated; cars lifted off ground.
F3	254–332	Severe damage. Roofs and some walls torn off well-constructed houses; trains overturned; most trees in forest uprooted; heavy cars lifted off the ground and thrown.
F4	333–419	Devastating damage. Well-constructed houses leveled; structures with weak foundations blown some distance; cars thrown; large missiles generated.
F5	> 419	Incredible damage. Strong frame houses lifted off foundations and carried away; automobile-sized missiles fly through the air in excess of 100 m; bark torn off trees.

Facts and Figures

The deadliest tornado in the United States occurred on March 18, 1925. The so-called Tri-State Tornado killed 695 people as it raced along at 96–117 km/h in a 352 km-long track across parts of Missouri, Illinois, and Indiana, producing F5 damage. This event also holds the known record for most tornado fatalities in a single city or town: at least 234 at Murphysboro, IL.

Hurricanes

If you've ever been to the tropics, you know that the usual weather consists of warm breezes, steady temperatures, and heavy but brief showers. However, these tranquil regions sometimes produce hurricanes, the most violent storms on Earth. **Whirling tropical cyclones that produce sustained winds of at least 119 kilometers per hour are known in the United States as hurricanes.** In other parts of the world, these severe tropical storms are called *typhoons, cyclones,* and *tropical cyclones.*

Hurricanes are powerful. At sea, they can generate 15-meter waves capable of destruction hundreds of kilometers away. If a hurricane hits land, strong winds and extensive flooding can cause billions of dollars in damage and great loss of life. Hurricane Katrina, shown in a satellite image in **Figure 20,** was one such storm. In August 2005, Katrina brought flooding rains and high winds to Louisiana and Mississippi. It was the costliest natural disaster in United States history, and the deadliest U.S. hurricane since 1928.

Hurricanes are becoming a growing threat because more and more people are living and working near coasts. At the start of the twenty-first century, more than 50 percent of the U.S. population lived within 75 kilometers of a coast. This number is expected to increase even more in the early decades of this century.

Location of Hurricanes Most hurricanes form between about 5 and 20 degrees north and south latitude. Hurricanes form in this area because ocean water is warm here—they do not form over cooler ocean water. For example, some of these storms develop in the Gulf of Mexico, but none start in the North Atlantic. Water temperatures are much warmer in the Gulf of Mexico than in the North Atlantic ocean.

FIGURE 20 Satellite View of a Hurricane This satellite image of Hurricane Katrina shows its position in the Gulf of Mexico a day before the hurricane moved onto land. Katrina eventually made landfall near the Louisiana-Mississippi border.

Weather Patterns and Severe Storms **575**

Facts and Figures

Of all the hurricane-prone areas of the United States, the area around Tampa Bay in Florida is considered one of the most vulnerable to severe flooding, damage, and loss of life in a major hurricane. There are several reasons for this. Tampa is located on a peninsula with long stretches of waterfront. This makes the area one of the most densely populated in Florida, and leads to limited evacuation routes. There is also a large population of elderly people in the area. The evacuation of this segment of the population could prove to be difficult for emergency workers. The geography around the bay could also increase the effects of a storm surge; the Gulf of Mexico has a broad, shallow continental shelf on which a storm surge could build to heights great enough to destroy or damage thousands of homes and businesses. The Tampa Bay area has not received a direct hit from a major hurricane in several decades.

LESSON 20.3

Build Science Skills `L2`

Compare and Contrast Ask students to explore the similarities and differences of tornadoes and hurricanes by making a chart. They should include in their chart information on location, associated storms, pressures associated with the storm, impact on society, and maximum wind strength.
Logical

Build Reading Literacy `L1`

Refer to **p. 502D** in **Chapter 18,** which provides the guidelines for visualizing.

Visualize Ask students to read the section under Development of Hurricanes on p. 576. After the first reading, instruct students to close their eyes and think of a hurricane. Have them suppose they are flying through the clouds of a hurricane and note the changes in wind velocity and pressure as they travel from one side to the other. Have students refer to Figure 21 to help them visualize their trip.
Intrapersonal

Build Science Skills `L2`

Analyze Data Hurricane season runs from June 1 through November 30 in the Atlantic Ocean and the Gulf of Mexico. Ask students to research the average monthly water temperatures in the Atlantic Ocean and in the Gulf of Mexico for the entire year. Students should present their data in a graph and discuss how water temperature relates to the development of hurricanes.
Logical, Visual

PLANET DIARY

For links about **Hurricanes,** go to PlanetDiary.com/HSES.

FIGURE 21 Cross Section of a Hurricane The eye of the hurricane is a zone of relative calm.
Describe *How does the air flow in different parts of a hurricane?*

In a yearly cycle, hurricanes begin most often in the late summer when water temperatures are warm enough to provide the necessary heat and moisture to the air. After beginning, hurricanes can travel thousands of kilometers. For example, a hurricane that begins off the west coast of Africa can move west across the Atlantic and then make its way up the east coast of the United States. A hurricane can last a week or more.

Development of Hurricanes A hurricane is fueled by the energy given off when huge quantities of water vapor condense. A hurricane begins as a tropical disturbance that consists of disorganized clouds and thunderstorms. Low atmospheric pressures and little or no rotation are characteristic of these disturbances.

Figure 21 shows a cross section of a well-developed hurricane. An inward rush of warm, moist surface air moves toward the core of the storm. The air then turns upward and rises in a ring of cumulonimbus clouds. This doughnut-shaped wall that surrounds the center of the storm is the **eye wall.** Here the greatest wind speeds and heaviest rainfall occur. Surrounding the eye wall are curved bands of clouds that trail away from the center of the storm. Notice that near the top of the hurricane, the rising air is carried away from the storm center. This outflow provides room for more inward flow at the surface.

At the very center of the storm is the eye of the hurricane. The **eye** is a zone where precipitation ceases and winds become less strong. The air within the eye gradually descends and heats, making it the warmest part of the storm.

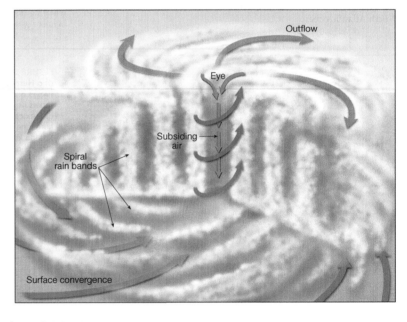

Outflow

Eye

Subsiding air

Spiral rain bands

Surface convergence

Facts and Figures

Hurricanes in the past were identified using awkward latitude/longitude methods. It became clear that the use of short, distinctive names would be quicker and less subject to error. These advantages are especially important in exchanging detailed storm information between hundreds of widely scattered stations, coastal bases, and ships at sea. Since 1953, Atlantic tropical storms have been named from lists originated by the World Meteorologic Organization. The lists featured only women's names until 1979, when men's and women's names were alternated. If a storm is deadly or very costly, the name is never used again.

Hurricane Intensity The intensity of a hurricane is described using the Saffir-Simpson scale shown in **Table 2**. The most devastating damage from a hurricane is caused by storm surges. A **storm surge** is a dome of water about 65 to 80 kilometers wide that sweeps across the coast where a hurricane's eye moves onto land.

A hurricane weakens when it moves over cool ocean waters that cannot supply adequate heat and moisture. Intensity also drops when storms move over land, because there is not sufficient moisture in the air. In addition, contact with the rough land surface causes winds to subside. Finally, when a hurricane reaches a location where the airflow aloft is unfavorable, it will die out.

Table 2 Saffir-Simpson Hurricane Scale		
Category	Sustained Wind Speeds (km/h)	Typical Damage
1	119–153	Storm surge 1.2–1.5 meters; some damage to unanchored mobile homes, shrubbery, and trees; some coastal flooding; minor pier damage.
2	154–177	Storm surge 1.6–2.4 meters; some damage to buildings' roofs, doors, and windows; considerable damage to mobile homes and piers; moderate coastal flooding.
3	178–209	Storm surge 2.5–3.6 meters; some structural damage to small buildings; some large trees blown over; mobile homes destroyed; some coastal and inland flooding.
4	210–249	Storm surge 3.7–5.4 meters; severe damage to trees and signs; complete destruction of mobile homes; extensive damage to doors and windows; severe flooding inland.
5	> 249	Storm surge >5.4 meters; complete roof failure on many buildings; some complete building failure; all trees and signs blown away; major inland flooding.

20.3 Assessment

Review Key Concepts

1. What is a thunderstorm?
2. What causes a thunderstorm?
3. What is a tornado?
4. How does a tornado form?
5. What is a hurricane?
6. How does a hurricane form?

Think Critically

7. **Draw Conclusions** What kind of front is associated with the formation of tornadoes? Explain.

8. **Relate Cause and Effect** Explain why a hurricane quickly loses its strength as the storm moves onto land.

BIGIDEA WEATHER AND CLIMATE

9. **Infer** Explain why even though hurricanes have lower wind speeds than tornadoes, they often cause more damage than tornadoes do.

How Earth Works

Objectives

In this feature, students will
- explain what causes wind and what factors affect wind speed.
- describe the development of the different types of storms.
- summarize the impact of storms.

Build Vocabulary `L2`

Key Terms Write these key terms on the board: *wind, tornado, blizzard, tropical cyclone, typhoon, storm surge.* Ask students to define them. Then have students explain what causes wind and what factors affect wind speed.

2 INSTRUCT

Bellringer `L2`

Have students read the feature caption heads that name different types of storms. **Ask:** Do any of these kinds of storms occur in your region? If so, have students estimate how frequently the storms occur. Discuss how location and regional climate account for the frequency of storms.
Verbal, Logical

Build Science Skills `L2`

Predict Satellite technology has had a significant impact on weather prediction and the tracking of severe storms, including hurricanes. Lead a discussion about the effect this technology has had in terms of lives and property saved. Ask students to predict the impact the loss of satellite technology might have on storm preparedness. *(Students should understand that satellite technology allows forecasters to predict storms earlier and with more accuracy. Without this technology, communities would be significantly less prepared for major storms and many lives would likely be lost.)*
Verbal, Interpersonal, Logical

Winds and Storms

The world's atmosphere is forever on the move. **Wind,** or air in horizontal motion, occurs because solar radiation heats up some parts of the sea and land more than others. Air above these hot spots becomes warmer and less dense than the surrounding air and therefore rises. Elsewhere, cool air sinks because it is more dense. Winds blow because air squeezed out by sinking, cold air flows toward regions of low pressure created by warm air. Wind may move slowly as in a gentle breeze, when air pressure and temperature change gradually. In extreme weather, when air pressure and temperature change rapidly, wind moves rapidly, creating terrifyingly destructive storms.

Southwest Monsoon
During the early summer, hot, dry air over Asia rises, creating low-pressure zones. Cool, moist, higher-pressure air from the Indian Ocean therefore flows inland. When the cooler, moist air collides with the hot, dry air over Asia, clouds form and rain falls.

Northeast Monsoon
The cold, dry, relatively dense winter air from Central Asia flows seaward toward regions of low air pressure, bringing chilly, dusty conditions to South Asia.

▲ **MONSOONS**
Seasonal winds called monsoons affect large areas of the tropics and subtropics. They occur in South Asia, southern North America, eastern Australia, and other regions of the world. In South Asia, southwest monsoons generally bring desperately needed rain from May until October.

◄ **THUNDERSTORMS**
Thunderclouds are formed by powerful updrafts of air that occur along cold fronts or over ground heated very strongly by the sun. Ice crystals and water droplets high in the cloud are torn apart and smashed together with such ferocity that they become charged with electricity. Thunderstorms can unleash thunder, lightning, wind, rain, and hail.

◄ **LIGHTNING AND THUNDER**
Electricity is discharged from a thundercloud in the form of lightning. A bolt of lightning can heat the air around it to a temperature four times as hot as the sun's surface. The heated air expands violently and sends out a rumbling shock wave that we hear as thunder. Some lightning bolts, like the one shown at left, can arc from the top of the thundercloud all the way to the ground, striking objects up to 16 kilometers (10 miles) away.

578 Chapter 20

Differentiated Instruction

GIFTED Explain to students that the term *tropical cyclones* is used to refer to certain hurricanes and typhoons. Have students find out how many tropical cyclones occurred last year and make a chart with the name, dates, and location (ocean) of each storm. Post the chart in your classroom and discuss whether there is a pattern in the chart.

TORNADOES ▶
Tornadoes may strike wherever thunderstorms occur. A **tornado** begins when a column of strongly rising warm air is set spinning by high winds at the top of a cloud. A funnel is formed and may touch the ground. With winds that can range from a damaging 104 kilometers per hour (65 mph) to a devastating speed greater than 400 kilometers per hour (250 mph), tornadoes can lift people, cars, and buildings high into the air and then smash them back to the ground.

▲ BLIZZARDS
When strong, 56 kilometers per hour (35 mph) winds combine with heavy snowfall to reduce visibility to just 400 meters (0.25 miles), a blizzard is the result. Winds pile up huge drifts of snow. Travel and communication systems can grind to a halt.

HOW TROPICAL STORMS DEVELOP
Tropical storms begin when water evaporates from warm ocean water to produce huge clouds and thunderstorms. When the storms cluster together and whirl around a low-pressure center, they form a **tropical cyclone.** Tropical cyclones with winds of at least 119 kilometers per hour (74 mph) are called hurricanes in some regions and **typhoons** in others. The sequence below shows satellite images of a hurricane. ▼

Stage 1:
Thunderstorms develop over the ocean.

Stage 2:
Storms group to form a swirl of cloud.

Stage 3:
Winds grow and a distinct center forms in the cloud swirl.

Eye

Stage 4:
Eye forms. The hurricane is now at its most dangerous.

Stage 5:
Eye passes over land. The hurricane starts to weaken.

IMPACT OF TROPICAL STORMS
Tropical storms are often devastating. The strongest winds, with gusts sometimes more than 249 kilometers per hour (156 mph), occur near the storm's center, within the eye wall. When a tropical storm strikes land, raging winds can uproot trees and destroy buildings. Vast areas may be swamped by torrential rain, and coastal regions may be overwhelmed by a **storm surge,** a bulge of water up to 8 meters (26 feet) high that rises in response to the extremely low air pressure of the storm's eye. When the tropical storm makes landfall, the storm surge rushes inland, swamping whatever lies in its path. ▼

These women wade through the streets of Dhaka, Bangladesh, flooded by a tropical cyclone. In 1991, a cyclone killed more than 130,000 Bangladeshis.

A Pacific typhoon struck this ship off the coast of Taiwan in November 2000.

Assessment

1. **Key Terms** Define **(a)** wind, **(b)** tornado, **(c)** blizzard, **(d)** tropical cyclone, **(e)** typhoon, **(f)** storm surge.

2. **Physical Processes** How do thunderstorms come into being?

3. **Economic Activities** **(a)** How can storms have a negative impact on economic activities? **(b)** How can monsoons benefit economic activities?

4. **Natural Hazards** How can a tropical cyclone result in the loss of thousands of lives?

5. **Critical Thinking Form a Hypothesis** Since 1991, the Bangladeshi government has constructed hundreds of concrete storm shelters in coastal regions of the country. **(a)** Why did the government likely decide to implement this policy? **(b)** How has this policy benefited the country?

579

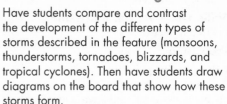
Assessment Answers

1. (a) air in motion horizontally; **(b)** a spinning column of air that reaches the ground; **(c)** a storm with heavy snowfall and strong winds; **(d)** a cluster of tropical thunderstorms that whirl around a low-pressure center; **(e)** a tropical cyclone that has winds moving at least 114 km/h **(f)** a wall of water sucked up by a hurricane's eye

2. Thunderstorms are formed by powerful updrafts of air that occur along cold fronts or over heated ground. Ice crystals and water droplets high in the cloud are torn apart and smashed together so energetically that they become charged with electricity.

3. (a) During a severe storm, economic activities may come to a halt. When property is destroyed, people spend money to replace or rebuild it. **(b)** Monsoons bring rain to South Asia, and rain is needed to grow crops.

4. Extremely strong winds can destroy buildings, bring torrential rain that results in floods, or cause a storm surge. Any of these can result in loss of life.

5. (a) Bangladesh is located in a region that is subject to tropical storms. The government hopes to offer shelter to the people who are most likely to be affected by the storms. **(b)** Sample answer: It has provided shelter for people who live in coastal areas.

MIDDLE-LATITUDE CYCLONES   L2

Objectives
In this activity, students will
- explain how middle-latitude cyclones affect the weather of the area over which they form.
- predict how middle-latitude cyclones change weather patterns as they move through an area.

Skills Observe, Compare and Contrast, Predict

Prep Time 10 minutes

Advance Prep If time is limited, provide students with light photocopies of the map on the facing page and have students color and mark the copies.

Class Time 40 minute

Teaching Tips
- If necessary, review the steps in the formation of a middle-latitude cyclone with students prior to their beginning the activity. Also review the information in Chapters 18 and 19 on humidity, precipitation, wind, and air pressure if needed.
- Walk around the room as students work on this activity and monitor students' progress. Should anyone have problems getting started or answering the questions, prompt him or her with appropriate questions.

Expected Outcome Students should be able to label the map and answer the questions. Note that the cold front is the front designated by the blue line with the triangular notches. The warm front is the red line with the semicircular notches. The occluded front is the front shown by the line with both the red and blue notches. Precipitation is falling at the center of the system and along the eastern boundaries of both the cold and warm fronts.

Middle-Latitude Cyclones

Problem How do middle-latitude cyclones affect weather patterns?

Materials tracing paper, sharp pencil, paper clips or removable tape, metric ruler, colored pencils

Skills Observe, Compare and Contrast, Predict

Connect to the Big idea You've learned that much of the day-to-day weather in the United States is caused by middle-latitude cyclones. In this lab, you will identify some of the atmospheric conditions associated with a middle-latitude cyclone. Then you will use what you know about Earth's atmosphere and weather to predict how the movement of the low-pressure system affects weather in the area.

Procedure

1. Use the paper clips or removable tape to secure the tracing paper over the map on the facing page.
2. Carefully trace all of the features and boundaries on the map. Be sure to include the isobars—the lines that show atmospheric pressure. Use the ruler to trace lines EA and GF.
3. Remove the tracing paper. Place it next to the map.
4. Transfer all of the letters and numbers on the map to your tracing.
5. Use the colored pencils to color the cold air, cool air, and warm air areas on the tracing. Also color the symbols used to designate the fronts.
6. Identify and label the cold front, warm front, and occluded front on your tracing.
7. Draw arrows that show the direction of surface winds at points A, C, E, F, and G.

Analyze and Conclude

1. **Describe** In which direction are the surface winds moving?
2. **Identify** At which stage of formation is the cyclone? Explain your answer. Refer to Figure 13 if necessary.
3. **Explain** Is the air in the center of the cyclone rising or falling? What effect does this have on the potential for condensation and precipitation?
4. **Infer** Find the center of the low, which is marked with the letter L. What type of front has formed here? What happens to the maritime tropical air in this type of front?
5. **Predict** Once the warm front passes, in which direction will the wind at point B blow?
6. **Predict** Describe the changes in wind direction and moisture in the air that will likely occur at point D after the cold front passes.
7. **Explain** Describe the wind directions, humidity, and precipitation expected for a city as the cyclone moves and the city's relative position changes from point A to B, point C, point D, and finally from point D to E.

GO FURTHER Find out and explain how subpolar lows affect middle-latitude cyclones over the United States in winter.

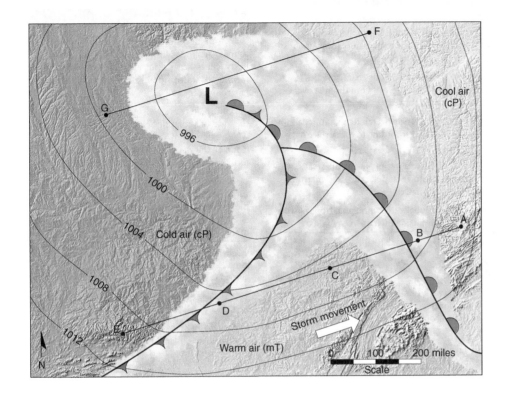

The figure shows a weather map with pressure contours labeled 996, 1000, 1004, 1008, and 1012. A low pressure center marked **L** is shown with fronts extending out. Air masses are labeled "Cool air (cP)," "Cold air (cP)," and "Warm air (mT)." Points A, B, C, D, E, F, and G are marked. An arrow indicates "Storm movement." A scale shows 0, 100, and 200 miles. A compass rose indicates N.

1. The winds at point A are blowing toward north-northwest. At point C, they are blowing almost directly north. At point E, the winds are moving almost directly east. At point F, the winds are blowing from the southeast toward the northwest. At point G, the winds are blowing from the northwest to the southeast.

2. The middle-latitude cyclone shown is at the mature stage as indicated by the occluded front.

3. The air at the center of the cyclone is rising. The potential for condensation and precipitation will be good because as the air rises, cooling will occur and the dew-point temperature may be reached.

4. An occluded front has formed at the center of the low pressure system. The warm mT air is lifted above the cooler air.

5. After the warm front passes, the wind at point B will be from the south.

6. The wind will blow from the northwest and the moisture content will decrease.

7. point A to point B: low stratus clouds, possible precipitation, wind from the southeast, moisture should increase, point C: wind from the south, warm and perhaps humid air; point D: vertical clouds, possible thunderstorms; point D to point E: wind from the northwest, cool or cold temperatures, clearing sky, moisture should decrease

GO FURTHER

During the winter, subpolar lows and the polar front are farthest south in North America. Thus, the central United States will experience a greater frequency of passing middle-latitude cyclones.
Kinesthetic, Visual

Organize New Information
Tell students to create outlines, charts, flashcards, timelines, and concept maps to help them visualize relationships.

Think Visually

Two air masses meet to form a front, which can be a warm front, cold front, stationary front, or an occluded front.

21st Century Learning

Problem Identification, Formulation, and Solution

What are the hazards of severe weather?

Severe weather can cause injury, damage to property, and even loss of human life. Ask students to use the Internet to research which type of weather-related events caused the greatest number of injuries and deaths in your state last year. Then, encourage them to find out what individuals can do to protect themselves when severe weather strikes. Students should be prepared to present their data and conclusions to the class.

Homework Guide

Lesson	Questions
1	1–4, 10, 11, 21–25
2	5, 6, 12–15, 26, 27, 37
3	7–9, 16–20, 28–36

20 Study Guide

Big idea ▸ Weather and Climate

20.1 Air Masses

🔑 An air mass is an extremely large body of air that is located in the troposphere and is characterized by similar temperatures and amounts of moisture at any given altitude.

🔑 As an air mass moves, its characteristics change, and so does the weather in the area over which the air mass moves.

🔑 In addition to their overall temperature, air masses are classified according to the surface over which they form.

🔑 Much of the weather in North America is influenced by continental polar (cP) and maritime tropical (mT) air masses.

🔑 Only occasionally do continental tropical (cT) air masses move outside their source regions.

air mass (559)

20.2 Fronts

🔑 When two air masses with different properties meet, they form a front, which is a boundary that separates two contrasting air masses.

🔑 A warm front forms when warm air moves into an area formerly covered by cooler air.

🔑 A cold front forms when cold, dense air moves into a region occupied by warmer air.

🔑 A stationary front forms when the surface position between two air masses does not move.

🔑 An occluded front forms when a cold front overtakes a warm front, producing a complex weather pattern.

🔑 A middle-latitude cyclone is a large center of low pressure that generally travels from west to east and causes stormy weather. More often than not, air high up in the atmosphere fuels a middle-latitude cyclone.

front (564)
warm front (565)
cold front (566)
stationary front (566)
occluded front (567)

20.3 Severe Storms

🔑 A thunderstorm generates lightning and thunder. Thunderstorms frequently produce gusty winds, heavy rain, and hail. Thunderstorms form when warm, humid air rises in an unstable environment.

🔑 Tornadoes are violent windstorms that take the form of a rotating column of air called a vortex, which extends downward from a cumulonimbus cloud all the way to the ground. Most tornadoes form in association with severe thunderstorms.

🔑 Hurricanes are whirling tropical cyclones with sustained high winds that sometimes develop over the ocean when water temperatures are warm enough to provide the necessary heat and moisture to fuel the storms.

thunderstorm (571)
tornado (573)
hurricane (575)
eye wall (576)
eye (576)
storm surge (577)

Think Visually

Use what you know about fronts and air masses to complete this concept map.

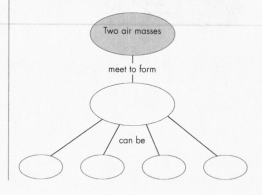

Assessment Answers

Review Content

1. a	**2.** d	**3.** b
4. c	**5.** a	**6.** d
7. c	**8.** d	**9.** b

Understand Concepts

10. In summer, cP air masses may bring a few days of relatively cool weather. In winter, this air brings the clear skies and cold temperatures you associate with a cold wave. Continental polar air masses can also cause lake-effect snow. Maritime tropical air masses are warm, moisture-laden, and usually unstable and the sources of most of the precipitation in the eastern two-thirds of the United States. In summer, when an mT air mass invades the central and eastern United States, it brings high temperatures and high humidity.

20 Assessment

Review Content

Choose the letter that best answers the question or completes the statement.

1. If a portion of the contiguous United States is experiencing consecutive days of constant weather, this weather is called
   a. air-mass weather.
   b. warm-front weather.
   c. cold-front weather.
   d. occluded-front weather.

2. An air mass that forms over the Gulf of Mexico is a(n)
   a. cP air mass.   c. cT air mass.
   b. mP air mass.   d. mT air mass.

3. Air masses that have the greatest influence on weather in the midwestern United States are
   a. mT and cT air masses.
   b. cP and mT air masses.
   c. mP and cP air masses.
   d. cT and cP air masses.

4. Lake-effect snow is associated with a(n)
   a. mP air mass.   c. cP air mass.
   b. mT air mass.   d. cT air mass.

5. "Rain long foretold, long last; short notice, soon past." The first five words of this weather proverb refer to a(n)
   a. warm front.   c. anticyclone.
   b. cold front.   d. tornado.

6. Which front often produces moderate-to-light precipitation over a large area?
   a. continental   c. cold
   b. maritime   d. warm

7. A thunderstorm is most intense during its
   a. cumulus stage.   c. mature stage.
   b. wave stage.   d. dissipating stage.

8. When a hurricane reaches land, its intensity decreases as the result of
   a. increase in pressure and temperature.
   b. lack of cold, dry air to fuel the storm.
   c. successive updrafts into the eye wall.
   d. friction and the lack of warm, moist air.

9. The eye of a hurricane
   a. has the greatest wind speeds.
   b. is warmer than the rest of the storm.
   c. experiences high pressures.
   d. is responsible for heavy precipitation.

Understand Concepts

10. Describe the effects of cP and mT air masses on much of the weather in the United States.

11. Describe weather associated with a warm front.

12. What kind of weather is associated with a cold front while it is over an area and once it passes?

13. What is a stationary front?

14. Sequence the steps that lead to the formation of an occluded front.

15. Describe the stages involved in the development of a middle-latitude cyclone.

16. Describe the formation of a thunderstorm.

17. What is a mesocyclone and how does it form?

18. Describe the different parts of a hurricane.

Use this map to answer Questions 19–22.

19. Name the three red air masses and identify the source region of each.

20. Identify the cold air masses, starting with the air mass farthest west and moving eastward.

21. Which air masses would supply the largest amount of precipitation to the area east of the Rocky Mountains?

22. Which of the air masses has the greatest influence on weather along the northwest coast?

Changes in air flow and pressure result in a counterclockwise flow of air. The rapidly moving cold front closes in on the warm front. As the cold front lifts, an occluded front forms. Eventually, the cyclone weakens.

16. Strong updrafts supply the initial volume of moist air. Each new surge of warm air causes the cloud to grow vertically. Usually within an hour of the initial updraft, the amount and size of the precipitation is too great for the updrafts to support. So, heavy precipitation is released from the cloud. Gusty winds, lightning, heavy precipitation, and sometimes hail are produced.

17. A mesocyclone is a vertical cylinder of rotating air that develops in the updraft of a thunderstorm. The formation of this large vortex begins as strong winds aloft cause winds lower in the atmosphere to roll. Strong thunderstorm updrafts cause this rolling air to tilt. Once the air is completely vertical, the mesocyclone is established.

18. Warm, moist surface air moves toward the center of a tropical storm, turns upward, and rises in a ring of cumulonimbus clouds. This doughnut-shaped wall that surrounds the center of the storm is the eye wall. Here the greatest wind speeds and heaviest rainfall occur. Surrounding the eye wall are curved bands of clouds that trail away from the center of the storm. At the very center of the storm is the eye of the hurricane. At the eye, which is the warmest part of a hurricane, precipitation ceases and winds subside.

19. Farthest west is the mT air mass, which forms over the Pacific Ocean. The cT air mass forms over the southwestern United Sates and Mexico. The mT mass, which is farthest east, has the Gulf of Mexico as its source region.

20. From west to east, the cold masses are mP, cP, cP, and mP.

21. mT

22. mP

---

11. Rain or snow begins and often continues for a long time. A gradual increase in temperature occurs with the passage of a warm front as well as a wind shift from the east to the southwest.

12. Weather along a cold front consists of heavy downpours and gusty winds. Once the front has passed, temperatures drop and wind shifts. The weather behind a cold front is dominated by a relatively cold air mass. Thus, weather clears soon after a cold front passes.

13. A stationary front forms when the flow of air on either side of a front is almost parallel to the line of the front.

14. A cold front moves toward a warm front, forcing warm air aloft. The cold front merges with the warm front to form an occluded front that drops heavy rains. The heavy rains are followed by periods of light precipitation.

15. The formation of a front sets the stage for the development of a middle-latitude cyclone. Over time, the front takes on a wave shape.

ASSESSMENT

Think Critically

23. Polar and tropical air masses are the same in that both are enormous bodies of air, each with similar temperatures and moisture conditions at any given altitude. Polar air masses, because of their high-latitude source regions, are colder than tropical air masses, which have source regions at low latitudes.

24. an mT air mass

25. Both are severe storms that can cause much damage. Tornadoes are small, quickly whirling vortices of air that form and move over land. Tornadoes last for only a short period of time—less than a few hours. Hurricanes are much larger than tornadoes and form and move over warm water. Hurricanes generally last for about a week. When they make landfall, hurricanes will die out.

26. Although the hurricane has diminished, heavy rains and inland flooding due to storm surges can last for several days, causing much damage and loss of life.

Map Skills

27. the Atlantic Ocean

28. As indicated by the differences in line patterns, Floyd was a tropical storm from September 7 through September 9 and again after September 16.

29. Hurricane Floyd moved towards the west-northwest and then between September 14 and 15 turned to the north-northeast.

30. Hurricanes are fueled by warm, wet air. Floyd was most intense from September 10 until it made landfall on September 16. At landfall, friction with the land and the lack of warm, wet air caused the hurricane to die out.

31. Hurricane Floyd moved onto land on September 16 when it crashed into the North Carolina coast.

Concepts in Action

32. As the low approached, one would experience cool temperatures because the warm part of the cyclone would be farther south. Air pressure would drop and clouds would form. Snow or rain would fall. As the occluded front passed, winds would shift and blow from the north or northeast. Skies would eventually clear and pressures would rise, but temperatures would remain cool.

33. Flooding, the mixing of salt water and fresh water, increased erosion, removal of low-lying vegetation, and the uprooting of trees are some of the changes that might affect coastal ecosystems.

---

23. **Compare and Contrast** Compare and contrast polar air masses with tropical air masses.

24. **Review** What type of air mass is responsible for most of the warm fronts east of the Rocky Mountains?

25. **Compare and Contrast** Compare and contrast tornadoes and hurricanes.

26. **Relate Cause and Effect** Great damage and significant loss of life can take place a day or more after a hurricane has moved ashore and weakened. Explain why this might happen.

Map Skills

Use the map to answer Questions 27–31.

Path of Hurricane Floyd, September, 1999

- - - - - tropical storm
——— hurricane

27. **Interpret Maps** Over which ocean did Hurricane Floyd develop and move?

28. **Interpret Maps** On which days was Floyd a tropical storm?

29. **Interpret Maps** Describe the path of Hurricane Floyd from September 10 through September 16.

---

30. **Infer** When was Hurricane Floyd most intense? Explain.

31. **Interpret Maps** When and where did Hurricane Floyd move onto land?

Concepts in Action

32. **Explain** Describe weather conditions that you would observe if the center of a middle-latitude cyclone passed two kilometers north of you.

33. **Apply Concepts** What kinds of negative effects might a hurricane have on coastal ecosystems?

34. **Explain** Use what you know about weather patterns to write a paragraph to explain which parts of the Earth system interact to produce the high snowfall in the Great Lakes region of North America.

Performance-Based Assessment

Apply Concepts Find out about precautions people should take during any of the three types of severe storms discussed in this chapter. Summarize your findings in three separate posters.

---

34. High snowfall on the leeward sides of the Great Lakes occurs when the atmosphere, hydrosphere, and lithosphere interact. The lake-effect snow develops as cold cP air travels over the warmer water and acquires moisture. This warming and increase in moisture causes the air mass to become unstable. The result is often heavy snow over the cooler land on the downwind shores of the lakes.

Performance-Based Assessment

Students' findings should include what should be done before, during, and after each type of storm strikes, as well as what should be done should storm watches and warnings be issued. This is probably a good time to review your school's or community's storm safety procedures.

Standardized Test Prep

Use the maps below and what you know about thunderstorms and tornadoes to answer Questions 1–3.

Choose the letter that best answers the question or completes the statement.

1 What part of Texas experiences the greatest average number of days with thunderstorms per year?
   A the southernmost tip
   B the southwestern portion of the state
   C the northern tip
   D the easternmost portion of the state

2 What part of Texas experiences the lowest average number of tornadoes per year per 26,000 km²?
   F central
   G eastern
   H northwestern
   J southwestern

3 How many tornadoes on average are experienced per year in the area referred to in Question 2?
   A 1.0–2.0
   B 2.0–3.0
   C 5.0–7.0
   D 7.0–9.0

4 What kind of air mass generally brings moisture to Virginia in summer?
   F maritime polar
   G maritime tropical
   H continental polar
   J continental tropical

5 Which kind of front generally produces the most violent weather?
   A cold front
   B warm front
   C occluded front
   D stationary front

> **Tips for Success**
>
> **Using Maps** Most maps in Earth science are used to show geographic features such as mountains and bodies of water, tectonic features such as plate boundaries, and different types of rocks. Maps, like those shown below, can also be used to show statistical information. When using such maps to answer questions, be sure you understand what each map is showing before you try to answer the questions.

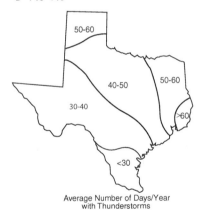

Average Number of Days/Year with Thunderstorms

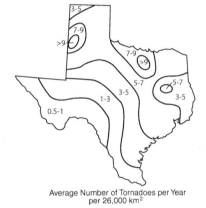

Average Number of Tornadoes per Year per 26,000 km²

If You Have Trouble With . . .

Question	1	2	3	4	5
See Lesson	20.3	20.3	20.3	20.1	20.2

Weather Patterns and Severe Storms **585**

21 Climate Planning Guide

Lesson Objectives		Activities	
21.1 Factors That Affect Climate, pp. 588–591 21.1 **Describe** how latitude affects climate. 21.2 **Describe** how elevation and mountain ranges affect climate. 21.3 **Describe** how large bodies of water affect climate. 21.4 **Describe** how global winds affect climate. 21.5 **Describe** how vegetation affects climate.		**TE** Teacher Demo: Heating and Angles, p. 589 **SE** Quick Lab: Observing How Land and Water Absorb and Release Energy, p. 590	L2 L2
21.2 World Climates, pp. 592–599 21.6 **Explain** the Köppen climate classification system. 21.7 **Describe** humid tropical climates. 21.8 **Compare and contrast** humid mid-latitude climates. 21.9 **List** the characteristics of dry climates. 21.10 **List** the characteristics of polar climates. 21.11 **Compare and contrast** highland climates with nearby lowland climates.		**SE** Map It: Global Climates, pp. 594–595 **TE** Teacher Demo: Modeling Humid Climates, p. 596 **SE** Map It: Extent of Dry Climate Zones, p. 598	L2 L2 L2
21.3 Climate Changes, pp. 600–603 21.12 **Describe** natural processes that can cause changes in climate. 21.13 **Explain** the greenhouse effect. 21.14 **Define** global warming. 21.15 **List** some of the consequences of global warming.		**TE** Teacher Demo: Earth's Motions and Climate, p. 601	L2
Chapter Features and Labs			
Try It Global Warming: Fact or Fiction? p. 587		**LM** Modeling the Greenhouse Effect	L2
How Earth Works Coniferous Forests, pp. 604–605			
Exploration Lab Human Impact on Climate and Weather, pp. 606–607			

Ability Levels		Components			
L1 For students who need additional help		**SE**	Student Edition	**LP**	Lesson Plans
L2 For all students		**TE**	Teacher's Edition	**AA**	Active Art
L3 For students who need to be challenged		**LM**	Laboratory Manual	**PD**	Planet Diary
		CT	Chapter Tests	**GEODe**	Geode CD-ROM
		GRSW	Guided Reading & Study Workbook	**eText**	
		CTB	Computer Test Bank		

Resources	Lesson Assessment
GRSW Lesson 21.1 **LP** Lesson Planning 21.1	**SE** Lesson 21.1 Assessment, p. 591 **eText** Lesson 21.1
GRSW Lesson 21.2 **LP** Lesson Planning 21.2	**SE** Lesson 21.2 Assessment, p. 599 **eText** Lesson 21.2
GRSW Lesson 21.3 **LP** Lesson Planning 21.3 **GEODe** Heating the Atmosphere: The Greenhouse Effect	**SE** Lesson 21.3 Assessment, p. 603 **eText** Lesson 21.3

Materials for Activities and Labs

Quantities for each group

STUDENT EDITION

Try It, p. 587
computer with Internet access, paper, pen, colored markers or highlighters

Quick Lab, p. 590
2 small, identical containers; 2 laboratory thermometers; water; dry sand; masking tape; watch or clock; book; paper towels or rags for spills

TEACHER'S EDITION

Teacher Demo, p. 589
black construction paper, metric ruler, scissors, tape, 3 thermometers, 100-W incandescent lamp

Teacher Demo, p. 596
water, 2 small plastic bowls, transparent plastic wrap, rubber band

Teacher Demo, p. 601
globe, lamp

Assessment

CHAPTER ASSESSMENT
SE Assessment, pp. 609–610
CT Chapter 21 Test
CTB Chapter 21
eText Chapter 21

21st Century Learning

Critical Thinking and Systems Thinking: How do forests affect the climate?, TE p. 586

Common Themes

Michael Wysession
Washington University

Earth's lands display a remarkable diversity of climates. The major factors that affect climate include latitude, elevation, topography, the nearness of large bodies of water, the patterns of global winds, and the type and amount of vegetation.

Space and Time Climate classifications, such as the Köppen classification system, are used to recognize how climate responds to the different factors such as latitude and elevation. The major climate types are humid tropical, dry, middle latitude (with mild or severe winters), and polar.

Forces and Motion Earth's climate changes significantly over time, sometimes very rapidly. The driving mechanism for climate change is the variation in the amount and distribution of solar radiation due to changes in Earth's revolution and rotation (Milankovitch cycles).

Matter and Energy Climate change, however, has many other natural factors. Volcanic eruptions can change climate by adding gases and dust into the atmosphere. Changes in global ocean currents greatly affect how heat from the sun is distributed. It is even possible that changes in solar activity, perhaps associated with sunspots, affects climate as well.

Earth as a System Human activity affects climate both locally, with the development of cities, and globally. We are in a period of global warming due to an increase in carbon dioxide emissions and the reduction in forest land. This global warming involves an increase in global temperatures as well as a change in patterns of precipitation.

EARTH SCIENCE REFRESHER

The History of Climate

The history of life is intimately connected with the history of climate. This is seen in the overall evolution of life, as well as the recent history of human culture and society.

When climates are warm, glacial ice melts, shorelines transgress, and large parts of the continents are covered with shallow seas, which are ideal environments for ocean life. The remarkable diversity of ocean life during the Cambrian period occurred during one of these times. The Cretaceous period, during the proliferation of the giant dinosaurs, was also extremely warm, and, on average, global climate has been cooling ever since.

Roughly 5 million years ago a major cooling trend began, and many forest habitats began to disappear, developing into plains. It has been proposed that this provided the selective force that caused our ancestors to evolve into bipedal hominids, leaving our hands free to develop tools. Many other important events, such as the emergence and dominance of *Homo sapiens* about 100,000 years ago, and the significant cultural expansion involving tools and jewelry about 50,000 to 40,000 years ago, are directly correlated with large climate changes.

> **Address Misconceptions**
>
> Students may think that Earth's climate was exactly the same for millions of years, and only changed recently as a result of human activity. In reality, there have been many major natural changes in Earth's history. For a strategy that helps to overcome this misconception, see **Address Misconceptions** on **TE p. 600**.

During the major ice age of about 20,000 years ago, sea level was low enough due to large land glaciers that all of the continents except for Antarctica were connected. This allowed northeast Asian people to cross the Bering Strait and settle in the Americas, and allowed Southeast Asian people to cross into Australia.

The rise of civilization began about 10,000 years ago, at the start of a stable global warm period. This allowed for the development of agriculture and the formation of cities. Most of the major migrations of peoples, including the movements of ancient tribes throughout the Middle East, the Greek and Roman conquests, the fall of Rome at the hands of the Goths and Huns, and many others, can be directly related to climate changes that either created prosperity or starvation.

On short time scales, volcanic eruptions have also been responsible for cultural change. For example, during the 1780s, volcanoes in Iceland and Japan significantly altered the global climates, and Europe suffered very cold temperatures and large-scale crop failures. Massive starvation lead to political unrest, and about a dozen European governments collapsed, including the French monarchy. Volcanoes caused the French Revolution!

The past 10,000 years have been remarkable not only in their unusually high temperatures, but also in the relatively small changes in temperature. While it seems that climate changes during this time were large, these changes were very small compared to previous times. If global climate patterns returned to the former level of large and rapid changes, the consequences for humanity would be severe.

BUILD READING LITERACY
SQ3R

Survey, Question, Read, Recite, and Review

Strategy Help students read material that contains technical information, diagrams, and figures. This strategy helps students focus on the main points in a section, making it easier for them to remember what they have read. Before students begin, assign a section in the textbook for them to read such as Factors That Affect Climate, pp. 588–591.

Example

1. **S** Have students survey the entire assignment and look at the heading, material in boldface and italics, and chapter summary. Have them write a short explanation of what they see in each diagram, photograph, or chart.

2. **Q** Have students write questions they will answer when they complete their survey. They should turn each heading into a question and leave room below it for the answer.

3. **R** Have students read the section and look for the answers to their questions.

4. **R** When students finish reading, tell them to think about what they read. They should recite the questions they wrote and—using their own words—give the answers they found. If students can't answer a question, have them reread the material for the related heading, looking more carefully to find the answer.

5. **R** Have students review the section by writing the answers they recited. Finally, refer students to the key concepts questions on the first page of the section. Have students answer each of these questions.

See TE p. 593 for a script on how to use this strategy with students. For additional strategies, see TE pp. 588 and 601.

ASSESS PRIOR KNOWLEDGE

Use the Chapter Pretest below to assess students' prior knowledge. As needed, review these concepts.

Review Science Concepts

Lesson 21.1 Review, from Lesson 17.3, factors that influence temperature.

Lesson 21.2 Review the idea of classification and why scientists classify things.

Lesson 21.3 Review, from Lesson 17.2, how the atmosphere is heated. Also review the concepts of El Niño and the greenhouse effect.

21 Climate

Big idea > **Weather and Climate**

Q: What factors determine and affect climate?

586

Chapter Pretest

1. As latitude increases, what generally happens to rays from the sun that strike Earth's surface? *(The rays become less vertical and more spread out.)*

2. Why do large bodies of water moderate nearby land climates? *(c)*

  a. Land heats and cools more slowly than water.

  b. Land heats more rapidly than water, but cools more slowly.

  c. Land heats and cools more rapidly than water.

  d. Land heats more slowly than water, but cools more rapidly.

3. True or False: As altitude in the lower atmosphere increases, temperature also increases. *(False)*

4. What are the major factors that determine climate? *(temperature and precipitation)*

5. True or False: El Niño is a change in ocean circulation that causes parts of the eastern tropical Pacific Ocean to become warmer than usual. *(True)*

6. What is the natural warming of Earth's atmosphere called? *(b)*

  a. El Niño

  b. the greenhouse effect

  c. global warming

  d. volcanism

INSIDE:

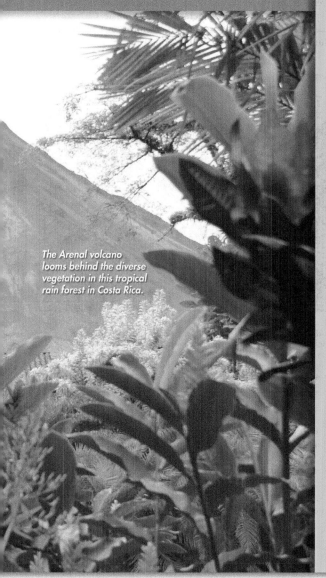

The Arenal volcano looms behind the diverse vegetation in this tropical rain forest in Costa Rica.

INQUIRY
TRY IT!

GLOBAL CLIMATE CHANGE: WHAT IS CAUSING IT?

Procedure

1. Use reliable Internet sources to gather information about whether global climate change (global warming) is caused by human activities or natural processes. Find several articles with different points of view.
2. Evaluate opposing points of view.
3. Formulate your own opinion based on your research.

Think About It

1. **Explain** List three facts about global climate change.
2. **Explain** List three uncertainties about global climate change.
3. **Draw Conclusions** What did you decide? Is global climate change due to human activity, or is it the result of natural fluctuations in climate? Or is the cause a combination of human activity and natural processes?
4. **Communicate** Write a letter in which you attempt to persuade your state senator to agree with your position. Support your stance with facts based on your research.

587

ENGAGE/EXPLORE

GLOBAL CLIMATE CHANGE: WHAT IS CAUSING IT?   L2

Purpose In this activity, students will research global climate change to form their own opinion about this environmental issue.

Skills Predict, Analyze Data, Draw Conclusions, Form an Opinion, Communicate

Prep Time 10–15 minutes

Materials computer with Internet access, paper, pen, colored markers or highlighters

Class Time 30 minutes

Teaching Tip Review with students how to research using the Internet and how to focus their searches. List some Web sites on the board that may be helpful, such as environmental sites, government sites, news sites, and educational sites. Suggest that students find three articles that support each of the following points of view: (1) Global climate change is primarily the result of human activities. (2) Global climate change is primarily due to natural processes.

Expected Outcomes Students will analyze the information they find and formulate an opinion. In the process, they will better understand the issue of global climate change. Students will also learn how to write a persuasive letter and support their articles with facts from their research.

Think About It
1. Students should list three facts that they found in their research. Accept all reasonable answers.
2. Students should list three uncertainties about global climate change they found in their research. Accept all reasonable answers.
3. Students should formulate an opinion based on their research.
4. Check students' letters to make sure that they are clearly and logically written, and that opinions are supported with facts.

1 FOCUS

Lesson Objectives

21.1 **Describe** how latitude affects climate.

21.2 **Describe** how elevation and mountain ranges affect climate.

21.3 **Describe** how large bodies of water affect climate.

21.4 **Describe** how global winds affect climate.

21.5 **Describe** how vegetation affects climate.

Build Vocabulary L2

LINCS Have students use the LINCS strategy to learn and review the terms *tropical, temperate,* and *polar.* In LINCS exercises, students **L**ist what they know about each term, **I**magine a picture that describes the word, **N**ote a "sound-alike" word, **C**onnect the terms to the sound-alike word by making up a short story, and then perform a brief **S**elf test.

Reading Strategy L2

a. Climates get cooler as latitude increases.
b. Climates get cooler as elevation increases.
c. Windward sides of mountains are wet; leeward sides are dry.
d. Places downwind of large water bodies have cooler summers and milder winters. Ocean currents transport heat over long distances.
e. Global winds influence climate by distributing heat and moisture.
f. Vegetation can moderate temperature and increase precipitation through processes such as transpiration and influencing the absorption and release of the sun's energy.

2 INSTRUCT

Build Reading Literacy L2

Refer to **p. 420D** in **Chapter 15,** which provides the guidelines for predicting.

Predict Before students read the lesson, **Ask:** Why do you think some areas of the world are very hot, and others are very cold? Once students have a list of predictions, have them read the lesson and evaluate whether their predictions were correct.

Logical, Interpersonal

Key Questions

How does latitude affect climate?

How does elevation affect climate?

What effect does a mountain range have on climate?

How do large bodies of water affect climate?

What effect do global winds have on climate?

How does vegetation affect climate?

Vocabulary

- climate
- tropical zone
- temperate zone
- polar zone

Reading Strategy

Summarize Information
Copy the table. As you read, summarize the effect(s) each factor has on climate.

Factor	Effect(s) on Climate
1. Latitude	a. ___?___
2. Elevation	b. ___?___
3. Topography	c. ___?___
4. Water bodies	d. ___?___
5. Global wind	e. ___?___
6. Vegetation	f. ___?___

POWERED BY THE SUN, Earth's climate system is a complex exchange of energy and moisture among Earth's different spheres—the hydrosphere, geosphere, and biosphere, as well as the atmosphere. All of the spheres interact to affect climate. **Climate** is the average weather conditions—such as precipitation, temperature, and humidity—in an area over a long period.

FIGURE 1 Maroon Bells Area, Colorado All of Earth's spheres—the atmosphere, hydrosphere, geosphere, and biosphere—interact to affect climate.
Identify *In the photograph, identify at least two components of each of the spheres shown.*

Factors That Determine Climate

What factors make the climate in Minneapolis, Minnesota, different from the climate in Virginia Beach, Virginia? The varied characteristics of Earth's surface and the many interactions that occur among Earth's spheres give every location a distinctive climate. Latitude, elevation, topography, large bodies of water, global winds, and vegetation affect the two most important elements of climate—temperature and precipitation.

588 Chapter 21 • Lesson 1

FIGURE 2 Earth's Major Climate Zones
A Near the poles, the sun's radiation strikes Earth at a smaller angle than at the equator.

B Earth can be divided into three zones based on these differences in solar intensity received at Earth's surface.

Latitude Latitude is the distance north or south of the equator. It is expressed in degrees. 🔑 **As latitude increases, the average intensity of solar energy received at Earth's surface decreases.** In **Figure 2A,** notice that near the equator, radiation from the sun strikes the planet most directly. Therefore, in this region, between about 23.5° north and 23.5° south of the equator, heat from the sun's rays is most intense. This region is called the **tropical zones,** or the tropics. Temperatures in the tropical zones are generally warm year-round. In the **temperate zones,** which are between about 23.5° and 66.5° north and south of the equator, the sun's radiation strikes Earth at a smaller angle than near the equator. Because the incoming radiation is slanted, solar energy is spread out over a larger area. In addition, the length of daylight in the summer is much greater than in the winter. As a result, temperate zones have hot summers and rather cold winters. In the **polar zones,** which are between 66.5° north and south latitudes and the poles, the energy strikes at an even smaller angle, causing the light and heat to spread out over an even larger area. Therefore, the polar regions are generally very cold.

Because of the effect of latitude, less solar energy per unit of area is transferred into the atmosphere in the polar regions than in the tropics. This difference in energy affects weather and climate from the equator to the poles. Differences in energy lead to the air-pressure differences that produce winds. Differences in energy affect evaporation rates and the formation of clouds, air masses, and storms. Over time, energy differences on a global scale also determine climate.

Elevation Elevation, or height above sea level, also affects an area's climate. For example, air temperature decreases with elevation by an average of about 6.5°C every 1000 meters. 🔑 **In general, the higher the elevation is, the colder the climate. Figure 3** shows how the climates of two cities at roughly the same latitude are affected by their height above sea level.

FIGURE 3 Climate Data for Two Cities This climate graph shows data for two cities in Arizona. Phoenix has an elevation of 338 m. Flagstaff has an elevation of 2134 m.
Interpret Graphs How does elevation affect annual temperatures and precipitation?

Climate **589**

LESSON 21.1

Use Visuals **L1**

Figure 4 Use this diagram to explain one way in which topography affects precipitation. **Ask:** What happens to humid air as it is blown up the windward side of the mountains? *(It cools, forming clouds.)* What often falls from these clouds? *(heavy precipitation)* What is the air like when it reaches the other side of the leeward side of the mountain? *(very dry)* What does the term "rain shadow" mean? *(It refers to an area where relatively little rain falls because of the effect of mountains.)*
Visual, Logical

INQUIRY QUICK LAB

OBSERVING HOW LAND AND WATER ABSORB AND RELEASE ENERGY **L2**

Objective
After completing this activity, students will be able to state that land and water absorb and release heat differently.

Skills Use Models, Compare and Contrast, Measure, Analyze Data, Draw Conclusions

Prep Time 10 minutes

Class Time 25–30 minutes

Materials safety goggles; 2 small, identical containers; 2 laboratory thermometers (alcohol); water; dry sand; masking tape; watch or clock; book; paper towels or rags for spills

Safety All students should wear safety goggles. Remind students to report any breakage of thermometers immediately. Wipe up any spills at once.

Expected Outcome Students will observe that water warms up and cools down more slowly than land.

Analyze and Conclude
1. The sand heated and cooled more quickly than the water.
2. A large body of water generally moderates the temperature of nearby land areas, which usually have cooler summers and warmer winters than land areas farther from the water.
Kinesthetic, Logical

FIGURE 4 The Rain Shadow Effect Mountains affect the amount of moisture in the air that travels over them. **Compare and Contrast** *How may the climates on the windward and leeward sides of mountains be different?*

Topography Topographic features such as mountains influence the amount of precipitation that falls over an area. As shown in **Figure 4**, humid air on the windward side of a mountain moves up the slopes and cools to form clouds that often release heavy precipitation. By the time air reaches the leeward side, it has lost most of its moisture, and that side of the mountain is dry. The dry area is called a *rain shadow*, and it may extend for hundreds of kilometers.

Bodies of Water Large bodies of water such as lakes and oceans have an important effect on the temperature of an area because the temperature of the water body influences the temperature of the air above it. Places downwind of a large body of water generally have cooler summers and milder winters than places at the same latitude and altitude that are farther inland.

INQUIRY QUICK LAB

OBSERVING HOW LAND AND WATER ABSORB AND RELEASE ENERGY

Materials
• 2 small, identical containers • 2 laboratory thermometers • water • dry sand • masking tape • watch or clock • book • paper towels or rags for spills

Procedure
1. On a separate sheet of paper, make a copy of the data table shown.
2. Fill one container three-quarters full of dry sand.
3. Fill the other container three-quarters full of water.
4. Place the containers in a sunny area on a flat surface such as a tabletop or a lab bench.
5. Place the bulb of one of the thermometers in the sand. Prop up the thermometer with a book. Tape the thermometer in place so that only the bulb is covered with sand.
6. Repeat Step 5 with the water. Tape the thermometer in place so only the bulb is covered with water.
7. Record the initial temperature of each substance in your data table.
8. Record the temperature of each thermometer every 5 minutes for about 20 minutes.
9. Remove the containers from the sunny area.
10. Record the temperature of each thermometer every five minutes for another 20 minutes.

Analyze and Conclude
1. **Compare and Contrast** Which substance heated faster? Which cooled faster?
2. **Draw Conclusions** How does a large body of water affect the temperature of nearby areas?

Heat Absorption and Retention of Water and Sand							
	Time	Temp H$_2$O	Temp Sand		Time	Temp H$_2$O	Temp Sand
Sunny Area	0			Shady Area	0		
	5				5		
	10				10		
	15				15		
	20				20		

Facts and Figures

Ocean currents have important effects on climates. Currents moving from low-latitude to high-latitude regions transfer heat from warmer to cooler areas on Earth. As the text indicates, the North Atlantic Drift is an extension of the Gulf Stream, the warm current that runs up the eastern shore of North America. The North Atlantic Drift keeps Great Britain and much of northwestern Europe much warmer during the winter than areas such as Labrador and Alaska that are at similar latitudes. Cold currents originate in cold high-latitude regions. As they travel towards the equator, they tend to moderate the warm temperatures of adjacent land areas. An example of this is the California Current, which moderates temperatures along the west coast of North America.

In addition, ocean currents affect climate by transporting heat over long distances. For example, the Gulf Stream is a warm current that originates in the Gulf of Mexico, travels northward, and eventually becomes the North Atlantic Drift that moves eastward across the Atlantic Ocean. The North Atlantic Drift transfers heat to the air over southern England and Ireland, giving these areas a mild climate in spite of their high latitudes.

Circulation in the Atmosphere ⚿ **Global winds are another factor that influences climate, because they distribute heat and moisture around Earth.** Recall that winds constantly move warm air toward the poles and cool air toward the equator. The low-pressure zones at the equator and in the middle latitudes lead to the formation of clouds. These clouds then drop precipitation as rain or snow.

Vegetation You probably know that the types of plants that grow in a region depend on climate, as shown in **Figures 5A** and **5B**. But did you know that vegetation affects climate? ⚿ **Vegetation can affect both temperature and the precipitation patterns in an area.** Vegetation influences how much of the sun's energy is absorbed and how quickly this energy is released. This influence, in turn, affects an area's temperature. During a process called *transpiration*, plants release water vapor from their leaves into the air. Transpiration influences the rate at which water vapor returns to the atmosphere, and therefore affects precipitation. Studies also indicate that pollen released by some plants can act as cloud seeds. If an increase in pollen promotes the formation of clouds, it can also influence regional precipitation patterns.

FIGURE 5 Arizona Vegetation
A Cacti and scrub are common types of vegetation in the hot, dry climate of Phoenix, Arizona. **B** The vegetation in the highlands of Flagstaff, Arizona, is much different.
Form a Hypothesis *Which of these areas would receive more precipitation? Why?*

21.1 Assessment

Reviewing Key Concepts ⚿

1. How does latitude affect climate?

2. How does elevation affect climate?

3. How does a mountain range affect climate?

4. How do large bodies of water affect climate?

5. What effect do global winds have on climate?

6. Describe different ways in which vegetation affects climate.

Think Critically

7. Describe Describe tropical zones, temperate zones, and polar zones in terms of location and the intensity of solar radiation that each receives.

8. Explain Why are deserts common on the leeward sides of mountain ranges?

9. Apply Concepts Look again at Figures 3 and 5. What two factors contribute to the average annual temperature in both areas?

BIGIDEA WEATHER AND CLIMATE

10. Relate Cause and Effect Write a paragraph to explain how three of the factors discussed in this section affect the climate of your area.

Climate **591**

21.2 World Climates

Lesson Objectives

21.6 **Explain** the Köppen climate classification system.

21.7 **Describe** humid tropical climates.

21.8 **Compare and contrast** humid mid-latitude climates.

21.9 **List** the characteristics of dry climates.

21.10 **List** the characteristics of polar climates.

21.11 **Compare and contrast** highland climates with nearby lowland climates.

Build Vocabulary `L2`

Concept Map Have students draw concept maps of the Köppen system. Have them start with "Köppen system" at the top, and put the five principal groups of climates on the next level. Below that, they should put the subgroups within each group and, on the last row, details about each climate.

Reading Strategy `L2`

Students' outlines should be consistent with the information in the chapter and include the temperature and precipitation for each climate type and one location for each climate type.

2 INSTRUCT

Build Science Skills `L2`

Classify Ask students to classify the five Köppen climate groups into two main groups. Invite several students to give their classifications; then point out that several different answers are possible. Ask students if they think the Köppen system is the only possible way to classify climates. *(no)* Point out that although classification systems are based on facts, they are invented by humans.
Visual, Logical

Key Questions

🔑 *What is the Köppen climate classification system?*

🔑 *What are humid tropical climates?*

🔑 *What are the characteristics of the different types of humid mid-latitude climates?*

🔑 *What are the characteristics of dry climates?*

🔑 *What are the characteristics of polar climates?*

🔑 *How do highland climates compare with nearby lowlands?*

Vocabulary

• Köppen climate classification system

Reading Strategy

Outline Make an outline for each climate type discussed in the section. Include temperature and precipitation information for each climate type, as well as at least one location with that climate type.

IF YOU WERE TO TRAVEL around the world, you would find an incredible variety of climates. There are so many different climates, in fact, that it might be hard to believe they could all occur on the same planet! Despite the diversity, climates can be classified according to average temperatures and amount of precipitation. In this section, you will learn about the Köppen climate classification system, which is commonly used to group climates.

The Köppen Climate Classification System

Many classification systems have been used to group climates. The Köppen climate classification system is probably the best known and the most commonly used. 🔑 **The Köppen climate classification system uses mean monthly and annual values of temperature and precipitation to classify climates.** This system classifies the world into climatic regions based on easily measured data.

The Köppen system has five principal groups: humid tropical climates, dry climates, humid mid-latitude climates, polar climates, and highland climates. **Figure 6** shows a place that has a polar climate. The five principal groups are defined on the basis of temperature and moisture. Each of the five major groups is further subdivided.

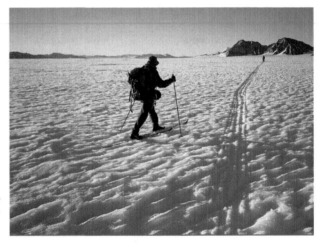

FIGURE 6 Polar Climate
An ice cap climate is a polar climate in which the average monthly temperature is always below freezing.

FIGURE 7 **Rain Forest in Malaysia** The vegetation in the tropical rain forest is the most luxuriant found anywhere on Earth.

Humid Tropical Climates

Humid tropical climates are climates without winters. Every month in such a climate has a mean temperature above 18°C. The amount of precipitation can exceed 200 cm per year. There are two types of humid tropical climates: wet tropical climates and tropical wet and dry climates.

Wet Tropical The *tropical rain forest* shown in **Figure 7** is typical of a wet tropical climate. *Wet tropical climates* have high temperatures and a great amount of annual precipitation. Why? Recall what you've learned about how latitude affects climate. The intensity of the sun's rays in the tropics is consistently high. The sun is directly overhead much of the time, and changes in the length of daylight throughout the year are slight. The winds that blow over the tropics cause the warm, humid, unstable air to rise and cool. The water vapor in the air condenses and falls as precipitation. Regions with humid tropical climates form a belt on either side of the equator. Wet tropical climates make up approximately 10 percent of Earth's land area, as shown in the map in **Figure 9** on the next two pages.

Tropical Wet and Dry Bordering the wet tropics are tropical wet and dry climates. *Tropical wet and dry climates* have temperatures and total precipitation similar to those in the wet tropics, but experience distinct periods of low precipitation. *Savannas,* which are tropical grasslands with drought-resistant trees, are typical of tropical wet and dry climates.

FIGURE 8 **African Savanna** Drought-resistant trees and tall grasses are typical vegetation for a savanna.

Climate **593**

LESSON 21.2

Use Visuals

L1

Figure 9 Use this map to explain global climates and how they are related. First, orient students to the map by pointing out the equator and lines of latitude. **Ask:** How are savannas and rainforests related? *(Savannas are usually found north and south of rain forests.)* How are steppes and deserts related? *(Steppes are usually found north and south of deserts.)* Explain that savannas and steppes are transition zones between rainforests and deserts, respectively, and the next climate zones. **Ask:** What pattern do you see as you go from south to north in eastern North America? *(Climates go from tropical wet and dry, to humid subtropical, to humid continental, to subarctic, to tundra.)*
Visual, Logical

Integrate Biology

L2

Biomes and Climate Regions Remind students that biomes are defined according to the organisms that live in an area, whereas climates are defined according to temperature and precipitation. Tell them that Köppen used the distribution of plants to determine climate regions. **Ask:** What is the typical vegetation in a savanna? *(tropical grasslands with drought-resistant trees)* What are the typical climate conditions in a rain forest? *(high temperatures and large amounts of precipitation year-round)*
Logical

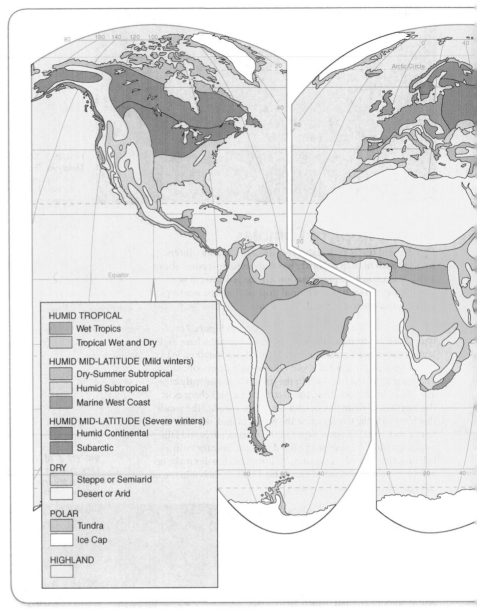

HUMID TROPICAL
- Wet Tropics
- Tropical Wet and Dry

HUMID MID-LATITUDE (Mild winters)
- Dry-Summer Subtropical
- Humid Subtropical
- Marine West Coast

HUMID MID-LATITUDE (Severe winters)
- Humid Continental
- Subarctic

DRY
- Steppe or Semiarid
- Desert or Arid

POLAR
- Tundra
- Ice Cap

HIGHLAND

FIGURE 9 Global Climates The map shows the distribution of climates worldwide.

Facts and Figures

Here is an overview of the major groups in the Köppen system:
A. Humid tropical: winterless climates; all months have a mean temperature above 18°C.
B. Humid mid-latitude with mild winters: average temperature of the coldest month is below 18°C but above −3°C.
C. Humid mid-latitude with severe winters: average temperature of the coldest month is below −3°C; warmest monthly mean exceeds 10°C.
D. Dry: climates where evaporation exceeds precipitation; there is a constant water deficiency.
E. Polar: summerless climates; average temperature of the warmest month is below 10°C.
F. Highland: Generally cooler and wetter than areas with lower elevations.

Map labels visible: 100, 120, 140, 160, 80, 60, 180, 40, 20, 0

Tropic of Cancer

Tropic of Capricorn

Climate **595**

LESSON 21.2

Use Visuals

Figure 10 Use this diagram to explain the format of climate graphs. Go over what each axis represents. Make sure students understand that temperature is shown using a line with units on the left axis. Precipitation is shown using bars with units on the right axis. **Ask:** In which month does Cape Town have the lowest temperature? *(July)* The highest temperature? *(January)* In which month does Guangzhou have the least precipitation? *(December)* The most precipitation? *(June)*
Visual, Logical

⬭ Teacher **Demo**

MODELING HUMID CLIMATES   L2

Purpose Students observe how temperature affects the humidity of a climate.

Materials water, 2 small plastic bowls, transparent plastic wrap, rubber band

Procedure Place equal amounts of water into each of two small plastic bowls. Cover each bowl with transparent plastic wrap and use a rubber band to hold each piece of wrap in place. Place one bowl in a warm location such as a sunny windowsill or near a radiator. Place the other bowl in a cool location. Ask students to predict in which bowl more evaporation will occur. *(Most students will say "the warm one.")* The next day, have students observe the two bowls. Ask them what they observed. *(The warmer bowl had more condensation on the underside of the plastic wrap.)* Ask students how they think this relates to the differences between humid tropical climates and humid mid-latitude climates. *(The higher temperatures in the tropics lead to greater evaporation and greater rainfall than in the mid-latitudes.)*

Expected Outcome The warmer bowl will have more condensation on the underside of the plastic wrap.
Logical, Visual

FIGURE 10 Humid Mid-Latitude Climates Each of these graphs shows typical climate data of the mid-latitude climates. Red curves indicate temperature. Blue bars indicate monthly precipitation.
Interpret Graphs What are the typical temperatures and amounts of precipitation for Chicago, Illinois, in May and June?

PLANET DIARY

For links about **Drought**, go to PlanetDiary.com/HSES

Humid Mid-Latitude Climates

Humid mid-latitude climates include climates with mild winters as well as those with severe winters. ⬭ Humid mid-latitude **climates with mild winters have an average temperature in the coldest month that is below 18°C but above −3°C. Humid mid-latitude climates with severe winters have an average temperature in the coldest month that is below −3°C.**

Humid Mid-Latitude With Mild Winters There are three types of humid mid-latitude climates with mild winters: humid subtropical climates, marine west-coast climates, and dry-summer tropical climates. Located between about 25° and 40° latitude on the eastern sides of the continents are the humid subtropical climates. In the summer, *humid subtropical climates* have hot, sultry weather as daytime temperatures are generally high. Although winters are mild, frosts are common in areas with higher latitudes. The graph in **Figure 10A** shows data for a city in China that has a typical humid subtropical climate. If you look at the map in Figure 9, you will see that humid subtropical climate dominates much of the eastern United States as well as the south-central part of the country. The state of Virginia, for example, lies within a humid subtropical region.

Coastal areas between about 40° and 65° north and south latitude have marine west coast climates. Maritime air masses over *marine west-coast climates* result in mild winters and cool summers with an ample amount of rainfall throughout the year. In North America, the marine west coast climate extends as a narrow belt from northernmost California into southern Alaska. The data in Figure 10B are typical of marine west coast climates. Note that in the Southern Hemisphere, marine west-coast climates are actually found on the east coast of Africa and Australia.

D
Humid Continental

Chicago, Illinois
42°N 88°W
Temp °C
Precip: 84 cm
Temp. range: 26°C
cm

E
Subarctic

Moose Factory, Ontario
51°N 80°W
Temp °C
Precip: 58 cm
Temp. range: 38°C
cm

As you can see in Figure 9, regions with *dry-summer subtropical climates* are located between about 30° and 45° latitude. These climate regions are unique because they are the only humid regions that have a high maximum winter rainfall, as shown in Figure 10C. A dry-summer subtropical climate is sometimes referred to as a *mediterranean climate.* In the United States, dry-summer subtropical climate is found only in California.

Humid Mid-Latitude With Severe Winters There are two types of humid mid-latitude climates with severe winters: the humid continental climates and the subarctic climates. Continental landmasses strongly influence both of these climates. As a result, such climates are absent in the Southern Hemisphere. There, oceans dominate the middle-latitude zone.

In a *humid continental climate,* the winters are severe, while the summers are typically quite warm. Note, too, that precipitation is generally greater in summer than in winter. Locate the regions having a humid continental climate, which are shown in blue, in Figure 9. Note that areas with such climates lie between approximately 40° and 50° north latitude.

In the Northern Hemisphere, there is an extensive subarctic climate region north of the humid continental climate and south of the tundra. Winters in *humid subarctic climates* are long and bitterly cold. In contrast, summers in the subarctic are remarkably warm but very short. The extremely cold winters and relatively warm summers combine to produce the highest annual temperature ranges on Earth. From Figure 9, you can see that this climate zone covers a broad expanse. Such climates stretch from western Alaska to Newfoundland in North America, and from Norway to the Pacific coast of Russia in Eurasia.

☑ **Reading Checkpoint** *Compare and contrast two types of humid mid-latitude climates that experience severe winters.*

Climate **597**

Address **Misconceptions**   L2

Students may think that it never gets hot in subarctic areas such as Alaska. Dispel this misconception by pointing out that summer temperatures in southern Alaska are usually between 15°–25°C). Also tell students that the record high temperature in Alaska is 38°C. This record was set on June 27, 1915, in Fort Yukon, a town along the Arctic Circle in the interior of Alaska.
Logical

Use Community Resources   L2

Invite a climatologist from a local college into the classroom to discuss climate regions and the factors that cause each one. Ask students to prepare questions in advance to ask the visitor.
Interpersonal

Answers

Figure 10 *Temperatures range from about 10°C to 20°C. Precipitation is nearly 10 cm.*

☑ **Reading Checkpoint** *Both are strongly influenced by continental landmasses. Humid continental climates experience severe temperatures, and precipitation is generally greater in summer than in winter. Subarctic climates have winters that are long and bitterly cold and summers that are remarkably warm but short. These differences combine to produce the highest annual temperature ranges on Earth.*

Facts and Figures

Winters in the subarctic region are nearly as cold as those in polar regions. Winter minimum temperatures are among the lowest ever recorded outside the ice sheets of Greenland and Antarctica. In fact, for many years the world's lowest temperature was attributed to Verkhoyansk in east central Siberia, where the temperature dropped to −68°C on February 5 and 7, 1892. Over a 23-year period, this same station had an average monthly minimum of −62°C during January. Although exceptional, these temperatures illustrate the extreme cold that envelops the subarctic region in winter.

Students may think that the terms *arid* and *drought* have roughly the same meaning. Explain that droughts occur temporarily as a result of atmospheric conditions. In contrast, arid regions are those where dry conditions are a permanent feature of the climate.
Logical, Verbal

FIGURE 11 **Extent of Dry Climate Zones**
As the map shows, there are deserts on every continent.

MAP IT!
ACTIVITY

Figure 11 shows the locations of dry climates worldwide.
Identify Identify the desert(s) in each place or region.
1. Chile
2. southwestern United States
3. central Australia
4. northwestern India
5. southern Africa
Describe About how much of Australia has a desert climate?

Dry Climates

🔑 **A dry climate is one in which the yearly precipitation is not as great as the potential loss of water by evaporation and transpiration.** In other words, dryness is not only related to annual rainfall, but is also a function of evaporation and transpiration. Evaporation, in turn, is closely dependent upon temperature and humidity. There are two types of dry climates: arid, or *desert climate,* and semi-arid, or *steppe,* as the map in **Figure 11** shows. Arid and semi-arid climates have many features in common. In fact, the difference between them is slight. The steppe is a more humid variant of the desert that separates the desert from climates that have even higher humidity. The steppe represents a transition zone that surrounds the desert and separates it from humid climates.

Dry climates exist as the result of the global distribution of air pressure and winds. In regions near the tropics of Cancer and Capricorn, air is subsiding. When air sinks, it is compressed and warmed. Such conditions are opposite of those needed for clouds to form precipitation. As a result, regions with dry climates have mostly clear, sunny skies and dry conditions. Other dry areas, including the Great Basin in North America and the Gobi Desert of Eurasia, occur where prevailing winds meet mountain barriers. These arid regions are called *rain shadow deserts.*

Some of Earth's driest desert climates occur where a cold ocean current affects the west coast of a continent. A cold current cools the air above it. This strengthens the sinking of air in the warm, dry airmasses that cause deserts. The Namib desert in Africa and the Atacama desert in Chile are examples of this type of extremely dry coastal desert.

Answers

MAP IT!

1. Atacama Desert; 2. Sonoran Desert;
3. Simpson Desert; 4. Great Indian Desert;
5. Namib Desert and Kalahari Desert

About 40 percent of Australia is desert.

Polar Climates

Polar climates are those in which the mean temperature of the warmest month is below 10°C. Winters in *polar climates* have periods of perpetual night, or nearly so, making temperatures extremely cold. During the summer, temperatures remain cool despite the long hours of daylight. Very little precipitation falls in polar regions.

There are two types of polar climates. The *tundra climate,* shown in **Figure 12,** is a treeless region found almost exclusively in the Northern Hemisphere. The *ice cap climate* does not have a single monthly mean temperature above 0°C. The landscape is covered by permanent ice and snow. Ice cap climates occur in high mountain areas and in Greenland and Antarctica.

FIGURE 12 Tundra North of Nome, Alaska Tundra plant life includes mostly mosses, shrubs, and flowering herbs.

Highland Climates

Mountains have climates that are different from climates in surrounding lowland areas. In general, highland climates are cooler and wetter than nearby areas at lower elevations. Conditions within highland climates often vary abruptly from one place to another. For example, in the Northern Hemisphere, south-facing slopes are warmer than north-facing slopes, and air on the windward sides of mountains is wetter than air on the leeward sides. Locate the highland climate regions on the map in Figure 9.

21.2 Assessment

Review Key Concepts

1. What is the Köppen climate classification system?

2. Describe the characteristics of humid tropical climates.

3. What are some characteristics of humid mid-latitude climates?

4. What defines a dry climate?

5. What are the characteristics of polar climates?

6. How do highland climates compare with nearby lowlands?

Think Critically

7. **Interpret Maps** Use Figure 9 to identify the climate type of your city or town. Describe some characteristics of your area's climate type.

8. **Draw Conclusions** Can tundra climates exist at low latitudes? Explain.

WRITING IN SCIENCE

9. **Explain** Write a paragraph in which you explain why Antarctica can be classified as a desert.

Climate **599**

Build Science Skills L2

Infer Have students refer back to Figure 9. Discuss why polar climates occur where they do. **Ask:** Why are tundra climates found almost exclusively in the Northern Hemisphere? *(There is very little land in the Southern Hemisphere that is at the same latitude as tundra climates in the Northern Hemisphere.)*
Visual, Logical

Build Science Skills L2

Apply Concepts Have students refer back to Lesson 21.1 to help them understand what causes highland climates. **Ask:** What two main factors cause highland climates? *(elevation and topography)* What effect does elevation have on highland climates? *(Temperature decreases with elevation, so highland climates are cooler than nearby climates at lower elevations.)*
Visual, Logical

3 ASSESS

Evaluate Understanding L2

Describe characteristics of various climate regions, and call on students to identify them. For example, if you say "very cold with no plants," students should respond "ice cap."

Reteach L1

Use Figure 9 to review the characteristics of each climate region and subregion.

Assessment Answers

1. The Köppen system uses mean monthly and annual values of temperature and precipitation to classify climates.
2. Humid tropical climates have no winters. Every month has a mean temperature above 18°C and has a lot of precipitation.
3. Humid mid-latitude climates with mild winters have an average temperature in the coldest month that is below 18°C but above −3°C. Humid mid-latitude climates with severe winters

have an average temperature in the coldest month that is below −3°C.
4. both the amount of precipitation that falls and the amount of water that can be lost as the result of evaporation and transpiration
5. Polar climates are extremely cold, even in the summer months. Very little precipitation falls in polar regions, and evaporation is limited.
6. Highland climates generally are cooler and wetter than nearby places at lower elevations.

7. Answers will vary depending on your location. If necessary, have students use a map.
8. yes, at high elevations where temperatures are very low
9. Deserts are dry climates that are defined primarily by the amount of precipitation that falls rather than temperature. Antarctica and other areas in Earth's polar regions are deserts because they receive very little precipitation that does not evaporate much annually.

LESSON 21.3

1 FOCUS

Lesson Objectives
21.12 **Describe** natural processes that can cause changes in climate.
21.13 **Explain** the greenhouse effect.
21.14 **Define** global warming.
21.15 **List** some of the consequences of global warming.

Build Vocabulary   L2
Paraphrase Explain the meaning of the vocabulary term and other science terms by using words that are familiar to students. For example, tell students that *global* can be thought of as "globe-like." Point out a classroom globe as an example.

Reading Strategy   L2
Sample answer: **a.** Plate Tectonics
b. Changes in land and oceans can cause long-term climate change.
c. Ocean Circulation
d. Changes can result in short-term fluctuations.
e. Earth's Orbital Motions
f. Changes in Earth's orbit and axis can cause intermediate-term climate change.

2 INSTRUCT

(Address **Misconceptions**)   L2

Students may think that Earth's climate was exactly the same for millions of years, and changed only recently as a result of human activity. Point out that there have been many major natural changes in Earth's history. For example, during the Ice Ages that began 2 to 3 million years ago, Earth's climate was much colder. At other times Earth's climate has been warmer than it is now. Emphasize that there are many different causes of climate change.

Key Questions

⊜ *Describe natural processes that can cause changes in climate.*

⊜ *What is the greenhouse effect?*

⊜ *What is global warming?*

⊜ *What are some of the consequences of global warming?*

Vocabulary
• global climate change

Reading Strategy
Identify Cause and Effect Copy the table, then complete the table as you read.

Climate Changes	
Causes	**Effects**
a. _____?_____	b. _____?_____
c. _____?_____	d. _____?_____
e. _____?_____ .	f. _____?_____

CLIMATE is always changing. Some of these changes are short-term, while others occur over long periods of geologic time. Some climate changes are the result of natural processes, such as flooding caused by El Niño. Other changes are related to human activities.

Natural Processes That Change Climate
Many different natural processes can cause climates to change. Some act over very long time periods, and some over much shorter periods. All occur together, making climate change a very complex process.

Plate Tectonics ⊜ **Geographic changes in Earth's land and oceans due to plate tectonics cause changes in climate over very long periods.** Oceans grow and shrink, changing the circulation patterns of ocean water. A large supercontinent like Pangaea would have affected patterns in wind and precipitation, as Asia does today.

But most important, mountain building cools global climates by removing carbon dioxide from the atmosphere. For example, Earth has been cooling over the past 50 million years because of the collision of India and Asia that created the Himalayas. In this process, exposed silicate rocks weather and erode quickly. The sediments wash into the ocean, where they form carbonate rocks. The carbon in these rocks begins as carbon dioxide in the atmosphere. Weathering removes carbon dioxide from the atmosphere and buries it on the sea floor. Before India collided with Asia, there was three times as much carbon dioxide in the atmosphere as there is now.

FIGURE 13 **Effect of El Niño** In 1998, bad weather conditions and flooding in Alabama were attributed to an extremely strong El Niño.

Earth's Orbital Motions **Changes in the shape of Earth's orbit and the tilt of Earth's axis of rotation affect global climates over intermediate time scales.** Earth's orbit is always elliptical. But over 100,000–400,000 year periods, the path becomes more and then less elliptical. This change in shape brings Earth closer to and then farther from the sun. This affects global climates: Earth is warmer when it is closer to the sun. The tilt of Earth's orbit also changes with respect to the rest of the solar system over a 100,000 year period. The tilt of Earth's axis changes over periods of about 20,000–40,000 years. The tilt of Earth's axis changes by about 3 degrees. This affects the severity of the seasons. When Earth's axis is less tilted, the temperature difference between summer and winter is less.

Ocean Circulation Recall that *El Niño* is a change in ocean circulation that causes parts of the eastern tropical Pacific Ocean to become warmer than usual. **The changes in ocean circulation caused by El Niño can also result in short-term climate fluctuations.** For example, some areas that are normally arid receive large amounts of rain during El Niño. Also, some regions that receive abundant precipitation may experience dry periods when the ocean circulation patterns change.

Solar Activity In general, the sun has been giving off increasing amounts of energy over its lifetime. **Over relatively short time scales, fluctuations in the amount of solar radiation can change global climates.** An increase in sunspots appears to correspond with warm periods in Europe and North America. A decrease in sunspots seems to correlate with cooler periods. For example, the "Little Ice Age" in Europe during the 1600s occurred during a period when there were very few sunspots.

Volcanic Eruptions Volcanic eruptions can emit large volumes of ash and dust into Earth's atmosphere. Volcanic eruptions also send tiny particles containing sulfur into the air. If the volume of these particles, called *aerosols*, is great enough, it can cause short-term changes in Earth's surface temperature. **Volcanic ash, dust, and sulfur-based aerosols in the air increase the amount of solar radiation that is reflected back into space. This causes Earth's lower atmosphere to cool.** But over longer time scales, volcanic eruptions can raise global temperatures by adding gases like carbon dioxide to the atmosphere, increasing the warming caused by the greenhouse effect.

☑ **Reading Checkpoint** *Identify five natural processes that cause climate changes.*

FIGURE 14 Ash in the Atmosphere In 2010, this volcano erupted in Iceland, ejecting volcanic ash into the atmosphere.

Climate **601**

LESSON 21.3

Address Misconceptions `L2`

Students may be misled by the term *greenhouse effect.* The term may make them think that the atmosphere is heated in exactly the same way as a greenhouse. The term was coined to describe the process that heats the atmosphere because it was once thought that greenhouses were heated in a similar way. One factor in heating a greenhouse is the blocking of heat radiation. However, a more important factor is that the glass of the greenhouse prevents warm air from escaping by convection.
Logical

Use Visuals `L1`

Figure 15 Use these graphs to explain how carbon dioxide emissions affect carbon dioxide concentrations in the atmosphere. Make sure that students understand that the emissions amounts and atmospheric concentrations in graph C are shown in different units. **Ask:** What unit is used for carbon dioxide emissions? *(gigatons of carbon/yr)* What unit is used for carbon dioxide concentrations in the atmosphere? *(ppm, or parts per million)* What do graphs A and B show? *(carbon dioxide concentrations in the atmosphere)*
Visual, Logical

Address Misconceptions `L2`

Students often think that the greenhouse effect and global warming are the same phenomenon. Emphasize that the greenhouse effect occurs naturally and is essential to keeping the atmosphere warm enough for living things to survive on Earth. Global warming, on the other hand, is an increase in the temperature of Earth's atmosphere that may be caused or influenced by human activities.
Logical

FIGURE 15 Change in CO₂ Levels
The rapid increase in carbon dioxide concentration (graphs **A** and **B**) since 1850 has closely followed the increase in carbon dioxide emissions from burning fossil fuels (graph **C**). The concentration of carbon dioxide is measured in parts per million (ppm).
Predict *Do you think that the concentration of carbon dioxide in the atmosphere will continue to increase? Explain your answer.*

Human Impact on Climate

Natural processes have certainly contributed to many climatic changes throughout Earth's 4.5-billion-year history. These processes will also cause some of the future shifts in Earth's climates. But human activities have contributed to, and will continue to contribute to, global climatic change.

The Greenhouse Effect Recall that the *greenhouse effect* is the process by which heat is trapped in the atmosphere by certain gases. 🔑 **The greenhouse effect is a natural warming of both Earth's lower atmosphere and Earth's surface.** The major gases involved in the greenhouse effect are water vapor, carbon dioxide, and methane. These *greenhouse gases,* as they are often called, do not prevent solar radiation from reaching Earth's surface. Most of the solar energy is then reradiated skyward. The greenhouse gases are good absorbers of Earth's reflected radiation. These gases maintain warm temperatures in the lower atmosphere, making Earth habitable for living things. Without the greenhouse effect, Earth would be much too cold to support most types of life that exist on Earth. But an increase in the greenhouse effect could prove devastating to living things.

Studies indicate that human activities for the past 200 or so years have strengthened the greenhouse effect. As **Figure 15** shows, carbon dioxide levels in the atmosphere have risen at a rapid pace since about 1850. Much of this greenhouse gas has been added by the burning of fossil fuels. The clearing of forests also contributes to an increase in carbon dioxide, because trees take in carbon dioxide during photosynthesis. In addition, this gas is released when vegetation is burned or when it decays.

Global Climate Change 🔑 **As a result of increases in carbon dioxide levels, as well as other greenhouse gases, global atmospheric temperatures have increased.** This increase in atmospheric temperature, along with climate changes that have resulted from it, is called **global climate change.** The term *global warming* is used to refer specifically to the increase in the temperature of Earth's atmosphere near the surface. During the twentieth century, Earth's average surface temperatures increased about 1.0°C. Scientists predict that temperatures on Earth will continue to increase in the twenty-first century.

Facts and Figures

Human influence on regional and global climates likely began long before the beginning of the modern industrial period. There is evidence that human activities have affected climate over extensive areas for thousands of years. The use of fire and the overgrazing of marginal lands by domestic animals have reduced the abundance and distribution of plants. Altering ground cover has affected important climate factors such as surface albedo, evaporation rates, and surface winds.

Scientists base their predictions about global warming on computer models, called climate models, of change in Earth's atmosphere. *Climate models* are complex computer programs that involve huge amounts of data on temperature, precipitation, and other variables. But climate models cannot describe Earth's atmosphere completely. For this reason, the results from a model are always an approximation. What follows is one prediction of how temperature increases could affect Earth.

Warmer surface temperatures increase evaporation rates. This, in turn, increases the amount of water vapor in the atmosphere. The combustion of fossil fuels also adds water vapor to the atmosphere. Water vapor is an even more powerful absorber of radiation emitted by Earth than is carbon dioxide. Therefore, more water vapor in the air will magnify the greenhouse effect.

Temperature increases will also cause sea ice to melt. Ice reflects more incoming solar radiation than liquid water does. The melting of the ice will cause a substantial increase in the solar energy absorbed at the surface. This, in turn, will magnify the temperature increase created by higher levels of greenhouse gases. The melting ice sheets and glaciers on land will also cause a global rise in sea level. This will lead to shoreline erosion and coastal flooding. Warmer oceans could also lead to stronger and more frequent storms, including hurricanes.

Scientists also expect that weather patterns will change as a result of the projected global warming. More intense heat waves and droughts in some regions and fewer such events in other places are also predicted. Hotter, more arid conditions have already led to more forest fires in the western United States.

FIGURE 16 Effect of Melting Ice
Polar bears swim between ice sheets when they hunt for food. Because ice is melting, the distance between ice sheets is increasing, and polar bears must now swim longer distances than they once did.

21.3 Assessment

Review Key Concepts

1. Describe five natural processes that can cause climate change.

2. What is the greenhouse effect?

3. What is global warming?

4. What are some possible effects of global climate change?

Think Critically

5. **Predict** How might cloud cover change as the result of global warming?

6. **Synthesize** How might global climate change affect Earth's inhabitants, including humans?

WRITING IN SCIENCE

7. **Propose a Solution** Write at least two paragraphs to persuade your friends and family to reduce their consumption of fossil fuels. Be sure to explain why the usage of such energy sources should be reduced.

Climate **603**

3 ASSESS

Evaluate Understanding [L2]

Ask students to describe three natural processes that change climate. Have them describe how each process works.

Reteach [L2]

Have students write several sentences that briefly explain what the greenhouse effect is.

Answers

Figure 15 *Many students will think that the concentration of carbon dioxide will continue to increase. Others, however, may think that government restrictions and people's voluntary lifestyle changes will reduce carbon dioxide emissions, eventually making the atmospheric concentration of carbon dioxide level off and possibly decrease.*

---

5. Global climate change would probably produce an increase in cloud cover due to the higher moisture content of the air. Clouds would also produce opposite effects: they could diminish the amount of solar energy available to heat the atmosphere, and they could absorb and emit radiation that would otherwise be lost from the troposphere.

6. It could harm or kill ocean organisms; cause both land and water habitats to shift or be destroyed; increase the spread of diseases; and increase drought, heat waves, and flooding. Global climate change might have positive effects for some organisms, including humans. For example, warming could increase organisms' range and open up land for farming in areas where the climate was previously too cool.

7. Answers will vary but should explain how burning fossil fuels is thought to be increasing global temperatures and why reducing the usage of fossil fuels will slow this increase.

Assessment Answers

1. Changes in land and oceans due to plate tectonics can cause long-term climate change. Changes in ocean circulation can result in short-term fluctuations. Changes in Earth's orbit and axis can cause intermediate-term climate change. Short-term fluctuations in solar activity can change global climates. Emissions from erupting volcanoes can reflect more solar radiation, lowering temperatures.

2. a natural warming of Earth's lower atmosphere and its surface caused by complex reactions between gases and particles in the air

3. an increase in global temperatures, due to increased levels of greenhouse gases and the climate changes that have resulted from the increase in temperature

4. short-term and long-term changes in temperature and precipitation patterns; a rise in sea level; an increase in shoreline erosion

How Earth Works

Objectives

In this feature, students will
- describe where the world's coniferous forests are located.
- recognize the features that enable conifers to withstand long, cold winters.
- identify the behaviors and adaptations that enable animals to survive in northern coniferous forests.

Build Vocabulary   L2

Word Origins Point out to students that *coniferous* sounds very much like another scientific term, *carnivorous*. Have them contrast the origins of these words. (*Coniferous comes from Latin and Greek roots that mean "cone-bearing." Carnivorous comes from the Latin words* caro, *which means "flesh," and* vorare, *which means "to swallow up."*) Encourage students to use both words correctly in sentences.

2 INSTRUCT

Bellringer   L2

Have students list features that make coniferous trees different from most other trees. *(Lists might include pointy leaves or needles, pine cones, and staying green all year.)* Have students list types of trees found in their region. **Ask:** Are the trees you listed conifers or deciduous trees? How do you know?
Verbal, Logical

Coniferous Forests

The world's largest forests extend across the far north, where winters can last for eight months. These dense **coniferous forests** consist mainly of spruces, pines, and other trees that carry their seeds in cones. They are particularly suited for coping with cold conditions. Animals in northern forests find plentiful food during the long days of summer, but the season is brief and cold weather soon returns. To survive the harsh winter, many animals migrate south, while others hibernate.

Distribution of northern coniferous forests

FORESTS AND LAKES
Conifer trees are well adapted for their harsh environment. Their trunks are covered with thick bark that helps them survive forest fires, a common problem during the long days of the brief, fairly dry growing season. The narrow, pointed shape of conifer trees helps them shed snow in winter and prevents their branches from breaking. Many conifers contain sap that is specially adapted to avoid freezing in the winter.▼

White spruce

◄**CONIFER LEAVES**
Most conifers have small, evergreen leaves called needles that are tough enough to withstand the coldest winters. A narrow shape helps the leaves to cope with strong winds and prevents water loss in the cool, dry Arctic air.

Waterlogged soil beneath trees is acidic and infertile.

Bobcat

◄**PREDATORS**
Mammals are relatively scarce in northern forests, so the **predators** that feed upon other animals sometimes have to cover vast distances to find food. Bobcats may roam many kilometers searching for small prey. Wolves hunt in packs for deer and other large mammals.

604 Chapter 21

Differentiated Instruction

GIFTED Mammals are not the only animals that hibernate in winter. Many fishes, amphibians, and reptiles are also hibernators. Divide students into groups and have each find out how one species of animal hibernates. Have each group compare that species' hibernation behavior to mammal hibernation.

1. A horntail lays eggs deep in a tree trunk.

2. Young larvae bore away from the drill-hole.

3. Each larva matures inside a chamber near the bark of the tree.

◄ **EATING WOOD**
Several insects of northern forests feed on wood. The horntail, or giant wood wasp, lays eggs by drilling deep beneath tree bark with a long egg-laying tube. Eggs hatch into larvae, which mature inside the tree while feeding on the wood.

Red crossbill

◄ **SEED EATERS**
Some birds rely on conifer seeds for food. Crossbill finches have unique bills that are crossed at the tips. This helps them remove seeds from cones. Clark's nutcracker, a member of the crow family, hides 20,000 or more seeds each fall. It is able to remember the locations of many of these seeds for up to nine months.

Spruce cone

Cold lake water contains few nutrients but is often rich in oxygen.

Caribou

ADAPTED FOR TRAVEL ►
To help them walk across thick layers of snow without sinking, caribou and elk have hooves with broadly splayed toes that help to distribute their weight. Lynx and snowshoe hares have similar adaptations.

Caribou hooves act as snowshoes.

COPING WITH COLD
To survive extreme winter temperatures, ground squirrels, woodchucks, and other small mammals hibernate. During the fall, they build up a store of fat in their bodies that will last until spring. They then go into **hibernation,** or deep sleep, which slows their bodily functions to a minimum.▼

Woodchuck

Assessment

1. Key Terms Define **(a)** coniferous forest, **(b)** predator, **(c)** hibernation.

2. Climates Describe the climatic conditions that are generally found in northern coniferous forests.

3. Ecosystems How do trees serve as a food source for birds and insects?

4. Ecosystems How are mammals of northern coniferous forests well suited for survival in their natural environment?

5. Critical Thinking Form a Hypothesis Deforestation has not reduced northern coniferous forests to the same degree that it has reduced mid-latitude deciduous forests. Why do you think that northern coniferous forests have fared better than deciduous forests to the south?

605

Build Science Skills   L2

Organize Data Have students read the introductory paragraph. **Ask:** What is the feature that all conifers share? *(They carry their seeds in cones.)* Then make a list on the board of all the conifers students can name. *(Possible answers: spruce, pine, juniper, cedar, sequoia, redwood, fir, and cypress)* **Logical**

❸ ASSESS

Evaluate Understanding   L2

Have students construct a three-column chart about the types of animals that live in coniferous forests. The columns should be labeled: "Type of Animal," "Feature or Habit," and "How It Promotes Survival." Have students complete the chart using information from the feature. Ask them to write a paragraph describing the plant and animal life in a coniferous forest.

Reteach   L1

Have students collect or draw the needles of different kinds of conifers. Then have them write a paragraph that explains how the leaves are well adapted for cold climates. Display collections and paragraphs in the classroom.

Assessment Answers

1. (a) large, dense forests composed mainly of trees that carry their seeds in cones; **(b)** animals that feed on other animals; **(c)** a state in which an animal's body functions slow to a minimum for a season

2. Winters are long and cold; summers are brief.

3. Some insects eat wood. Some birds eat conifer seeds.

4. Some mammals, such as elk, have splayed toes that help them walk on snow. Other mammals build up stores of fat during the fall that will last until spring. In winter some mammals hibernate.

5. Sample answer: Fewer people have wanted to settle in cold, northern areas. The land is not suited to farming, so humans have not cut these forests to clear land.

HUMAN IMPACT ON CLIMATE AND WEATHER L2

Objective
After completing this activity, students will be able to understand how human activity changes Earth's climates.

Skills Calculate, Measure, Interpret Tables, Analyze Data

Class Time 30 minutes

Teaching Tip Review the tables and graphs in this lab. Make sure students understand how to interpret the information properly. **Ask:** What units are used for Table 1? *(millions of metric tons/year)* What information does Table 2 provide? *(Average Climatic Changes Produced by Cities)* What effect do these data represent? *(the urban heat island effect)* What data does Figure A provide? *(emissions of three pollutants each year)* What data does Figure B provide? *(carbon dioxide concentration per year)*

Expected Outcome Students will use data to understand some of the ways that human activities change the atmosphere and Earth's climates.

Human Impact on Climate and Weather

Problem How do we know that human activity is changing Earth's climates?

Materials paper, pen or pencil

Skills Calculate, Measure, Interpret Tables, Analyze Data

Connect to the Big idea Scientists are now closely monitoring how daily human activity is changing microclimates. There is concern that changing microclimates can have an effect on global climates. In this investigation, you will explore some of the ways that human activities are changing the atmosphere.

Procedure

1. **Table 1** lists many of the types, sources, and amounts of primary pollutants. Use this table to answer Questions 1, 2, 3, and 4 under Analyze and Conclude.

2. Look at **Figure A.** The pollutants listed are linked to a wide variety of negative health effects such as eye irritation, heart damage, and lung damage. The pollutants shown are also linked to reduced visibility, reduced crop yields, and damage to ecosystems. Study the figure and answer Questions 5, 6, and 7.

3. Look at **Figure B.** Scientists have noted the increasing levels of carbon dioxide in the atmosphere. Research continues to determine whether this increase is affecting global climates. Use Figure B to answer Question 8.

4. Look at **Table 2.** This table presents data on the effects of large cities on their surrounding microclimates. Temperatures in cities can be higher than the surrounding countryside. Meteorologists call this effect "the urban heat island." Study the data in the table and answer Questions 9, 10, and 11.

Analyze and Conclude

1. **Analyze Data** What is the leading source (by weight) of primary pollutants? How many metric tons of this pollutant are added to the atmosphere each year?

2. **Analyze Data** Which of the following is the most abundant primary pollutant?
   a. carbon monoxide
   b. sulfur oxides

3. **Calculate** Your answer for Question 2 is what percentage of all primary pollutants?
   a. 25%   **b.** 50%   **c.** 75%

4. **Calculate** What is the approximate total weight (in million metric tons) of all primary pollutants added to the atmosphere?

Table 1 Estimated Nationwide Emissions (millions of metric tons/year)						
Source	**Carbon Monoxide**	**Partic-ulates**	**Sulfur Oxides**	**Volatile Organics**	**Nitrogen Oxides**	**Total**
Transportation	43.5	1.6	1.0	5.1	7.3	58.5
Stationary Source Fuel Combustion	4.7	1.9	16.6	0.7	10.6	34.5
Industrial Processes	4.7	2.6	3.2	7.9	0.6	19.0
Solid Waste Disposal	2.1	0.3	0.0	0.7	0.1	3.2
Miscellaneous	7.2	1.2	0.0	2.8	0.2	11.4
Total	62.2	7.6	20.8	17.2	18.8	126.6

Source: U.S. Environmental Protection Agency

606 Chapter 21

FIGURE A

FIGURE B

5. **Analyze Data** Describe the trend you see in the data for atmospheric pollutants prior to 1970.

6. **Analyze Data** Describe the trend you see in the data for atmospheric pollutants since 1970.

7. **Infer** Suggest a reason for the changing trend.

8. **Calculate** What has been the approximate percentage increase in atmospheric carbon dioxide near Mauna Loa since 1958?

9. **Analyze Data** Compared to rural areas, which factors are increased by urbanization? Which factors are decreased?

10. **Analyze Data** Of all of the factors shown, which shows the greatest increase due to urbanization?

11. **Relate Cause and Effect** Suggest a possible reason for each of the following effects on the weather that is influenced by a city.
    a. increased frequency of thunderstorms
    b. lower wind speed
    c. increased precipitation

GO FURTHER Use the Internet to search for climate data for your region. What trends do you see in the data since 1970? Suggest a hypothesis that could account for any changes you discover.

Table 2 Average Climatic Changes Produced by Cities

Element	Comparison with Rural Areas
Particulate matter	10 times more
Temperature	
Annual mean	0.5–1.5°C higher
Winter	1–2°C higher
Solar radiation	15–30% less
Ultraviolet, winter	30% less
Ultraviolet, summer	5% less
Precipitation	5–15% more
Thunderstorm frequency	16% more
Winter	5% more
Summer	29% more
Relative humidity	6% lower
Winter	2% lower
Summer	8% lower
Cloudiness (frequency)	5–10% more
Fog (frequency)	60% more
Winter	100% more
Summer	30% more
Wind speed	25% lower
Calms	5–20% more

Source: After Landsberg, Changnon, and others.

Analyze and Conclude

1. transportation; 58.5 million metric tons
2. a
3. b
4. 126.6 million metric tons
5. Emissions of atmospheric pollutants were generally on the rise prior to 1970.
6. Atmospheric pollutant emissions have generally decreased since 1970.
7. Industrialization and increased transportation using fossil fuels increased atmospheric pollutant concentrations until 1970, when government regulations took effect and began lowering these concentrations.
8. net change: 370 ppm − 315 ppm = 55 ppm; 55 ppm ÷ 370 ppm = approximately 15 percent increase in atmospheric carbon dioxide
9. Increased: particulate matter, temperature, precipitation, thunderstorm frequency, cloudiness, fog, calms. Decreased: solar radiation, relative humidity, wind speed
10. fog in winter
11. a. Urban heating reduces the stability of the atmosphere.
    b. Buildings impede the flow of air.
    c. Urban heating reduces the stability of the atmosphere; there are more condensation nuclei from industrial pollution; buildings impede the movement of weather systems causing rain producing weather to linger.

GO FURTHER

Accept all reasonable answers.
Logical

Climate **607**

Study Tip

Study With a Partner
Once in a while, study with a partner. Quiz each other, compare notes from class lectures, and go over homework answers. Also, discuss concepts that you need help understanding.

Think Visually

1. Colder climate
2. High elevation/mountains
3. Global climate change
4. Rise in sea level
5. Short-term lower temperatures
6. More moderate climate than if the lake were not present

21st Century Learning

Critical Thinking and Systems Thinking

How do forests affect climate?
Have students research the role of forests in maintaining Earth's energy balance, the water cycle, and the carbon cycle. Ask students to find out how cutting down trees can impact the climate by interfering with these natural processes. Students should produce an illustration that summarizes their research.

Homework Guide

Lesson	Questions
1	1, 11–13, 21, 22
2	2, 3, 8–10, 14–16, 23–29
3	4–7, 17–20, 30–32

Big idea ▶ Weather and Climate

21.1 Factors That Affect Climate

As latitude increases, the average intensity of solar energy received at Earth's surface decreases.

In general, the higher the elevation is, the colder the climate.

Topographic features such as mountains influence the amount of precipitation that falls over an area.

Large bodies of water such as lakes and oceans have an important effect on the temperature of an area because the temperature of the water body influences the temperature of the air above it.

Global winds affect climate because they distribute heat and moisture around Earth.

Vegetation can affect both temperature and the precipitation patterns in an area.

climate (588)   temperate zone (589)
tropical zone (589)   polar zone (589)

21.2 World Climates

The Köppen climate classification system uses mean monthly and annual values of temperature and precipitation to classify climates.

Humid tropical climates have no winters. Every month has a mean temperature above 18°C, and precipitation can exceed 200 cm per year.

Humid mid-latitude climates with mild winters have an average temperature in the coldest month that is below 18°C but above −3°C. In areas with severe winters, the average temperature in the coldest month is below −3°C.

A dry climate is one in which the yearly precipitation is not as great as the potential loss of water by evaporation and transpiration.

Polar climates have a mean temperature in the warmest month that is below 10°C.

Highland climates are generally cooler and wetter than nearby areas at lower elevations.

Köppen climate classification system (592)

21.3 Climate Changes

Geographic changes in Earth's land and oceans due to plate tectonics cause changes in climate over very long time scales.

Changes in the shape of Earth's orbit and the tilt of Earth's axis affect global climates over intermediate time periods.

Changes in ocean circulation caused by El Niño can result in short-term climate fluctuations.

Over relatively short time scales, fluctuations in the amount of solar radiation can change global climates.

Aerosols (volcanic ash, dust, and sulfur-based aerosols) in the air can cause a short-term cooling of the lower atmosphere.

The greenhouse effect is a natural warming of Earth's lower atmosphere and Earth's surface.

As a result of increases in carbon dioxide levels, as well as other greenhouse gases, global temperatures have increased.

global climate change (602)

Think Visually

The table below shows some causes and effects related to climate. Copy the table onto a sheet of paper and complete the table.

Some Factors That Influence Climate	
Causes	**Effects**
1. Increase in latitude	1. ___?___
2. ___?___	2. Highland climate
3. Increase in greenhouse gases	3. ___?___
4. ___?___	4. More coastal erosion
5. Large volcanic eruption	5. ___?___
6. Nearby lake	6. ___?___

Assessment Answers

Review Content

1. c	**2.** d	**3.** a
4. b	**5.** c	**6.** a
7. a		

Understand Concepts

8. arid or desert
9. semiarid or steppe, marine west coast, humid subtropical, tropical wet and dry
10. the effect of warm air blowing off the ocean
11. Powered by the sun, the climate system is a complex exchange of energy and moisture among Earth's atmosphere, biosphere, hydrosphere, and lithosphere.

21 Assessment

Review Content

Choose the letter that best answers the question or completes the statement.

1. Which of the following is true?
   a. Climates at high latitudes are very warm.
   b. A nearby lake causes a climate to be colder.
   c. Vegetation can increase the amount of precipitation that falls over an area.
   d. Places at lower elevations generally have lower temperatures.

2. Humid tropical climates typically experience
   a. severe winters.   c. low humidity.
   b. dry summers.   d. warm temperatures.

3. In a dry climate, yearly precipitation is
   a. less than the potential rate of evaporation.
   b. greater than the rate of evaporation.
   c. greater in a desert than a steppe.
   d. less than that in a polar climate.

4. The greenhouse effect is best described as
   a. solely an increase in Earth's surface temperature.
   b. a natural warming effect of the atmosphere.
   c. a result of global warming.
   d. any short-term change in climate.

5. Recent global climate change appears to be the result of
   a. changes in global wind patterns.
   b. a decrease in the greenhouse effect.
   c. increases in greenhouse gases in the air.
   d. changes in Earth's revolution around the sun.

6. Melting ice caps can result in which of the following?
   a. a rise in sea level
   b. a fall in sea level
   c. colder temperatures
   d. less precipitation

7. An increase in ocean temperatures can cause
   a. melting of sea ice.
   b. most forms of ocean life to flourish.
   c. a decrease in sea level.
   d. global wind patterns to stabilize.

Understand Concepts

Use this map to answer Questions 8–10.

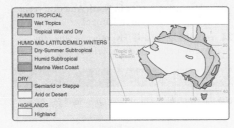

8. Describe the dominant climate in Australia.

9. Identify the type of climate found on the other parts of the continent.

10. What causes much of the east-southeastern part of the continent to experience warm, humid, and marine west coast climates?

11. What powers Earth's climate system, and which of Earth's spheres are involved in this system?

12. Name the three major climate zones, and explain why their overall temperatures differ.

13. Explain how two places at the same latitude can have different climates.

14. What climate data are needed in order to classify a climate using the Köppen climate classification system?

15. Describe the characteristics of a wet tropical climate.

16. Describe the characteristics of a humid continental climate. Give one example of a place with such a climate.

17. Explain the greenhouse effect caused by Earth's atmosphere.

18. How have humans contributed to the increase in the levels of carbon dioxide in the atmosphere?

19. What is global warming?

20. How might global climate change affect global precipitation?

---

15. Wet tropical climates have high temperatures and year-round precipitation.

16. Areas with humid continental climates lie between approximately 40° and 50° north latitude. Both winter and summer temperatures in such climates are relatively severe and precipitation is generally greater in summer than in winter. One example is Chicago, Illinois.

17. The greenhouse effect is a natural warming of Earth's lower atmosphere and its surface. This effect is caused by complex interactions between gases and solar radiation. Certain gases, including carbon dioxide and water vapor, absorb solar energy and are heated. As the gases cool, they send some of the energy back into space. Some of the energy radiates back toward Earth and warms it.

18. Burning fossil fuels and clearing forests have contributed to increased levels in carbon dioxide in the air.

19. Global warming is an increase in Earth's average surface temperature over time, which many scientists think is caused by the increase of greenhouse gases in the atmosphere.

20. Warmer surface temperatures will increase evaporation rates, which will put more water vapor into the atmosphere. With increased water vapor, there will probably be increased precipitation.

---

12. The three major zones are the tropical zone, the temperate zones, and the polar regions. They differ in the intensity at which sunlight strikes the surface in the region. In the tropics, the sun's rays strike at almost 90° angles, causing this region to be warm all year round. In the temperature zones, the sun's energy strikes Earth at a smaller angle. This causes solar energy to be spread out over a larger area, making these regions have moderate yearly temperatures. In the polar regions, solar energy strikes at a more acute angle, causing the light and heat to spread out over even a larger area. Therefore, the polar regions experience very low temperatures year-round.

13. Latitude is only one factor that affects a climate. The places may be at different elevations and may have different topographies and different kinds and amounts of vegetative cover. Proximity to a body of water can also influence climate.

14. Mean monthly and annual values of temperature and precipitation are used to classify climates in the Köppen scheme.

ASSESSMENT

Think Critically

21. Yes, if the region is at a high enough elevation, it can be cold enough to experience snow.

22. Because it is cooler, air at higher elevations generally contains less moisture than air at lower elevations. Thus, regions at higher elevations often experience less precipitation than areas at lower elevations.

23. Marine west coast climates are dominated by the onshore flow of oceanic air. Only a narrow region of such climates exists in North America because mountains block the oceanic air and prevent it from flowing over land. In western Europe, there are no mountainous regions to block this flow of air. Thus, such climates dominate this part of Europe.

24. Most fogs form when enough water vapor is added to air to bring about saturation. Desert regions lack enough water to produce fog.

Analyze Data

25. The highest monthly temperature of 26°C occurred in July.

26. The lowest monthly temperature of 0°C occurred in January.

27. The range is 0°C to 26°C , or 26°C.

28. The wettest season of the year in St. Louis is late winter or early spring.

29. The climate is humid subtropical.

Concepts in Action

30. Cities are warmer than nearby undeveloped areas because sidewalks, buildings, streets, and roads radiate heat, causing urban temperatures to be higher than areas with more vegetation or nearby bodies of water.

31. Answers will vary, but should include alternatives to burning fossil fuels and a reduction in the clearing of forests and other vegetated areas.

32. Answers will vary, but students' stories should include at least three effects on temperature and precipitation patterns. Depending on your location, the effects on sea levels might also be included.

Think Critically

21. Synthesize Can a region at low latitudes have snow? Explain.

22. Apply Concepts How does elevation affect the amount of precipitation that falls over an area?

23. Infer Why do marine west coast climates exist only as narrow strips in North America, yet are widespread in western Europe?

24. Form a Hypothesis Hypothesize why rain shadow deserts rarely experience fog.

Analyze Data

Use the graph below to answer Questions 25–29.

25. Interpret Graphs What is the highest average monthly temperature, and during which month does it occur?

26. Interpret Graphs What is the lowest monthly temperature, and during which month does it occur?

27. Calculate What is the average annual temperature range for St. Louis?

28. Draw Conclusions What is the wettest season of the year in St. Louis?

29. Classify Classify the climate of St. Louis using the Köppen climate classification system.

Concepts in Action

30. Synthesize Cities are referred to as urban heat islands. Use what you know about factors that affect climate to explain this statement.

31. Apply Concepts What do you think can be done to reduce the steady increase in global carbon dioxide levels?

32. Writing in Science Suppose you're a writer for the school newspaper. You are doing a story on how global climate change might affect your area. Write an article that explains at least three effects that an increase in Earth's surface temperature might have on the climate of your area.

Performance-Based Assessment

Apply Concepts Make flyers with catchy slogans to suggest ways to reduce your community's use of fossil fuels. Get permission to post the flyers in grocery stores, community halls, shopping malls, and other common areas.

Performance-Based Assessment

Encourage students to be creative in generating their slogans. Assist them with posting the flyers, if necessary.

Standardized Test Prep

Use the graphs to answer the questions on this page. Choose the letter that best answers the question.

Antarctic Temperature over 160,000 years in degrees Fahrenheit

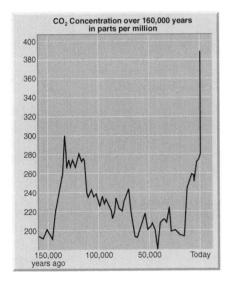

CO_2 Concentration over 160,000 years in parts per million

1 Antarctica's temperatures were similar to the temperatures there today—
   A about 150,000 years ago
   B about 130,000 years ago
   C about 50,000 years ago
   D about 25,000 years ago

2 Which part of the temperature graph shows the global warming trend discussed in the chapter?
   F the time from about 170,000 to 140,000 years ago
   G the time from about 120,000 to 100,000 years ago
   H the time from about 70,000 to 60,000 years ago
   J the time from about 100 years ago to the present

3 When during the past 160,000 years were carbon dioxide concentrations the highest?
   A about 135,000 years ago
   B about 120,000 years ago
   C about 40,000 years ago
   D about 1000 years ago

4 What were the carbon dioxide levels in the atmosphere during Antarctica's coldest period in the past 160,000 years?
   F between about 190 and 200 ppm
   G between about 220 and 240 ppm
   H between about 240 and 260 ppm
   J between about 260 and 280 ppm

If You Have Trouble With . . .				
Question	1	2	3	4
See Lesson	21.3	21.3	21.1	21.1

22 Origin of Modern Astronomy Planning Guide

Lesson Objectives		Activities
22.1 Early Astronomy, pp. 614–621 22.1 **Describe** the contributions of ancient Greeks to astronomy. 22.2 **Compare and contrast** the geocentric and heliocentric models of the solar system. 22.3 **Explain** the contributions to astronomy of Copernicus, Brahe, Kepler, Galileo, and Newton.		TE **T**eacher Demo: Visualizing Planetary Orbits, p. 618 L2 TE **T**eacher Demo: A Simple Mirror Telescope, p. 620 L2
22.2 The Earth-Moon-Sun System, pp. 622–629 22.4 **Describe** the movements of Earth known as rotation, revolution, and precession. 22.5 **Explain** how the moon goes through phases. 22.6 **Explain** how eclipses occur.		TE **T**eacher Demo: Observing Precession, p. 625 L2
22.3 Earth's Moon, pp. 630–634 22.7 **Describe** how the physical features of the lunar surface were created. 22.8 **Explain** the history of the moon.		TE Build Science Skills, p. 632 L2
Chapter Features and Labs		
Try It How Do Impact Craters Form? p. 613		LM Measuring the Angle of the Sun at Noon L2
Earth & Its Resources Foucault's Pendulum, p. 635		
Exploration Lab Modeling Synodic and Sidereal Months, pp. 636–637		

Ability Levels		Components			
L1 For students who need additional help		SE	Student Edition	LP	Lesson Plans
L2 For all students		TE	Teacher's Edition	AA	Active Art
L3 For students who need to be challenged		LM	Laboratory Manual	PD	Planet Diary
		CT	Chapter Tests	GEODe	Geode CD-ROM
		GRSW	Guided Reading & Study Workbook	eText	
		CTB	Computer Test Bank		

Resources	Lesson Assessment
GRSW Lesson 22.1 **LP** Lesson Planning 22.1 **PD** Links on astronomy	**SE** Lesson 22.1 Assessment, p. 621 **eText** Lesson 22.1
GRSW Lesson 22.2 **LP** Lesson Planning 22.2 **AA** Phases of the Moon Activity	**SE** Lesson 22.2 Assessment, p. 629 **eText** Lesson 22.2
GRSW Lesson 22.3 **LP** Lesson Planning 22.3 **GEODe** Astronomy: Earth's Moon	**SE** Lesson 22.3 Assessment, p. 634 **eText** Lesson 22.3

Materials for Activities and Labs

Quantities for each group

STUDENT EDITION

Try It, p. 613
plastic container, sand, wooden ruler, 3 different-sized balls, meter stick

Exploration Lab, pp. 636–637
pencil, paper, lamp, basketball, softball

TEACHER'S EDITION
Teacher Demo, p. 618
several sheets of paper, heavy cardboard, 2 pushpins, metric ruler, string, pencils

Teacher Demo, p. 620
lightbulb in a lamp base, magnifying lens, mirror with concave surface (magnifying mirror with 2 sides—used for makeup and shaving)

Teacher Demo, p. 625
toy top

Build Science Skills, p. 632
foam poster board, soft modeling clay, toothpicks, narrow paper strips, tape, marker (or pencil or pen)

Assessment

CHAPTER ASSESSMENT
SE Assessment, pp. 639–640
CT Chapter 22 Test
CTB Chapter 22
eText Chapter 22

21st Century Learning

Information and Media Literacy: What is the Origin of the Moon? TE p. 638

Common Themes

Michael Wysession
Washington University

Satellites, moons, planets, and stars travel along predictable paths that are determined by the mass of the objects and the laws of gravity.

Space and Time Many early people believed in a geocentric model of the universe, where all objects revolved around Earth. The Ptolemaic system adapted the geocentric model to include explanations of the apparent retrograde motions of planets. Copernicus showed that the heliocentric model, with Earth revolving around the sun, was simpler. Planets, moons, and satellites follow elliptical orbits when they revolve around another body, as shown by Kepler.

Forces and Motion Earth rotates once per day. This day is 24 hours with respect to the sun, but 23 hours and 56 minutes with respect to the stars. Earth revolves around the sun once every 365.25 days, or one year. The seasons are a result of the tilt of Earth's axis of rotation, which is 23.5° toward the solar ecliptic. The direction that Earth's axis points to changes, or precesses, over a period of 26,000 years. The phases of the moon are a result of the relative positions of the sun, moon, and Earth. Solar and lunar eclipses occur when these three bodies are lined up.

Matter and Energy The Apollo missions, during which astronauts visited the moon, revealed a great deal about our nearest neighbor. The moon most likely formed from the ejected debris of an enormous impact of a Mars-sized planetesimal with Earth early in our planet's history. Because the moon has so little mass, it lacks an atmosphere, hydrosphere, or biosphere, and so its structure and surface are very different from Earth's.

EARTH SCIENCE REFRESHER

General Relativity and Motions in Space

As with many things in science, simple explanations can give you 99 percent of the story, but the full picture is somewhat more complicated. This certainly holds true for gravity and the motions of objects in space. Most all orbital motions can be nicely explained by the simple laws discovered by Kepler and Newton. However, some could not, and the most famous was the precession of the orbit of Mercury. It took Einstein and his theory of general relativity to explain these motions.

The problem with Mercury had to do with the precession, or rotational shift of its elliptical orbit. Newton's laws of gravity predicted a certain continual shift in the orbit, but not enough. Einstein's theory of general relativity exactly predicted this orbital precession, which was considered to be proof of his theory.

Einstein predicted that all mass actually distorts the fabric of space and time. For larger masses, the effect is more noticeable. This has some interesting implications, the most important of which for astronomy is that light does not always go in a straight line. For example, light will be bent around a massive object, like a galaxy. Einstein would say that the light is not actually bent, but that space itself is warped. The result, however, is that the galaxy acts like a refracting lens, and light from the distant object is focused together and therefore more visible. This phenomenon, called a gravitational lens, allows astronomers to see very distant objects that would otherwise be too faint to see.

Some students may think that modern astronomy was developed recently by a small number of scientists. The body of astronomical knowledge is an accumulation of work by many scientists over many centuries of time. Modern astronomers study the works of earlier scientists and build on the foundation of knowledge that they have laid. In fact, Sir Isaac Newton has been quoted as saying, "If I have seen further, it is by standing on the shoulders of giants." For a strategy that helps to overcome this misconception, see **Address Misconceptions** on **TE p. 617.**

Another interesting result of general relativity is that time slows down the closer you are to a large object. A clock running at the bottom of a tower, closer to Earth, actually runs slower than a clock at the top of a tower. All clocks on Earth run slower when Earth is closest to the sun, at around January 5, and run faster in August, even though the accumulated difference is only a fraction of a second. These gravitational time effects also need to be taken into account with global positioning systems (GPS), which rely upon time signals sent through satellites. So, this effect won't make you late to any appointments, and your wristwatch will do for most applications. But if you want to know the time exactly, or use GPS to know your location exactly, you need to use general relativity.

BUILD READING LITERACY
Think Aloud

Verbalize Thought Processes While Reading

Strategy Model cognitive and metacognitive processes that students can use to build meaning, self-correct, and monitor their own comprehension. Choose part of a Lesson from Chapter 22, such as Ancient Greeks on pp. 614–616, and preview it. As you do so, imagine that you are reading these paragraphs for the first time, just as your students will be. Make a copy of the section, and on it write comments and questions that you can use as "think-aloud" models.

Example

1. Read several paragraphs aloud and have your students follow along silently. Have them listen to how you pause to check your own comprehension and to determine meaning at trouble spots. You might model some of the following strategies aloud as you read:

• Make a prediction, then revise or verify it.

• Describe mental pictures as they form.

• Connect new information with prior knowledge or related ideas; share an analogy.

• Verbalize confusing points and work out steps to clarify their meanings; adjust your reading pace if needed.

2. Select a logical stopping point. Then, have students read the next paragraph silently and apply similar strategies internally. Afterward, ask students to share the strategies they used. Repeat this step several times.

3. Have students work in pairs, taking turns applying think-aloud strategies to the next several paragraphs.

See TE p. 619 for a script on how to use this strategy with students. For additional strategies, see TE pp. 624 and 631.

ASSESS PRIOR KNOWLEDGE

Use the Chapter Pretest below to assess students' prior knowledge. As needed, review these concepts.

Review Science Concepts

Lesson 22.1 Review the relationships between the orbits of the planets in our solar system to be sure that students fully understand the misconceptions of early astronomers.

Lesson 22.2 Have students review the concept of rotational motion.

Lesson 22.3 A knowledge of the Apollo moon missions will give students a greater appreciation and understanding of their study of the moon.

Use Visuals

Lunar Surface This photograph of the lunar surface shows amazing details. The central peak shown here is in the middle of Crater Tycho. Tycho is 85 km in diameter (about 52 miles) and the central peak complex shown in the photogtraph is 15 km wide and the tallest peak is 2 km tall. Some students may not have thought about sunrise occurring on the moon, so this photo provides a great opportunity for a class discussion about what sunrise on the moon would look like and how long it would take.

22 Origin of Modern Astronomy

Big idea **Earth and the Universe**

Q: What is the origin of the Moon?

612

Chapter Pretest

1. True or False: Early Greek astronomers (600 B.C.–A.D. 150) used telescopes to observe the stars. *(False)*

2. What lies at the center of our solar system? *(a)*
   a. the sun   **b.** Mars
   c. Earth   **d.** the moon

3. What is rotation? *(the turning, or spinning, of a body on its axis)*

4. What is the approximate time that it takes Earth to rotate on its axis? *(a)*
   a. 24 hours   **b.** 12 hours
   c. 30 days   **d.** 365 days

5. What was the most important accomplishment of the Apollo moon missions? *(landing on the moon and collecting data and samples from the moon's surface)*

6. Approximately how long does it take for the moon to go through all of its phases? *(c)*
   a. 24 hours   **b.** 12 hours
   c. 30 days   **d.** 365 days

7. How would geometry and trigonometry have been useful to early astronomers? *(These would have provided a method of approximating sizes and distances.)*

INSIDE:

NASA's Lunar Reconnaissance Orbiter spacecraft captured this view of the central peak in the lunar crater named Tycho. The peak is 2 km tall! Astronomers think a central peak forms in a crater when a large meteoroid or asteroid strikes the surface. The long shadows in the photograph are the result of sunrise occurring on the moon.

INQUIRY
TRY IT!

HOW DO IMPACT CRATERS FORM?

Procedure

1. Fill a large, plastic container with sand to a depth of about 3 cm. Flatten the surface of the sand with a wooden ruler.
2. Design a data table to record your measurements.
3. One at a time, drop each of the different-sized balls from heights of 0.5 m, 1 m, and 2 m into the container. Make sure to smooth the surface of the sand between each drop.
4. Measure the diameter and height of the crater produced each time. Record your measurements in your data table.

Think About It

1. **Make Graphs** Identify your dependent and independent variables. Then plot your data on a line graph.
2. **Control Variables** Which of the variables is directly related to the velocity of the falling objects?
3. **Draw Conclusions** Examine your data closely. What can you conclude about the general relationships between crater size and the size, mass, and velocity of the object that produced the crater?

613

ENGAGE/EXPLORE

INQUIRY
TRY IT!

HOW DO IMPACT CRATERS FORM?　L2

Purpose In this activity, students will observe the relationship between crater size and the size, mass, and velocity of the object that produced the crater.

Skills Observe, Measure, Use Tables and Graphs, Draw Conclusions

Prep Time 5 minutes

Materials plastic container, sand, wooden ruler, 3 different-sized balls, meter stick

Advance Prep Sand and large plastic containers can be purchased inexpensively from hardware stores or home improvement centers.

Class Time 10 minutes

Safety Students should wear safety goggles.

Teaching Tip The balls should vary in mass so that students will see the mass and crater depth relationship.

Expected Outcome If two or more balls are dropped from the same height, the ball with the greater mass will produce a deeper crater. A ball dropped from a greater height will have greater velocity upon impact and will produce a deeper crater.

Think About It
1. Dependent variable: size of ball; independent variable: height from which ball is dropped
2. the height from which the ball is dropped
3. Mass and velocity have the greatest influence on the size and depth of the craters.

1 FOCUS

Lesson Objectives

22.1 Describe the contributions of ancient Greeks to astronomy.

22.2 Compare and contrast the geocentric and heliocentric models of the solar system.

22.3 Explain the contributions to astronomy of Copernicus, Brahe, Kepler, Galileo, and Newton.

Build Vocabulary `L2`

Word Origins Explain to students that the prefix *geo-* is a Greek prefix that means "Earth." *Centric* is from the Greek word *kentrikos,* which means "located in the center." So the word *geocentric* means "having Earth as the center." *Helio-* is a Greek prefix that means "sun." So the word *heliocentric* means "having the sun as the center."

Reading Strategy `L2`

a. orbits Earth
b. Aristotle, Ptolemy
c. orbits sun
d. center of universe
e. Aristarchus, Copernicus

2 INSTRUCT

Integrate Social Studies `L2`

Aristotle was an ancient Greek philosopher and scientist who had a broad range of capabilities. He worked in many areas including physics, chemistry, biology, zoology, botany, psychology, political theory, logic, metaphysics, and philosophy. Have students research the life and works of Aristotle. Encourage students to make an oral presentation to the class.
Verbal

22.1 Early Astronomy

Key Questions

 How does the geocentric model of the solar system differ from the heliocentric model?

 What were the accomplishments of early astronomers?

Vocabulary

- astronomy • geocentric
- orbit • heliocentric
- retrograde motion • ellipse
- astronomical unit (AU)

Reading Strategy

Compare and Contrast Copy the table below. As you read about the geocentric and heliocentric models of the solar system, fill in the table.

	Location of Earth	Location of Sun	Supporters of Model
Geocentric Model	center of universe	a. ?	b. ?
Heliocentric Model	c. ?	d. ?	e. ?

EARTH IS ONE of the planets and many smaller bodies that orbit the sun. The sun is part of a much larger family of perhaps 400 billion stars that make up our galaxy, the Milky Way. There are billions of galaxies in the universe. A few hundred years ago scientists thought that Earth was the center of the universe. In this chapter, you will explore some events that changed the view of Earth's place in space. You will also examine Earth's moon.

Ancient Greeks

Astronomy is the science that studies the universe. It deals with the properties of objects in space and the laws under which the universe operates. The "Golden Age" of early astronomy (600 B.C.–A.D. 150) was centered in Greece. The early Greeks used philosophical arguments to explain natural events. However, they also relied on observations. These early astronomers used instruments such as the astrolabe in **Figure 1** to find the positions of the sun and stars. The Greeks developed the basics of geometry and trigonometry, which was used to measure the sizes and distances of the sun and the moon.

The famous Greek philosopher Aristotle (384–322 B.C.) concluded that Earth is round because it always casts a curved shadow on the moon when it passes between the sun and the moon. Aristotle's belief that Earth is round was abandoned during the Middle Ages.

FIGURE 1 Astrolabe
Early astronomers often used instruments called astrolabes to locate and predict the positions of the sun and stars.

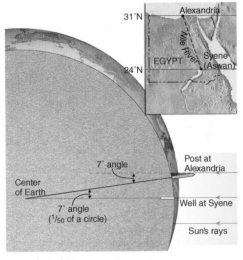

CALCULATING EARTH'S
CIRCUMFERENCE
**FIGURE 2 The Geometry
of Astronomy** This diagram
shows the angle of the sun's
rays at Syene (Aswan) and
Alexandria in Egypt on June 21.
Eratosthenes used these
measurements to calculate the
circumference of Earth.

The first successful attempt to establish the size of Earth is
credited to Eratosthenes (276–194 B.C.). As shown in **Figure 2,** he
observed the angles of the noonday sun on the same day of the year
in two Egyptian cities—Syene (now Aswan) and Alexandria. The
angles differed by 7 degrees, or 1/50 of a circle, so he concluded
that the circumference of Earth must be 50 times the distance
between these two cities. The cities were 5000 stadia apart, giving
him a calculation of 250,000 stadia. Many historians think that one
stadion (plural, stadia) was equivalent to 157.6 meters. This would
make Eratosthenes's calculation of Earth's circumference—about
39,400 kilometers—a measurement very close to the modern value
of 40,075 kilometers.

Geocentric Model Ancient Greeks believed in a **geocentric**
universe, in which Earth was a sphere that stayed motionless at the
center of the universe. ⊂⊃ In the geocentric model, the moon,
sun, and the known planets—Mercury, Venus, Mars, Jupiter and
Saturn—go around Earth. The path of an object as it goes around
another object in space is called an **orbit.** Beyond the planets was a
transparent, hollow sphere on which the stars traveled daily around
Earth. This was called the celestial sphere. To the Greeks, all of the
heavenly bodies, except seven, appeared to remain in the same
relative position to one another. These seven wanderers included the
sun, the moon, Mercury, Venus, Mars, Jupiter, and Saturn. Each was
thought to have a circular orbit around Earth. The Greeks were able
to explain the apparent movements of all celestial bodies in space by
using this model. Although the geocentric model of the universe was
not correct, astronomers still use the concept of the celestial sphere
to describe the motion of objects in the sky as seen from Earth.
Figure 3A on the next page illustrates the geocentric model.

Origin of Modern Astronomy **615**

Address **Misconceptions**   L2

Some students may confuse astrology
and astronomy to the point of thinking
that they are the same. *Astronomy* is a
scientific probing of the universe to derive
the properties of celestial objects and the
laws under which the universe operates.
Astrology is a pseudoscience that is based
on ancient superstitions, which claim that
an individual's actions and personality are
determined by the positions of the planets
and stars at the present time, and at the time
of the person's birth. Pseudoscience means
false science. Astrological claims cannot
be tested by scientific methods. **Ask:** Why
don't scientists accept astrological beliefs as
scientific fact? *(Astrological claims cannot
be tested by scientific methods.)*
Verbal

Build Science Skills   L2

Calculate Have students confirm
Eratosthenes's calculations of the
circumference of Earth and calculate the
percent error of the calculation.

$$\frac{7}{360} = \frac{1}{50}$$

5000 stadia × 50 = 250,000 stadia;
if 1 stadia = 157.6 m, then,

$$250,000 \text{ stadia} \times \frac{157.6 \text{ m}}{1 \text{ stadia}}$$

= 39,400,000 m = 39,400 km;
percent error

$$= \frac{39,400 \text{ km} - 40,075 \text{ km}}{40,075 \text{ km}} \times 100$$

= 1.7%

Eratosthenes's calculation of Earth's
circumference is amazing considering this
was calculated before 194 B.C.
Logical

Differentiated Instruction

ENGLISH LANGUAGE LEARNERS Encourage
English language learners to make a science
glossary as they read the section. Students
should start with the vocabulary terms and
add any other new words they encounter.

Have students write brief definitions of each
term or draw an illustration that helps them
understand the term. Students may want to
include definitions in both English and their
native language in their glossary.

LESSON 22.1

Figure 3 Have students compare the geocentric and heliocentric models represented in the figure. **Ask:** What is the main difference in these two models of the solar system? *(In the geocentric model, Earth is at the center. In the heliocentric model, the sun is at the center.)* How do the changing models of the solar system demonstrate the self-correcting nature of science? *(As new information was discovered about the solar system, the models were changed to incorporate the new information. As more and more information was collected and as technology improved, the model of the solar system became more accurate.)*
Verbal, Portfolio

Note to teacher Ptolemy's system of planetary motion was complicated, and it can sometimes be hard for students to visualize. For Ptolemy's model to have planets orbit in perfect circles around Earth, he had to postulate that planets moved on epicycles, which in turn orbited along circles called deferents. This was because planets don't really orbit in perfect circles around Earth, but in ellipses around the sun. Ptolemy's model did provide an explanation for retrograde motion, as it meant that although planets would generally appear to move eastward towards the sky, every now and then they would appear to move backwards. To help students picture this, draw a circle with the Earth at the center, and then another circle whose center is a point is on the first circle. Trace the motion of a planet along a moving epicycle to show students how Ptolemy's system helped explain retrograde motion.

FIGURE 3 A Geocentric Model of the Universe In a geocentric system, the planets and sun orbit Earth.

B Heliocentric Model of the Universe In a heliocentric system, Earth and the other planets orbit the sun.

Heliocentric Model Aristarchus (312–230 B.C.) was the first Greek to propose a sun-centered, or **heliocentric,** universe. 🔗 **In the heliocentric model, Earth and the other planets orbit the sun.** Aristarchus used geometry to calculate the relative distances from Earth to the sun and from Earth to the moon. He later used these distances to calculate the size of the sun and the moon. But Aristarchus came up with numbers that were much too small. However, he did determine that the sun was many times more distant than the moon and many times larger than Earth. Though there was evidence to support the heliocentric model, shown in **Figure 3B,** the Earth-centered view dominated Western thought for nearly 2000 years.

Ptolemaic System Much of our knowledge of Greek astronomy comes from Claudius Ptolemy. In A.D. 141, Ptolemy presented a model of the universe that was later called the Ptolemaic system. The precision with which his theory was able to predict the motion of the planets allowed it to go unchallenged for nearly 13 centuries.

Just like the Greek model, Ptolemy's model had the planets moving in circular orbits around a motionless Earth. However, the motion of the planets against the background of stars seemed odd. Each planet, if watched night after night, moves slightly eastward among the stars. But periodically, each planet appears to stop, reverse direction for a time, and then resume an eastward motion. The apparent westward drift is called **retrograde motion** and is illustrated in **Figure 4.** This rather odd apparent motion actually results from the combination of the motion of Earth and the planet's own motion around the sun. However, Ptolemy explained retrograde motion by saying that planets moved along smaller circles, called *epicycles,* which in turn moved along their orbits around Earth. Ptolemy's theory was wrong—the planets do not orbit Earth. Yet his theory accounted for the planets' apparent motions.

☑ **Reading Checkpoint** *What is retrograde motion?*

Facts and Figures

Ptolemy's most famous work was a 13-volume text written in Greek called *He mathematike syntaxis,* or *The Mathematical Collection.* This great work was translated into Arabic by Arab scholars and renamed *al-Majisti,* or *Great Work.* The book is now known as the *Almagest.* In this work, Ptolemy used mathematical terms to explain the motions of the heavenly bodies. Ptolemy's explanations of the planets' movements were widely accepted.

Figure 4 To help students understand the concept of retrograde motion, have them trace the eye's line of sight with their finger. Tell students to find the number 1 in the left part of the diagram and follow the dotted line to the position of Mars. Then have students repeat this process for each numbered position.

Ask: Why does Mars appear to have retrograde motion? *(Earth has a faster orbital speed than Mars has and overtakes it.)* Using Newton's laws of motion, explain why retrograde motion is impossible. *(Mars would not reverse its direction of motion unless it was acted upon by an outside force that would change its direction. Inertia and gravity will keep it moving in a forward direction.)*
Visual

The Birth of Modern Astronomy

The development of modern astronomy involved a break from previous philosophical and religious views. Scientists began to discover a universe governed by natural laws. We will examine the work of five noted scientists: Nicolaus Copernicus, Tycho Brahe, Johannes Kepler, Galileo Galilei, and Sir Isaac Newton.

Nicolaus Copernicus For almost 13 centuries after the time of Ptolemy, very few astronomical advances were made in Europe. The first great astronomer to emerge after the Middle Ages was Nicolaus Copernicus (1473–1543) from Poland. ⊙ **Copernicus concluded that Earth is a planet. He proposed a model of the solar system with the sun at the center.** This was a major break from the ancient idea that a motionless Earth lies at the center. Copernicus used circles, which were considered to be the perfect geometric shape, to represent the orbits of the planets. However, the actual path of the planets seemed to stray from the paths predicted by Copernicus.

Tycho Brahe Tycho Brahe (1546–1601) was born of Danish nobility three years after the death of Copernicus. Brahe became interested in astronomy while viewing a solar eclipse that had been predicted by astronomers. He persuaded King Frederick II to build an observatory near Copenhagen. The telescope had not yet been invented. At the observatory, Brahe designed and built other instruments, such as the angle-measuring device shown in **Figure 5.** He used these instruments for 20 years to measure the positions of the the moon, planets, and stars. ⊙ **Brahe's observations, especially of Mars, were far more precise than any made previously.** In the last year of his life, Brahe found an able assistant, Johannes Kepler. Kepler kept most of Brahe's observations and put them to exceptional use.

FIGURE 4 Retrograde Motion
When viewed from Earth, Mars moves eastward among the stars each day. Then periodically it appears to stop and reverse direction. This apparent movement, called retrograde motion, occurs because Earth has a faster orbital speed than Mars and overtakes it.

FIGURE 5 Tycho Brahe in His Observatory Brahe (seated) is painted on the wall within the arc of a sighting instrument called a quadrant.

Origin of Modern Astronomy **617**

(**Address Misconceptions**)   L2

Some students may think that modern astronomy was developed recently by a small number of scientists. The body of astronomical knowledge is an accumulation of work by many scientists over many centuries of time. Modern astronomers study the works of earlier scientists and build on the foundation of knowledge that they have laid. In fact, Sir Isaac Newton has been quoted as saying, "If I have seen further, it is by standing on the shoulders of giants."
Ask: What is an example of a field of science that does not contain an accumulation of knowledge that was acquired over many years? *(There is no such field of science. All fields of science are accumulations of knowledge.)*
Verbal

Answers

☑ **Reading Checkpoint** *Retrograde motion is the apparent westward drift of a planet resulting from the combination of the motion of Earth and the planet's own motion around the sun.*

Facts and Figures

The Copernican explanation of the solar system challenged the belief that Earth was the center of the universe and was considered heretical by the Roman Catholic Church. Copernicus's text, *De Revolutionibus, Orbium Coelestium (On the Revolution of the Heavenly Spheres)*, was published as he lay on his deathbed in 1543. One of Copernicus's followers, Giordano Bruno, was seized in 1600 during the Inquisition, a Roman Catholic tribunal for the discovery and punishment for heresy. He refused to denounce the Copernican theory and was burned at the stake.

LESSON 22.1

VISUALIZING PLANETARY ORBITS L2

Purpose Students will draw ellipses to develop an understanding of the shape of an orbit.

Materials several sheets of paper, heavy cardboard, 2 pushpins, metric ruler, string, pencils

Procedure Have students place the paper over the cardboard. Tell students to place the two pushpins into the paper a short distance from each other. Have them tie the string in a loop and place it around the pins. Using the pencil, students should pull the string tight and drag the pencil around the pins to draw the ellipse. Have students draw a few ellipses, each time changing the distance between the pins.

Expected Outcome Students will discover that some ellipses look more elongated than others. Point out to the students that most planetary orbits, although ellipses, look very close to circles.

Kinesthetic, Logical

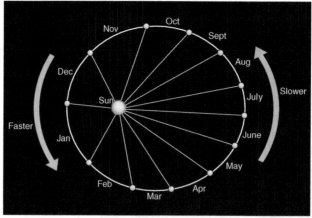

FIGURE 6 Planet Revolution
A line connecting a planet to the sun moves in such a manner that equal areas are swept out in equal times. Thus, planets revolve slower when they are farther from the sun and faster when they are closer.

Table 1 Period of Revolution and Solar Distances of Planets

Planet	Solar Distance (d) (AU)*	Period (T) (Earth years)
Mercury	0.39	0.24
Venus	0.72	0.62
Earth	1.00	1.00
Mars	1.52	1.88
Jupiter	5.20	11.86
Saturn	9.54	29.46
Uranus	19.18	84.01
Neptune	30.06	164.80
Pluto**	39.44	247.70

*AU = astronomical unit. **As of 2007, Pluto is a dwarf planet.

Johannes Kepler Johannes Kepler (1571–1630) was an astronomer with a strong belief in the accuracy of Brahe's work. **Kepler discovered three laws of planetary motion.** The first two laws resulted from his inability to fit Brahe's observations of Mars to a circular orbit. Kepler concluded that the orbit of Mars around the sun is not a perfect circle. Instead, it is an oval-shaped path, called an **ellipse.** Two points inside the ellipse, each called a *focus* (plural, foci), help to determine the shape of the ellipse. The further apart the foci, the more stretched out the ellipse. About the same time, Kepler realized that the speed of Mars in its orbit changes in a predictable way. As Mars approaches the sun, it speeds up. As it moves away from the sun, it slows down.

Kepler summarized three laws of planetary motion:

1. The path of each planet around the sun is an ellipse, with the sun at one focus. The other focus is located at the symmetrically opposite end of the ellipse.

2. Each planet revolves so that an imaginary line connecting it to the sun sweeps over equal areas in equal time intervals, as shown in **Figure 6.** If a planet is to sweep equal areas in the same amount of time, it must travel more rapidly when it is nearer the sun and more slowly when it is farther from the sun.

3. The square of the length of time it takes a planet to orbit the sun (*orbital period*) is proportional to the cube of its mean distance to the sun.

In its simplest form, the orbital period of revolution is measured in Earth years. A planet's distance to the sun is expressed in **astronomical units (AU),** which is the average distance between Earth and the sun. One AU is about 150 million kilometers.

Using these units, Kepler's third law states that a planet's orbital period squared is equal to its mean solar distance cubed ($T^2 = d^3$). Therefore, the solar distances of the planets can be calculated when their periods of revolution are known. For example, Mars has a period of 1.88 Earth years, which squared equals 3.54. The cube root of 3.54 is 1.52, and that is the distance from the sun to Mars in astronomical units. The solar distance and orbital period of all the planets and Pluto—a dwarf planet—are shown in **Table 1.** The farther from the sun, the greater a planet's orbital period.

Galileo Galilei Galileo Galilei (1564–1642) was thought by many to be the greatest Italian scientist of the Renaissance. 🔑 **Galileo's most important contributions were his descriptions of the behavior of moving objects.** All astronomical discoveries before his time were made without the aid of a telescope. But in the early 1600s, Dutch lensmakers invented a device for "seeing faraway things as though nearby." The device consisted of two lenses in a tube that magnified objects about three times the size seen by the unaided eye. By 1609, these devices were available in Italy. Galileo built his own versions of these early three-power telescopes. In a short time, however, Galileo built improved versions of these early telescopes. His improved telescopes had twenty- and thirty-power magnifications.

Using these telescopes, Galileo was able to view the universe in a new way. He made many important discoveries that supported Copernicus's heliocentric view of the universe, such as the following:

1. *The discovery of four satellites, or moons, orbiting Jupiter.* This proved that the old idea of Earth being the only center of motion in the universe was wrong. Here, plainly visible, was another center of motion—Jupiter. People who opposed the sun-centered system said that the moon would be left behind if Earth really revolved around the sun. Galileo's discovery disproved this argument.

2. *The discovery that the planets are circular disks, not just points of light, as was previously thought.* This showed that the planets were not stars.

3. *The discovery that Venus has phases just like the moon.* So Venus orbits its source of light—the sun. Galileo saw that Venus appears smallest when it is in full phase and therefore farthest from Earth, as shown in **Figure 7.**

4. *The discovery that the moon's surface was not smooth.* Galileo saw mountains, craters, and plains. Before Galileo, people thought that the objects in the sky were smooth and perfect.

5. *The discovery that the sun had sunspots, or dark regions.* These blemishes on the sun showed that the sun was not perfect. Galileo tracked the movement of these spots and estimated the rotational period of the sun as just under a month.

Many influential people during the time of Galileo strongly believed in the geocentric model of the universe. Galileo's new discoveries directly contradicted these firmly held beliefs. As a result, Galileo lived the last years of his life under house arrest.

☑ **Reading Checkpoint** What is a telescope?

THE SOLAR SYSTEM MODEL EVOLVES

FIGURE 7
Relate Cause and Effect *In the geocentric model, which phase of Venus would be visible from Earth?*

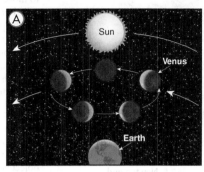

In the Ptolemaic system, the orbit of Venus lies between the sun and Earth.

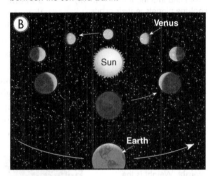

In the Copernican system, Venus orbits the sun and more of its phases are visible from Earth.

As Galileo observed, Venus goes through phases similar to the moon.

Origin of Modern Astronomy **619**

Refer to **p. 612D** at the beginning of this chapter, which provides the guidelines for thinking aloud.

Think Aloud Set the example for this strategy by verbalizing your own thought processes while reading about "Galileo Galilei." Encourage students to read "Sir Isaac Newton" on the next page while quietly verbalizing their thought processes. Then have a class discussion about the advantages students found in staying focused on a logical thought process when reading in this manner.
Intrapersonal, Auditory

Answers

Figure 7 *only the crescent phase*

☑ **Reading Checkpoint** *A telescope is a tool used to magnify objects that are far away. Early telescopes consisted of two lenses in a tube and magnified objects about three times the size seen by the unaided eye.*

LESSON 22.1

A SIMPLE MIRROR TELESCOPE L2

Purpose Students will observe how a mirror telescope works.

Materials lightbulb in a lamp base, magnifying lens, mirror with concave surface (magnifying mirror with 2 sides—used for makeup and shaving)

Procedure Place the light on a table in a darkened room. Turn the light on and use the concave surface of the mirror to reflect the lightbulb on the wall. Move the mirror toward or away from the lightbulb until you get a sharp image on the wall. Observe the image of the bulb on the wall through the magnifying glass. Move the magnifying glass toward or away from the image to get the largest and clearest image.

Expected Outcome Students will observe how a mirror telescope enlarges an image to make it easier to study.
Kinesthetic, Visual

Integrate Physics L2

Gravitational force is one of four fundamental forces. The other three are the electromagnetic force, the strong nuclear force, and the weak nuclear force. Fundamental forces describe all interactions between objects. As its name implies, the strong nuclear force is the strongest fundamental force. It also has the shortest range, meaning that particles must be extremely close together in order for its effects to be felt. The strong nuclear force holds the protons in the nucleus together. The weak nuclear force plays a role in radioactive decay. The electromagnetic force is the force of attraction between like charges and the force of repulsion between unlike charges.
Verbal

FIGURE 8 Newton and Gravity Sir Isaac Newton explained that the force of gravity kept the planets in their orbits.

Sir Isaac Newton Sir Isaac Newton (1642–1727), shown in **Figure 8**, was born in the year of Galileo's death. Many scientists had attempted to explain the forces involved in planetary motion. Kepler believed that some force pushed the planets along in their orbits. Galileo correctly reasoned that no force is required to keep an object in motion. And he proposed that a moving object will continue to move at a constant speed and in a straight line. This concept is called *inertia*.

The problem, then, was not to explain the force that keeps the planets moving but rather to determine the force that prevents them from going in a straight line out into space. Newton described a force that holds the moon in orbit around Earth. 🔑 **Although others had theorized the existence of such a force, Newton was the first to formulate and test the law of universal gravitation.**

Universal Gravitation According to Newton, every body in the universe attracts every other body with a force that is directly proportional to their masses and inversely proportional to the square of the distance between their centers of mass. The mass of an object is a measure of the total amount of matter it contains.

Gravitational force decreases with distance. Two objects 3 kilometers apart have 3^2, or 9, times less gravitational attraction than if the same objects were 1 kilometer apart.

The law of universal gravitation also states that the greater the mass of the object, the greater is its gravitational force. For example, the mass of the moon creates a gravitational force strong enough to cause ocean tides on Earth. But the tiny mass of an artificial satellite has no measurable effect on Earth.

Weight is not the same as mass. *Weight* is the force of gravity acting upon an object. Therefore, weight varies when gravitational forces change, even if mass is constant. Weight is properly expressed in newtons (N). See **Figure 9.**

FIGURE 9 Gravity Affects Weight Weight is the force of gravity acting on an object. **A** An astronaut with a mass of 88 kg weighs 863 N on Earth. **B** An astronaut with a mass of 88 kg weighs 141 N on the moon.

Astronaut on Earth
Mass = 88.0 kg; Weight = 863 N

Astronaut on Moon
Mass = 88.0 kg; Weight = 141 N

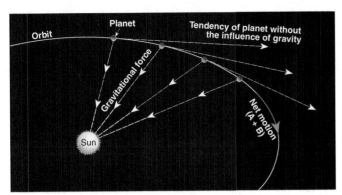

FIGURE 10 Earth's Path Without Gravity Without the influence of gravity, planets would move in a straight line out into space.

Evaluate Understanding   L2

Have students write three review questions for this section. Students should then work in small groups and ask one another their questions.

Reteach L1

Use Figures 3 and 4 to review geocentric and heliocentric models of the solar system.

Newton proved that the force of gravity, combined with the concept of inertia, results in the elliptical orbits that Kepler discovered. Earth, for example, moves forward in its orbit about 30 kilometers each second. During the same second, the force of gravity pulls it toward the sun about 0.5 centimeter. Newton concluded that it is the combination of Earth's forward motion and its "falling" motion that defines its orbit. As **Figure 10** shows, if gravity were somehow eliminated, Earth would move in a straight line out into space. If Earth's forward motion suddenly stopped, gravity would pull it directly toward the sun.

Newton used the law of universal gravitation to redefine Kepler's third law. When restated, Kepler's third law takes into account the masses of the bodies involved in addition to the distance between the bodies when calculating the orbital period of an object.

22.1 Assessment

Review Key Concepts 🔑

1. Compare and contrast the geocentric and heliocentric models of the universe.

2. What produces the retrograde motion of Mars?

3. What geometric arrangements did Ptolemy use to explain retrograde motion?

4. What major change did Copernicus make in the Ptolemaic system? Why was this change significant?

Think Critically

5. Apply Concepts What role did the telescope play in Galileo's contributions to science?

6. Summarize In your own words, summarize Kepler's three laws of planetary motion.

MATH PRACTICE

7. Calculate Use Kepler's third law to show that the distance of a hypothetical planet whose period is 5 years is 2.9 AU from the sun. Do the same for hypothetical planets with a period of 10 years at 4.6 AU from the sun and a period of 10 days at 0.09 AU from the sun.

Origin of Modern Astronomy **621**

Assessment Answers

1. In the geocentric model, the sun and planets revolve around Earth. In the heliocentric model, Earth and the other planets revolve around the sun.
2. Retrograde motion occurs when Earth, which travels faster than Mars, passes Mars. This makes Mars appear to go westward.
3. Ptolemy said that planets moved on small circles called epicycles, which in turn moved along their orbits around Earth.

4. Copernicus placed the sun at the center of the solar system. This was a major break from the ancient idea that Earth lies at the center.
5. Sample answer: The telescope allowed Galileo to view the universe in a new way, leading to many discoveries on his part.
6. The path of a planet around the sun is an ellipse. Each planet revolves so that an imaginary line connecting it to the sun sweeps over equal areas at equal time intervals. The

squares of the orbital periods of the planets to the cubes of their average distances from the sun.
7. $P^2 = a^3$
$5^2 = 2.9^3$
$10^2 = 4.6^3$
$\dfrac{10^2}{365} = 0.09^3$

22.2 The Earth-Moon-Sun System

1 FOCUS

Lesson Objectives
22.4 **Describe** the movements of Earth known as rotation, revolution, and precession.

22.5 **Explain** how the moon goes through phases.

22.6 **Explain** how eclipses occur.

Build Vocabulary **L2**
Word-Part Analysis List on the board the following word parts and meanings: *helios*, "sun"; *ge* or *gee*, "earth"; *peri-*, "around or near"; *ap-* or *apo-*, "away from." Have students identify these word parts in the vocabulary terms. Discuss the terms' meanings with students.

Reading Strategy **L2**
a. Earth comes between the moon and sun.
b. solar eclipse.
c. lunar eclipse.

2 INSTRUCT

Integrate Language Arts **L2**
Archaeologists think that Stonehenge was built in three stages between about 3000 to 1000 B.C. Stonehenge was probably used as a religious center or a type of astronomical clock or calendar. Have students research information on the construction and possible purposes for Stonehenge. Students should prepare a short report and make a visual aid showing the layout of Stonehenge.
Verbal, Portfolio

Key Questions
🔑 *In what ways does Earth move?*

🔑 *What causes the phases of the moon?*

🔑 *Why are eclipses relatively rare events?*

Vocabulary
- rotation • revolution
- precession • perihelion
- aphelion • perigee
- apogee • phases of the moon
- solar eclipse • lunar eclipse

Reading Strategy
Monitor Your Understanding
Copy and complete the flowchart below.

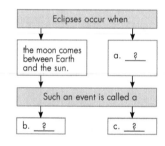

Flowchart
- Eclipses occur when
  - the moon comes between Earth and the sun.
  - a. ?
- Such an event is called a
  - b. ?
  - c. ?

IF YOU FIND a spot for star gazing away from city lights, it will seem that the stars are fixed to a giant dome that covers Earth. This impression seems so real that it is easy to understand why many early Greek astronomers regarded the stars as being fixed to a solid, celestial sphere. The sun and moon, on the other hand, constantly change their positions against the stars. Prehistoric people built observatories to chart their motions. The structure known as Stonehenge, shown in **Figure 11,** was probably an attempt at better solar predictions. At the beginning of summer in the Northern Hemisphere (on June 21), the rising sun comes up directly above the heel stone (small stone in the center of Figure 11) of Stonehenge. Besides keeping this calendar, Stonehenge may also have provided a method of predicting eclipses. In this lesson, you'll learn more about the movements of bodies in space that cause events such as eclipses.

FIGURE 11 Early Astronomical Instrument? On the summer solstice, the sun can be observed rising above the heel stone (small stone in the center) of Stonehenge, an ancient observatory in England.

Motions of Earth
🔑 **The two main motions of Earth are rotation and revolution.**
Rotation is the turning, or spinning, of a body on its axis.
Revolution is the motion of a body, such as a planet or moon, along its orbit around some point in space. For example, Earth revolves around the sun, and the moon revolves around Earth. Earth also has another very slow motion known as **precession,** which is the slight cone-shaped movement of where, in the sky, Earth's axis points. The period of Earth's rotation is one day and one revolution takes one year. However, the period of Earth's precession is 26,000 years.

Rotation The main results of Earth's rotation are day and night. Earth's rotation has become a standard method of measuring time because it is so dependable and easy to use. Each rotation of Earth around its axis equals about 24 hours. The result of Earth's rotation is an apparent circular motion by most of the stars in the sky, as shown in **Figure 12.** We can measure Earth's day in two ways. Most familiar is the apparent solar day, the time interval from one noon to the next, which is about 24 hours. Noon is when the sun has reached its highest point in the sky for that day.

The *sidereal day* is the time it takes for Earth to make one complete rotation with respect to a star other than our sun. The sidereal day is measured by the time required for a star to reappear at the identical position in the sky where it was observed the day before. The sidereal day has a period of 23 hours, 56 minutes, and 4 seconds, which is almost 4 minutes shorter than the average solar day. This difference comes from the fact that the direction to distant stars barely changes from day to day as a result of Earth's revolution around the sun. The direction to the sun from one day to the next, on the other hand, changes by almost 1 degree. This difference is shown in **Figure 13.**

Why do we use the mean solar day instead of the sidereal day as a measurement of our day? In sidereal time, "noon" occurs four minutes earlier each day. Therefore, after six months, "noon" occurs at "midnight." Sidereal time is more useful to astronomers because the stars appear in the same position every 24 sidereal hours.

☑ **Reading Checkpoint** *How is the solar day measured?*

FIGURE 12 Evidence of Earth's Rotation A long exposure pointed at the star Polaris shows the apparent paths of the stars. In fact, this apparent motion is caused by Earth's rotation.

FIGURE 13 Sidereal Day It takes Earth 23 hours and 56 minutes to make one rotation with respect to the stars (sidereal day). However, after Earth has completed one sidereal day, point Y has not yet returned to the "noon position" with respect to the sun. Earth has to rotate another 4 minutes to complete the solar day.

Origin of Modern Astronomy **623**

Origin of Modern Astronomy **623**

Integrate Mathematics

It takes 24 hours for the apparent motion of an individual star to make one complete circle around Polaris—the center of the concentric circles. Focus students' attention on Figure 12. **Ask:** How can you determine the length of the time exposure in this photograph? *(Take any one star trail arc and draw a line from the each end of the arc to Polaris. Use a protractor to measure the angle made by these two lines. Divide that angle by 360 degrees. Multiply the result by 24 hours—that's the length of the time exposure. For example, if the lines made a 90 degree angle, divide 90 degrees by 360 degrees to get 0.25. Then, multiply 0.25 times 24 hours to get 6 hours. In that case, the time exposure would have been 6 hours.)*

Use Visuals

Figure 13 Have students examine the movement of Earth and the locations of points X and Y carefully. **Ask:** What are the reference points for a mean solar day and a sidereal day? *(A mean solar day is measured using the sun as a reference point. A sidereal day is measured using a star other than the sun as a reference point.)* Why do these two reference points give two different results? *(The direction from Earth to a distant star barely changes, but the direction from Earth to the sun changes each day because Earth revolves about one degree in its orbit each day.)* Why do astronomers choose to use the sidereal day instead of the mean solar day? *(The stars appear in the same position in the sky every 24 sidereal hours.)*
Visual, Logical

Answers

☑ **Reading Checkpoint** *A solar day is the time interval between noon on one day to noon on the next. Noon is the hour at which the sun has reached the highest point in the sky. A solar day is about 24 hours.*

Differentiated Instruction

ENGLISH LANGUAGE LEARNERS Have students draw simple illustrations for the motions of Earth, the motions of the Earth-moon-sun system, and eclipses. Have them explain each illustration to a partner. Then have each pair of students discuss why the motions occur as they do.

Build Reading Literacy L1

Refer to **p. 334D** in **Chapter 12,** which provides the guidelines for outlining.

Outline Have students read the text on pp. 622–629 relating to the Earth-moon-sun system. Then ask students to use the headings as major divisions in an outline. Suggest that students refer to their outlines when answering the questions in the Lesson 22.2 Assessment.
Verbal

FIGURE 14 The Celestial Sphere Earth's revolution around the sun causes the apparent position of the sun to shift about one degree each day on the celestial sphere.

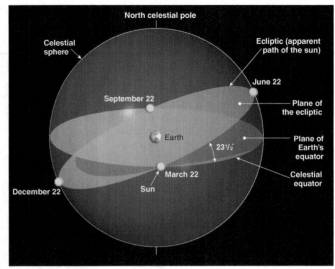

Revolution Earth revolves around the sun in an elliptical orbit at an average speed of 107,000 kilometers per hour. Its average distance from the sun is 150 million kilometers. But because its orbit is an ellipse, Earth's distance from the sun varies. At **perihelion,** Earth is closest to the sun—about 147 million kilometers. Perihelion occurs around January 3. At **aphelion,** Earth is farthest from the sun— about 152 million kilometers. Aphelion occurs about July 4. So Earth is farthest from the sun in July and closest to the sun in January.

Because of Earth's annual movement around the sun, each day the sun appears to move among the constellations. The apparent annual path of the sun against the backdrop of the celestial sphere is called the *ecliptic*, as shown in **Figure 14.**

Earth's Axis and Seasons The imaginary plane that connects Earth's orbit with the celestial sphere is called the *plane of the ecliptic*. The projection of Earth's equator onto the sky is the *celestial equator*. Earth's axis of rotation is tilted about 23.5 degrees toward the plane of the ecliptic. This angle is very important to Earth's inhabitants. Because of the inclination of Earth's axis to the plane of the ecliptic, Earth has a yearly cycle of seasons.

When the apparent position of the sun is plotted on the celestial sphere over a period of a year's time, its path intersects the celestial equator at two points. From a Northern Hemisphere point of view, these intersections are called the spring equinox (March 19 or 20) and autumnal equinox (September 22 or 23). On June 20 or 21, the date of the summer solstice, the sun appears 23.5 degrees north of the celestial equator. Six months later, on December 21 or 22, the date of the winter solstice, the sun appears 23.5 degrees south of the celestial equator.

624 Chapter 22 • Lesson 2

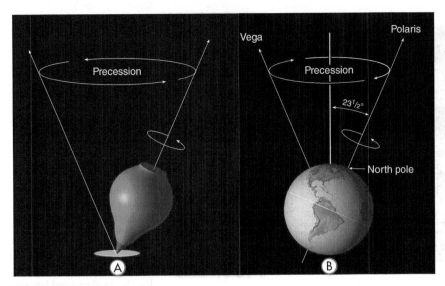

FIGURE 15 Precession
A Precession is similar to a spinning top. It causes the North Pole to point at different parts of the sky during a 26,000-year cycle.

B Today, the North Pole points to Polaris.

Interpret Visuals *What star will the North Pole point to in about 13,000 years?*

Precession A slow movement of Earth, called *precession*, is the motion of Earth's axis as it traces out a circle on the sky. Earth's axis varies in tilt between 21.5° and 24.5° with a repeating period of 41,000 years. This shifting axis is important in affecting climate change. In addition, the direction in which the axis points continually changes. This movement is very similar to the wobble of a spinning top, as shown in **Figure 15A.** At the present time, the axis points toward the bright star Polaris. In about 13,000 years, it will point toward the bright star Vega, which will then become the North Star, as shown in **Figure 15B.** The period of precession, or the amount of time for the axis to complete one circle, is 26,000 years. So, by the year 28,000, Polaris will once again be the North Star.

Earth-Sun Motion In addition to its own movements, Earth accompanies the sun as the entire solar system speeds in the direction of the bright star Vega at 20 kilometers per second. Also, the sun, like other nearby stars, revolves with the Milky Way Galaxy. This trip takes 230 million years to traverse at speeds approaching 250 kilometers per second. The galaxies themselves are also in motion. The Milky Way Galaxy is presently approaching one of its nearest galactic neighbors, the Andromeda Galaxy.

☑ **Reading Checkpoint** What is precession?

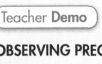

Interpret Diagrams and Photographs
Compare the photographs at the bottom of the page, Figure 16B, with those in Figure 16A. Ask students to label the photographs with the phase of the moon that is shown from left to right. *(Crescent, waning; Third quarter; Gibbous, waning; and Full.)* Challenge students to recognize the patterns for a waxing and waning moon. *(When the right side of the moon is lit, the moon is in its waxing phase. When the left side is lit, the moon is waning.)*
Visual, Logical

Address **Misconceptions** L2

Students may have four different misconceptions of why the moon goes through phases. (1) Clouds cover part of the moon. (2) Planets cast a shadow on the moon. (3) The shadow of the sun falls on the moon. (4) The shadow of Earth falls on the moon. Help students realize that lunar phases are a result of the motion of the moon and the sunlight that is reflected from its surface.
Logical

FIGURE 16 Phases of the Moon
A The outer figures show the phases as seen from Earth's Northern Hemisphere.
B Compare these photographs with the diagram. Clockwise from the top left, they show four phases: waning crescent, third quarter, waning gibbous, and full.

Motions of the Earth-Moon System

Earth has one natural satellite, the moon. It takes about one month for our moon to orbit Earth. When viewed from above the North Pole, the direction of the moon's motion is counterclockwise. Because the moon's orbit is elliptical, its distance to Earth varies but averages 384,401 kilometers. At a point known as **perigee,** the moon is closest to Earth. At **apogee,** the moon is farthest from Earth. The terms *perigee* and *apogee* are also used to describe the closest and farthest orbital points of artificial satellites orbiting Earth.

Phases of the Moon On a monthly basis, we observe the **phases of the moon** as a change in the amount of the moon that appears lit. Look at the new moon shown in **Figure 16A.** About two days after the new moon, a thin sliver (crescent phase) appears low in the western sky just after sunset. During the following week, the lighted portion of the moon visible from Earth increases (waxing) to a half circle (first-quarter phase) and is visible from noon to midnight. A week later, the full disk (full-moon phase) can be seen rising in the east as the sun is sinking in the west. During the next two weeks, the percentage of the moon that can be seen decreases (waning), until the moon disappears altogether (new-moon phase). The cycle begins again with the reappearance of the crescent moon.

Lunar phases are caused by the changes in how much of the sunlit side of the moon faces Earth. This is illustrated in **Figure 16B.** Half of the moon is illuminated at all times. But to an observer on Earth, the percentage of the bright side that is visible depends on the location of the moon with respect to the sun and Earth. When the moon lies between the sun and Earth, none of its bright side faces Earth.

When the moon lies on the side of Earth opposite the sun, all of its lighted side faces Earth. So we see the full moon. At all positions between the new moon and the full moon, a part of the moon's lit side is visible from Earth.

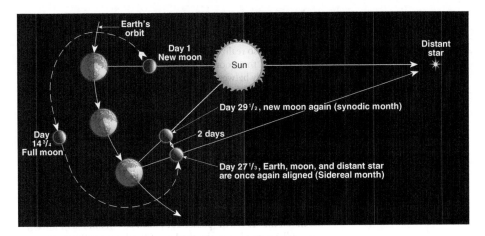

Lunar Motions

The cycle from new moon to full moon and back to new moon takes about $29\frac{1}{2}$ days, or one *synodic month*. This cycle was the basis for the first Roman calendar, which included twelve synodic periods per year. However, a synodic month is the apparent period of the moon's revolution around Earth. The true period, which takes only $27\frac{1}{3}$ days, is known as the *sidereal month*.

The reason for the difference of nearly two days between synodic and sidereal months is illustrated in **Figure 17**. Note that as the moon orbits Earth, the Earth-moon system also revolves in an orbit around the sun. Assume that the starting position of one period occurs when the moon is directly between Earth and the sun. Even after the moon has made a complete revolution around Earth, it is not yet directly between Earth and the sun. It takes another two days for the moon to reach its starting position (relative to the sun).

An interesting fact about the moon is that the same side of the moon constantly faces Earth. It takes the moon the same amount of time to rotate (spin) on its axis as it does to revolve around Earth. Both motions take $27\frac{1}{3}$ days. So, as the moon revolves around Earth, the same side of the moon is always facing Earth. Humans had their first views of the far (or back) side of the moon only when artificial satellites with cameras orbited the moon and took the first pictures of the far side. The far side of the moon appears to have many more craters than the side we see. One reason for this is that the far side is constantly pointed toward space.

Another interesting fact is that the length of one daylight period on the moon is two Earth weeks. Since the moon rotates on its axis only once every $27\frac{1}{3}$ days, any spot on the moon's surface has two weeks of daylight followed by two weeks of night. This partially accounts for the high temperature of 127°C on the day side of the moon and the low temperature of −173°C on its night side.

☑ **Reading Checkpoint** *Why does the same side of the moon always face Earth?*

FIGURE 17 Lunar Motion As the moon orbits Earth, the Earth-moon system also revolves around the sun. Thus, even after the moon makes one revolution around Earth, it has not yet reached its starting point in relation to the sun.

INQUIRY
APPLY IT!

Q: *Why do we sometimes see the moon in daytime?*

A: During phases of the lunar cycle other than the full moon, the moon and sun are not directly opposite each other. This makes it possible to see the moon during daylight hours.

Origin of Modern Astronomy **627**

Facts and Figures

Ancient calendars were based on phases of the moon. The month was originally defined as the time between two full moons, or 29 1/2 days. The lunar calendar year was 354 days, which is 11 1/4 days short of a solar year.

An additional month was occasionally added to lunar calendars to align the calendar with the seasons. Ancient Egyptians were the first to devise a calendar based on a solar year.

LESSON 22.2

Use Community Resources L2

Arrange for your class to visit a planetarium. Have students prepare questions regarding the topics in this chapter in advance.
Interpersonal

Use Visuals L1

Figure 18A Have students examine this figure. **Ask:** During a solar eclipse, why do observers in the umbra see a total solar eclipse? *(The moon completely blocks the sun from the viewer.)* Why do observers in the penumbra see a partial eclipse? *(The moon only partially blocks the sun from the viewer.)*

Figure 18B Have students examine this figure. **Ask:** When does a total lunar eclipse occur? *(A total lunar eclipse occurs when Earth completely blocks the moon from the sun and the moon is completely in Earth's shadow. This only happens during the full-moon phase)* When does a partial lunar eclipse occur? *(A partial lunar eclipse occurs when Earth partially blocks the moon from the sun and only a portion of the moon is in Earth's umbra (shadow).)*
Visual, Logical

Eclipses

Along with understanding the moon's phases, early Greek astronomers also realized that eclipses are the result of the shadows that Earth and the moon project into space. When the moon moves in a line directly between Earth and the sun, it casts a dark shadow on Earth. This produces a **solar eclipse.** This situation occurs during new-moon phases. When the moon's orbit takes it into Earth's shadow, this produces a **lunar eclipse.** This situation occurs during full-moon phases. **Figure 18** illustrates solar and lunar eclipses.

Why doesn't a solar eclipse occur with every new moon and a lunar eclipse with every full moon? If the orbit of the moon lay exactly along the plane of Earth's orbit around the sun, then we would have one solar and lunar eclipse each month. However, the moon's orbit is inclined about 5 degrees to the plane that contains Earth and the sun. During most new-moon phases, the shadow of the moon misses Earth (passes above or below). Similarly, during most full-moon phases, the shadow of Earth misses the moon. **During a new-moon or full-moon phase, the moon's orbit must cross the plane of the ecliptic for an eclipse to take place.** Because these conditions are normally met only twice a year, the usual number of eclipses is four. These occur as a set of one solar and one lunar eclipse, followed six months later with another set. Occasionally, the alignment can result in additional eclipses. However, the total number of eclipses in one year isn't more than seven. The exact day, time, and path of eclipses is very predictable. The NASA Web site lists timetables for upcoming eclipses.

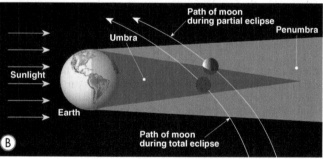

Facts and Figures

One of the earliest surviving records of eclipse observations is from ancient China. Astronomers recorded their observations from 722 to 481 B.C. in a chronicle called *Ch'un-ch'iu (Spring and Autumn Annals).* As many as 32 of the eclipses recorded in the *Ch'un-ch'iu* can be identified by modern calculations.

During a total lunar eclipse, Earth's circular shadow can be seen moving slowly across the disk of the full moon. When totally eclipsed, the moon is completely within Earth's shadow, but it is still visible as a coppery disk. This happens because Earth's atmosphere bends and transmits some light into its shadow. A total eclipse of the moon can last up to four hours and is visible to anyone on the side of Earth facing the moon.

During a total solar eclipse, the moon casts a circular shadow that is never wider than 275 kilometers, about the length of South Carolina. Anyone observing within this region will see the moon slowly and completely block the sun from view and the sky darken. When the eclipse is almost complete, the temperature sharply drops a few degrees. The solar disk is completely blocked for seven minutes at the most. The reason for the short duration of a solar eclipse is that the diameter of the moon's shadow is so small. Then one edge of the solar disk reappears and the moon continues moving until it no longer covers any part of the sun.

When the eclipse is complete, the dark moon is seen covering the complete solar disk. Only the sun's brilliant white outer atmosphere is visible. Total solar eclipses are visible only to people in the dark part of the moon's shadow known as the *umbra*. A partial eclipse is seen by those in the light portion of the shadow, known as the *penumbra*.

A total solar eclipse is a rare event at any location. The next one that will be visible from parts of the United States will take place on August 21, 2017. It will sweep southeast across the country from Oregon to South Carolina.

Review Concepts 🗝

1. In what ways does Earth move?

2. What phenomena result from Earth's rotation and revolution?

3. What causes the phases of the moon?

4. How does the crescent phase that precedes the new moon differ from the crescent phase that follows the new moon?

5. Why don't eclipses occur during every full-moon or new-moon phase?

6. Describe the locations of the sun, moon, and Earth during a solar eclipse and during a lunar eclipse.

Think Critically

7. Predict Currently, Earth is closest to the sun in January (perihelion) and farthest from the sun in July (aphelion). However, 13,000 years from now, perihelion and aphelion will be reversed. How might this affect average summer and winter temperatures?

BIGIDEA EARTH AND THE UNIVERSE

8. Communicate Even when you are standing still you are moving rapidly through space. Write a paragraph that summarizes the many different motions you undergo during one Earth day as a result of Earth's movement through the universe.

Origin of Modern Astronomy **629**

---

3 ASSESS

Evaluate Understanding L2

Call out different phases of the moon. Have students draw the phases on the board or in their notebooks.

Reteach L1

Write *rotation, revolution,* and *precession* on the board. Have students quiz each other on these motions of Earth.

6. During a solar eclipse, the moon is between the sun and Earth. During a lunar eclipse, Earth is between the sun and moon.

7. Sample answer: The difference between perihelion and aphelion has little influence on the quantity of radiation received by Earth. The primary cause of seasons is Earth's tilted axis, not its distance from the sun. So any changes in summer or winter temperatures would be small. The overall impact on the biosphere and hydrosphere would also be small.

8. Students should write a paragraph that includes the motion of Earth's rotation and revolution. They should also include the motion of the sun moving in the galaxy and the galaxy moving in the universe.

Origin of Modern Astronomy **629**

Assessment Answers

1. Earth revolves around the sun, rotates on its axis, and undergoes precession. It also revolves with the solar system around the Milky Way and moves with the Milky Way towards the Andromeda Galaxy.

2. rotation: day and night; revolution: seasons

3. the motion of the moon and the amount of sunlight reflected from its surface that can be seen from Earth

4. The left edge of the moon is visible during the crescent phase that precedes the new moon, while the right side of the moon is visible during the crescent phase that follows the new moon.

5. The moon's orbit must cross the plane of the ecliptic for an eclipse to take place. Because the moon's orbit is tilted to the plane of the ecliptic, it does not always cross the ecliptic at full-moon or new-moon phase.

22.3 Earth's Moon

1 FOCUS

Lesson Objectives
22.7 **Describe** how the physical features of the lunar surface were created.
22.8 **Explain** the history of the moon.

Build Vocabulary L2
Vocabulary Rating Chart Have students construct a chart with four columns labeled Term, Can Define or Use It, Heard or Seen It, and Don't Know. Have students copy the terms *crater, ray, mare, rille,* and *lunar regolith* into the first column and rate their term knowledge by putting a check in one of the other columns. Ask how many students actually know each term. Have them share their knowledge. Ask focused questions to help students predict text content based on the term, thus enabling them to have a purpose for reading. After students have read the section, have them rate their knowledge again.

Reading Strategy L2
a. Huge quantities of crust and mantle were ejected into space.
b. The debris began orbiting Earth.
c. Debris united to form the moon.

Key Questions

What processes created surface features on the moon?

How did the moon form?

Vocabulary
- crater • ray • mare
- rille • lunar regolith

Reading Strategy
Sequence Copy Copy the flowchart below. As you read, fill in the stages leading to the formation of the moon.

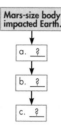

Mars-size body impacted Earth.

a. ?

b. ?

c. ?

EARTH HAS ONE natural satellite, the moon. Earth's moon, shown in **Figure 19,** is thought to be about the same age as Earth. The moon is at least 4.5 billion years old, based on the analysis of moon rocks brought back by astronauts and on other factors. The moon's average diameter is 3475 kilometers, about the same as the distance from Maine to Colorado. Its size makes the moon unique in our solar system. While other planets have moons, those moons are much smaller compared to the size of their parent planets. Earth's moon is large compared to the size of Earth.

Since Galileo first aimed a telescope at the moon, astronomers have been gathering new information. Using human and nonhuman space missions, scientists are constantly learning more about Earth's moon. For example, the moon's density is 3.3 grams per cubic centimeter (g/cm^3). That density is much less than Earth's density ($5.5\ g/cm^3$). Comparing lunar density with the density of Earth helps scientists understand the internal structure of the moon.

FIGURE 19 The Moon Through a Telescope This is what the moon's surface looks like from Earth when viewed through a telescope.

The Lunar Surface

Through his telescopes, Galileo saw two different types of lunar landscape—dark lowlands and bright highlands. Because the dark regions resembled seas on Earth, they were later named *maria*, which comes from the Latin word for *sea*. We know now that there is no water on the surface of the moon and virtually no atmosphere. So the lunar surface is not eroded in the same way that Earth's surface is. Instead, the moon's surface is eroded from impact by *meteoroids*, solid particles that travel through space. These particles can range in size from microscopic to a kilometer or more in diameter. Continual bombardment over billions of years has given the moon a surface that is much different from Earth's surface.

Craters The most obvious features of the lunar surface are **craters,** which are round depressions in the surface of the moon. ⬤ **Most craters were produced by the impact of rapidly moving debris or meteoroids.** Some astronomers think it is impossible to count the number of craters on the moon because the closer you look, the more small craters you find. The moon's surface probably has many billions of craters, from microscopic to very large. The largest craters are about 250 kilometers in diameter, about the width of Indiana.

By contrast, Earth has fewer easily recognized impact craters. Friction with Earth's atmosphere burns up small debris before it reaches the ground. Evidence for craters that formed early in Earth's history has been destroyed by erosion and other forces that change Earth's surface.

The formation of an impact crater is modeled in **Figure 20.** Upon impact, the colliding object compresses the material it strikes. This process is similar to the splash that occurs when a rock is dropped into water. In larger craters, a central peak forms as a result of the impact.

Most of the ejected material lands near the crater, building a rim around it. Heat generated by the impact is enough to melt rock. Astronauts brought back to Earth samples of lunar glass and rock formed by such impact.

A meteoroid only 3 meters in diameter can blast out a 150-meter-wide crater. A few of the large craters, such as those named *Kepler* and *Copernicus*, formed from the impact of bodies one kilometer or more in diameter. These two large craters are thought to be relatively young because the bright **rays,** or elongated streaks that radiate outward for hundreds of kilometers, are still visible.

VISUAL SUMMARY

FORMATION OF A CRATER

FIGURE 20 Impact Craters
The energy of the rapidly moving meteoroid is transformed into heat energy. Rock compresses and then quickly rebounds. The rebounding rock causes debris to be ejected from the crater.

Origin of Modern Astronomy **631**

LESSON 22.3

Build Science Skills L2

Student Activity: Use Models

Purpose Students will model the surface features of the lunar surface.

Materials foam poster board; soft modeling clay; toothpicks; narrow paper strips; tape; pencil, pen, or marker

Class Time 30 minutes

Procedure Have students use Figure 21 as a guide for their topographic map. First, instruct students to draw the physical features on the foam poster board. Next, have students use the soft modeling clay to build the surface features. Then students should make flag-type labels for the physical features, using narrow strips of paper, toothpicks, and tape. Finally, have students use the markers to identify the physical features on the surface of their topographical map.

Expected Outcome Students learn the major topographical surface features on the lunar surface.

Visual, Kinesthetic

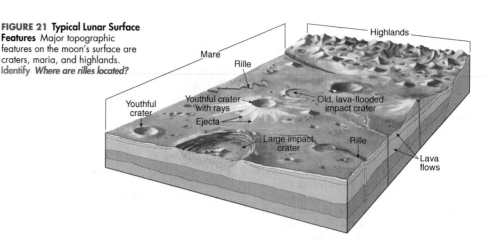

FIGURE 21 Typical Lunar Surface Features Major topographic features on the moon's surface are craters, maria, and highlands. **Identify** *Where are rilles located?*

Highlands — Mare — Rille — Youthful crater — Youthful crater with rays — Old, lava-flooded impact crater — Ejecta — Large impact crater — Rille — Lava flows

Highlands Most of the lunar surface is made up of light-colored, mountainous areas known as highlands. **Figure 21** shows highlands and other features of the moon. In fact, highlands cover most of the surface of the far side of the moon. Within the highland regions are mountain ranges and large concentrations of impact craters. The highest lunar peaks reach elevations of almost 8 kilometers. This height is only one kilometer lower than Mount Everest, the highest mountain on Earth. The origin of lunar mountains is thought to be a different process than the origin of mountains on Earth. Many astronomers think that the mountains in lunar highlands were formed when very large space debris, called *asteroids*, struck the moon's surface.

Maria The dark, relatively smooth areas on the moon's surface are called maria (singular: **mare**). **Maria, ancient beds of basaltic lava, originated when asteroids punctured the lunar surface, letting magma "bleed" out.** Apparently, the craters were flooded with layer upon layer of very fluid basaltic lava somewhat resembling the Columbia Plateau in the northwestern United States. The lava flows are often over 30 meters thick. The total thickness of the material that fills the maria could reach thousands of meters.

Long channels called **rilles** are associated with maria. Rilles look somewhat similar to river valleys. Rilles may be the remnants of ancient rivers of lava.

Regolith All lunar terrains are covered with a layer of gray debris that came from billions of years of bombardment from space debris. This uppermost layer, called **lunar regolith,** is composed of igneous rocks, beads, and fine lunar dust. In the maria explored by astronauts, the lunar regolith is just over 3 meters thick. It is thought that in other areas, the regolith could be more than 20 meters thick.

☑ **Reading Checkpoint** *What is lunar regolith?*

Diagram NOT drawn to scale

FIGURE 22 Formation of the Moon The moon may have formed when a large object collided with Earth. The resulting debris was ejected into space. The debris began orbiting around Earth and eventually united to form the moon.

Lunar History

The moon is our nearest planetary neighbor. Although astronauts have walked on its surface, much is still unknown about its origin. **The most widely accepted model for the origin of the moon is that when the solar system was forming, a body the size of Mars impacted Earth.** The impact, shown in **Figure 22,** would have liquefied Earth's surface and ejected huge quantities of crustal and mantle rock from an infant Earth. A portion of this ejected debris would have entered an orbit around Earth where it combined to form the moon.

The giant-impact hypothesis is consistent with other facts known about the moon. The ejected material would have been mostly iron-poor mantle and crustal rocks. These would account for the lack of a sizable iron core on the moon. The ejected material would have remained in orbit long enough to have lost the water that the moon lacks. Despite this supporting evidence, many more questions need to be answered about how and when the moon formed.

Space geologists have worked out the basic details of the moon's more recent history. One of their methods is to observe variations in crater density (the number of craters per unit area). The greater the crater density, the older the surface must be. From such evidence, scientists concluded that the moon evolved in three phases—the original crust (highlands), followed by maria basins, and finally rayed craters.

During its early history, the moon was continually impacted as it swept up debris. This continuous bombardment, combined with radioactive decay, generated enough heat to melt the moon's outer shell and possibly some of the interior as well. Remnants of this original crust occupy the densely cratered highlands. These highlands have been estimated to be as much as 4.5 billion years old, about the same age as Earth.

Origin of Modern Astronomy **633**

Facts and Figures

The United States is not the only country with a space program. The former Union of Soviet Socialist Republics also had one. In fact, the U.S.S.R. was the first country to launch an artificial Earth satellite, *Sputnik 1,* in 1957. In early 1959, the Soviet spacecraft, *Luna 1,* became the first artificial object to orbit the sun, which was actually an error caused by a computer malfunction. Later in 1959, *Luna 2* crashed into the moon to become the first artificial object on the lunar surface. Also in 1959, *Luna 3* took the first pictures of the moon's far side. The Soviet goal to send the first crewed spacecraft to the moon was never realized. In 1969, the United States became the first country that landed a person on the moon.

LESSON 22.3

Evaluate Understanding   **L2**

Have students make flashcards on the details found in this section. Tell students to write a question on one side of the card and the answer on the other. Students can use these flashcards to quiz each other in class.

Reteach   **L1**

Write the headings *Lunar Surface* and *Lunar History* on the board. Ask students to give you facts from the section about each topic. Write the information under the appropriate heading. Students can copy this information from the board and use it as a study aid.

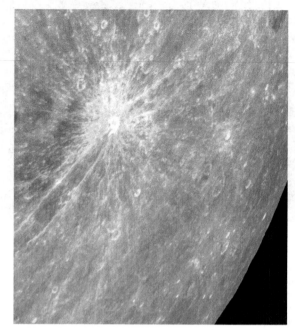

FIGURE 23 Most Recent Lunar Features Bright-rayed craters such as this one, located on the far side of the moon, are the most recent major features that formed on the lunar surface. Notice how the rays can be seen on top of other surface features. This is evidence that the rays are younger than those other features.

The next phase of the moon's history was the formation of maria basins. Analysis of rock samples from lunar maria has shown the maria to be between 3.2 billion and 3.8 billion years old. This is about a billion years younger than the moon's original crust. In other words, the maria formed about a billion years after the moon formed. In places, these lava flows overlap the highlands, which is further evidence that the maria are younger than the highlands.

The most recent prominent features that formed are the rayed craters. Material ejected from these relatively young depressions can be clearly seen covering the lunar surface and many older craters. Even a young crater like the one shown in **Figure 23** is probably millions of years old. If this crater had formed on Earth, erosional forces would have erased it long ago. Compared with Earth, the lunar surface changes very slowly. For example, footprints left by astronauts on the moon will likely remain, little changed, for millions of years. However, a million years from now if you could view a lunar footprint through a microscope, you would probably see many, many craters formed by the impact of microscopic meteoroids.

22.3 Assessment

Review Concepts 🔑

1. How did most lunar craters form?

2. How did maria originate?

3. What is one hypothesis that explains how the moon formed?

Think Critically

4. **Apply Concepts** On Earth, the four major spheres (atmosphere, hydrosphere, geosphere, and biosphere) interact as a system. Which of these spheres are absent, or nearly absent, on the moon? Based on your answer, identify at least five processes that operate on Earth but not on the moon.

5. **Infer** Why are craters more common on the moon than on Earth, even though the moon is a smaller target?

CONNECTING CONCEPTS

6. **Explain** Write a paragraph explaining what evidence scientists use to reconstruct the history of the moon.

634 Chapter 22 • Lesson 3

Assessment Answers

1. Craters form from the impact of rapidly moving debris.
2. Maria originated when asteroids punctured the lunar surface, letting magma bleed out, forming extensive lava flows.
3. A Mars-sized object collided with Earth. Huge quantities of crust and mantle were ejected into space. The debris began orbiting Earth and eventually united to form the moon.

4. Of the four spheres, the atmosphere, hydrosphere, and biosphere are absent, or nearly absent, on the moon. Because the moon lacks these spheres, processes such as chemical weathering, most types of erosion, soil formation, weather in general, and most types of sedimentation are all absent.
5. Erosion and subduction have removed most craters from Earth's surface.

6. Scientists observe variations in crater density. They also analyze material gathered from space missions.

Foucault's Experiment

Today, scientists understand that Earth rotates on its axis once each day, which produces periods of daylight and darkness. However, day and night can be accounted for equally well by a sun and a celestial sphere that revolve around a stationary Earth. How to prove that Earth rotates?

In the 1500s, Copernicus realized that a rotating Earth that also revolves around the sun greatly simplified the model of the universe. But he was unable to prove his theory. The first proof was presented 300 years after the death of Copernicus by French physicist Jean Foucault.

The Swinging Pendulum

In 1851, Foucault used a free-swinging pendulum to demonstrate that Earth does, in fact, turn on its axis. To picture Foucault's experiment, imagine a large pendulum swinging over the North Pole, as shown in the illustration on this page. Keep in mind that once a pendulum is put into motion, it continues swinging in the same plane unless acted upon by some outside force. Assume that a sharp point is attached to the bottom of this pendulum, marking the snow as it swings. If we were to observe the marks made by the point, we would see that the pendulum is slowly but continually changing position. At the end of 24 hours, the pendulum would have returned to its starting position.

Evidence of Earth's Rotation

No outside force acted on the pendulum to change its position. So what we observed must have been Earth rotating beneath the pendulum. Foucault conducted a similar experiment when he suspended a long pendulum from the dome of the Pantheon in Paris. Today, Foucault pendulums can be found in some museums to recreate this famous science experiment.

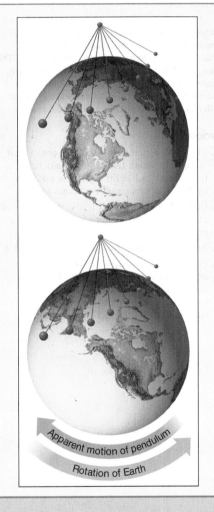

Apparent motion of pendulum

Rotation of Earth

Origin of Modern Astronomy **635**

Foucault's Experiment L2

Background The Foucault pendulum was constructed in 1851 by Jean Bernard Foucault and was demonstrated for the first time at the world's fair in Paris. The pendulum consisted of a 28-kg iron ball suspended from the dome of the Pantheon by a 67-m long steel wire.

Teaching Tips

After students have read p. 635, **Ask:** Once the pendulum is set in motion, it will continue to swing in the same direction unless it is pushed or pulled by a force. Why is this true? *(The pendulum's motion will obey Newton's first law of motion.)*

Ask: What outside force is acting on the pendulum to change its postion? *(None. Gravity keeps the pendulum swinging, but doesn't change its position.)*

Ask: Why does the pendulum change position over time? *(The pendulum did not change position, Earth moved beneath the pendulum.)*

Ask: How does this prove that Earth is rotating? *(The pendulum continued moving in the same direction because no outside force acted upon it. Since the pendulum did not change its motion, Earth beneath it must be moving.)*

Ask: Will Foucault's Experiment work at other places on Earth, and not just at the North Pole? *(Yes. A Foucault pendulum shows that our Earth is rotating, no matter where on Earth the experiment is performed (except for locations on the equator). However, a Foucault pendulum will return to its starting position in 24 hours only if the pendulum is hung over the North Pole or the South Pole. A Foucault pendulum hung over any other location on Earth will take longer than 24 hours to return to its initial position.)*

Ask: Why won't the experiment work at the equator? *(At the equator, the Foucault pendulum's direction of swing lines up perfectly with the direction of Earth's rotation, so the apparent motion and actual motion of the pendulum are identical. This means that the pendulum's direction of swing will not change over the course of a day.)*

Verbal

MODELING SYNODIC AND SIDEREAL MONTHS

L2

Objective After completing this activity, students will be able to explain the difference between synodic and sidereal months.

(Address **Misconceptions**)

Students might think that the time it takes for the moon to go through its phases, 29 1/2 days, is the same as the time it takes the moon to make one revolution around the Earth, 27 1/3 days. After performing this lab, ask students to explain the difference between these two cycles.

Skills Observe, Use Models, Analyze Data, Draw Conclusions

Prep Time 5 minutes

Advance Prep Obtain lamps, basketballs, and softballs for each lab group.

Class Time 30 minutes

Safety Position the electrical cords for the lamps so that they are not near a water source. Additionally, be sure that cords do not become tripping hazards.

Teaching Tips

• Borrow softballs and basketballs from the athletic department at your school.
• Encourage students to repeat Step 5 until they get the movements synchronized correctly.

Modeling Synodic and Sidereal Months

Problem How do synodic and sidereal months differ?

Materials pencil, paper, lamp, basketball, softball

Skills Observe, Use Models, Analyze Data, Draw Conclusions

Connect to the Big idea The time interval required for the moon to complete a full cycle of phases is 29.5 Earth days, or one synodic month. The true period of the moon's revolution around Earth, however, is only 27.3 Earth days and is known as the sidereal month. In this lab, you will model the differences between synodic and sidereal months.

Procedure

1. Copy the diagram on the next page onto a sheet of paper. In Month 1, indicate the dark half of the moon on each of the eight lunar positions by shading the appropriate area with a pencil.
2. On the diagram of Month 1, label the position of the new moon. Do the same for the other lunar phases.
3. Repeat Steps 1 and 2 for the diagram of Month 2.
4. Place the lamp on a desk or table. The lamp represents the sun. Hold the softball, which represents the moon. Have a partner hold the basketball, which represents Earth. Turn on the lamp and turn off all other lights in the room.

5. Stand so that the "moon" is in the position of the new-moon phase in Month 1, relative to "Earth" and the "sun." Revolve the moon around Earth while at the same time moving both Earth and the moon to Month 2. Stop at the same numbered position at which you began. Use the diagrams to guide your movements.

Analyze and Conclude

1. **Use Models** After one complete revolution beginning at the new-moon phase in Month 1, in what position is the moon located in Month 2?
2. **Interpret Data** Based on your answer to the previous question, does this position occur before or after the moon has completed one full cycle of phases?
3. **Identify** In Month 2, what position represents the new-moon phase? When the moon reaches this position, will it have completed a synodic or sidereal month?
4. **Explain** In your own words, explain the difference between a sidereal and synodic month.

GO FURTHER With your partner's help, use the lamp, softball, and basketball to model the positions of the sun, Earth, and moon during a lunar eclipse and a solar eclipse. On your diagram, label the position of the moon during each eclipse.

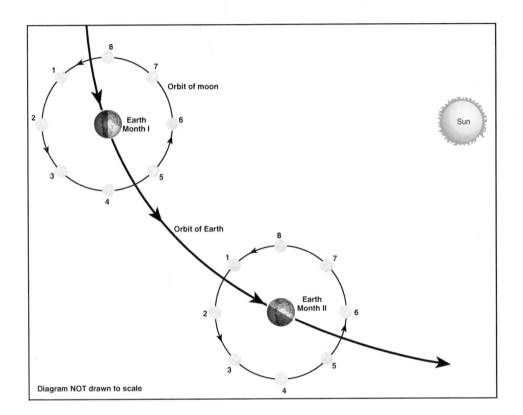

Diagram NOT drawn to scale

Analyze and Conclude
1. Position 6
2. before
3. Position 7; a synodic month
4. A sidereal month is one complete revolution of the moon around Earth. During a synodic month, the moon completes one cycle of phases. The synodic month is about two days longer than the sidereal month because of the motion of the Earth-moon system around the sun.

GO FURTHER

During a lunar eclipse, Earth is between the sun and moon. During a solar eclipse, the moon is between Earth and the sun. Lunar eclipses can only occur during full moons (position 2 in Month 1 and position 3 in Month 12). Solar eclipses can only occur during new moons (position 6 in Month 1 and position 7 in Month 2).
Kinesthetic, Verbal

Origin of Modern Astronomy **637**

Study Tip

Study With a Partner

On occasion, study with a friend. Quiz each other, compare notes from class lectures, go over homework answers, and discuss concepts that you need help with understanding.

Think Visually

a. Tycho Brahe
b. Galileo Galilei
c. Newton
d. heliocentric model
e. astronomical observations
f. laws of planetary motion
g. many possible answers, such as the discovery of Venus's phases

21st Century Learning

Information and Media Literacy

What is the origin of the Moon?

Current scientific opinion mostly supports the "giant impact" hypothesis of the origin of Earth's moon. However, there are several other hypotheses and not all of the key evidence is available. Ask students to work in pairs to investigate this topic on the Web and to find two articles that discuss competing hypotheses about the origin of the Moon. One of the articles should be from a reliable source, and the other from a less reliable source. Student pairs should discuss what makes each article reliable or unreliable on a blog or in their notes. Students should provide links to each of the articles.

Homework Guide

Lesson	Questions
1	1, 2, 11–16, 31, 32
2	3–7, 17–21, 24–27, 33
3	8–10, 22, 23, 28–30, 34

22 Study Guide

Big idea Earth and the Universe

22.1 Early Astronomy

🔑 In the geocentric model, the moon, sun, and the known planets—Mercury, Venus, Mars, Jupiter, and Saturn—orbit Earth.

🔑 In the heliocentric model, Earth and the other planets orbit the sun.

🔑 Copernicus placed the sun at the center of the solar system, with the planets orbiting around it.

🔑 Brahe's observations, especially of Mars, were far more precise than any made previously.

🔑 Using Brahe's precise observations, Kepler discovered three laws of planetary motion.

🔑 Galileo described the behavior of moving objects.

🔑 Newton was the first to formulate and test the law of universal gravitation.

astronomy (614)
geocentric (615)
orbit (615)
heliocentric (616)
retrograde motion (616)
ellipse (618)
astronomical unit (AU) (618)

22.2 The Earth-Moon-Sun System

🔑 The two main motions of Earth are rotation and revolution.

🔑 Lunar phases are caused by the changes in how much of the sunlit side of the moon faces Earth.

🔑 An eclipse can only occur during a new moon or full moon when the moon's orbit crosses the plane of the ecliptic.

rotation (622)
revolution (622)
precession (622)
perihelion (624)
aphelion (624)
perigee (626)
apogee (626)
phases of the moon (626)
solar eclipse (628)
lunar eclipse (628)

22.3 Earth's Moon

🔑 Most craters were produced by the impact of rapidly moving debris or meteoroids.

🔑 Maria, ancient beds of basaltic lava, originated when asteroids punctured the lunar surface, letting magma "bleed" out.

🔑 The most widely accepted model for the origin of the moon is that when the solar system was forming, a body the size of Mars impacted Earth.

crater (631)
ray (631)
mare (632)
rille (632)
lunar regolith (632)

Think Visually

Use the information from the chapter to complete the concept map below.

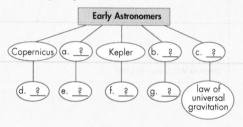

Assessment Answers

Review Content

1. b	2. b	3. c
4. b	5. d	6. c
7. c	8. d	9. b
10. a		

Understand Concepts

11. Ptolemy said that the planets moved along smaller circles, which in turn moved along their orbits around Earth. His theory was wrong because planets do not orbit Earth.

12. He observed and calculated the difference between the angles of the noonday sun in two cities.

13. His contribution was his accurate observations of Mars that were later used by Kepler to determine the three laws of planetary motion.

22 Assessment

Choose the letter that best answers the question or completes the statement.

1. Who first proposed that the sun was the center of the universe?
   a. Aristotle
   b. Aristarchus
   c. Anaxogoras
   d. Ptolemy

2. One astronomical unit averages about
   a. 93 million kilometers.
   b. 150 million kilometers.
   c. 210 million kilometers.
   d. 300 million kilometers.

3. During which month is Earth farthest from the sun?
   a. January
   b. April
   c. July
   d. October

4. In 13,000 years, Earth's axis will point toward
   a. Polaris.
   b. Vega.
   c. the sun.
   d. the moon.

5. At what point is the moon nearest to Earth during its orbit?
   a. at apogee
   b. at perihelion
   c. during an eclipse
   d. at perigee

6. What type of eclipse occurs when the moon casts its shadow on Earth?
   a. lunar
   b. sidereal
   c. solar
   d. synodic

7. During the period that the moon's phases are changing from new to full, the moon is always
   a. waning.
   b. approaching Earth.
   c. waxing.
   d. receding from Earth.

8. The large, dark regions on the moon are called
   a. highlands.
   b. craters.
   c. mountains.
   d. maria.

9. Rilles are associated with which of the following lunar features?
   a. craters
   b. maria
   c. rays
   d. highlands

10. The oldest lunar features are
    a. highlands.
    b. rayed craters.
    c. rilles.
    d. maria.

Understanding Concepts

11. How did Ptolemy explain what is now known as retrograde motion? How was his explanation flawed?

12. Describe how Eratosthenes measured the size of Earth.

13. What was Tycho Brahe's contribution to science?

14. Use Kepler's third law ($T^2 = d^3$) to determine the period of a hypothetical planet whose solar distance is 10 AU.

15. What is an astronomical unit?

16. Newton learned that the orbits of planets are the result of what interaction?

17. Explain the difference between the mean solar day and the sidereal day.

18. What is the approximate length of the cycle of the phases of the moon?

19. What phase of the moon occurs approximately one week after the new moon?

20. How many eclipses normally occur each year?

21. How long can a total eclipse of the moon last? A total eclipse of the sun?

22. Describe three features found on the moon's surface.

23. Briefly outline the history of the moon.

23. Accumulation of debris formed the moon; heat may have melted the moon's outer layer, remnants of which exist in lunar highlands; maria basins formed, which are later filled in by basaltic lava; large rayed craters formed last.

14. 31.6 years
15. The average distance between Earth and the sun, or about 150 million kilometers
16. The interaction of gravity and inertia
17. Earth takes 23 hours and 56 minutes to make one rotation with respect to a star, a period known as a sidereal day. Earth must rotate another 4 minutes to return to the noon position with respect to the sun, a period known as a mean solar day.

18. 29 1/2 days, or one synodic month
19. First-quarter phase
20. Four
21. A total eclipse of the moon can last up to four hours. A total eclipse of the sun lasts only about seven minutes.
22. Sample answer: depressions called craters, light-colored highlands, dark regions called maria

ASSESSMENT

Think Critically

24. Earth moves faster in January. Therefore, the longest solar day occurs in January.

25. The slow lunar rotation, along with the absence of an atmosphere, cause high surface temperatures on the side of the moon facing the sun and low surface temperatures on the side of the moon facing away from the sun.

26. A lunar eclipse is visible to anyone on the side of Earth facing the moon. A solar eclipse is visible only by those in the narrow region covered by the moon's shadow.

27. Sample answer: The two most obvious interactions may be gravity and the light cast on Earth during the brighter phases of the moon. Without the moon's gravity, there would be smaller tides. Without those tides, heat exchange between ocean and atmosphere would be altered, and ocean life would be affected. Without moonlight, lives of nocturnal animals would be affected, as well as the migratory habits of some species.

Analyze Data

28. Mare; when layer upon layer of basaltic lava flooded the moon's surface

29. Point D is a rayed crater; point C shows highlands.

30. Point C is oldest. It marks the highlands, which are densely cratered.

Concepts in Action

31. Venus is full when it is on the opposite side of the sun from Earth, an alignment that could only happen in the Copernican view of the universe.

32. It showed that a body other than Earth could be a center of motion.

33. The same side of the moon always faces Earth.

34. The greater the crater density, the longer the topographic feature must have existed.

Think Critically

24. Draw Conclusions Does Earth move faster in its orbit near perihelion (January) or near aphelion (July)? Based on your answer, is the solar day longest in January or July?

25. Predict The moon rotates very slowly on its axis. Predict how this affects the lunar surface temperature.

26. Apply Concepts Solar eclipses are slightly more common than lunar eclipses. Why then is it more likely that your region of the country will experience a lunar eclipse?

27. Draw Conclusions In what ways do the interactions between Earth and its moon influence the Earth-moon system? If Earth did not have a moon, would the atmosphere, hydrosphere, geosphere, and biosphere be any different? Explain.

Analyze Data

Use the photograph below to answer Questions 28–30.

Concepts in Action

28. Interpret Visuals What feature exists at point A? How did this feature likely form?

29. Interpret Visuals Which point represents a ray? Which point represents highlands?

30. Infer What is the oldest feature in the photograph? How do you know?

Concepts in Action

31. Relate Cause and Effect How does the fact that Venus appears full when it is smallest support Copernicus's view rather than the Ptolemaic system?

32. Explain How did Galileo's discovery of Jupiter's moons support the heliocentric model?

33. Identify What is the result of the moon having the same period of rotation and revolution?

34. Apply Concepts How is crater density used in the relative dating of features on the moon?

Performance-Based Assessment

Observe Record at least four observations of the moon over the next two weeks. Sketch the moon at each observation. Use shading to show the phase you see. Note the date and time of each observation. Afterward, write a paragraph describing how the size and shape of the lit portion of the moon changed over the length of your observations.

Performance-Based Assessment

Students should choose a safe location from which to view the moon. Have them begin their observations on a clear night. They should take along a notebook to record the observations and make sketches.

Standardized Test Prep

Tips for Success

Eliminating Unreasonable Answers When you answer a multiple-choice question, you can often eliminate at least one answer because it is clearly incorrect. If you eliminate one or more choices, you increase your odds of choosing the correct answer. In the question below, you can immediately eliminate choice A because the moon does not have rivers on its surface. Clearly, choices B and D cannot both be true because they relate to the same phenomenon. You can eliminate both of these choices because volcanic activity is not currently occurring on the moon. The remaining choice, C, must be the correct answer.

The most important factors currently modifying the moon's surface are—
A rivers
B lava flows
C tiny particles from space
D volcanoes

(Answer: C)

1 **The Ptolemaic system assumed that—**
A Earth revolved around the sun
B the sun was the center of the universe
C Earth was a wanderer
D Earth was the center of the universe

2 **What is the shape of a planet's orbit?**
F circular
G irregular
H elliptical
J constantly changing

Use the diagram below to answer Questions 3 and 4.

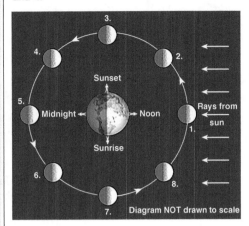

Diagram NOT drawn to scale

3 **Which number illustrates the moon's position in its orbit during a full moon? A new moon?**
A full: 1; new: 5
B full: 3; new: 7
C full: 5; new: 1
D full: 7; new: 3

4 **What number represents the position of the moon during a lunar eclipse? A solar eclipse?**
F lunar: 1; solar: 5
G lunar: 3; solar: 7
H lunar: 5; solar: 1
J lunar: 7; solar: 3

If You Have Trouble With . . .

Question	1	2	3	4
See Lesson	22.1	22.2	22.3	22.3

Origin of Modern Astronomy **641**

23 Touring Our Solar System Planning Guide

BIGIDEA: EARTH AND THE UNIVERSE

Lesson Objectives		Activities
23.1 The Solar System pp. 644–648 23.1 **List** the major differences between the terrestrial and Jovian planets. 23.2 **Explain** how the solar system formed.		TE Teacher Demo: Speeding Up a Spinning Nebula, p. 647 L2
23.2 The Terrestrial Planets pp. 649–653 23.3 **Describe** the distinguishing characteristics of each terrestrial planet.		
23.3 The Outer Planets (and Pluto) pp. 654–659 23.4 **Describe** the distinguishing characteristics of each Jovian planet. 23.5 **Explain** why Pluto is not considered a planet.		TE Teacher Demo: Discovering the Rings of Uranus p. 658 L2
23.4 Minor Members of the Solar System pp. 660–664 23.6 **Identify** the location within our solar system where most asteroids are found. 23.7 **Describe** the structure of a comet. 23.8 **Explain** the possible origins for a meteoroid.		TE Teacher Demo: Modeling a Comet's Tail, p. 662 L2

Chapter Features and Labs		
Try It What is the Shape of a Planetary Orbit? p. 643		LM Exploring Orbits L2
Earth & Space Is Earth on a Collision Course? p. 665		
Exploration Lab Modeling the Solar System, pp. 666–667		

Ability Levels

L1 For students who need additional help
L2 For all students
L3 For students who need to be challenged

Components

SE	Student Edition	LP	Lesson Plans
TE	Teacher's Edition	AA	Active Art
LM	Laboratory Manual	PD	Planet Diary
CT	Chapter Tests	GEODe	Geode CD-ROM
GRSW	Guided Reading & Study Workbook	eText	
CTB	Computer Test Bank		

Resources	Lesson Assessment
GRSW Lesson 23.1 **LP** Lesson Planning Lesson 23.1 **AA** Solar System Activity **GEODe** Astronomy: The Planets: An Overview Earth's Moon	**SE** Lesson 23.1 Assessment, p. 648 **eText** Lesson 23.1
GRSW Lesson 23.2 **LP** Lesson Planning Lesson 23.2 **GEODe** Astronomy: Calculating Your Age and Weight on Other Planets	**SE** Lesson 23.2 Assessment, p. 653 **eText** Lesson 23.2
GRSW Lesson 23.3 **LP** Lesson Planning Lesson 23.3	**SE** Lesson 23.3 Assessment, p. 659 **eText** Lesson 23.2
GRSW Lesson 23.4 **LP** Lesson Planning Lesson 23.4 **PD** Links on comets and meteor showers **GEODe** Astronomy: A Brief Tour of the Planets	**SE** Lesson 23.4 Assessment, p. 664 **eText** Lesson 23.4

Materials for Activities and Labs

Quantities for each group

STUDENT EDITION

Try It, p. 643
cardboard (about 20 cm²), 2 pushpins, ruler, piece of string, pencil, tape, unlined paper

Exploration Lab, p. 666–667
meter stick, colored pencils, calculator, 6-m length of adding machine paper

TEACHER'S EDITION

Teacher Demo, p. 647
chair that spins in place

Teacher Demo, p. 658
meter stick, flashlight

Teacher Demo, p. 662
table-top fan, light-weight paper, tape

Assessment

CHAPTER ASSESSMENT
SE Assessment, pp. 669–670
CTB Chapter 23
eText Chapter 23

21st Century Learning

Communication Skills: Where in the Solar System have we probed and why?, TE p. 668

Common Themes

Michael Wysession
Washington University

Earth is part of a solar system, which consists of the sun, eight planets and their moons, three dwarf planets, asteroids, meteoroids, and comets.

Space and Time The solar system is enormous, extending outward from the sun more than 10,000 times the Earth-sun distance (10,000 AU). The solar system formed from the contraction of a pre-solar nebula, a vast cloud of gas and dust. The center of the nebula became the sun, and the outer parts accreted to form millions of planetesimals, which eventually collided and coalesced to form the planets.

Forces and Motion All of the planets revolve around the sun in the same direction, and most rotate around their axes in the same direction. Planets further from the sun take longer to revolve around it.

Matter and Energy The sun makes up 99.85 percent of the mass of the solar system. The terrestrial planets (Mercury, Venus, Earth, Mars) are relatively small, and are mostly made of a rocky mantle and metal core. The gas giants (Jupiter, Saturn, Uranus, Neptune) are relatively large, have thick layers of gas and liquid above a rock/metal interior, and are orbited by moons and rings. The Kuiper belt objects, like Pluto, extend 100 AU out from the sun, and are mostly rock and ice. Small icy comets also orbit the sun, though most are found in the Oort cloud, which extends to edge of the solar system.

Earth as a System Earth is constantly bombarded by tiny meteoroids, which streak across the sky as meteors, and by cometary debris, which has been a source of Earth's water. Some meteoroids originate in the Asteroid belt.

EARTH SCIENCE REFRESHER

Astrobiology

Are we alone in the universe? This is perhaps the most culturally significant question that planetary science is addressing. Much of the current efforts of NASA involve the search for life on other planets. Some of these efforts involve direct investigations of other planetary bodies. Mars is very important in this respect, because it appears likely that this neighbor once had plentiful water on its surface, and as we have found on Earth, where there is water there is life. Another important target for robotic missions is the moon of Jupiter, Europa, which likely has a salt-water ocean beneath an outer layer of ice. Life on Earth began in a salt-water ocean, and scientists are excited to investigate the possibility that there may currently be life on Europa.

Some of NASA's investigations, however, are of a more theoretical nature. Using what we have learned from the planets and moons in our solar system, can we determine what kind of a planet would be needed to develop intelligent life? Life on Earth took 4 billion years before it learned to play the piano. That is a long time to require the presence of liquid water on the surface. If Earth was twice as big, would this still have happened? If Earth was twice as far from the sun, or if the sun was twice as big, would life still have evolved?

It is beginning to look like the conditions needed for intelligent life to evolve on a planet are very narrow. If Earth were a little different in size, a little different in distance

> **Address Misconceptions**
>
> *The solar system and outer space in general are very crowded.* Actually, the planets and stars are very far apart. For a strategy that helps to overcome this misconception, see **Address Misconceptions** on **TE p. 646.**

Scientific knowledge is gathered solely through controlled experiments. Many advances in science actually come from fieldwork and careful observations. For a strategy that helps to overcome this misconception, see **Address Misconceptions** on **TE p. 649.**

from the sun, or the sun a little different in size, water would not be continuously liquid. Earth has the right composition and amount of water to allow plate tectonics to occur, which is the reason that we have land (and there is some debate as to whether civilizations could have developed if life never left the oceans). Earth also benefits from a nearly circular orbit, which keeps annual temperatures nearly constant; the presence of a large moon, which helps to stabilize its axis of rotation; and the presence of large outer planets such as Jupiter, which have the right size and orbit to stabilize the asteroid belt and to gravitationally hurl out of the solar system rogue asteroids that might collide with Earth. Our sun is small enough to last for a long time (large suns burn out quickly), but large enough to keep us warm. Our solar system is also in the right location within the right kind of galaxy—go too close to the center of the Milky Way and the radiation is too intense and the impacts too frequent; go too far out, and stars are too small and metal-poor. There are whole galaxies that seem to be too poor in metals to allow for planets such as Earth.

A couple of decades ago a formula was developed called the Drake equation, which took into account many aspects of planetary, galactic, and cultural evolution, to predict how many other planets in our galaxy might have sufficiently advanced societies that would be trying to contact us. Some early predictions put the number in the millions. However, with what we are now learning about the stringent conditions required to support life on a planet for billions of years, Earth might be the only one.

BUILD READING LITERACY
Compare and Contrast
Identify Similarities and Differences

Strategy Help students read and understand material that discusses two or more related topics or concepts. This strategy helps students identify similarities and differences, thus enabling them to link prior knowledge with new information. Before students begin, assign a lesson in Chapter 23 for them to read, such as Lesson 23.1, pp. 644–648.

Example

1. Have students compare two or more topics or concepts under a section heading. Tell them that when they compare, they should focus on both similarities and differences. Remind them to look for these signal words:

- Similarities: similar, similarly, also, just as, like, likewise, in the same way
- Differences: but, however, although, whereas, on the other hand, different, unlike

2. Have students contrast two or more topics or concepts. Remind students that when they contrast, they should focus only on differences.

3. Have students create a chart or diagram comparing or contrasting two or more topics or concepts they read about in the section. Suggest that they create either a compare/contrast table or a Venn diagram to present their information.

See TE p. 645 and 650 for a script on how to use this strategy with students. For additional strategies, see TE pp. 652, 656, 661, 663, and 664.

CHAPTER 23

23 Touring Our Solar System

Big idea

Earth and the Universe

Q: Where in the solar system have we probed and why?

If you were able to stand on the surface of Mars, this is a landscape you might see. This "natural color" image of a crater about the length of a football field was taken by the Mars Exploration Rover named Opportunity. The image is made by pasting together many smaller images. The pasting process leaves some blanks such as the ones you see at the bottom of the image.

642

Chapter Pretest

1. An object with a density of 1.2 g/cm³ placed in a cup filled with water, will *(a)*
  a. sink to the bottom.
  b. float on top of the water.
  c. float in the middle of the water.

2. Earth's atmosphere is mostly made of *(c)*
  a. water vapor.
  b. carbon dioxide.
  c. nitrogen.

3. It takes Earth about _____ to rotate once. *(b)*
  a. 1 year
  b. 24 hours
  c. 30 days

4. Convection currents can occur in *(d)*
  a. solids only.
  b. liquids only.
  c. gases only.
  d. liquids, gases, and solids.

5. True or False: In a convection current, the warmer, less dense fluid rises. *(True)*

6. Convection currents in Earth's atmosphere are caused by *(a)*
  a. solar energy.
  b. heat from Earth's interior.
  c. gravity.
  d. plate movements.

7. True or False: A shooting star is actually a star that is falling from the sky. *(False)*

TRY IT!

WHAT IS THE SHAPE OF A PLANETARY ORBIT?

Procedure

1. Place a piece of cardboard about 20 cm square on a flat surface. Place two push pins into the cardboard about 3 cm apart.
2. Tie the ends of a 10-cm length of string together. Loop the string around the pushpins.
3. Using a pencil to keep the string taut, trace around the pins.
4. Repeat Steps 1 through 3, varying the distance between the two pins.

Think About It

1. **Observe** What type of shape did you draw?
2. **Observe** What happened when you moved the pins farther apart?
3. **Compare** How do your drawings compare with the shapes of planetary orbits? *[HINT: See the illustrations of orbits inside the chapter.]*

643

ENGAGE/EXPLORE

WHAT IS THE SHAPE OF A PLANETARY ORBIT?   L2

Purpose In this activity, students will discover how ellipses are made and observe that changing the foci of an ellipse changes its eccentricity.

Skill Observe

Prep Time 10 minutes

Materials cardboard (about 20 cm^2), 2 pushpins, ruler, piece of string, pencil, tape, unlined paper

Advance Prep Precut the pieces of string, making each piece about 10 cm long.

Class Time 25 minutes

Teaching Tips
- Have students tape a piece of unlined paper onto their cardboard before putting the pins in. If students draw on the paper, rather than directly on the cardboard, the cardboard may be reused for multiple classes or multiple years.
- This activity will have more meaning if you explain that ellipses have two foci that are used to draw the shape. The pins students use in this activity serve as the foci for each ellipse they draw.

Expected Outcome Students will discover that ellipses can be drawn by using two foci. They will learn that all planets orbit the sun in ellipses of varying eccentricities.

Think About It
1. Students should have drawn three different ellipses.
2. Students should find that the farther the pins were moved apart, the more flattened the ellipse became.
3. Students should note that their drawings and the planetary orbits pictured in this chapter are ellipses.

LESSON 23.1

☐ FOCUS

Lesson Objectives

23.1 **List** the major differences between the terrestrial and Jovian planets.

23.2 **Explain** how the solar system formed.

Build Vocabulary · L2

Word Part Analysis Teach students that *terr-* means "Earth," and *-ial* and *-ian* mean "of, or related to" so *terrestrial* means "Earthly" or "Earth-like." Terrestrial planets are those similar to Earth while Jovian planets are those similar to Jupiter.

Advise students that *nebula* is related to the word *nebulous,* which means "hazy" or "unclear." The word *nebula* is used to describe a "hazy mass of gases and dust seen among the stars." Tell students that *infinitesimal* means "infinitely small," and have them predict the meaning of *planetesimal.* (*Planetesimals are small solid bodies that combine to form planets.*)

Reading Strategy · L2

a. The sun formed at the center of a disk.
b. Matter collided to form planetesimals.
c. Planetesimals eventually grow into planets.

☐ INSTRUCT

Use Visuals · L1

Figure 1 This diagram shows the orbits of all 8 planets around the sun. **Ask:** Which planet is the closest to the sun? *(Mercury)* The asteroid belt is found between which two planets? *(Mars and Jupiter)*

Tell students that the diagram is not drawn to scale. However, the scale along the bottom of the figure shows the scale distances from planet to planet. Tell students that the inner planets are those found before the asteroid belt, and the outer planets are found after the asteroid belt. **Ask:** How does the distance between the inner planets differ from the distance between the outer planets? *(The inner planets are much closer together than the outer planets.)*
Visual

23.1 The Solar System

Key Questions

🔹 *How do terrestrial planets differ from Jovian planets?*

🔹 *How did the solar system form?*

Vocabulary

- terrestrial planet
- Jovian planet
- nebula • planetesimal

Reading Strategy

Relate Text and Diagrams
As you read, refer to Figure 3 to complete the flowchart on the formation of the solar system.

THE SUN IS the hub of a huge rotating system of planets, their satellites, and numerous smaller celestial (meaning *of the sky*) bodies. An estimated 99.85 percent of the mass of our solar system is contained within the sun. The planets collectively make up most of the remaining 0.15 percent. As **Figure 1** shows, the planets, listed in order starting nearest from the sun, are Mercury, Venus, Earth, Mars, Jupiter, Saturn, Uranus, and Neptune.

Held in place by the sun's gravitational force, each planet moves in an elliptical orbit, and all travel in the same direction. The nearest planet to the sun—Mercury—has the fastest orbital motion at 48 kilometers per second, and it has the shortest period of revolution. By contrast, the most distant planet, Neptune, has an orbital speed of 5 kilometers per second, and it requires 165 Earth years to complete one revolution.

Imagine a planet's orbit drawn on a flat sheet of paper. The paper represents the planet's orbital plane. The orbital planes of seven planets lie within three degrees of the plane of the sun's equator. Mercury's orbit is inclined by seven degrees.

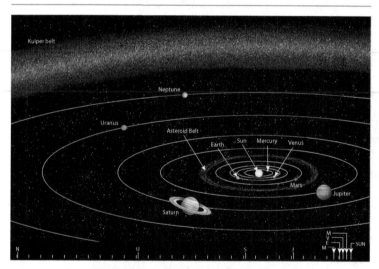

FIGURE 1 Orbits of the Planets Notice the elliptical orbits of the planets. The lines and letters at the bottom show the scale distances of each planet from the sun.

The Planets: An Overview

Careful examination of **Table 1** shows that the planets fall quite nicely into two groups. The **terrestrial planets**—Mercury, Venus, Earth, and Mars—are relatively small and rocky. (*Terrestrial* = Earth-like.) The **Jovian planets**—Jupiter, Saturn, Uranus, and Neptune—are huge gas giants. (*Jovian* = Jupiter-like.)

🔑 **Size is the most obvious difference between the terrestrial and the Jovian planets.** The diameter of the largest terrestrial planet, Earth, is only one-quarter the diameter of the smallest Jovian planet, Neptune. Also, Earth's mass is only 1/17 as great as Neptune's. Hence, the Jovian planets are often called giants. Because of their distant locations from the sun, the four Jovian planets are also called the *outer planets*. The terrestrial planets are closer to the sun and are called the *inner planets*. As we shall see, there appears to be a correlation between the positions of these planets and their sizes.

🔑 **Density, chemical makeup, and rate of rotation are other ways in which the two groups of planets differ.** The densities of the terrestrial planets average about five times the density of water. The Jovian planets, however, have densities that average only 1.5 times the density of water. For example, Saturn, has a density only 0.7 times that of water, which means that Saturn would theoretically float if placed in a large enough body of water. The outer planets are less dense because much of their huge volume consists of gas and ice. The outer planets rotate on their axes more quickly than the inner planets.

☑ **Reading Checkpoint** *Compare the densities of terrestrial planets and Jovian planets.*

Table 1 Planetary Data

Planet	Average Distance from Sun AU	Average Distance from Sun Millions of km	Period of Revolution	Orbital Velocity km/s	Period of Rotation	Diameter (km)	Relative Mass (Earth = 1)	Average Density (g/cm^3)	Number of Known Satellites*
Mercury	0.39	58	88^d	47.5	59^d	4878	0.06	5.4	0
Venus	0.72	108	225^d	35.0	244^d	12,104	0.82	5.2	0
Earth	1.00	150	365.25^d	29.8	23^h 56^m 04^s	12,756	1.00	5.5	1
Mars	1.52	228	687^d	24.1	24^h 37^m 23^s	6794	0.11	3.9	2
Jupiter	5.20	778	12^{yr}	13.1	9^h 50^m	143,884	317.87	1.3	64
Saturn	9.54	1427	29.5^{yr}	9.6	10^h 14^m	120,536	95.14	0.7	62
Uranus	19.18	2870	84^{yr}	6.8	17^h 14^m	51,118	14.56	1.2	27
Neptune	30.06	4497	165^{yr}	5.3	16^h 03^m	49,528	17.21	1.7	13
Pluto**	39.44	5900	248^{yr}	4.7	6.4^d	approx. 2300	0.002	1.8	3

*Includes all satellites discovered as of May 2011.

**Pluto is included for purposes of comparison.

Build Reading Literacy 🔲 L1

Refer to **p. 642D,** which provides guidelines for comparing and contrasting.

Compare and Contrast Have students make a chart comparing the characteristics of the terrestrial planets and the Jovian planets. Have them start with what they observed about the distances between planets in the **Use Visuals** activity on p. 644, and use the reading, tables, and figures on pp. 645–647. For example:

Terrestrial Planets	Jovian Planets
Orbits are close together	Orbits are far apart
Smaller diameter	Larger diameter
More dense	Less dense
Rotate slower	Rotate faster
Thin or no atmosphere	Thick atmosphere
Composed mostly of rocky and metallic substances, with few gases and ices	Mostly made of gases, liquids, and ices, but with rocky and metallic materials in their cores

Visual, Verbal

Answers

☑ **Reading Checkpoint** *The terrestrial planets have greater densities than the Jovian planets.*

Differentiated Instruction

SPECIAL NEEDS Help students complete Compare and Contrast activities by providing them with scaffolding. Give them a chart to fill in that lists the categories they should be comparing. For example, these students could be given a chart such as the one below to use for the Compare and Contrast activity on this page.

Characteristic	Terrestrial Planets	Jovian Planets
Distance from one planet to the next		
Diameter		
Density		
Rotation rate		
Atmosphere		
Composition		

Use Visuals L1

Figure 2 Have students study Figure 2 and answer the caption question. **Ask:** Which planet is the smallest? *(Mercury)* Which planet is the largest? *(Jupiter)* How does the size of the largest planet compare to the size of the sun? *(Jupiter is much smaller than the sun.)*
Visual

FIGURE 2 Scale Sizes The planets and Pluto are drawn to scale.
Interpret Diagrams How do the sizes of the terrestrial planets compare with the sizes of the Jovian planets?

The Interiors of the Planets The materials that make up the planets are divided into three groups: gases, rocks, and ices. These groups are classified by the melting points of the substances.

1. Gases—hydrogen and helium—have melting points near absolute zero ($-273°C$ or 0 kelvin).
2. Rocks are mainly silicate minerals and metallic iron, which have melting points above 700°C.
3. Ices include ammonia (NH_3), methane (CH_4), carbon dioxide (CO_2), and water (H_2O). They have intermediate melting points, around 0°C.

The terrestrial planets are dense, consisting mostly of rocky and metallic substances, and only minor amounts of gases and ices. The Jovian planets are less dense and contain large amounts of gases and ices. The outer planets also contain substantial amounts of rocky and metallic materials, which are concentrated in their cores. Outer planet rocky cores are small compared to the overall size of the planets.

The Atmospheres of the Planets The Jovian planets have very dense atmospheres of hydrogen, helium, methane, and ammonia. By contrast, the terrestrial planets, including Earth, have thin atmospheres at best. A planet's ability to retain an atmosphere depends on its gravitational force, which depends on its mass, and its temperature.

A gas molecule can escape from a planet if it reaches a speed known as the *escape velocity*. Escape velocity for a given planet depends on its gravitational force. For Earth, escape velocity is 11 kilometers per second. Any material, including a rocket, must reach this velocity before it can escape Earth's gravity and go into space.

The motion, or velocity, of a gas molecule depends upon its temperature. Planets closer to the sun have a higher temperature, so gas molecules of the inner planets would move relatively fast. A warm, small body, such as Mercury, cannot hold gases, and has almost no atmosphere. The inner planets larger than Mercury—Earth, Venus, and Mars—have more mass and retain some heavy gases. Still, their atmospheres make up only a small portion of their total mass.

In contrast, the larger Jovian planets have much greater surface gravities. This gives them escape velocities of 21 to 60 kilometers per second. Also, the temperatures of the outer planets are much colder. So it is more difficult for even the lightest gases to acquire the velocity needed to escape. As a result, the outer planets have dense atmospheres.

Facts and Figures

Why are the Jovian planets so much larger than the terrestrial planets? According to the nebular hypothesis, the planets formed from a rotating disk of dust and gases that surrounded the sun. The growth of planets began as solid bits of matter began to collide and clump together. In the inner solar system, the temperatures were so high that only the metals and silicate materials could form solid grains. It was too hot for ices of water, carbon dioxide, and methane to form. Thus, the innermost (terrestrial) planets grew mainly from the high melting point substances found in the solar nebula. By contrast, in the frigid outer reaches of the solar system, it was cold enough for ices of water and other substances to form. Consequently, the outer planets are thought to have grown not only from accumulations of solid bits of metals and silicate minerals but also from large quantities of ices. Eventually, the outer planets became large enough to gravitationally capture the lightest gases (hydrogen and helium), and thus grow to become "giant" planets.

Formation of the Solar System

Perhaps you have heard the phrase "the vacuum of space." Space is not, however, a pure vacuum. In addition to stars and other bodies, it is populated with regions of widely spread dust and gases. A cloud of dust and gas in space is called a **nebula** (*nebula* = cloud; plural: *nebulae*). A nebular cloud is similar to fog in the sense that it does not have very defined edges. A nebula, shown in **Figure 3A,** often consists of roughly 90 percent hydrogen, nine percent helium, and a small percentage of the remaining heavier elements.

Nebular Theory Obviously there is no direct evidence to help scientists understand how our solar system formed. Instead, one of the goals of astronomy is to discover indirect evidence by observing other bodies in space that appear to be in various stages of development. Observing the stages that other nebula seem to be going through provides scientists with some of the information necessary to develop a theory about how solar systems form.

Scientific studies of nebulae have led to a theory concerning the origin of our solar system. **According to the nebular theory, the sun and planets formed from a rotating disk of dust and gases.** As nebular material contracted due to gravity, most of the material collected in the center. The remaining materials formed a thick, flattened rotating disk. Within this disk, the material cooled and formed grains and clumps of icy, rocky material. All of this took many millions of years to complete.

FIGURE 3 Formation of the Solar System
A According to the nebular theory, the solar system formed from a rotating cloud of dust and gas. **B** The sun formed at the center of the rotating disk. **C** Planetesimals collided, eventually gaining enough mass to be planets.

Touring Our Solar System **647**

Evaluate Understanding   L2

Have students develop quiz questions from this lesson and put them on flashcards. Then put the students in small groups where they will compete to see who can answer the most questions correctly. Put the cards in the center of the table, and have students take turns selecting a card and trying to answer it. If a student cannot answer the question, the card is returned to the bottom of the pile. Students earn the card of each question they answer correctly. The winner is the one with the most cards at the end of the game. You may want to continue this activity throughout the chapter. This will give any students who are behind after the first lesson an incentive to improve their studying so they are able to catch up and even win the game.

Reteach   L1

Have students summarize the differences between the terrestrial and Jovian planets by using the figures and tables in this lesson.

Assessment Answers

1. Terrestrial: Mercury, Venus, Earth, and Mars; Jovian: Jupiter, Saturn, Uranus, and Neptune

2. Mercury, Venus, Earth, Mars, Jupiter, Saturn, Uranus, Neptune

3. The terrestrial planets are small and rocky. The Jovian planets are gas giants.

4. A nebula is a cloud of dust and gas in space.

5. Close to the sun, temperatures were so high that only metals and silicate minerals could form solid grains. Thus, the inner planets grew mainly from substances with high melting points. In the outer reaches of the solar system, ices of water and other substances formed. Consequently, the Jovian

Planetesimals The growth of planets began as solid bits of matter collided and clumped together through a process known as *accretion*. The colliding matter formed small, irregularly shaped bodies called **planetesimals.** As the collisions continued, the planetesimals grew larger, as shown in **Figure 3C** on the previous page. Eventually, they acquired enough mass to exert a gravitational pull on surrounding objects. In this way, they added still more mass and grew into true planets.

In the inner solar system, close to the sun, temperatures were so high that only metals and silicate minerals could form solid grains. It was too hot for ices of water, carbon dioxide, and methane to form. As shown in **Figure 4,** the inner planets grew mainly from substances with high melting points.

In the much colder outer reaches of the solar system, it was cold enough for ices of water and other substances to form. Consequently, the Jovian planets grew not only from accumulations of solid bits of material but also from large quantities of ices. Eventually, the Jovian planets became large enough to gravitationally capture even the lightest gases, such as hydrogen and helium. This enabled them to grow into giants.

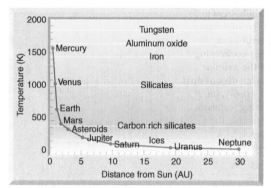

FIGURE 4 Materials That Formed the Planets The terrestrial planets formed mainly from materials with high melting points. The Jovian planets formed from large quantities of gases and ices.

23.1 Assessment

Review Key Concepts

1. Which planets are classified as terrestrial? Which planets are classified as Jovian?

2. List the planets in order, beginning with the planet closest to the sun.

3. How do the terrestrial planets differ from the Jovian planets?

4. What is a nebula?

5. How does distance from the sun affect the size and composition of the planets?

Think Critically

6. Review Explain the nebular theory of the formation of the solar system.

7. Infer Among the planets in our solar system, Earth is unique because water exists in all three states—solid, liquid, and gas—on Earth's surface. How would Earth's water cycle be different if its orbit were outside the orbit of Mars?

MATH PRACTICE

8. Calculate Jupiter is 6.3×10^8 (630 million) kilometers from Earth. Calculate how long it would take to reach Jupiter if you traveled at
1) 100 km/h (freeway speed);
2) 1,000 km/h (jetliner speed);
3) 40,000 km/h (rocket speed); and
4) 3.0×10^8 km/s (speed of light).

---

planets grew not only from accumulations of solid bits of material but also from large quantities of gases and ices.

6. The sun and planets formed from a rotating disk of dust and gases. As the speed of rotation increased, the center of the disk began to flatten out. Matter became more concentrated in this center, where the sun eventually formed.

7. Sample answer: Only ice would exist. With only frozen water, there would be no precipitation, runoff, or infiltration—the water cycle and life itself would not exist.

8. (1) 6.3×10^8 km ÷ 100 km/h = 6,300,000 h ÷ 24 h/day = 262,500 days ÷ 365 days/yr = 719 yrs
(2) 6.3×10^8 km ÷ 1000 km/h = 630,000 h ÷ 24 h/day = 26,250 days ÷ 365 days/yr = 72 yrs
(3) 6.3×10^8 km ÷ 40,000 km/h = 15,750 h ÷ 24 h/day = 656 days ÷ 365 days/yr = 1.8 yrs
(4) 6.3×10^8 km ÷ 300,000 km/s = 2100 s ÷ 60 s/ 1 min = 35 minutes

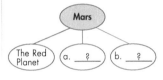

23.2 The Terrestrial Planets

THE ROBOTIC EXPLORER, *Curiosity*, a NASA Mars Science Laboratory rover, has several interesting features. *Curiosity* is tasked, among other things, with discovering evidence that microbial life does exist (or could have existed) on Mars—the fourth planet from the sun. To help in this task, the "head" of the rover has the ability to rise to 2.1 meters—about as tall as some professional basketball players. The head has dual cameras for stereo color viewing of the Martian surface, or for viewing rock samples collected by the "arms." Another feature of the head is a powerful laser beam that can vaporize rock samples from about 9 meters away. Sensors on the rover can then anlayze the vapors and determine what elements were in the rock. Other features, such as a drill and a scoop, enable the rover to pick up samples for analysis by its onboard instruments.

Mercury: The Innermost Planet

Mercury, the planet closest to the sun, is only slightly larger than Earth's moon and smaller than three moons in the solar system. Mercury has a high orbital velocity, taking only 88 Earth days for one orbit around the sun. Yet, Mercury rotates on its axis slowly, so that a sidereal day has a period of about 59 Earth days. A result of this fast revolution and slow rotation is that a solar day on Mercury has a period of 176 Earth days, or about six Earth months. So, a Mercurial solar day is twice as long as a Mercurial year.

Key Questions

🔑 *What are the distinguishing characteristics of each terrestrial planet?*

Reading Strategy

Use Prior Knowledge Copy the web diagram below. Before you read, add properties that you already know about Mars. Then add details about each property as you read. Make a similar web diagram for the other terrestrial planets.

FIGURE 5 Mars Rover *Curiosity*, a Mars Science Laboratory rover, is tasked with exploring evidence of microbial life. (Artist's concept)

LESSON 23.2

1 FOCUS

Lesson Objective
23.3 **Describe** the distinguishing characteristics of each terrestrial planet.

Build Vocabulary   L2
Vocabulary List Encourage students to keep a list of new terms they encounter as they read this chapter. Have them use the context of each term to predict its definition. Go over the terms with the class. Some terms they may select are *rover, nonexistent, penetrate, veiled, summit, flank,* and *prominent.*

Reading Strategy L2
Sample answers:
a. explored by rovers
b. numerous large volcanoes

Address **Misconceptions** L2

Some students may think that scientific knowledge is only acquired from controlled experiments. However, a great deal of scientific knowledge is a result of fieldwork and careful observations. In fact, a great deal of what we know about the universe and our solar system, we learned strictly from observation. To help students realize this, ask these questions as you teach this lesson. **Ask:** What did we learn about Venus from the Magellan spacecraft? *(Venus has varied topography like Earth.)* What did we learn about Mars from the orbiting spacecraft Mariner 9? *(Mars has volcanoes and canyons.)* What did we learn about Mars from the rovers Spirit and Opportunity? *(Mars has evaporite minerals and evidence of geological processes caused by liquid water; Mars has sand dunes and impact craters.)* What did we learn from Mars Global Surveyor? *(Underground springs may have existed on Mars.)* Could we have learned these things simply from controlled experiments on Earth? *(no)*
Verbal

Build Reading Literacy [L1]

Refer to **p. 362D** in **Chapter 13,** which provides guidelines for using prior knowledge.

Use Prior Knowledge Have students make a web diagram that includes information they already know about Mercury. Have them add new information to their web as they read. Possible characteristics of Mercury include: small, hot, closest to sun, has craters, very dense, revolves around sun quickly, rotates slowly, greatest temperature extremes of any planet. **Visual, Verbal**

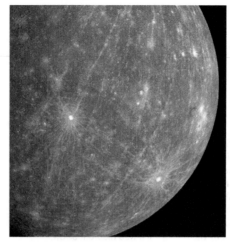

FIGURE 6 Craters on Mercury This image of Mercury was obtained by the uncrewed spacecraft *Messenger*. The bright crater to the left of center is Kuiper, which has a width of about 60 kilometers and is thought to be relatively young.

Structure Mercury has a weak magnetic field, which is evidence that there is a liquid core. The convection currents of a liquid core can generate a magnetic field. The solid surface of Mercury has cratered highlands, much like the moon, and some smooth terrains that resemble lunar maria. The largest known impact crater on Mercury is about 1300 kilometers wide—about the distance from Indiana to Louisiana.

Surface Temperature Mercury's surface reflects very little sunlight. Instead, most solar radiation is absorbed, resulting in daytime temperatures higher than 427°C—hot enough to melt lead. Since Mercury has very little atmosphere, nighttime temperatures drop as low as −173°C. **Mercury has the greatest temperature extremes of any planet.** The odds of "life as we know it" existing on Mercury are almost nonexistent.

☑ **Reading Checkpoint** *How does Mercury's period of rotation compare with Earth's?*

Venus: The Veiled Planet

Venus is the second planet from the sun and the second brightest natural object in the nighttime sky. Venus is almost the same size as Earth and orbits the sun once every 225 Earth days. A sidereal day on Venus has a period of about 244 Earth days, while a solar day has a period of about 117 Earth days. On Venus, the sun rises in the west and sets in the east—opposite from what occurs on Earth and the other planets.

Structure Venus is thought to have an iron core and rocky crust, similar to Earth's. Numerous uncrewed spacecraft have taken measurements and found little or no magnetic field around Venus. Scientists used these and other data to conclude that the core is solid and there are no convection currents operating inside the planet. The surface of Venus has only about 1000 noticeable impact craters, far fewer than Mercury, but more than Earth. **Data have confirmed that basaltic volcanism and tectonic activity shape Venus's surface. Based on the low density of impact craters, these forces must have been very active during the recent geologic past.**

About 80 percent of Venus's surface consists of plains covered by volcanic flows. Some lava channels extend hundreds of kilometers—one is 6800 kilometers long. Scientists have identified thousands of inactive volcanic structures. Most are small shield volcanoes, although more than 1500 volcanoes greater than 20 kilometers across have been mapped. **Figure 8** shows two of these volcanoes—one is Sapas Mons, 400 kilometers across and 1.5 kilometers high. Flows from this volcano mostly erupted from its flanks rather than its summit, in the manner of Hawaiian shield volcanoes.

FIGURE 7 Venus This global view of the surface of Venus is computer generated from two years of Magellan Project radar mapping. The twisting bright features that cross the planet are highly fractured mountains and canyons.

Differentiated Instruction

ENGLISH LANGUAGE LEARNERS Have students use a thesaurus rather than a dictionary to look up unfamiliar words. This will help them learn the meaning of multiple words simultaneously. It is likely that at least one synonym listed is a word they know.

FIGURE 8 Sapas Mons and Maat Mons In this computer-generated image from Venus, Sapas Mons (*Mons* = mountain) is the bright feature in the foreground. Maat Mons, a large volcano, is near the horizon.
Compare and Contrast *What features on Venus are similar to those on Earth? What features are different?*

Surface Temperature Venus has the densest atmosphere of the terrestrial planets. On the surface, the atmospheric pressure on Venus is more than 90 times greater than on Earth's surface. This pressure is equivalent to the pressure a diver would experience at about 900 meters below the surface of the ocean. Spacecraft that have landed on Venus were crushed—as expected—within an hour.

Even though much of the solar energy hitting Venus is reflected—that is why Venus is so bright—the surface temperature on the planet is 462°C, which is even hotter than Mercury. The atmospheric conditions on Venus are thought to be a model for the planetary phenomonom called the *greenhouse effect*. Most solar energy that reaches the planet's surface is converted to heat and remains trapped on the planet by the dense atmosphere.

The main reason for the runaway greenhouse effect on Venus is that its atmosphere is 97 percent carbon dioxide. By comparison, Earth's atmosphere has less than 0.1 percent carbon dioxide. Carbon dioxide prevents heat energy from escaping and is a contributing factor to the greenhouse effect. Venus lacks oceans in which carbon dioxide gas could dissolve, thus removing it from the atmosphere. Any oceans on Venus probably evaporated early in its history. Evaporation added water vapor to the atmosphere and accelerated the greenhouse effect. Venus's atmosphere eventually lost most of its water vapor. Ultraviolet radiation broke down water molecules into hydrogen and oxygen. These gases then escaped into space.

☑ **Reading Checkpoint** *Describe the composition of Venus's atmosphere.*

Facts and Figures

Mars has two natural satellites (moons), Phobos and Deimos. Although Mars is easy to observe from Earth, these moons were not discovered until 1977. Perhaps this is because they are only 24 and 15 km in diameter. Because Phobos is very close to Mars, it requires just 7 hours and 39 minutes for one revolution. *Mariner 9* found that both moons are irregularly shaped and have numerous impact craters.

Build Reading Literacy   L1

Refer to **p. 1D** in **Chapter 1,** which provides guidelines for this reading strategy.

Anticipation Guide Ask students to respond to the following questions in writing before they read the section on Mars. Have the students check over their answers and make changes as needed after they finish reading the section. Students should answer True or False to the following series of statements: Mars's polar ice caps are mostly made of water. *(False)* There are active volcanoes on Mars. *(False)* Mars often has dust storms with hurricane-force winds. *(True)* Mars has canyons that are much larger than Earth's Grand Canyon. *(True)* There is evidence that liquid water once flowed on Mars. *(True)* Liquid water currently flows on the Martian surface. *(False)*
Verbal

Use Community Resources   L2

If possible, invite an astronomer or geologist in your community to talk to students about the findings of the rovers *Spirit* and *Opportunity* on Mars. Encourage students to list questions they have about Mars before the speaker comes to visit.
Verbal, Interpersonal

Integrate Chemistry   L3

Polar Ice Caps Inform students that Mars has polar ice caps that are made mostly of frozen carbon dioxide, with some frozen water. Have advanced students brainstorm how these ice caps could be used to help make Mars habitable for humans.
Verbal, Logical

FIGURE 9 Martian Scenery Many parts of Mars's landscape resemble desert areas on Earth.

FIGURE 10 Valles Marineris Mars's Valles Marineris canyon system is more than 5000 kilometers long and up to 8 kilometers deep. The dark spots on the left edge of the image are huge volcanoes.

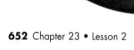

Volcanoes

Valles Marineris

Mars: The Red Planet

Mars has evoked great interest throughout history. It is the outermost terrestrial planet, averaging about 80,000,000 kilometers farther from the sun than Earth is. Mars is a little more than half the size of Earth, yet has two natural moons: Deimos and Phobos. It takes 687 Earth days for Mars to orbit the sun. Both a sidereal day and a solar day on Mars have a period of about 25 Earth hours.

Structure Uncrewed spacecraft missions have detected no magnetic field surrounding Mars. However, certain areas of the surface of Mars are magnetized. These clues help scientists conclude that Mars may have had a magnetic field—and therefore internal convection currents—in the past. Most Martian surface features are old by Earth standards. The highly cratered southern hemisphere is probably 3.5 billion to 4.5 billion years old. On Earth, any features that old would have eroded away long ago. Even the relatively "fresh" volcanic features of the northern hemisphere may be older than one billion years. Spacecraft images of Mars' northern hemisphere have revealed numerous large inactive volcanoes. The biggest, Olympus Mons, is the size of Ohio and is 23 kilometers high—over two and a half times higher than Mount Everest.

Surface Temperature The Martian atmosphere is only one percent as dense as Earth's atmosphere. It is made up primarily of carbon dioxide with tiny amounts of water vapor. Data from Mars probes confirm that the polar caps of Mars are made of water ice, covered by a thin layer of frozen carbon dioxide. During the Martian winter, temperatures drop to −125°C, and more frozen carbon dioxide is deposited.

Although the atmosphere of Mars is very thin, extensive dust storms occur and may cause the color changes observed from Earth. Hurricane-force winds as high as 270 kilometers per hour can persist for weeks. The composition of Mars's atmosphere is similar to that of Venus. But Mars is very cold and Venus very hot. The reason for this difference is that Mars's atmosphere is extremely thin compared with the atmosphere of Venus. Early in its history, Mars likely had a dense atmosphere, but most of the gases escaped due to its relatively weak gravity.

Facts and Figures

Students may ask why the volcanoes on Earth are so much smaller than volcanoes on Mars. The reason is that Earth's crust is tectonically active, so the crust over a mantle plume is constantly moving. This motion produces a series of smaller volcanoes. Because Mars does not have plates that move, a volcano was able to grow larger and larger each time it erupted. Also, the lower gravity and surface air pressure on Mars allowed the volcanoes to grow taller than they do on Earth.

Water on Mars Some areas of Mars exhibit drainage patterns similar to those created by streams on Earth. The rover *Opportunity,* for example, found evidence of minerals that form by the evaporation of water and geologic formations associated with liquid water. In addition, images from the Mars lander *Viking* revealed ancient islands in what is now a dry streambed. When these streamlike channels were first discovered, observers speculated that a dense water-laden atmosphere capable of generating torrential downpours once existed on Mars. If so, what happened to this water? The present Martian atmosphere contains only traces of water.

Images from the *Mars Global Surveyor* indicate that groundwater has recently migrated to the surface. These spring like seeps have formed gullies where they emerge from valley and crater walls. Some of the escaping water may have initially frozen due to the average Martian temperatures that range between −70°C and −100°C. Eventually, however, it seeped out as a slurry of sediment, ice, and liquid that formed the gullies.

Many scientists do not accept the theory that Mars once had an active water cycle similar to Earth's. Rather, they believe that most of the stream like valleys were formed by the collapse of surface material caused by the slow melting of subsurface ice. Data from *Opportunity* indicate that some areas were "drenched" in water. It will take scientists many months, if not years, to analyze the data gathered by the latest Mars missions. Since water is an essential ingredient for life, scientists are hoping that additional data from *Curiosity* can help answer many questions about the possibility of life on Mars.

FIGURE 11 Warm Season Flows These features that appear on the edges of craters in the spring and summer, might be evidence of liquid water activity on the surface of Mars.

3 ASSESS

Evaluate Understanding **L2**

Review with the class by stating a characteristic of one of the planets. Have students respond with the name of the planet that has that characteristic.

Reteach **L1**

Have students make a colored sketch of each terrestrial planet. They should list each planet's characteristics next to their sketch. Then have students put their sketches in order (Mercury out to Mars) and display their work.

23.2 Assessment

Review Key Concepts

1. Which inner planet is smallest?

2. How does Venus compare with Earth?

3. Identify one distinguishing characteristic of each inner planet.

4. What surface features does Mars have that are also common on Earth?

Think Critically

5. **Make Judgments** Besides Earth, which inner planet may have been most able to support life? Explain your answer.

6. **Relate Cause and Effect** Why are surface temperatures so high on Venus?

BIGIDEA EARTH AND THE UNIVERSE

7. **Communicate** A space mission to Mars can cost millions of dollars. Yet, it is hoped that space exploration can give us valuable knowledge about the solar system. Consider the pros and cons of space exploration. Then write a paragraph explaining whether or not you believe the costs are worth the potential benefits.

Assessment Answers

1. Mercury
2. Venus is similar to Earth in size, density, mass, and location in the solar system. But it is covered in thick clouds and its surface temperature is much higher.
3. Sample answer: Mercury has the greatest temperature extremes of any planet. Venus shows evidence of recent volcanic and tectonic activity. Earth is the only place where water exists in all three states at the planet's surface.

Mars experiences extensive dust storms and high winds.
4. volcanoes, sand dunes, and large canyons
5. Sample answer: Mars may have been the most able to support life because it may have had liquid water on its surface.
6. Venus's atmosphere is very dense and mainly made up of carbon dioxide, which traps radiation so the heat cannot escape.

7. Students' paragraphs should discuss both the costs and benefits of space exploration. Student opinions should be supported by facts.

23.3 The Outer Planets (and Pluto)

Lesson Objectives

23.4 **Describe** the distinguishing characteristics of each Jovian planet.

23.5 **Explain** why Pluto is not considered a planet.

Build Vocabulary L2

Vocabulary Rating Chart Have students construct a chart with four columns labeled Term, Can Define or Use It, Heard or Seen It, and Don't Know. As students read the lesson, have them copy difficult terms into the first column and rate their knowledge by putting a check in one of the other columns. Ask how many students actually know each term. Have them share their knowledge. Ask focused questions to help students predict text content based on the term, thus enabling them to have a purpose for reading. After students have read the lesson, have them rate their knowledge again.

Reading Strategy L2

Sample answers:

a. Saturn
b. largest ring system
c. Uranus
d. axis tilted more than 90°
e. Neptune
f. winds exceed 1000 km per hour

2 INSTRUCT

Build Reading Literacy L1

Refer to **p. 392D** in **Chapter 14,** which provides guidelines for previewing.

Preview Have students preview this lesson by skimming the headings and visuals. This will help students to activate their previous knowledge about the outer planets and will likely make them interested to read more about each planet.
Visual, Verbal

Key Questions

🔑 **What characteristics distinguish each outer planet?**

🔑 **Why is Pluto not considered a planet?**

Vocabulary

• dwarf planet

Reading Strategy

Summarize Make a table similar to the one shown that includes a row for each outer planet. Write a brief summary of the characteristics of each planet.

Outer Planets	Characteristics
Jupiter	largest; most mass; Great Red Spot
a. ?	b. ?
c. ?	d. ?

NASA'S *CASSINI* orbiter is on an extended mission to explore Saturn. A shining example of international cooperation, the *Cassini* mission involves three different space agencies. The spacecraft has a mass of more than 5000 kilograms and is the size of a school bus.

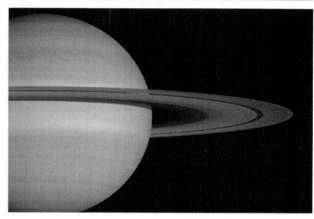

FIGURE 12 Majestic Jovian This *Cassini* orbiter image was made by pasting numerous smaller images together. It shows the natural colors of Saturn—what you would see if you were actually there.

Jupiter: Giant Among Planets

🔑 **Jupiter, which is the largest planet in the solar system, has a mass that is 2 1/2 times greater than the mass of all the other planets and moons combined.** Jupiter rotates more rapidly than any other planet, completing one rotation in less than 10 Earth hours. In the time it takes Jupiter to orbit the sun once—4,332 Earth days—Earth orbits the sun nearly 12 times. Jupiter is large and bright enough to be visible with the naked eye.

Structure Although Jupiter is referred to as a gas giant, it is not simply a ball of gas. At 1000 kilometers below the clouds, the pressure is great enough to compress hydrogen gas into a liquid. Consequently, Jupiter is thought to be a gigantic ocean of liquid hydrogen. Less than halfway into Jupiter's interior, extreme pressures cause the liquid hydrogen to turn into liquid metallic hydrogen. Jupiter is also believed to have a rocky and metallic central core.

Jupiter's hydrogen-helium atmosphere also contains small amounts of methane, ammonia, water, and sulfur compounds. Observing the atmosphere over time shows that it undergoes constant motion. The wind systems generate the light- and dark-colored bands that encircle this giant. Jupiter itself gives off nearly twice as much heat as it receives from the sun. Thus, the interior heat from Jupiter produces huge convection currents in the atmosphere.

Jupiter's Moons Jupiter's satellite system, consisting of 50 moons and 14 provisional moons, resembles a miniature solar system. The four largest moons—Io, Europa, Ganymede, and Callisto—were discovered by Galileo in 1610. Each of the four Galilean satellites is a unique geological world. The innermost of the Galilean moons, Io, is one of four known volcanically active bodies in our solar system. The others are Earth, Saturn's moon Enceladus, and Neptune's moon Triton. The heat source for volcanic activity on Io is thought to be tidal energy generated by the gravitational power of Jupiter and other nearby moons. These gravitational forces pull and push on Io's tidal bulge causing 100-meter tall "tides" on Io's surface. This gravitational flexing of Io is transformed into frictional heat energy and results in Io's volcanic eruptions.

Jupiter's Rings Jupiter's ring system was one of the most unexpected discoveries made by *Voyager 1*. By analyzing how these rings scatter light, researchers concluded that the rings are composed of fine, dark particles, similar in size to smoke particles. The faint nature of the rings also indicates that these minute fragments are widely dispersed. The particles are thought to be fragments blasted by meteorite impacts from the surfaces of Metis and Adrastea, two small moons of Jupiter.

☑ **Reading Checkpoint** *Which Galilean moon is volcanically active?*

FIGURE 13 Jupiter's Atmosphere
A When photographed by *Voyager 2*, the Great Red Spot was the size of two Earth-size circles placed side by side.
B The dark clouds are regions where gases are sinking and cooling. The convection currents and the rapid rotation of the planet generate high-speed winds.

FIGURE 14 Jupiter's Moons
A Io is one of only four volcanically active bodies in the solar system. **B** Europa—the smallest of the Galilean moons—has an icy surface that is crossed by many linear features. **C** Ganymede is the largest moon in our solar system, and it contains cratered areas, smooth regions, and areas covered by numerous parallel grooves. **D** Callisto—the outermost of the Galilean moons—is densely cratered, much like Earth's moon.

Use Visuals L1

Figure 14 This diagram shows Jupiter's four largest moons. **Ask:** What do these moons have in common with each other? *(They are all round, and they orbit around Jupiter.)* Could Europa have craters? *(Yes, but its surface is covered in ice.)* Which of these moons has volcanoes? *(Io)*
Visual

Integrate Language Arts L2

Mythological Characters All of the planets in our solar system, except for Earth, are named for characters or gods in Roman mythology. Have students work in groups. Each group should select the name of one planet to research. They should find out which mythological character or god the planet was named after, learn about the character, and determine why the name may have been given to the planet. For example, Mercury was named after the Roman messenger god because it is the planet with the fastest revolution rate around the sun. Each group should present its findings to the class.
Verbal, Interpersonal

Answers

☑ **Reading Checkpoint** *Io is volcanically active.*

Differentiated Instruction

ENGLISH LANGUAGE LEARNERS Have students make a concept map to organize what they will learn about the outer planets. Have them start with the main concept of the outer planets. Then have students add branches for Jupiter, Saturn, Uranus, and Neptune. Students can complete the map by filling in characteristics of each planet as they read.

LESSON 23.3

Build Reading Literacy `L1`

Refer to **p. 124D** in **Chapter 5,** which provides the guidelines for summarizing.

Summarize Have students summarize the major characteristics of Saturn as they read. For example, Saturn has wind, storms, many moons, and rings.
Verbal

Use Visuals `L1`

Figure 15 This diagram shows the rings of Saturn. **Ask:** How are rings A and B different from ring C? *(Ring C is a darker color.)* What do you think is the cause of this difference? *(They have different compositions.)* How are the outer rings different from the inner rings? *(The outer rings are much thinner than the inner rings.)* How is ring E different from the other rings? *(Ring E looks green, and is more diffuse.)*
Visual

Saturn: The Elegant Planet

Located more than 1.5 billion kilometers from the sun at aphelion (farthest point), Saturn takes nearly 11,000 Earth days to complete one orbit. Saturn is 764 times larger (in volume) than Earth. However, for every one rotation that Earth completes, Saturn rotates on its axis more than twice. **The most prominent feature of Saturn is its system of rings.** In 1610, Galileo used an early version of the telescope to observe the structures that were later identified to be the rings. To Galileo they appeared as two small bodies adjacent to the planet. Their ring nature was explained 50 years later by the Dutch astronomer Christian Huygens.

Features of Saturn Two uncrewed spacecraft—*Voyager 1* and *Voyager 2*—are on an extended mission to explore the outer reaches of our solar system. In an earlier phase of their missions, the spacecraft came within 100,000 kilometers of Saturn. More information was gained in a few days than had been acquired in nearly four centuries since Galileo first viewed this elegant planet.

1. Saturn's atmosphere is very active, with winds roaring at up to 1500 kilometers per hour.
2. Large cyclonic "storms" similar to Jupiter's Great Red Spot, although smaller, occur in Saturn's atmosphere.
3. Eleven additional moons were discovered.
4. The rings of Saturn were found to be more complex than expected.

More recently, observations from ground-based telescopes, the Hubble Space Telescope, and *Cassini* have added to our knowledge of Saturn's ring and moon system. *Cassini* carried a probe called *Huygens* that descended to the surface of Saturn's largest moon, Titan. The probe sent back photographs and other data about Titan's atmosphere and surface.

FIGURE 15 Saturn's Rings
Saturn's rings fall into two categories based on particle density. The main rings (A and B) are densely packed. In contrast, the outer rings are composed of widely dispersed particles.

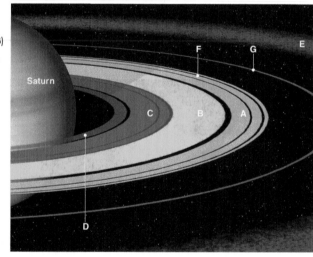

Facts and Figures

Scientists think that liquid water is the key to the development of life, so they carefully search other planets and moons for this key ingredient. Studies of Jupiter's moon, Europa, have revealed that it is covered with a thick layer of ice, and scientists have inferred that there may be liquid water beneath this layer. This makes Europa a prime target for future space probes to look for evidence of life on this moon.

Saturn's Rings Much has been learned about Saturn's rings since Galileo first observed them. Yet, much remains a mystery. Scientists know that there are more than 20 separate rings in the ring system. The ring system is about one kilometer thick and approximately 282,000 kilometers wide. By comparison, the average distance between Earth and Earth's moon is about 380,000 kilometers.

The rings are made up of particles of ice and rock that range in size from as small as dust to as large as mountains. Scientists think that the particles are debris from broken up moons, asteroids, and other space bodies.

Most rings fall into one of two categories based on particle density. Saturn's main rings, designated A and B in **Figure 15,** are densely packed and contain a wide variety of particle sizes. These particles are thought to collide frequently as they orbit the planet.

At the other extreme, the faintest rings, such as the outermost rings, are composed of very fine particles that are widely dispersed. Saturn's outermost rings are designated E in Figure 15. In addition to having very low particle densities, these rings tend to be thicker than Saturn's bright rings.

Saturn's Moons Saturn's satellite system consists of 53 known, natural moons and nine provisional (or, yet-to-be-named) moons. Titan is Saturn's largest moon and is bigger than Mercury. It has a thick, smog-like atmosphere consisting mainly of nitrogen. The *Huygens* space probe provided evidence that large bodies of liquid, possibly liquid methane, exist on Titan's surface. In addition, the probe recorded air pressure, temperature, air composition, and wind speed. For example, the temperature at the *Huygen* touch-down site was −180°C.

Many moons have an interesting story. Phoebe orbits Saturn in the opposite direction to the orbits of the larger moons. Mimas has an extremely large impact crater. Hyperion has a wobbly rotation, possibly because it was recently impacted by a huge asteroid.

☑ **Reading Checkpoint** *How many moons of Saturn have been discovered thus far?*

FIGURE 16 Saturn's Moons
This Saturn image from Hubble shows some of its moons crossing the face of the planet.

Touring Our Solar System **657**

Build Science Skills **L2**

Infer After reading the section on Saturn's rings, have students take another look at the image of Saturn's rings in Figure 15. Ask students to use what they read and observed, in addition to their prior knowledge of how the solar system formed, to infer how Saturn's rings might have formed. Have students share their ideas with the class. Then share the information in the Facts and Figures box below with the class. **Visual, Logical**

Answers

☑ **Reading Checkpoint** *Fifty-three known, natural moons and nine provisional moons have been discovered orbiting Saturn.*

Facts and Figures

There are several theories regarding the origin of ring particles. Some scientists think the rings formed out of a cloud of gas and dust from which the planet formed. Others think the rings formed later when a moon or asteroid was pulled apart by the planet's gravity. Still others think a crash with a foreign body blasted apart one of the planet's moon. Scientists hope that future missions to Saturn will help them resolve this controversy.

LESSON 23.3

Teacher **Demo**

DISCOVERING THE RINGS OF URANUS

L2

Purpose Students will experience a simulation of how the rings of Uranus were discovered.

Materials meter stick, small flashlight

Procedure Darken the classroom, and have one student hold the flashlight at the front of the room. Hold the meter stick horizontally to represent the rings of Uranus. While the student holds the flashlight steadily, pass the meter stick slowly up and down in front of the flashlight so it appears to blink on and off. Explain to students that the flashlight represents the distant star which was blocked by Uranus in 1977. Help students understand that the rings would have caused the light of the star to blink on and off a few times as Uranus and its rings passed in front of the distant star.

Expected Outcome Students will see that Uranus's rings would have caused the occluded star to blink on and off a few times before and after the passing of Uranus's body in front of the star.

Visual, Kinesthetic

FIGURE 17 Did a Giant Collision Tilt Uranus? The axis of rotation of Uranus is nearly parallel with the plane of its orbit. This photo also shows the planet's ring system.

FIGURE 18 Neptune The Great Dark Spot of Neptune (photographed by *Voyager 2*) is visible in the center left of the image. Bright cirrus-like clouds that travel at high speeds around the planet are also visible.
Identify *What did scientists assume the Great Dark Spot was?*

Uranus: The Sideways Planet

Uranus is more than 3,000,000,000 kilometers from the sun at aphelion. It is 14 times more massive than Earth. Uranus takes more than 30,000 Earth days to orbit the sun. The planet rotates from east to west, taking about 17 Earth hours for one rotation. A unique feature of Uranus is that it rotates "on its side." **Instead of being generally perpendicular to the plane of its orbit like the other planets, Uranus's axis of rotation lies nearly parallel with the plane of its orbit.** Uranus's spin may have been altered by a giant impact with an Earth-sized object.

Uranus's atmosphere contains mostly hydrogen and helium. There are also small amounts of methane, water, and ammonia in the atmosphere. Most of the mass of the planet is contained in its core, which consists primarily of icy water, methane, and ammonia.

Observers have discovered that Uranus has a ring system with at least nine distinct ring belts. Uranus has 27 moons. The five largest moons show widely varied terrain. Some of the moons have long, deep canyons and linear scars, while other moons have large, smooth areas on otherwise crater-riddled surfaces. The moon Miranda has a greater variety of landforms than any body yet examined in the solar system.

☑ **Reading Checkpoint** *What is unique about Uranus's axis of rotation?*

Neptune: The Windy Planet

Neptune, the outermost planet in our solar system, is more than 4,500,000,000 kilometers from the sun at aphelion. Neptune has about the same mass as Uranus. It takes more than 60,000 Earth days to orbit the sun, and it rotates on its axis once every 16 Earth hours.

Neptune has a dynamic atmosphere, much like those of Jupiter and Saturn. **Winds exceeding 1000 kilometers per hour encircle Neptune, making it one of the windiest places in the solar system.** At one time, it had an Earth-size blemish called the Great Dark Spot, which was similar to Jupiter's Great Red Spot. The Great Dark Spot was assumed to be a large rotating storm. About five years after the Great Dark Spot was discovered, it vanished, only to be replaced by another dark spot in a different location, which also vanished within a few years.

Neptune has many other surprising features. Perhaps most surprising are the cirrus-like clouds that occupy a layer about 50 kilometers above the main cloud deck. The clouds are most likely frozen methane. *Voyager 2* images revealed that the bluish planet also has a very faint ring system.

Neptune has 13 known moons. Triton, Neptune's largest moon, is nearly the size of Earth's moon. Triton has the lowest surface temperature yet measured on any body in the solar system at −240°C. A *Voyager 2* image of Triton's surface shows an ice volcano erupting 8 kilometers high. The eruption most likely consisted of liquid nitrogen and methane that instantly froze.

Facts and Figures

The existence of Neptune was predicted before it was discovered. This prediction was based on irregularities in the orbit of Uranus and Newton's Universal Law of Gravitation. In 1846, scientists discovered Nepune exactly where it had been predicted. This discovery is an excellent example of a hypothesis being tested not in a lab, but in outer space itself by observation.

Pluto: Dwarf Planet

For 76 years Pluto was considered a planet. However, the International Astronomical Union (IAU) redefined the word *planet* as a celestial body that orbits the sun, has sufficient mass for its own gravity to produce a nearly round shape, and has enough gravitational force to clear the space debris in the neighborhood of its orbit. **Pluto is not considered a planet, because it has not cleared the neighborhood around its orbit.**

At the same time, the IAU established a new designation called dwarf planet. A **dwarf planet** is a celestial body in orbit around the sun, has sufficient mass for its own gravity to produce a nearly round shape, has not cleared the neighborhood around its orbit, and is not the satellite of another planet.

Pluto is the most well known of the dwarf planets. However, it is neither the largest nor the first to be discovered. The dwarf planet Ceres, which is in the asteroid belt, was discovered in 1801. And the dwarf planet Eris, discovered in 2005, is about the same size as Pluto. The IAU established an additional category, called *plutoids,* for celestial bodies such as Pluto—dwarf planets that are beyond the orbit of Neptune. Initially, plutoids included Pluto, Eris, and a few other objects. Eventually, several more bodies could be categorized as plutoids.

While no longer considered a true planet, Pluto is still a significant celestial body. It is about two-thirds the size of Earth's moon but has moons of its own. Pluto orbits the sun slowly at 4.7 kilometers per second, or about 17,000 kilometers per hour. By comparison, Earth orbits the sun at 107,000 kilometers per hour—more than six times faster than Pluto. It takes Pluto 248 Earth years to complete one orbit.

Pluto's orbit is so elliptical that at aphelion it is about 7.4 billion kilometers from the sun. At perihelion, it is 3 billion kilometers closer to the sun. When it is closest to the sun, the ice on Pluto's surface thaws and forms a thin atmosphere.

FIGURE 19 Pluto and Its Largest Moon This Hubble image shows Pluto and its moon Charon.

23.3 Assessment

Review Key Concepts

1. What is the largest planet? What is the smallest?

2. What is Jupiter's Great Red Spot?

3. Identify one distinguishing characteristic of each outer planet and Pluto.

4. How are Saturn's moon Titan and Neptune's Triton similar?

5. In what way is Io similar to Earth? What other body shows this similarity?

Think Critically

6. **Relate Cause and Effect** What may have caused Uranus's unique axis of rotation?

7. **Make Judgments** Should Pluto have been reclassified as a dwarf planet? Explain your answer.

CONNECTING CONCEPTS

8. **Compare and Contrast** Write a brief paragraph comparing and contrasting atmospheric convection currents on Jupiter and Earth.

Touring Our Solar System **659**

Assessment Answers

1. Jupiter is the largest planet. Mercury is the smallest.

2. a cyclonic storm

3. Sample answer: Jupiter is the largest planet. Saturn has an amazing ring system. Uranus's axis of rotation is nearly parallel with the plane of its orbit. Neptune is one of the windiest places in the solar system. Pluto is small and cold with a very eccentric orbit.

4. Titan is Saturn's largest moon and Triton is Neptune's largest moon.

5. Io is volcanically active, just like Earth. Neptune's moon Triton is also volcanically active.

6. A giant impact may have changed Uranus's spin.

7. Sample answer: Further study is likely required to determine if our definition of a dwarf planet should apply to Pluto.

8. Before students begin writing, review with them how convection currents in Earth's atmosphere work. Describe their cause (*solar energy*), what they look like (*hot, less dense air rises while*

cooler, denser air sinks), and some results of convection currents (*wind*).

Sample answer: On Earth, atmospheric convection currents are driven by solar energy. Jupiter, however, gives off nearly twice as much heat as it receives from the sun. The interior heat from Jupiter produces huge convection currents in the atmosphere.

23.4 Minor Members of the Solar System

Lesson Objectives
23.6 **Identify** the location within our solar system where most asteroids are found.

23.7 **Describe** the structure of a comet.

23.8 **Explain** the possible origins for a meteoroid.

Build Vocabulary `L2`
Concept Map Have students make a concept map for the vocabulary terms in this lesson. The center of the map should be "Minor members of the solar system," the terms *asteroid, comet,* and *meteoroid* should branch off of this topic, and students should expand their map with the other vocabulary terms as they learn about each term.

Reading Strategy `L2`
Have students expand their tables with enough space to enter all five terms and their definitions. Sample answers:
a. small rocky body
b. comet
c. body made up of rocky and metallic materials held together by frozen gases
d. coma
e. glowing head of a comet
f. meteoroid
g. small solid particle that travels through space
h. meteor
i. meteoroid that enters Earth's atmosphere and burns up
j. meteorite
k. meteoroid that reaches Earth's surface

Key Questions
🔑 **Where are most asteroids located?**

🔑 **What is the structure of a comet?**

🔑 **What is the origin of most meteoroids?**

Vocabulary
- asteroid • comet
- coma • meteoroid
- meteor • meteorite

Reading Strategy
Build Vocabulary Copy the table below. Then as you read the section, write a definition for each vocabulary term in your own words.

Vocabulary	Definition
asteroid	a. ?
b. ?	c. ?
d. ?	e. ?

FIGURE 20 Giant Asteroid Vesta
This image of Vesta was taken by the *Dawn* spacecraft at a distance of about 5200 kilometers. It shows evidence of many impact craters.

NASA'S *DAWN* spacecraft became the first probe to orbit an asteroid in the asteroid belt. The uncrewed *Dawn* probe took high-resolution photos of the asteroid as it approached, as shown in **Figure 20**. Explorations of our solar system such as this are important because they provide scientists with evidence of how the solar system formed.

Asteroids
Asteroids are small rocky bodies that orbit the sun and are larger than 10 meters in diameter. The largest, the dwarf planet Ceres, is about 1000 kilometers in diameter, but more than a million asteroids are greater than 1 kilometer across. 🔑 **Most asteroids lie in the asteroid belt between the orbits of Mars and Jupiter. They have orbital periods of three to six years.** Some asteroids have very elongated orbits and travel very near the sun, and a few larger ones regularly pass close to Earth and the moon, as shown in **Figure 21**. Many of the most recent impact craters on the moon and Earth were probably caused by collisions with asteroids. Inevitably, more asteroids will strike Earth in the future.

Many asteroids have irregular shapes, as shown in **Figure 22**. Because of this, planetary geologists first speculated that they might be fragments of a broken planet that once orbited between Mars and Jupiter. However, the total mass of the asteroids is estimated to be only 1/1000 (0.1 percent) that of Earth, which itself is not a large planet. What happened to the remainder of the original planet?

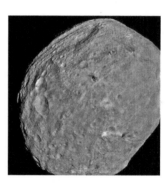

Others have hypothesized that several larger bodies once coexisted in close proximity, and their collisions produced numerous smaller ones. The existence of several asteroids with related features has been used to support this explanation. However, no conclusive evidence has been found for either hypothesis.

☑ **Reading Checkpoint** *What is an asteroid?*

FIGURE 21 Asteroid Orbits
The orbits of most asteroids lie between Mars and Jupiter. Also shown are the orbits of a few near-Earth asteroids. Perhaps a thousand or more asteroids pass close to Earth. Luckily, only a few dozen of these are thought to be larger than one kilometer in diameter.

Comets

Comets are among the most interesting and unpredictable bodies in the solar system. **Comets** are pieces of rocky and metallic materials held together by frozen water, ammonia, methane, carbon dioxide, and carbon monoxide. Many comets travel in very elongated orbits that carry them far beyond Pluto. These comets take hundreds of thousands of years to complete a single orbit around the sun. However, a few have orbital periods of less than 200 years and make regular encounters with the inner solar system.

Coma When first observed, a comet appears very small. But as it approaches the sun, solar energy begins to vaporize the frozen gases. This produces a glowing head called a **coma**. 🔲 **A small glowing nucleus with a diameter of only a few kilometers can sometimes be detected within a coma. As comets approach the sun, some, but not all, develop a tail that extends for millions of kilometers.**

The tail of a comet is produced by a combination of two solar forces. One force, called radiation pressure, pushes dust particles away from the coma. The second force, known as solar wind, is responsible for moving the ionized gases, particularly carbon monoxide. Sometimes a single tail composed of both dust and ionized gases is produced, but often two tails are observed.

As a comet moves away from the sun, the gases forming the coma recondense, the tail disappears, and the comet returns to cold storage. Material that was blown from the coma to form the tail is lost from the comet forever. Therefore it is believed that most comets cannot survive more than a few hundred close orbits of the sun. Once all the gases are expelled, the remaining material—a swarm of tiny metallic and stony particles—continues the orbit without a coma or a tail.

FIGURE 22 Asteroid Example
Asteroid 951, also called Gaspra, is probably the fragment of a larger body that was torn apart by a collision.

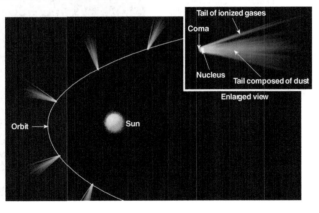

FIGURE 23 Which Way Does the Tail Point? No matter in which direction it is traveling, a comet's tail always points away from the sun.

Touring Our Solar System **661**

 INSTRUCT

Use Visuals

Figure 21 This image shows the orbital paths of several asteroids in our solar system. Have students look carefully at the figure and read the caption. **Ask:** Where are most asteroids found? *(between Mars and Jupiter, in the asteroid belt)* Are most of the asteroids near Earth found in the asteroid belt? *(no)* What is the shape of all of the asteroid orbits? *(elliptical)*
Visual

Build Reading Literacy L1

Refer to **p. 306D** in **Chapter 11,** which provides guidelines for this reading strategy.

KWL Construct a KWL chart with students before reading the section on comets. Students will probably already know that comets are "dirty snowballs," and will be able to name at least one comet. What students want to know will vary. After teaching the section on comets, have students complete the chart with what they learned. Clarify learning as needed.
Verbal

Answers

☑ **Reading Checkpoint** *An asteroid is a small, rocky body that orbits the sun.*

Differentiated Instruction

ENGLISH LANGUAGE LEARNERS Put beginning English language learners in groups with native English speakers of average to below-average ability. These groups will allow the conversations to be at appropriate levels. Have students work together over a few class periods to complete their concept maps for this section's vocabulary words. Once ELL students reach the intermediate level, they can work with average to above-average students.

LESSON 23.4

MODELING A COMET'S TAIL **L2**

Purpose The demonstration will help students understand why a comet's tail always points away from the sun.

Materials tabletop fan, light-weight paper, tape

Procedure Have students make simple models of comets using a ball of paper or an actual ball as the coma with light-weight paper streamers as the tail. Turn on the fan, and have students hold their models in the breeze. The streamers will always point away from the fan's breeze.

Expected Outcome Students will see how radiation pressure and solar wind will cause a comet's tail to point away from the sun.

Visual, Kinesthetic

Kuiper Belt Comets apparently originate in two regions of the outer solar system. Those with short orbital periods are thought to orbit beyond Neptune in a region called the *Kuiper belt*. Similar to the asteroids in the inner solar system, most Kuiper belt comets move in nearly circular orbits that lie roughly in the same plane as the planets. A chance collision between two Kuiper belt comets, or the gravitational influence of one of the Jovian planets, may occasionally alter the orbit of a comet enough to send it to the inner solar system, and into our view.

☑ **Reading Checkpoint** *In which direction does the tail of a comet point?*

Oort Cloud Unlike Kuiper belt comets, comets with long orbital periods aren't confined to the plane of the solar system. These comets appear to be distributed in all directions from the sun, forming a spherical shell around the solar system called the *Oort cloud*. The gravitational effect of another object in space is thought to send an occasional Oort cloud comet into a highly eccentric orbit that carries it toward the sun. However, only a tiny portion of the Oort cloud comets pass into the inner solar system.

Comet Halley The most famous short-period comet is Comet Halley, shown in **Figure 24.** Its orbital period averages 76 years. When it passed near Earth in 1910, Comet Halley had developed a tail nearly 1.6 million kilometers long and was visible during the daylight hours.

In March 1986, the European probe *Giotto* approached to within 600 kilometers of the nucleus of Comet Halley and obtained the first images of this elusive structure. We now know that the nucleus is potato-shaped, 16 kilometers by 8 kilometers. The surface is irregular and full of craterlike pits. Gases and dust that vaporize from the nucleus to form the coma and tail appear to gush from parts of its surface as bright jets or streams.

FIGURE 24 When Will It Return? Comet Halley will return to the inner solar system in 2061.

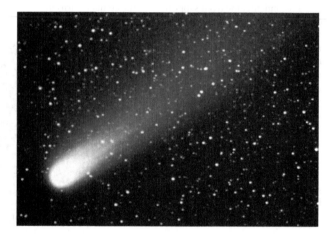

Facts and Figures

Many of the scientists who classified Pluto as a dwarf planet consider it a Kuiper belt object. The highly eccentric orbit of Pluto, its size, and its icy and rocky composition, give it the characteristics of many other objects orbiting the sun in the Kuiper belt.

Meteoroids

Nearly everyone has seen a "shooting star" while gazing at the nighttime sky. This streak of light occurs when a meteoroid enters Earth's, or any planet's, atmosphere. A **meteoroid** is a small solid particle that travels through space. **Most meteoroids originate from one of three sources: (1) interplanetary debris that was not gravitationally swept up by the planets during the formation of the solar system, (2) material from the asteroid belt, or (3) the solid remains of comets that once traveled near Earth's orbit.** A few meteoroids are believed to be fragments of the moon, or possibly Mars, that were ejected when an asteroid impacted these bodies.

Meteors Some meteoroids are as large as asteroids. Most, however, are the size of sand grains. Small meteoroids vaporize before reaching Earth's surface. Meteoroids that enter Earth's atmosphere and burn up are called **meteors.** The light that we see is caused by friction between the particle and the air, which produces heat.

Occasionally, meteor sightings can reach 60 or more per hour. These displays, called *meteor showers*, result when Earth encounters a swarm of meteoroids traveling in the same direction and at nearly the same speed as Earth. As shown in **Table 2,** some meteor showers are closely associated with the orbits of some comets, strongly suggesting that they are material lost by these comets. The Perseid meteor shower, which occurs each year around August 12, may be the remains of Comet 1862 III.

Table 2 Major Meteor Showers		
Shower	Approximate Dates Each Year	Associated Comet
Quadrantids	Jan. 4–6	
Lyrids	Apr. 20–23	Comet 1861 I
Eta Aquarids	May 3–5	Comet Halley
Delta Aquarids	July 30	
Perseids	Aug. 12	Comet 1862 III
Draconids	Oct. 7–10	Comet Giacobini-Zinner
Orionids	Oct. 20	Comet Halley
Taurids	Nov. 3–13	Comet Encke
Andromedids	Nov. 14	Comet Biela
Leonids	Nov. 18	Comet 1866 I
Geminids	Dec. 4–16	

TABLE 2 Meteor Showers You can see by the data in this table that the occurrence of meteor showers is quite predictable.

FIGURE 25 Orionids Meteor Shower The light streak in this image is a sand-sized meteoroid that has entered Earth's atmosphere and is burning up. Scientists think that meteoroids such as this one were left behind during one of Comet Halley's journeys into the inner solar system.

Build Reading Literacy L1

Refer to **p. 612D** in **Chapter 22,** which provides the guidelines for this reading strategy.

Think Aloud The first paragraph of the Meteoroids section is very important, but it contains many words that may confuse students. Read this paragraph out loud, and stop at the end of each sentence to ask yourself (and the class) a question to check for comprehension. For example, after the first sentence you can ask, "Have I ever seen a shooting star?" When you read the Key Concept aloud, you may want to ask multiple questions, such as "What is interplanetary debris? Where's the asteroid belt? What would the remains of a comet look like?" If your students are not able to answer your questions, encourage them to go back in the chapter to find the answers. For example, students may need to reread the section on comets to figure out what the remains of a comet are.
Verbal, Intrapersonal

Answers

☑ **Reading Checkpoint** *away from the sun*

Facts and Figures

Scientists have hypothesized that comets may contain organic material, and the Giotto probe observed what appeared to be organic material on the surface of Halley's comet. Because comets occasionally come close to Earth, or even crash into Earth's surface, some people think that life on Earth originated from organic material carried to our planet by a comet.

LESSON 23.4

Build Reading Literacy L1

Refer to **p. 474D** in **Chapter 17**, which provides the guidelines for monitoring your understanding.

Monitor Your Understanding After students have read the paragraphs on meteoroids, advise them to make sure they understand the difference between meteoroids, meteors, and meteorites. Also, have them verify that they recognize the relationship between meteor showers and comets. Recommend to students that they reread the passage if they did not understand these ideas.
Verbal, Intrapersonal

3 ASSESS

Evaluate Understanding L2

Check for understanding by putting the students in groups and having the groups write an answer for each Key Question in the chapter.

Reteach L1

Review the content in this chapter with a series of Venn diagrams or concept maps.

FIGURE 26 Large Meteorite
Many meteorites, such as this sample, are made up mostly of iron.

Meteorites A meteoroid that actually reaches Earth's surface is called a **meteorite.** A few very large meteorites have blasted out craters on Earth's surface, similar to those on the moon. One of the most famous is Meteor Crater in Arizona. Prior to moon rocks brought back by astronauts, meteorites were the only extraterrestrial materials that could be directly examined. Some scientists estimate that between 900 and 9,000,000 kilograms of meteorites fall toward Earth each day! Much of this is meteoroid dust—particles so small that Earth's atmosphere slows each particle down enough so that it doesn't burn up. Instead, the particles float gently to Earth. NASA has a program that has recovered more than 16,000 meteorite pieces from Antarctica.

Meteorites and the Age of the Solar System How did scientists determine the age of the solar system? They used evidence from meteorites, Moon rocks, and Earth rocks. Radiometric dating of meteorites found on Earth shows that the oldest meteorites formed more than 4.5 billion years ago. These meteorites are the oldest-known materials in the solar system. Some are made mostly of iron. Others, called stony meteorites, contain silicates. Scientists think that the composition of meteorites is similar to the composition of other materials in the inner solar system during its formation.

Some Moon rocks have a composition similar to that of stony meteorites. These Moon rocks date to about 4.5 billion years ago, almost as old as the oldest meteorites. From these facts, scientists infer that the Moon must be just slightly younger than the formation of the solar system, which occured more than 4.5 billion years ago.

The ages of the oldest known Earth rocks are consistent with this conclusion. Scientists have dated rocks found in northwestern Canada at about 4 billion years old. These are the oldest rocks found on Earth so far. In addition, some tiny crystals of the mineral zircon found in sedimentary rocks in Australia are 4.4 billion years old.

23.4 Assessment

Review Key Concepts

1. Where are most asteroids located?

2. Describe the structure of a comet.

3. Where do short-period comets come from? What about long-period comets?

4. Meteoroids originate from what three sources?

Think Critically

5. **Compare and Contrast** Compare and contrast a meteoroid, meteor, and meteorite.

6. **Predict** What do you think would happen if Earth passed through the tail of a comet?

MATH PRACTICE

7. **Calculate** It has been estimated that Comet Halley has a mass of 1×10^{11} metric tons. This comet is estimated to lose 1×10^8 metric tons of material each time its orbit brings it close to the sun. With an orbital period of 76 years, what is the maximum remaining life span of Comet Halley?

Assessment Answers

1. Most asteroids lie between the orbits of Mars and Jupiter.
2. A comet is made up of frozen gases and pieces of rocky and metallic materials. As the comet approaches the sun, vaporizing gases produce a glowing head called a coma. Within the coma, a small glowing nucleus is sometimes present. Most comets have long tails.
3. Short-period comets come from the Kuiper belt. Long-period comets come from the Oort cloud.

4. Most meteoroids originate from: (1) interplanetary debris that was not gravitationally swept up by the planets during the formation of the solar system, (2) material from the asteroid belt, or (3) the solid remains of comets that once traveled near Earth's orbit.
5. Meteoroids are small solid particles traveling through space. Meteors are meteoroids that enter Earth's atmosphere and burn up. Meteorites are meteoroids that strike Earth's surface.
6. Sample answer: There may be a huge meteor shower.

7. 1×10^{11} tons of mass ÷ 1×10^8 tons of mass lost/orbit = 1×10^3 or 1000 orbits remaining; 76 years/orbital period × 1,000 orbits = 76,000 years of life remaining

Is Earth on a Collision Course?

The solar system is cluttered with meteoroids, asteroids, active comets, extinct comets, and other celestial bodies.

These fragments travel at great speeds and can strike Earth with the explosive force of a powerful nuclear weapon.

Ancient Collisions

During the last few decades, it has become increasingly clear that asteroids have collided with Earth far more frequently than was previously known. The evidence for these collisions is giant impact structures, called *craters*, as shown in **Figure 27**. The map in **Figure 28** shows the location of over 100 such impact structures. Most are so old and eroded that they no longer resemble impact craters. Relatively young impact craters, such as Meteor Crater near Winslow, Arizona, are easier to recognize.

Evidence is mounting that about 65 million years ago a large asteroid about 10 kilometers (more than 100 football fields) in diameter collided with Earth. This impact may have changed the climate in a way that caused the extinction of the dinosaurs, as well as nearly 50 percent of all plant and animal species on Earth.

FIGURE 27 Eroded Impact Crater Manicouagan, Quebec, is a 200-million-year-old eroded impact structure. The lake outlines the crater remnant.

Close Calls

More recently, a spectacular explosion was linked to the collision of a comet or asteroid with our planet. In 1908, in a remote region of Northern Asia, a "fireball" that appeared more brilliant than the sun exploded with a violent force. The shock waves rattled windows and triggered reverberations heard up to 1000 kilometers (625 miles) away. The "Tunguska event," as it is called, scorched, de-limbed, and flattened trees up to 30 kilometers (19 miles) from the impact site. However, expeditions to the area did not find any evidence of an impact crater or asteroid fragments. It is believed that the explosion—which equaled at least a 10-megaton nuclear bomb—occurred a few kilometers above the surface. It was most likely the end of a comet or perhaps a stony asteroid. The reason it exploded prior to impact remains unclear.

A reminder of the dangers of living with these small but deadly objects from space came in 1989 when an asteroid—nearly 1 kilometer across—shot past Earth. The asteroid came close to Earth, missing it by only twice the distance to the moon. If it had struck Earth, it could have made an impact crater 10 kilometers in diameter and perhaps 2 kilometers deep.

FIGURE 28 Major Impact Structures

• Impact structures

Is Earth on a Collision Course? L2

Background
The solar system is cluttered with meteoroids, asteroids, active comets, and extinct comets. These fragments travel at great speeds and can strike Earth with the explosive force of a powerful nuclear weapon.

Teaching Tip
Tell students to imagine they were close enough to the Tunguska event to see it. Have them write what they experienced—saw, heard, or smelled—during the event, how they felt, and what they thought it was. This can be written in the format of a newspaper article or diary entry.
Verbal

MODELING THE SOLAR SYSTEM   `L2`

Objective After completing this activity, students will be able to model the distances among the planets and their distances from the sun.

(Address **Misconceptions**)

Emphasize that students are constructing a scale model of the solar system. The distances on the adding machine paper are proportionally the same as the actual distances between planets. However, the actual distances between planets are much greater than the actual distances between the marks on the paper.

Skills Calculate, Use Models

Prep Time less than 5 minutes

Class Time 40 minutes

Teaching Tip You may want to calculate the proper scale distances as a class to make sure students are doing it correctly.

Expected Outcome Students will realize that the outer planets have much greater distances between them than the inner planets have.

Modeling the Solar System

Problem How can you model distances among the planets and their distances from the sun?

Materials meter stick, colored pencils, calculator, 6-meter length of adding machine paper

Skills Calculate, Use Models

Connect to the `Big idea` An examination of any scale model of the solar system reveals that the distances from the sun and the spacing between the planets appear to follow a regular pattern. The best way to examine this pattern is to build an actual scale model of the solar system.

Procedure

Note: **Figure A** on the next page may help you model the solar system.

1. Place the 6-meter length of adding machine paper on the floor.

2. Draw an "X" about 10 centimeters from one end of the adding machine paper. Label this mark "sun."

Table 3			
Planet	Distance from Sun		Diameter (km)
	AU	Millions of km	
Mercury	0.39	58	4878
Venus	0.72	108	12,104
Earth	1.00	150	12,756
Mars	1.52	228	6794
Jupiter	5.30	778	143,884
Saturn	9.54	1427	120,536
Uranus	19.18	2870	51,118
Neptune	30.06	4497	49,528
Pluto*	39.44	5900	2300

*Pluto is a dwarf planet.

3. **Table 3** shows the mean distances of the planets and Pluto—a dwarf planet— from the sun. The table also shows the diameter of each object. Use the table and the following scale to calculate the proper scale distance of each object from the sun:

1 millimeter = 1 million kilometers
1 centimeter = 10 million kilometers
1 meter = 1000 million kilometers

4. After calculating the scale distances, draw a small circle for each object at its proper scale distance from the sun. Use a different-colored pencil for the inner and outer planets and for Pluto. Write the name of each object next to its position.

Analyze and Conclude

1. **Use Models** Where is Earth located on your model? Where are the rest of the planets located? Where is Pluto located?

2. **Observe** What pattern of spacing do you observe? Summarize the pattern for both the inner and outer planets?

3. **Analyze Data** Which object or objects vary most from the general pattern of spacing?

`GO FURTHER` Determine how to expand your model to include the scale sizes of the planets. Refer to the table for the diameters of each planet (Table 3). Develop a scale, and then calculate the proper scale size of the planets. Draw the planets to scale on your model.

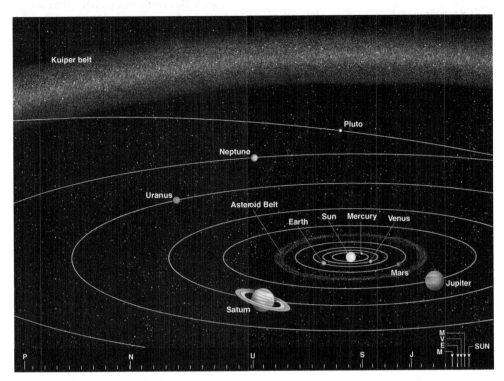

Kuiper belt

Pluto

Neptune

Uranus

Asteroid Belt

Earth Sun Mercury Venus

Mars

Jupiter

Saturn

M
V
E
M SUN

P N U S J

FIGURE A Illustration of the Solar System
This illustration shows the sun, eight planets, and the dwarf planet Pluto.

Analyze and Conclude
1. Earth: 15 cm; Mercury: 5.8 cm; Venus: 10.8 cm; Mars: 22.8 cm; Jupiter: 77.8 cm; Saturn: 1.4 m; Uranus: 2.9 m; Neptune: 4.5 m; Pluto: 5.9 m
2. The inner planets are closely spaced together. The largest space exists between Earth and Mars. The outer planets are widely spaced apart. The smallest space is between Jupiter and Saturn.
3. The space between Neptune and Pluto varies the most from the general pattern.

GO FURTHER

Using a scale of 1 cm = 4000 km, the scale model diameter of each planet would be: Mercury: 1.2 cm; Venus: 3 cm; Earth: 3.2 cm; Mars: 1.7 cm; Jupiter: 36 cm; Saturn: 30.3 cm; Uranus: 11.8 cm; Neptune: 11.7 cm
Logical

Study Tip

Write Questions

Encourage students to create their own chapter test by writing and answering questions based on the key concepts and vocabulary terms for the chapter. Suggest that students write at least one short answer question for each key concept and at least one fill-in-the-blank or multiple choice question for every vocabulary term. Encourage students to review the chapter by quizzing each other using the tests they created.

Think Visually

a. Venus; 12,104 km (diameter); 0.72 AU (distance from sun)
b. Earth; 12,756 km (diameter); 1.00 AU (distance from sun)
c. Mars; 6794 km (diameter); 1.52 AU (distance from sun)
d. Saturn; 120,536 km (diameter); 9.54 AU (distance from sun)
e. Uranus; 51,118 km (diameter); 19.18 AU (distance from sun)
f. Neptune; 50,530 km (diameter); 30.06 AU (distance from sun)

21st Century Learning

Communication Skills

Where in the Solar System have we probed and why?

Humans have sent out numerous probes into our solar system. Have students research these missions and learn where they went and why. Ask them to find out where they are now if the mission is ongoing. Ask students to use a paper or computer graphic diagram of the solar system to illustrate these solar-system missions. Have them draw the track of each of the missions, showing where the mission visited, halted, or where it is now. Their diagrams should have a legend that contains each mission's name, purpose, dates, and other relevant information.

23 Study Guide

Big idea ▸ Earth and the Universe

23.1 The Solar System

🔑 Size is the most obvious difference between the terrestrial and the Jovian planets.

🔑 Density, chemical makeup, and rate of rotation are other ways in which the two groups of planets differ.

🔑 According to the nebular theory, the sun and planets formed from a rotating disk of dust and gases.

terrestrial planet (645)
Jovian planet (645)
nebula (647)
planetesimal (648)

23.2 The Terrestrial Planets

🔑 Mercury has the greatest temperature extremes of any planet.

🔑 Data have confirmed that basaltic volcanism and tectonic activity shape Venus's surface.

🔑 The thin atmosphere of Mars has dust storms with hurricane-force winds.

23.3 The Outer Planets (and Pluto)

🔑 Jupiter has a mass that is 2 1/2 times greater than the mass of all the other planets and moons combined.

🔑 The most prominent feature of Saturn is its system of rings.

🔑 Instead of being generally perpendicular to the plane of its orbit like the other planets, Uranus's axis of rotation lies nearly parallel with the plane of its orbit.

🔑 Winds exceeding 1000 kilometers per hour encircle Neptune, making it one of the windiest places in the solar system.

🔑 Pluto is not considered a planet because it has not cleared the neighborhood around its orbit.

dwarf planet (659)

23.4 Minor Members of the Solar System

🔑 Most asteroids lie between the orbits of Mars and Jupiter. They have orbital periods of three to six years.

🔑 A small glowing nucleus with a diameter of only a few kilometers can sometimes be detected within a coma. As comets approach the sun some develop a tail that extends for millions of kilometers.

🔑 Most meteoroids originate from one of three sources: (1) interplanetary debris that was not gravitationally swept up by the planets during the formation of the solar system, (2) material from the asteroid belt, or (3) the solid remains of comets that once traveled near Earth's orbit.

asteroid (660)   meteoroid (663)
comet (661)   meteor (663)
coma (661)   meteorite (664)

Think Visually

Copy and complete the table below comparing and contrasting the inner and outer planets. Include information about each planet's diameter, distance from the sun, composition, and number of moons.

Inner and Outer Planets		
Inner Planets		
	Diameter	Distance from Sun
Mercury	4878 km	0.39 AU
a. ___?___		
b. ___?___		
c. ___?___		
Outer Planets		
	Diameter	Distance from Sun
Jupiter	143,884 km	5.20 AU
d. ___?___		
e. ___?___		
f. ___?___		

Homework Guide

Lesson	Questions
1	1–3, 11, 12, 35, 36
2	4, 5, 13–16, 26, 27, 31–34
3	6, 7, 17–21, 29, 30
4	8–10, 22–25, 28, 37

Assessment Answers

Review Content

1. d	**2.** b	**3.** c
4. c	**5.** b	**6.** d
7. a	**8.** c	**9.** a
10. d		

Understand Concepts

11. The solar system includes the sun, the planets and their moons, the dwarf planets, asteroids, comets, and meteoroids.

12. Most of the solar system is made up of the gases hydrogen and helium, the rocky substances silicate minerals and metallic iron, and the icy substances ammonia, methane, carbon dioxide, and water.

13. In general, the terrestrial planets are small and rocky. They are closer to the sun than the Jovian planets.

23 Assessment

Review Content

Choose the letter that best answers the question or completes the statement.

1. Which of these planets is not a terrestrial planet?
   a. Earth   c. Venus
   b. Mercury   d. Uranus

2. What theory describes the formation of the solar system from a huge cloud of dust and gases?
   a. protoplanet theory
   b. nebular theory
   c. planetesimal theory
   d. solar theory

3. Which of the following is NOT a characteristic of Jovian planets?
   a. large size
   b. composed mostly of gases and ice
   c. lack of moons
   d. located beyond the orbit of Mars

4. Which planet was explored by the rover *Curiosity?*
   a. Mercury   c. Mars
   b. Jupiter   d. Venus

5. Which two planets are most alike?
   a. Jupiter and Mercury
   b. Earth and Mercury
   c. Mars and Uranus
   d. Uranus and Venus

6. Which of the following is NOT true of Jupiter?
   a. It is more massive than all the other planets and moons combined.
   b. It has huge rotating storms.
   c. It has a thin ring system.
   d. It has a solid surface.

7. Which moon is known to have active volcanism?
   a. Io   c. Europa
   b. Phobos   d. Titan

8. What bodies in the solar system orbit between Mars and Jupiter?
   a. comets   c. asteroids
   b. stars   d. meteorites

9. A comet's tail always points
   a. away from the sun.
   b. toward the sun.
   c. up.
   d. down.

10. Meteoroids that strike Earth are called
    a. asteroids.   c. meteors.
    b. comets.   d. meteorites.

Understand Concepts

11. What objects are found in the solar system?

12. What substances make up most of the solar system? Classify them as gas, rock, or ice.

13. Describe general characteristics and location of the terrestrial planets.

14. What is Olympus Mons? Where is it found?

15. Why has Mars been the planet most studied by telescopes?

16. Why is life unlikely to exist on Venus?

17. Which planets have ring systems?

18. What four bodies in the solar system exhibit volcanic activity?

19. How are Uranus and Neptune similar?

20. Why isn't Pluto classified as either a terrestrial planet or a Jovian planet?

21. How big is the largest known asteroid in our solar system?

22. What are two explanations scientists have proposed for the origin of the asteroid belt between Mars and Jupiter?

23. Which minor members of the solar system are thought to have formed beyond the orbit of Pluto?

24. What is the bright glowing head of a comet called?

25. What evidence indicates that our solar system is about 4.5 billion years old?

22. One explanation is that the asteroids are remnants of a planet that once existed between Mars and Jupiter. Another explanation is that they are remnants of several larger bodies that were broken up due to collisions.
23. Comets are thought to have formed beyond the orbit of Pluto.
24. The bright, glowing head of a comet is called a coma.
25. Meteorite dating and lunar rocks indicate that the solar system is 4.6 billion years old.

14. Olympus Mons is a volcano. It is found on Mars.
15. Mars is the only planet whose surface can be easily viewed using a telescope.
16. Atmospheric pressure and surface temperatures are very high on Venus.
17. Jupiter, Saturn, Uranus, and Neptune have ring systems.
18. The four bodies in the solar system that exhibit volcanic activity are Earth, Io, Enceladus, and Triton.

19. They are about the same size and have a similar composition and structure.
20. Pluto is not considered a planet because it has not cleared the neighborhood around its orbit of space debris.
21. The largest asteroid is about 1000 km in diameter.

ASSESSMENT

Think Critically

26. Mars has drainage patterns and geologic structures associated with liquid water, as well as polar ice caps. The Martian atmosphere contains very little water vapor.

27. Venus's atmosphere traps heat on its surface. The CO_2 and its thick dense atmosphere result in a strong greenhouse effect.

28. It would be classified as a dwarf planet because of its location.

29. The Jovian planets are more massive and have greater escape velocities. They are also colder.

30. Uranus does not have a solid surface so no evidence of the impact remains.

Analyze Data

31. Venus and Mars have similar atmospheric compositions.

32. Venus has a much greater surface atmospheric pressure.

33. Oxygen is present in Earth's atmosphere. Earth's oxygen-rich atmosphere reflects the presence of life.

34. Greater atmospheric pressure leads to less variation in surface temperature.

Concepts in Action

35. You might expect to weigh the least on Mercury because it is the planet with the least mass. (However, you would actually weigh least on Mars.)

36. A year on Jupiter is equivalent to 12 Earth-years. A 15-year-old student would be 1.25 years old in Jupiter-years.

37. impact craters

---

26. Analyze Data What evidence supports the theory that liquid water may have existed on Mars? What evidence refutes the possibility of a wet Martian climate?

27. Draw Conclusions Mercury is closer to the sun than Venus. Venus, however, is hotter. Why?

28. Classify Suppose a new object is discovered in the Kuiper belt. If this new object is roughly the size of Earth's moon, how would you classify it? Why?

29. Draw Conclusions Why is it more difficult for gases to escape from the Jovian planets than from the terrestrial planets?

30. Apply Concepts Why would it be difficult to verify that an impact may have altered Uranus's axis of rotation?

Analyze Data

Use the table below to answer Questions 31–34.

Comparison of the Atmospheres and Surface Temperatures of Mercury, Venus, Earth, Mars

Planet or Body	Gases (% by volume)			Surface Temperature (range)	Surface Atmospheric Pressure (bars)
	N_2	O_2	CO_2		
Mercury	0	trace	0	−173° to 427°C	10^{-15}
Venus	3.5	< 0.01	96.5	475°C (small range)	92
Earth	78.01	20.95	0.03	−40° to 75°C	1.014
Mars	2.7	1.3	95.32	−120° to 25°C	0.008

31. Identify Which two terrestrial planets have similar atmospheric compositions?

32. Analyze Data What makes these two planets' atmospheres very different?

33. Infer What gas is present in Earth's atmosphere, but nearly absent in the atmospheres of Venus and Mars? What do you think explains its presence on Earth? (*Hint:* What does Earth have that Venus and Mars both lack?)

34. Analyze Data Based on the data in the table, how would you describe the effect of increasing atmospheric pressure on surface temperature?

Concepts in Action

35. Relate Cause and Effect Weight is a function of the gravitational attraction of an object on your mass. On which planet would you expect to weigh the least? Explain your answer.

36. Calculate Refer to Table 1 within the chapter. Using the table, determine how old you are in Jupiter-years.

37. Identify Which features on Earth offer clear evidence that comets and asteroids have struck its surface?

Performance-Based Assessment

Use Models Use a fan, a Styrofoam ball, several pushpins, and several pieces of ribbon to create a model of a comet. Explain what each part of the model represents. Work with a partner to demonstrate the orbit of your model. Make sure that the "tail" points in the proper direction.

Performance-Based Assessment

Students should explain that the fan represents the sun, the ball represents the nucleus of the comet, and the ribbons represent the tail. The push pins are used to attach the ribbons to the ball. Students should make sure that the "tail" always points away from the sun. While one partner holds the comet, the other partner can rotate the fan so that the air blows the tail away from the sun.

Standardized Test Prep

1 Which is *not* the most obvious difference between the terrestrial and Jovian planets?
A mass
B color
C density
D chemical makeup

2 Which planet does *not* have a density that is greater than water?
F Mercury
G Mars
H Venus
J Saturn

3 Why was Mercury unable to retain an atmosphere during its formation?
A Mercury has a high surface temperature and has a low mass.
B Mercury is the largest planet.
C Mercury is the farthest planet from the sun.
D Mercury revolves slowly.

Use the photograph below to answer Questions 4 and 5.

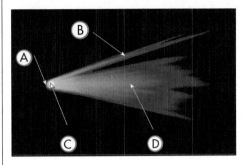

4 What features do labels B and D represent?
F Both are comet tails.
G Both are comet comas.
H B is a comet tail, and D is a comet coma.
J B is a comet coma, and D is a comet tail.

5 What are features A and C?
A Both are comet comas.
B Both are comet nuclei.
C A is a comet coma, and C is a comet nucleus.
D A is a comet nucleus, and C is a comet coma.

If You Have Trouble With . . .					
Question	1	2	3	4	5
See Lesson	23.1	23.3	23.2	23.4	23.4

Standardized Test Prep
1 B
2 J
3 A
4 F
5 C

24 Studying the Sun Planning Guide

Lesson Objectives		Activities
24.1 The Study of Light, pp. 674–677 24.1 **Describe** the waves that compose the electromagnetic spectrum. 24.2 **Describe** what the different types of spectra reveal about stars. 24.3 **Explain** how the Doppler effect is applied to the motion of stars in relation to Earth.		**TE** Teacher Demo: Making a Simple Spectrometer, p. 676 L2
24.2 Tools for Studying Space, pp. 678–683 24.4 **Explain** how refracting, reflecting, and radio telescopes work. 24.5 **Describe** the advantages and disadvantages of each type of telescope. 24.6 **Explain** the advantages that a space telescope has over an Earth-based telescope.		**TE** Teacher Demo: Making a Simple Refracting Telescope, p. 679 L2
24.3 The Sun, pp. 684–690 24.7 **Explain** the structure of the sun. 24.8 **Describe** the physical features on the surface of the sun. 24.9 **Explain** how the sun produces energy.		**TE** Teacher Demo: Earth and Solar Winds, p. 686 L2 **TE** Build Science Skills, p. 687 L2
Chapter Features and Labs		
Try It How Does the Position of the Setting Sun Change? p. 673		**LM** Measuring the Diameter of the Sun L2
Earth & Space Solar Variability and Climate Change, p. 691		
Exploration Lab TEACHER DEMO: Tracking Sunspots, pp. 692–693		

Ability Levels		Components			
L1 For students who need additional help		**SE**	Student Edition	**LP**	Lesson Plans
L2 For all students		**TE**	Teacher's Edition	**AA**	Active Art
L3 For students who need to be challenged		**LM**	Laboratory Manual	**PD**	Planet Diary
		CT	Chapter Tests	**GEODe**	Geode CD-ROM
		GRSW	Guided Reading & Study Workbook	**eText**	
		CTB	Computer Test Bank		

Resources	Lesson Assessment
GRSW Lesson 24.1 **LP** Lesson Planning 24.1	**SE** Lesson 24.1 Assessment, p. 677 **eText** Lesson 24.1
GRSW Lesson 24.2 **LP** Lesson Planning 24.2	**SE** Lesson 24.2 Assessment, p. 683 **eText** Lesson 24.2
GRSW Lesson 24.3 **LP** Lesson Planning 24.3 **PD** Sunspots and Weather	**SE** Lesson 24.3 Assessment, p. 690 **eText** Lesson 24.3

Materials for Activities and Labs

Quantities for each group

STUDENT EDITION

Try It, p. 673
paper, pencil

Exploration Lab, pp. 692–693
telescope, small cardboard box, large cardboard box, piece of white paper, metric ruler, pencil, tape

TEACHER'S EDITION

Teacher Demo, p. 676
empty paper towel cardboard tube, diffracting grating (about 5 cm × 5 cm), piece of black paper (about 9 cm × 9 cm), tape, rubber band, razor blade, bright light

Teacher Demo, p. 679
2 magnifying lenses

Teacher Demo, p. 686
bar magnet, 2 sheets of notebook paper, iron filings, drinking straw

Build Science Skills, p. 687
2 empty 2-L plastic soda bottles, water, colored glitter, duct tape, paper towel, washer (same diameter as the mouth of the plastic soda bottle)

Assessment

CHAPTER ASSESSMENT
SE Assessment, pp. 695–696
CT Chapter 24 Test
CTB Chapter 24
eText Chapter 24

21st Century Learning

Health Literacy: How does Earth protect humans from dangerous radiation?

Common Themes

Michael Wysession
Washington University

Space and Time Reflecting telescopes are usually used to collect visible light because they can be built larger and more inexpensively than refractors. Also, they do not suffer from chromatic aberration. Radio telescopes can "see" objects not viewable with visible light because of intervening interstellar dust. The Doppler shift of light is used to determine if objects are moving away or toward us. The sun can be divided into four layers: the interior, photosphere, chromosphere, and corona. The photosphere is the visible surface of the sun.

Forces and Motion The solar wind consists of protons and electrons generated from the sun's corona. Sunspots, cooler regions of the photosphere, come and go in an 11-year cycle. The sun's surface is turbulent, occasionally erupting in prominences and generating solar flares.

Matter and Energy All luminous objects emit electromagnetic radiation, which takes the form of gamma rays, X-rays, ultraviolet and visible light, infrared radiation, microwaves, and radio waves. Light behaves as both a particle and a wave in different situations. The spectroscopic emission and absorption spectra are used to determine the composition of stars and the matter of interstellar space. The sun generates light through the fusion of hydrogen to form helium, and is about 15 million degrees K in its interior.

Earth as a System Telescopes in space like the Hubble telescope produce the clearest images because they are not distorted by Earth's atmosphere.

EARTH SCIENCE REFRESHER

Chance and the Sun's Chromosphere

Science tends to be suspicious of chance and coincidence. However, statistically, that is just how things are bound to happen sometimes. One example has been our ability to view the outer structure of the sun, which has been best observed during total solar eclipses. The solar corona is very observable because the usually overwhelming light from the photosphere has been entirely blocked by the moon. By total coincidence, both the sun and moon appear to be the same size when viewed from Earth, about 0.5°. This led people in ancient times to think that there was some special reason they were created this way. There isn't. By coincidence, the sun's diameter is about 400 times wider than the moon's, but the sun is also about 400 times further from Earth than the moon.

Interestingly, the sun and moon haven't always appeared the same size when viewed from Earth. The moon used to be much closer to Earth, which would have meant not only that the moon would have appeared much larger, but that the size of the tides along shorelines would have been much greater. At that time Earth also rotated much faster, so that there were fewer hours in the day and more days in the year. We know this from the layers of calcium carbonate in fossil marine shells. Over time, the moon has spiraled further away from Earth, and in the future, it will appear

Address Misconceptions

Many students may think that since the sun is an enormous ball of gas it does not have a surface. The visible surface of the sun, the photosphere, is a layer of gas about 500 km thick. For a strategy that helps to overcome this misconception, see **Address Misconceptions** *on TE p. 685.*

smaller than the sun. So, if we had evolved a billion years from now, we would not have been able to use solar eclipses to study the chromosphere.

Of course, the sun and moon do not appear to be the exact same size. The sun's average size appears to be 0.015° larger than the moon's. What's more, because the orbits of the moon and Earth are both elliptical this changes over the course of the year. Because Earth is closer to the sun in January, the sun appears to be 0.54° in diameter. In the summer time, it is only 0.52°. The moon's orbit around Earth is even more elliptical, and its apparent size varies between 0.49° and 0.56°. When the moon appears as large or larger than the sun, solar eclipses are total, and the sun's photosphere is totally blocked, allowing good viewing of the outer corona. When the orbital distances are such that the moon appears smaller than the sun, then solar eclipses are annular, and there is still a ring of the sun's bright outer corona visible.

BUILD READING LITERACY
Summarize

Briefly Restating the Main Ideas

Strategy Help students understand a topic by restating the main ideas. Students read a section of the text and then identify main ideas and supporting details. They summarize what they have read by briefly restating the main concepts in a sentence or two. Summarizing can be employed to review brief subsections as well as entire lessons and chapters. Have students read the beginning of Lesson 24.2, pp. 678–679.

Example

1. Ask students to carefully read the selected passage. Then, have them review the passage and identify the main ideas. Demonstrate this process by using the bold headings, Key Concept statements, and vocabulary as aids in determining what the passage is mostly about. List the main ideas on the board.

2. Direct students to write brief summaries of the passage by restating each of the main ideas in one or two sentences, using their own words. Remind students to focus on the most important concepts, omitting details and examples. Students should check to be sure that their summary covers the terms mentioned in the bold headings.

3. Assign the next passage for students to read and summarize. You may want to have students work in small groups to compare their summaries.

4. Have students read and summarize the rest of Lesson 24.2.

See TE p. 675 for a script on how to use this strategy with students. For additional strategies, see TE pp. 678 and 684.

CHAPTER 24

ASSESS PRIOR KNOWLEDGE

Use the Chapter Pretest below to assess students' prior knowledge. As needed, review these concepts.

Review Science Concepts

Lesson 24.1 Encourage students to recall what they have learned about electromagnetic waves and the Doppler effect in previous science courses.

Lesson 24.2 Review the wave properties of refraction and reflection to help students understand how refracting and reflecting telescopes work.

Lesson 24.3 Encourage students to recall what they have learned about nuclear fusion in previous science courses.

24 Studying the Sun

Big idea — **Earth and the Universe**

Q: How do the sun and solar radiation affect Earth?

672

Chapter Pretest

1. Name one type of electromagnetic radiation. *(Students should name one of the following: gamma rays, X rays, ultraviolet rays, visible light, infrared, microwaves, and radio waves.)*

2. What do all waves transport from one place to another? *(energy)*

3. The sun is a *(a)*
   a. star.
   b. planet.
   c. asteroid.
   d. comet.

4. True or False: As light travels from one medium into another, such as from air to water, it will refract. *(True)*

5. Which wave property is demonstrated when you look into a mirror and see yourself? *(reflection)*

6. What is nuclear fusion? *(a nuclear reaction in which the nuclei of two atoms combine to form a larger nucleus)*

INSIDE:

This full-disk image of the sun was taken by NASA's Solar Dynamics Observatory (SDO). The image shows material streaming away from sunspots. The clarity of SDO images is ten times better than high-definition television and will help scientists measure solar flares.

INQUIRY
TRY IT!

HOW DOES THE POSITION OF THE SETTING SUN CHANGE?

Procedure

1. Several minutes before sunset, estimate where the sun will set on the western horizon. On a separate sheet of paper, draw prominent features, such as buildings and trees, to the north and south of the sun's estimated setting position.
2. As the sun sets, draw its position relative to the fixed features on the horizon. **CAUTION:** *Never look directly at the sun; eye damage may result.*
3. Note the date and time of your observation on your drawing.
4. Return to the same position several days later. Using the same drawing, repeat the activity and note the position of the setting sun. Wait several more days and do the activity one more time.

Think About It

1. **Observe** How did the sun's position at sunset change over the course of your observations?
2. **Predict** Based on your observations, predict where the sun might set in several weeks time. Sketch that location on your drawing relative to the fixed features on the horizon.

673

ENGAGE/EXPLORE

INQUIRY
TRY IT!

HOW DOES THE POSITION OF THE SETTING SUN CHANGE?

Purpose In this activity, students will realize that the sun does not set in the same location every day.

Skills Observe, Predict

Prep Time 5 minutes

Materials paper and pencil

Class Time none; 60 minutes outside class time over several days

Safety Remind students never to look directly at the sun because it can cause eye injury and possible blindness.

Expected Outcome Students will observe the sun's setting position change over time.

Think About It

1. In general, observations made between June 21 and December 22 will show the sun setting farther south with each successive observation. Observations made between December 21 and June 21 will show the sun setting farther north with each successive observation. The opposite occurs in the southern hemisphere.
2. If the observations were made between June 21 and December 22, drawings should show the sun setting farther south along the horizon. If the observations were made between December 22 and June 21, drawings will show the sun setting farther north along the horizon.

24.1 The Study of Light

Lesson Objectives

24.1 **Describe** the waves that compose the electromagnetic spectrum.

24.2 **Describe** what the different types of spectra reveal about stars.

24.3 **Explain** how the Doppler effect is applied to the motion of stars in relation to Earth.

Build Vocabulary L2

Vocabulary Rating Chart Have students make a chart with four columns with the headings Term, Can Define or Use It, Heard or Seen It, and Don't Know. Have students copy the seven vocabulary terms into the first column and rate their knowledge by putting a checkmark in one of the other columns. Ask how many students actually know each term. Then, give students a purpose for reading by asking focused questions to help students predict text content based on each term. After students have read the lesson, have them rate themselves again.

Reading Strategy L2

a. Look for answers that show whether the student has prior understanding of the words *electromagnetic* and *spectrum*.

b. The electromagnetic spectrum is the arrangement of electromagnetic radiation including gamma rays, X-rays, ultraviolet light, visible light, infrared radiation, microwaves, and radio waves according to their wavelengths and frequencies.

Key Questions

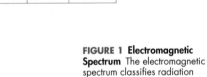 **What types of radiation make up the electromagnetic spectrum?**

What can scientists learn about a star by studying its spectrum?

How can astronomers determine whether a star is moving toward or away from Earth?

Vocabulary

- electromagnetic spectrum
- photon • spectroscopy
- continuous spectrum
- absorption spectrum
- emission spectrum
- Doppler effect

Reading Strategy

Predict Copy the table. Before you read, predict the meaning of the term *electromagnetic spectrum*. After you read, revise your definition if it was incorrect.

Vocabulary Term	Before You Read	After You Read
electromagnetic spectrum	a. ?	b. ?

ASTRONOMERS STUDY LIGHT. When the Ancient Greek astronomers first tilted their heads to the nighttime sky, the light they could see included the moon and thousands of other points. By studying the sky, they were able to draw conclusions about the structure and nature of the universe. Almost everything we currently know about the universe comes from our study of the light that stars emit and the light that planets and moons reflect. But today's space scientists work with a vast array of instruments that capture and analyze "light" that can't even be detected by the human eye.

Electromagnetic Radiation

Stars and other bodies in space emit light that can be used to study them. Although visible light is most familiar to us, it makes up only a small part of the different types of energy known as *electromagnetic radiation*. **Electromagnetic radiation includes gamma rays, X-rays, ultraviolet light, visible light, infrared radiation, microwaves, and radio waves.** The arrangement of these waves according to their wavelengths and frequencies is called the **electromagnetic spectrum**, shown in **Figure 1**. All energy, regardless of wavelength, travels through the vacuum of space at the speed of light, or 300,000 kilometers per second. Over a 24-hour day, this equals a staggering 26 billion kilometers. Nothing known to humans is faster than the speed of light in a vacuum. In addition, the speed of light is the same to all observers, whether or not they are moving with respect to the light.

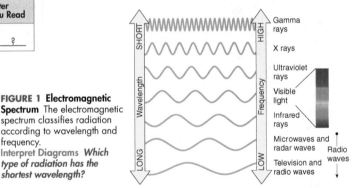

FIGURE 1 Electromagnetic Spectrum The electromagnetic spectrum classifies radiation according to wavelength and frequency.
Interpret Diagrams *Which type of radiation has the shortest wavelength?*

Nature of Light Experiments—some dating as far back as Sir Isaac Newton—have shown that light can be described in two ways. In some instances light behaves like waves, and in other instances like particles. In the wave sense, light can be thought of as swells in the ocean. This motion is characterized by a property known as *wavelength*, which is the distance from one wave crest to the next. Wavelengths vary from several kilometers for radio waves to less than a billionth of a centimeter for gamma rays. Most of these waves are either too long or too short for our eyes to see.

The narrow band of electromagnetic radiation we can see is sometimes called *visible light*. However, visible light is made up of a range of waves with various wavelengths. This fact was clearly demonstrated in an experiment by Newton hundreds of years ago using a prism, as shown in **Figure 2.** As visible light passes through a prism, the color with the shortest wavelength, violet, is bent more than blue, which is bent more than green, and so forth. Thus, visible light can be separated into its component colors in the order of their wavelengths, producing the familiar rainbow of colors.

Photons Wave theory, however, cannot explain some effects of light. In some cases, light acts like a stream of particles called **photons.** Photons can be thought of as extremely small bullets fired from a machine gun. Photons can exert force on matter called *radiation pressure*. For example, photons from the sun produce a comet's tail by pushing material away from the comet. Each photon has a specific amount of energy, which is related to its wavelength in a simple way: the photons of shorter wavelength have more energy. Thus, the photons of blue light have more energy than the photons of red light.

Which theory of light—the wave theory or the particle theory—is correct? Both, because each predicts the behavior of light for certain phenomena. As George Abell, a famous astronomer from UCLA, stated about all scientific laws, "The mistake is only to apply them [the laws] to situations that are outside their range of validity."

☑ **Reading Checkpoint** *What are photons?*

Table 1 Colors and Corresponding Wavelengths	
Color	Wavelength (nanometers*)
Violet	380–440
Blue	440–500
Green	500–560
Yellow	560–590
Orange	590–640
Red	640–750

*One nanometer is 10^{-9} meter.

FIGURE 2 Spectrum A spectrum is produced when sunlight or visible light is passed through a prism, which bends each wavelength at different angles.

Studying the Sun **675**

LESSON 24.1

MAKING A SIMPLE SPECTROMETER `L2`

Purpose Students will observe how a spectrometer breaks light into the wavelengths that compose it.

Materials empty paper towel cardboard tube, diffracting grating (about 5 cm × 5 cm), piece of black paper (about 9 cm × 9 cm), tape, rubber band, razor blade, bright light

Procedure Tape the diffracting grating over one end of the cardboard tube. Cover the opposite end of the tube with black paper. Secure the black paper over the end of the tube with a rubber band. Carefully cut a narrow slit in the center of the black paper. The length of the slit should be about two-thirds the width of the opening. Hold the diffraction-grating end of the tube close to your eye and point the slit end of the tube toward a bright light. Look for the spectrum image to appear on the inside walls of the tube. Allow students to use the spectrometer to view the spectrum.

Safety Do not allow students to use this spectrometer to view the sun directly.

Expected Outcomes The diffraction grating works like a prism and breaks visible light into its basic colors. Students will be able to use this simple spectrometer to see bright light broken into its component colors or wavelengths.
Visual, Kinesthetic

For Enrichment `L3`

Use the spectrometer to view the spectrum emitted by an incandescent bulb. Then, view the spectrum emitted by a fluorescent bulb. **Ask:** What difference do you notice in the spectra? *(The incandescent spectrum is a continuous spectrum. The fluorescent spectrum is a broken line or emission spectrum.)* This difference in spectra is typically the result of fluorescent bulbs emitting light in narrow bands of the full spectrum.

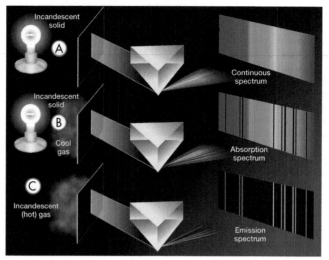

FIGURE 3 Formation of Spectra
A A continuous spectrum consists of a band of uninterrupted color.
B An absorption spectrum contains dark lines. **C** An emission spectrum contains bright lines.

Spectroscopy

When Sir Isaac Newton used a prism to disperse visible light into its component colors, he unknowingly introduced the field of spectroscopy. **Spectroscopy** is the study of the properties of light that depend on wavelength. The rainbow of colors Newton produced included all wavelengths of visible light. It was later learned that two other types of spectra exist. Each is generated under somewhat different conditions.

Continuous Spectrum A **continuous spectrum** is produced by an incandescent solid, liquid, or gas under high pressure. (*Incandescent* means "to emit light when hot.") An example of an incandescent light source is a light bulb. The continuous spectrum consists of an uninterrupted band of color, as shown in **Figure 3A**. The light generated by a light bulb would produce a continuous spectrum. This is the type of spectrum Newton produced in his experiments.

Absorption Spectrum An **absorption spectrum** is produced when visible light is passed through a relatively cool gas under low pressure. The gas absorbs certain wavelengths of light. So the spectrum appears continuous, but with a series of dark lines running through it, as shown in **Figure 3B**. The dark lines represent wavelengths that were absorbed.

Emission Spectrum An **emission spectrum** is produced by a hot gas under low pressure. It is a series of bright lines of particular wavelengths, depending on the gas that produces them. As shown in **Figure 3C**, if the same gaseous element produced an absorption and an emission spectrum, the bright lines of the emission spectrum would line up exactly in the same location as the dark lines in the absorption spectrum.

The spectra of most stars are of the dark-line, or absorption, type. The importance of these spectra is that each element or compound in its gaseous state produces a unique set of spectral lines. When the spectrum of a star is studied, the spectral lines act as "fingerprints." These lines identify the elements present and thus the star's chemical composition. The spectrum of the sun contains thousands of dark lines. More than 60 elements have been identified by matching these lines with those of elements known on Earth.

☑ **Reading Checkpoint** *What is spectroscopy?*

676 Chapter 24 • Lesson 1

The Doppler Effect

When you are standing in place and an ambulance approaches, the siren seems to have a higher-than-normal pitch. The opposite effect happens when the ambulance is moving away from you. The pitch sounds lower. These changes in pitch, which occur for both sound and light waves, are called the Doppler effect. The **Doppler effect** refers to the perceived change in frequency of a wave that is emitted from a source that is moving away from or toward an object. It takes time for the wave to be emitted. If the source is moving away from you, the time between wave fronts increases. The opposite is true for a wave moving toward you.

Frequency and wavelength are inversely proportional. As frequency decreases, wavelength increases. The visible light from a source that is moving away from an observer appears redder because its waves are lengthened. Objects moving toward an object have their light waves shifted toward the blue, or shorter, wavelength. In addition, the amount of shift is related to the rate of movement. The same effect would be produced if you moved and the light source was stationary.

▭ **In astronomy, the Doppler effect is used to determine whether a star or other body in space is moving away from or toward Earth.** Larger Doppler shifts indicate higher speeds; smaller Doppler shifts indicate slower speeds. Doppler shifts are generally measured from the dark lines in the spectra of stars by comparing them with a standard spectrum produced in the laboratory.

FIGURE 4 The Doppler Effect
The frequency of sound waves from an approaching ambulance increase as it approaches an observer. For a receding ambulance, the frequency decreases and the observer notes a lower-pitched sound. When this effect is applied to light, a shorter wavelength is noted for an approaching object and is seen as blue light. A longer wavelength is noted for a receding object, which is seen as red light.

Integrate Physics L2

A Sonic Boom The Doppler effect and a sonic boom are similar phenomena. When an object such as an airplane is traveling near the speed of sound, the compression waves bunch up near the nose of the aircraft. When the aircraft exceeds the speed of sound, a loud explosion, known as a sonic boom, is heard. The sonic boom occurs because some of the sound wavefronts arrive at the same instant. Have students research how a sonic boom and a Mach cone are formed. Have students make posters showing how each of these phenomena occurs.
Verbal

3 ASSESS

Evaluate Understanding   L2

Have students write one question on each of the following topics: electromagnetic radiation, spectroscopy, and the Doppler effect. Have groups of students ask one another their questions.

Reteach   L1

Use Figure 3 on p. 676 to review the different types of spectra.

24.1 Assessment

Review Key Concepts ▭

1. What types of radiation make up the electromagnetic spectrum?

2. Compare and contrast the three different types of spectra.

3. How do scientists determine the elements present in a star?

4. How can scientists determine whether a star is moving toward or away from Earth?

Think Critically

5. **Sequence** Sequence the components of visible light according to wavelength, beginning with the shortest wavelength.

6. **Apply Concepts** Based on what you know about prisms and visible light, how do you think rainbows form in Earth's atmosphere?

WRITING IN SCIENCE

7. **Summarize** Make a list of questions that you would like to ask a scientist about the nature of light. Your questions should cover both the wave theory and the particle theory of light.

Studying the Sun **677**

Answers

☑ **Reading Checkpoint** *Spectroscopy is the study of the properties of light that depend on wavelength.*

Assessment Answers

1. Electromagnetic radiation includes gamma rays, X-rays, ultraviolet light, visible light, infrared radiation, microwaves, and radio waves.
2. A continuous spectrum is produced by an incandescent solid, liquid, or gas under high pressure. It consists of an uninterrupted band of color. An absorption spectrum is produced when visible light is passed through a relatively cool gas under low pressure. The spectrum appears continuous, but with a series of dark lines running through it. An emission spectrum is produced by a hot gas under low pressure. It is a series of bright lines of particular wavelengths, depending on the gas that produces them.

3. Scientists study the star's spectrum. The spectral lines act as "fingerprints," which identify the elements present and thus the star's chemical composition.
4. Scientists study Doppler shifts. A red shift indicates that a star is moving away from Earth. A blue shift indicates that a star is moving toward Earth.
5. violet, blue, green, yellow, orange, and red

6. Visible light is bent when it encounters water droplets in the atmosphere and is separated into its component colors.
7. Sample questions: In which circumstances does light behave like a wave? When does it behave like a stream of particles? Who developed the theories? If time permits, have students research the answers to their questions.

24.2 Tools for Studying Space

1 FOCUS

1 FOCUS

Lesson Objectives

24.4 **Explain** how refracting, reflecting, and radio telescopes work.

24.5 **Describe** the advantages and disadvantages of each type of telescope.

24.6 **Explain** the advantages that a space telescope has over an Earth-based telescope.

Build Vocabulary L2

Concept Map Have students make a concept map using the term *telescopes* as the starting point. All of the vocabulary terms in this lesson should be used.

Reading Strategy L2

a. uses a lens to bend and redirect light to a focal point behind a mirror

b. uses a concave mirror to focus light to a point in front of a mirror

2 INSTRUCT

Build Reading Literacy L1

Refer to p. **642D** in **Chapter 23**, which provides the guidelines for comparing and contrasting.

Compare and Contrast Have students read the lesson. As they read, they should make lists of how the various types of telescopes are similar and different.
Verbal

Key Questions

🔑 *How does a refracting telescope produce an image?*

🔑 *Why are most large telescopes reflecting telescopes?*

🔑 *How does a radio telescope gather data?*

🔑 *What advantages do space telescopes have over Earth-based telescopes?*

Vocabulary

- refracting telescope
- chromatic aberration
- reflecting telescope
- radio telescope

Reading Strategy

Compare and Contrast
Copy the Venn diagram. As you read, complete it to show the differences between refracting and reflecting telescopes.

```
Refracting                Reflecting
Telescopes                Telescopes

   a.  ?    light-gathering,   b.  ?
           resolving, and
           magnifying power
```

THERE IS only so faint a light the unaided eye can observe. So, what tools do astronomers use to improve their ability to study light? It all started in the early 1600s when Galileo got his hands on an invention that's credited to Dutch lens makers—the telescope. The concept of a basic telescope is pretty simple. Two lenses are inserted in a tube. The lenses act together to produce a brighter, larger, sharper image than could be seen by the unaided eye. The first telescope—the original Dutch invention—magnified objects three times their actual size. But Galileo quickly improved upon that design, ending up with a telescope that could magnify objects more than 30 times. The images that Galileo viewed through his telescopes were fuzzy and distorted. Yet, the discoveries that he made with those early instruments changed astronomy forever.

Over the centuries, scientists and engineers have continuously improved the tools of astronomy. Galileo's farthest subjects were stars in our own galaxy. Today, astronomers use advanced tools to study light and other electromagnetic radiation from objects at the edge of the known universe.

FIGURE 5
Yerkes Telescope
The telescope at Yerkes Observatory is the largest refracting telescope in the world.

Refracting Telescopes

The early telescopes used by Galileo and other astronomers used lenses to bend or refract light. This type of telescope is known as a **refracting telescope.**

Focus 🔑 **The objective lens of a refracting telescope produces an image by bending light from a distant object so that the light converges at an area called the focus** (*focus* = central point). A star, for example, appears as a point of light.

You can easily demonstrate an image produced by refraction by holding a lens in one hand and placing a white card behind the lens. Now vary the distance between the lens and the card until an image, such as a window, appears on the card. The distance between the lens and the card is called the *focal length* of the lens.

Astronomers usually study an image from a telescope by first photographing the image. However, if a telescope is used to examine an image directly, a second lens, called an eyepiece, is required. The *eyepiece* magnifies the image produced by the objective lens. In this respect, it is similar to a magnifying glass. The objective lens produces a very small, bright image of an object, and the eyepiece enlarges the image so that details can be seen.

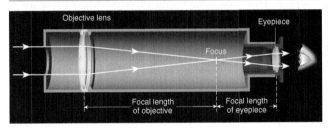

FIGURE 6 Simple Refracting Telescope A refracting telescope uses an objective lens to bend light and an eyepiece to enlarge the refracted image.

Chromatic Aberration Although used extensively in the nineteenth century, refracting telescopes suffer a major optical defect. A lens, like a prism, bends the shorter wavelengths of light more than the longer ones. Consequently, when a refracting telescope is in focus for red light, blue and violet light are out of focus. When blue light is in focus, a reddish halo appears. When red light is in focus, a bluish halo appears. The troublesome effect, called **chromatic** (*chroma* = color) **aberration** (*aberrare* = to go astray), weakens the image and produces that halo of color around it. Although this effect cannot be eliminated completely, it is reduced by using a second lens made of a different type of glass.

☑ **Reading Checkpoint** What is chromatic aberration?

Use Community Resources L2

Invite an astronomer to talk to your class about telescopes. Ask if he or she could bring small telescopes to use for demonstrations. If possible, see if the astronomer could come at night and have a moon-gazing or star-gazing party.
Verbal, Interpersonal

(Teacher **Demo**)

MAKING A SIMPLE REFRACTING TELESCOPE L2

Purpose Students will observe the simple concepts behind a refracting telescope.

Materials 2 magnifying lenses

Procedure Observe an object in the distance with one of the magnifying lenses. Move the lens back and forth until you get a sharp image. Place the second magnifying lens in front of your eye. Move the second lens back and forth until you get a clear image. The image should appear larger. Pass the lenses around the classroom to give students an opportunity to view an image.

Expected Outcome Students will see that a simple refracting telescope consists of two lenses. In this example, it consists of two convex lenses. A convex lens is thicker in the middle and thinner around the edges.
Visual, Kinesthetic

Answers

☑ **Reading Checkpoint** *Chromatic aberration is an effect associated with refracting telescopes that weakens an image and produces a halo of color around it.*

Differentiated Instruction

SPECIAL NEEDS For students with difficulty absorbing concepts by reading, use Figures 6, 7, and 8 as visual aids as you describe how each of these telescopes works. Be sure students understand the differences among these telescopes.

Figure 7 Have students examine the figure. **Ask:** Where is the viewer positioned for each type of reflecting telescope? *(In A, the viewer is in a viewing cage inside the telescope, positioned at the focal point. In B, the viewer is seated below the telescope at the focal point. In C, the viewer is at the side of the telescope, viewing the image at an angle.)* Infer why the prime method is used only for large telescopes. *(The telescope has to be large enough for a person to sit inside the telescope to view the image.)*
Verbal, Logical

Students may think that increasing the magnification of a reflecting telescope will improve the clarity of an image. This is not necessarily true. What can be viewed telescopically is limited by atmospheric conditions and the resolving power of the telescope. Any part of an image that is not clear at low magnification will appear only as a larger blur at higher magnification. Increasing magnification spreads out the light and decreases the brightness of the object. Astronomers describe telescopes not in terms of their magnification, but by the diameter of the objective mirror or lens, because it is this factor that determines both the light-gathering power and the resolving power of a telescope.

A good rule of thumb for amateur astronomers is that every inch of aperture enables you to increase magnification up to 60 power. A three inch telescope would have a useful magnification of 180×.
Verbal

Prime method

Cassegrain method

Newtonian method

FIGURE 7 Viewing Methods With Reflecting Telescopes A The Prime method is only used with very large telescopes. **B** The Cassegrain method is most commonly used. Note that a small hole in the center of the mirror allows light to pass through. **C** This figure shows the Newtonian method.

Reflecting Telescopes

Newton solved the problem of chromatic aberration by building telescopes that reflected light from a shiny surface—a mirror. Because reflected light is not dispersed into its component colors, chromatic aberration is avoided. **Reflecting telescopes** use a concave mirror that focuses light in front of a mirror, rather than behind it, like a lens. The mirror, called the objective, is generally made of glass that is finely ground and coated with a highly reflective material, usually an aluminum compound.

Because the focus of a reflecting telescope is in front of the mirror, the observer, too, must be in front of the mirror. This blocks some light from falling on the objective mirror. **Figure 7A** shows a viewing cage for the observer within the telescope. **Figures 7B** and **7C** show how secondary mirrors can be used to view the image from outside the telescope.

Advantages of Reflecting Telescopes As you might imagine, it's a huge task to produce a large piece of high-quality, bubble-free glass for refracting telescopes. 🔖 **Most large optical telescopes are reflectors. Light does not pass through a mirror so the glass for a reflecting telescope does not have to be of optical quality.** In addition, a lens can be supported only around the edge, so over time it sags and images become distorted. But mirrors can be supported fully from behind so there is no problem of the mirror sagging and distorting the image. As you can see in the illustrations in Figure 7, the major disadvantage of the reflecting telescope is that the viewing location blocks some light from entering the telescope and falling on the objective mirror. Thus, a reflecting telescope with a 25-centimeter opening will not collect as much light as a 25-centimeter refracting telescope.

Properties of Optical Telescopes Both refracting and reflecting telescopes have three properties that aid astronomers in their work: 1) light-gathering power, 2) resolving power, and 3) magnifying power. Light-gathering power refers to the telescope's ability to collect more light—more than the unaided eye—from distant objects, thereby producing brighter images. Telescopes with large lenses or mirrors are able to "see" farther into space than those with small ones.

Another advantage of telescopes with large objectives is their greater resolving power, which allows for sharper images and finer detail. For example, with the unaided eye, the Milky Way appears as a vague band of light in the night sky. But even a small telescope is capable of resolving, or separating it into, individual stars. Lastly, telescopes have magnifying power, which is the ability to make an image larger, or appear closer than it actually is. Magnification is calculated by dividing the focal length of the objective by the focal length of the eyepiece. Thus, the magnification of a telescope can be changed by simply changing the eyepiece.

☑ **Reading Checkpoint** *What is light-gathering power?*

RADIO TELESCOPES
FIGURE 8
A The 43-meter Radio Telescope at Green Bank, West Virginia The dish acts like the mirror of a reflecting telescope, focusing radio waves onto the antenna.

B The Very Large Array Near Socorro, New Mexico Twenty-seven identical antennas operate together to form this radio network.

Identify *What is a network of radio telescopes called?*

Detecting Invisible Radiation

Solar radiation is made up of more than just the radiation that is visible to our eyes. Gamma rays, X-rays, ultraviolet radiation (UV), infrared radiation (IR), and radio waves are also produced by stars. Photographic film and digital sensors that are sensitive to UV and IR radiation have been developed. This extends the limits of our vision. However, most UV and IR radiation cannot penetrate our atmosphere, so balloons, rockets, and satellites must transport cameras "above" the atmosphere to record it.

A narrow band of radio waves is able to penetrate the atmosphere. Measurement of this radiation is important because it enables astronomers to measure the galactic distribution of hydrogen. Hydrogen is the main material from which stars are made.

Radio Telescopes The detection of radio waves is accomplished by large dishes called **radio telescopes,** shown in **Figures 8A** and **8B.** The dish of one of these telescopes operates in the same manner as the objective mirror of an optical telescope. 🔊 **A radio telescope focuses incoming radio waves on an antenna, which absorbs and transmits the waves to an amplifier, similar to a radio antenna.**

Because radio waves are about 100,000 times longer than visible radiation, the surface of the dish doesn't need to be as smooth as a mirror. Except for the shortest radio waves, a wire mesh is a good reflector. However, because radio signals from celestial sources are very weak, large dishes are necessary to intercept an adequate signal.

Radio telescopes have poor resolution, making it difficult to pinpoint the radio source. Pairs or groups of telescopes reduce this problem. When several radio telescopes are wired together, as shown in Figure 8B, the resulting network is called a *radio interferometer.*

Studying the Sun **681**

Facts and Figures

The Very Large Array consists of 27 radio antennas set up in a Y-shaped configuration. The site is located on the Plains of San Augustin 50 miles west of Socorro, New Mexico. Each antenna measures 25 m in diameter. When the antennae are combined electronically, they give an equivalent resolution of an antenna 36 km in diameter. The combination of the antennae has the sensitivity of a dish that is 130 m in diameter.

Integrate Language Arts L2

The Hubble Space Telescope The Hubble Space Telescope has provided spectacular images of the universe. This program also has experienced difficulties. Have students in groups research the Hubble Space Telescope project and make a computer presentation to share with their classmates. The Internet contains many photographs that can be included in the presentation.
Verbal, Interpersonal

For Enrichment L2

Ask students to research to determine speeds of current spacecraft and to use this information to evaluate the probability of travel to nearby solar systems. *(Students should realize that travel to nearby solar systems would be too slow to be realistic, given current technology.)*
Verbal, Logical

Answers

☑ **Reading Checkpoint** *They do not need visible light to obtain images.*

INQUIRY
APPLY IT!

Q: *Why do astronomers build observatories on mountaintops?*

A: Observatories are most often located on mountaintops because sites above the densest part of the atmosphere provide better conditions for "seeing."

FIGURE 9 Hubble Space Telescope Hubble was deployed into Earth's orbit by the space shuttle *Discovery.*

682 Chapter 24 • Lesson 2

Advantages of Radio Telescopes Radio telescopes have some advantages over optical telescopes. They are much less affected by turbulence in the atmosphere, clouds, and the weather. No protective dome is required, which reduces the cost of construction. "Viewing" is possible 24 hours a day. More important, radio telescopes can "see" through interstellar dust clouds that obscure visible wavelengths. Radio telescopes can also detect clouds of gases that are too cool to emit visible light. These cold gas clouds still emit radio waves. Studying these clouds is important because they are the sites of star formation.

Radio telescopes are, however, hindered by human-made radio interference. While optical telescopes are placed on remote mountaintops to reduce interference from city lights, radio telescopes are often hidden in valleys to block human-made radio interference.

Radio telescopes have revealed such spectacular events as the collision of two galaxies. They also allowed for the discovery of intense and distant radio wave sources called *quasars*—quasi-stellar radio sources. Quasars are radio wave sources that appear to exist in the center of newly formed galaxies.

☑ **Reading Checkpoint** Why can radio telescopes be used 24 hours a day?

Space Telescopes

Have you ever noticed how the air above a hot parking lot in the summer can shimmer and blur? That same blurring effect also distorts the images produced by most telescopes on Earth.

One effective way to get around the distorting effects of Earth's atmosphere is to send telescopes into space. **Space telescopes orbit above Earth's atmosphere and thus produce clearer images than Earth-based telescopes.**

Hubble Space Telescope The Hubble Space Telescope, built by NASA, was the first space telescope. The Hubble spacecraft, shown in **Figure 9,** is about 43 meters long—about the size of a school bus. It was put into orbit around Earth in 1990. This 2.4-meter (about 95-inch) space telescope has 10 billion times more light-gathering power than the unaided human eye. Hubble has provided data about the birth of stars, objects known as black holes, and the age of the universe.

Among the many important discoveries made possible by Hubble have been numerous extrasolar planets. An *extrasolar planet* is a planet in orbit around a star other than the sun. How do astronomers detect extrasolar planets? An extrasolar planet is not viewed directly. Instead, the gravity of an extrasolar planet causes a Doppler shift in light emitted by the planet's star. By measuring the Doppler shift in the star's emission spectrum, astronomers can infer that a planet is present. Most known extrasolar planets are thought to be gas giants larger than Jupiter.

Special Purpose Telescopes Space telescopes have been built for a variety of specialized purposes. Similar to radio telescopes, these space telescopes often reveal surprising features of the objects they study. They are often designed to observe objects in space at wavelengths outside the visible spectrum. Data from space telescopes enable space scientists to better classify these objects and study the complex processes involved in their formation.

For example, to study X-rays, NASA uses the Chandra X-Ray Observatory. One of Chandra's missions is to gather data about *black holes*—objects whose gravity is so strong that visible light cannot escape them. Another space telescope, the Compton Gamma-Ray Observatory, was used to study both visible light and gamma rays emitted by black holes and other objects in space. For example, it observed exploding stars that gave off powerful bursts of gamma radiation. The James Webb Space Telescope's mission is to study infrared radiation. This telescope is designed to detect infrared radiation from the oldest stars and galaxies that formed early in the history of the universe.

FIGURE 10 The Milky Way Galaxy Different types of telescopes have been used to observe the Milky Way at different parts of the spectrum, including visible light, X-ray, gamma ray, and infrared.

3 ASSESS

Evaluate Understanding L2

Have students write down the following types of telescopes: refracting, reflecting, and radio. Then, have students write down three facts about each telescope. Have them share their facts with the class.

Reteach L1

Use Figures 6, 7, and 8 to review how each of the these telescopes works.

24.2 Assessment

Review Key Concepts

1. How does a refracting telescope work?

2. How does a reflecting telescope differ from a refracting telescope?

3. Why are most large optical telescopes reflecting telescopes?

4. How do radio telescopes gather data?

5. Why do space telescopes obtain clearer images than Earth-based telescopes?

Think Critically

6. **Calculate** If a telescope has an objective with a focal length of 50 centimeters and an eyepiece with a focal length of 25 millimeters, what will be the magnification?

7. **Apply Concepts** Using the numbers from the previous question, would an eyepiece with a greater focal length increase or decrease magnification? Explain.

BIGIDEA EARTH AND THE UNIVERSE

8. **Draw Conclusions** Recall the different types of electromagnetic radiation. Based on what you've learned in this lesson, would you recommend sending a telescope into space to study radio waves? Why or why not?

Studying the Sun **683**

Assessment Answers

1. The objective lens produces an image by bending light from a distant object so that the light converges at an area called the focus.
2. A reflecting telescope uses a concave mirror to produce an image. A refracting telescope uses a lens to bend or refract light.
3. Because light does not pass through a mirror, the glass for a reflecting telescope does not have to be of optical quality. In addition, a lens can be supported only around the edge, so it sags. Mirrors, on the other hand, can be supported fully from behind. Finally, with mirrors there is no chromatic aberration.

4. A radio telescope focuses the incoming radio waves on an antenna, which absorbs and transmits the waves to an amplifier.
5. Space telescopes orbit above Earth's atmosphere and thus produce clearer images than Earth-based telescopes. There is no blurring of images and no interference from city lights.
6. Magnification is calculated by dividing the focal length of the objective by the focal length of the eyepiece. In this example, 500 mm ÷ 25 mm = 20; magnification would be 20 times.

7. An eyepiece with a greater focal length, such as 50 mm, would decrease magnification because 500 mm ÷ 50 mm = 10 times magnification.
8. Sample answer: Radio waves can easily pass through Earth's atmosphere. Therefore, there is little advantage in sending a radio telescope into space.

24.3 The Sun

Lesson Objectives

24.7 **Explain** the structure of the sun.

24.8 **Describe** the physical features on the surface of the sun.

24.9 **Explain** how the sun produces energy.

Build Vocabulary   L2

LINCS There are several words in the vocabulary list that sound like other words students may be familiar with. Have students: **L**ist the parts that they know; **I**magine a picture; **N**ote a reminding sound-alike word; **C**onnect the terms; and **S**elf-test.

Reading Strategy   L2

a. Answers will vary.
b. Answers will vary.
c. Answers will vary.
d. Answers will vary.

2 INSTRUCT

Build Reading Literacy   L1

Refer to p. **392D** in **Chapter 14,** which provides the guidelines for previewing.

Preview Before they read the lesson, have students skim the titles, headings, visual elements, and boldfaced type to preview how the text is organized.
Visual

Key Questions

🔑 **What is the structure of the sun?**

🔑 **What are the characteristics of features on the sun?**

🔑 **How does the sun produce energy?**

Vocabulary

- photosphere
- chromosphere • corona
- solar wind • sunspot
- prominence • solar flare
- aurora • nuclear fusion

Reading Strategy

Monitor Your Understanding Preview the Key Concepts, topic headings, vocabulary, and figures in this section. Copy the table below, listing two things you expect to learn. After reading, fill in the table below, stating what you have learned about each item you listed.

What I Expect to Learn	What I Learned
a. ?	b. ?
c. ?	d. ?

THE SUN is one of the billions of stars that make up the Milky Way galaxy. The sun is Earth's primary source of energy. Everything—from the fossil fuels we burn in our automobiles to the food that we eat—is ultimately derived from solar energy. The sun is also important to astronomers, since until just a few years ago it was the only star whose surface we could study. Even with the largest telescopes, most other stars appear only as points of light.

Because of the sun's brightness and its damaging radiation, it is not safe to observe it directly. However, a telescope can project its image on a flat surface held behind the telescope's eyepiece. In this manner, the sun can be studied safely. This basic method is used in several telescopes around the world. One of the finest is at the Kitt Peak National Observatory (see **Figure 11**). It consists of an enclosure with moving mirrors that direct sunlight to an underground mirror. From the mirror, an image of the sun is projected to an observing room, where it is studied.

Compared to other stars, the sun is an average star. However, compared with the other objects in our solar system, it is truly gigantic. Its diameter is equal to 109 Earth diameters, or 1.35 million kilometers. Its volume is 1.25 million times as great as Earth's. Its mass is 332,000 times the mass of Earth and its density is only one quarter that of solid Earth.

FIGURE 11 The McMath-Pierce Solar Telescope at Kitt Peak Near Tucson, Arizona Movable mirrors at the top follow the sun, reflecting its light down the sloping tunnel.

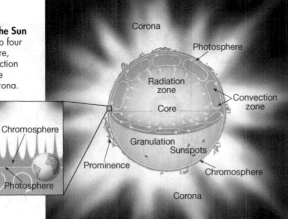

FIGURE 12 Structure of the Sun
The sun can be divided into four parts: the solar interior (core, radiation zone, and convection zone), the photosphere, the chromosphere, and the corona.

Structure of the Sun

Because the sun is made of ionized gas, or *plasma*, no sharp boundaries exist between its various layers. 🔑 **Keeping this in mind, we can divide the sun into four parts: the solar interior, the visible surface (the photosphere), the chromosphere, and the corona.** These parts are shown in **Figure 12.** The sun's interior makes up all but a tiny fraction of the total solar mass. Unlike the outer three layers of the sun, the solar interior cannot be directly observed. Let's discuss the visible layers first.

Photosphere The **photosphere** (*photos* = light, *sphere* = a ball) radiates most of the sunlight we see and can be thought of as the visible surface of the sun. The photosphere consists of a layer of plasma less than 500 kilometers thick. It is neither smooth nor uniformly bright, as the ancient astronomers had imagined.

When viewed through a telescope, the photosphere's grainy texture is apparent. This is the result of numerous relatively small, bright markings called *granules* which are surrounded by narrow, dark regions, as shown in **Figure 13.** Individual granules are typically the size of Texas, and they owe their brightness to hotter gases that are rising from below. As this gas spreads, cooling causes it to darken and sink back toward the interior. Each granule survives only 10 to 20 minutes. The combined motion of new granules replacing old ones gives the photosphere the appearance of boiling. This up-and-down flow of plasma is called *convection*. Besides producing the grainy appearance of the photosphere, convection is believed to be responsible for the transfer of energy in the uppermost part of the sun's interior.

The composition of the photosphere is revealed by the dark lines of its absorption spectrum. Studies show that 90 percent of the sun's surface atoms are hydrogen, almost 10 percent are helium, and only minor amounts of the other detectable elements are present. Other stars also have high proportions of these two elements—the lightest elements in the periodic table.

FIGURE 13 Granules Granules are the yellowish-orange patches on the photosphere.
Describe **How do gases move in the convection zone?**

Studying the Sun **685**

Answers

Figure 13 *Gases rise to the surface of the sun, cool, then sink back into the interior.*

LESSON 24.3

EARTH AND SOLAR WINDS L2

Purpose Students will observe how Earth is protected from solar winds.

Materials bar magnet, 2 sheets of notebook paper, iron filings, drinking straw

Procedure Cover the magnet with a sheet of paper. Fold the other sheet of paper in half. Sprinkle iron filings in the fold. Hold the paper about 15 cm from the magnet. Blow through the straw, directing the stream of air at the iron filings. The iron filings should be attracted to the magnet.

Expected Outcome Students will observe how a magnetic field attracts charged particles. The solar wind is composed of ionized or charged particles. Just as the iron filings are drawn to the magnet, the solar wind is attracted to Earth's magnetic field. Earth's magnetic field prevents the solar wind from reaching Earth's surface and bombarding it.
Visual, Logical

FIGURE 14 Chromosphere The chromosphere is a thin layer of hot gases that appears as a red rim around the sun when photographed through a special filter.

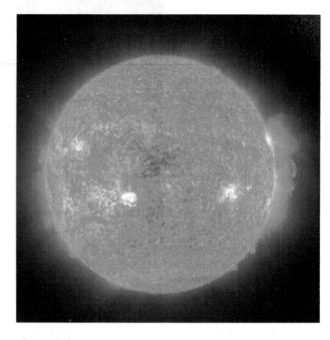

Chromosphere Just above the photosphere is the **chromosphere,** a relatively thin layer of hot plasma a few thousand kilometers thick. Astronomers can observe the chromosphere for a few moments during a total solar eclipse or by using a special instrument that blocks out the brighter light from the photosphere. Under such conditions, the chromosphere appears as a thin red rim around the sun. Because the chromosphere consists of hot, incandescent ionized gases under low pressure, it produces an emission spectrum that is nearly the reverse of the absorption spectrum of the photosphere.

Corona The outermost portion of the solar atmosphere, the **corona** (*corona* = crown) is visible only when the brilliant photosphere is covered. This envelope of ionized gases normally extends a million kilometers from the surface of the sun and produces a glow about half as bright as the full moon.

At the outer fringe of the corona, the ionized gases have speeds great enough to escape the gravitational pull of the sun. The streams of protons and electrons that flow from the corona constitute the **solar wind.** This wind travels outward through the solar system at speeds up to 800 kilometers per second and eventually is lost to space. During its journey, the solar wind interacts with the bodies of the solar system, continually bombarding lunar rocks and altering their appearance. Earth's magnetic field prevents the solar winds from reaching our surface.

☑ **Reading Checkpoint** *What is the solar wind?*

686 Chapter 24 • Lesson 3

Facts and Figures

The high temperature of the corona is probably caused by sound waves generated by the convection motion of the photosphere. Just as boiling water makes noise, the energetic sound waves generated in the photosphere are believed to be absorbed by the gases of the corona and thereby raise their temperatures.

The Active Sun

The most conspicuous features on the surface of the sun are the dark regions, shown in **Figure 15A.** They were occasionally observed before the advent of the telescope, but were generally regarded as objects located somewhere between the sun and Earth. In 1610, Galileo concluded that these regions were part of the solar surface. From their motion, he deduced that the sun rotates on its axis about once a month. Later observations indicated that not all parts of the sun rotate at the same speed. The sun's equator rotates once in 25 days, while a location 70 degrees from the solar equator, whether north or south, requires 33 days for one rotation. This nonuniform rotation of the sun is evidence that it is made up of ionized gases.

Sunspots What are those dark areas Galileo observed? The dark regions on the surface of the photosphere are called **sunspots.** As **Figure 15B** shows, an individual spot contains a black center rimmed by a lighter region. ☞ **Sunspots appear dark because of their temperature, which is about 1500 K less than that of the surrounding solar surface.** But sunspots only appear dark by comparison with the hotter gases surrounding them. If these dark spots could be observed away from the sun, they would appear many times brighter than the full moon.

According to NASA research, sunspots are thought to be "islands" of magnetism floating on the sun's surface. Many sunspots are about the size of Earth. It is also thought that convection currents beneath the sun's surface help keep the sunspots afloat.

For the past 400 years, records of sunspot occurrences have been kept. This sunspot data reveals that the number of sunspots observable varies in an 11-year cycle. First, the number of sunspots increases to a maximum, with an average of between 100 to 200 sunspots occurring each year. Then their numbers gradually decline to a minimum, when only a few or even none occur during a year.

PLANET DIARY

For an activity on **sunspots and weather**, visit PlanetDiary.com/HSES.

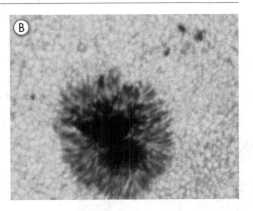

FIGURE 15 Sunspots
A Sunspots often appear as groups of dark areas on the sun.

B A close-up of an individual sunspot shows a black center surrounded by a lighter region.

Studying the Sun **687**

Build Science Skills

L2

Student Activity: Use Models
Have students complete the following activity. Fill an empty soda bottle half full with water. Add 5 mL of glitter to the bottle of water. Place the washer on the mouth of the bottle. Dry the mouths of this bottle and a second empty soda bottle with a paper towel to be sure that tape sticks to them both. Place the mouth of the second bottle on top of the washer. Tape the two bottles together securely with duct tape. Swirl the two bottles several times. Then, turn the bottles upside down, placing the empty bottle on the table. The glitter demonstrates how fluids travel at different rates as the fluid moves through the funnel. Because the sun is not a solid body, the fluids are free to rotate at various speeds and different parts of the sun rotate at different rates, just as they do in the bottles.
Kinesthetic, Visual

Answers

☑ **Reading Checkpoint** *streams of protons and electrons that flow from the corona*

Facts and Figures

An interesting characteristic of sunspots was discovered by astronomer George Hale, for whom the Hale telescope is named. Hale found that the large sunspots are strongly magnetized, and when they occur in pairs, they have opposite magnetic poles. Also, every pair located in the same hemisphere is magnetized in the same manner. However, all pairs in the other hemisphere are magnetized in the opposite manner. At the beginning of each sunspot cycle, the polarity reverses. The cause of this change in polarity is not fully understood.

FIGURE 16
Solar Prominence
Solar prominences are huge, arched structures, best observed when they are on the edge of the sun.

Prominences Among the more spectacular features of the active sun are prominences (*prominere* = to jut out). **Prominences** are huge cloudlike structures consisting of chromospheric ionized gases. They often appear as great arches that extend well into the corona. Many prominences have the appearance of a fine tapestry and seem to hang motionless for days at a time, as shown in **Figure 16**. Others rise explosively away from the sun. These eruptive prominences reach speeds of as much as 1000 kilometers per second—enough speed to escape the sun's gravity completely. **Prominences are ionized gases trapped by magnetic fields that extend from regions of intense solar activity.**

Solar Flares The most explosive events associated with sunspots are solar flares. **Solar flares** are brief outbursts that normally last about an hour and appear as a sudden brightening of the region above a sunspot cluster. **During their existence, solar flares release enormous amounts of energy, much of it in the form of ultraviolet, radio, and X-ray radiation.** At the same time, fast-moving atomic particles are ejected, causing solar wind to intensify. Although a major flare could conceivably endanger the crew of a space flight, they are relatively rare. About a day after a large outburst, the ejected particles reach Earth, where they can affect long-distance radio communications.

The most spectacular effects of solar flares, however, are the **auroras,** also called the northern and southern lights. Following a strong solar flare, Earth's upper atmosphere near its magnetic poles is set aglow for several nights. The auroras appear in a wide variety of forms, one example of which is shown in **Figure 17.** Sometimes the display looks like colorful ribbons moving with the breeze. At other times, the auroras appear as a series of luminous arcs or as a foglike glow. Auroral displays, like other solar activities, vary in intensity with the 11-year sunspot cycle.

☑ **Reading Checkpoint** *What are solar flares?*

FIGURE 17 Aurora Borealis or Northern Lights in Alaska The same phenomenon occurs toward the south pole, where it is called the aurora australis or southern lights.

The Solar Interior

The interior of the sun cannot be observed directly. For that reason, everything we know about it is based on information acquired from the energy it radiates and from theoretical studies. The source of the sun's energy was not discovered until the late 1930s.

Nuclear Fusion Deep in its interior, the sun produces energy by a process known as **nuclear fusion.** This nuclear reaction converts four hydrogen nuclei into the nucleus of a helium atom. When this fusion occurs, tremendous energy is released. **During nuclear fusion, energy is released because some matter is actually converted to energy.** The nuclear fusion process is illustrated in **Figure 18.** How does this process work? Consider that four hydrogen atoms have a combined atomic mass of 4.032 atomic mass units (4×1.008). The atomic mass of helium is 4.003 atomic mass units, or 0.029 units less than the combined mass of the hydrogen. The small amount of missing mass is emitted as energy, according to Albert Einstein's equation:

$$E = mc^2$$

E equals energy, *m* equals mass, and *c* equals the speed of light. Because the speed of light is very great (300,000 km/s), the amount of energy released from even a small amount of mass is enormous.

The conversion of just one pinhead's worth of hydrogen to helium generates more energy than burning thousands of tons of coal. Most of this energy is in the form of high-energy photons that work their way toward the solar surface. The photons are absorbed and reemitted many times in the radiation zone until they reach a layer just below the photosphere. Here, convection currents help transport this energy to the solar surface, where it radiates through the transparent chromosphere and corona.

Only a small percentage of the hydrogen in the nuclear reaction is actually converted to energy. Nevertheless, the sun is consuming an estimated 600 million tons of hydrogen each second. Of this amount, about 4 million tons are converted to energy. As hydrogen is consumed, the product of this reaction— helium—forms the solar core. The solar core continually grows in size.

☑ **Reading Checkpoint** *What happens during the process of nuclear fusion?*

FIGURE 18 Nuclear Fusion
During nuclear fusion, four hydrogen nuclei combine to form one helium nucleus. Some matter is converted to energy.

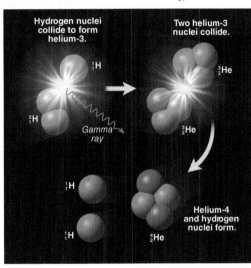

Hydrogen nuclei collide to form helium-3.

Two helium-3 nuclei collide.

Gamma ray

Helium-4 and hydrogen nuclei form.

Studying the Sun **689**

LESSON 24.3

For Enrichment   L3

Challenge students to write an essay that explains how the position of Earth in the solar system, the size of Earth and the sun, and Earth's tilt affected the evolution of Earth and of life on Earth.

Verbal, Logical

3 ASSESS

Evaluate Understanding   L2

Have students draw and label a diagram of the sun. Have students include all of the applicable vocabulary words in the diagram. Then, have students explain how the sun produces energy and what an aurora is.

Reteach   L1

Use Figure 12 to review the structure of the sun.

FIGURE 19 Earth's Energy Source
The sun is the source of more than 99 percent of all energy on Earth.

How Old Is the Sun? Just how long can the sun produce energy at its present rate before all of its hydrogen fuel is consumed? Even at the enormous rate of consumption, the sun has enough fuel to last 100 billion years. However, evidence gathered by studying the life cycles of others stars similar to the sun indicates that the sun will grow dramatically in diameter and engulf Earth and several other planets long before it runs out of hydrogen fuel. It is thought that a medium-sized star such as the sun can continue in its present stable state for about 10 billion years. Much scientific evidence suggests that the sun is currently 4.5 billion years old, so it is "middle-aged."

For nuclear fusion to have started, the sun's internal temperature had to have reached several million degrees. But what caused this increase in temperature? The solar system is thought to have formed from an enormous compressed cloud of dust and gases—mostly hydrogen. When gases are compressed, their temperature increases due to the higher pressure. All of the bodies in the solar system were compressed by gravity. However, the sun was the only one, because of its size and the size of its gravitational force, that became hot enough for nuclear fusion to occur. Astronomers currently estimate the sun's internal temperature at 15 million K.

Jupiter is basically a hydrogen-rich ball; if it were about 10 times more massive, it too might have become a star. The idea of one star orbiting another may seem odd, but recent evidence indicates that a large percentage of the stars in the universe probably occur in pairs or multiples.

24.3 Assessment

Review Key Concepts 🔑

1. What is the structure of the sun?

2. Which layer of the sun can be thought of as its surface?

3. Describe some characteristics of features on the sun.

4. Are the same number of sunspots always present on the sun? Explain.

5. How does the sun produce energy?

6. How much longer will the sun likely exist in its present state?

Think Critically

7. Relate Cause and Effect Why do sunspots appear dark?

8. Apply Concepts What is the effect on Earth's atmosphere of a strong solar flare?

MATH PRACTICE

9. Calculate Of the 6×10^8 tons of hydrogen the sun consumes each second, about 4×10^6 tons are converted to energy. What percentage of the total hydrogen consumed per second is converted to energy?

690 Chapter 24 • Lesson 3

Assessment Answers

1. The sun contains the following parts: the solar interior, the photosphere, the chromosphere, and the corona.
2. the photosphere
3. Sunspots appear dark because of their temperature, which is about 1500 K less than that of the surrounding solar surface. Prominences are huge cloudlike structures of chromospheric gases. Solar flares release enormous amounts of energy.

4. No, because the number of sunspots varies in an 11-year cycle.
5. Deep in its interior, the sun produces energy by a process known as nuclear fusion, wherein four hydrogen nuclei are converted into the nucleus of a helium atom and tremendous energy is released.
6. The sun is estimated to last another 5 billion years in its present state.
7. Sunspots are somewhat cooler than the surrounding surface.

8. During a solar flare, fast-moving particles are ejected from the sun, increasing the solar wind. The ejected particles reach Earth and disturb long-distance radio communication. They also produce auroras.
9. 4×10^6 tons ÷ 6×10^8 tons = $0.0066 \times 100 = 0.7$ percent

EARTH & SPACE

Solar Variability and Climate Change

Sunspots, the dark regions on the sun's surface shown in **Figure 20,** are prominent solar features. Since the early 1600s, astronomers have recorded the number of sunspots that occur each year. **Figure 21** shows that the average number of sunspots each year varies in an 11-year cycle. Notice a period between about 1645 to 1715, known as the *Maunder Minimum*, with little or no sunspot activity.

Reliable historical records indicate that Europe and North America experienced lower-than-normal temperatures during that same period. Did the reduced number of sunspots result in lower air temperatures on Earth? Sunspot cycles and historical temperature records do not provide enough scientific evidence to draw this conclusion. What additional evidence is available?

Solar Variability

For the past 40 years, space scientists have measured solar radiation. These studies show that solar radiation varies in the same 11-year cycle as sunspots. When sunspot activity is high, solar radiation is high. When sunspot activity is low, solar radiation is also low. The fluctuation of solar radiation is called *solar variability*.

The significance of solar variability here on Earth is that when solar radiation decreases, the amount of solar energy that Earth receives from the sun also decreases. It might seem logical to assume that during the Maunder Minimum solar radiation was low so the amount of solar energy reaching Earth was low. Perhaps this resulted in the lower temperatures. But since solar variation measurements only go back 40 years, there's not enough evidence to support that conclusion.

That's where sunspot cycles come in. If solar variation and sunspot cycles are both on the same 11-year cycle, then it's reasonable to infer that solar radiation was low during the Maunder Minimum.

Effect on Climate Change

There are still many unanswered questions. Why were there so few sunspots from 1645 to 1715? Will there be another period of low sunspot activity in the future? If so, how might that affect Earth's climate? NASA's *Solar Dynamics Observatory (SDO)* is a spacecraft designed to study the sun and provide data that can help answer these questions. Perhaps someday you will become a space scientist and make important contributions to our understanding of the relationship between solar energy and Earth's climate.

FIGURE 20
Sunspots
Scientists have observed that sunspot frequency occurs in an 11-year cycle.

Yearly Averaged Sunspot Numbers 1610–2010

FIGURE 21 Sunspot Cycles This graph of average sunspot numbers spans about 400 years. Note the period of very low activity around the late 1600s.

EARTH & SPACE

Solar Variability and Climatic Change [L2]

Background A National Aeronautics and Space Administration (NASA) computer climate model suggests that low solar activity from the 1400s to the 1700s could have triggered the "Little Ice Age" in North America and Europe. Changes in the sun's energy were one of the biggest factors influencing climatic changes during this time period. There is evidence that the accumulation of greenhouse gases in the atmosphere, caused by human activities, is the primary catalyst for temperature changes today.

Teaching Tip Have students research information available from NASA, National Oceanic and Atmospheric Administration (NOAA), and other reliable sources on the relationship between Earth temperature and solar activity. Students should write a short report detailing the information they have found.
Verbal

TEACHER DEMO: TRACKING SUNSPOTS L2

Objective
Students will observe sunspots and their movement over several days.

Skills Observe, Interpret Data, Make and Use Graphs

Prep Time 20 minutes for setup

Class Time 150 minutes total viewing time, 30 minutes for 5 sessions

Safety Tell students never to look directly at the sun.

Teaching Tips
- Have students take turns tracing the sunspots each day.
- Make copies of the drawings so each lab group can do the calculations.

Expected Outcome Students will observe the sunspots move over time.

TEACHER DEMO: Tracking Sunspots

Problem How can a telescope be used to *safely* view, count, measure, and track the sunspots on the sun's surface over a period of time?

Materials telescope, small cardboard box, large cardboard box, piece of white paper, metric ruler, pencil, tape

Skills Observe, Interpret Data, Make and Use Graphs

Connect to the Big idea Sunspots begin as small areas about 1600 kilometers in diameter. Most last for only a few hours. However, some grow into dark regions many times larger than Earth and last for a month or more. In this lab you will count the number of sunspots over the course of several days.

Procedure

1. Your teacher will position a telescope on a tripod outdoors in a sunny spot away from obstacles. The eyepiece should face away from the sun. **⚠CAUTION:** *Never look at the sun directly. Do not view the sun through the telescope. These actions could cause eye damage or blindness.*

2. Place the large cardboard box on the ground with the front edge of the box about 15 centimeters in front of the telescope's eyepiece.

3. Use the pencil to punch a hole in one side of the small cardboard box. Tape a sheet of white paper inside the opposite end of the box, as shown in the illustration below.

4. Place the small box on its side on top of the large box so you can see into the box. The hole in the small box should face the telescope eyepiece. Your teacher will adjust the telescope so the eyepiece, the hole, and the white paper are aligned.

SAFETY CAUTION:
Never look at the sun directly through a telescope. Doing so can cause eye damage and possible blindness.

5. With your teacher's help, adjust the small box until you see an image of the sun projected onto the paper. Your teacher may adjust the telescope to obtain a clearer image. *Do not look through the viewer, even momentarily,* to accomplish the alignment. You may also vary the distance between the box and the telescope to obtain better images.

6. Copy the data table below on a separate sheet of paper. In your data table, record the number of sunspots that you observe. Trace the outlines of sunspots on the paper. Shade in the sunspots and use the ruler to measure their width.

7. As weather permits and with your teacher's help, make several more viewings of sunspots over the course of the next few days. During each viewing, repeat Steps 1–6. Be sure to track any movement of the sunspots.

Analyze and Conclude

1. **Draw Graphs** How many sunspots did you observe? Draw a line graph of your data using your data table.

2. **Observe** How did the number of sunspots vary over the course of your observations?

3. **Interpret Data** Why did the sunspots move?

4. **Interpret Data** Based on your observations, could you detect any meaningful pattern in the number of sunspots? Why or why not?

5. **Design Experiments** Is it possible to design an experiment to test the hypothesis that sunspots affect Earth's climate? Explain.

GO FURTHER The diameter of the sun is approximately 1.35 million kilometers. Use this number to develop a scale to estimate the sizes of the sunspots you measured in this activity.

Sample Data Table		
Day	Number of Sunspots	Movement?
1		
2		
3		
4		
5		

Analyze and Conclude

1. Sample answer: about 15 large sunspots; check students' graphs.
2. Sample answer: The number of sunspots remained fairly steady over the course of the observations.
3. The sunspots moved because the sun rotates on its axis.
4. Students will probably respond that they could not detect any pattern in sunspot activity because they made too few observations for a pattern in the data to emerge.
5. It would be difficult, or perhaps impossible, to test such a hypothesis because so many other variables affect weather and climate.

GO FURTHER

Sample answer: A possible scale might be 1 mm = 10,000 km. The estimated size of a large sunspot might be 60,000 km.
Visual, Logical

Study Tip

Choose a Quiet Place to Study
Tell students that they will absorb concepts better if they study in a quiet place. Stress that they should minimize distractions, such as music and television.

Think Visually

a. reflecting
b. lens

21st Century Learning

Health Literacy

How does Earth protect humans from dangerous radiation?
Life on Earth depends on solar radiation, but some forms of radiation can be dangerous for humans. Ask students to research the kinds of radiation that are dangerous to human life, the problems this radiation can cause, and the natural protection Earth provides against radiation damage. Instruct students to write a blog entry that explains the types of solar radiation and the problems they have discovered. The blog entries should also include descriptions of the protection that Earth provides and what might happen without this protection.

Homework Guide

Lesson	Questions
1	1–3, 11–15, 24, 32
2	4–6, 16–19, 25, 33
3	7–10, 20–23, 26–31, 34

---

24 Study Guide

Big idea ▶ **Earth and the Universe**

24.1 The Study of Light

🔑 Electromagnetic radiation includes gamma rays, X-rays, ultraviolet light, visible light, infrared radiation, microwaves, and radio waves.

🔑 When the spectrum of a star is studied, the spectral lines act as "fingerprints." These lines identify the elements present and thus the star's chemical composition.

🔑 In astronomy, the Doppler effect is used to determine whether a star or other body in space is moving away from or toward Earth.

electromagnetic spectrum (674)
photon (675)
spectroscopy (676)
continuous spectrum (676)
absorption spectrum (676)
emission spectrum (676)
Doppler effect (677)

24.2 Tools for Studying Space

🔑 The objective lens of a refracting telescope produces an image by bending light from a distant object so that the light converges at an area called the focus.

🔑 Most large optical telescopes are reflectors. Light does not pass through a mirror so the glass for a reflecting telescope does not have to be of optical quality.

🔑 A radio telescope focuses the incoming radio waves on an antenna, which absorbs and transmits these waves to an amplifier, similar to any radio antenna.

🔑 Space telescopes orbit above Earth's atmosphere and thus produce clearer images than Earth-based telescopes.

refracting telescope (679)
chromatic aberration (679)
reflecting telescope (680)
radio telescope (681)

24.3 The Sun

🔑 The sun can be divided into four parts: the solar interior; the visible surface, or photosphere; and two atmospheric layers, the chromosphere and corona.

🔑 Sunspots appear dark because of their temperature, which is about 1500 K less than that of the surrounding solar surface.

🔑 Prominences are ionized gases trapped by magnetic fields that extend from regions of intense solar activity.

🔑 Solar flares release enormous amounts of energy, much of it in the form of ultraviolet, radio, and X-ray radiation.

🔑 During nuclear fusion, energy is released because some matter is converted to energy.

photosphere (685)
chromosphere (686)
corona (686)
solar wind (686)
sunspot (687)
prominence (688)
solar flare (688)
aurora (688)
nuclear fusion (689)

Think Visually

Use information from the chapter to complete the concept map below.

Assessment Answers

Review Content

1. a	**2.** d	**3.** b
4. b	**5.** c	**6.** b
7. c	**8.** a	**9.** d
10. c		

Understand Concepts

11. wavelength and frequency
12. red; violet
13. The wave theory states that light can be thought of as similar to swells in the ocean. This motion is characterized by a property known as wavelength, which is the distance from one wave crest to the next. The particle theory states that light sometimes acts like a stream of particles, called photons, that push on matter, exerting radiation pressure.

24 Assessment

Choose the letter that best answers the question or completes the statement.

1. Which type of radiation has the shortest wavelength?
   a. gamma rays   c. visible light
   b. X-rays   d. radio waves

2. The energy of a photon is related to its
   a. size.   c. density.
   b. mass.   d. wavelength.

3. As light passes through a prism, which color will bend the most?
   a. red   c. yellow
   b. violet   d. blue

4. Which type of telescope uses a concave mirror?
   a. refracting   c. ultraviolet
   b. reflecting   d. infrared

5. Which of the following is not a property of optical telescopes?
   a. resolving power
   b. magnifying power
   c. reflecting power
   d. light-gathering power

6. When several radio telescopes are wired together, the resulting network is called a radio
   a. receiver.
   b. interferometer.
   c. tuner.
   d. antenna.

7. The numerous, relatively small bright markings on the sun's photosphere are called
   a. auroras.
   b. sunspots.
   c. granules.
   d. prominences.

8. The thin, red rim seen around the sun during a total solar eclipse is the
   a. chromosphere.
   b. corona.
   c. solar wind.
   d. photosphere.

9. Which features of the sun look like huge cloudlike arches?
   a. solar flares
   b. sunspots
   c. auroras
   d. prominences

10. What is the source of the sun's energy?
    a. magnetism
    b. nuclear fission
    c. nuclear fusion
    d. radiation pressure

Understand Concepts

11. What two factors determine how radiation is arranged on the electromagnetic spectrum?

12. Which color has the longest wavelength? The shortest?

13. Compare and contrast the wave theory and the particle theory of light.

14. Describe a continuous spectrum. Give an example of a natural phenomenon that exhibits a continuous spectrum.

15. Which type of spectrum do most stars have?

16. What optical defect is associated with refracting telescopes?

17. What three properties do optical telescopes have that aid astronomers?

18. What are some advantages of radio telescopes over optical telescopes?

19. List three space telescopes and describe the type of radiation studied by each.

20. Compare the diameter of the sun to that of Earth.

21. What is solar wind?

22. What "fuel" does the sun consume?

23. What happens to the matter that is consumed in nuclear fusion?

20. The diameter of the sun is equal to 109 Earth diameters.
21. Streams of protons and electrons that flow from the corona and travel outward through the solar system at high speeds constitute the solar wind.
22. hydrogen
23. The hydrogen nuclei are converted to helium nuclei with a small percentage of the matter converted to energy.

14. A continuous spectrum is produced by an incandescent solid, liquid, or gas under high pressure. One example would be light generated by a common light bulb.
15. Most stars have an absorption, or dark-line, spectrum.
16. chromatic aberration
17. light-gathering power, resolving power, and magnifying power

18. Radio telescopes can operate 24 hours a day, are generally cheaper to construct, and can "see" through interstellar dust clouds.
19. The Chandra X-Ray Observatory studies X-rays. The Compton Gamma-Ray Observatory studied both gamma rays and visible light. The mission of the James Webb Space telescope is to study infrared radiation.

ASSESSMENT

Think Critically

24. Larger Doppler shifts indicate higher speeds; smaller Doppler shifts indicate slower speeds.

25. The absence of an atmosphere on the moon would greatly increase the resolving power of a telescope.

26. Hot gases rise to the photosphere, forming granules. Granules cool, darken, and sink back into the sun's interior. Each granule lasts only 10 to 20 minutes. New granules constantly replace old ones. The up-and-down motion gives the photosphere a boiling appearance.

27. No, because the particles of the solar wind are ions, not photons.

Analyze Data

28. The lowest sunspot activity occurred around 1712 and 1811. The highest sunspot activity occurred around 1990.

29. Sunspot activity peaks about every 11 years. Some peak years have relatively few sunspots, while others have many.

30. The last peak occurred in 2001. The next peak will occur about 11 years later, or in 2012.

31. No, it is not possible to predict how many sunspots will occur in a given peak year because the number of sunspots changes with every cycle. Some peak years have close to 200 sunspots, while other peak years have less than 50.

Concepts in Action

32. The star is moving away from Earth.
33. Telescopes with large lenses or mirrors gather more light and produce brighter images. Consequently, large telescopes can view very dim objects, which are often located at great distances. Also, large telescopes have greater resolving powers than do telescopes with smaller objectives.
34. A strong solar flare has occurred on the sun.

Think Critically

24. **Summarize** Briefly summarize the relationship between Doppler shift and the speed of a moving object.

25. **Infer** Why would the moon make a good site for an optical observatory?

26. **Relate Cause and Effect** The photosphere has a boiling appearance. Why?

27. **Draw Conclusions** Can the solar wind be thought of as evidence for the particle theory of light? Explain your answer.

Analyze Data

Use the graph to answer Questions 28–31.

28. **Identify** Which years had the lowest number of sunspots? The highest?

29. **Interpret Data** Describe any patterns in the data.

30. **Predict** When will the next period of maximum sunspot activity most likely occur?

31. **Analyze Data** Based on the data alone, is it possible to predict how many sunspots will occur during the next peak? Why or why not?

Concepts in Action

32. **Infer** What can you infer about a star that exhibits a red shift in its spectra?

33. **Explain** Why do astronomers seek to design telescopes with larger and larger objectives?

34. **Relate Cause and Effect** What could you infer about solar activity if you spotted an aurora that lasted several nights?

Performance-Based Assessment

Summarize The sun is Earth's main source of energy. Work in a group to develop a presentation describing what might happen if the sun's energy increased by 10 percent. Discuss the effects on global temperatures, ocean shorelines, and polar caps. Be sure to consider changes in the amount of surface vegetation, and the impact of these changes on levels of atmospheric carbon dioxide.

Performance-Based Assessment

Students should note that if the sun's energy increased by 10 percent, global temperatures would increase. Polar caps would melt and sea level would rise. Shorelines would move inland. Warmer temperatures would also produce an increase in vegetation, which, in turn, would remove more carbon dioxide from the air during photosynthesis. Because carbon dioxide is a greenhouse gas, a reduction in the amount of carbon dioxide would decrease global temperatures.

Standardized Test Prep

Choose the letter that best answers the question.

1 The sun produces energy by converting
   A oxygen nuclei to carbon dioxide.
   B oxygen nuclei to nitrogen nuclei.
   C hydrogen nuclei to helium nuclei.
   D helium nuclei to hydrogen nuclei.

2 Which of the following best describes the composition of the sun?
   F The sun's surface is about 90 percent hydrogen and 10 percent helium.
   G The sun's surface is about 90 percent helium and 10 percent hydrogen.
   H The sun's surface is about 50 percent hydrogen and 50 percent helium.
   J The sun's surface is almost 100 percent helium, with trace amounts of hydrogen.

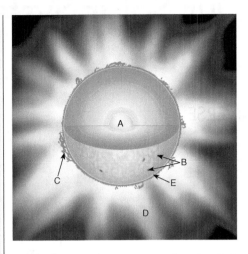

Use the diagram above to answer Questions 3–5.

3 What is the innermost layer of the sun called?
   A the core
   B the radiation zone
   C the chromosphere
   D the corona

4 What is the outermost layer of the sun called?
   F the core
   G the radiation zone
   H the chromosphere
   J the corona

5 What letters represent features found on the sun's photosphere?
   A B only
   B B and C only
   C C and E only
   D B, C, and E

If You Have Trouble With . . .

Question	1	2	3	4	5
See Lesson	24.3	24.3	24.3	24.3	24.3

25 Beyond Our Solar System Planning Guide

Lesson Objectives		Activities
25.1 Properties of Stars, pp. 700–706		TE Teacher Demo: Binary Star Motion, p. 701 L2
25.1 **Describe** what astronomers can learn by studying star properties.		
25.2 **Explain** how distance affects parallax.		TE Teacher Demo: Apparent and Absolute Magnitude, p. 703 L2
25.3 **List** the factors that determine a star's apparent magnitude.		
25.4 **Describe** the relationship shown on a Hertzprung-Russell diagram.		
25.2 Stellar Evolution, pp. 707–714		TE Build Science Skills, p. 707 L2
25.5 **Identify** which stage marks the birth of a star.		
25.6 **Explain** why all stars eventually die.		TE Teacher Demo: Modeling a Pulsar, p. 713 L2
25.7 **List** the stages of the sun's life cycle.		
25.3 The Universe, pp. 715–721		TE Build Science Skills, p. 716 L2
25.8 **Describe** the size and structure of the Milky Way Galaxy.		TE Build Science Skills, p. 717 L2
25.9 **List** the ways in which galaxies differ from one another.		TE Teacher Demo: "Stretching" Light Waves, p. 718 L2
25.10 **Cite** the evidence that indicates that the universe is expanding.		
25.11 **Describe** how the universe began according to the big bang theory.		TE Build Science Skills, p. 719 L2
Chapter Features and Labs		
Try It How Do Astronomers Measure Distance to Nearby Stars? p. 699		LM Modeling the Rotation of Neutron Stars L3
Earth & History How Can Constellations Help Someone Locate a Star? p. 722		
Exploration Lab Observing Stars, p. 723		

Ability Levels

L1	For students who need additional help
L2	For all students
L3	For students who need to be challenged

Components

SE	Student Edition
TE	Teacher's Edition
LM	Laboratory Manual
CT	Chapter Tests
GRSW	Guided Reading & Study Workbook
CTB	Computer Test Bank

LP	Lesson Plans
AA	Active Art
PD	Planet Diary
GEODe	Geode CD-ROM
eText	

Resources	Lesson Assessment
GRSW Lesson 25.1 **LP** Lesson Planning 25.1 **PD** Links on Earth's orbit and parallax	**SE** Lesson 25.1 Assessment, p. 706 **eText** Lesson 25.1
GRSW Lesson 25.2 **LP** Lesson Planning 25.2 **AA** Lives of Stars activity	**SE** Lesson 25.2 Assessment, p. 714 **eText** Lesson 25.2
GRSW Lesson 25.3 **LP** Lesson Planning 25.3	**SE** Lesson 25.3 Assessment, p. 721 **eText** Lesson 25.3

Materials for Activities and Labs

Quantities for each group

STUDENT EDITION

Exploration Lab, p. 723
star charts (in the Appendix), penlight, notebook

TEACHER'S EDITION

Teacher Demo, p. 701
string, tape, 2 tennis balls, pencil, table tennis ball

Teacher Demo, p. 703
2 equally bright flashlights, 1 dimmer flashlight

Build Science Skills, p. 707
series of photographs of people of different ages, series of photographs of the life cycle of an insect such as a butterfly that undergoes complete metamorphosis

Teacher Demo, p. 713
string; long, thin flashlight

Build Science Skills, p. 716
sharp pencil, sheet of paper, tape, cardboard

Build Science Skills, p. 717
cotton balls, coat hangers, and other materials of students' choice

Teacher Demo, p. 718
old bicycle inner tube, scissors, chalk

Build Science Skills, p. 719
coiled spring toy

Assessment

CHAPTER ASSESSMENT
SE Assessment, pp. 725–726
CT Chapter 25 Test
CTB Chapter 25
eText Chapter 25

21st Century Learning

Problem Identification, Formulation, and Solution: What can you find out about extrasolar planets in our galaxy?, TE p. 724

Common Themes

Michael Wysession
Washington University

Our sun is one of about 400 billion stars in the Milky Way galaxy, which may be one of about 125 billion galaxies in the universe. The universe formed about 13.7 billion years ago from the big bang, and is still rapidly expanding.

Space and Time Galaxies exist in spiral, elliptical, or irregular forms. The Milky Way is about 100,000 light years across and contains about 400 billion stars. Galaxies are often found in groups called galaxy clusters.

Forces and Motion Stars form from the dust and gas of interstellar matter that gets pulled together by the force of gravity. For about 90 percent of its life, a star will fuse hydrogen to make helium during its main-sequence stage. During a supergiant phase, some stars expand to enormous size because their outer layers are forced outward from radiation emitted by a contracting core. For some stars, a final supernova phase follows the completion of fusion reactions, resulting in an implosion that creates a shock wave and ejects heavier elements into space.

Matter and Energy The color of stars is an indication of their temperature. Binary star orbits can be used to find the mass of the stars. The mass of a star determines its evolution. Low-mass stars last a long time, but massive stars have short lives. Low-mass and medium-mass stars end as white dwarves. Massive stars go through supergiant and supernova phases, and end as neutron stars or black holes.

EARTH SCIENCE REFRESHER

The Birth of the Universe

Using the laws of physics, scientists have been able to reconstruct the infancy of our universe, starting a fraction of a second after the big bang. What happened at the instant of the big bang remains a mystery, because the laws of physics break down when all of space and time collapse to a single point. But once our universe got its start, we have a fairly good idea of what might have happened.

Our universe began extremely small and extremely hot—so hot, in fact that there was no matter, only radiated energy. As the universe expanded, it cooled, and the radiation began to convert into matter. By 10^{-32} seconds after the big bang, there were particles like electrons and quarks, but the quarks had not yet come together to form protons and neutrons. At this time, the temperature of the universe was 3×10^{26} K, and it was about 30 cm across—the size of a beach ball!

By 10^{-5} seconds after the big bang (1/100,000 of a second), the sub-atomic particles called quarks were able to combine to make protons and neutrons. At this time, the temperature of the universe was 10^{13} K, and it was about 0.002 light-years across (this is about 100 times the current distance from Earth to the sun).

Address **Misconceptions**

Students are often confused by the term light-year *and think that it is a unit of time. Explain that the "year" refers to the time that it takes for light to travel the distance known as a light-year. For a strategy that helps to overcome this misconception, see* **Address Misconceptions** *on TE p. 702.*

By three minutes after the big bang, the universe had cooled enough that the neutrons and protons could combine to make atomic nuclei, of which were about 75 percent hydrogen nuclei and 25 percent helium nuclei. At this point in time, the temperature of the universe was 10^9 K (1 trillion degrees), and it was about 50 light-years across.

By 10,000 years after the big bang, the universe had cooled to the point that the energy of the radiation was less than the energy of matter (atomic particles). At this time, the temperature of the universe was 30,000 K, and it was about 2 million light-years across.

By 300,000 years after the big bang, the atomic nuclei were able to combine with electrons to make the first true atoms. This stage is called decoupling, because the radiation was separated from the atomic particles, allowing light to travel unhindered by the free-flying electrons. This is as far back in time as a telescope like the Hubble telescope could ever see. At this point in time, the temperature of the radiation within the universe was only 5000 K, and the universe was already 15 million light-years across.

The first stars and protogalaxies formed after about a billion years, and the first galac-tic disks formed about 3 billion years after the big bang. Now, 13.7 billion years after the big bang, the universe has expanded so much that radiation left over from the big bang is in the form of microwaves traveling through space with a very low temperature of only 2.7° above absolute zero.

BUILD READING LITERACY

Sequence

Ordering Events

Strategy Help students understand and visualize the steps in a process, or the order in which events occur. Sequences frequently involve cause-effect relationships. Readers can construct graphic organizers to help them visualize and comprehend a sequence. For most sequences, flowcharts are the graphic of choice. However, cycle diagrams are more appropriate for cycles. Before students begin, locate in the text a several-step process or a chain of causes and effects, such as the passage, Star Birth, on pp. 707–709 and the figure, Life Cycle of Sunlike Star, on p. 709.

Example

1. Have students read the passage, thinking about what takes place first, second, third, and so on. Point out that the text will not always use order words such as *first, next, then,* and *finally.*

2. Review the passage, listing the steps or events in order.

3. If the passage describes a chain of steps or events, draw a flowchart on the board, having students tell the sequence of events, steps, or causes and effects, and writing each part of the process in a separate box.

4. If the passage describes a cycle, use a cycle diagram to show the sequence.

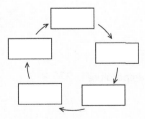

5. Have students locate additional examples of sequential relationships in the text or visuals of the chapter. Students can depict the steps or events using graphic organizers.

See TE p. 720 for a script on how to use this strategy with students. For additional strategies, see TE pp. 703 and 708.

ASSESS PRIOR KNOWLEDGE

Use the Chapter Pretest below to assess students' prior knowledge. As needed, review these concepts.

Review Science Concepts

Lesson 25.1 Review temperature scales and how the Kelvin scale is related to the Celsius and Fahrenheit scales.

Lesson 25.2 Review the concept of fusion. Also review the structure of the atom and what protons, neutrons, and electrons are.

Lesson 25.3 Review electromagnetic radiation and the Doppler effect.

25 Beyond Our Solar System

Big idea

Earth and the Universe

Q: How do astronomers study objects in our galaxy and beyond?

A nebula is a dust cloud in space that consists mostly of hydrogen and nitrogen. The Lagoon Nebula, pictured here, is located about 5000 light-years from Earth in the part of the sky called Sagittarius. This image was captured by specialized cameras on the Hubble Space Telescope. Astronomers think that areas such as this are where stars are born. A nebula does not emit light on its own. Instead, energy from a nearby bright star is either reflected by the cloud or is absorbed and causes gases to give off light. In this image, light from hydrogen is red; light from nitrogen is green.

698

Chapter Pretest

1. To what Celsius temperature is 273 K equivalent? *(d)*
   a. 273°C
   b. 546°C
   c. 146°C
   d. 0°C

2. What happens during nuclear fusion? *(Less massive nuclei are forced together to form a more massive nucleus.)*

3. What is the nucleus of a helium atom made up of? *(b)*
   a. protons and electrons
   b. protons and neutrons
   c. neutrons and electrons
   d. protons only

4. True or False: Electrons are small positively charged particles. *(False)*

5. If a light source is moving toward you at a very high speed, how will the light from it be affected? *(It will be shifted toward the blue.)*

6. True or False: Visible light is a form of electromagnetic radiation. *(True)*

INQUIRY

TRY IT!

HOW DO ASTRONOMERS MEASURE DISTANCES TO NEARBY STARS?

Procedure

1. Close your left eye. Hold your index finger in a vertical position. Use your right eye to line up your finger with a distant object, such as a tree or edge of a building.
2. Without moving your finger, close your right eye and open your left eye. Notice the alignment now of your finger with the distant object.

Think About It

1. **Observe** What happened to the position of your finger when you observed it with your left eye?
2. **Predict** What might happen if you repeated the activity, holding your finger farther from your eyes? Test your prediction.

699

ENGAGE/EXPLORE

HOW DO ASTRONOMERS MEASURE DISTANCES TO NEARBY STARS?   L2

Purpose Students will infer the considerations astronomers must make when measuring distances to nearby stars.

Skills Observe, Predict, Infer

Class Time 5–10 minutes

Teaching Tip Assist visually impaired students by describing what occurs when doing the activity.

Expected Outcome Students' fingers will appear to shift.

Think About It
1. The finger appeared to shift to the right.
2. The farther away you hold your finger, the less its position seems to shift.

25.1 Properties of Stars

Lesson Objectives

25.1 **Describe** what astronomers can learn by studying star properties.

25.2 **Explain** how distance affects parallax.

25.3 **List** the factors that determine a star's apparent magnitude.

25.4 **Describe** the relationship shown on a Hertzsprung-Russell diagram.

Build Vocabulary L2

Word Parts and Roots Have students look up the prefix *bi-* to help them understand what *binary* means. *("two," "having two distinct parts")* Have them look up the origin of *nova* and relate it to its meaning. *(from the Latin* novus, *meaning "new"; refers to a bright star that suddenly appears in the sky)*

Reading Strategy L2

Possible answers:

a. What information does the H-R diagram show?

b. absolute magnitude and temperature

c. What is the largest group of stars on the H-R diagram?

d. the main sequence

2 INSTRUCT

INTEGRATE LANGUAGE ARTS L2

Greek Mythology Tell students that many of the constellations were named by the ancient Greeks after characters in stories. Other peoples, such as Native Americans, had different names and stories associated with various star patterns. Ask each student to research a different constellation and write a paragraph describing the story associated with it. Students can also make up their own patterns and stories if they wish.
Verbal

Key Questions

🔑 **What can we learn by studying star properties?**

🔑 **How does distance affect parallax?**

🔑 **What factors determine a star's apparent magnitude?**

🔑 **What relationship is shown on a Hertzsprung-Russell diagram?**

Vocabulary

- constellation
- binary star • light-year
- apparent magnitude
- absolute magnitude
- Hertzsprung-Russell diagram
- main-sequence star
- red giant • supergiant
- Cepheid variable
- nova

Reading Strategy

Preview Copy the table below. Before you read, find the Hertzsprung–Russell diagram in the lesson. Look at the diagram and write two questions about it. As you read, write answers to your questions.

Questions about the Hertzsprung-Russell Diagram	
Question	Answer
a. ___?___	b. ___?___
c. ___?___	d. ___?___

THE CLOSEST star to Earth is the sun—about 150,000,000 kilometers away. After that, the next closest star is Proxima Centauri, which is 39,900,000,000,000 kilometers from Earth. Even though Proxima Centauri and Earth are space neighbors, it still takes light from that star 4.3 years to reach Earth. The light from other stars takes billions of years to reach us. The universe is incomprehensibly large. Astronomers have developed units of length (distance) for use in measuring the distance of objects in space. These units enable us to express how far away a star is without writing so many zeros!

Thousands of years ago, humans didn't know how vast the universe was. Yet, people were fascinated with the star-studded skies and began to name the patterns they saw. Some of these patterns of stars were named after characters from mythology, such as Orion, shown in **Figure 1.**

A **constellation** is used to designate an area of the sky that contains a specific pattern of stars. A star within one of these areas is considered part of the constellation, even if that star is not part of the pattern. The International Astronomical Union (IAU) divided the nighttime sky into 88 separate constellations, similar to a world map of countries. Now, the location of any star can be referred to by which constellation the star is in.

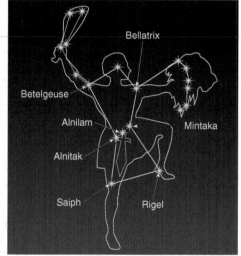

FIGURE 1 Orion This constellation was named after Orion—a great hunter from Greek mythology.

Characteristics of Stars

A great deal is known about the universe beyond our solar system. This knowledge hinges on the fact that stars, and even gases in the "empty" space between stars, radiate electromagnetic energy in all directions into space. The key to understanding the universe is to collect this radiation energy and study it. By analyzing the energy emitted or reflected by objects in the universe, astronomers have been able to determine many properties of stars, such as color, temperature, and mass.

Star Color and Temperature All objects, including stars and planets, emit and absorb radiation. We can see planets because they reflect some of the light that hits them. Stars, on the other hand, are *blackbody radiators*. A blackbody absorbs all of the electromagnetic radiation that strikes it. It also gives off the maximum amount of radiation possible at a given temperature. The energy of radiation given off by stars depends on their temperatures. Study the stars in **Figure 2** and note their color. ⬤ **Color is a clue to a star's temperature.** Very hot stars with surface temperatures above 30,000 K emit most of their energy in the form of short-wavelength light and therefore appear blue. Cooler stars emit most of their energy as longer-wavelengths and appear red. Stars with temperatures between 5000 and 6000 K appear yellow, like the sun.

Binary Stars and Stellar Mass In the early nineteenth century, astronomers discovered that many stars orbit each other. These pairs of stars, pulled toward each other by gravity, are called **binary stars.** More than 50 percent of the stars in the universe may occur in pairs or multiples.

⬤ **Binary stars are used to determine the star property most difficult to calculate—its mass.** The mass of a body can be calculated if it is attached by gravity to a partner. As shown in **Figure 3,** binary stars orbit each other around a common point called the center of mass. For stars of equal mass, the center of mass lies exactly halfway between them. If one star is more massive than its partner, the center of mass moves closer to the more massive star, as shown in Figure 3B. If the sizes of the orbits of binary stars are known, the stars' masses can be calculated.

☑ **Reading Checkpoint** What is a binary star system?

FIGURE 2 Stars of Orion This time-lapse photograph shows stars as streaks across the night sky as Earth rotates. The streaks clearly show different star colors.

FIGURE 3 Common Center of Mass A For stars of equal mass, the center of mass lies in the middle. **B** A star twice as massive as its partner is twice as close to the center of mass. It therefore has a smaller orbit than its less massive partner.

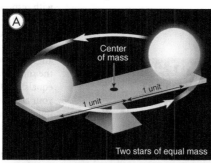

Center of mass

1 unit   1 unit

1 unit

Two stars of equal mass

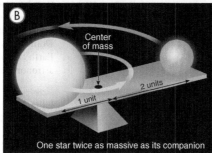

Center of mass

1 unit   2 units

One star twice as massive as its companion

Beyond Our Solar System **701**

Figure 4 Use this figure to explain how parallax works. Emphasize that the drawing is not to scale; the star would actually be much farther away and the parallax angle very small. **Ask:** What does the simulated photograph at the top left show? *(It shows the star as seen from Earth's original position.)* What does the simulated photograph at the bottom left show? *(It shows the star as seen from Earth 6 months later.)* How is the parallax angle related to the distance between the star and Earth? *(The farther away the star is, the smaller the angle.)*
Visual, Logical

Students are often confused by the term *light-year* and think that it is a unit of time. Explain again that the "year" refers to the time it takes for light to travel the distance known as a *light-year*. Have students calculate the distance to Proxima Centauri in kilometers. *(4.3 light-years × 9.5 × 10^{12} km = ≈41 × 10^{12} km)*
Logical

Note to teacher: The parallax method of measuring star distance led to a new unit for measuring distances in space. A star that appears to shift by 1 second of arc against the night sky is said to be a distance of 1 parallax-second away from Earth, or 1 parsec. The parsec turns out to be equal to a distance of 3.26 light-years, so astronomers will sometimes use the parsec instead of the light-year to describe the distance to a star. This also explains why absolute magnitude is defined as the magnitude a star would have if viewed at a standard distance of 32.6 light-years. The standard distance is actually a round number of 10 parsecs. Advanced students may appreciate this information.

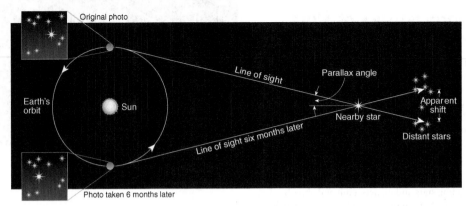

Original photo
Line of sight
Parallax angle
Earth's orbit
Sun
Apparent shift
Nearby star
Distant stars
Line of sight six months later
Photo taken 6 months later

FIGURE 4 Parallax The parallax angle shown here is exaggerated to illustrate the principle. Because the distances to even the nearest stars are huge, astronomers work with very small angles.
Relate Cause and Effect *What caused the star to appear to shift?*

Measuring Distances to Stars

In order to accurately calculate the distance to stars, astronomers must make very precise measurements. Today's astronomers have a wide array of specialized instruments to help them make precise measurements.

Parallax The most basic way to measure star distance is parallax. *Parallax* is the slight shifting in the apparent position of a nearby star due to the orbital motion of Earth. Parallax is determined by photographing a nearby star against the background of distant stars. Then, six months later, when Earth has moved halfway around its orbit, a second photograph is taken. When these photographs are compared, the position of the nearby star appears to have shifted with respect to the background stars. **Figure 4** shows this shift and the resulting parallax angle.

⬤ **The nearest stars have the largest parallax angles, while those of distant stars are too small to measure.** In fact, all parallax angles are very small. The parallax angle to the nearest star (besides the sun), Proxima Centauri, is less than 1 second of arc, which equals 1/3600 of a degree. To put this in perspective, fully extend your arm and raise your little finger—roughly 1 degree wide. Now imagine tracking a movement only 1/3600 as wide as your finger.

Before the invention of precise instruments for measuring parallax, astronomers did not understand the scale of the universe. Astronomers once inferred that the planets were closer than the stars because the planets could be seen to pass in front of the stars. They knew the principle of parallax, but the parallax angles of the stars were too small to be measured. It was not until 1673 that Gian Domenico Cassini used parallax to measure the distance between Earth and Mars. Later, in 1838, Friedrich Bessel and two other astronomers used parallax to determine the distances to several stars.

Light-Year Distances to stars are so great that units such as kilometers or even astronomical units are often not practical to use. A better unit to express stellar distance is the **light-year,** which is the distance light travels in one year—about 9.5 × 10^{12} or 9.5 trillion kilometers (9,500,000,000,000 kilometers).

Stellar Brightness

The measure of a star's brightness is its magnitude. The stars in the night sky have an assortment of sizes, temperatures, and distances, so their brightnesses vary widely.

Apparent Magnitude Some stars may appear dimmer than others only because they are farther away. A star's brightness as it appears from Earth is called its **apparent magnitude.** ▣ **Three factors control the apparent brightness of a star as seen from Earth: how big it is, how hot it is, and how far away it is.**

Astronomers use numbers to rank apparent magnitude. The brighter a star is, the smaller the number. This is similar to the finishing order of a race—the best finish is first place, the next-best finish is second place, etc. The dimmest stars that are just barely visible from Earth through a telescope have an apparent magnitude of about 25. The brightest single star in our sky, other than the sun, has an apparent magnitude of −1.4. This star is called *Sirius*. As you can see from **Table 1,** Alpha Centauri has less magnitude—0.0—than Sirius. However, Alpha Centauri is actually a three-star system (similar to a binary system, except with three stars instead of two). Alpha Centauri appears brighter than Sirius, but that is because the combined brightness of the three stars appears brighter than the single star, Sirius.

Absolute Magnitude Astronomers are also interested in how bright a star actually is, or its **absolute magnitude.** Two stars of the same absolute magnitude usually do not have the same apparent magnitude because one may be much farther from us than the other. The star that is farther away will appear dimmer. To compare their absolute brightness, astronomers determine what magnitude the stars would have if they were at a standard distance of about 32.6 light-years. For example, the sun, which has an apparent magnitude of −26.7, would, if located at a distance of 32.6 light-years, have an absolute magnitude of about 5. Stars with absolute magnitude values lower than 5 are brighter than the sun. The absolute magnitude of Betelgeuse is much greater than the sun's absolute magnitude. Betelgeuse appears dimmer than the sun because it is 520 light-years from Earth.

▣ **Reading Checkpoint** *If one star is closer to Earth than another star, will the closer star always appear brighter? Explain.*

Table 1 Distance, Apparent Magnitude, and Absolute Magnitude of Some Stars

Name	Distance (light-years)	Apparent Magnitude*	Absolute Magnitude*
Sun	NA	−26.7	5.0
Alpha Centauri	4.27	0.0	4.4
Sirius	8.70	−1.4	1.5
Arcturus	36	−0.1	−0.3
Betelgeuse	520	0.8	−5.5
Deneb	1600	1.3	−6.9

*The more negative, the brighter; the more positive, the dimmer.

Beyond Our Solar System **703**

Students often think that the H-R diagram is a star chart that shows the locations of stars in the sky. Emphasize that the H-R diagram is a graph that shows the characteristics of stars. Go over the units shown on the axes so that students understand why it is a graph. Explain that the stars are shown different sizes on the graph for illustration only. Also explain that an H-R diagram can be used to plot any sample of stars.
Visual

Use Visuals   L1

Figure 5 Use this diagram to explain the main groups of stars on the H-R diagram. **Ask:** To what group of stars does the sun belong? *(It belongs to the main sequence.)* How are absolute magnitude and temperature related within the main sequence? *(As absolute magnitude increases, so does temperature.)* What types of stars have high absolute magnitude but low temperature? *(giants and supergiants)* What types of stars have low absolute magnitudes and medium temperatures? *(white dwarfs)*
Visual, Logical

Hertzsprung-Russell Diagram

An important tool used by astronomers when studying stars is the diagram shown in **Figure 5**—the Hertzsprung-Russell (H-R) diagram. **A Hertzsprung-Russell diagram shows the relationship between the absolute magnitude and temperature of stars.** The H-R diagram shows that about 90 percent of all stars are **main-sequence stars** that fall along a band that runs from the upper-left corner to the lower-right corner of the diagram. The hottest main-sequence stars are the brightest, and the coolest main-sequence stars are the dimmest.

The brightness of the main-sequence stars is also related to their mass. The hottest blue stars are about 50 times more massive than the sun, while the coolest red stars are only 1/10 as massive. Therefore, on the H-R diagram, the main-sequence stars appear in decreasing order, from hotter, more massive blue stars to cooler, less massive red stars.

Above and to the right of the main-sequence stars in the H-R diagram lies a group of very bright stars called **red giants.** Some stars are so large that they are called **supergiants.** Betelgeuse, a bright red supergiant in the constellation Orion, has a radius about 800 times that of the sun. Stars in the lower-central part of the H-R diagram are much fainter than main-sequence stars of the same temperature. Some probably are no bigger than Earth. This group is called *white dwarfs*, although not all are white.

FIGURE 5 Hertzsprung-Russell (H-R) Diagram In this idealized chart, stars are plotted according to temperature and absolute magnitude. The H-R diagram also provides clues to stellar evolution—stars are born, age, and then die.

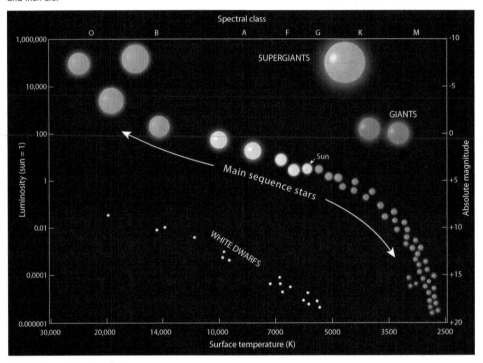

Facts and Figures

Einar Hertzsprung was born in 1873 in Denmark. He worked as a chemist before switching to studying astronomy. In 1912, he discovered that for most stars temperature is closely related to absolute magnitude. Before this discovery, astronomers had thought that stars could have any combination of temperature and absolute magnitude. Henry

Norris Russell was born in 1877 in the United States. While working in England in 1921, Russell independently found the same relationship that Hertzsprung had. Hertzsprung continued to work into his nineties. Russell spent six decades at Princeton University.

FIGURE 6 Nova
These photographs, taken two months apart, show the decrease in brightness that follows a nova flare-up.

Variable Stars Space scientists have learned that some stars fluctuate in brightness. **Cepheid variables** are stars that get brighter and fainter in a regular pattern. The interval between two successive occurrences of maximum brightness is called a *light period*. In general, the longer the light period of a Cepheid, the greater its absolute magnitude is. Once the absolute magnitude is known, it can be compared to the apparent magnitude of the Cepheid. Based on this comparison, astronomers can figure out how far away the Cepheid is. Measuring Cepheid variable periods is an important means of determining distances within our universe.

A different type of variable is associated with a **nova,** or sudden brightening of a star. During a nova eruption, the outer layer of the star is ejected at high speed. A nova (shown in **Figure 6**) generally reaches maximum brightness in a few days, remains bright for only a few weeks, then slowly returns in a year or so to its original brightness. Only a small amount of its mass is lost during the flare-up. Some stars have experienced more than one such event. In fact, the process probably occurs repeatedly.

Scientists think that most novas occur in binary systems consisting of an expanding red giant and a nearby hot white dwarf. Hydrogen-rich gas from the oversized giant is transferred by gravity to the white dwarf. Eventually, the added gas causes the dwarf to ignite explosively. Such a reaction rapidly heats and expands the outer layer of the hot dwarf to produce a nova. In a relatively short time, the white dwarf returns to its prenova state, where it remains inactive until the next buildup occurs.

☑ **Reading Checkpoint** *What is a light period?*

Beyond Our Solar System **705**

LESSON 25.1

FIGURE 7 Dark Nebula The Horsehead Nebula is found in the constellation Orion.

Interstellar Matter Between existing stars is "the vacuum of space." However, it is not a pure vacuum, for there are nebulae—clouds of dust and gases. If this interstellar matter is close to a very hot star, it will glow and is called a *bright nebula*. The two main types of bright nebulae are emission nebulae and reflection nebulae.

Emission nebulae consist largely of hydrogen. They absorb ultraviolet radiation emitted by a nearby hot star. Because these gases are under very low pressure, they emit this energy as visible light. This conversion of ultraviolet light to visible light is known as fluorescence. You can see this effect in fluorescent lights. *Reflection nebulae*, as the name implies, merely reflect the light of nearby stars. Reflection nebulae are thought to be composed of dense clouds of large particles called interstellar dust.

Some nebulae are not close enough to a bright star to absorb or reflect light. They are called *dark nebulae*. Dark nebulae, such as the one shown in **Figure 7**, can easily be seen as starless, or dark, regions when viewed against the backdrop of the Milky Way.

Although nebulae appear very dense, they actually consist of thinly scattered matter. Because of their enormous size, however, their total mass may be many times that of the sun. Astronomers study nebulae because it is thought that stars and planets form from this interstellar matter.

25.1 Assessment

Review Key Concepts 🔑

1. What can astronomers learn by studying a star's color?

2. Binary stars can be used to establish what property of stars?

3. How does distance affect parallax?

4. What factors determine a star's apparent magnitude?

5. The H-R diagram shows the relationship between what two factors?

Think Critically

6. **Compare and Contrast** What are similarities and differences between Cepheid variables and novas?

7. **Infer** Scientists think that only a small amount of a star's mass is lost during a nova. Based on what you have learned about stars and novas, infer what evidence scientists use to support this theory.

WRITING IN SCIENCE

8. **Summarize** Make an educational Web site about the H-R diagram for younger students. Use Figure 5 as a guide. Include a color key and other elements to help clarify concepts such as star temperature, the Kelvin scale, and absolute magnitude.

25.2 Stellar Evolution

A STAR IS NOT a living thing—at least not according to the biological definition of life. However, each star begins, progresses through certain stages, and ends. Astronomers call this progression the *life cycle* of a star. The stellar (meaning "pertaining to a star") life cycle is hard to study, because it can span billions of years. However, by studying stars of different ages, astronomers can piece together the typical progression of events of the stellar life cycle. This progression is called *stellar evolution*. It includes the changes that occur during the birth, life, and death of a star.

Star Birth

In the Milky Way, nebulae consist of roughly 90 percent hydrogen, nine percent helium, and less than one percent of the remaining heavier elements. For some reason not yet fully understood, some nebulae become dense enough to begin to contract due to gravity. A shock wave from an explosion of a nearby star might trigger the contraction. Once the contraction process begins, gravity pulls every particle in the nebula toward the center. As the overall nebula shrinks, the center of the nebula increases in mass. As mass increases, the force of gravity also increases. Gradually, gravitational force is converted to heat energy. As heat builds to tremendous temperatures, the processes that shape stellar development begin to unfold. A star is born.

FIGURE 8 Nebula
Large, interstellar clouds of dust and gas are thought to be areas where stars form.

Key Questions

🔑 **What stage marks the birth of a star?**

🔑 **Why do all stars eventually die?**

🔑 **What stages make up the sun's life cycle?**

Vocabulary

- protostar • supernova
- white dwarf • neutron star
- pulsar • black hole

Reading Strategy

Sequence Copy the flowchart below. As you read, complete it to show how the sun evolved. Expand the chart to show the evolution of low-mass and high-mass stars.

Evolution of Sun

a. ___?___

b. ___?___

1 FOCUS

Lesson Objectives
25.5 **Identify** which stage marks the birth of a star.
25.6 **Explain** why all stars eventually die.
25.7 **List** the stages of the sun's life cycle.

Build Vocabulary [L2]
Concept Map As students read the lesson, have them make a concept map showing how the vocabulary terms are related. The concept map should show how a star changes during its lifetime.

Reading Strategy [L2]
a. cloud of dust and gases (nebula stage)
b. protostar stage

2 INSTRUCT

Build Science Skills [L2]
Student Activity: Use Analogies Show students a series of photographs of people of different ages. Ask them to put the photos in order by age. Then, show students a series of photographs of the life cycle of an insect, such as a butterfly, that undergoes complete metamorphosis. Ask them to put the photos in order by age. **Ask:** Why was the second series harder to sequence than the first one? *(You can't easily tell by looking at the photos which stage comes in what order.)* Point out that astronomers have the same problem with stars. It's not obvious just from looking at various stages of stars how old they are.
Logical, Visual

Integrate Physics L2

Fission and Fusion Review the concepts of fission and fusion with students. During fission, atomic nuclei are split apart to make smaller nuclei. This is the process used in nuclear power plants. During fusion, atomic nuclei combine to make larger nuclei. Sustained fusion occurs only within stars. Main-sequence stars fuse four hydrogen nuclei to form a helium nucleus. The helium nucleus has slightly less mass than the hydrogen nuclei. The remaining mass is converted into energy. Hotter stars can produce carbon and other elements by fusion.
Logical, Verbal

Build Reading Literacy L1

Refer to **p. 392D** in **Chapter 14,** which provides guidelines for previewing.

Preview Before they read the lesson, have students skim the headings, visuals, and boldfaced words to preview how the text is organized.
Verbal, Visual

Protostar Stage It is thought that the initial nebular contraction typically spans a million years or so. As time passes, the temperature slowly rises until the nebula is hot enough to radiate energy from its surface in the form of long-wavelength red light. This large red object is called a protostar. A **protostar** is a developing star not yet hot enough to engage in nuclear fusion.

During the protostar stage, gravitational contraction continues—slowly at first, then much more rapidly. This rapid contraction causes the core of the protostar to heat much more intensely than the outer layer. **When the core of a protostar reaches 10 million K, pressure within it is so great that nuclear fusion of hydrogen begins, forming helium and releasing energy.**

Heat from hydrogen fusion causes the gases to increase their motion. This in turn causes an increase in the outward gas pressure. At some point, this outward pressure exactly balances the inward force of gravity, as shown in **Figure 9.** When this balance is reached, the star becomes a stable main-sequence star. Stated another way, a stable main-sequence star is balanced between two forces: gravity, which is trying to squeeze it into a smaller sphere, and gas pressure, which is trying to expand it.

Main-Sequence Stage From this point in the evolution of a main-sequence star until its death, internal gas pressure struggles to offset the constant force of gravity. Typically, hydrogen fusion continues for a few billion years and provides the outward pressure required to support the star from gravitational collapse.

Different stars age at different rates. Hot, massive blue stars radiate energy at such an enormous rate that they deplete their hydrogen fuel in only a few million years. By contrast, the least massive main-sequence stars may remain stable for hundreds of billions of years. A yellow star, such as the sun, remains a main-sequence star for about 10 billion years.

By counting how many stars are in each life cycle stage, astronomers have determined that a very large percentage of stars are main-sequence stars. This information enables scientists to conclude that an average star spends 90 percent of its life as a hydrogen-fusion, main-sequence star. Once the hydrogen fuel in the star's core is depleted, it evolves rapidly and dies. However, with the exception of the least-massive red stars, a star may go into a different phase of nuclear reaction where heavier elements are fused. If this happens, the star becomes a giant and lives longer.

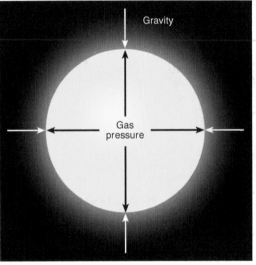

FIGURE 9 Balanced Forces A main-sequence star is balanced between gravity, which is trying to squeeze it, and gas pressure, which is trying to expand it.

708 Chapter 25 • Lesson 2

Differentiated Instruction

GIFTED Have students develop a computer graphic presentation that compares the life cycles of different masses of stars. The presentations should include scale diagrams of each stage along with labels and a brief caption. Invite students to share their presentations with the class.

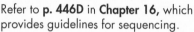

FIGURE 10 Life Cycle of a Sunlike Star A medium-mass star, similar to the sun, will evolve along the path shown here.
Interpret Diagrams *What is the first stage in the formation of the star? What is the last stage?*

Red-Giant Stage The red-giant stage occurs because the zone of hydrogen fusion continually moves outward, leaving behind a helium core. Eventually, all the hydrogen in the star's core is consumed. While hydrogen fusion is still progressing in the star's outer shell, no fusion is taking place in the core. Without a source of energy, the core no longer has enough pressure to support itself against the inward force of gravity. As a result, the core begins to contract.

As the core contracts, the overall star expands. The core grows hotter by converting gravitational energy into heat energy. Some of this energy is radiated outward, increasing the rate of hydrogen fusion in the star's outer shell. This additional energy heats and expands the star's outer layer. The result is a giant body hundreds to thousands of times its main-sequence size, as shown in **Figure 10.**

As the star expands, its surface cools, which explains the star's reddish appearance. During expansion, the core continues to collapse and heat until it reaches 100 million K. At this temperature, it is hot enough to convert helium to carbon. So, a red giant consumes both hydrogen and helium and produces energy.

Eventually, all the usable nuclear fuel in these giants will be consumed. The sun, as a medium-sized star, will spend less than a billion years as a giant. More massive stars will pass through this stage more rapidly. The force of gravity will control the star's destiny as it squeezes the star into a much smaller, denser piece of matter.

☑ **Reading Checkpoint** *Why do red giants have a reddish appearance?*

Beyond Our Solar System **709**

Facts and Figures

Earth's sun is a medium-sized yellow star with an estimated 10 billion year main sequence life span. Astrobiologists have predicted that a planet that might support life as we know it would most likely revolve around a star with an ideal surface temperature of 4000–7000 K. The surface temperature of Earth's star (the sun) is approximately 6000 K, which falls within the ideal range. The surface temperature of a blue giant can be more than 20,000 K, far outside the ideal range. Additionally, the life span of blue giants is relatively short—from 10 million to 1 billion years. Experts feel that this is too short a period of time for life to evolve as it did on Earth.

FIGURE 11
Stellar Evolution
A A low-mass star uses fuel at a low rate and has a long life span.
B Similar to a low-mass star, a medium-mass star ends as a black dwarf.
C Massive stars end in huge explosions, then become either neutron stars or black holes.

Burnout and Death

The processes involved in the birth and life of stars are relatively easy to confirm by studying existing stars. By comparison, the last stages of the stellar life cycle are more theoretical. **We do know that all stars, regardless of their size, eventually run out of fuel and collapse due to gravity.** Exactly how this collapse occurs for various size stars is less well known.

Death of Low-Mass Stars As shown in **Figure 11A,** stars less than one half the mass of the sun consume their fuel at a slower rate than larger stars. Consequently, these small, cool red stars may remain on the main sequence for up to 100 billion years. Because the interior of a low-mass star never reaches high enough temperatures and pressures to fuse helium, its only energy source is hydrogen. So, low-mass stars never evolve into red giants. Instead, they remain as stable main-sequence stars until they consume their hydrogen fuel and collapse.

FIGURE 12 Planetary Nebula
During its collapse from a red giant, a medium-mass star ejects its outer layer, which forms a round cloud of gas called a planetary nebula.

Death of Medium-Mass Stars As shown in **Figure 11B,** medium-mass stars evolve in a similar way as low-mass stars. During their red giant phase, medium-mass stars fuse hydrogen and helium fuel at a fast rate. Once this fuel is exhausted, they collapse.

During their collapse medium-mass stars are thought to cast off their enlarged outer layer, which forms an expanding round cloud of gas. The remaining hot, central star heats the gas cloud, causing it to glow. These often beautiful, gleaming spherical clouds are called *planetary nebulae.* An example of a planetary nebula is shown in **Figure 12.**

710 Chapter 25 • Lesson 2

Facts and Figures

In a few billion years, the sun's core will run out of hydrogen fuel, triggering hydrogen fusion in the surrounding shell. As a result, the sun's outer envelope will expand, producing a red giant hundreds of times larger and brighter. Intense solar radiation will boil Earth's oceans, and solar winds will drive away Earth's atmosphere. Another billion years later, the sun will expel its outermost layer, producing a planetary nebula. The interior will collapse to produce a small, dense white dwarf. Gradually the sun will emit its remaining energy and become a cold black dwarf.

FIGURE 13 Crab Nebula
This nebula, found in the constellation Taurus, is the remains of a supernova that took place in the year 1054.

Death of Massive Stars In contrast to sunlike stars, stars with masses four times that of the sun have relatively short life spans. As shown in **Figure 11C,** these stars end in a brilliant explosion called a **supernova.** During a supernova, a star becomes millions of times brighter than its prenova stage—so bright that it can sometimes be seen during the day on Earth. Supernovae are rare. None have been observed in our galaxy since the invention of the telescope. However, astronomers Tycho Brahe recorded a supernova in 1572 and Galileo recorded one in 1604. An even larger supernova was recorded in 1054 by the Chinese. This supernova was apparently so bright, people could read at night by its light. Today, the remnant of this great outburst is the Crab Nebula, shown in **Figure 13.**

A supernova event is thought to be triggered when a massive star consumes most of its nuclear fuel. Without a heat engine to generate the gas pressure required to balance its immense gravitational field, the star collapses. This *implosion*, or bursting inward, is huge, resulting in a shock wave that moves out from the star's interior. This energetic shock wave destroys the star and blasts the outer shell into space, generating the supernova event.

☑ **Reading Checkpoint** *What is a supernova?*

Beyond Our Solar System **711**

LESSON 25.2

Use Analogies Use an analogy of a star to a charcoal briquette in a barbecue grill to describe the life of a low-mass star. When the briquette is first lit, it begins to consume its fuel and glows red-hot (main sequence). As it runs out of fuel, it becomes cooler and dimmer (white dwarf). Eventually it runs out of fuel and becomes a cold cinder (black dwarf). Ask students how the briquette is different from an actual star. *(The briquette burns because of chemical reactions, not fusion. It doesn't get hotter in the "white dwarf" stage.)*
Logical, Visual

Nucleosynthesis A dying star can be a factory where new elements form. Stars produce all the naturally occurring chemical elements beyond helium in the periodic table. The process that produces chemical elements inside stars is called *nucleosynthesis*.

Nucleosynthesis starts with the fusion of hydrogen nuclei to form helium. Over time, the helium nuclei begin to fuse, forming nuclei of heavier elements. These heavier elements may also fuse. Elements between lithium and iron in the periodic table form in this way. Certain elements heavier than iron form as iron nuclei absorb neutrons released during fusion. The rarest heavy elements form at temperatures up to one billion degrees Celsius when a star explodes in a supernova. The explosion scatters the star's elements across space. There, they are available to form new stars and planets.

The mass of a star determines the highest atomic number of the elements it can produce. Only the most massive stars produce elements heavier than iron. By comparison, the sun will not be able to produce elements heavier than oxygen.

Stellar Remnants

Eventually, all stars consume their nuclear fuel and collapse into one of three states—white dwarf, neutron star, or black hole. Although different in some ways, these small, compact objects are all composed of incomprehensibly dense material with extreme surface gravity.

White Dwarfs **White dwarfs** are the remains of low-mass and medium-mass stars. They are extremely small stars with densities greater than any known material on Earth. Although some white dwarfs are no larger than Earth, the mass of such a dwarf can equal 1.4 times that of the sun. A spoonful of such matter would weigh several tons. Densities this great are possible only when electrons are displaced inward from their regular orbits, around an atom's nucleus, allowing these atoms to take up less than a "normal" amount of space.

As a star contracts into a white dwarf, its surface becomes very hot, sometimes exceeding 25,000 K. Even so, without a source of energy, a white dwarf can only evolve into a cooler and dimmer object. **Table 2** summarizes the evolution of stars of various masses.
🔑 **The sun began as a nebula, will spend much of its life as a main-sequence star, and then will become a red giant, planetary nebula, white dwarf, and finally, a black dwarf.**

Table 2 Summary of Evolution for Stars of Various Masses				
Initial Mass of Interstellar Cloud (Sun = 1)	Main-Sequence Stage	Giant Phase	Evolution After Giant Phase	Final Stage
1–3	Yellow	Yes	Planetary nebula	White dwarf
6	White	Yes	Supernova	Neutron star
20	Blue	Yes (Supergiant)	Supernova	Black hole

Neutron Stars After studying white dwarfs, scientists made what might at first appear to be a surprising conclusion. The smallest white dwarfs are the most massive, and the largest are the least massive. The explanation for this is that a more massive star, because of its greater gravitational force, is able to squeeze itself into a smaller, more densely packed space than can a less massive star. So, the smaller white dwarfs are thought to have been produced from the collapse of larger, more massive stars than were the larger white dwarfs.

This conclusion led to the prediction that stars smaller and more massive than white dwarfs must exist. These objects, called **neutron stars,** are thought to be the remnants of supernova events. In a white dwarf, the electrons in the atoms are pushed close to the nucleus, while in a neutron star, the electrons are forced to combine with protons to produce neutrons. If Earth were to collapse to the density of a neutron star, it would have a diameter equal to the length of a football field. A pea-size sample of this matter would weigh more than 90 million kilograms. This is approximately the same density as an atomic nucleus. In a way, neutron stars can be thought of as large atomic nuclei.

Supernovae During a supernova, the outer layer of the star is ejected, while the core collapses into an extremely small, hot neutron star about 20 kilometers in diameter. Imagine an entire star becoming so small that it would almost fit inside the city limits of Dallas, Texas. Although neutron stars have high surface temperatures, their small sizes would greatly limit their brightness. Finding one with a telescope would be extremely difficult.

However, astronomers think that a neutron star would have a very strong magnetic field. As a star collapses, it rotates faster, for the same reason a spinning ice skater rotates faster when she pulls in her arms. Radio waves generated by these rotating stars would be concentrated into two narrow zones that would align with the star's magnetic poles. Consequently, these stars would resemble a rapidly rotating beacon emitting strong radio waves. If Earth happened to be in the path of these beacons, the star would appear to blink on and off, or pulsate, as the waves swept past. A spinning neutron star that appears to give off pulses of radio waves is called a **pulsar.**

In the early 1970s, a pulsar was discovered in the Crab Nebula. This pulsar is undoubtedly the remains of the supernova of 1054. If so, that would mean the star evolved from supernova to pulsar in about 1000 years. By astronomical standards, that is a very short period of time.

FIGURE 14 Veil Nebula Located in the constellation Cygnus, this nebula is the remnant of an ancient supernova.

...

LESSON 25.2

Use Visuals　L1

Figure 15 Use this figure to explain how black holes can be detected. **Ask:** Can a black hole be detected directly? Why or why not? *(no, because its gravity is so strong that not even light can escape)* What may happen if a black hole has a companion star? *(The black hole may pull material out of the star and into itself.)* What happens to material as it falls into a black hole? *(It becomes very hot and emits X-rays.)* What would be good evidence for a black hole? *(stellar material being heated and then apparently disappearing into nothingness)* **Visual, Logical**

3 ASSESS

Evaluate Understanding　L2

Call on students to describe the stages that stars of different masses go through during their life cycles.

Reteach　L1

Use Figure 10 to review the life cycle of a sunlike star and to emphasize that the H-R diagram is a graph, not a star chart.

Black Holes Are neutron stars made of the most dense materials possible? No. During a supernova event, remnants of stars at least 20 times more massive than the sun apparently collapse into objects even smaller and denser than neutron stars. Dense objects with gravity so strong that not even light can escape their surface are called **black holes.** Anything that moves too near a black hole would be swept in by its gravity and added to the mass of the black hole.

How can astronomers find an object whose gravitational field prevents the escape of all matter and energy? One strategy is to find evidence of matter being rapidly swept into a region of apparent nothingness. Scientists think that as matter is pulled into a black hole, it should become very hot and emit a flood of X-rays before being pulled in. Because isolated black holes would not have a source of matter to swallow up, astronomers first looked at binary-star systems.

A likely candidate for a black hole is Cygnus X-1, a strong X-ray source in the constellation Cygnus. In this case, the X-ray source can be observed orbiting a supergiant companion with a period of 5.6 Earth days. It appears that gases are pulled from this companion and spiral into the disk-shaped structure around the black hole. An artist's impression of this is shown in **Figure 15.** Some scientists also think that there are supermassive black holes in the centers of many galaxies. Our own galaxy may have a black hole in the center with a mass equivalent to 1 to 2 billion suns.

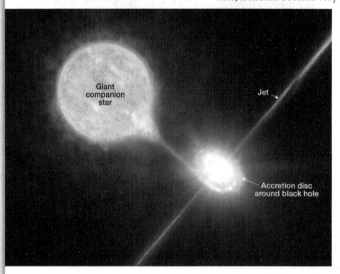

FIGURE 15 Black Hole
Gases from the red giant spiral into the black hole.

Giant companion star

Jet

Accretion disc around black hole

25.2 Assessment

Review Key Concepts 🔑

1. What is a protostar?

2. At what point is a star born?

3. What causes a star to die?

4. Describe the life cycle of the sun.

Think Critically

5. Infer Why are less massive stars thought to age more slowly than more massive stars, even though less massive stars have much less "fuel"?

6. Relate Cause and Effect Why is interstellar matter important to stellar evolution?

BIGIDEA　EARTH AND THE UNIVERSE

7. Compare and Contrast Compare the sun with Deneb, a massive blue-white star that is 1600 light-years from Earth. How likely is it that each star will experience a supernova?

Assessment Answers

1. A protostar is a developing star not yet hot enough to engage in nuclear fusion.
2. When the core of a protostar has reached about 10 million K, pressure within it is so great that nuclear fusion of hydrogen begins, and a star is born.
3. A star runs out of fuel and collapses due to gravity.

4. The sun began as a nebula, became a protostar and then a main-sequence star. It will become a red giant, planetary nebula, white dwarf, and finally a black dwarf.
5. A less massive star will live longer because it consumes fuel at a slower rate than do more massive stars.
6. Stars are born out of clouds of interstellar matter.

7. The sun is a medium-sized yellow star and is unlikely to experience a supernova. Scientists think that only massive stars, such as Deneb, experience a supernova. As a massive blue-white star, Deneb is very likely to experience a supernova.

25.3 The Universe

❶ FOCUS

Lesson Objectives

25.8 **Describe** the size and structure of the Milky Way Galaxy.

25.9 **List** the ways in which galaxies differ from one another.

25.10 **Cite** the evidence that indicates that the universe is expanding.

25.11 **Describe** how the universe began according to the big bang theory.

Build Vocabulary L2

LINCS Have students use the LINCS strategy to learn and review the terms *galaxy, galactic cluster,* and *elliptical galaxy.* In LINCS exercises, students **L**ist what they know about each term, **I**magine a picture that describes the word, **N**ote a sound-alike word, **C**onnect the terms to the sound-alike word by making up a short story, and then perform a brief **S**elf-test.

Reading Strategy L2

A. Milky Way Galaxy
1. Size—100,000 light-years wide and 10,000 light-years thick
2. Structure—at least three spiral arms, nearly round halo

B. Types of Galaxies
1. Spiral galaxy—disk-shaped, large
2. Elliptical galaxy–round to oval, mostly small
3. Irregular galaxy—Only 10 percent of galaxies have irregular shapes.
4. Galactic clusters—groups of galaxies

C. Expanding Universe
1. Red shifts—Light from distant galaxies is "stretched."
2. Hubble's law—The universe is expanding.

ON A CLEAR and moonless night away from city lights, you can see a truly marvelous sight—our own Milky Way Galaxy, as shown in **Figure 16. Galaxies** are large groups of stars, dust, and gases held together by gravity. There may be 400 billion stars in the Milky Way Galaxy alone. Our galaxy looks milky because our solar system is located within a flat disk of the galaxy—the galactic disk. We view the Milky Way from the inside and see a high concentration of stars when we look toward the center of the galaxy.

The Milky Way Galaxy

Imagine that you are hiking in an enormous forest. You look around and see equal numbers of trees in every direction. Are you in the center of the forest? Not necessarily. Because the trees block your view, almost anywhere in the forest could seem to be the center. When astronomers began to survey the stars located along the plane of the Milky Way, it appeared that equal numbers of stars lay in every direction. The stars made it look like Earth was at the center. But that is not actually the case.

Size of the Milky Way It's hard to study the Milky Way Galaxy with optical telescopes because large quantities of interstellar dust and gas block our view. Partly with the aid of radio telescopes, scientists can see "through" the dust and gas and have determined the likely structure of our galaxy. **The Milky Way is a large spiral galaxy whose disk is about 100,000 light-years wide and about 10,000 light-years thick at the nucleus.** As viewed from Earth, the center of the galaxy lies beyond the constellation Sagittarius.

☑ **Reading Checkpoint** *How big is the Milky Way Galaxy?*

FIGURE 16 Milky Way Galaxy Notice the dark band caused by interstellar dark nebulae.

Key Questions

🔑 What are the size and structure of the Milky Way Galaxy?

🔑 In what ways do galaxies differ from one another?

🔑 What evidence indicates that the universe is expanding?

🔑 According to the big bang theory, how did the universe begin?

Vocabulary
- galaxy • galaxy cluster
- Hubble's law
- Big Bang theory

Reading Strategy

Outline As you read, make an outline of the most important ideas in this section.

I. The Universe
  A. Milky Way Galaxy
    1. _____ ?
    2. _____ ?
  B. _____ ?
    1. Spiral Galaxy
    2. Elliptical Galaxy
    3. _____ ?

Beyond Our Solar System **715**

Answers

☑ **Reading Checkpoint** *The Milky Way Galaxy is about 100,000 light-years wide and 10,000 light-years thick at the nucleus.*

② INSTRUCT

Build Science Skills L2

Student Activity: Infer Tell groups of students to use a sharp pencil to carefully poke several dozen holes in a sheet of paper. Have them tape the sheets to a piece of cardboard and then look at them from the other side of the room. Ask students whether they can see the individual holes. *(no)* Ask students to compare the sheets to Figure 16 on p. 715 and explain why both the Milky Way and the holes look fuzzy in both cases. *(The holes and stars are too small compared to their distances to be clearly visible.)*
Logical, Visual

Use Visuals L1

Figure 17 Use this figure to discuss the structure of the Milky Way Galaxy. **Ask:** How wide is the Milky Way Galaxy? *(about 100,000 light-years)* What is at the center of the Milky Way Galaxy? *(the nucleus)* What part of the Milky Way Galaxy lies outside the main disk? What is it made up of? *(the halo; thin gas and globular clusters)* Where is the sun in the Milky Way Galaxy? *(It is about two thirds of the way from the center on one of the spiral arms.)*
Visual, Logical

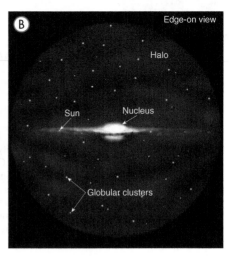

FIGURE 17 Structure of the Milky Way A The spiral arms are clearly visible in a simulated overhead view of our galaxy. **B** Our solar system is located about 30,000 light-years from the galactic nucleus.

Structure of the Milky Way Today's astronomer has a vast array of instruments to measure electromagnetic radiation emitted by the stars. These instruments are located on Earth, they orbit the planet in artificial satellites, and they are onboard spacecraft that are streaking into various parts of space. By analyzing the readings of these instruments, astronomers know that the Milky Way has at least three distinct spiral arms. Some of the arms show signs of splintering. The sun is positioned in one of these arms about two thirds of the way from the center, or *galactic nucleus*, at a distance of about 30,000 light-years. The stars in the arms of the Milky Way rotate around the galactic nucleus. The most outward arms move the slowest, and the ends of the arms appear to trail behind the main bodies of the arms. Our solar system orbits the galactic nucleus once about every 230 million years.

Surrounding the galactic disk is a nearly round halo consisting of thin gas and numerous star clusters. These star clusters do not rotate around the nucleus in the same way that the stars in the spiral arms rotate. Instead, they have their own orbits that carry them through the disk. Although some star clusters are quite dense, they pass between the stars of the arms without colliding.

In recent years, NASA's *Fermi Gamma-ray Space Telescope* has aided astronomers in discovering new facts about the Milky Way. For example, there appears to be two very large bubbles of gamma radiation emerging from the "top" and "bottom" of the nucleus. The source of this gamma radiation is not known, but one possibility is that the radiation could be related to a black hole in the nucleus.

☑ **Reading Checkpoint** *Where is our solar system located within the Milky Way Galaxy?*

716 Chapter 25 • Lesson 3

Differentiated Instruction

ENGLISH LANGUAGE LEARNERS Concepts such as galaxies, redshift, Hubble's law, and the big bang theory can be difficult to understand. Help English language learners understand these concepts by having them construct a Reading/Learning log. Have students write what they understand in the left column and what they still have questions about in the right column.

Types of Galaxies

In the mid-1700s, German philosopher Immanuel Kant proposed that the fuzzy patches of light scattered among the stars were actually distant galaxies like the Milky Way. Today we know that the universe includes hundreds of billions of galaxies, each containing hundreds of billions of stars. From these hundreds of billions of galaxies, scientists have identified several basic types.

Spiral Galaxies As shown in **Figure 18A,** spiral galaxies are usually disk-shaped, with a greater concentration of stars near their nuclei. There are numerous variations, though. Viewed broadside, the arms are often seen extending from the central nucleus and sweeping gracefully away. The outermost stars of these arms rotate most slowly, giving the galaxy the appearance of a pinwheel.

One type of spiral galaxy, however, has its stars arranged in the shape of a bar, which rotates as a rigid system. Attached to each end of these bars are curved spiral arms. These have become known as barred spiral galaxies, as shown in **Figure 18B.** Recent evidence indicates that the Milky Way may be a barred spiral galaxy. Spiral galaxies are generally quite large. About 10 percent of all galaxies are thought to be barred spirals, and another 20 percent are regular spiral galaxies.

Elliptical Galaxies About 60 percent of galaxies are classified as elliptical galaxies. Elliptical galaxies range in shape from round to oval. Although most are small, the very largest known galaxies—200,000 light-years in diameter—are elliptical. This type of galaxy, shown in **Figure 19,** was once thought to be very old galaxies with limited star-making capabilities. However, thanks to Hubble imagery, scientists are learning that elliptical galaxies do, indeed, give birth to new, young stars.

Irregular Galaxies Only 10 percent of the known galaxies have irregular shapes and are classified as irregular galaxies. The best-known irregular galaxies, the Large and Small Magellanic Clouds, are easily visible from the Southern Hemisphere with the unaided eye. These galaxies were named after the explorer Ferdinand Magellan, who observed them when he sailed around Earth in 1520. They are our nearest galactic neighbors—only 150,000 light-years away. An irregular galaxy is shown in **Figure 20.**

🔑 **In addition to shape and size, one of the major differences among different types of galaxies is the age of their stars.** Irregular galaxies are composed mostly of young stars, while elliptical galaxies contain many old stars. The Milky Way and other spiral galaxies have both young and old stars, with the youngest located in the arms.

FIGURE 18 Spiral Galaxies
A A spiral galaxy looks somewhat like a pinwheel. **B** A barred spiral galaxy has a bar through its center, with arms extending outward from the bar.

FIGURE 19 Elliptical Galaxy Most galaxies are classified as elliptical with shapes ranging from round to oval.

FIGURE 20 Irregular Galaxy Irregular galaxies have a variety of shapes. Describe *What type of stars would you find in an irregular galaxy?*

Beyond Our Solar System **717**

LESSON 25.3

Doppler Effect Review the electro-magnetic spectrum and the Doppler effect. **Ask:** What is the electromagnetic spectrum? *(the full range of frequencies of electromagnetic radiation)* What is visible light? *(the part of the spectrum that the human eye can see)* What is wavelength? *(the distance from the peak of one wave to the peak of the next)* How does the Doppler effect affect wavelength if the source of the waves is moving toward the observer? *(The waves will seem to be closer together. They will have a smaller wavelength.)*
Logical

(Teacher **Demo**)

"STRETCHING" LIGHT WAVES   L2

Purpose Students observe a model of how light is redshifted.

Materials old bicycle inner tube, scissors, chalk

Teaching Tip This demonstration would also work well with a long party balloon in place of the inner tube.

Procedure Before the demo, cut an old bicycle inner tube on both sides of the valve to form a long tube. Cut the tube lengthwise to form a long narrow band of rubber. In front of the students, use white chalk to draw a galaxy at one end of the tube to represent the Milky Way. Draw another galaxy at the other end. Draw a wavy line to represent light coming from the other galaxy toward the Milky Way. Then, hold both ends of the strip and stretch them apart. Ask students what happens to the "wave." *(It gets stretched out.)* Ask how this affects the color of the light. *(The wavelength increases, so the light is shifted toward the red end of the spectrum.)* Tell students that light from distant galaxies is redshifted by a similar process.

Expected Outcome Students will observe the "wave" being "redshifted."
Visual, Logical

FIGURE 21 Galaxy Cluster
This cluster of galaxies is located about 1 million light-years from Earth.

Galaxy Clusters Once astronomers discovered that stars were found in groups, they wondered whether galaxies also were grouped or just randomly distributed throughout the universe. They found that, like stars, galaxies are grouped in **galaxy clusters.** One such cluster is shown in **Figure 21.** Some clusters may contain thousands of galaxies. The Milky Way Galaxy is part of a galaxy cluster, called the Local Group. It contains at least 28 galaxies. Of these, three galaxies are spiral, 11 are irregular, and 14 are elliptical. Galaxy clusters also make up huge groups called superclusters, which make up vast threadlike structures called *filaments*, the largest known structures in the universe.

Quasars In the 1960s, astronomers discovered objects that were very bright and very far away. They called them quasi-stellar radio sources, or *quasars*, since they looked like stars. Because it takes their light billions of years to reach Earth, quasars must have existed when the universe was very young. Quasars must emit huge amounts of radiation, or they would be too dim for us to detect. The leading theory is that they are massive black holes in the center of very young galaxies.

The Expanding Universe

When a source is moving away from an observer, its light appears redder than it actually is, because its waves appear lengthened. This is called the *Doppler effect*. Objects approaching have their frequency shifted toward the blue or shorter wavelengths. Therefore, the Doppler effect reveals whether a star or other body in space is moving away from Earth or toward Earth. The amount of shift allows us to calculate the rate of this relative movement. Large Doppler shifts indicate higher speeds; smaller Doppler shifts indicate lower speeds.

Red Shifts One of the most important discoveries of modern astronomy was made in 1929 by Edwin Hubble. Observations completed several years earlier revealed that most galaxies have Doppler shifts toward the red end of the spectrum. The red shift occurs because the light wave frequency is reduced, which shows that Earth and the source are moving away from each other. Hubble set out to explain this red shift phenomenon.

Hubble realized that dimmer galaxies were probably farther away than were brighter galaxies. He tried to determine whether a relationship existed between the distances to galaxies and their red shifts. Hubble used estimated distances based on relative brightness and Doppler red shifts to discover that galaxies that exhibit the greatest red shifts are the most distant.

Hubble's Law A consequence of the universal red shift is that it predicts that most galaxies—except for a few nearby—are moving away from us. The amount of Doppler red shift depends on the speed at which the object is moving away. Greater red shifts indicate faster speeds. Because more distant galaxies have greater red shifts, Hubble concluded that they must be retreating from us at greater speeds. This idea is currently termed **Hubble's law.** It states that galaxies are retreating from us at a speed that is proportional to their distance—the farthest galaxies are retreating the fastest.

Hubble was surprised at this discovery because it implied that the most distant galaxies are moving away from us many times faster than those nearby. What does this mean? ☞ **The red shifts of distant galaxies indicate that the universe is expanding.**

FIGURE 22
Raisin Dough Analogy
As the dough rises, raisins that are farther apart travel a greater distance in the same time than those that are closer together. Like galaxies in an expanding universe, the distant raisins move away from one another more rapidly than those that are near one another.

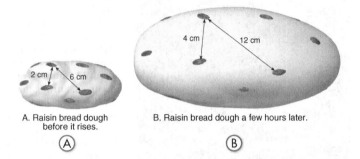

A. Raisin bread dough before it rises.

B. Raisin bread dough a few hours later.

To visualize the nature of this expanding universe, imagine a loaf of raisin bread dough that has been set out to rise for a few hours. As shown in **Figure 22,** raisins are distributed throughout the dough. As the dough doubles in size, so does the distance between all of the raisins. However, the raisins that were initially farther apart traveled a greater distance in the same time span than those located closer together. Any object covering a greater distance in the same amount of time as an object moving a shorter distance must be traveling faster. Scientists can therefore conclude that in an expanding universe, as in the raisin bread dough analogy, those space objects located farther apart move away from each other more rapidly than objects located closer to each other.

Another feature of the expanding universe can also be demonstrated using the raisin dough analogy. No matter which raisin you select, it will move away from all the other raisins. Likewise, no matter where a galaxy is located in the universe, every other galaxy—except those in the same cluster—will be moving away. Hubble indeed advanced our understanding of the universe. The Hubble Space Telescope is named in his honor.

☑ **Reading Checkpoint** *What is Hubble's law?*

Beyond Our Solar System **719**

Use Visuals   L1

Figure 22 Use this figure to explain how the universe is expanding. Tell students to imagine that the galaxy at the top left is our galaxy. **Ask:** If the raisin that is 2 cm from us becomes 6 cm away 2 hours later, how fast is it moving relative to us? *([6 cm − 2 cm]/2hr = 2 cm/hr)* If the raisin that is 5 cm from us becomes 15 cm away 2 hours later, how fast is it moving relative to us? *([15 cm − 5 cm]/2 hr = 5 cm/hr)* How do your answers relate to Hubble's law? *(The farther away a galaxy is, the faster it is moving.)*
Visual, Logical

Build Science Skills   L2

Student Activity: Use Analogies The text cites the raisin dough analogy as a way of explaining the expansion of the universe. Model a coiled spring toy as an analogy for red shifts. Have groups of two grip each end of a spring toy. Instruct one student to stay in place, and another to back away slowly. Ask students to discuss the following: Which of you represents our galaxy? *(the stationary student)* Which of you represents a galaxy that is moving away? *(the student who is backing up)* How does the toy represent a red shift? *(As the coils stretch, the distance between each one grows, modeling the lengthening of wavelengths over distance.)*
Kinesthetic, Interpersonal

Answers

☑ **Reading Checkpoint** *Hubble's law states that galaxies are receding from Earth at a speed that is proportional to their distance.*

Facts and Figures

Edwin Hubble was born in 1889 in Marshfield, Missouri. He initially studied law and only later decided to go into astronomy. In the early 1920s, astronomers did not know whether some "spiral nebulae" were small clouds of stars within our galaxy or separate galaxies entirely. Hubble measured the distance to the Andromeda nebula in 1924 and showed that it was about 100,000 times as far away as nearby stars. He concluded that it was a separate galaxy. In 1929, Hubble established that the red shift of galaxies was proportional to their distance, and thus that the universe is expanding. Much of Hubble's work was done using what at the time was the world's best telescope—the 100-in. telescope on Mt. Wilson in California. Hubble died in 1953.

Build Reading Literacy **L1**

Refer to **p. 698D**, which provides guidelines for sequencing.

Sequence While students read about the big bang, have them draw a flowchart showing the chain of events starting with the big bang and ending with the formation of stars and galaxies. *(big bang → atoms form → gases cool and condense → stars and galaxies form)*
Visual, Verbal

(Address **Misconceptions**) **L2**

Students may think that the Big Bang occurred at a certain point at the center of the universe. They may also think that material from the Big Bang exploded into already existing space. Tell students that space itself expanded as a result of the Big Bang. Space is within the universe rather than the universe being within space. There is no center from which the universe is expanding. The Big Bang essentially occurred everywhere at once. Evidence for this is that the cosmic background radiation comes from every direction, not just from a specific location.
Verbal

Answers

☑ **Reading Checkpoint** *The red shift of distant galaxies and cosmic background radiation support the big bang.*

☑ **Reading Checkpoint** *Most scientists think that the universe is open, or ever expanding. The current view is that the universe has no ending point.*

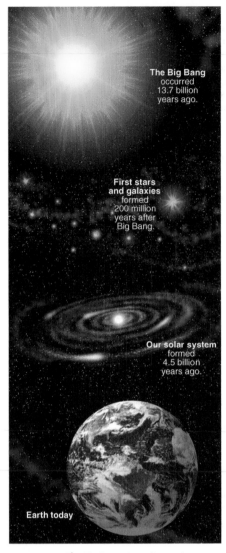

The Big Bang
occurred
13.7 billion
years ago.

First stars
and galaxies
formed
200 million
years after
Big Bang.

Our solar system
formed
4.5 billion
years ago.

Earth today

FIGURE 23 The Big Bang According to the Big Bang theory, the universe began 13.7 billion years ago. Two hundred million years later, the first stars and galaxies began to form.

The Big Bang

How did the universe begin? Any theory about the origin of the universe must account for the fact that all distant galaxies are moving away from us at a faster rate than are nearby galaxies. Although all galaxies appear to be moving away from Earth, it seems unlikely that our planet is the center of the universe.

A more probable explanation exists. Imagine a balloon with paper-punch dots glued to its surface. When the balloon is inflated, each dot spreads apart from every other dot. Similarly, if the universe is expanding, every galaxy would be moving away from every other galaxy.

This concept of an expanding universe led to the widely accepted Big Bang theory. According to the **Big Bang theory,** the universe began as a violent explosion from which the universe continues to expand, evolve, and cool. **The Big Bang theory states that at one time, the entire universe was confined to a dense, hot, supermassive ball. Then, about 13.7 billion years ago, a violent explosion occurred, hurling this material in all directions.** The Big Bang, illustrated in **Figure 23,** marks the beginning of the universe.

Scientists think that protons, neutrons, and electrons formed from the energy of the Big Bang. Scientists can model conditions in the early universe, using machines called particle accelerators. These devices smash subatomic particles together at very high speeds. The collision produces other particles that may exist for only a few billionths of a second. But they give scientists a brief glimpse of matter in the early universe. After several hundred thousand years, the universe became cool enough for atoms to form. As time passed, gases in the universe continued to cool and condense and eventually formed the stars.

Supporting Evidence Scientists have gathered substantial evidence that supports the Big Bang theory. For example, the red shift of galaxies indicates that the universe is still expanding. Scientists also discovered a type of energy called cosmic microwave background radiation. This energy has been detected as faint radio signals coming from every direction in space. Scientists think that this radiation was produced during the Big Bang.

☑ **Reading Checkpoint** *What evidence supports the Big Bang theory?*

The Big Crunch? If the universe began with a big bang, how will it end? One view is that the universe will last forever. In this scenario, the stars will slowly burn out, being replaced by an invisible form of matter and black holes that will travel outward through an endless, dark, cold universe. The other possibility is that the outward flight of the galaxies will slow and eventually stop. Gravitational contraction could follow, causing the galaxies to collapse into the high-energy, high-density mass from which the universe began. This scenario, the big bang operating in reverse, has been called the "big crunch."

Material called "dark matter" could affect the rate at which the universe expands. Dark matter is matter that cannot be directly observed because it does not give off radiation. Galaxies contain most of the visible mass of the universe, but there is evidence that what we see makes up less than one-tenth its total mass. Measurements of galactic rotation suggest that dark matter accounts for the rest of the universe's mass.

Whether the universe will expand forever or collapse upon itself depends on its average density. If the average density of the universe is more than its critical density—about one atom for every cubic meter—the gravitational field is enough to stop the outward expansion and cause the universe to contract. But, if the density of the universe is less than the critical value, it will expand forever. Current estimates place the density of the universe below the critical density, which predicts an ever-expanding, or open, universe. However, the universe is expanding even faster now than in the past. This may be due to a theoretical new force that astronomers have named "dark energy." The view currently favored by most scientists is that we live in an expanding universe with no ending point.

☑ **Reading Checkpoint** *How will the universe end?*

25.3 Assessment

Review Key Concepts 🔑

1. What is a galaxy?

2. Describe the size and structure of the Milky Way Galaxy.

3. How do galaxies differ?

4. What evidence indicates that the universe is expanding?

5. What is the Big Bang theory?

Think Critically

6. Compare and Contrast Compare and contrast the three types of galaxies.

7. Infer If the universe is an open universe, what can you infer about its average density?

WRITING IN SCIENCE

8. Summarize Scientists are continuously searching the Milky Way Galaxy for other stars that may have planets. What types of stars would most likely have a planet or planets suitable for life as we know it? Write a paragraph describing these stars.

Beyond Our Solar System **721**

Integrate History   L2

Current understanding of the universe is based on observations and research by many astronomers over hundreds of years. Encourage interested students to research online and in the library about key events in astronomy and space exploration. Ask them to make a timeline and to present the information to the class. Their timelines are likely to include information on the *Apollo* missions. *(Sample answer: In May of 1961, President John F. Kennedy challenged the American space program to put a person on the moon before the end of the decade. There were 15 missions, called the Apollo missions, between January 1967 and December 1972. Highlights of the Apollo missions include:*

- **Apollo 7** *October 1968 first 3-person crew; 163 orbits of Earth; first television images*
- **Apollo 8** *December 1968 10 orbits of the moon; first humans to see the far side of the moon*
- **Apollo 10** *May 1969 31 lunar orbits; first color television images*
- **Apollo 11** *July 1969 first crewed landing on moon and return to Earth*
- **Apollo 13** *April 1970 an oxygen tank exploded and forced the mission to circle the moon once and return to Earth*
- **Apollo 15** *July 1971 first use of the lunar rover vehicle; collected 170 pounds of moon rocks*
- **Apollo 17** *December 1972 the final crewed lunar mission)*

3 ASSESS

Evaluate Understanding   L2

Write "The Expanding Universe" on the board. Ask students to contribute ideas that indicate that the universe is expanding.

Reteach   L1

Have students use Figures 18–20 to review the basic types of galaxies.

Assessment Answers

1. A galaxy is a large group of stars, dust, and gases held together by gravity.

2. The Milky Way is a large spiral galaxy whose disk is about 100,000 light-years wide and about 10,000 light-years thick at the nucleus.

3. Galaxies differ in size, shape, and the ages of their stars.

4. The red shifts of distant galaxies indicate that the universe is expanding.

5. The big bang theory states that about 13.7 billion years ago, the universe began at one point and has been expanding ever since.

6. The most obvious difference is their shape: spiral galaxies have arms; elliptical galaxies range in shape from round to oval; irregular galaxies have no regular shape. Irregular galaxies are composed mostly of young stars, while elliptical galaxies contain mostly older stars. Spiral galaxies are composed of stars of various ages, with the youngest stars in the arms.

7. Its average density must be less than its critical density.

8. Medium-mass stars, like our sun, may be the most likely candidates to have planets that support life. In our own galaxy, there are millions of sun-like stars. If these stars are orbited by planets, the existence of life would depend on the planets' composition and temperature, among other factors.

HOW CAN CONSTELLATIONS HELP SOMEONE LOCATE A STAR? **L2**

Background

- Until about 400 years ago, science was not a separate field of study as it is today. It was rare for anyone to study the natural world merely out of curiosity. Belief in what we would now call unscientific superstitions was quite common even among well-educated people. Kepler, for example, believed that observations of the stars could be used to predict future events. Part of his job as an astronomy professor was to make such predictions.

- The International Astronomical Union (IAU) is an international group of professional astronomers. Among other things, the IAU is responsible for naming stars and other celestial bodies, defining important astronomical and physical constants, and promoting astronomy education.

Teaching Tip

Have students research early astronomers and the connections between astronomy and the rest of society at that time. Have students develop a definition of *pseudoscience* and to explain how pseudoscience is different from science. *(Students should understand that pseudoscience is often presented as if it is based on scientific evidence but that the ideas have not been tested and often cannot be tested reliably.)* Ask them to present a brief report to the class.
Logical

Use Visuals

Figure 24 To help students understand Figure 24, present a model in your classroom. Place table tennis balls, or similar small objects, in positions similar to the stars shown in Figure 24A. If possible, hang the model so that students can view it from all angles. Ask students to draw the "constellation" from at least three positions. Once students have completed their drawings, point out that the appearance of groups of stars is even more variable because they are so far apart. At distances visible within the classroom, people have accurate depth perception. However, when the objects are light years apart, humans are unable to discern the differences in distance.
Visual

EARTH & HISTORY
How Can Constellations Help Someone Locate a Star?

For centuries, human stargazers have identified patterns in the nighttime sky, called *constellations*. Early Greek philosophers believed that the position of the constellations could influence, and be used to predict, human behavior and natural events. This belief developed into the practice called *astrology*. In order to make their predictions, astrologists had to make precise measurements.

These early measurements laid a valuable foundation for the scientific study of the stars, planets, and other celestial bodies. By the 1600s, the study of the stars developed into the science of astronomy—a science because each hypothesis can be tested. By comparison, astrology is a *pseudoscience* (meaning *false science*), because the claims of astrology lack evidence and cannot be reliably tested.

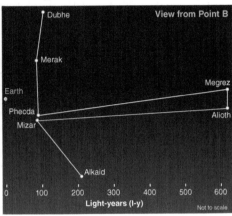

FIGURE 24 Different Views of the Big Dipper Drawing imaginary lines that connect the seven stars above, you see a shape of a dipper. **A** This arrangement of stars only produces a dipper shape when viewed from Earth.

B If these same stars are viewed from a different location in space—*Point B* in Figure 24A—the same lines result in a much different shape. The reason for the difference is some stars are closer to Earth and some farther away.

If someone asked you to find the town of Gretna on a map of the United States, it might take you a while. However, if your map was divided into states and you were told that Gretna is in Virginia, you'd at least have a better idea of where to start looking.

In a similar way, if someone asked you to locate the red star Betelgeuse somewhere in the nighttime sky, it would be a daunting task. Several decades ago the International Astronomical Union (IAU) recognized this challenge and did something to help. The IAU divided the sky around Earth into 88 sections. Why 88 sections? At the time of their action, there were 88 named constellations. So they divided the sky and named each section after the constellation that is located in that section. Any star located in that segment of the sky, even if the star isn't part of the constellation shape, is considered "in" that constellation.

As a result of the IAU action, your search for the location of Betelgeuse would now be much easier. Betelgeuse is a red star in the constellation Orion. With a star map in hand, you could quickly complete your task.

However, the constellation-reference system is only useful for observers on or near Earth. As explained in **Figure 24,** once you journey beyond our solar system, the constellations no longer have the same shape. The IAU developed a coordinate system that is not geocentric. The International Celestial Reference System (ICRS) is a detailed coordinate system that helps astronomers describe the position of any celestial body. For amateur sky watchers there is an easier method. Computer applications for smartphones and tablets do all the work for you. Type in "betelgeuse" and the device will show you exactly where to look.

Observing Stars

Problem How can you use star charts to identify constellations and track star movements?

Materials star charts (in the Appendix), penlight, notebook

Skills Observe, Summarize, Interpret Data

Connect to the **Big idea** Throughout history, people have been recording the nightly movement of stars that results from Earth's rotation, as well as the seasonal changes in the constellations as Earth revolves around the sun. Early astronomers offered many explanations for these changes before the true nature of the motions was understood in the seventeenth century. In this lab, you'll observe and identify stars.

Procedure

1. On a clear, moonless night as far from street lights as safely possible, go outside and observe the stars.

2. In a data table like the one below, make a list of the different colors of stars that you see.

3. Select one star that is directly overhead or nearly so. Observe and record its movement over a period of one hour. Also note the direction of its movement (eastward, westward).

4. Select a star chart suitable for your location and season. Locate several constellations. Sketch and label the constellations in your notebook.

5. Locate the North Star (Polaris) in the night sky. Observe the motion of stars that surround the North Star.

6. Return to the exact same location several weeks later and repeat Steps 1–5.

Analyze and Conclude

1. **Observe** How many different colors of stars did you observe? How do these colors relate to star temperature?

2. **Interpret Data** In which direction did the star that you observed appear to move? How is this movement related to the direction of Earth's rotation?

3. **Summarize** Write a brief summary of the motion of the stars that surround the North Star. Be sure to include any changes you observed during your second viewing.

GO FURTHER Find the Big Dipper, which is part of the constellation Ursa Major. A binary star system makes up the stars of the Big Dipper. Locate the star pair and sketch them in their proper location in the Big Dipper.

Data Table				
Date	Star Colors	Star Movement	Constellations	Motions of Stars Around North Star

ES.1 The student will plan and conduct investigations in which **c.** scales, diagrams, charts, graphs, tables, imagery, models, and profiles are constructed and interpreted; and **e.** variables are manipulated with repeated trials. **ES.2** The student will demonstrate an understanding of the nature of science and scientific reasoning and logic. Key concepts include **c.** observation and logic are essential for reaching a conclusion.

Beyond Our Solar System **723**

INQUIRY
EXPLORATION LAB

Observing Stars [L2]

Objective
In this activity, students will observe and identify stars by using star charts.

Skills Observe, Summarize, Interpret Data

Advance Prep Allow 5–10 minutes to copy star charts, if desired.

Class Time 20–30 minutes for after-lab discussion

Teaching Tips Because students will be observing stars at night from home, you may wish to help them choose the appropriate nights for viewing.

Students who live in urban areas may be hindered by light pollution. If possible, help students consider locations far enough away from light sources. Alternatively, you could schedule a field trip to a local planetarium.

Expected Outcome Students will observe different colors of stars. They will also observe that the stars appeared to move.

Analyze and Conclude

1. Observed colors might be blue, blue-white, red, and yellow. Blue and blue-white stars are hot, red stars are cool, and yellow stars are of medium temperature.

2. The star appeared to move westward. The rotation of Earth from west to east (eastward) makes the position of the star appear to move east to west (westward) throughout the night.

3. The stars surrounding the North Star appear to move in circles around the North Star, with the circles becoming larger the farther a star appears to be from the North Star.

GO FURTHER

The binary star system is the second star in the handle of the Big Dipper.
Kinesthetic, Visual

STUDY GUIDE

Study Tip

Review Notes

Tell students to make reviewing their notes part of their homework plan. By reviewing their notes for a few minutes each day, students will need to spend less time studying for tests.

Think Visually

a. Irregular
b. Elliptical
c. has round to oval shape
d. usually disk-shaped
e. contains young stars
f. contains both old and young stars

21st Century Learning

Problem Identification, Formulation, and Solution

What can you find out about extrasolar planets in our galaxy?

Since 1992, astronomers have been discovering planets revolving around stars other than the sun in our galaxy. These planets are called extrasolar planets because they are outside our solar system. Encourage interested students to research the currently known extrasolar planets. Instruct them to find information about the planets revolving around the three stars closest to the sun. Each student should make a data table with information about each star and its orbiting planets. Students should be prepared to present the data in class or on the class blog. Remind them to provide any other interesting facts they discover about these stars or planets. As an extension, students can do additional research to answer questions asked during their presentations.

Homework Guide

Lesson	Questions
1	1–5, 11–15, 26–31
2	6–8, 16–20
3	9, 10, 21–25

Big idea ▶ Earth and the Universe

25.1 Properties of Stars

🔑 Color is a clue to a star's temperature.

🔑 Binary stars can be used to determine stellar mass.

🔑 The nearest stars have the largest parallax angles, while those of distant stars are too small to measure.

🔑 Three factors control the apparent brightness of a star as seen from Earth: how big it is, how hot it is, and how far away it is.

🔑 A Hertzsprung-Russell diagram shows the relationship between the absolute magnitude and temperature of stars.

constellation (700)
binary star (701)
light-year (702)
apparent magnitude (703)
absolute magnitude (703)
Hertzsprung-Russell diagram (704)
main-sequence star (704)
red giant (704)
supergiant (704)
Cepheid variable (705)
nova (705)

25.2 Stellar Evolution

🔑 When the core of a protostar has reached at least 10 million K, pressure within it is so great that nuclear fusion of hydrogen begins.

🔑 All stars, regardless of their size, eventually run out of fuel and collapse due to gravity.

🔑 Stars similar to the sun begin as a nebula, spend much of their lives as main-sequence stars, become red giants, planetary nebulae, white dwarfs, and finally, black dwarfs.

protostar (708)
supernova (711)
white dwarf (712)

neutron star (713)
pulsar (713)
black hole (714)

25.3 The Universe

🔑 The Milky Way is a large spiral galaxy whose disk is about 100,000 light-years wide and about 10,000 light-years thick at the nucleus.

🔑 In addition to shape and size, one of the major differences among different types of galaxies is the age of their stars.

🔑 The red shifts of distant galaxies indicate that the universe is expanding.

🔑 The Big Bang theory states that at one time, the entire universe was confined to a dense, hot, supermassive ball. Then, about 13.7 billion years ago, a violent explosion occurred, hurling this material in all directions.

galaxy (715)
galaxy cluster (718)
Hubble's law (719)
Big Bang theory (720)

Think Visually

Summarize Use information from the chapter to complete the concept map below.

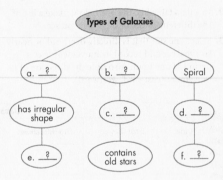

Assessment Answers

Review Content

1. c	**2.** d	**3.** b
4. d	**5.** c	**6.** c
7. a	**8.** b	**9.** a
10. d		

Understand Concepts

11. A star's temperature can be determined by its color.

12. About 50 percent of stars are estimated to occur in pairs or multiples.

13. Parallax is the slight shifting in the apparent position of a nearby star due to the orbital motion of Earth.

14. Apparent magnitude is how bright a star appears from Earth. Absolute magnitude is how bright a star actually is.

25 Assessment

Review Content

Choose the letter that best answers the question or completes the statement.

1. Distances to stars are usually expressed in units called
   a. miles.
   b. kilometers.
   c. light-years.
   d. astronomical units.

2. The measure of a star's brightness is called its
   a. parallax.
   b. color index.
   c. visual binary.
   d. magnitude.

3. Distances to nearby stars can be determined from
   a. fluorescence.
   b. stellar parallax.
   c. stellar mass.
   d. emission nebulae.

4. Which color stars have the highest surface temperature?
   a. red
   b. orange
   c. yellow
   d. blue

5. Which type of star is the sun?
   a. black hole
   b. black dwarf
   c. main sequence
   d. red giant

6. What does a sunlike star become after it has burned the fuel in its core?
   a. supernova
   b. neutron star
   c. red giant
   d. nebula

7. Which object has such a strong surface gravity that light cannot escape it?
   a. black hole
   b. black dwarf
   c. red giant
   d. white dwarf

8. Stars that are composed of matter in which electrons have combined with protons are called
   a. black holes.
   b. neutron stars.
   c. red giants.
   d. white dwarfs.

9. Hubble's law states that galaxies are retreating from Earth at a speed that is proportional to their
   a. distance from Earth.
   b. volume.
   c. mass.
   d. temperature.

10. What theory states that the universe began in a violent explosion?
    a. the big crunch
    b. the Doppler effect
    c. Hubble's law
    d. the Big Bang

Understand Concepts

11. Which property of a star can be determined by its color?

12. Approximately what percentage of stars in the universe are estimated to occur in pairs or multiples?

13. What is parallax?

14. Compare and contrast apparent magnitude and absolute magnitude.

15. What color is the most massive type of main-sequence star? The least massive?

16. At what temperature does nuclear fusion begin?

17. A stable main-sequence star is balanced between which two forces?

18. What element is the main fuel for main-sequence stars? For red giants?

19. What type of stars end their lives as supernovae?

20. What is a pulsar?

21. How long does it take our solar system to orbit the nucleus of the Milky Way Galaxy?

22. The farther a galaxy is from the Milky Way, the greater its red shift. What does this indicate about the universe?

23. What is cosmic microwave background radiation?

Beyond Our Solar System **725**

15. The most massive type of main-sequence stars are hot, blue stars. The least massive are cool, red stars.
16. 10 million K
17. A stable main-sequence star is balanced between the forces of gravity and gas pressure.
18. Hydrogen is the main fuel for main-sequence stars. Red giants consume hydrogen in their outer shells and eventually helium in their cores.
19. massive stars

20. A pulsar is a spinning neutron star that appears to give off pulses of radio waves.
21. It takes about 200 million years for our solar system to orbit the Milky Way Galaxy.
22. It indicates that the universe is expanding.
23. Cosmic microwave background radiation is energy produced during the Big Bang. It can be detected coming from space in all directions.

Beyond Our Solar System **725**

ASSESSMENT

Think Critically

24. Large quantities of interstellar matter block much of the visible light.
25. You would study the arms of the spiral galaxy because most young stars are located in the arms.

Analyze Data

26. Rigel is the brightest star. Sirius B is the hottest star.
27. White dwarfs have low absolute brightnesses compared with supergiants.
28. The greater the absolute brightness of a main-sequence star, the higher its temperature is.

Concepts in Action

29. The mass of a body can be calculated if it is gravitationally attached to a partner, which is the case for any binary star system. Binary stars orbit each other around a common point called the center of mass. For stars of equal mass, the center of mass lies exactly halfway between them. If one star is more massive than its partner, their common center will be closer to the more massive one.
30. No, because the parallax angle of distant stars is too small to measure.
31. One light-year equals about 9.5×10^{12} km; 9.5×10^{12} km/light-year $\times$ 4.3 light-years $= 40.9 \times 10^{12}$ km.

24. Explain Why are radio telescopes instead of optical telescopes used to determine the structure of the Milky Way Galaxy?

25. Draw Conclusions Imagine that you are a scientist studying the birth of stars in a spiral galaxy. Which part of the galaxy would you study? Explain your answer.

Analyze Data

Use the diagram below to answer Questions 26–28.

Hertzsprung-Russell Diagram

26. Interpret Graphs What is the brightest star in the diagram? The hottest?

27. Analyze Data How does the absolute brightness of white dwarfs compare with that of supergiants?

28. Summarize What is the relationship between absolute brightness and temperature for a main-sequence star?

Concepts in Action

29. Explain How can a binary star system be used to determine a star's mass?

30. Infer Would you use parallax to determine the distance to a faraway star? Why or why not?

31. Calculate The closest star to the sun, *Proxima Centauri*, is 4.3 light-years away. How many kilometers from the sun is *Proxima Centauri*?

Performance-Based Assessment

Use Models Use materials provided by your teacher to construct a scale model of the Milky Way Galaxy. Before you begin, be sure to develop a workable scale for your model.

Performance-Based Assessment

Provide students with clay, paper, paint, and other materials to construct their models. A workable scale might be 1 cm = 10,000 light-years. Models should reflect that the Milky Way is about 100,000 light-years wide and 10,000 light-years thick at its nucleus.

Standardized Test Prep

Choose the letter that best answers the question or completes the statement.

1 What can you estimate about a Cepheid variable if you know its absolute magnitude and apparent magnitude?
   A mass
   B distance
   C temperature
   D volume

2 Based on the red shifts of distant galaxies, astronomers conclude that—
   F Earth is in the center of the universe
   G the universe is contracting
   H the universe is expanding
   J new galaxies are continually being added to the universe

3 What types of stars are thought to be the remnants of supernova explosions?
   A protostars
   B neutron stars
   C red giant stars
   D white dwarf stars

4 Which sequence of events describes the evolution of a medium-mass star, such as the sun? Begin with the earliest event.
   F dust and gases, protostar, main-sequence star, white dwarf, black dwarf
   G dust and gases, protostar, main-sequence star, giant, planetary nebula, white dwarf, black dwarf
   H dust and gases, protostar, main-sequence star, supergiant, supernova explosion, black hole
   J dust and gases, protostar, main-sequence star, supergiant, supernova explosion, neutron star

If You Have Trouble With . . .				
Question	1	2	3	4
See Lesson	25.1	25.3	25.2	25.2

STEM Activity: The Bycatch Problem

Next Generation Science Standards

PERFORMANCE EXPECTATIONS:
HS-ESS3-3; HS-ESS3-4; HS-ETS1-3

DISCIPLINARY CORE IDEAS: ESS3.C

SEP: Use Mathematical and Computational Thinking

Common Core Standards

ELA: RST.9-10.7; RST.11-12.7; WHST.9-12.7

MATHEMATICS: MP.2; MP.4; HSN-Q.A.1

Incorporating Mathematics Standards

Students may encounter mathematical data in many forms, including words, tables, and graphs. Line graphs and bar graphs can display information efficiently. Suggest that students use automatic graphing software (available in many software applications) to graph variables such as commercial value in dollars, fish population changes over time, and current trends in market prices.

Procedure Suggestions

Journal articles and reports from national and international entities focusing on conservation can be useful sources of information. Annual commercial figures from fisheries or from the government can also be helpful. Depending on the particular fishing market students choose, they will discover different approaches to reduce the problem of bycatch. Encourage them to anticipate possible unintended effects of these approaches. For example, keeping bycatch and selling it makes more economic sense for struggling professional fishing operations, but existing regulations may not allow them to keep the bycatch if they are over limit for that species in their areas. As a result, fish may be wasted due to well-intended regulations.

EARTH AND HUMAN ACTIVITY

Science and Engineering Practices
Using Mathematical and Computational Thinking

The Bycatch Problem

Seafood harvesting is a multibillion-dollar industry. The high volume of seafood production is driven by factors such as an increasing world population, a trend toward healthier eating, and technological advances in packaging and transportation.

Such a huge industry is bound to have some negative effects, and bycatch is one them. *Bycatch* is the name given to fish and other marine animals that are inadvertently caught in fishing gear meant for a different species (the targeted species is called the "catch"). Many fish, mammals, birds, and turtles die after getting caught in fishing nets intended for other species. Often the bycatch includes species such as grouper, halibut, red snapper, rockfish, and other commonly eaten species that are tossed back into the sea regardless of whether the fish are alive or dead. This represents an estimated $1 billion in wasted fish resources.

Scientists and people in the fishing industry are working together to find solutions to the problem of bycatch. These solutions may involve the use of fishing methods that reduce the capture of non-targeted species, as well as finding ways to use commercially valuable bycatch instead of tossing it back into the sea.

Use Mathematical and Computational Thinking

Choose a species that is used as seafood (for example, bluefin tuna). Research the issues associated with its bycatch: What is the most common fishing method? What species make up the bycatch? What is their commercial value in dollars? How have these fish populations changed over the years? What are the current trends in market prices? Use quantitative data from your research to develop a presentation that does one of the following:

- Compare the profitability of traditional and bycatch-friendly fishing methods.
- Estimate the impact of a particular fishing method on fish populations over a specific number of years.

Support your conclusions with graphs and use appropriate calculations.

Professional Development

Commercial fishing operations are causing fish populations to plummet faster than they can be replenished. To buy time until global solutions can be found, some experts recommend simply adjusting our fishing methods to better suit the targeted catch. For example, nets are trawled along the sea floor to catch shrimp, halibut, and sole. This method also picks up a huge variety of bottom-dwelling organisms that are simply discarded dead or dying. Therefore, trawling regulations could have a very positive impact. For large fish, harpooning is a more environmentally responsible method than gillnetting. Jigging, which uses grappling hooks attached to a line, targets the desired fish well enough that bycatch is not a serious problem. In some cases, simply changing the types of hooks or sinking longlines can reduce the amount of bycatch.

STEM ACTIVITY

EARTH AND HUMAN ACTIVITY

Science and Engineering Practices
Designing Solutions

Design to Reduce Waste

As the world's human population soars, so does the problem of solid waste management. By 2025, some warn that people will be producing more than 6 billion kilograms of solid waste every day as compared to the more than 3.5 billion kilograms they produced each day in 2010. Managing all this waste costs hundreds of billions of dollars a year. However, without effective management, solid waste will pollute the environment, sicken people, and contribute greenhouse gases to the atmosphere.

Developed countries, especially the United States, contribute the major share of the daily solid waste produced globally. According to the Environmental Protection Agency (EPA), Americans generated about 707 million kilograms of solid waste every day in 2013. You might be surprised to learn that containers and packaging made up almost 30%, or about 211 million kilograms of that solid waste every day in 2013.

To reduce the amount of packaging heading to landfills, companies must find new ways to package their products. By redesigning their packaging, businesses can reduce the amount of solid waste entering landfills. However, different products need different types of packaging. Therefore, many new packaging options need to be developed.

Design Solutions

Break down the problem of packaging into a more manageable problem by designing, building, and testing a package for either a food or a product you often purchase. Your packaging needs to be compact, cost effective, and environmentally safe. It should also use less material than it currently does. Do some research. Identify and prioritize the criteria for your design before you settle on a design solution for your packaging. Then, build and test a prototype. Troubleshoot and redesign your prototype before evaluating your solution based on your prioritized criteria and the trade-offs you made to account for the constraints.

When you are satisfied with your prototype, communicate your results. Include a list of sources used to research the design of your packaging, a list of materials with an explanation of why you chose them, a sketch of your design, and a description of how you evaluated your solution based on your criteria and constraints. Also include a model of the impacts of your design solution on the costs of the food or product and on landfills over time.

729

Differentiated Instruction

If students are struggling to develop a design solution, suggest that they collect six samples of product or food packaging from purchases made by family or friends. Ask them to explain why each type of packaging is likely to add to the landfill problem. Then ask students to describe a different kind of packaging for the same product or food that would still protect the product but not contribute to the landfill problem. The goal is to encourage students to analyze the factors that make the current packaging undesirable and to address the changes needed to solve the problem.

STEM Activity: Design to Reduce Waste

Next Generation Science Standards

PERFORMANCE EXPECTATIONS: HS-ESS3-4; HS-ETS1-1; HS-ETS1-2; HS-ETS1-3

DISCIPLINARY CORE IDEAS: ESS3.C; ETS1.A; ETS1.B; ETS1.C

SEP: Designing Solutions

Common Core Standards

ELA: RST.11-12.7

MATHEMATICS: HSN-Q.A.3

Incorporating ELA Standards

Before students begin their research, remind them that they may see many claims about manufacturers' products. Tell them to evaluate each claim in terms of the validity of the manufacturer's reasoning and the relevance and sufficiency of the evidence that the manufacturer presents. Remind students that they should incorporate their evaluations into their design solutions.

Procedure Suggestions

Work with students to identify the constraints for their packaging idea—compact, cost effective, and environmentally safe. Differentiate between constraints and criteria by providing examples of criteria they might select for their packaging solution, such as size measurements, weight measurements, or composting time. Allow for creativity in packaging solutions. For example, compostable take-out containers are available to food retailers. A student might propose a design solution that makes those containers reusable for a certain number of times before the container was thrown into the trash.

STEM Activity: Plate Tectonics: Measuring Plate Movement

Next Generation Science Standards

PERFORMANCE EXPECTATIONS:
HS-ESS2-1

DISCIPLINARY CORE IDEAS: ESS2.B

SEP: Developing and Using Models

Common Core Standards

ELA: WHST.9-12.7; SL.11–12.4; SL.11–12.5

Incorporating ELA Standards

Many students have good command of the subject but don't know how to present their information effectively. Focus them on the following presentation aspects to help them succeed in using their models to explain how the technology works.

- Organize the content into a beginning, middle, and end. For example, begin by describing the model and explaining the relationships among its components. Then describe how the technology works and the data it generates. Finally, relate this data to what it reveals about plate movement.
- In addition to the model, use visuals to help the audience understand.
- Use accepted presentation skills (eye contact, voice modulation, purposeful movement, etc.).
- Practice and revise the presentation until it achieves a natural flow.

Procedure Suggestions

Explain that satellite technology supports all of the technologies that directly measure the motion of Earth's plates. Remind students that GPS is a system consisting of satellites, ground stations, and receivers. The position of each satellite at any given time is known; ground stations track it using radar. The receiver in your phone or GPS device uses signals from four or more satellites to calculate its distance from them and thus determine its location on Earth. Tell students to use what they know about GPS to help them understand how the technology they research works so they can build an accurate model.

730

STEM ACTIVITY

EARTH'S PLACE IN THE UNIVERSE

Science and Engineering Practices
Developing and Using Models

Plate Tectonics: Measuring Plate Movement

Without advances in technology, the theory of plate tectonics would still be considered pseudoscience. Past movements of plates have been documented using technologies to collect data. Sonar technology was used to map the topography of the ocean floor, leading to the discovery of mid-ocean ridges. Sonar technology was also used to measure the depth of ocean floor sediment, revealing very little sediment deposit near mid-ocean ridges and increasing amounts of sediment as the distance from the ridges increased. Magnetometers were used to measure the strength and direction of magnetic fields associated with rocks on the ocean floor. This resulted in magnetic maps of the ocean floor that scientists used to determine the rate at which plates had moved away from mid-ocean ridges. But ocean rock is no older than 200 million years. To find out about plate movements before then, scientists used magnetometers to collect data from ancient continental rocks and use it to estimate how much continents had rotated as their plates moved.

Technologies also allow scientists to calculate present-day movements of plates and predict future movements. SLR (Satellite Laser Ranging) is one of these technologies. It allows scientists to measure the distance between plates by positioning two laser systems on different sides of a plate boundary. Each system shoots a laser pulse at the same special orbiting satellite, which reflects the pulses back to their systems. The systems record the round-trip time of their pulses and the difference in the times is used ultimately to determine the distance between the two laser systems on Earth.

Developing and Using Models

Research SLR, GPS (Global Positioning System), VLBI (Very Long Baseline Interferometry) and other technologies used to directly measure the present-day movements of Earth's plates. Select one of the technologies and develop a model of it that shows the relationship among its components. Present your model to the class and use it to explain how the technology works and how it can reveal Earth's hidden processes.

730

Focus on Technology

Tracking plate movements back in time requires fast analysis of enormous amounts of data. New software is constantly being designed for supercomputers that 'crunch' the data. A team of scientists including paleogeologist Dietmar Mueller, at the University of Sydney, geophysicist Mike Gurnis at Cal Tech, and geologist Trond Torsvik at the University of Oslo has developed 3-D software for charting the movements of plates over the past 410 million years. The model produced by this software charts longitude and lacks a 2-D model's distortion of the appearance and movement of tectonic plates. It also includes factors associated with the convecting mantle that affect plate movements. When using this model, you can pick a past geological time and return to it, seeing what Earth's surface and it depths looked like at that time.

STEM ACTIVITY

EARTH'S PLACE IN THE UNIVERSE

Science and Engineering Practices
Defining Problems

Space Weather Readiness

During the early morning hours of March 13, 1989, the 9,460-megawatt power grid serving the Canadian province of Quebec stopped working. No electricity meant no heat or light for millions of residents in Montreal and surrounding areas. Newspaper presses shuddered to a stop. Traffic lights went dark. And weak battery-powered back-up lights snapped on to illuminate the underground walkways.

Meanwhile, observers as far south as Florida and Cuba witnessed the night sky explode into the beautiful shimmering colors of the aurora borealis, which is normally visible only in northern latitudes. Earlier that day, residents in certain areas of southern California were equally puzzled by their automatic garage doors, which kept opening and closing on their own. In the northeast, microchip manufacturers had to shut down production several times due to the intense and fluctuating magnetic activity in Earth's ionosphere.

What did the collapse of the extensive and powerful Quebec power grid have to do with the odd behavior of automatic garage door openers in California? Both events were the result of a powerful solar explosion that took place three days earlier, releasing as much energy as thousands of nuclear bombs all exploding simultaneously. The explosion released a billion-ton cloud of gas that hurtled towards Earth at a million miles per hour. The solar flare that was created by the explosion jammed radio signals and caused short-wave radio interference. The magnetic disturbance from this solar storm was immense and far-reaching.

Although the strength of this particular solar storm was unusual, solar storms are not rare. They are an important aspect of what is known as "space weather."

Define a Problem

A 2009 report found that modern power systems are more vulnerable than traditional systems to the effects of severe geomagnetic storms. Why would this be the case? Research the details of how the 1989 solar storm disabled the Quebec power grid. Identify one problem faced by engineers as they try to build reliable power grids or reduce the vulnerability of existing ones. Use what you learn to define the problem by describing the criteria and constraints that a reliable system must meet. Include relevant graphs and comparison data tables as needed.

Career Connections

Public utilities engineers are highly trained and educated individuals who are responsible for the performance, repair, and safety of public utilities. Using their engineering education and experience, public utilities engineers devise methods to increase the stability of electricity delivery systems to commercial and private customers. They design the transmission systems, including grids and poles, to homes and businesses. The job usually requires a substantial amount of work in the field because the engineers work with utility company linemen to install systems that can withstand the weather restrictions in any given area. Along with electrical engineering, these professionals must also have extensive course work in mechanics, hydraulics, and building structures.

STEM Activity: Space Weather Readiness

Next Generation Science Standards

PERFORMANCE EXPECTATIONS: HS-ESS1-1; HS-ETS1-1

DISCIPLINARY CORE IDEAS: ESS1.A; ETS1.A

SEP: Defining Problems

Common Core Standards

ELA: RST.9-10.1; RST.9-10.7; WHST.9-12.7

MATHEMATICS: HSF.IF.B.4 and HSF.IF.B.6

Incorporating ELA Standards

Encourage students to translate technical information into a visual format, and quantitative data into tables, charts, or graphs. For example, text about the components of a power grid system can be translated into a graphic model that shows all the components in a visual way to help others understand how the system works. Students can then use this graphic to help them determine the criteria and constraints of a reliable power grid system.

Procedure Suggestions

Before beginning, ask students how a loss of electrical power can affect their lives. They may mention inconveniences such as the loss of electric lights and appliances, but if they seem unable to go beyond the obvious, divide them into groups and inform them that solar storms not only affect power grids, but also satellites. Have them brainstorm more subtle and serious disruptions that a solar storm can cause, such as the inability to pump gasoline, use ATMs, or travel.

Answer

Why are modern power systems more vulnerable than traditional systems to the effects of severe geomagnetic storms? The total length of high-voltage power lines turns power grids into giant antennas for geomagnetically induced currents. The currents are attracted and passed along much more quickly than when there were fewer high power lines attached to a grid.

Science Skills

Basic Process Skills

During a science course, you often carry out some short lab activities as well as more detailed experiments. Here are some skills that you will use as you work.

Observing

In every science activity, you make a variety of observations. **Observing** is using one or more of the five senses to gather information. Many observations involve the senses of sight, hearing, touch, and smell.

Sometimes you will use tools that increase the power of your senses or make observations more precise. For example, hand lenses enable you to see things in greater detail. Tools may help you eliminate personal opinions or preferences.

In science it is customary to record your observations at the time they are made, usually by writing or drawing in a notebook. You may occasionally make records by using computers, cameras, videotapes, and other tools. As a rule, scientists keep complete accounts of their observations, often using tables to help organize their observations in a regular way.

Inferring

In science as in everyday life, observations are usually followed by inferences. **Inferring** is interpreting an observation or statement based on prior knowledge. For example, you can make several observations using the strobe photograph below. You can observe that the ball is moving. Based on the motion of the ball, you might infer that the ball was thrown downward at an angle by an experi-

menter. In making that inference, you would use your knowledge about the motion of projectiles. Someone who knew more about projectile motion might infer that the ball loses energy with each bounce. That is why the height decreases with each bounce.

Comparing Observations and Inferences	
Sample Observation	**Sample Inference**
The ball moves less and less vertical distance in the time between each flash of the strobe light.	Gravity is slowing down the ball's upward motion.
The ball moves the same distance to the right in the time between each flash of the strobe light.	Air resistance is so small that it does not slow down the ball's horizontal motion.

Notice that an inference is an act of reasoning, not a fact. That means an inference may be logical but not true. It is often necessary to gather further information before you can be confident that an inference is correct. For scientists, that information may come from further observations or from research into the work done by others.

Predicting

People often make predictions, but their statements about the future could be either guesses or inferences. In science, a **prediction** is an inference about a future event based on evidence, experience, or knowledge. For example, you can say, *On the first day next month, it will be sunny all day.* If your statement is based on evidence of weather patterns in the area, then the prediction is scientific. If the statement was made without considering any evidence, it's just a guess.

Predictions play a major role in science because they offer scientists a way to test ideas. If scientists understand an event or the properties of a particular object, they should be able to make accurate predictions about that event or object. Some predictions can be tested simply by making observations. For others, carefully designed experiments are needed.

Measuring

Measurements are important in science because they provide specific information and help observers avoid bias. **Measuring** is comparing an object or process to a standard. Scientists use a common set of standards, called the International System of Units, abbreviated as SI (for its French name, *Système International d'Unités*).

What distance does the ball travel in each time interval in the strobe photograph? You can make measurements on the photograph to make more precise statements about the ball's motion.

Calculating

Once scientists have made measurements, calculations are a very important part of analyzing data. How fast is a ball moving? You could directly measure the speed of a ball using probeware such as a motion sensor. But you can also calculate the speed using distance and time measurements. **Calculating** is a process in which a person uses mathematical operations to manipulate numbers and symbols.

Classifying

Classifying is grouping items according to some organizing idea or system. Classifying occurs in every branch of science but it's especially important in chemistry because there are so many different ways that elements can combine to form compounds.

Sometimes you place objects into groups using an established system. Other times you create a system by observing a variety of objects and

identifying their properties. For example, you could group household cleaners into those that are abrasive and those that are not. Or you could categorize cleaners as toxic or non-toxic. Ammonia is toxic, whereas vinegar is not.

Using Tables and Graphs

Scientists represent and organize data in tables and graphs as part of experiments and other activities. Organizing data in tables and graphs makes it easier to see patterns in data. Scientists analyze and interpret data tables and graphs to determine the relationship of one variable to another and to make predictions based on the data.

Space-filling
model

Electron dot
model

Using Models

Some cities refuse to approve new tall buildings if they would cast shadows on existing parks. As architects plan buildings in such locations, they use models to show where a proposed building's shadow will fall at any time of day at any season of the year. A **model** is a mental or physical representation of an object, process, or event. In science, models are usually made to help people understand natural objects and the processes that affect these objects.

Models can be varied. Mental models, such as mathematical equations, can represent some kinds of ideas or processes. For example, the equation for the surface area of a sphere can model the surface of Earth, enabling scientists to determine its size. Models can be two-dimensional (flat) or three-dimensional (having depth). In chemistry, for example, there are several ways to model the arrangement of atoms in a molecule. Two models for a water molecule are shown above. The electron dot model is two-dimensional. It has the advantage of clearly showing how electrons are shared among atoms in the molecule. The space-filling model cannot show the number of electrons inside the atoms or between atoms, but it does show the arrangement of atoms in space.

Experimental Methods

A science experiment is a procedure designed so that there is only one logical explanation for the results. Some types of experiments are fairly simple to design. Others may require ingenious problem solving.

Posing Questions

As a gardener harvested corn in her vegetable garden, she noticed that on one side of the garden the plants produced very few ears of corn. The gardener wondered, *Why didn't the plants on one side of the garden produce as much corn?*

An experiment may begin when someone like the gardener asks a specific question or wants to solve a particular problem. Sometimes the original question leads directly to an experiment, but often researchers need to restate the problem before they can design an appropriate experiment. The gardener's question about the corn, for example, is too broad to be tested by an experiment, since there are so many possible different answers. To narrow the topic, the gardener might think about several related questions: *Were the seeds the same on both sides of the garden? Was the sunlight the same? Is there something different about the soil?*

Formulating Hypotheses

In science, a question about an event is answered by developing a possible explanation called a **hypothesis**. The hypothesis may be developed after long thought and research or come to a scientist "in a flash." To be useful, a hypothesis must lead to predictions that can be tested.

In this case, the gardener decided to focus on the quality of the soil on each side of her garden. She did some tests and discovered that the soil had a lower pH on the side where the plants did not produce well. That led her to propose this hypothesis: *If the pH of the soil is too low, the plants will produce less corn.* The next step is to make a prediction based on the hypothesis, for example, *If the pH of the soil is increased using lime, the plants will yield more corn.* Notice that the prediction suggests the basic idea for an experiment.

Designing Experiments

A carefully designed experiment can test a prediction in a reliable way, ruling out other possible explanations. As scientists plan their experimental procedures, they pay particular attention to the variables that must be controlled and the procedures that must be defined.

The gardener decided to study three groups of plants:

Group 1—20 plants on the side of the garden with a low pH;

Group 2—20 plants on the side of the garden with a low pH, but with lime added; and

Group 3—20 plants on the side of the garden with a high pH.

Controlling Variables

As researchers design an experiment, they identify the **variables**, factors that can change. Some common variables include mass, volume, time, temperature, light, and the presence or absence of specific materials. An experiment involves three categories of variables. The factor that scientists purposely change is called the **manipulated variable**. The factor that may change because of the manipulated variable and that scientists want to observe is called the **responding variable**. And the factors that scientists purposely keep the same are called the **controlled variables**. Controlling variables helps make researchers confident that the observed changes in the responding variable are due to changes in the manipulated variable.

For the gardener, the manipulated variable is the pH of the soil. The responding variable is the number of ears of corn produced by the plants. Among the variables that must be controlled are the amount of sunlight received each day, the time of year when seeds are planted, and the amount of water the plants receive.

Forming Operational Definitions

In an experiment, it is often necessary to define one or more variables explicitly so that any researcher could measure or control the variable in exactly the same way. An **operational definition** describes how a particular variable is to be measured or how a term is to be defined. In this context, the term *operational* means "describing what to do."

The gardener, for example, has to decide exactly how much lime to add to the soil. Can lime be added after the seeds are planted or only before planting? At what pH should no more lime be added to the soil? In this case, the gardener decided to add lime only before planting, and to add enough lime to make the pH equal in Groups 2 and 3.

Analyzing Data

The observations and measurements that are made in an experiment are called **data**. Scientists customarily record data in an orderly way. When an experiment is done, the researcher analyzes the data for trends or patterns, often by doing calculations or making graphs, to determine whether the results support the hypothesis.

For example, the gardener regularly measured and recorded data such as the soil moisture, daily sunlight, and pH of the soil. She found that the soil pH in Groups 2 and 3 started the same, but after two months the soil pH for Group 3 was a little higher

than the soil pH for Group 2.

After harvesting the corn, the gardener recorded the numbers of ears of corn produced by each plant. She totaled the number of ears for each group. Her results were the following.

Group 1: 67 ears of corn
Group 2: 102 ears of corn
Group 3: 126 ears of corn

The overall trend was clear: The gardener's prediction was correct.

Drawing Conclusions

Based on whether the results confirm or refute the hypothesis, researchers make a final statement that summarizes the experiment. That final statement is called the **conclusion**. For example, the gardener's conclusion was, *Adding lime to soil with a low pH will improve the production of corn plants.*

Communicating Results

When an experiment has been completed, one or more events may follow. Researchers may repeat the experiment to verify the results. They may publish the experiment so that others can evaluate and replicate their procedures. They may compare their conclusion with the discoveries made by other scientists. And they may raise new questions that lead to new experiments. For example, *Why does the pH level decrease over time when soil is treated with lime?*

Evaluating and Revising

Scientists must be flexible about the conclusions drawn from an experiment. Further research may help confirm the results of the experiment or make it necessary to revise the initial conclusions. For example, a new experiment may show that lime can be effective only when certain microbes are present in the soil. Scientists continuously evaluate and revise experiments based on the findings in new research.

Science Safety

Laboratory work can be exciting, but it can be dangerous if you don't follow safety rules. Ask your teacher to explain any rules you don't understand. Always pay attention to safety symbols and **CAUTION** statements.

General Safety Rules and First Aid

1. Read all directions for an experiment several times. Follow the directions exactly as they are written. If you are in doubt, ask your teacher for assistance.
2. Never perform unauthorized or unsupervised labs, or handle equipment without specific permission.
3. When you design an experiment, do not start until your teacher has approved your plan.
4. If a lab includes physical activity, use caution to avoid injuring yourself or others. Tell your teacher if there is a reason that you should not participate.
5. Never eat, drink, or bring food into the laboratory.
6. Report all accidents to your teacher immediately.
7. Learn the correct ways to deal with a burn, a cut, and acid splashed in your eyes or on your skin.
8. Be aware of the location of the first-aid kit. Your teacher should administer any required first aid.
9. Report any fire to your teacher immediately. Find out the location of the fire extinguisher, the fire alarm, and the phone where emergency numbers are listed.

Dress Code

10. Always wear safety goggles to protect your eyes when working in the lab. Avoid wearing contact lenses. If you must wear contact lenses, ask your teacher what precautions you should take.
11. Wear a laboratory apron to protect your skin and clothing from harmful chemicals or hot materials.
12. Wear disposable plastic gloves to protect yourself from contact with chemicals that can be harmful. Keep your hands away from your face. Dispose of gloves according to your teacher's instructions.
13. Tie back long hair and loose clothing. Remove any jewelry that could contact chemicals or flames.

Heating and Fire Safety

14. Hot plates, hot water, and hot glassware can cause burns. Never touch hot objects with your bare hands. Use an oven mitt or other hand protection.
15. Use a clamp or tongs to hold hot objects. Test an object by first holding the back of your hand near it. If you feel heat on the back of your hand, the object may be too hot to handle.
16. Tie back long hair and loose clothing, and put on safety goggles before using a burner. Follow instructions from your teacher for lighting and extinguishing burners. If the flame leaps out of a burner as you are lighting it, turn the gas off. Never leave a flame unattended or reach across a flame. Make sure your work area is not cluttered with materials.
17. If flammable materials are present, make sure there are no flames, sparks, or exposed sources of heat.
18. Never heat a chemical without your teacher's permission. Chemicals that are harmless when cool can be dangerous when heated. When heating a test tube, point the opening away from you and others in case the contents splash or boil out of the test tube.
19. Never heat a closed container. Expanding hot gases may cause the container to explode.

Using Electricity Safely

20. To avoid an electric shock, never use electrical equipment near water, or when the equipment or your hands are wet. Use ground fault circuit interrupter (GFCI) outlets if you or your equipment may come into contact with moisture.
21. Use only sockets that accept a three-prong plug. Never use two-prong extension cords or adapters. When removing an electrical plug from a socket or extension cord, grasp the plug, not the cord.
22. Disconnect equipment that is not in use. Be sure cords are untangled and cannot trip anyone.
23. Do not use damaged electrical equipment. Look for dangerous conditions such as bare wires or frayed cords. Report damaged equipment immediately.

Using Glassware Safely

24. Handle fragile glassware, such as thermometers, test tubes, and beakers, with care. Do not touch broken glass. Notify your teacher if glassware breaks. Never use chipped or cracked glassware.
25. Never force glass tubing into a stopper. Your teacher will demonstrate the proper methods.
26. Never heat glassware that is not thoroughly dry. Use a wire screen to protect glassware from flames.
27. Hot glassware may not appear hot. Never pick up glassware without first checking to see if it is hot.
28. Never eat or drink from laboratory glassware.

Using Chemicals Safely

29. Do not let any corrosive or poisonous chemicals get on your skin or clothing, or in your eyes. When working with poisonous or irritating vapors, work in a well-ventilated area and wash your hands thoroughly after completing the activity.

30. Never test for an odor unless instructed by your teacher. Avoid inhaling a vapor directly. Use a wafting motion to direct vapor toward your nose.

31. Never mix chemicals "for the fun of it." You might produce a dangerous, possibly explosive substance.

32. Never touch, taste, or smell a chemical that you do not know for certain to be harmless.

33. Use only those chemicals listed in an investigation. Keep the lids on the containers when chemicals are not being used. To avoid contamination, never return chemicals to their original containers.

34. Take extreme care not to spill any chemicals. If a spill occurs, immediately ask your teacher about the proper cleanup procedure. Dispose of all chemicals as instructed by your teacher.

35. Be careful when working with acids or bases. Pour these chemicals over the sink, not over your workbench. If an acid or base gets on your skin or clothing, rinse it off with plenty of cold water. Immediately notify your teacher about an acid or base spill.

36. When diluting an acid, pour the acid into water. Never pour water into the acid.

Using Sharp Instruments

37. Use sharp instruments only as directed. Scissors, scalpels, pins, and knives are sharp and can cut or puncture your skin. Always direct sharp edges and points away from yourself and others.

38. Notify your teacher immediately if you cut yourself when in the laboratory.

End-of-Experiment Rules

39. All chemicals and any other materials used in the laboratory must be disposed of safely. Follow your teacher's instructions.

40. Clean up your work area and return all equipment to its proper place. Thoroughly clean glassware before putting it away.

41. Wash your hands thoroughly with soap, or detergent, and warm water. Lather both sides of your hands and between your fingers. Rinse well.

42. Check that all burners are off and the gas supply for the burners is turned off.

Safety Symbols

 General Safety Awareness
Follow all safety instructions.

 Physical Safety
Use caution in physical activities.

 Safety Goggles
Always wear goggles in the laboratory.

 Lab Apron
Always wear a lab apron in the laboratory.

 Plastic Gloves
Protect your hands from unsafe chemicals.

 Heating
Be careful using sources of heat.

 Heat-Resistant Gloves
Do not touch hot objects with bare hands.

 Flames
Work carefully around open flames.

 No Flames
Flammable materials may be present.

 Electric Shock
Take precautions to avoid electric shock.

 Fragile Glassware
Handle glassware carefully.

 Corrosive Chemical
Work carefully with corrosive chemicals.

 Poison
Avoid contact with poisonous chemicals.

 Fumes
Avoid inhaling dangerous vapors.

 Sharp Object
Use caution with sharp or pointed tools.

 Disposal
Follow instructions for disposal.

 Hand Washing
Wash your hands before leaving the lab.

Reading and Study Skills

At the beginning of each section, you will find a reading strategy to help you study. Each strategy uses a graphic organizer to help you stay organized. The following strategies and graphic organizers are used throughout the text.

Reading Strategies

Using Prior Knowledge

This strategy helps you think about your own experience before you read a section. Research has shown that you learn new material better if you can relate it to something you already know.

Previewing

Previewing a lesson can give you a sense of how the textbook is organized and what lies ahead. One technique is to look at the section topics (in green and blue type). You also can preview by reading captions. Sometimes previewing helps you simply because you find out a topic isn't as hard as you thought it might be.

Predicting

You can preview a section and then make a prediction. For example, you might predict the meaning of an important concept. Then, as you read, check to see if your prediction was correct. Often you find out that you knew more about a topic than you realized.

Building Vocabulary

Start building new vocabulary by previewing a section and listing boldface terms you don't recognize. Then look for each term as you read. Writing a sentence with a term, and defining a term in your own words are two techniques that will help you remember definitions.

Identifying the Main Idea

The key symbols next to boldface sentences identify the main ideas in a section. You can use topic sentences to find the main idea in a paragraph. Often, a topic sentence is the first or second sentence in a paragraph.

Identifying Cause and Effect

Cause-and-effect relationships are very important in science. A flowchart will help you identify cause-and-effect relationships as you read about a process.

Comparing and Contrasting

Comparing and contrasting can help you understand how concepts are related. Comparing is identifying both similarities and differences, while contrasting focuses on the differences. Compare-and-contrast tables and Venn diagrams work best with this strategy.

Sequencing

When you sequence events, it helps you to visualize the steps in a process and to remember the order in which they occur. Sequences often involve cause-and-effect relationships. Use flowcharts for linear sequences and cycle diagrams for repeating sequences.

Relating Text and Figures

You can use diagrams and photographs to focus on the essential concepts in a section. Then find text that extends the information in the figures. You can also reinforce concepts by comparing different figures.

Summarizing

Summarizing requires you to identify key ideas and state them briefly in your own words. You will remember the content of an entire section better even if you summarize only a portion of the section.

Outlining

You can quickly organize an outline by writing down the green and blue headings in a section. Then add phrases or sentences from the boldface sentences to expand the outline with the most important concepts.

Monitoring Your Understanding

You can evaluate your progress with graphic organizers such as a Know-Write-Learn (KWL) table. To make a KWL table, construct a table with three columns, labeled K, W, and L. Before you read, write what you already know in the first column (K). In the middle column, write what you want to learn (W). After you read, write what you learned (L).

Graphic Organizers

Concept Maps and Web Diagrams

A **concept map** is a diagram that contains concept words in ovals and connects the ovals with linking words. Often the most general concept is placed at the top of the map. The content of the other ovals becomes more specific as you move away from the main concept. Linking words are written on a line between two ovals.

A **web diagram** is a type of concept map that shows how several ideas relate to one central idea. Each subtopic may also link to subtopics, creating the visual effect of a spider web. Linking words are usually not included.

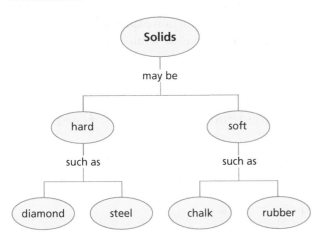

Compare-and-Contrast Tables

A **compare-and-contrast table** is a way of showing the similarities and differences between two or more objects or processes. The table provides an organized framework for making comparisons based on specific characteristics.

Compare-and-Contrast Table		
Contents	**Book**	**CD-ROM**
Paper pages	Yes	No
Photographs	Yes	Yes
Videos	No	Yes

The items to be compared are usually column headings across the top of the table. Characteristics for comparison are listed in the first column. You complete the table by filling in information for each item.

Venn Diagrams

A **Venn diagram** consists of two or more ovals that overlap. Each oval represents a particular object or idea. Unique characteristics are shown in the part of each oval that does not overlap. Shared characteristics are shown in the area of overlap.

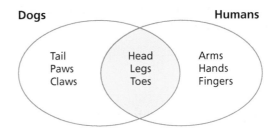

Flowcharts

A **flowchart** is used to represent the order in which a set of events occurs. Each step in the sequence is described in a box. Each box is linked to the next box with an arrow. The flowchart shows a sequence from beginning to end.

Cycle Diagrams

A **cycle diagram** shows boxes representing a cyclical sequence of events. As in a flowchart, boxes are linked with arrows, but the sequence does not have a beginning or end. The boxes are usually arranged in a clockwise circle.

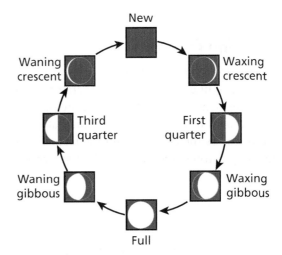

Throughout your study of science, you will often need to solve math problems. This appendix is designed to help you quickly review the basic math skills you will use most often.

Fractions

Adding and Subtracting Fractions

To add or subtract fractions that have the same denominator, add or subtract the numerators, and then write the sum or difference over the denominator. Express the answer in lowest terms.

Examples

$$\frac{3}{10} + \frac{1}{10} = \frac{3+1}{10} = \frac{4}{10} = \frac{2}{5}$$

$$\frac{5}{7} - \frac{2}{7} = \frac{5-2}{7} = \frac{3}{7}$$

To add or subtract fractions with different denominators, find the least common denominator. Write an equivalent fraction for each fraction using the least common denominator. Then add or subtract the numerators. Write the sum or difference over the least common denominator and express the answer in lowest terms.

Examples

$$\frac{1}{3} + \frac{3}{5} = \frac{5}{15} + \frac{9}{15} = \frac{5+9}{15} = \frac{14}{15}$$

$$\frac{7}{8} - \frac{1}{4} = \frac{7}{8} - \frac{2}{8} = \frac{7-2}{8} = \frac{5}{8}$$

Multiplying Fractions

When multiplying two fractions, multiply the numerators to find the product's numerator. Then multiply the denominators to find the product's denominator. It helps to divide any numerator or denominator by the greatest common factor before multiplying. Express the answer in lowest terms.

Examples

$$\frac{3}{5} \times \frac{2}{7} = \frac{3 \times 2}{5 \times 7} = \frac{6}{35}$$

$$\frac{4}{14} \times \frac{6}{9} = \frac{2 \times 2}{7 \times 2} \times \frac{2 \times 3}{3 \times 3} = \frac{2 \times 2}{7 \times 3} = \frac{4}{21}$$

Dividing Fractions

To divide one fraction by another, invert and multiply. Express the answer in lowest terms.

Examples

$$\frac{2}{5} \div \frac{3}{4} = \frac{2}{5} \times \frac{4}{3} = \frac{2 \times 4}{5 \times 3} = \frac{8}{15}$$

$$\frac{9}{16} \div \frac{5}{8} = \frac{9}{16} \times \frac{8}{5} = \frac{9 \times 1}{2 \times 5} = \frac{9}{10}$$

Ratios and Proportions

A ratio compares two numbers or quantities. A ratio is often written as a fraction expressed in lowest terms. A ratio also may be written with a colon.

Examples

The ratio of 3 to 4 is written as 3 to 4, $\frac{3}{4}$, or 3 : 4.

The ratio of 10 to 5 is written as $\frac{10}{5} = \frac{2}{1}$, or 2 : 1.

A proportion is a mathematical sentence that states that two ratios are equivalent. To write a proportion, place an equal sign between the two equivalent ratios.

Examples

The ratio of 6 to 9 is the same as the ratio of 8 to 12.

$$\frac{6}{9} = \frac{8}{12}$$

The ratio of 2 to 4 is the same as the ratio of 7 to 14.

$$\frac{2}{4} = \frac{7}{14}$$

You can set up a proportion to determine an unknown quantity. Use x to represent the unknown. To find the value of x, cross multiply and then divide both sides of the equation by the number that comes before x.

Example

Two out of five students have blue notebooks. If this same ratio exists in a class of twenty students, how many students in the class have blue notebooks?

$$\frac{2}{5} = \frac{x}{20}$$ ← **Cross multiply.**

$$2 \times 20 = 5x$$ ← **Divide.**

$$8 = x$$

Percents and Decimals

To convert a percent to a decimal value, write the number without the percent sign and move the decimal point two places to the left. Add a zero before the decimal point.

Examples

$38\% = 0.38$
$13.92\% = 0.1392$

You can convert a decimal value to a percent value by moving the decimal point two places to the right and adding the percent sign.

Examples

$0.46 = 46\%$
$0.8215 = 82.15\%$

Exponents

A base is a number that is used as a factor. An exponent is a number that tells how many times the base is to be used as a factor.

Example

$2^5 = 2 \times 2 \times 2 \times 2 \times 2 = 32$

A power is any number that can be expressed as a product in which all of the factors are the same. Any number raised to the zero power is 1. Any number raised to the first power is that number. The only exception is the number 0, which is zero regardless of the power it is raised to.

Exponents	
Powers of 2	**Powers of 10**
$2^2 = 4$	$10^2 = 100$
$2^1 = 2$	$10^1 = 10$
$2^0 = 1$	$10^0 = 1$
$2^{-1} = \frac{1}{2}$	$10^{-1} = \frac{1}{10}$
$2^{-2} = \frac{1}{4}$	$10^{-2} = \frac{1}{100}$

Multiplying Exponents

To multiply exponential expressions with the same base, add the exponents. The general expression for exponents with the same base is $x^a \times x^b = x^{a+b}$.

Example

$3^2 \times 3^4 = (3 \times 3) \times (3 \times 3 \times 3 \times 3) = 3^6 = 729$

To raise a power to a power, keep the base and multiply the exponents. The general expression is $(x^a)^b = x^{ab}$.

Example

$(3^2)^3 = (3^2) \times (3^2) \times (3^2) = 3^6 = 729$

To raise a product to a power, raise each factor to the power. The general expression is $(xy)^n = x^n y^n$.

Example

$(3 \times 9)^2 = 3^2 \times 9^2 = 9 \times 81 = 729$

Dividing Exponents

To divide exponential expressions with the same base, keep the base and subtract the exponents. The general expression is:

$$\frac{x^a}{x^b} = x^{a-b}$$

Example

$$\frac{5^6}{5^4} = 5^{6-4} = 5^2 = 25$$

When the exponent of the denominator is greater than the exponent of the numerator, the exponent of the result is negative. A negative exponent follows the general expression:

$$x^{-n} = \frac{1}{x^n}$$

Example

$$2^3 \div 2^5 = 2^{3-5} = 2^{-2} = \frac{1}{2^2} = \frac{1}{4}$$

Scientific Notation

Scientific notation is used to express very large numbers or very small numbers. To convert a large number to scientific notation, move the decimal point to the left until it is located to the right of the first nonzero number. The number of places that you move the decimal point becomes the positive exponent of 10.

Example

$$18,930,000 = 1.893 \times 10^7$$

To write a number less than 1 in scientific notation, move the decimal point to the right of the first nonzero number. Use the number of places you moved the decimal point as the negative exponent of 10.

Example

$$0.0027 = \frac{2.7}{10 \times 10 \times 10} = 2.7 \times 10^{-3}$$

Adding and Subtracting

To add or subtract numbers in scientific notation, the exponents must be the same. If they are different, rewrite one of the numbers to make the exponents the same. Then write the answer so that only one number is to the left of the decimal point.

Example

$$3.20 \times 10^3 + 5.1 \times 10^2$$
$$= 32.0 \times 10^2 + 5.1 \times 10^2$$
$$= 37.1 \times 10^2$$
$$= 3.71 \times 10^3$$

Multiplying and Dividing

To multiply or divide numbers in scientific notation, the exponents are added or subtracted.

Examples

$$(1.2 \times 10^3) \times (3.4 \times 10^4) = (4.1 \times 10^{3 + 4})$$
$$= 4.1 \times 10^7$$
$$(5.0 \times 10^9) \div (2.5 \times 10^6) = (2.0 \times 10^{9 - 6})$$
$$= 2.0 \times 10^3$$

Significant Figures

When measurements are combined in calculations, the uncertainty of each measurement must be correctly reflected in the final result. The digits that are accurate in the answer are called significant figures. When the result of a calculation has more significant figures than needed, the result must be rounded off. If the first digit after the last significant digit is less than 5, round down. If the first digit after the last significant digit is 5 or more, round up.

Examples

1577 rounded to three significant figures is 1580.
1574 rounded to three significant figures is 1570.
2.458462 rounded to three significant figures is 2.46.
2.458462 rounded to four significant figures is 2.458.

Adding and Subtracting

In addition and subtraction, the number of significant figures in the answer depends on the number with the largest uncertainty.

Example

$$\begin{array}{r} 25.34 \text{ g} \\ 152 \text{ g} \\ + \quad 4.009 \text{ g} \\ \hline 181 \text{ g} \end{array}$$

The measurement with the largest uncertainty is 152 g and it is measured to the nearest gram. Therefore, the answer is given to the nearest gram.

Multiplying and Dividing

In multiplication and division, the measurement with the smallest number of significant figures determines the number of significant figures in the answer.

Example

$$\text{Density} = \frac{\text{Mass}}{\text{Volume}}$$
$$= \frac{20.79 \text{ g}}{5.5 \text{ mL}}$$
$$= 3.8 \text{ g/mL}$$

Because 5.5 mL has only two significant figures, the answer must be rounded to two significant figures.

Formulas and Equations

An equation is a mathematical sentence that contains one or more variables and one or more mathematical operators (such as $+, -, \div, \times$, and $=$). An equation expresses a relationship between two or more quantities.

A formula is a special kind of equation. A formula such as $V = l \times w \times h$ states the relationship between unknown quantities represented by the variables V, l, w, and h. The formula means that volume (of a rectangular solid) equals length times width times height. Some formulas have numbers that do not vary, such as the formula for the perimeter of a square: $P = 4s$. In this formula, the number 4 is a constant.

To solve for a quantity in an equation or formula, substitute known values for the variables. Be sure to include units.

Example

An airplane travels in a straight line at a speed of 600 km/h. How far does it fly in 3.5 hours?

Write the formula that relates speed, distance, and time.

$$\text{Speed} = \frac{\text{Distance}}{\text{Time}}$$
$$v = \frac{d}{t}$$

To solve for distance, multiply both sides of the equation by t.

$$v = \frac{d}{t}$$
$$v \times t = \frac{d}{t} \times t$$
$$v \times t = d$$

Substitute in the known values.

$$600 \text{ km/h} \times 3.5 \text{ h} = d$$
$$d = 2100 \text{ km}$$

Conversion Factors

Many problems involve converting measurements from one unit to another. You can convert units by using an equation that shows how units are related. For example,

1 in. $= 2.54$ cm relates inches and centimeters.

To write a conversion factor, divide both sides of the equation by 1 in.

$$\frac{1 \text{ in.}}{1 \text{ in.}} = \frac{2.54 \text{ cm}}{1 \text{ in.}}$$
$$1 = 2.54 \text{ cm/in.}$$

Because the conversion factor is equal to 1, you can multiply one side of an equation by it and preserve equality. You can make a second conversion factor by dividing both sides of the equation by 2.54 cm.

$$\frac{1 \text{ in.}}{2.54 \text{ cm}} = \frac{2.54 \text{ cm}}{2.54 \text{ cm}} = 1$$

One conversion factor converts inches to centimeters and the other converts centimeters to inches. Choose the conversion factor that cancels out the unit that you have a measurement for.

Example

Convert 25 inches to centimeters. Use d to represent the unknown number of centimeters.

$$d = 25 \text{ in.} \times \frac{2.54 \text{ cm}}{1 \text{ in.}}$$
$$= 64 \text{ cm}$$

Some conversions are more complicated and require multiple steps.

Example

Convert 23°F to a Celsius temperature.

The conversion formula is
$$°F = \left(\frac{9}{5} \times °C\right) + 32°F$$

Substitute in 23°F:

$$23°F = \left(\frac{9}{5} \times °C\right) + 32°F$$

$$23°F - 32°F = \frac{9}{5} \times °C$$

$$-9°F = \frac{9}{5} \times °C$$

$$-9°F \times \frac{5}{9} = -5°C$$

Data Tables

Data tables help to organize data and make it easier to see patterns in data. If you plan data tables before doing an experiment, they will help you record observations in an orderly fashion.

The data table below shows United States immigration data for the year 2001. Always include units of measurement so people can understand the data.

Immigration to the United States, 2001	
Place of Origin	Number of Legal Immigrants
Africa	53,948
Asia	349,776
Europe	175,371
North America	407,888
South America	68,888

Bar Graphs

To make a bar graph, begin by placing category labels along the bottom axis. Add an overall label for the axis Place of Origin. Decide on a scale for the vertical axis. An appropriate scale for the data in the table is 0 to 500,000. Label the vertical axis Number of People. For each continent, draw a bar whose height corresponds to the number of immigrants. You will need to round off the values. For example, the bar for Africa should correspond to 54,000 people. Add a graph title to make it clear what the graph shows.

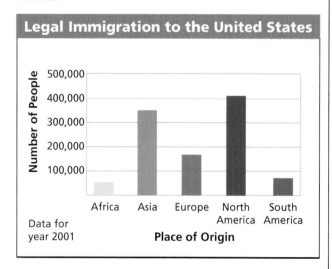

Circle Graphs

Use the total number to calculate percentages. For example, the percentage of immigrants from Africa in 2001 was $53,948 \div 1,061,984 = 0.051 \approx 5\%$. Multiply each percent by 360° to find the central angle of each wedge. For Africa, the central angle is 18°. Use a protractor to draw each central angle. Color and label the wedges and finish your graph with a title.

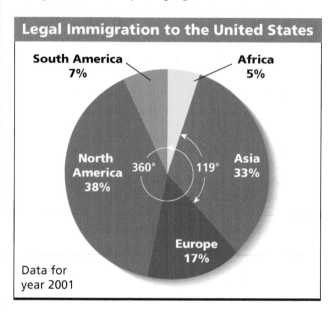

Line Graphs

The slope of a straight-line graph equals the "rise over the run." The rise is the change in the y values and the run is the change in the x values. Using points A and B on the graph below gives

$$\text{Slope} = \frac{\text{Rise}}{\text{Run}} = \frac{5-3}{9-3} = \frac{2}{6} = 0.33$$

APPENDIX A SI Units

SI *(Système International d'Unités)* is a revised version of the metric system, which was originally developed in France in 1791. SI units of measurement are used by scientists throughout the world. The system is based on multiples of ten. Each unit is ten times larger or ten times smaller than the next unit. The most commonly used SI units are given below.

You can use conversion factors to convert between SI and non-SI units. Try the following conversions. How tall are you in meters? What is your weight in newtons? What is your normal body temperature in degrees Celsius?

Commonly Used Metric Units

Length	The distance from one point to another
meter (m)	A meter is slightly longer than a yard. 1 meter = 1000 millimeters (mm) 1 meter = 100 centimeters (cm) 1000 meters = 1 kilometer (km)

Volume	The amount of space an object takes up
liter (L)	A liter is slightly more than a quart. 1 liter = 1000 milliliters (mL)

Mass	The amount of matter in an object
gram (g)	A gram has a mass equal to about one paper clip. 1000 grams = 1 kilogram (kg)

Temperature	The measure of hotness or coldness
degrees	0°C = freezing point of water at sea level
Celsius (°C)	100°C = boiling point of water at sea level

Metric–Customary Equivalents

2.54 centimeters (cm) = 1 inch (in.)
1 meter (m) = 39.37 inches (in.)
1 kilometer (km) = 0.62 miles (mi)
1 liter (L) = 1.06 quarts (qt)
250 milliliters (mL) = 1 cup (c)
9.8 newtons (N) = 2.2 pounds (lb)
°C = 5/9 × (°F – 32)

10 mm = 1 cm

Metric ruler

Riders   Beams

Triple-Beam Balance

Boiling point of water at sea level

Human body temperature

Freezing point of water

Thermometer

Graduated cylinder

Using a Laboratory Balance

The laboratory balance is an important tool in scientific investigations. You can use a balance to determine the masses of materials that you study or experiment with in the laboratory.

Different kinds of balances are used in the laboratory. One kind of balance is the triple-beam balance. The balance that you may use in your science class is probably similar to the balance illustrated. To use the balance properly, you should learn the name, location, and function of each part of the balance you are using.

The Triple-Beam Balance

The triple-beam balance is a single-pan balance with three beams The back, or 100-gram, beam is divided into ten units of 10 grams. The middle, or 500-gram, beam is divided into five units of 100 grams. The front, or 10-gram, beam is divided into ten major units, each of which is 1 gram. Each 1-gram unit is further divided into units of 0.1 gram. What is the largest mass you could measure with a triple-beam balance?

The following procedure can be used to find the mass of an object with a triple-beam balance.

1. When no object is on the pan, and the riders are at zero, make sure the pointer is at zero. If it is not, use the adjustment screw to zero the balance.
2. Place the object on the pan.
3. Move the rider on the middle beam notch by notch until the horizontal pointer drops below zero. Move the rider back one notch.
4. Move the rider on the back beam notch by notch until the pointer again drops below zero. Move the rider back one notch.
5. Slowly slide the rider along the front beam until the pointer stops at zero. The mass of the object is the sum of the readings on the three beams.

Pointer
(at zero)

Pan

Riders

Beams

Adjustment
screw

TRIPLE BEAM BALANCE
2610g   5 lb 2 oz

Triple-Beam Balance

The Chemical Elements

Element	Symbol	Atomic Number	Atomic Mass†	Element	Symbol	Atomic Number	Atomic Mass†
Actinium	Ac	89	(277)	Neodymium	Nd	60	144.24
Aluminum	Al	13	26.982	Neon	Ne	10	20.179
Americium	Am	95	(243)	Neptunium	Np	93	(237)
Antimony	Sb	51	121.75	Nickel	Ni	28	58.71
Argon	Ar	18	39.948	Niobium	Nb	41	92.906
Arsenic	As	33	74.922	Nitrogen	N	7	14.007
Astatine	At	85	(210)	Nobelium	No	102	(259)
Barium	Ba	56	137.33	Osmium	Os	76	190.2
Berkelium	Bk	97	(247)	Oxygen	O	8	15.999
Beryllium	Be	4	9.0122	Palladium	Pd	46	106.4
Bismuth	Bi	83	208.98	Phosphorus	P	15	30.974
Bohrium	Bh	107	(264)	Platinum	Pt	78	195.09
Boron	B	5	10.81	Plutonium	Pu	94	(244)
Bromine	Br	35	79.904	Polonium	Po	84	(209)
Cadmium	Cd	48	112.41	Potassium	K	19	39.098
Calcium	Ca	20	40.08	Praseodymium	Pr	59	140.91
Californium	Cf	98	(251)	Promethium	Pm	61	(145)
Carbon	C	6	12.011	Protactinium	Pa	91	231.04
Cerium	Ce	58	140.12	Radium	Ra	88	(226)
Cesium	Cs	55	132.91	Radon	Rn	86	(222)
Chlorine	Cl	17	35.453	Rhenium	Re	75	186.21
Chromium	Cr	24	51.996	Rhodium	Rh	45	102.91
Cobalt	Co	27	58.933	Roentgenium	Rg	111	(272)
Copernicium	Cn	112	(277)	Rubidium	Rb	37	85.468
Copper	Cu	29	63.546	Ruthenium	Ru	44	101.07
Curium	Cm	96	(247)	Rutherfordium	Rf	104	(261)
Darmstadtium	Ds	110	(269)	Samarium	Sm	62	150.4
Dubnium	Db	105	(262)	Scandium	Sc	21	44.956
Dysprosium	Dy	66	162.50	Seaborgium	Sg	106	(263)
Einsteinium	Es	99	(252)	Selenium	Se	34	78.96
Erbium	Er	68	167.26	Silicon	Si	14	28.086
Europium	Eu	63	151.96	Silver	Ag	47	107.87
Fermium	Fm	100	(257)	Sodium	Na	11	22.990
Fluorine	F	9	18.998	Strontium	Sr	38	87.62
Francium	Fr	87	(223)	Sulfur	S	16	32.06
Gadolinium	Gd	64	157.25	Tantalum	Ta	73	180.95
Gallium	Ga	31	69.72	Technetium	Tc	43	(98)
Germanium	Ge	32	72.59	Tellurium	Te	52	127.60
Gold	Au	79	196.97	Terbium	Tb	65	158.93
Hafnium	Hf	72	178.49	Thallium	Tl	81	204.37
Hassium	Hs	108	(265)	Thorium	Th	90	232.04
Helium	He	2	4.0026	Thulium	Tm	69	168.93
Holmium	Ho	67	164.93	Tin	Sn	50	118.69
Hydrogen	H	1	1.0079	Titanium	Ti	22	47.90
Indium	In	49	114.82	Tungsten	W	74	183.85
Iodine	I	53	126.90	Ununhexium	Uuh	116	(293)
Iridium	Ir	77	192.22	Ununoctium	*Uuo	117	(299)
Iron	Fe	26	55.847	Ununpentium	*Uup	115	(288)
Krypton	Kr	36	83.80	Ununquadium	*Uuq	114	(289)
Lanthanum	La	57	138.91	Ununtrium	*Uuz	113	(284)
Lawrencium	Lr	103	(262)	Uranium	U	92	238.03
Lead	Pb	82	207.2	Vanadium	V	23	50.941
Lithium	Li	3	6.941	Xenon	Xe	54	131.30
Lutetium	Lu	71	174.97	Ytterbium	Yb	70	173.04
Magnesium	Mg	12	24.305	Yttrium	Y	39	88.906
Manganese	Mn	25	54.938	Zinc	Zn	30	65.38
Meitnerium	Mt	109	(268)	Zirconium	Zr	40	91.22
Mendelevium	Md	101	(258)				
Mercury	Hg	80	200.59				
Molybdenum	Mo	42	95.94				

† Number in parentheses gives the mass number of the most stable isotope.

* Name not officially assigned.

United States Physical Map

KEY

- ▪ Capital city
- ◉ State capital city
- ○ Major city
- —— International border
- —— State border

Elevation

Meters	Feet
3,960	13,000
1,980	6,500
480	1,600
200	650
Sea level	Sea level
–200	–650

Weather Map

This weather map shows data collected from many weather stations.
Below the map is an explanation of what the symbols mean.

Weather Map

Explanation of Fronts

Cold Front
Boundary between a cold air mass and a warm air mass. Brings brief storms and cooler weather.

Warm Front
Boundary between a warm air mass and a cold air mass. Usually accompanied by precipitation.

Stationary Front
Boundary between warm and cold air masses when no movement occurs. Long periods of precipitation.

Occluded Front
Boundary on which a warm front has been overtaken by a cold front. Brings precipitation.

Weather	Symbol
Drizzle	⌐
Fog	≡
Hail	△
Haze	∞
Rain	●
Shower	▽
Sleet	◬
Smoke	⌇
Snow	✳
Thunderstorm	⌐
Hurricane	↜

Wind Speed (mph)	Symbol
1–2	
3–8	
9–14	
15–20	
21–25	
26–31	
32–37	
38–43	
44–49	
50–54	
55–60	
61–66	
67–71	
72–77	

Cloud Cover (%)	Symbol
0	○
10	◑
20–30	◔
40	◕
50	◖
60	◑
70–80	◕
90	◑
100	●

How Symbols Are Used on a Weather Map

Amount of cloud cover (100%)

Atmospheric pressure (millibars)

Temperature (°F)

38 ● 1018

Wind direction (from the southwest)

Wind speed (21–25 mph)

Relative Humidity Chart

To find the relative humidity, measure the wet-bulb and dry-bulb temperatures with a sling psychrometer. Find the dry-bulb reading in the left column and the difference between readings at the top of the table. The number where these readings intersect is the relative humidity in percent.

Relative Humidity (percent)														
Dry-Bulb Reading (8C)	Difference Between Wet-Bulb and Dry-Bulb Readings (8C)													
	1	2	3	4	5	6	7	8	9	10	11	12	13	14
5	86	72	58	45	33	20	7							
6	86	73	60	48	35	24	11							
7	87	74	62	50	38	26	15							
8	87	75	63	51	40	29	19	8						
9	88	76	64	53	42	32	22	12						
10	88	77	66	55	44	34	24	15	6					
11	89	78	67	56	46	36	27	18	9					
12	89	78	68	58	48	39	29	21	12					
13	89	79	69	59	50	41	32	23	15	7				
14	90	79	70	60	51	42	34	26	18	10				
15	90	80	71	61	53	44	36	27	20	13	6			
16	90	81	71	63	54	46	38	30	23	15	8			
17	90	81	72	64	55	47	40	32	25	18	11			
18	91	82	73	65	57	49	41	34	27	20	14	7		
19	91	82	74	65	58	50	43	36	29	22	16	10		
20	91	83	74	66	59	51	44	37	31	24	18	12	6	
21	91	83	75	67	60	53	46	39	32	26	20	14	9	
22	92	83	76	68	61	54	47	40	34	28	22	17	11	6
23	92	84	76	69	62	55	48	42	36	30	24	19	13	8
24	92	84	77	69	62	56	49	43	37	31	26	20	15	10
25	92	84	77	70	63	57	50	44	39	33	28	22	17	12
26	92	85	78	71	64	58	51	46	40	34	29	24	19	14
27	92	85	78	71	65	58	52	47	41	36	31	26	21	16
28	93	85	78	72	65	59	53	48	42	37	32	27	22	18
29	93	86	79	72	66	60	54	49	43	38	33	28	24	19
30	93	86	79	73	67	61	55	50	44	39	35	30	25	21

Autumn Sky

To use this chart, hold it up in front of you and turn it so the direction you are facing is at the bottom of the chart. The chart works best at 35° N latitude, but it can be used at other latitudes. It works best at the following dates and times: September 1 at 10:00 P.M., October 1 at 8 P.M., and November 1 at 6 P.M.

Winter Sky

To use this chart, hold it up in front of you and turn it so the direction you are facing is at the bottom of the chart. The chart works best at 35° N latitude, but it can be used at other latitudes. It works best at the following dates and times: December 1 at 10:00 P.M., January 1 at 8 P.M., and February 1 at 6 P.M.

Spring Sky

To use this chart, hold it up in front of you and turn it so the direction you are facing is at the bottom of the chart. The chart works best at 35° N latitude, but it can be used at other latitudes. It works best at the following dates and times: March 1 at 10:00 P.M. and April 1 at 8 P.M.

Summer Sky

To use this chart, hold it up in front of you and turn it so the direction you are facing is at the bottom of the chart. The chart works best at 35° N latitude, but it can be used at other latitudes. It works best at the following dates and times: May 15 at 11:00 P.M. and June 15 at 9 P.M.

Dew Point Chart

Dew-point temperature (°C)																						
Dry bulb (°C)	(Dry-Bulb Temperature Minus Wet-Bulb Temperature ī Depression of the Wet Bulb)																					
	1	2	3	4	5	6	7	8	9	10	11	12	13	14	15	16	17	18	19	20	21	22
−20	−33																					
−18	−28																					
−16	−24																					
−14	−21	−36																				
−12	−18	−28																				
−10	−14	−22																				
−8	−12	−18	−29																			
−6	−10	−14	−22																			
−4	−7	−12	−17	−29																		
−2	−5	−8	−13	−20																		
0	−3	−6	−9	−15	−24																	
2	−1	−3	−6	−11	−17																	
4	1	−1	−4	−7	−11	−19																
6	4	1	−1	−4	−7	−13	−21															
8	6	3	1	2	−5	−9	−14															
10	8	6	4	1	−2	−5	−9	−14	−18													
12	10	8	6	4	1	−2	−5	−9	−16													
14	12	11	9	6	4	1	−2	−5	−10	−17												
16	14	13	11	9	7	4	1	−1	−6	−10	−17											
18	16	15	13	11	9	7	4	2	−2	5	10	−19										
20	19	17	15	14	12	10	7	4	2	−2	−5	−10	−19									
22	21	19	17	16	74	12	10	8	5	3	−1	−5	−10	−19								
24	23	21	20	18	16	14	12	10	8	6	2	−1	−5	−10	−18							
26	25	23	22	20	18	17	15	13	11	9	6	3	0	−4	−9	−18						
28	27	25	24	22	27	19	17	16	14	11	9	7	4	1	−3	−9	16					
30	29	27	26	24	23	21	19	18	16	14	12	70	8	5	1	−2	−8	−15				
32	31	29	28	27	25	24	22	21	19	17	15	13	11	8	5	2	−2	−7	−14			
34	33	31	30	29	27	26	24	23	21	20	18	16	14	12	9	6	3	−1	−5	−12	−29	
36	35	33	32	31	29	28	27	25	24	22	20	19	17	15	13	10	7	4	0	−4	−10	
38	37	35	34	33	32	30	29	28	26	25	23	21	19	17	15	13	11	8	5	1	−3	9
40	39	37	36	35	34	32	31	30	28	27	25	24	22	20	18	16	14	12	9	6	2	−2

Dry-Bulb (Air) Temperature

Dew-Point Values

World Soils

The map on the next page shows the generalized pattern of global soil orders according to the Comprehensive Soil Classification System (CSCS). It should be examined in conjunction with the table below, which briefly describes each of the soil orders depicted on the map. To avoid subjective decisions as to classification (a problem that plagued earlier systems), the CSCS defined its classes strictly in terms of soil characterisitics. That is, it is based on features that can be observed or inferred.

The CSCS uses a hierarchy of six categories, or levels. The system recognizes 10 major global orders that can be further subdivided into suborders, great groups, subgroups, families, and series. Note, however, that on the scale of a world map, only the largest units (soil orders) can be shown and then only in an extremely generalized way. Although the distribution pattern of major soil orders is more complex than can be shown, the major distinguishing regional properties of world soils are depicted.

World Soil Orders

Entisols	Youngest soils on the Earth. Just beginning to develop in response to the weathering phenomena in the environment. Do not display natural horizons. Found in all climates. They weather slowly over thousands of years; consequently, volcanic ash deposits or sand deposits form the basis for entisols.
Vertisols	Soils containing large amounts of clay, which shrink upon drying and swell with the addition of water. Found in subhumid to arid climates, provided that adequate supplies of water are available to saturate the soil after periods of drought. Soil expansion and contraction exert stresses on human structures.
Inceptisols	Young soils that reveal developmental characteristics (horizons) in response to climate and vegetation. Exist from the Arctic to the tropics on young land surfaces. Common in alpine areas, on river floodplains, in stables and dune areas, and in areas once glaciated.
Aridsols	Soils that develop in dry places, such as the desert, where water—precipitation and groundwater—is insufficient to remove soluble minerals. Frequently irrigated for intensive agricultural production, although salt accumulation poses a problem.
Mollisols	Dark, soft soils that have developed under grass vegetation, generally found in prairie areas. Soil fertility is excellent because potential evaporation generally exceeds precipitation. Also found in hardwood forests with significant earthworm activity. Climatic range is boreal or alpine to tropical. Dry seasons are normal.
Spodosols	Soils found only in humid regions on sandy material. Range from the boreal coniferous forests into tropical forests. Beneath the dark upper horizon of weathered organic material lies a light-colored horizon of leached material, the distinctive property of this soil.
Alfisols	Mineral soils that form under boreal forests or broadleaf deciduous forests, rich in iron and aluminum. Clay particles accumulate in a subsurface layer in response to leaching in moist environments. Fertile, productive soils, because they are neither too wet nor too dry.
Ultisols	Soils that represent the products of long periods of weathering. Water percolating through the soil concentrates clay particles in the lower horizons (argillic horizons). Restricted to humid climates in the temperate regions and the tropics where the growing season is long. Abundant water and a long frost-free period contribute to extensive leaching, hence poorer soil quality.
Oxisols	Soils that occur on old land surfaces unless parent materials were strongly weathered before they were deposited. Generally found in the tropics and subtropical regions. Rich in iron and aluminum oxides, oxisols are heavily leached; hence are poor soils for agricultural activity. Few, if any, exist in the United States.
Histosols	Organic soils with little or no climatic implications. Can be found in any climate where organic debris can accumulate to form a bog soil. Dark, partially decomposed organic material commonly referred to as *peat*.

Source: Robert E. Norris et al., *Geography: An Introductory Perspective*, Columbus, Ohio: Merrill, 1982.

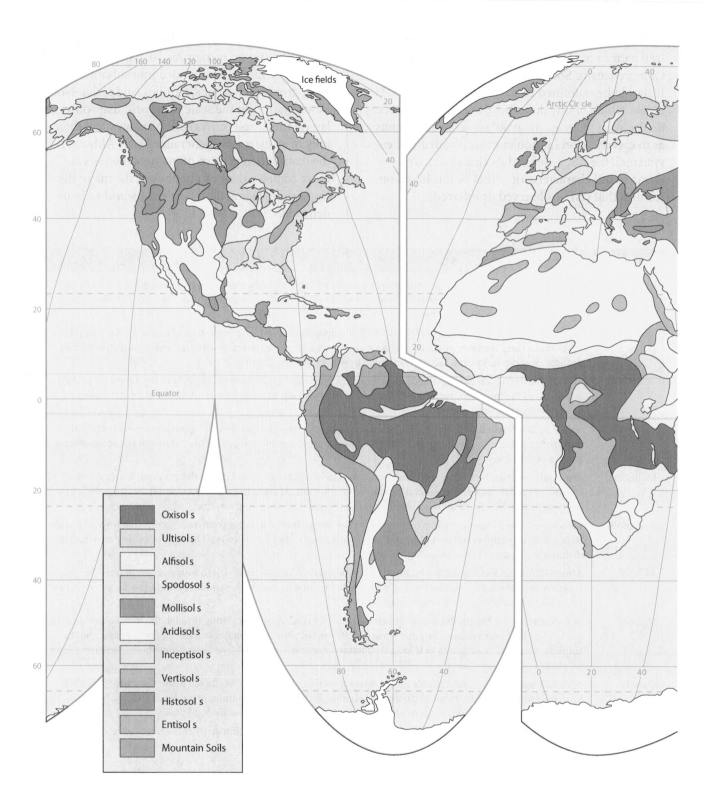

Soil distribution. The pattern of global soil orders is remarkably similar to the pattern of major climates. Soil classification is from the *Comprehensive Soil Classification System*.

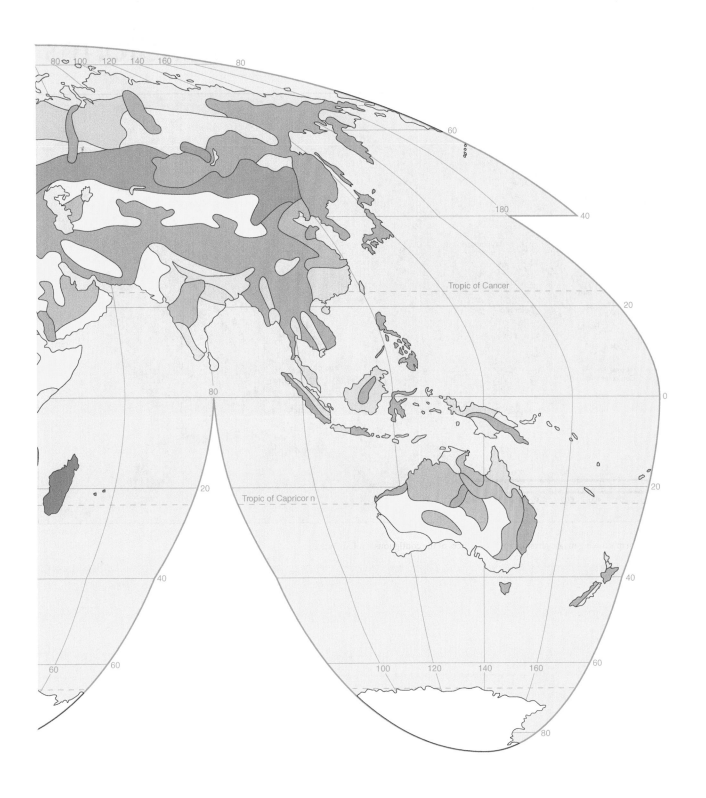

Contiguous United States Landforms

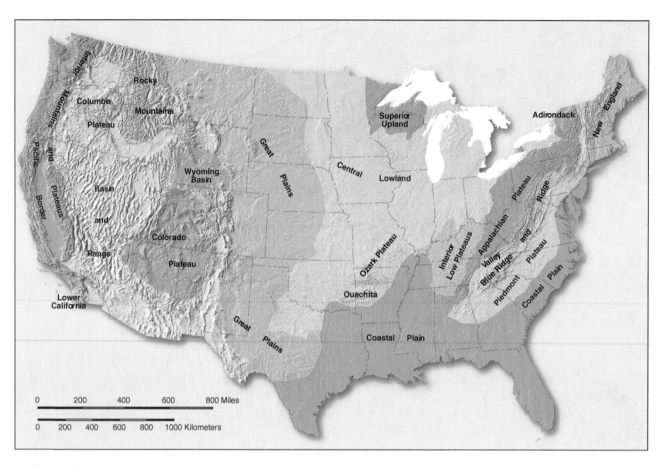

Outline map showing major physiographic provinces of the contiguous United States.

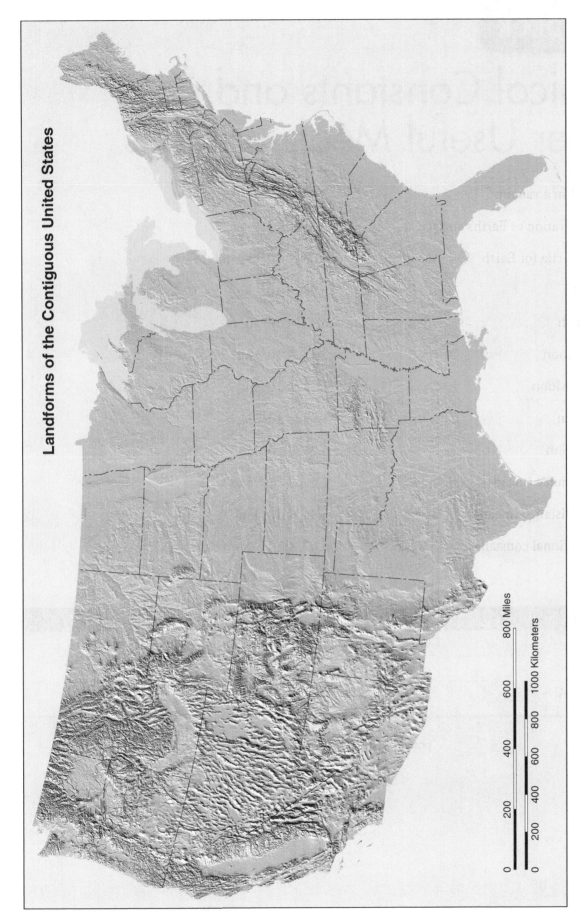

Landforms of the Contiguous United States

0	200	400	600	800 Miles	
0	200	400	600	800	1000 Kilometers

Digital shaded relief landform map of the United States. (Data provided by the U.S. Geological Survey)

Physical Constants and Other Useful Measurements

Speed of light in a vacuum	3.00×10^8 m/s
Free fall acceleration of Earth's surface	9.81 m/s^2
Moment of inertia for Earth	8.03×10^{31} kg•m^2
Mass of Earth	5.98×10^{24} kg
Radius of Earth	6.37×10^6 m
Mass of the Moon	7.35×10^{22} kg
Radius of the Moon	1.74×10^6 m
Mass of the Sun	1.99×10^{30} kg
Radius of the Sun	6.96×10^5 km
Earth-Sun distance (mean)	1.496×10^8 km
Earth-Moon distance (mean)	3.84×10^5 km
Earth's gravitational constant	6.67×10^{11} N•m^2/kg^2

Some SI Derived Units		
Quantity	**Unit name**	**Abbreviation**
Force	newton	N
Energy and work	joule	J
Power	watt	W
Pressure	pascal	Pa

Glossary

A

abrasion the grinding and smoothing of a rock surface by rock fragments that are carried by ice, wind, or water. (p. 192)

    abrasion/abrasión desgaste y alisamiento de la superficie de una roca causados por fragmentos de roca que son transportados por el hielo, el viento o el agua (pág. 192)

absolute magnitude the apparent brightness of a star if it were viewed from a distance of 32.6 light-years; used to compare the true brightness of stars (p. 703)

    absolute magnitude/magnitud absoluta luminosidad aparente de una estrella si se observara a una distancia de 32.6 años luz; usada para comparar la luminosidad real de las estrellas (pág. 703)

absorption spectrum a continuous spectrum produced when white light is passed through a cool gas under low pressure; The gas absorbs selected wavelengths of light, and the spectrum looks like it has dark lines superimposed. (p. 676)

    absorption spectrum/espectro de absorción espectro continuo producido cuando pasa luz blanca a través de un gas frío a presión baja; El gas absorbe determinadas longitudes de onda de luz y el espectro pareciera tener líneas oscuras superpuestas. (pág. 676)

abyssal plain very level area of the deep-ocean floor consisting of thick layers of sediment transported by turbidity currents (p. 404)

    abyssal plain/planicie abisal área muy nivelada del fondo oceánico profundo formada por capas gruesas de sedimentos que han sido transportados por corrientes de turbidez (pág. 404)

abyssal zone a subdivision of the benthic zone characterized by extremely high pressures, low temperatures, low oxygen, few nutrients, and no sunlight (p. 432)

    abyssal zone/zona abisal subdivisión de la zona bentónica caracterizada por tener presiones extremadamente altas, bajas temperaturas, poco oxígeno, pocas sustancias nutrientes y ausencia de luz solar (pág. 432)

accretion process that occurs when crustal fragments collide with and stay connected to a continental plate (p. 324)

    accretion/acreción proceso que ocurre cuando los fragmentos corticales chocan con una placa continental y permanecen conectados a ella (pág. 324)

accretionary wedge a large wedge-shaped mass of sediment that accumulates in subduction zones; Here sediment is scraped from the subducting oceanic plate and accreted to the overriding crustal block. (p. 321)

    accretionary wedge/prisma acrecionario masa grande de sedimento en forma de prisma que se acumula en las zonas de subducción; El sedimento es raspado de la placa oceánica de subducción y acrecentado al bloque cortical preponderante. (pág. 321)

adaptation a trait that helps an organism survive and reproduce (p. 345)

    adaptation/adaptación rasgo que ayuda a sobrevivir y a reproducirse a un organismo (pág. 345)

aftershock a small earthquake that follows the main earthquake (p. 221)

    aftershock/replica terremoto pequeño que sigue al terremoto mayor (pág. 221)

air mass a large body of air that is located in the troposphere and is characterized by similar temperatures and amounts of moisture at any given altitude (p. 559)

    air mass/masa de aire cuerpo grande de aire ubicado en la troposfera, que se caracteriza por tener temperatura y humedad similares a cualquier altitud dada (pág. 559)

air pressure the force exerted by the weight of a column of air above a given point (p. 532)

    air pressure/presión de aire fuerza ejercida por el peso de una columna de aire sobre un punto dado (pág. 532)

albedo the fraction of total radiation that is reflected back by a surface (p. 492)

    albedo/albedo fracción de la radiación total que es reflejada por una superficie (pág. 492)

alluvial fan a fan-shaped deposit of sediment formed when a stream's slope is abruptly reduced (p. 201)

Glossary, *continued*

alluvial fan/abanico aluvial depósito de sedimentos en forma de abanico, formado cuando la vertiente de una corriente de agua se reduce abruptamente (pág. 201)

amphibian a vertebrate that lives part of its life on land and part of its life in water (p. 373)
amphibian/anfibio vertebrado que vive parte de su vida en la tierra y parte en el agua (pág. 373)

andesitic composition the composition of igneous rocks lying between granitic and basaltic (p. 73)
andesitic composition/composición andesítica composición de rocas ígneas que se encuentra entre las rocas graníticas y las rocas basálticas (pág. 73)

anemometer an instrument used to determine wind speed (p. 545)
anemometer/anemómetro instrumento usado para determinar la velocidad del viento (pág. 545)

angiosperm flowering plant that produces flowers and seeds with an outer covering (p. 380)
angiosperm/angiosperma planta que da flores y produce semillas que tienen una cubierta exterior (pág. 380)

anticline a fold in sedimentary strata resembling an arch (p. 312)
anticline/anticlinal pliegue en el estrato sedimentario que parece un arco (pág. 312)

anticyclone a high-pressure center characterized by a clockwise flow of air in the Northern Hemisphere (p. 537)
anticyclone/anticiclón centro de alta presión en el hemisferio norte que se caracteriza por una masa de aire que se mueve en dirección de las agujas del reloj (pág. 537)

aphelion the place in the orbit of a planet where the planet is farthest from the sun (p. 624)
aphelion/afelio punto en la órbita de un planeta en el que éste se encuentra más alejado del Sol (pág. 624)

apogee the point where the moon is farthest from Earth (p. 626)

apogee/apogeo punto donde la Luna se encuentra más alejada de la Tierra (pág. 626)

apparent magnitude the brightness of a star when viewed from Earth (p. 703)
apparent magnitude/magnitud aparente luminosidad de una estrella vista desde la Tierra (pág. 703)

aquifer rock or soil through which groundwater moves easily (p. 171)
aquifer/acuífero roca o tierra a través de la cual el agua subterránea se mueve fácilmente (pág. 171)

artesian well a well in which the water naturally rises above the level of the water table (p. 174)
artesian well/pozo artesiano pozo en el cual el agua sube naturalmente por encima del nivel freático (pág. 174)

asteroid a small, rocky body, which can range in size from a few hundred kilometers to less than a kilometer; The asteroids' orbits lie mainly between those of Mars and Jupiter. (p. 660)
asteroid/asteroide cuerpo rocoso y pequeño, cuyo tamaño puede variar entre cientos de kilómetros a menos de un kilómetro; Las órbitas de los asteroides se encuentran principalmente entre las órbitas de Marte y Júpiter. (pág. 660)

asthenosphere a weak plastic layer of the mantle situated below the lithosphere; The rock within this zone is easily deformed. (p. 235)
asthenosphere/astenosfera capa plástica y débil del manto situada debajo de la litosfera; La roca en esta zona se deforma fácilmente. (pág. 235)

astronomical unit (AU) average distance from Earth to the sun; 1.5×10^8, or 150 million kilometers (p. 618)
astronomical unit (AU)/unidad astronómica (UA) distancia promedio de la Tierra al Sol; 1.5×10^8, ó 150 millones de kilómetros (pág. 618)

astronomy the scientific study of the universe; It includes the observation and interpretation of celestial bodies and phenomena. (pp. 3, 614)
astronomy/astronomía estudio científico del universo; incluye la observación y la interpretación de cuerpos y fenómenos celestes (págs. 3, 614)

atmosphere the gaseous portion of a planet; the planet's envelope of air; one of the traditional subdivisions of Earth's physical environment (p. 8)

    atmosphere/atmósfera porción gaseosa de un planeta; envoltura de aire del planeta; una de las subdivisiones tradicionales del medio ambiente físico de la Tierra (pág. 8)

atomic number the number of protons in the nucleus of an atom (p. 35)

    atomic number/número atómico número de protones en el núcleo de un átomo (pág. 35)

aurora a bright display of ever-changing light caused by solar radiation interacting with the upper atmosphere in the region of the poles (p. 688)

    aurora/aurora polar luz brillante en constante movimiento causada por la radiación solar que interactúa con la parte superior de la atmósfera en la región de los polos (pág. 688)

autumnal equinox the equinox that occurs on September 22 or 23 in the Northern Hemisphere and on March 21 or 22 in the Southern Hemisphere (p. 482)

    autummal equinox/equinoccio de otoño que ocurre el 22 ó el 23 de septiembre en el hemisferio norte y el 21 ó el 22 de marzo en el hemisferio sur (pág. 482)

B

barometer an instrument that measures atmospheric pressure (p. 533)

    barometer/barómetro instrumento que mide la presión atmosférica (pág. 533)

barrier island a low, elongated ridge of sand that parallels the coast (p. 466)

    barrier island/isla barrera lomo de arena bajo y alargado que se encuentra paralelo a la costa (pág. 466)

basaltic composition igneous rocks that contain at least 45% dark silicate minerals; sometimes called mafic rocks (p. 73)

    basaltic composition/composición basáltica rocas ígneas que contienen al menos 45% de minerales de silicato oscuros; a veces se les llama rocas máficas (pág. 73)

batholith a large mass of igneous rock that formed when magma intruded at depth, became crystallized, and subsequently was exposed by erosion; Batholiths have a surface exposure greater than 100 square kilometers. (p. 297)

    batholith/batolito masa grande de roca ígnea que se forma cuando el magma penetra en la profundidad, se cristaliza y luego queda expuesta debido a la erosión; los batolitos tienen una superficie expuesta mayor a los 100 kilómetros cuadrados (pág. 297)

bathymetry the measuring of ocean depths and the charting of the shape or topography of the ocean floor (p. 397)

    bathymetry/batimetría medición de las profundidades marinas y trazado de la forma o topografía del fondo marino (pág. 397)

beach the accumulation of sediment found along the shore of a lake or an ocean (p. 461)

    beach/playa acumulación de sedimento que se encuentra a lo largo de la costa de un lago u océano (pág. 461)

bed load sediment that is carried by a stream along the bottom of its channel (p. 165)

    bed load/carga del lecho sedimento arrastrado por una corriente de agua a lo largo del fondo de su canal (pág. 165)

benthic zone the marine-life zone that includes any sea-bottom surface regardless of its distance from shore (p. 432)

    benthic zone/zona béntica zona de vida marina que incluye cualquier superficie del fondo del mar sin importar su distancia de la costa (pág. 432)

benthos the forms of marine life that live on or in the ocean bottom; includes marine algae, sea stars, and crabs (p. 429)

    benthos/bentos organismos marinos que viven en el fondo marino; incluyen algas marinas, estrellas de mar y cangrejos (pág. 429)

Bergeron process a theory that relates the formation of precipitation to supercooled clouds, freezing nuclei, and the different saturation levels of ice and liquid water (p. 521)

Glossary, *continued*

Bergeron process/proceso de Bergeron teoría que relaciona la formación de precipitación con nubes sobreenfriadas, núcleos congelados y los diferentes niveles de saturación del agua helada y el agua líquida (pág. 521)

Big Bang theory the theory that proposes that the universe originated as a single mass, which subsequently exploded (p. 720)

> **Big Bang theory/teoría del Big Bang** teoría que propone que el universo se originó como una masa única, la cual estalló posteriormente (pág. 720)

binary star one of two stars revolving around a common center of mass under their mutual gravitational attraction (p. 701)

> **binary star/estrella binaria** una de dos estrellas que giran alrededor de un centro de masa común atraídas por su fuerza gravitacional mutua (pág. 701)

biochemical sedimentary rock sedimentary rock consisting of sediments that come from biological processes; sometimes called organic sedimentary rocks (p. 78)

> **biochemical sedimentary rock/roca sedimentaria bioquímica** roca sedimentaria formada por sedimentos derivados de procesos biológicos; a veces se le llama roca sedimentaria orgánica (pág. 78)

biogenous sediment seafloor sediment of biological origin, such as shells and skeletons of marine life (p. 408)

> **biogenous sediment/sedimento biogénico** sedimento del fondo marino de origen biológico, como conchas y esqueletos de organismos marinos (pág. 408)

biosphere all life on Earth; the parts of the solid Earth, hydrosphere, and atmosphere in which living organisms can be found (p. 9)

> **biosphere/biosfera** toda la vida en la Tierra; partes de la Tierra sólida, la hidrosfera y la atmósfera en las que se encuentran los organismos vivos (pág. 9)

black hole a massive star that has collapsed to such a small volume that its gravity prevents the escape of everything, including light (p. 714)

> **black hole/agujero negro** estrella masiva que se ha reducido a un volumen tan pequeño que su fuerza de gravedad no permite que nada se escape, incluyendo la luz (pág. 714)

C

calcareous ooze thick, common biogenous sediment formed from dissolving calcium carbonate shells (p. 408)

> **calcareous ooze/fango calcáreo** sedimento biógeno común y grueso, producido por la disolución de conchas de carbonato de calcio (pág. 408)

caldera a large depression typically caused by collapse or ejection of the summit area of a volcano (p. 292)

> **caldera/caldera** depresión grande causada típicamente por el colapso o la expulsión de la cima de un volcán (pág. 292)

capacity the total amount of sediment a stream is able to transport (p. 165)

> **capacity/capacidad** cantidad total de sedimento que puede transportar una corriente de agua (pág. 165)

cavern a naturally formed underground chamber or series of chambers most commonly produced by solution activity in limestone (p. 177)

> **cavern/caverna** cámara subterránea o serie de cámaras subterráneas formadas naturalmente y producidas comúnmente por actividad de solución sobre piedra caliza (pág. 177)

cementation solidification of sediments by the deposition of dissolved minerals in the tiny spaces between the sedimentary particles (p. 76)

> **cementation/cementación** solidificación de sedimentos por el depósito de minerales disueltos en los espacios diminutos entre las partículas sedimentarias (pág. 76)

Cepheid variable a star whose brightness varies periodically because it expands and contracts; a type of pulsating star (p. 705)

> **Cepheid variable/variable Cefeida** estrella cuya luminosidad varía periódicamente porque se expande y se contrae; tipo de estrella púlsar (pág. 705)

chemical bond a force that holds together atoms that form a compound (p. 39)

    chemical bond/enlace químico fuerza que une los átomos que forman un compuesto (pág. 39)

chemical sedimentary rock sedimentary rock consisting of dissolved sediments that precipitate directly from water (p. 77)

    chemical sedimentary rock/roca sedimentaria química roca sedimentaria formada por sedimentos disueltos precipitados del agua (pág. 77)

chemical weathering the processes by which the internal structure of a mineral is altered by the removal and/or addition of elements (p. 129)

    chemical weathering/meteorización química proceso mediante el cual la estructura interna de un mineral es alterada por la extracción y/o la suma de elementos (pág. 129)

chemosynthesis the process by which certain microorganisms use chemical energy to produce food (p. 433)

    chemosynthesis/quimiosíntesis proceso por el cual ciertos microorganismos usan energía química para producir alimento (pág. 433)

chromatic aberration the property of a lens whereby light of different colors is focused at different places (p. 679)

    chromatic aberration/aberración cromática propiedad de una lente en la cual se enfoca luz de diferentes colores en distintos lugares (pág. 679)

chromosphere the first layer of the solar atmosphere found directly above the photosphere (p. 686)

    chromosphere/cromosfera primera capa de la atmósfera solar que se encuentra directamente por encima de la fotosfera (pág. 686)

cinder cone a small volcano built primarily of pyroclastic material ejected from a single vent (p. 290)

    cinder cone/cono de escoria volcán pequeño formado principalmente de material piroclástico expulsado por una sola abertura (pág. 290)

cirque an amphitheater-shaped basin at the head of a glaciated valley produced by frost wedging and plucking (p. 194)

    cirque/circo cuenca en forma de anfiteatro en la cabecera de un valle glaciar producida por la erosión de hielo (pág. 194)

cirrus one of three basic cloud forms; also one of the three high cloud types; They are thin, delicate ice-crystal clouds often appearing as veil-like patches or thin, wispy fibers. (p. 517)

    cirrus/cirro una de las tres formaciones básicas de las nubes; también uno de los tres tipos de nubes altas; son nubes cristalinas delicadas que parecen retazos de velo o fibras tenues y finas (pág. 517)

clastic sedimentary rock a sedimentary rock made of fragments of pre-existing rock (p. 77)

    clastic sedimentary rock/roca sedimentaria clástica roca sedimentaria formada por fragmentos de roca preexistente (pág. 77)

cleavage the tendency of a mineral to break along planes of weak bonding (p. 53)

    cleavage/clivaje tendencia de un mineral a fracturarse a lo largo de planos de enlace débiles (pág. 53)

climate the average weather conditions in an area over a long period (p. 588)

    climate/clima promedio de las condiciones del tiempo atmosférico en un área durante un período largo de tiempo (pág. 588)

cold front a front along which a cold air mass thrusts beneath a warmer air mass (p. 566)

    cold front/frente frío frente en el que una masa de aire frío avanza bajo una masa de aire caliente (pág. 566)

collision-coalescence process a theory of raindrop formation in warm clouds (above 0°C) in which large cloud droplets collide and join together with smaller droplets to form a raindrop; Opposite electrical charges may bind the cloud droplets together. (p. 521)

    collision-coalescence process/proceso de coalescencia y colisión teoría sobre la formación de gotas de agua en nubes cálidas (por encima de los 0 °C), en la cual las gotas grandes de agua en una nube chocan y se unen con gotitas más pequeñas para formar una gota de mayor tamaño; Las corrientes eléctricas opuestas pueden unir las gotitas. (pág. 521)

Glossary, *continued*

coma the fuzzy, gaseous component of a comet's head (p. 661)

coma/coma componente gaseoso y difuso que rodea el núcleo de un cometa (pág. 661)

comet a small body made of rocky and metallic pieces held together by frozen gases; Comets generally revolve about the sun in an elongated orbit. (p. 661)

comet/cometa cuerpo pequeño formado por materiales rocosos y metálicos unidos por medio de gases congelados; Los cometas generalmente giran alrededor del Sol en una órbita alargada. (pág. 661)

compaction process by which sediments are squeezed together by the weight of overlying materials driving out water (p. 76)

compaction/compactación proceso por el cual los sedimentos se unen y expulsan agua debido al peso de los materiales que los cubren (pág. 76)

composite cone a volcano composed of both lava flows and pyroclastic material (p. 291)

composite cone/estratovolcán volcán compuesto de flujos de lava y material piroclástico (pág. 291)

compost partly decomposed organic material that is used as fertilizer (p. 115)

compost/compost material orgánico parcialmente descompuesto que se usa como fertilizante (pág. 115)

compound a substance formed by the chemical combination of two or more elements in definite proportions and usually having properties different from those of its constituent elements (p. 39)

compound/compuesto sustancia formada por la combinación química de dos o más elementos en proporciones definidas y que tiene usualmente propiedades diferentes a las de los elementos que la componen (pág. 39)

condensation the change of state from a gas to a liquid (p. 506)

condensation/condensación cambio de estado de un gas a un líquido (pág. 506)

condensation nuclei tiny bits of particulate matter that serve as surfaces on which water vapor condenses (p. 516)

condensation nuclei/núcleos de condensación partículas muy pequeñas de materia que sirven como superficies para que se condense el vapor (pág. 516)

conduction the transfer of heat through matter by molecular activity; Energy is transferred through collisions from one molecule to another. (p. 483)

conduction/conducción transferencia de calor a través de la materia por actividad molecular; la energía se transfiere a través de choques de una molécula contra otra (pág. 483)

conservation the careful use of resources (p. 113)

conservation/conservación uso cuidadoso de los recursos (pág. 113)

constellation an apparent group of stars originally named for mythical characters; The sky is presently divided into 88 constellations. (p. 700)

constellation/constelación grupo aparente de estrellas nombrado originalmente a partir de personajes míticos; el cielo se encuentra en la actualidad dividido en 88 constelaciones (pág. 700)

contact metamorphism localized changes in rock caused by the heat from a nearby magma body (p. 81)

contact metamorphism/metamorfismo de contacto cambios que sufre una roca en un lugar específico de su superficie debido al calor de un cuerpo de magma cercano (pág. 81)

continental drift a hypothesis that originally proposed that the continents had once been joined to form a single supercontinent; The supercontinent broke into pieces, which drifted into their present-day positions. (p. 248)

continental drift/deriva continental hipótesis que propuso originalmente que los continentes estuvieron unidos formando un solo supercontinente; El supercontinente se quebró en pedazos, los cuales se desplazaron hasta sus posiciones actuales. (pág. 248)

continental glacier a very large, thick mass of glacial ice that covers a large region and flows outward in all directions from one or more accumulation centers; also called a continental ice sheet (p. 189)

continental glacier/glaciar continental masa muy grande y gruesa de hielo glacial que cubre una región grande y fluye hacia afuera en todas direcciones desde uno o más centros de acumulación; también se le llama capa de hielo continental (pág. 189)

continental margin that portion of the seafloor adjacent to the continents; It may include the continental shelf, continental slope, and continental rise. (p. 401)

    continental margin/margen continental porción del suelo marino adyacente a los continentes; puede incluir la plataforma continental, el talud continental y el pie continental (pág. 401)

continental rise the gently sloping surface at the base of the continental slope (p. 403)

    continental rise/pie continental superficie que se encuentra levemente en declive en la base del talud continental (pág. 403)

continental shelf the gently sloping submerged portion of the continental margin, extending from the shoreline to the continental slope (p. 402)

    continental shelf/plataforma continental porción sumergida y levemente en declive del margen continental, que se extiende desde la costa hasta el talud continental (pág. 402)

continental slope the steep gradient that leads to the deep-ocean floor and marks the seaward edge of the continental shelf (p. 402)

    continental slope/talud continental pendiente empinada que conduce al suelo marino profundo y marca el límite de la plataforma continental que da al mar (pág. 402)

continental volcanic arc mountains formed in part by volcanic activity caused by the subduction of oceanic lithosphere beneath a continent (p. 265)

    continental volcanic arc/arco volcánico continental montañas formadas en parte por actividad volcánica causada por la subducción de la litosfera volcánica debajo de un continente (pág. 265)

continuous spectrum an uninterrupted band of light emitted by an incandescent solid, liquid, or gas under pressure (p. 676)

continuos spectrum/espectro continuo banda de luz continua emitida por un sólido, un líquido o un gas incandescente bajo presión (pág. 676)

contour interval on a topographic map, tells the distance in elevation between adjacent contour lines (p. 14)

    contour interval/intervalo entre curvas de nivel en un mapa topográfico, indica la diferencia de altitud entre dos curvas de nivel adyacentes (pág. 14)

contour line line on a topographic map that indicates an elevation; Every point along a contour line has the same elevation. (p. 14)

    contour line/curva de nivel línea en un mapa topográfico que indica una altitud; Todos los puntos a lo largo de una curva de nivel tienen la misma altitud. (pág. 14)

convection the transfer of heat by the movement of a mass or substance; It can take place only in fluids. (p. 485)

    convection/convección transferencia de calor por el movimiento de una masa o sustancia; puede ocurrir sólo en líquidos (pág. 485)

convection current the motion of matter resulting from changes in temperature; The convective flow of material in the mantle is due to Earth's unequal heating and causes the tectonic plates to move. (p. 470)

    convection current/corriente de convección movimiento de materia resultante de cambios en la temperatura; El flujo convectivo de material en el manto se debe al calentamiento desigual de la tierra y hace que las placas tectónicas se muevan. (pág. 470)

convergent boundary a boundary in which two plates move together (p. 262)

    convergent boundary/límite convergente límite en el cual dos placas se muevan juntas (pág. 262)

core the innermost layer of Earth, located beneath the mantle; The core is divided into an outer core and an inner core. (p. 8)

    core/núcleo capa más interna de la Tierra, ubicada debajo del manto; El núcleo está dividido en un núcleo exterior y un núcleo interior. (pág. 8)

Glossary, *continued*

Coriolis effect the apparent deflective force of Earth's rotation on all free-moving objects, including the atmosphere and oceans; Deflection is to the right in the Northern Hemisphere and to the left in the Southern Hemisphere. (pp. 449, 535)

    Coriolis effect/efecto de Coriolis aparente fuerza desviadora que la rotación de la Tierra ejerce sobre todos los objetos que están en movimiento libre, incluyendo la atmósfera y los océanos; El desvío es hacia la derecha en el hemisferio norte y hacia la izquierda en el hemisferio sur. (págs. 449, 535)

corona the outer weak layer of the solar atmosphere (p. 686)

    corona/corona solar débil capa exterior de la atmósfera solar (pág. 686)

correlation establishing the equivalence of rocks of similar age in different areas (p. 340)

    correlation/correlación establecimiento de la equivalencia de rocas de edades similares en diferentes áreas (pág. 340)

covalent bond a bond that forms when atoms share electrons (p. 41)

    covalent bond/enlace covalente enlace que se forma cuando los átomos comparten electrones (pág. 41)

crater the depression at the summit of a volcano or that which is produced by a meteorite impact (pp. 289, 631)

    crater/cráter depresión en la cumbre de un volcán o la que se produce por el impacto de un meteorito (págs. 289, 631)

creep the slow downhill movement of soil and regolith (p. 147)

    creep/reptación movimiento lento cuesta abajo de tierra y regolitos (pág. 147)

crevasse a deep crack in the brittle surface of a glacier (p. 190)

    crevasse/hendidura grieta profunda en la superficie frágil de un glaciar (pág. 190)

cross-cutting relationships, principle of a principle of relative dating; A fault or intrusion is younger than any geologic feature through which it cuts. (p. 338)

cross-cutting relationships, principle of/ relaciones de corte transversal, principio de principio de datación relativa; una falla o intrusión es más reciente que cualquier accidente geológico que ésta atraviesa (pág. 338)

crust the thin, rocky outer layer of Earth (pp. 8, 223)

    crust/corteza capa exterior fina y rocosa de la Tierra (págs. 8, 223)

crystal form the external appearance of a mineral as determined by its internal arrangement of atoms (p. 51)

    crystal form/forma cristalina apariencia externa de un mineral determinada según la distribución interna de los átomos (pág. 51)

cumulus one of three basic cloud forms; also the name given to one of the clouds of vertical development; They are billowy individual cloud masses that often have flat bases. (p. 517)

    cumulus/cúmulo una de las tres formas básicas de las nubes; nombre dado también a una de las nubes de desarrollo vertical; son masas de nubes individuales ondulantes que tienen a menudo bases planas (pág. 517)

cyclone a low-pressure center characterized by a counterclockwise flow of air in the Northern Hemisphere (p. 537)

    cyclone/ciclón centro de baja presión en el hemisferio norte caracterizado por una corriente de aire que corre en sentido contrario a las manecillas del reloj (pág. 537)

D

decompression melting melting due to a drop in confining pressure that occurs as rock rises (p. 280)

    decompression melting/fusión por descompresión fusión debida a una disminución de la presión restrictiva que ocurre a medida que una roca va subiendo (pág. 280)

deep-ocean trench a surface feature in the seafloor produced by the descending plate during subduction (p. 255)

    deep-ocean trench/fosa oceánico depresión en el fondo oceánico causada por la placa descendiente durante la subducción (pág. 255)

deflation the lifting and removal of loose material by wind (p. 203)

    deflation/deflación levantamiento y remoción de material suelto por el viento (pág. 203)

deformation general term for the processes of folding, faulting, shearing, compression, or extension of rocks as the result of various natural forces (p. 308)

   deformation/deformación término general para los procesos de plegamiento, formación de fallas, partición, compresión o extensión en rocas, como resultado de diferentes fuerzas naturales (pág. 308)

delta an accumulation of sediment formed where a stream enters a lake or an ocean (p. 166)

   delta/delta acumulación de sedimento que se forma donde una corriente de agua entra a un lago u océano (pág. 166)

density mass per unit volume of a substance, usually expressed as grams per cubic centimeter (pp. 53, 425)

   density/densidad masa por unidad de volumen de una sustancia, expresada por lo general en gramos por centímetro cúbico (págs. 53, 425)

density current current of ocean water that results from density differences among water masses (p. 451)

   density current/corriente de densidad corriente de agua oceánica que resulta de las diferencias de densidad entre las masas de agua (pág. 451)

deposition the process by which an agent of erosion loses energy and drops the sediment it is carrying; also the process by which water vapor is changed directly to a solid without passing through the liquid state (pp. 76, 506)

   desposition/deposición proceso por el cual un agente de erosión pierde energía y deja caer el sedimento que arrastra; también es el proceso por el cual el vapor de agua pasa al estado sólido sin pasar por el estado líquido (págs. 76, 506)

desert pavement a layer of coarse pebbles and gravel created when wind removed the finer material (p. 204)

   desert pavement/pavimento desértico capa de guijarros gruesos y grava que se forma cuando el viento remueve el material más fino (pág. 204)

dew point the temperature to which air has to be cooled in order to reach saturation (p. 508)

dew point/punto de condensación temperatura a la cual se tiene que enfriar el aire para que alcance la saturación (pág. 508)

dike a tabular-shaped intrusive igneous feature that occurs when magma is injected into fractures in the surrounding rock, cutting across preexisting rock layers (p. 296)

   dike/dique masa intrusiva de magma solidificado de forma tabular que se forma cuando el magma es inyectado en las fracturas de la roca circundante, penetrando transversalmente las capas de rocas preexistentes (pág. 296)

dinosaur land-dwelling reptile of the Mesozoic era (p. 377)

   dinosaur/dinosaurio reptil de tierra de la era Mesozoica (pág. 377)

discharge the quantity of water in a stream that passes a given point in a period of time (p. 161)

   discharge/caudal cantidad de agua en una corriente que pasa por un punto determinado en un período (pág. 161)

divergent boundary a region where the rigid plates are moving apart, typified by the oceanic ridges (p. 262)

   divergent boundary/límite divergente zona donde las placas tectónicas se separan, tipificada por las dorsales oceánicas (pág. 262)

divide an imaginary line that separates the drainage of two streams; often found along a ridge (p. 170)

   divide/divisoria de aguas línea imaginaria que separa el drenaje de dos corrientes de agua; frecuentemente se encuentra a lo largo de una elevación (pág. 170)

Doppler effect the apparent change in frequency of electromagnetic or sound waves caused by the relative motions of the source and the observer (p. 677)

   Doppler effect/efecto Doppler variación aparente en la frecuencia de una onda sonora o electromagnética debido al movimiento relativo entre la fuente de la onda y el observador (pág. 677)

drainage basin the land area that contributes water to a stream (p. 170)

   drainage basin/cuenca de avenamiento área de tierra que aporta agua a un arroyo (pág. 170)

Glossary, *continued*

drumlin a streamlined, asymmetrical hill composed of glacial till; The steep side of the hill faces the direction from which the ice advanced. (p. 196)

    drumlin/drumlin colina asimétrica compuesta de tilita glacial; El lado empinado de la colina mira hacia la dirección desde la cual avanzó el hielo. (pág. 196)

dry adiabatic rate the rate of adiabatic cooling or warming in unsaturated air; The rate of temperature change is 1°C per 100 meters. (p. 511)

    dry adiabatic rate/tasa adiabática seca tasa de enfriamiento o calentamiento adiabático en el aire no saturado; la tasa de cambio en la temperatura es de 1 °C por cada 100 metros (pág. 511)

dune a hill or ridge of wind-deposited sand (p. 205)

    dune/duna colina o elevación formada por arena depositada por el viento (pág. 205)

dwarf planet a round object that orbits the sun but has not cleared the neighborhood around its orbit (p. 659)

    dwarf planet/planeta enano un cuerpo esférico que está en órbita alrededor del Sol, pero no ha limpiado la vecindad de su órbita (pág. 659)

E

earthflow slow-moving downslope movement of water-saturated, clay-rich sediment, most characteristic of humid regions (p. 146)

    earthflow/deslizamiento de tierra movimiento lento y descendente de sedimento saturado con agua, rico en arcilla, muy característico de las regiones húmedas (pág. 146)

earthquake the vibration of Earth produced by the rapid release of energy (p. 218)

    earthquake/terremoto vibración de la Tierra producida por una liberación rápida de energía (pág. 218)

Earth science the name for all the sciences that collectively seek to understand Earth; It includes geology, oceanography, meteorology, and astronomy. (p. 2)

Earth science/ciencias de la Tierra nombre dado a todas las ciencias que colectivamente estudian la Tierra; incluye la geología, la oceanografía, la meteorología y la astronomía (pág. 2)

elastic rebound tendency for deformed rock along a fault to spring back to its original shape after an earthquake (p. 220)

    elastic rebound/rebote elástico tendencia de la roca deformada a lo largo de una falla geológica a volver a su configuración original después de un sismo (pág. 220)

electromagnetic spectrum the arrangement of electromagnetic radiation according to wavelength (p. 674)

    electromagnetic spectrum/espectro electromagnético orden de la radiación electromagnética según la longitud de onda (pág. 674)

element a substance that cannot be broken down into simpler substances by ordinary chemical or physical means (p. 34)

    element/elemento sustancia que no puede ser descompuesta en sustancias más sencillas a través de métodos químicos o físicos comunes (pág. 34)

ellipse an oval (p. 618)

    ellipse/elipse óvalo (pág. 618)

El Niño the name given to the periodic warming of the ocean that occurs in the central and eastern Pacific; A major El Niño episode can cause extreme weather in many parts of the world. (p. 546)

    El Niño/El Niño nombre dado al calentamiento periódico que ocurre en las regiones central y oriental del océano Pacífico; Un episodio intenso de El Niño puede causar fenómenos climáticos extremos en muchas partes del mundo. (pág. 546)

emission spectrum a series of bright lines of particular wavelengths produced by a hot gas under low pressure (p. 676)

    emission spectrum/espectro de emisión serie de luces brillantes con longitudes de onda específicas, producidas por un gas caliente sometido a bajas presiones (pág. 676)

energy level one of several distinct regions around the nucleus of an atom where electrons are located (p. 35)

energy level/nivel de energía una de varias regiones específicas que rodea el núcleo de un átomo y en donde se ubican los electrones (pág. 35)

eon the largest time unit on the geologic time scale, next in order of magnitude above era (p. 354)

  eon/eón unidad de mayor intervalo en la escala geocronológica, mayor que una era (pág. 354)

epicenter the location on Earth's surface directly above the focus, or origin, of an earthquake (p. 218)

  epicenter/epicentro punto en la superficie de la Tierra que está justo sobre el foco, u origen, de un terremoto (pág. 218)

epoch a unit of the geologic time scale that is a subdivision of a period (p. 355)

  epoch/época unidad de la escala geocronológica, que es una subdivisión de un período (pág. 355)

era a major division on the geologic time scale, smaller only than eons; divided into shorter units called periods (p. 355)

  era/era una de las grandes divisiones de la escala geocronológica, menor que un eón; se divide en unidades más pequeñas llamadas períodos (pág. 355)

erosion the incorporation and transportation of material by a mobile agent, such as water, wind, or ice (p. 76)

  erosion/erosión incorporación y transporte de un material por un agente móvil, como el agua, el viento o el hielo (pág. 76)

esker sinuous ridge composed largely of sand and gravel deposited by a stream flowing in a tunnel beneath a glacier near its terminus (p. 196)

  esker/esker elevación alargada y sinuosa, compuesta por arena y grava que han sido depositadas por un arroyo que fluye por el túnel de un glaciar, cerca de su punta. (pág. 196)

eukaryote an organism whose cells contain nuclei (p. 368)

  eukaryote/eucariota organismo cuyas células contienen núcleos (pág. 368)

evaporation the process of converting a liquid to a gas (p. 505)

  evaporation/evaporación proceso mediante el cual un líquido se convierte en gas (pág. 505)

evolution change over time (p. 345)

  evolution/evolución cambio a lo largo del tiempo (pág. 345)

exfoliation type of weathering caused by reducing pressure on a rock surface, allowing slabs of outer rock to break off in layers (p. 128)

  exfoliation/exfoliación tipo de meteorización causada por la disminución de la presión en una superficie rocosa, lo que permite que los estratos externos de la roca se desprendan en láminas (pág. 128)

extinct term used to describe a type of organism that no longer exists anywhere on Earth (p. 342)

  extinct/extinto describe un tipo de organismo que ya no existe en la Tierra (pág. 342)

extrusive igneous rock igneous rock that has formed on Earth's surface (p. 71)

  extrusive igneous rock/roca ígnea extrusiva roca ígnea que ha sido formada en la superficie de la Tierra (pág. 71)

eye a zone of scattered clouds and calm averaging about 20 kilometers in diameter at the center of a hurricane (p. 576)

  eye/ojo zona de calma, con pocas nubes, que en promedio mide 20 kilómetros de diámetro y que se encuentra en el centro de un huracán (pág. 576)

eye wall the doughnut-shaped area of intense cumulonimbus development and very strong winds that surrounds the eye of a hurricane (p. 576)

  eye wall/pared del ojo zona en forma de rosquilla con gran intensidad de cumulonimbos y fuertes vientos, que rodea el ojo de un huracán (pág. 576)

F

fault a fracture in Earth along which movement has occurred (p. 218)

  fault/falla fractura en la Tierra en la cual ha habido movimiento (pág. 218)

fault-block mountain a mountain formed when large blocks of crust are tilted, uplifted, or dropped between large normal faults (p. 317)

  fault-block mountain/montaña de bloque de falla montaña formada cuando los bloques grandes de corteza terrestre se inclinan, se elevan o caen entre fallas grandes (pág. 317)

Glossary, continued

fetch the distance that the wind has traveled across open water (p. 456)

    fetch/alcance del viento distancia que ha recorrido el viento sobre aguas abiertas (pág. 456)

flood occurs when the discharge of a stream becomes so great that it exceeds the carrying capacity of its channel and overflows its banks (p. 168)

    flood/inundación ocurre cuando el caudal de una corriente de agua es tan grande que sobrepasa la capacidad de su canal y se desborda por sus riberas (pág. 168)

floodplain the flat, low-lying portion of a stream valley subject to periodic flooding (p. 167)

    floodplain/planicie aluvial parte plana y baja del valle de un arroyo que está expuesta a inundaciones periódicas (pág. 167)

focus the point within Earth where an earthquake originates (p. 218)

    focus/foco punto dentro de la Tierra en el cual se origina un terremoto (pág. 218)

folded mountain a mountain created primarily by compressional stresses, which create folds in the rock layers (p. 316)

    folded mountain/montaña de pliegues montaña que ha sido creada principalmente por esfuerzos de compresión, los caules causan pliegues en los estratos de roca (pág. 316)

foliated metamorphic rock a metamorphic rock with minerals oriented perpendicular to the direction of greatest exerted pressure, giving it a layered texture (p. 82)

    foliated metamorphic rock/roca metamórfica esquistosa roca metamórfica cuyos minerales están dispuestos en forma perpendicular a la dirección en la cual la roca recibe mayor presión, lo cual le da una textura de capas (pág. 82)

food chain a succession of organisms through which food energy is transferred, starting with primary producers (p. 437)

    food chain/cadena alimentaria serie de organismos a través de los cuales se transfiere la energía de los alimentos y que empieza por los productores primarios (pág. 437)

food web a group of interrelated food chains (p. 437)

    food web/red alimentaria grupo de cadenas alimentarias interrelacionadas (pág. 437)

foreshock a small earthquake that often precedes a major earthquake (p. 221)

    foreshock/sismo premonitor pequeño terremoto que generalmente precede a un terremoto mayor (pág. 221)

fossil the remains or traces of an organism preserved from the geologic past (p. 342)

    fossil/fósil remanentes o vestigios de un organismo que ha sido preservado del pasado geológico (pág. 342)

fossil fuel a carbon-containing fuel that formed over millions of years from the remains of living things (p. 95)

    fossil fuel/combustible fósil combustible que contiene carbón y que se ha formado a lo largo de millones de años a partir de los restos de seres vivos (pág. 95)

fossil succession, principle of geologic principle stating that fossil organisms tend to be found in the same general order at different locations (p. 344)

    fossil succession, principle of/sucesión faunística, principio de la principio geológico según el cual los fósiles tienden a encontrarse en el mismo orden general en diferentes lugares (pág. 344)

fracture any break or rupture in rock along which no appreciable movement has taken place (p. 53)

    fracture/fractura discontinuidad en una roca en la cual no se manifiesta que haya ocurrido movimiento alguno (pág. 53)

front the boundary between two adjoining air masses having contrasting characteristics (pp. 512, 564)

    front/frente límite entre dos masas de aire adyacentes que tienen características que contrastan (págs. 512, 564)

frost wedging the mechanical breakup of rock caused by the expansion of freezing water in cracks and crevices (p. 127)

frost wedging/gelifracción fragmentación mecánica de una roca, causada por la expansión tras la congelación del agua en sus grietas y poros (pág. 127)

G

galaxy a group of stars, dust, and gases held together by gravity (p. 715)

galaxy/galaxia grupo de estrellas, polvo y gas unidos por la gravedad (pág. 715)

galaxy cluster a system of galaxies containing from several to thousands of member galaxies (p. 718)

galaxy cluster/cúmulo de galaxias sistema que puede contener hasta miles de galaxias (pág. 718)

gas hydrate compact chemical structures made of water and natural gas (p. 411)

gas hydrate/hidrato de gas estructura química compacta formada por agua y gas natural (pág. 411)

geocentric describes the concept of an Earth-centered universe (p. 615)

geocentric/geocéntrico describe un universo cuyo centro es la Tierra (pág. 615)

geologic time scale timeline of Earth's history divided into units of varying length, such as eons, eras, periods, and epochs (p. 353)

geologic time scale/escala geocronológica línea cronológica de la historia de la Tierra, dividida en unidades que varían en longitud, como eones, eras, períodos y épocas (pág. 353)

geology the science that examines Earth, its form and composition, and the changes it has undergone and is undergoing (p. 2)

geology/geología ciencia que estudia la Tierra, su forma, su composición y los cambios que ha tenido y que continúa teniendo (pág. 2)

geosphere layer of Earth under both the atmosphere and the oceans; It is composed of the core, the mantle, and the crust. (p. 8)

geosphere/geosfera estrato de la Tierra que se encuentra bajo la atmósfera y los océanos; está compuesta por el núcleo, el manto y la corteza (pág. 8)

geothermal energy energy that can be extracted from Earth's internal heat, for example, natural steam used for power generation (p. 105)

geothermal energy/energía geotérmica energía que puede extraerse del calor interno de la Tierra; por ejemplo, el vapor natural que se usa para generar electricidad (pág. 105)

geyser a hot spring or fountain that ejects water at various intervals (p. 173)

geyser/géiser manantial o fuente de agua caliente que expele agua a intervalos (pág. 173)

glacial erratic an ice-transported rock not derived from bedrock near its present site (p. 194)

glacial erratic/bloque errático roca transportada por el hielo y que no se originó del lecho rocoso donde se encuentra (pág. 194)

glacier a thick mass of ice originating on land from the compaction and recrystallization of snow that shows evidence of past or present flow (p. 188)

glacier/glaciar masa gruesa de hielo que se origina en la superficie terrestre por compactación y recristalización de la nieve, mostrando evidencias de flujo en el pasado o en la actualidad (pág. 188)

global climate change the increase in average temperatures of the atmosphere, along with climate changes that have resulted from it, due in part to increased carbon dioxide levels (pp. 110, 602)

global climate change/cambio climático global aumento de la temperatura media de la atmósfera y los cambios climáticos derivados de éste, causado en parte por el aumento de los niveles de dióxido de carbono (págs. 110, 602)

Gondwana Paleozoic supercontinent that formed the southern portion of Pangaea, consisting of all or parts of present-day South America, Africa, Australia, India, and Antarctica (p. 371)

Gondwana/Gondwana supercontinente del Paleozoico, que formaba la porción austral de Pangea y que abarcaba lo que hoy en día son América del Sur, África, Australia, India y la Antártida (pág. 371)

graben a valley formed by the downward displacement of a fault-bounded block (p. 317)

graben/fosa tectónica valle formado por el desplazamiento descendente de un bloque rodeado de fallas (pág. 317)

Glossary, *continued*

gradient the slope of a stream over a certain distance (p. 160)

    gradient/gradiente pendiente de un arroyo a lo largo de una distancia determinada (pág. 160)

granitic composition igneous rocks that contain between 10% and 25% dark silicate minerals; sometimes called felsic rocks (p. 72)

    granitic composition/composición de granito rocas ígneas que contienen entre 10% y 25% de minerales de silicato oscuros; a veces se les llama rocas félsicas (pág. 72)

greenhouse effect the heating of Earth's surface and atmosphere from solar radiation being absorbed and emitted by the atmosphere, mainly by water vapor and carbon dioxide (p. 487)

    greenhouse effect/efecto invernadero calentamiento de la superficie y la atmósfera de la Tierra debido a la absorción y emisión de radiación solar por la atmósfera, principalmente por el vapor de agua y el dióxido de carbono (pág. 487)

groundwater water underground in the zone of saturation (p. 172)

    groundwater/agua subterránea agua que se encuentra bajo la tierra, en las zonas de saturación (pág. 172)

gymnosperm seed-bearing plant that bears its seeds on the surfaces of cones (p. 378)

    gymnosperm/gimnosperma planta cuyas semillas se encuentran en las superficies de los conos (pág. 378)

gyre a large circular surface current pattern found in each ocean (p. 449)

    gyre/giro patrón de corriente circular grande que se encuentra en todos los océanos (pág. 449)

H

half-life the time required for one half of the atoms of a radioactive substance to decay (p. 348)

    half-life/vida media tiempo requerido para que se desintegre la mitad de los átomos de una sustancia radiactiva (pág. 348)

hardness the resistance a mineral offers to scratching (p. 52)

    hardness/dureza resistencia que ofrece un mineral a ser rayado (pág. 52)

heat thermal energy transferred from one object to another (p. 483)

    heat/calor energía térmica que se transfiere de un objeto a otro (pág. 483)

heliocentric describes the view that the sun is at the center of the solar system (p. 616)

    heliocentric/heliocéntrico describe la idea de que el Sol es el centro del sistema solar (pág. 616)

Hertzsprung-Russell diagram *See* H-R diagram

    Hertzsprung-Russell diagram/diagrama Hertzsprung-Russell *ver* diagrama HR

horst an elongated, uplifted block of crust bounded by faults (p. 317)

    horst/pilar tectónico bloque de corteza alargado que ha sido empujado hacia arriba y se encuentra rodeado de fallas (pág. 317)

hot spot a concentration of heat in the mantle capable of producing magma, which rises to Earth's surface; The Pacific plate moves over a hot spot, producing the Hawaiian Islands. (p. 285)

    hot spot/punto caliente concentración de calor en el manto capaz de producir magma, la cual sube a la superficie terrestre; la placa tectónica del Pacífico se mueve sobre un punto caliente que formó las islas hawaianas (pág. 285)

H-R diagram a plot of stars according to their absolute magnitudes and temperatures (p. 704)

    H-R diagram/diagrama HR diagrama de estrellas basado en las temperaturas y magnitudes absolutas de las mismas (pág. 704)

Hubble's law a law that states that the galaxies are retreating from the Milky Way at a speed that is proportional to their distance (p. 719)

    Hubble's law/ley de Hubble ley que establece que las galaxias se alejan de la vía láctea a una velocidad proporcional a sus distancias (pág. 719)

humidity a general term referring to water vapor in the air but not to liquid droplets of fog, cloud, or rain (p. 506)

humidity/humedad término general que se refiere al vapor de agua en el aire, excluyendo las gotas líquidas de niebla, nubes o lluvia (pág. 506)

hurricane a tropical cyclonic storm having winds in excess of 119 kilometers per hour (p. 575)

hurricane/huracán tormenta tropical ciclónica con vientos cuyas velocidades exceden los 119 kilómetros por hora (pág. 575)

hydroelectric power the power generated by falling water (p. 105)

hydroelectric power/energía hidroeléctrica energía generada por el agua en movimiento (pág. 105)

hydrogenous sediment seafloor sediment consisting of minerals that crystallize from seawater (p. 408)

hydrogenous sediment/sedimento hidrogenado sedimento del fondo oceánico, formado por minerales que se han cristalizado a partir del agua marina (pág. 408)

hydrosphere the water portion of Earth; one of the traditional subdivisions of Earth's physical environment (p. 8)

hydrosphere/hidrosfera parte acuática de la Tierra; una de las divisiones tradicionales del medio ambiente físico de la Tierra (pág. 8)

hydrothermal solution the hot, watery solution that escapes from a mass of magma that may alter the surrounding rock (p. 82)

hydrothermal solution/solución hidrotérmica solución acuosa y caliente que sale del magma y que puede alterar las rocas que la rodean (pág. 82)

hygrometer an instrument designed to measure relative humidity (p. 508)

hygrometer/higrómetro instrumento diseñado para medir la humedad relativa (pág. 508)

hypothesis a scientific explanation for a set of observations that can be tested in ways that support or reject it (p. 23)

hypothesis/hipótesis explicación científica de un conjunto de observaciones, que se puede poner a prueba para comprobarla o rechazarla (pág. 23)

I

ice age a period of time when much of Earth's land is covered by glaciers (p. 188)

ice age/era glacial período en el que gran parte de la Tierra estaba cubierta por glaciares (pág. 188)

igneous rock a rock formed from cooled magma or lava (p. 67)

igneous rock/roca ígnea roca formada por magma o lava que se ha enfriado (pág. 67)

index fossil fossil that is particularly useful for correlation because it is both geographically widespread and abundant in the fossil record, but is limited to a particular span of geologic time (p. 345)

index fossil/fósil índice fósil particularmente útil para establecer correlaciones porque es geográficamente extenso y abundante, pero se limita a una época geológica específica (pág. 345)

infiltration the movement of surface water into rock or soil through cracks and pore spaces (p. 159)

infiltration/infiltración movimiento del agua desde la superficie hacia las rocas o la tierra a través de grietas y aperturas porosas (pág. 159)

inner core the solid innermost layer of Earth, about 1220 kilometers in radius (p. 235)

inner core/núcleo interno estrato sólido más profundo de la Tierra; tiene un radio de 1220 kilómetros (pág. 235)

intertidal zone the area where land and sea meet and overlap; the zone between high and low tides (p. 431)

intertidal zone/zona intermareal área donde se encuentran y se solapan la tierra y el mar; zona entre la marea alta y la marea baja (pág. 431)

intraplate volcanism igneous activity that occurs within a tectonic plate away from plate boundaries (p. 285)

intraplate volcanism/vulcanismo de placa actividad ígnea que ocurre en una placa tectónica lejos de sus límites (pág. 285)

intrusive igneous rock igneous rock that formed below Earth's surface (p. 71)

intrusive igneous rock/roca ígnea intrusiva roca ígnea formada bajo la superficie de la Tierra (pág. 71)

Glossary, *continued*

invertebrate animal that lacks a backbone (p. 370)

    invertebrate/invertebrado animal que no tiene columna vertebral (pág. 370)

ion an atom or a molecule that possesses an electrical charge (p. 40)

    ion/ion átomo o molécula que tiene una carga eléctrica (pág. 40)

ionic bond a bond that forms between negative and positive ions (p. 40)

    ionic bond/enlace iónico enlace que se forma entre iones negativos e iones positivos (pág. 40)

isobars lines on a map that connect places of equal air pressure (p. 534)

    isobars/isobaras líneas de un mapa que unen lugares que tienen la misma presión atmosférica (pág. 534)

isostasy the concept that Earth's crust is floating in gravitational balance upon the material of the mantle (p. 310)

    isostasy/isostasia concepto que explica que la corteza terrestre está flotando sobre el material del manto gracias a un equilibrio gravitacional (pág. 310)

isostatic adjustment process of establishing a new level of gravitational equilibrium (p. 310)

    isostatic adjustment/ajuste isostático proceso en el cual se establece un nuevo nivel de equilibrio gravitacional (pág. 310)

isotherm a line connecting points of equal temperature (p. 492)

    isotherm/isoterma línea que conecta puntos que tienen temperaturas idénticas (pág. 492)

isotope an atom with the same number of protons but different numbers of neutrons for a given element; An isotope's mass number is different from that of the given element. (p. 38)

    isotope/isótopo para cualquier elemento, es un átomo con igual número de protones pero distinto número de neutrones; el número de masa de un isótopo es distinto al de ese elemento (pág. 38)

J

jet stream swift (120–240 kilometers per hour), high-altitude winds (p. 536)

    jet stream/corriente de chorro vientos de alta velocidad (120–240 kilómetros por hora) que se encuentran a grandes altitudes (pág. 536)

Jovian planet the Jupiter-like planets: Jupiter, Saturn, Uranus, and Neptune; These planets have relatively low densities and are huge gas giants. (p. 645)

    Jovian planet/planeta joviano cualquier planeta de la familia de Júpiter: Júpiter, Saturno, Urano y Neptuno; Estos planetas tienen densidades relativamente bajas y están compuestos principalmente de gas. (pág. 645)

K

karst topography an area that has a land surface or topography with numerous depressions called sinkholes (p. 178)

    karst topography/relieve kárstico zona cuya superficie o topografía presenta numerosas depresiones llamadas dolinas (pág. 178)

kettle depression created when a block of ice became lodged in glacial deposits and subsequently melted (p. 196)

    kettle/marmita depresión creada cuando se derrite un bloque de hielo que se había alojado en un depósito glacial (pág. 196)

Köppen climate classification system a system for classifying climates that is based on mean monthly and annual values of temperature and precipitation (p. 592)

    Köppen climate classification system/ sistema de clasificación de climas de Köppen sistema para clasificar los climas en base a los valores promedio de las temperaturas y de las precipitaciones mensuales y anuales (pág. 592)

L

La Niña an episode of strong trade winds and unusually low sea-surface temperatures in the central and eastern Pacific; the opposite of *El Niño* (p. 547)

La Niña/La Niña vientos alisios muy fuertes y bajas temperaturas de la superficie del mar que se registran en el océano Pacífico central y en el océano Pacífico oriental; fenómeno contrario a El Niño (pág. 547)

laccolith a massive igneous body intruded between preexisting strata (p. 296)

laccolith/lacolito cuerpo ígneo gigantesco que ha penetrado entre dos estratos preexistentes (pág. 296)

lahar mudflow made up of water-soaked volcanic ash and rock (p. 294)

lahar/lahar, el colada de barro formado por ceniza volcánica y roca saturadas de agua (pág. 294)

latent heat the energy absorbed or released during a change in state (p. 505)

latent heat/calor latente energía absorbida o desprendida durante un cambio de estado físico (pág. 505)

laterite a red, highly leached soil type found in the tropics that is rich in oxides of iron and aluminum (p. 139)

laterite/laterita suelo rojizo y altamente lixiviado de las regiones tropicales, rico en óxidos de hierro y aluminio (pág. 139)

latitude the distance north or south of the equator, measured in degrees (p. 11)

latitude/latitud distancia al norte o al sur del ecuador, que se mide en grados (pág. 11)

Laurasia supercontinent that formed the northern portion of Pangaea, which included portions of present-day North America, northern Europe, and Siberia (p. 372)

Laurasia/Laurasia supercontinente que se formó en la parte norte de Pangea, y que abarcaba regiones de lo que hoy en día son América del Norte, Europa septentrional y Siberia (pág. 372)

lava magma that reaches Earth's surface (p. 67)

lava/lava magma que ha llegado a la superficie de la Tierra (pág. 67)

lava plateau landform produced by repeated eruptions of fluid basaltic magma that builds up in thick layers (p. 293)

lava plateau/llanura de lava formación producida por sucesivas erupciones volcánicas y la acumulación de magma basáltica en capas gruesas (pág. 293)

light-year the distance light travels in a year, about 9.5 trillion kilometers (p. 702)

light-year/año luz distancia recorrida por la luz en un año o aproximadamente 9.5 trillón de kilómetros (pág. 702)

liquefaction a phenomenon, sometimes associated with earthquakes, in which soils and other unconsolidated materials saturated with water are turned into a liquid that is not able to support buildings (p. 229)

liquefaction/licuefacción fenómeno, a veces asociado con los terremotos, en el cual la tierra, junto con otros materiales no consolidados saturados con agua, se convierten en un líquido que no es capaz de sostener los edificios (pág. 229)

lithosphere the rigid outer layer of Earth, including the crust and upper mantle (p. 235)

lithosphere/litosfera capa externa y rígida de la Tierra, que incluye la corteza y el manto superior (pág. 235)

loess deposits of windblown silt, lacking visible layers, generally light yellow, and capable of maintaining a nearly vertical cliff (p. 204)

loess/loes depósitos de limo transportado por el viento, generalmente amarillos y sin estratos visibles, y que son capaces de crear precipicios casi verticales (pág. 204)

longitude the distance east or west of the prime meridian, measure in degrees (p. 11)

longitude/longitud distancia hacia el este o el oeste del Primer meridiano; se mide en grados (pág. 11)

longshore current a near-shore current that flows parallel to the shore (p. 463)

longshore current/corriente litoral corriente que está cerca de la costa y que fluye paralela a la misma (pág. 463)

lunar eclipse an eclipse of the moon; A lunar eclipse occurs when the moon passes through Earth's shadow. (p. 628)

lunar eclipse/eclipse lunar eclipse de la Luna; ocurre cuando la Luna pasa a través de la sombra de la Tierra (pág. 628)

lunar regolith a thin, gray layer on the surface of the moon, consisting of loosely compacted, fragmented material believed to have been formed by repeated impacts of meteorites (p. 632)

Glossary, *continued*

lunar regolith/regolito lunar capa gris y delgada sobre la superficie lunar compuesta de material fragmentado y ligeramente compactado, el cual se cree que fue formado por los impactos repetidos de meteoritos (pág. 632)

luster the appearance or quality of light reflected from the surface of a mineral (p. 51)

    luster/brillo apariencia o calidad de la luz que es reflejada por la superficie de un mineral (pág. 51)

M

magma molten rock beneath Earth's surface, including any dissolved gases and crystals (p. 67)

    magma/magma roca fundida que se encuentra bajo la superficie de la Tierra; incluye gases y cristales disueltos (pág. 67)

main-sequence star a star that falls into the main-sequence category on the H-R diagram; This category contains the majority of stars and runs diagonally from the upper left to the lower right on the H-R diagram (p. 704)

    main-sequence star/estrella de secuencia principal estrella que pertenece a la categoría de Secuencia Principal en el diagrama HR; esta categoría contiene la mayoría de las estrellas y pasa diagonalmente de la esquina superior izquierda a la esquina inferior derecha en el diagrama HR (pág. 704)

mammal animal that has hair, nourishes its young with milk, and maintains a steady body temperature (p. 378)

    mammal/mamífero animal que tiene pelo, amamanta a sus crías y es capaz de regular su temperatura corporal (pág. 378)

manganese nodule rounded lump of hydrogenous sediment scattered on the ocean floor, consisting mainly of manganese and iron and usually containing small amounts of copper, nickel, and cobalt (p. 408)

    manganese nodule/nódulo de manganeso masa redonda de sedimento hidrogenado que se encuentra esparcida por el fondo oceánico; está formado principalmente por manganeso y hierro, y generalmente tiene pequeñas cantidades de cobre, níquel y cobalto (pág. 408)

mantle the 2890-kilometer-thick layer of Earth located below the crust (pp. 8, 234)

    mantle/manto estrato de la Tierra que se encuentra justo por debajo de la corteza; tiene 2890 kilómetros de profundidad (págs. 8, 234)

mantle plume a mass of hotter-than-normal mantle material that ascends toward the surface, where it may lead to igneous activity (p. 271)

    mantle plume/pluma eruptiva masa de material del manto caliente que sube hacia la superficie, donde puede desencadenar una actividad ígnea (pág. 271)

mare (*plural* maria) the Latin name for the smooth areas of the moon formerly thought to be seas (p. 632)

    mare/mare (plural: maria) nombre en Latín para las zonas lisas de la Luna que antiguamente se pensaba eran mares (pág. 632)

mass extinction the extinction of many groups of organisms in a relatively short time (p. 369)

    mass extinction/extinción en masa extinción de muchos tipos de organismos en un tiempo relativamente corto (pág. 369)

mass movement the downslope movement of rock, regolith, and soil under the direct influence of gravity (p. 143)

    mass movement/movimiento de masas movimiento descendente de rocas, regolito y tierra por influencia directa de la gravedad (pág. 143)

mass number the number of neutrons and protons in the nucleus of an atom (p. 38)

    mass number/número de masa número de neutrones y protones en el núcleo de un átomo (pág. 38)

meander a looplike bend in the course of a stream (p. 163)

    meander/meandro sinuosidad en el recorrido de un arroyo (pág. 163)

mechanical weathering the physical disintegration of rock, resulting in smaller fragments (p. 126)

    mechanical weathering/meteorización mecánica desintegración física de las rocas que produce fragmentos más pequeños (pág. 126)

mesosphere the layer of the atmosphere immediately above the stratosphere and characterized by decreasing temperatures with height (p. 480)

mesosphere/mesosfera estrato de la atmósfera que se encuentra inmediatamente por encima de la estratosfera y está caracterizada por el descenso de la temperatura con el aumento de la altura (pág. 480)

metallic bond a bond that forms when electrons are shared by metal ions (p. 43)

metallic bond/enlace metálico enlace que se forma cuando los iones metálicos comparten electrones (pág. 43)

metamorphic rock rock formed by the alteration of pre-existing rock by heat, pressure, and/or fluids (p. 67)

metamorphic rock/roca metamórfica roca formada por la alteración de una roca preexistente debido al calor, la presión o la acción de líquidos (pág. 67)

metamorphism the changes in mineral composition and texture of a rock subjected to high temperature and pressure within Earth (p. 80)

metamorphism/metamorfismo cambios en la composición mineral y la textura de una roca sometida a temperaturas y presiones elevadas dentro de la Tierra (pág. 80)

meteor the luminous phenomenon observed when a meteoroid enters Earth's atmosphere and burns up, popularly called a shooting star (p. 663)

meteor/meteoro fenómeno luminoso que se observa cuando un meteoroide entra a la atmósfera de la Tierra y se desintegra, conocido popularmente como estrella fugaz (pág. 663)

meteorite any portion of a meteoroid that reaches Earth's surface (p. 664)

meteorite/meteorito cualquier fragmento de un meteoroide que llega a la superficie terrestre (pág. 664)

meteoroid a small, solid particle that travels through space (p. 663)

meteoroid/meteoroide partícula sólida y pequeña que viaja a través del espacio (pág. 663)

meteorology the scientific study of the atmosphere and atmospheric phenomena; the study of weather and climate (p. 3)

meteorology/meteorología estudio científico de la atmósfera y los fenómenos que ocurren en ella; estudio del estado del tiempo y el clima (pág. 3)

mid-ocean ridge a continuous elevated zone on the floor of all the major ocean basins and varying in width from 1000 to 4000 kilometers; The rifts at the crests of ridges represent divergent plate boundaries. (pp. 255, 405)

mid-ocean ridge/dorsal oceánica zona de elevación continua en el fondo de todas las cuencas de los océanos, cuya anchura varía entre 1000 y 4000 kilómetros; las grietas en las cimas de las elevaciones representan límites divergentes de las placas tectónicas (págs. 255, 405)

Milankovitch cycles cycles related to Earth's movements, such as its orbit around the sun, that scientists think may help to cause ice ages (p. 384)

Milankovitch cycles/ciclos de Milankovitch ciclos relacionados a los movimientos de la Tierra, tales como el cambio de su órbita alrededor del Sol, que los científicos creen influencian períodos glaciales (pág. 384)

mineral a naturally occurring, inorganic crystalline material with a unique chemical composition (p. 45)

mineral/mineral material cristalino inorgánico que ocurre de manera natural y que tiene una composición química única (pág. 45)

Moho the Mohorovičić discontinuity, which is shortened to Moho; It is the boundary separating the crust from the mantle, discernible by an increase in the velocity of seismic waves. (p. 236)

Moho/Moho la discontinuidad de Mohorovičić, abreviada Moho; es el límite que separa la corteza del manto y que se distingue por un aumento en la velocidad de las ondas sísmicas (pág. 236)

Mohs scale a series of 10 minerals used as a standard in determining hardness (p. 52)

Mohs scale/escala de Mohs serie de 10 minerales usados como guía para determinar la dureza (pág. 52)

moment magnitude a more precise measure of earthquake magnitude than the Richter scale, which is derived from the amount of displacement that occurs along a fault zone and estimates the energy released by an earthquake (p. 225)

moment magnitude/magnitud de momento medida más exacta para la magnitud de un terremoto que la escala de Richter, que se deriva del desplazamiento que ocurre a lo largo de una zona de falla y estima la energía que libera un terremoto (pág. 225)

Glossary, *continued*

monocline a large, steplike fold in otherwise horizontal sedimentary strata (p. 313)

monocline/pliegue monoclinal pliegue grande en forma de escalón en un estrato horizontal de sedimento (pág. 313)

monsoon seasonal reversal of wind direction associated with large continents, especially Asia; In winter, the wind blows from land to sea. In summer, the wind blows from sea to land. (p. 542)

monsoon/monzón cambio estacional en la dirección del viento asociado con los grandes continentes, particularmente Asia; En invierno, el viento sopla de la tierra al mar y en verano, sopla del mar a la tierra. (pág. 542)

moraine a ridge of unsorted sediment left by a glacier (p. 195)

moraine/morrena loma de sedimento mixto depositado por un glaciar (pág. 195)

mudflow quickly moving downhill flow of soil and rock fragments containing a large amount of water (p. 146)

mudflow/corriente de barro movimiento descendente y rápido de tierra y fragmentos de roca que contienen gran cantidad de agua (pág. 146)

N

natural levee an elevated landform that parallels a stream and acts to confine its waters, except during floodstage (p. 167)

natural levee/terraplén natural formación de tierra elevada paralela a un arroyo y que sirve para contener sus aguas, excepto durante una etapa de inundación (pág. 167)

natural selection evolutionary mechanism proposed by Charles Darwin in which traits that improve an individual's reproductive success are passed on more frequently to future generations than those that do not (p. 345)

natural selection/selección natural mecanismo evolutivo propuesto por Charles Darwin según el cual los rasgos que aumentan las posibilidades reproductivas de un individuo se transmiten a generaciones futuras con mayor frecuencia que los rasgos que no aumentan esas posibilidades (pág. 345)

neap tide lowest tidal range, occurring near the times of the first-quarter and third-quarter phases of the moon (p. 459)

neap tide/marea muerta menor rango entre mareas, que ocurre aproximadamente cuando la Luna está en cuarto creciente y en cuarto menguante (pág. 459)

nebula a cloud of gas and dust in space (p. 647)

nebula/nébula nube de gas y/o polvo en el espacio (pág. 647)

nekton organisms that can move independently of ocean currents by swimming or other means of propulsion; includes most adult fish and squid, marine mammals, and marine reptiles (p. 429)

nekton/necton grupo de organismos que pueden moverse independientemente de las corrientes del océano, nadando o mediante otros medios de propulsión; incluye la mayoría de los peces y calamares adultos, y los mamíferos y reptiles marinos (pág. 429)

neritic zone the marine-life zone that extends from the low-tide line and across the continental shelf (p. 431)

neritic zone/zona nerítica zona con vida marítima que se extiende desde la línea de marea baja y abarca la plataforma continental (pág. 431)

neutron star a star of extremely high density composed entirely of neutrons (p. 713)

neutron star/estrella de neutrones estrella de gran densidad, compuesta enteramente de neutrones (pág. 713)

nonfoliated metamorphic rock metamorphic rock that does not exhibit a banded or layered appearance (p. 83)

nonfoliated metamorphic rock/roca metamórfica no esquistosa roca metamórfica que no tiene una apariencia estratificada (pág. 83)

nonpoint source pollution water pollution that does not have a specific point of origin (p. 109)

nonpoint source pollution/contaminación no localizada contaminación del agua que no tiene un origen determinado (pág. 109)

nonrenewable resource resource that takes millions of years to form (p. 94)

nonrenewable resource/recurso no renovable recurso que toma millones de años en formarse (pág. 94)

normal fault a fault in which the rock above the fault plane has moved down relative to the rock below (p. 314)

    normal fault/falla normal falla en la que la roca que está por encima del plano de la falla se desplaza hacia abajo, en relación a la roca que está por debajo (pág. 314)

normal polarity a magnetic field that is the same as that which exists at present (p. 258)

    normal polarity/polaridad normal campo magnético igual al que existe en el presente (pág. 258)

nova a star that explosively increases in brightness (p. 705)

    nova/nova estrella cuyo brillo aumenta repentinamente (pág. 705)

nuclear fusion the way in which the sun produces energy; Nuclear fusion occurs when less massive nuclei combine into more massive nuclei, releasing tremendous amounts of energy. (p. 689)

    nuclear fusion/fusión nuclear proceso mediante el cual el Sol genera energía; La fusión nuclear ocurre cuando los núcleos menos masivos se unen para formar núcleos más masivos y desprenden enormes cantidades de energía en el proceso. (pág. 689)

O

occluded front a front formed when a cold front overtakes a warm front; It marks the beginning of the end of a middle-latitude cyclone. (p. 567)

    occluded front/frente ocluido frente que se forma cuando un frente frío alcanza a un frente cálido; indica el principio del fin de un ciclón de las latitudes medias (pág. 567)

ocean basin floor area of the deep-ocean floor between the continental margin and the oceanic ridge (p. 403)

    ocean basin floor/cuenca del fondo oceánico zona del fondo de los océanos profundos, ubicada entre el margen continental y la elevación oceánica (pág. 403)

ocean current mass of ocean water that flows from one place to another (p. 448)

    ocean current/corriente oceánica masa de agua oceánica que fluye de un lugar a otro (pág. 448)

oceanic zone the marine-life zone beyond the continental shelf (p. 431)

    oceanic zone/zona oceánica zona con vida marina que se encuentra más allá de la plataforma continental (pág. 431)

oceanography the scientific study of the oceans and oceanic phenomena (p. 3)

    oceanography/oceanografía estudio científico de los océanos y sus fenómenos (pág. 3)

orbit the path of an object as it goes around another object in space (p. 615)

    orbit/órbita camino que sigue un objeto al girar alrededor de otro objeto en el espacio (pág. 615)

ore a material from which a useful mineral or minerals can be mined at a profit (p. 98)

    ore/mena material a partir del cual se pueden explotar minerales útiles para obtener un beneficio económico (pág. 98)

original horizontality, principle of a principle of relative dating; Layers of sediments are generally deposited in a horizontal or nearly horizontal position. (p. 338)

    original horizontality, principle of/ horizontalidad original, principio de la principio de la datación relativa; Los estratos de sedimentos generalmente son depositadas en posición horizontal o casi horizontal. (pág. 338)

orogenesis the processes that collectively result in the formation of mountains (p. 316)

    orogenesis/orogénesis aquellos procesos que en colectivo resultan en la formación de las montañas (pág. 316)

orographic lifting mountains acting as barriers to the flow of air, forcing the air to ascend; The air cools adiabatically, and clouds and precipitation may result. (p. 512)

    orographic lifting/elevación orográfica montaña o montañas que forman una barrera para el flujo del aire, empujando el aire hacia arriba; El aire se enfría de manera adiabática, lo cual causa la formación de nubes y precipitación. (pág. 512)

outer core a layer beneath the mantle about 2260 kilometers thick; The outer core contains liquid iron and generates Earth's magnetic field. (p. 235)

Glossary, *continued*

outer core/núcleo exterior estrato que se encuentra por debajo del manto, con un grosor de aproximadamente 2260 kilómetros; El núcleo exterior contiene hierro líquido y genera el campo magnético de la Tierra. (pág. 235)

outwash plain a relatively flat, gently sloping plain consisting of materials deposited by meltwater streams in front of the margin of an ice sheet (p. 196)

    outwash plain/llanura aluvial llanura relativamente plana y con leves inclinaciones formada por materiales depositados por los arroyos de aguanieve al borde de un helero (pág. 196)

ozone a molecule of oxygen containing three oxygen atoms (p. 478)

    ozone/ozono molécula de oxígeno que contiene tres átomos de oxígeno (pág. 478)

P

P wave earthquake wave that pushes and pulls rocks in the direction of the wave; also known as a compression wave (p. 222)

    P wave/onda P onda sísmica que empuja y atrae las rocas; también se llama onda de compresión (pág. 222)

paleomagnetism the study of changes in Earth's magnetic field, as shown by patterns of magnetism in rocks that have formed over time (p. 258)

    paleomagnetism/paleomagnetismo El estudio de los cambios en el campo magnético de la Tierra, según lo muestran los patrones de magnetismo en las rocas que se han formado a través del tiempo (pág. 258)

Pangaea the proposed supercontinent that 200 million years ago began to break apart and form the present landmasses (pp. 248, 375)

    Pangaea/Pangea supercontinente que hace 200 millones de años comenzó a fragmentarse y a formar las masas de tierra actuales (págs. 248, 375)

parent rock rock that was changed by an agent of metamorphism or erosion (p. 80)

    parent rock/roca madre roca que ha cambiado debido a la acción de un agente metamórfico o de la erosión (pág. 80)

pedalfer soil of humid regions characterized by the accumulation of iron oxides and aluminum-rich clays in the B horizon (p. 139)

    pedalfer/pedalfer suelo de las regiones húmedas que se caracteriza por la acumulación de óxidos de hierro y de arcillas ricas en aluminio en el horizonte B (pág. 139)

pedocal soil associated with drier regions and characterized by an accumulation of calcium carbonate in the upper horizons (p. 139)

    pedocal/pedocal suelo asociado con las regiones más secas y que se caracteriza por una acumulación de carbonato de calcio en los horizontes superiores (pág. 139)

pelagic zone open ocean of any depth; Animals in this zone swim or float freely. (p. 432)

    pelagic zone/zona pelágica océano abierto de cualquier profundidad; Los animales de esta zona nadan o flotan libremente. (pág. 432)

perigee the point at which the moon is closest to Earth (p. 626)

    perigee/perigeo el punto en el que la Luna está más cerca de la Tierra (pág. 626)

perihelion the point in the orbit of a planet where it is closest to the sun (p. 624)

    perihelion/perihelio el punto en la órbita de un planeta en el que éste está más cerca del Sol (pág. 624)

period a basic unit of the geologic time scale that is a subdivision of an era; Periods may be divided into smaller units called epochs. (p. 355)

    period/período unidad básica de la escala geocronológica que es una subdivisión de una era; los períodos pueden dividirse en unidades más pequeñas llamadas épocas (pág. 355)

permeability a measure of a material's ability to transmit fluids (p. 171)

    permeability/permeabilidad la capacidad de un material para transmitir fluidos (pág. 171)

phases of the moon the progression of changes in the moon's appearance during the month (p. 626)

    phases of the moon/fases de la Luna la progresión de los cambios de la apariencia de la Luna a lo largo del mes (pág. 626)

phenocryst large crystal in an igneous rock with porphyritic texture (p. 72)

    phenocryst/fenocristal cristal grande de una roca ígnea que tiene textura porfídica (pág. 72)

photic zone the upper part of the ocean into which sunlight penetrates (p. 430)
  photic zone/zona fótica parte superior del océano en la que penetra la luz solar (pág. 430)

photon a small packet of light energy (p. 675)
  photon/fotón partícula de energía luminosa (pág. 675)

photosphere the region of the sun that radiates energy to space; visible surface of the sun (p. 685)
  photosphere/fotosfera región del Sol que irradia energía al espacio; la superficie visible del Sol (pág. 685)

photosynthesis the process by which plants, algae, and certain prokaryotes use light energy to convert water and carbon dioxide into energy-rich glucose molecules (pp. 367, 428)
  photosynthesis/fotosíntesis proceso mediante el cual plantas, algas y ciertos procariotas usan la energía luminosa para convertir agua y dióxido de carbono en moléculas de glucosa ricas en energía (págs. 367, 428)

phytoplankton plankton that perform photosynthesis, making them the most important community of primary producers in the ocean (p. 429)
  phytoplankton/fitoplancton plancton que realiza la fotosíntesis y constituye la comunidad más importante de productores primarios del océano (pág. 429)

planetesimal small, irregularly shaped body formed by colliding matter (p. 648)
  planetesimal/planetésimo cuerpo pequeño, de forma irregular, formado por materia en colisión (pág. 648)

plankton passively drifting or weakly swimming organisms that cannot move independently of ocean currents; includes microscopic algae, protozoa, jellyfish, and larval forms of many animals (p. 428)
  plankton/plancton organismos que flotan pasivamente o nadan débilmente, que no se pueden mover independientemente de corrientes oceánicas; incluyen algas microscópicas, protozoos, medusas y formas larvales de muchos animales (pág. 428)

plate one of numerous rigid sections of the lithosphere that moves as a unit over the material of the asthenosphere (p. 261)

plate/placa una de las numerosas secciones rígidas de la litosfera que se mueve como unidad sobre la materia de la astenosfera (pág. 261)

plate tectonics the theory that proposes that Earth's outer shell consists of individual plates that interact in various ways and thereby produce earthquakes, volcanoes, mountains, and the crust itself (p. 261)
  plate tectonics/tectónica de placas teoría que propone que la capa exterior de la Tierra se compone de placas individuales que interactúan de varias maneras y producen como resultado terremotos, volcanes, montañas y la corteza en sí (pág. 261)

playa lake a flat area on the floor of an undrained desert basin (playa) that fills and becomes a lake after heavy rain (p. 202)
  playa lake/salar superficie plana en el suelo de una cuenca desértica sin drenaje que se llena y se convierte en un lago tras lluvias fuertes (pág. 202)

pluton an intrusive igneous structure that results from the cooling and hardening of magma beneath the surface of Earth (p. 295)
  pluton/plutón estructura intrusiva ígnea que resulta del enfriamiento y endurecimiento del magma bajo la superficie de la Tierra (pág. 295)

point source pollution water pollution that comes from a known and specific location (p. 108)
  point source pollution/contaminación de fuentes localizadas contaminación acuática que procede de una fuente conocida y específica (pág. 108)

polar easterlies in the global pattern of prevailing winds, winds that blow from the polar high toward the subpolar low; These winds, however, should not be thought of as persistent winds, such as the trade winds. (p. 541)
  polar easterlies/vientos polares del este en el patrón global de vientos dominantes, los vientos que soplan desde la zona polar de alta presión a la zona subpolar de baja presión; Sin embargo, estos vientos no deben considerarse como vientos persistentes, como por ejemplo los vientos alisios. (pág. 541)

polar front the stormy frontal zone separating cold air masses of polar origin from warm air masses of tropical origin (p. 541)

Glossary, *continued*

polar front/frente polar la zona frontal tormentosa que separa masas de aire frío de origen polar de masas de aire cálido de origen tropical (pág. 541)

polar zone the region between 66.5° north and south latitudes and the poles; The sun's rays strike at a very small angle in the polar zone. (p. 589)

polar zone/zona polar la región entre los 66.5° de latitud y los polos; Los rayos del Sol llegan a la zona polar en un ángulo muy pequeño. (pág. 589)

porosity the volume of open spaces in rock or soil (p. 171)

porosity/porosidad el volumen de espacios abiertos en una roca o suelo (pág. 171)

Precambrian time the long time span from Earth's formation to the beginning of the Cambrian period; made up of the Hadean, Archaean, and Proterozoic eons (p. 354)

Precambrian time/tiempo Precámbrico el lapso de tiempo desde la formación de la Tierra hasta el comienzo del período Cámbrico; comformado por los eones Hadeico, Arcaico y Proterozoico (pág. 354)

precession a slow motion of Earth's axis that traces out a cone over a period of 26,000 years (p. 622)

precession/precesión movimiento lento del eje de la Tierra que traza un cono a lo largo de un período de 26,000 años (pág. 622)

precipitation any form of water that falls from a cloud (p. 504)

precipitation/precipitación cualquier forma de agua que cae de una nube (pág. 504)

pressure gradient the amount of pressure change occurring over a given distance (p. 534)

pressure gradient/gradiente de presión medida del cambio de presión que ocurre a lo largo de una distancia dada (pág. 534)

prevailing wind a wind that consistently blows from one direction more than from another (p. 545)

prevailing wind/viento dominante un viento que sopla constantemente de una dirección más que de otra (pág. 545)

primary productivity the production of organic matter from inorganic substances through photosynthesis or chemosynthesis (p. 433)

primary productivity/productividad primaria la producción de materia orgánica a partir de sustancias inorgánicas a través de la fotosíntesis o quimiosíntesis (pág. 433)

prokaryote single-celled organism that lacks a nucleus (p. 368)

prokaryote/procariota organismo unicelular que carece de núcleo (pág. 368)

prominence a concentration of gases above the solar surface that appears as a bright archlike structure (p. 688)

prominence/prominencia concentración de gases sobre la superficie solar que aparece como una estructura brillante en forma de arco (pág. 688)

protostar a collapsing cloud of gas and dust destined to become a star; a developing star not yet hot enough to engage in nuclear fusion (p. 708)

protostar/protoestrella nube de gas y polvo en colapso destinada a convertirse en una estrella; una estrella en desarrollo que todavía no está lo suficientemente caliente para iniciar la fusión nuclear (pág. 708)

pulsar a variable radio source of small size that emits radio pulses in very regular periods (p. 713)

pulsar/púlsar fuente de radio variable de tamaño pequeño que emite pulsaciones de radio en períodos muy regulares (pág. 713)

pycnocline a layer of water in which there is a rapid change of density with depth (p. 426)

pycnocline/picnoclina capa de agua en la que se produce un rápido cambio de densidad con la profundidad (pág. 426)

pyroclastic material the volcanic rock ejected during an eruption, including ash, bombs, and blocks (p. 289)

pyroclastic material/material piroclástico roca volcánica expulsada durante una erupción, incluyendo cenizas, bombas y bloques (pág. 289)

R

radiation the transfer of energy (heat) through space by electromagnetic waves (p. 485)

radiation/radiación transferencia de energía (calor) a través del espacio mediante ondas electromagnéticas (pág. 485)

radioactivity the spontaneous decay of certain unstable atomic nuclei (p. 347)

    radioactivity/radiactividad desintegración espontánea de ciertos núcleos atómicos inestables (pág. 347)

radiocarbon dating method for determining age by comparing the amount of radioactive carbon-14 to the amount of stable carbon-12 in a sample (p. 350)

    radiocarbon dating/datación por radiocarbono método para determinar la edad mediante la comparación de la cantidad de carbono-14 radiactivo con la cantidad de carbono-12 estable de una muestra (pág. 350)

radiometric dating the procedure of calculating the absolute ages of rocks and minerals that contain radioactive isotopes (p. 348)

    radiometric dating/datación radiométrica procedimiento para calcular las edades absolutas de rocas y minerales que contienen isótopos radiactivos (pág. 348)

radio telescope a telescope designed to make observations in radio wavelengths (p. 681)

    radio telescope/radiotelescopio telescopio diseñado para hacer observaciones en longitud de ondas de radio (pág. 681)

ray any of a system of bright elongated streaks, sometimes associated with a crater on the moon (p. 631)

    ray/rayo cualquiera de los sistemas de haces alargados luminosos, a veces asociados con un cráter en la Luna (pág. 631)

recycling the collecting and processing of used items so they can be made into new products (p. 116)

    recycling/reciclaje recolección y procesamiento de objetos usados para que puedan convertirse en nuevos productos (pág. 116)

red giant a large, cool star of high luminosity; a star occupying the upper-right portion of the H-R diagram (p. 704)

    red giant/gigante roja estrella grande, fría, de gran luminosidad; estrella que ocupa la parte superior derecha del diagrama HR (pág. 704)

reflecting telescope a telescope that concentrates light from distant objects by using a concave mirror (p. 680)

reflecting telescope/telescopio reflector telescopio que concentra la luz de objetos distantes usando un espejo cóncavo (pág. 680)

reflection the process whereby light bounces back from an object at the same angle at which it encounters a surface and with the same intensity (p. 486)

    reflection/reflexión proceso por el cual la luz rebota de un objeto en el mismo ángulo en el que llega a su superficie y con la misma intensidad (pág. 486)

refracting telescope a telescope that uses a lens to bend and concentrate the light from distant objects (p. 679)

    refracting telescope/telescopio refractor telescopio que usa una lente para doblar y concentrar la luz de objetos distantes (pág. 679)

refraction *See* wave refraction.

    refraction/refracción *Ver* onda de refracción.

regional metamorphism metamorphism associated with large-scale mountain-building processes (p. 81)

    regional metamorphism/metamorfismo regional metamorfismo asociado con procesos de formación de montañas a gran escala (pág. 81)

regolith the layer of rock and mineral fragments that nearly everywhere covers Earth's surface (p. 133)

    regolith/regolito manto de fragmentos de rocas y minerales que cubre casi toda la superficie de la Tierra (pág. 133)

relative dating process by which rocks are placed in their proper sequence or order; Only the chronological order of events is determined, not the absolute age in years. (p. 337)

    relative dating/datación relativa proceso por el que las rocas se colocan en su propia secuencia u orden; Sólo se determina el orden cronológico de los sucesos, no la edad absoluta en años. (pág. 337)

relative humidity the ratio of the air's water-vapor content to its water-vapor capacity (p. 506)

    relative humidity/humedad relativa la proporción del contenido de vapor de agua en el aire y su capacidad de vapor de agua (pág. 506)

Glossary, *continued*

renewable resource a resource that is virtually inexhaustible or that can be replenished over relatively short time spans (p. 94)

    renewable resource/recurso renovable recurso que virtualmente no se puede agotar o que se puede renovar en un lapso relativamente corto (pág. 94)

reptile group of generally terrestrial and scaly animals that lay amniotic eggs (p. 374)

    reptile/reptil grupo de animales generalmente terrestres que están cubiertos de escamas y ponen huevos amnióticos (pág. 374)

retrograde motion the apparent westward motion of the planets with respect to the stars (p. 616)

    retrograde motion/movimiento retrógrado el aparente movimiento hacia el oeste de los planetas con respecto a las estrellas (pág. 616)

reverse fault a fault in which the material above the fault plane moves up in relation to the material below (p. 314)

    reverse fault/falla inversa falla en la que el material sobre el plano de la falla se desliza hacia arriba en relación con el material de abajo (pág. 314)

reverse polarity a magnetic field opposite to that which exists at present (p. 258)

    reverse polarity/polaridad inversa campo magnético opuesto al que existe en el momento (pág. 258)

revolution the motion of one body about another, as Earth about the sun (p. 622)

    revolution/revolución o traslación movimiento de un cuerpo alrededor de otro, como el de la Tierra alrededor del Sol (pág. 622)

ridge-push a mechanism that may contribute to plate motion; It involves the oceanic lithosphere sliding down the oceanic ridge under the pull of gravity. (p. 271)

    ridge-push/empuje de dorsal mecanismo que puede contribuir al movimiento de placas; implica que la litosfera oceánica se desliza hacia abajo por la dorsal oceánica bajo la atracción de la gravedad (pág. 271)

rift valley deep faulted structure found along the axes of divergent plate boundaries; Rift valleys can develop on the seafloor or on land. (p. 255)

    rift valley/valle de rift estructura de fallas profundas que se encuentra a lo largo de los ejes de los límites de placas divergentes; Los valles de rift pueden formarse en el suelo marino o en la tierra. (pág. 255)

rille long channel associated with lunar maria; A rille looks similar to a valley or a trench. (p. 632)

    rille/rille canal alargado asociado con los maria lunares; Un rille es parecido a un valle o una fosa. (pág. 632)

Ring of Fire volcano belt that rims the Pacific Ocean (p. 284)

    Ring of Fire/Cinturón de Fuego gran cadena de volcanes que rodea el océano Pacífico (pág. 284)

rock a solid made of minerals or mineral-like materials (p. 66)

    rock/roca objeto sólido formado por minerales o materiales parecidos a los minerales (pág. 66)

rock cycle a model that describes the ways in which rocks change from one type to another (p. 66)

    rock cycle/ciclo de la roca modelo que describe las maneras en que una roca cambia de un tipo a otro (pág. 66)

rockfall occurs when rocks or rock fragments fall freely through the air; common on steep slopes (p. 145)

    rockfall/desprendimiento de rocas ocurre cuando rocas o fragmentos de roca caen libremente por el aire; son comunes en pendientes pronunciadas (pág. 145)

rockslide occurs when a mass of rock slides rapidly downslope along planes of weakness (p. 145)

    rockslide/deslizamiento de rocas ocurre cuando una masa de rocas se desliza rápidamente pendiente a lo largo de taludes inestables (pág. 145)

rotation the spinning of a body, such as Earth, about its axis (p. 622)

    rotation/rotación el giro de un cuerpo, como la Tierra, alrededor de su eje (pág. 622)

runoff water that flows over the land surface rather than seeping into the ground (p. 109)

    runoff/escorrentía agua que fluye sobre la superficie del suelo, en lugar de filtrarse en ella (pág. 109)

S

S wave a seismic wave that shakes particles perpendicular to the direction the wave is traveling (p. 222)

    S wave/onda S onda sísmica que sacude partículas perpendiculares a la dirección en que viaja la onda (pág. 222)

salinity the proportion of dissolved salts to pure water, usually expressed in parts per thousand (‰) (p. 422)

    salinity/salinidad la proporción de sales disueltas en agua pura, generalmente expresada en partes por miles (‰) (pág. 422)

saturated the state of air that contains the maximum quantity of water vapor that it can hold at any given temperature and pressure (p. 506)

    saturated/saturado el estado del aire que contiene la máxima cantidad de vapor de agua que puede retener a una temperatura y presión determinadas (pág. 506)

scattering the redirecting (in all directions) of light by small particles and gas molecules in the atmosphere; The result is more light rays with weaker intensity. (p. 486)

    scattering/dispersión la redirección (en todas direcciones) de luz por pequeñas partículas y moléculas de gas en la atmósfera; El resultado es más rayos de luz con menos intensidad. (pág. 486)

seafloor spreading the process by which plate tectonics produces new oceanic lithosphere at ocean ridges (pp. 256, 405)

    seafloor spreading/expansión de los suelos oceánicos proceso por el cual la tectónica de placas produce una nueva litosfera oceánica en las dorsales oceánicas (págs. 256, 405)

seamount an isolated volcanic peak that rises at least 1000 meters above the deep-ocean floor (p. 404)

    seamount/monte marino pico volcánico aislado que se eleva al menos 1000 metros sobre el suelo oceánico (pág. 404)

sediment loose particles created by the weathering of rock (p. 67)

    sediment/sedimento partículas sueltas formadas por la meteorización de una roca (pág. 67)

sedimentary rock rock formed from layers of weathered, eroded, and deposited sediment (p. 67)

    sedimentary rock/roca sedimentaria roca formada por capas de sedimentos que resultan de la meteorización, la erosión o que se han acumulado en depósitos (pág. 67)

seismic gap an area along a fault where there has not been any earthquake activity for a long period of time (p. 231)

    seismic gap/brecha sísmica área a lo largo de una falla donde no ha habido actividad sísmica durante un largo período (pág. 231)

seismic waves vibrations that travel through Earth carrying the energy released during an earthquake (p. 218)

    seismic waves/ondas sísmicas vibraciones que se desplazan por la Tierra, llevando la energía liberada durante un terremoto (pág. 218)

seismogram the record made by a seismograph (p. 224)

    seismogram/sismograma registro hecho por un sismógrafo (pág. 224)

seismograph an instrument that records seismic waves (p. 224)

    seismograph/sismógrafo instrumento que registra ondas sísmicas (pág. 224)

shield exposed Precambrian rocks found in the interior of each continent (p. 366)

    shield/escudo roca precámbrica que se encuentra en el interior de cada continente (pág. 366)

shield volcano a broad, gently sloping volcano built from fluid basaltic lavas (p. 290)

    shield volcano/volcán en escudo volcán ancho, de laderas poco inclinadas, formado por el fluido de lavas basálticas (pág. 290)

silicate any one of numerous minerals that have the oxygen and silicon tetrahedron as their basic structure (p. 47)

    silicate/silicato cualquiera de los numerosos minerales que tienen como su estructura básica el tetraedro de oxígeno y silicio (pág. 47)

Glossary, *continued*

siliceous ooze biogenous sediment composed of the silica-based shells of some single-celled organisms (p. 408)

    siliceous ooze/fango silíceo sedimento biógeno compuesto de esqueletos de sílice de organismos unicelulares (pág. 408)

silicon-oxygen tetrahedron a structure composed of four oxygen atoms surrounding a silicon atom, which constitutes the basic building block of silicate minerals (p. 47)

    silicon-oxygen tetrahedron/tetraedro de oxígeno y silicio estructura compuesta de cuatro átomos de oxígeno que rodean un átomo de silicio, que constituye la pieza clave para formar los silicatos (pág. 47)

sill a tabular igneous body formed when magma is injected along sedimentary bedding surfaces (p. 296)

    sill/sill cuerpo tabular ígneo que se forma cuando el magma es inyectado a lo largo de superficies de lechos sedimentarios (pág. 296)

sinkhole a depression produced in a region where soluble rock has been removed by groundwater (p. 178)

    sinkhole/dolina depresión que se produce en una región cuando el agua subterránea disuelve la roca soluble (pág. 178)

slab-pull a mechanism that contributes to plate motion in which cool, dense oceanic crust sinks into the mantle and "pulls" the trailing lithosphere along (p. 271)

    slab-pull/subducción de placa mecanismo que contribuye al movimiento de placas en el cual la corteza oceánica, densa y fría se hunde en el manto, arrastrando consigo la litosfera (pág. 271)

slump the downward slipping of a mass of rock or unconsolidated material moving as a unit along a curved surface (p. 146)

    slump/desprendimiento el movimiento hacia abajo de una masa de rocas o material no consolidado que se mueve como unidad a lo largo de una superficie curva (pág. 146)

snowline lowest elevation in a particular area that remains covered in snow all year (p. 189)

    snowline/línea de nieve elevación más baja en un área concreta que queda cubierta por la nieve todo el año (pág. 189)

soil a combination of mineral and organic matter, water, and air; that portion of the regolith that supports plant growth (p. 133)

    soil/suelo combinación de materia mineral y orgánica, agua y aire; parte del regolito que permite el crecimiento de plantas (pág. 133)

soil horizon a layer of soil that has identifiable characteristics produced by chemical weathering and other soil-forming processes (p. 138)

    soil horizon/horizonte capa del suelo que tiene unas características identificables producidas por alteraciones químicas y otros procesos de formación del suelo (pág. 138)

soil profile a vertical section through a soil showing its succession of horizons and the underlying parent material (p. 138)

    soil profile/perfil del suelo sección vertical de un suelo que muestra la sucesión de horizontes y los materiales litológicos subyacentes (pág. 138)

solar eclipse an eclipse of the sun; A solar eclipse occurs when the moon moves in a line directly between Earth and the sun, casting a shadow on Earth. (p. 628)

    solar eclipse/eclipse solar eclipse del Sol; Un eclipse solar ocurre cuando la Luna se mueve en línea directa entre la Tierra y el Sol, formando una sombra sobre la Tierra. (pág. 268)

solar flare a sudden and tremendous eruption in the solar chromosphere (p. 688)

    solar flare/destello solar gran erupción de energía repentina en la cromosfera solar (pág. 688)

solar wind streams of protons and electrons ejected at high speed from the solar corona (p. 686)

    solar wind/viento solar ráfagas de protones y electrones lanzadas a alta velocidad desde la corona solar (pág. 686)

sonar an electronic depth-sounding mechanism; *Sonar* is an acronym for *sound navigation and ranging*. Sonar calculates ocean depth by recording the time it takes for an energy pulse to reach the ocean floor and return. (p. 254)

sonar/sonar mecanismo electrónico de sonido de profundidad; *Sonar* es un acrónimo en inglés para *sound navigation and ranging* (navegación y rango de sonido); un sonar calcula la profundidad del océano al registrar el tiempo que tarda una pulsación de energía en llegar al suelo oceánico y volver. (pág. 254)

spectroscopy the study of the properties of light that depend on wavelength (p. 676)

spectroscopy/espectroscopia estudio de las propiedades de la luz que depende de la longitud de onda (pág. 676)

spring a flow of groundwater that emerges naturally at the ground surface (p. 172)

spring/manantial fuente de agua subterránea que emerge de forma natural en la superficie de la tierra (pág. 172)

spring equinox the equinox that occurs on March 19 or 20 in the Northern Hemisphere (p. 482)

spring equinox/equinoccio de primavera el equinoccio que tiene lugar el 19 ó 20 de marzo en el hemisferio norte (pág. 482)

spring tide highest tidal range that occurs due to the alignment of Earth, the moon, and the sun (p. 459)

spring tide/marea viva rango de marea más alto que ocurre debido a la alineación de la Tierra, la Luna y el Sol (pág. 459)

stalactite an icicle-like structure that hangs from the ceiling of a cavern (p. 177)

stalactite/estalactita estructura en forma de carámbano que cuelga del techo de una caverna (pág. 177)

stalagmite a columnlike form that grows upward from the floor of a cavern (p. 177)

stalagmite/estalagmita estructura en forma de columna que crece hacia arriba desde el suelo de una caverna (pág. 177)

stationary front a front in which two air masses come together but neither displaces the other (p. 566)

stationary front/frente estacionario frente en el cual dos masas de aire se unen pero ninguna desplaza a la otra (pág. 566)

storm surge the abnormal rise of the sea along a shore as a result of strong winds (p. 577)

storm surge/marea de tempestad la subida anormal del mar a lo largo de la costa como resultado de fuertes vientos (pág. 577)

strain the change in shape or volume of a body of rock as a result of stress (p. 308)

strain/deformación el cambio en la forma o el volumen de un cuerpo rocoso como resultado del esfuerzo (pág. 308)

stratosphere the layer of the atmosphere immediately above the troposphere, characterized by increasing temperatures with height, due to the concentration of ozone (p. 480)

stratosphere/estratosfera la capa de la atmósfera inmediatamente por encima de la troposfera, que se caracteriza por el aumento de la temperatura con la altura, debido a la concentración de ozono (pág. 480)

stratus one of three basic cloud forms; They are sheets or layers that cover much or all of the sky. (p. 518)

stratus/estrato una de las tres formas básicas de las nubes; son como sábanas o capas que cubren todo o casi todo el cielo (pág. 518)

streak the color of a mineral in powdered form (p. 50)

streak/raya el color de un mineral en forma pulverizada (pág. 50)

stream channel the course that the water in a stream follows (p. 160)

stream channel/cauce el curso que sigue el agua de una corriente (pág. 160)

stress the force per unit area acting on a solid (p. 308)

stress/esfuerzo la fuerza por unidad de área que actúa sobre un sólido (pág. 308)

strike-slip fault a fault along which the movement is horizontal and parallel to the trend of the fault (p. 315)

strike-slip fault/falla de desgarre falla a lo largo de la cual el movimiento es horizontal y paralelo a la tendencia de la falla (pág. 315)

stromatolite layered mound of calcium carbonate deposited by cyanobacteria (p. 367)

stromatolite/estromatolito acumulación en forma de capas de carbonato de calcio producido por cianobacterias (pág. 367)

Glossary, *continued*

subduction the process by which oceanic crust sinks beneath a trench and back into the mantle at a colliding plate boundary (p. 257)

> **subduction/subducción** proceso mediante el cual la corteza oceánica se hunde debajo de una fosa y vuelve al manto por el borde de una placa convergente (pág. 257)

sublimation the conversion of a solid directly to a gas without passing through the liquid state (p. 506)

> **sublimation/sublimación** conversión de un sólido directamente a gas sin pasar por estado líquido (pág. 506)

submarine canyon a seaward extension of a valley that was cut on the continental shelf during a time when sea level was lower; a canyon carved into the outer continental shelf, slope, and rise by turbidity currents (p. 402)

> **submarine canyon/cañón submarino** extensión de un valle hacia el mar que se cortó en la plataforma continental durante una era en la que el nivel del mar era más bajo; un cañón cavado en la parte exterior de la plataforma continental, el talud continental y el pie continental por corrientes de turbidez (pág. 402)

submersible a small underwater craft used for deep-sea research (p. 400)

> **submersible/sumergible** nave submarina pequeña que se usa en la investigación oceánica (pág. 400)

summer solstice the solstice that occurs on June 20 or 21 in the Northern Hemisphere and on December 20 or 21 in the Southern Hemisphere (p. 482)

> **summer solstice/solsticio de verano** solsticio que tiene lugar el 20 ó 21 de junio en el hemisferio norte y el 20 ó 21 de diciembre en el hemisferio sur (pág. 482)

sunspot a dark spot on the sun, which is cool by contrast to the surrounding photosphere (p. 687)

> **sunspot/mancha solar** área oscura del Sol que está más fría que la fotosfera que la rodea (pág. 687)

supercooled water the condition of water droplets that remain in the liquid state at temperatures well below 0°C (p. 521)

supercooled water/agua subenfriada condición en que las gotas de agua permanecen en estado líquido a temperaturas inferiores a 0°C (pág. 521)

supergiant a very large, very bright red giant star (p. 704)

> **supergiant/supergigante** estrella roja muy grande y muy brillante (pág. 704)

supernova an exploding star that increases in brightness many thousands of times (p. 711)

> **supernova/supernova** estrella en explosión que aumenta su brillo muchos miles de veces (pág. 711)

superposition, law of a law that states that in any undeformed sequence of sedimentary rocks, each bed is older than the layers above and younger than the layers below. (p. 337)

> **superposition, law of/ley de superposición** ley que enuncia que en cualquier secuencia no deformada de rocas sedimentarias, cada capa es más antigua que los estratos de arriba y más joven que los estratos de abajo (pág. 337)

supersaturated air the condition of air that is more highly concentrated than is normally possible under given temperature and pressure conditions; When describing humidity, it refers to a relative humidity that is greater than 100 percent. (p. 521)

> **supersaturated air/aire sobresaturado** condición del aire con un nivel de concentración mucho más alto de lo que es normalmente posible bajo ciertas condiciones de temperatura y presión; al describir la humedad, se refiere a una humedad relativa que es mayor que el 100 por ciento (pág. 521)

surface current movement of water that flows horizontally in the upper part of the ocean's surface (p. 448)

> **surface current/corriente superficial** movimiento de agua que fluye horizontalmente en la parte superior de la superficie oceánica (pág. 448)

surface wave a seismic wave that travels along the surface of Earth (p. 223)

> **surface wave/onda superficial** onda sísmica que viaja a lo largo de la superficie de la Tierra (pág. 223)

syncline a linear downfold in sedimentary strata; the opposite of anticline (p. 312)

syncline/sinclinal pliegue lineal en el estrato sedimentario; lo opuesto de anticlinal (pág. 312)

system any size group of interacting parts that form a complex whole (p. 18)

system/sistema grupo de cualquier tamaño de partes relacionadas que forman un conjunto complejo (pág. 18)

T

talus an accumulation of rock debris at the base of a cliff (p. 127)

talus/talud acumulación de restos de roca al pie de un acantilado (pág. 127)

temperate zone region located between 23.5° and 66.5° north and south of the equator; The sun's rays strike Earth at a smaller angle in the temperate zone than near the equator. (p. 589)

temperate zone/zona templada región situada entre 23.5° y 66.5° norte y sur del ecuador; Los rayos de Sol llegan a la Tierra formando un ángulo más pequeño en la zona templada que en el ecuador. (pág. 589)

temperature a measure of the average kinetic energy of individual atoms or molecules in a substance (p. 483)

temperature/temperatura medición de la energía cinética promedio de los átomos o moléculas individuales en una sustancia (pág. 483)

temperature inversion a layer of limited depth in the atmosphere where the temperature increases rather than decreases with height (p. 514)

temperature inversion/inversión de temperatura capa de poca densidad en la atmósfera donde la temperatura aumenta con la altura en vez de descender (pág. 514)

terrane a crustal block bounded by faults, whose geologic history is distinct from the histories of adjoining crustal blocks (p. 324)

terrane/terreno formación de rocas de la corteza rodeada de fallas, cuya historia geológica es distinta a las historias de las formaciones de rocas lindantes (pág. 324)

terrestrial planet any of the Earth-like planets, including Mercury, Venus, Mars, and Earth (p. 645)

terrestrial planet/planeta terrestre cualquiera de los planetas similares a la Tierra, como Mercurio, Venus, Marte y Tierra (pág. 645)

terrigenous sediment seafloor sediment derived from eroded rocks on land (p. 407)

terrigenous sediment/sedimento terrígeno sedimento en el fondo oceánico que se deriva de la erosión de rocas en la tierra (pág. 407)

texture the size, shape, and arrangement of a rock's component parts (p. 71)

texture/textura tamaño, forma y distribución de los componentes de una roca (pág. 71)

theory a well-established, reliable explanation of a natural or physical phenomenon (p. 24)

theory/teoría explicación sólida y confiable de un fenómeno natural o físico (pág. 24)

thermocline a layer of water in which there is a rapid change in temperature with depth (p. 424)

thermocline/termoclina capa de agua en la cual se observa un rápido cambio de temperatura con la profundidad (pág. 424)

thermosphere the region of the atmosphere immediately above the mesosphere and characterized by increasing temperatures due to absorption of very short-wave solar energy by oxygen (p. 480)

thermosphere/termosfera capa de la atmósfera inmediatamente superior a la mesosfera y que se caracteriza por un aumento de temperatura causado por la absorción de energía solar de ondas muy cortas por el oxígeno (pág. 480)

thrust fault a reverse fault with a dip less than 45°, normally about 10–15° (p. 314)

thrust fault/falla de empuje falla inversa con una depresión de menos de 45°, normalmente entre 10° y 15° (pág. 314)

thunderstorm a storm produced by a cumulonimbus cloud and always accompanied by lightning and thunder; It is of relatively short duration and usually accompanied by strong wind gusts, heavy rain, and sometimes hail. (p. 571)

thunderstorm/tormenta eléctrica tormenta causada por una nube cumulonimbo y siempre acompañada de relámpagos y truenos; es de duración relativamente corta y va generalmente acompañada de fuertes ráfagas de viento, precipitaciones y a veces granizo (pág. 571)

Glossary, *continued*

tidal range the difference in height between successive high and low tides (p. 459)

    tidal range/rango de marea diferencia en altura entre sucesivas mareas altas y bajas (pág. 459)

tide daily change in the elevation of the ocean surface (p. 458)

    tide/marea cambios diarios en el ascenso de la superficie oceánica (pág. 458)

till sediment of different sizes deposited directly by a glacier (p. 194)

    till/tillita sedimentos de diferentes tamaños depositados directamente por un glaciar (pág. 194)

topographic map a map that represents Earth's surface in three dimensions; It shows elevation, distance, directions, and slope angles. (p. 14)

    topographic map/mapa topográfico mapa que representa la superficie de la Tierra en tres dimensiones; muestra elevación, distancia, direcciones y ángulos de inclinación (pág. 14)

tornado a small, very intense cyclonic storm with exceedingly high winds, most often produced along cold fronts in conjunction with severe thunderstorms (p. 573)

    tornado/tornado pequeña tormenta ciclónica pero sumamente intensa, con vientos de gran velocidad, que a menudo ocurre a lo largo de frentes fríos acompañados de poderosas tormentas eléctricas (pág. 573)

trade winds two belts of winds that blow almost constantly from easterly directions and are located on the north and south sides of the subtropical highs (p. 541)

    trade winds/vientos alisios dos cinturones de viento que soplan casi constantemente desde la dirección del este y que se encuentran al norte y al sur de los centros de las altas presiones subtropicales (pág. 541)

transform fault boundary a boundary in which two plates slide past each other without creating or destroying lithosphere (p. 263)

    transform fault boundary/límite de falla de transformación límite en el que dos placas se deslizan a lo largo de la falla sin generar o destruir litosfera (pág. 263)

travertine a form of limestone that is deposited by hot springs or as a cave deposit (p. 177)

    travertine/travertino tipo de piedra caliza que es depositada por fuentes termales o que forma parte del depósito de cuevas (pág. 177)

tributary a stream that empties itself into another stream (p. 162)

    tributary/afluente corriente de agua que desemboca en otra corriente (pág. 162)

trophic level a nourishment level in a food chain; Plant and algae producers constitute the lowest level, followed by herbivores and a series of carnivores at progressively higher levels. (p. 436)

    trophic level/nivel trófico nivel de alimentación en la cadena alimentaria; los productores como las plantas y las algas forman parte del nivel más bajo, seguidos de herbívoros y una serie de carnívoros en los niveles superiores progresivos (pág. 436)

tropical zone region between 23.5° north (the tropic of Cancer) and 23.5° south (the tropic of Capricorn) of the equator; The sun's rays are most intense and the temperatures are always warm. (p. 589)

    tropical zone/zona tropical región entre 23.5° norte (trópico de Cáncer) y 23.5° sur (trópico de Capricornio) del ecuador; los rayos solares son de mayor intensidad y la temperatura es siempre cálida (pág. 589)

troposphere the lowermost layer of the atmosphere; It is generally characterized by a decrease in temperature with height. (p. 480)

    troposphere/troposfera capa más inferior de la atmósfera; generalmente se caracteriza por un decrecimiento de la temperatura con la altura (pág. 480)

tsunami the Japanese word for a seismic sea wave (p. 230)

    tsunami/tsunami palabra japonesa con la que se denomina a una ola sísmica marina (pág. 230)

turbidity current a downslope movement of dense, sediment-laden water formed when sand and mud on the continental shelf and slope are dislodged and thrown into suspension (p. 402)

turbidity current/corriente de turbidez
movimiento descendente de una densa masa
de agua cargada de sedimentos que se forma
cuando la arena y el barro de la plataforma y
el talud continental se desplazan y quedan en
suspensión (pág. 402)

U

unconformity a surface that represents a break
in the rock record, caused by erosion or lack of
deposition (p. 339)

unconformity/discordancia superficie que
representa una interrupción en la evolución
de la roca, causada por erosión o por falta de
deposición (pág. 339)

uniformitarianism the concept that processes
that have shaped Earth in the past are essentially the
same as those operating today (p. 336)

uniformitarianism/uniformismo principio
que dice que los procesos que dieron forma a la
Tierra en el pasado geológico son esencialmente
los mismos que ocurren en la actualidad
(pág. 336)

uplifted mountain a circular or an elongated
structure formed by uplifting of the underlying
basement rock (p. 316)

**uplifted mountain/montaña formada por
elevación** estructura circular o elongada
formada por el levantamiento de rocas
subyacentes del basamento (pág. 316)

upwelling the rising of cold water from deeper
layers to replace warmer surface water that has been
moved away (p. 450)

upwelling/afloramiento movimiento
ascendente de aguas frías desde las
profundidades del mar para reemplazar las
aguas más calidas de la superficie que han sido
desplazadas (pág. 450)

V

valley glacier a glacier confined to a mountain
valley, which in most instances had previously been
a stream valley; also known as an alpine glacier
(p. 189)

valley glacier/glaciar de valle glaciar localizado
en un valle de montaña, que en varias etapas
anteriores había sido un valle fluvial; también
conocido como glaciar alpino (pág. 189)

vent an opening in the surface of Earth through
which molten rock and gases are released (p. 287)

vent/chimenea abertura en la superficie de la
Tierra a través de la cual salen roca derretida y
gases (pág. 287)

vertebrate animal with a backbone (p. 370)

vertebrate/vertebrado animal que tiene
columna vertebral (pág. 370)

viscosity a measure of a fluid's resistance to flow
(p. 286)

viscosity/viscosidad una medida que indica la
resistencia de un líquido al fluir (pág. 286)

volcanic island arc a chain of volcanic islands
generally located a few hundred kilometers from
a trench where subduction of one oceanic slab
beneath another is occurring (p. 266)

volcanic island arc/arco de islas volcánicas
una cadena de islas volcánicas generalmente
ubicada a unos cientos de kilómetros de una
fosa donde está ocurriendo la subducción de
una placa océanica debajo de otra (pág. 266)

volcanic neck hardened magma in a volcano's pipe
(p. 293)

volcanic neck/cuello volcánico depósito de
magma solidificada en la chimenea de un volcán
(pág. 293)

volcano a mountain formed of lava and/or
pyroclastic material (p. 289)

volcano/volcán montaña formada de lava y/o
material piroclástico (pág. 289)

W

warm front a front along which a warm air mass
overrides a retreating mass of cooler air (p. 565)

warm front/frente cálido zona frontal de una
masa de aire cálido que avanza para reemplazar
una masa de aire frío que retrocede (pág. 565)

water cycle the constant movement of water
among the oceans, the atmosphere, geosphere, and
the biosphere (p. 158)

water cycle/ciclo del agua movimiento
constante del agua en los océanos, la atmósfera,
la geosfera y la biosfera (pág. 158)

Glossary

water table the upper level of the saturated zone of groundwater (p. 172)

> **water table/nivel freático** nivel superior de la zona de saturación de las aguas subterráneas (pág. 172)

wave height the vertical distance between the trough and crest of a wave (p. 456)

> **wave height/altura de la ola** distancia vertical entre el valle y la cresta de una ola (pág. 456)

wavelength the horizontal distance separating successive crests or troughs (p. 456)

> **wavelength/longitud de la ola** distancia horizontal que separa crestas o valles sucesivos (pág. 456)

wave period the time interval between the passage of successive crests at a stationary point (p. 456)

> **wave period/período de la ola** el intervalo entre el paso de crestas sucesivas por un mismo punto (pág. 456)

wave refraction the process by which the portion of a wave in shallow water slows and bends until it is nearly parallel to shore (p. 462)

> **wave refraction/refracción de la ola** proceso en que la porción de una ola en aguas poco profundas disminuye su velocidad y se rompe hasta quedar casi paralela a la costa (pág. 462)

weathering any process that breaks down rock (p. 67)

> **weathering/meteorización** cualquier proceso mediante el cual se desintegra la roca (pág. 67)

well an opening bored into the zone of saturation (p. 173)

> **well/pozo** abertura excavada dentro de la zona de saturación (pág. 173)

westerlies the dominant west-to-east motion of the atmosphere that characterizes the regions on the poleward side of the subtropical highs (p. 541)

> **westerlies/vientos del oeste** el movimiento dominante de oeste a este de la atmósfera que caracteriza las regiones en el lado polar de las zonas de alta presión subtropicales (pág. 541)

wet adiabatic rate the rate of adiabatic temperature change in saturated air; The rate of temperature change is variable, but it is always less than the dry adiabatic rate. (p. 511)

> **wet adiabatic rate/tasa adiabática húmeda** la tasa del cambio de temperatura adiabática en el aire saturado; La tasa de cambio de temperatura es variable, pero siempre es menor que la tasa adiabática seca. (pág. 511)

white dwarf a star that has exhausted most or all of its nuclear fuel and has collapsed to a very small size, believed to be near its final stage of evolution (p. 712)

> **white dwarf/enana blanca** estrella que ha agotado todo o casi todo su combustible nuclear y que se desvanece hasta alcanzar un tamaño pequeño, que se considera el estado final de su evolución (pág. 712)

winter solstice the solstice that occurs on December 21 or 22 in the Northern Hemisphere and on June 21 or 22 in the Southern Hemisphere (p. 482)

> **winter solstice/solsticio de invierno** el solsticio que tiene lugar el 21 ó 22 de diciembre en el hemisferio norte, y el 21 ó 22 de junio en el hemisferio sur (pág. 482)

Z

zone of saturation zone where all open spaces in sediment and rock are completely filled with water (p. 172)

> **zone of saturation/zona de saturación** zona donde todos los espacios abiertos en el sedimento y la roca están completamente llenos de agua (pág. 172)

zooplankton animal plankton (p. 429)

> **zooplankton/zooplancton** plancton animal (pág. 429)

Index

Index, *continued*

Index, *continued*

Index, *continued*

Index, *continued*

Index, *continued*

Acknowledgments

Editorial development, design, and production

Pages 148–149, **Soil** Taken from *Dictionary of the Earth*, published by Dorling Kindersley Limited. © Dorling Kindersley Limited, 1994, pp. 130–132; *Ecology* published by Dorling Kindersley Limited. © Dorling Kindersley Limited, 2000, pp. 22–23; *Earth*, published by Dorling Kindersley Limited. © Dorling Kindersley Limited, 2000, pp. 52–53. Pages 208–209, **Erosion** Taken from *Earth*, published by Dorling Kindersley Limited. © Dorling Kindersley Limited, 2000, pp. 54–55; *Dictionary of the Earth*, published by Dorling Kindersley Limited, 1994, pp. 112–113, 123. Pages 238–239, **Effects of Earthquakes** Taken from *Volcano & Earthquake*, published by Dorling Kindersley Limited. © Dorling Kindersley Limited, 2000, pp.46–47, 56–57. Pages 298–299, **Effects of Volcanoes** Taken from *Volcano & Earthquake*, published by Dorling Kindersley Limited. © Dorling Kindersley Limited, 2000, pp. 14–15, 22, 34–35, 39, 40–41. Pages 438–439, **Ocean Life** Taken from *Nature Encyclopedia*, published by Dorling Kindersley Limited. © Dorling Kindersley Limited, 1998, pp. 68–69, 72–73, 188. Pages 494–495, **Earth's Atmosphere** Taken from *Earth*, published by Dorling Kindersley Limited. © Dorling Kindersley Limited, 2000, pp. 10–11. Pages 578–579, **Winds and Storms** Taken from *Weather*, published by Dorling Kindersley Limited. © Dorling Kindersley Limited, 2000, pp. 38–39, 44–45. Pages 604–605, **Coniferous Forests** Taken from *Nature Encyclopedia*, published by Dorling Kindersley Limited. © Dorling Kindersley Limited, 1998, pp. 78–79.

Illustration

All illustrations by Dennis Tasa

Photographs

Cover

Front Cover Jim Lopes/Shutterstock; **Back Cover** (Bkgrd) Jim Lopes/Shutterstock, (L) Joseph C. Justice Jr./iStockphoto, (CL) S. Solum/Photolink/Getty Images, (CR) Mary Terriberry/Shutterstock, (R) amygdala_imagery/iStockphoto. Additional credits for custom covers can be found on the copyright page.

Front Matter

See the copyright page for Front Matter acknowledgments.

Chapter 1

1 ©Xin Qiu/Shutterstock; 2 (B) James L. Amos/Corbis; 3 Randy M. Ury/Corbis; 7 (CL) NASA, (CR) NASA/Science Source/Photo Researchers, Inc.; 9 Photos to Go/Photolibrary; 15 U.S. Geological Survey; 16 U.S. Geological Survey; 17 NASA; 19 Jack Dykinga Photography; 20 Roger Wood/Corbis; 21 (TL) Guy Vanderelst/Getty Images; 22 Mass Communication Specialist 3rd Class Dylan McCord/U.S. Navy; 25 (C) NASA;

Chapter 2

32 ©Carsten Peter/Speleoresearch & Film/National Geographic Image Collection; 41 (T) Dennis Tasa/Tasa Graphic Arts, Inc.; 42 (CL) Dennis Tasa/Tasa Graphic Arts, Inc.; 43 (CR) Nicholas Rigg/Getty Images; 44 (L) MarcelClemens/Shutterstock, (BL) Thom Lang/Corbis; 46 (TBR, CR) E. J. Tarbuck, (TR, CR) GeoScience Resources/American Geological Institute, (TL) Martin Zwick/AGE Fotostock/SuperStock; 47 (BR) Breck P. Kent Natural History Photography, (B) Dennis Tasa/Tasa Graphic Arts, Inc.; 49 (TR, CR) GeoScience Resources/American Geological Institute; 50 (B) Fred Ward/Black Star; 51 (TL, TC) E. J. Tarbuck, (BR) Herve Berthoule/Photo Researchers, Inc.; 53 (TR) ©Chip Clark/Smithsonian Institution, (CR) E. J. Tarbuck; 54 (BL) Paul Silverman/Fundamental Photographs; 56 (BR) ©DK Images, (BL) Lawrence Lawry/Photo Researchers, Inc.; 57 (TR) Rosemary Weller/Getty Images; 58 Dennis Tasa/Tasa Graphic Arts, Inc.; 60 Dennis Tasa/Tasa Graphic Arts, Inc.;

Chapter 3

64 Shutterstock; 66 (CL, BL) GeoScience Resources/American Geological Institute; 69 (TR) E. J. Tarbuck; 70 (B) Brad Lewis Photography; 71 (TR, TL) E. J. Tarbuck; 72 (BL) E. J. Tarbuck; 73 (CR) Hubert Stadler/Corbis; 75 (B) ©John R. McNair/Shutterstock; 76 (TL, BL) E. J. Tarbuck; 77 (T, B) E. J. Tarbuck; 78 (BR) Gary Yeowell/Getty Images; 80 (BL) Michael Collier; 81 (TR) Andrew Ward/Life File/Getty Images; 82 (CL) ©Philip Dombrowski; 83 (R) Breck P. Kent Natural History Photography, (L) E. J. Tarbuck; 86 (T) E. J. Tarbuck; 87 (CL, BR) E. J. Tarbuck; 90 E. J. Tarbuck; 91 (TR, TL, BR, BL) E. J. Tarbuck, (BR) GeoScience Resources/American Geological Institute;

Chapter 4

92 ©Danita Delimont/Alamy Images; 94 ©Greenshoots Communications/Alamy Images; 100 Bettmann/Corbis; 102 (TR) Bettmann/Corbis, (B) Thomas Del Brase Photography; 103 (TR) Martin Bond/Photo Researchers, Inc.; 104 (BL) J. Mead/Photo Researchers, Inc.; 105 Michael Collier; 106 Ted J. Clutter/Photo Researchers/Inc.; 109 (TR) Janis Burger/Bruce Coleman, Inc./Photoshot; 110 (TL) Stefan Zaklin/Stringer/Getty Images; 111 R. Ian Lloyd/Masterfile Corporation; 113 (BR) Steve Starr/Corbis; 114 (BL) SuperStock; 116 Monty Rakusen/Photolibrary Group, Inc.; 117 (C) Michael Collier;

Chapter 5

125 Frans Lemmens/Alamy Images; 126 (L) Jane Hallin/Alamy Inc.; 127 (BL) Susan Rayfield/Photo Researchers, Inc.; 128 (T) Breck P. Kent Natural History Photography; 129 (L) ©Egmont Strigl/AGE Fotostock; 130 (TR) E. J. Tarbuck, (TR) Martin Schmidt; 131 (BR, BC) E. J. Tarbuck; 132 (TL) Art Wolfe Inc.; 136 ©Danie Nei/Shutterstock; 138 ©Kenneth W. Fink/Photo Researchers, Inc.; 139 R. Ian Lloyd Productions; 140 (B) U.S. Department of Agriculture, (TL) Wayne Lawler/Photo Researchers, Inc.; 141 Carl Purcell/Photo Researchers, Inc.; 144 ©YURI CORTEZ/AFP/Getty Images; 145 ©Rob Kruyt/Reuters/Landov LLC; 146 (T) Chuck Place Photography, (B) E. J. Tarbuck; 147 (R) ©Daniel Goodchild/Alamy; 148 (C) Andrew Green/©DK Images, (B) Georg Gerster/Photo Researchers, Inc.; 149 (TL,) ©DK Images, (C) Clive Streeter/DK Images, (BR) Mike Saunders/©DK Images;

Chapter 6

156 Dmitry Naumov/Shutterstock; 163 (R, L) Michael Collier; 165 (B) Michael Tercha/NewsCom; 167 Art Wolfe Inc.; 168 (B) GeoEye Inc. Satellite Image; 172 (L) Ken Hamblin; 175 (C) Roy Morsch/Corbis; 176 (B) F. Rossotto/Corbis, (T) U.S. Geological Survey; 177 ©Michael Nichols/Getty Images; 178 Martin Zwick/AGE Fotostock/SuperStock;

Chapter 7

186 Nigel Hicks/©DK Images; 188 (B) Ron Niebrugge/Alamy Inc.; 190 (T) Bill Stevenson/Alamy Inc.; 191 (T) Steve Allen/Getty Images; 192 Kevin Schafer/Alamy Inc.; 194 (C, B) E. J. Tarbuck, (T) Marli Bryant Miller; 195 John Schwieder/Alamy Inc.; 196 ©Washington Imaging/Alamy; 199 (B) Michael Melford/Getty Images; 200 (T) E. J. Tarbuck; 201 (TL) Michael Collier; 202 Guy Edwardes/Getty Images, Terry Donnelly/Getty Images; 203 (CR) State Historical Society of North Dakota; 204 (TR) Dave Hamman/Getty Images, (B) Fred Lutgens; 205 (TR) Don W Fawcett/Photo Researchers/Getty Images, (TL) Michael Collier; 208 (BL) Andrzej Gibasiewicz/Shutterstock, (C) James Stevenson/©DK Images, (TLT, TLC, TLB) Mike Saunders/©DK Images; 209 (TL) Jack Sharpe/Shutterstock, (BC) ©DK Images, (BR) Michael Martin/SPL/Photo Researchers, Inc., (TR) Tetra Images/Alamy;

Chapter 8

216 ©Mark Pearson/Alamy Images; 219 ©Roy Garner/Alamy Images, Bettmann/Corbis; 228 (B) Matthew McDermott/Polaris Images; 229 (TR) La Prensa Grafica/©AP Images, (TL) NOAA; 232 FLETCHER & BAYLIS/Getty Images; 238 (T) ©The Granger Collection, NY, (B) Jorge Silva/Reuters/Corbis; 239 (BR) Andrew Green/©DK Images, (TR, TC) Andrew S. Dalsimer/Bruce Coleman/Photoshot, (BL) Bettmann/Corbis, (TL) Lenny Ignelzi/©AP Images;

Chapter 9

246 ©John Warburton-Lee Photography/Alamy Images; 253 Thomas Barrat/Shutterstock; 254 ©Science Source/Photo Researchers, Inc.; 256 NASA;

Chapter 10

278 ©George Burba/Shutterstock; 280 (B) Dolores Ochoa R./©AP Images; 286 (BR, BL) U.S. Geological Survey; 288 (L) Philippe Bourseiller/Getty Images, (TR) U.S. Geological Survey; 290 (T) Greg Vaughn Photography, (BR) Michael Collier; 291 Diane N. Ennis/Shutterstock; 292 (B) Kevin Ebi/Alamy; 293 (T) ©Bob Stefko/Getty Images, (CR) Special Collections Division, University of Washington Libraries; 295 (CR) Laura Crossey, Ph.D.; 296 (TL) E. J. Tarbuck; 297 (R) Art Wolfe Inc.; 298 (C) Andrey Lebedev/Shutterstock, (C) Phyllis Picardi/Imagestate Media, (TL) Rapho Agence/Photo Researchers, Inc.; 299 (TC, BR, BCR) ©DK Images, (CC) dalish/Shutterstock;

Chapter 11

306 Comstock/Thinkstock; 308 (BL) Art Wolfe Inc.; 312 (B) Darwin Wiggett/Corbis; 313 (B) Stephen Studd/Getty Images; 314 Fletcher & Baylis/Photo Researchers, Inc.; 316 (BR) Chris Noble/Getty Images; 317 (BL) Michael Collier; 320 (BL) Terry Donnelly/Alamy Images;

Chapter 12

334 ©Adam Burton/Nature Picture Library; 336 (BL) U.S. Geological Survey; 337 Photos to Go/Photolibrary; 338 (T) Francois Gohier/Photo Researchers, Inc.; 340 (B) E. J. Tarbuck; 342 (CL) Reuters/Corbis; 343 (TL) Patrick Poendl/Shutterstock, (BC) Breck P. Kent Natural History Photography, (TC, BL) E. J. Tarbuck, (TR) Florissant Fossil Beds National Monuments/US National Park Service/Herb Meyer; 345 Colin Keates/Getty Images; 346 Carl Buell; 350 Reuters/Corbis; 352 All Canada Photos/SuperStock; 353 (BR) Martin Bond/Photo Researchers, Inc.; 355 ©loong/Shutterstock, Ed Reschke/PhotoLibrary Group, Inc.;

Chapter 13

362 Diego Barucco/Shutterstock; 364 (BL) James L. Amos/Corbis; 367 (BR) Biophoto Associates/Photo Researchers, Inc., (BL) SPL/Photo Researchers, Inc.; 368 (T) Chase Studio/Photo Researchers, Inc., (B) Sinclair Stammers/Photo Researchers, Inc.; 370 (T) GeoScience Resources/American Geological Institute, (B) Publiphoto/Photo Researchers, Inc.; 371 Neg #GEO 80820C/©The Field Museum of Natural History, Chicago; 372 Kaj R. Svensson/Photo Researchers, Inc.; 373 (BR) Publiphoto/Photo Researchers, Inc.; 374 Neg #GEO 85637C/©The Field Museum of Natural History, Chicago; 375 (B) Francois Gohier/Photo Researchers, Inc.; 376 (T) Arnold Newman/PhotoLibrary Group, Inc.; 378 Biophoto Associates/Photo Researchers, Inc.; 379 (B) Chris Butler/Photo Researchers, Inc.; 380 (BL) Francois Gohier/Photo Researchers, Inc.; 385 Photo Researchers, Inc.; 389 SPL/Photo Researchers, Inc.;

Chapter 14

392 Jupiterimages/Thinkstock; 400 ©Kip Evans/Alamy Images; 405 Louise Fornander/©Jonas Stenstrom; 408 Deep Sea Drilling Project/Scripps Institution of Oceanography; 410 (BL) Greg Ochocki/Photo Researchers, Inc.; 411 (TR, TL) ©IFM-GEOMAR; 412 W. Townsend, Jr./Photo Researchers, Inc.; 413 Institute of Oceanographic Sciences/NERC/Photo Researchers, Inc.;

Chapter 15

420 ©Josef78/Shutterstock; 423 (TR) Peter Adams/Getty Images, (BL) NASA, (BR) Paul Steel/Corbis, (TL) Steve Allen/Getty Images; 425 ©Wilmar Photography/Alamy Images; 428 (BR, BL) Norman T Nicoll/Natural Visions; 429 (BL) David Hall/Photo Researchers, Inc., (BR) Images & Stories/Alamy, (T) Tom McHugh/Photo Researchers, Inc.; 430 (T) Dudley Foster/©Woods Hole Oceanographic Institution, (B) Thinkstock; 433 (B) Debra James/Shutterstock; 438 (TR) ©DK Images, (C) Helmut Cornell/imagebroker/Alamy; 439 (BR) blickwinkel/Schmidbauer/Alamy, (TR) Kelvin Aitken/PhotoLibrary Group, Inc., (TL) Malcolm McGregor/©DK Images, (CR) Ronald Sefton/Bruce Coleman/Photoshot; 440 E. J. Tarbuck;

Chapter 16

446 Jupiterimages/Thinkstock; 448 (B) sergioboccardo/Shutterstock; 450 (L) Rosenstiel School of Marine and Atmospheric Science; 451 Fotolia, (TR) NASA; 452 (T) British Antarctic Survey/Photo Researchers, Inc.; 455 (B) Rafael Macia/Photo Researchers, Inc.; 459 (BR, BL) Norman Pogson/Shutterstock; 462 (T) W.K. Fletcher/Photo Researchers, Inc.; 464 (T) Sinclair Stammers/Photo Researchers, Inc., (B) U.S. Department of Agriculture; 466 ©crystalseye/Fotolia; 467 (T, B) Courtesy U. S. Army Corps of Engineers, (B) Nova Scotia Archives and Records Management; 468 (T) Nova Scotia Archives and Records Management;

Chapter 17

474 (C) Shutterstock; 476 (BL) Mike Groll/Stringer/Getty Images; 479 (B) Natalia Bratslavsky/Shutterstock; 485 Gary Yeowell/Getty Images; 488 (CL) Bobbe Z. Christopherson; 494 (TR) Johnson Space Center/NASA Image Exchange, (BL) Nicholas Hall/©DK Images, (BL) SPL E540/072/Photo Researchers, Inc., (TL) Wayne Lawler/Photo Researchers, Inc.; 495 (TR) NASA Image Exchange, (TL, BL) Stephen Bull/©DK Images; 496 E. J. Tarbuck;

Chapter 18

502 ©DK Images, Dina Calvarese/Shutterstock; 508 (T) Jacek Chabraszewski, (B) E. J. Tarbuck; 510 E. J. Tarbuck; 515 tttuna/iStockphoto; 517 (B) E. J. Tarbuck; 520 Ales Liska/Shutterstock; 522 NOAA; 523 (B) ©David Butow/Corbis;

Chapter 19

530 ©Bob Reynolds/Shutterstock; 532 (B) Annie Griffiths Belt/Getty Images; 537 ©Gregory James Van Raalte/Shutterstock, (B) Jake Rajs/Getty Images; 545 (TR) Belfort Instrument Company; 549 (B) NASA;

Chapter 20

556 Mike Hollingshead/Solent News/©Associated Press; 557 (TR) National Gallery of Art, Washington, DC; 558 (B) NOAA; 562 (T) Tony Arruza/Corbis; 563 Layne Kennedy/Corbis; 564 (B) Kenneth Garrett/National Geographic Image Collection; 568 NOAA; 574 Tornadovideo/©Associated Press, Warren Faidley/Weatherstock®; 575 NOAA; 578 (TR) ©DK Images, (BL) 1989 - Warren Faidley/Weatherstock®; 579 (TL) 1996 - Warren Faidley/Weatherstock®, (BL) AFP PHOTO/Jewel SAMAD/Getty Images, (R) Naval Research Laboratory, (TR) Scott Olson/Getty Images;

Chapter 21

586 ©papijoe/Fotolia; 588 (B) Andrew Zarivny/123RF; 591 (L) Charlie Ott Photography/Photo Researchers, Inc., (R) iStockphoto/Thinkstock; 592 (B) David Keaton/Corbis; 593 (T) Art Wolfe/Photo Researchers, Inc., (B) Stan Osolinski/Dembinsky Photo Associates; 599 (T) Natalie Fobes/Corbis; 601 ©klikk/Fotolia, StockTrek/Getty Images; 603 ©age fotostock/SuperStock; 604 (BC) ©DK Images, (CR) Matthew Ward/©DK Images, (BL, Bkgrd) Winfried Wisniewski/Corbis; 605 (CR) ©DK Images, (CR) Cyril Laubscher/©DK Images, (BR) Joe McDonald/Corbis, (TR) Johnny Johnson/Stone/Getty Images, (TL) Malcolm McGregor/©DK Images, (CR) Peter Chadwick/©DK Images; 606 (BL) Winfried Wisniewski/Corbis;

Chapter 22

612 Goddard Space Flight Center/Arizona State University/NASA; 614 (B) David Lees/Corbis; 616 (R) Bettman/Corbis, (L) Stapleton Collection/Corbis; 617 (BR) Royal Ontario Museum; 619 (B) SSPL/Getty Images; 620 ©Georgios Kollidas/Fotolia, (BR) NASA; 622 (B) SPL/Photo Researchers, Inc.; 623 ©Richard Wainscoat/Alamy Images; 626 (CR, CL, BR, BL) Lick Observatory; 628 (Inset) alnilam/iStockphoto; 630 (B) Lick Observatory; 634 NASA; 635 (L) Museum of Science and Industry; 640 (B) Lick Observatory;

Chapter 23

642 JPL-Caltech/Cornell/ASU/NASA; 649 JPL-Caltech/NASA; 650 (T) Johns Hopkins University Applied Physics Laboratory/Carnegie Institution of Washington/NASA, (B) JPL/USGS/NASA; 651 SPL/Photo Researchers, Inc.; 652 (T) NASA, (B) U.S. Geological Survey; 653 JPL-Caltech/Univ. of Arizona/NASA; 654 JPL/Space Science Institute/NASA; 655 Nasa/National Geographic Image Collection; 657 ESA and the Hubble Heritage Team (STScI/AURA)/NASA; 658 (T) California Association for Research in Astronomy/Photo Researchers, Inc., (B) Jet Propulsion Laboratory/NASA; 659 NASA; 660 JPL-Caltech/UCLA/MPS/DLR/IDA/NASA; 663 ©bk3/ZUMA Press/NewsCom, Jerry Lodriguss/Photo Researchers, Inc.; 664 James P. Mandaville/Aramco World Magazine; 665 (C) U.S. Geological Survey;

Chapter 24

672 GSFC/AIA/NASA; 678 (B) Yerkes Observatory Photograph; 681 (L) David Parker/SPL/Photo Researchers, Inc., (R) National Radio Astronomy Observatory; 682 NASA; 683 NASA; 684 (B) Kent Wood/Photo Researchers, Inc.; 685 (B) National Solar Observatory/NOAO/AURA/NSF; 686 NASA; 687 (R) National Solar Observatory/NOAO/AURA/NSF; 688 (B) Pi-Lens/Shutterstock; 690 Péter Gudella/Shutterstock; 691 Science Source/Photo Researchers, Inc.;

Chapter 25

698 ESA/NASA; 701 (T) NOAO/AURA/NSF; 705 (T, B) Lick Observatory; 706 Anglo-Australian Observatory; 707 (B) NASA; 710 (BL) Anglo-Australian Observatory; 711 Lick Observatory; 713 (TR) California Institute of Technology/Palomar Observatory; 715 (B) Dr. Axel Mellinger; 717 (T) Anglo-Australian Observatory, (CR) California Institute of Technology/Palomar Observatory, (BL) ESO Education & Public Relations, (BR) NASA; 718 (BL) NASA; 722 Fundamental Photographs;

Skill and Reference Handbook

729 (B) Russ Lappa; 730 Benjamin Volant/Alamy Images; 731 Martin Shields/Photo Researchers/Getty Images.